The Kinetic Basis of
Molecular Biology

The Kinetic Basis of Molecular Biology

FRANK H. JOHNSON
DEPARTMENT OF BIOLOGY
PRINCETON UNIVERSITY

HENRY EYRING
DEPARTMENT OF CHEMISTRY AND THE
GRADUATE SCHOOL, UNIVERSITY OF UTAH

MILTON J. POLISSAR
DEPARTMENT OF CHEMISTRY, CITY COLLEGE
OF SAN FRANCISCO AND BIOMECHANICS GROUP
UNIVERSITY OF CALIFORNIA MEDICAL SCHOOL
SAN FRANCISCO

JOHN WILEY & SONS, INC., NEW YORK
CHAPMAN & HALL, LIMITED, LONDON

Library of Congress Catalog Card Number: 54–7856

Printed in the United States of America

Preface

In theory at least, all the chemical and physical processes which molecules enter into are now calculable from first principles. Processes in living organisms seem to be no exception. The chief purpose of this book is to apply modern molecular theory, in so far as it is now possible, to some representative biological processes.

Although there have been many publications dealing with biological reactions from a physical chemical point of view, the present approach has the advantage of incorporating a relatively new understanding of the mechanisms governing rate processes in general. This new understanding is largely the outgrowth of modern research in quantum and statistical mechanics. It rests heavily upon the notion that reactants are in equilibrium with an activated complex, and it puts at our disposal the theoretical methods useful for equilibria. The theory, usually referred to as the theory of absolute reaction rates, has been extensively applied to processes encountered not only in ordinary chemical reactions but also in a wide variety of other fields. Biological applications of the theory that have already been made have been sufficiently successful to encourage our undertaking of the more comprehensive treatment set forth in this book.

For some years biology has progressed steadily toward an ultimate goal of rational interpretations of both structure and function at the molecular level—toward a broad and basic science of molecular biology. The present work is a step in this direction, with the emphasis primarily on the kinetic basis rather than on the purely structural, biochemical, or other more or less distinct aspects appropriate to the general subject. Although remarkable progress has been made on these other aspects, it would be difficult, indeed, within the space of a single book, to do justice to the many outstanding studies that have been made, especially during recent years. As it stands, the material that has been included is by no means complete. The limitations of space and time have made it impractical to include, among other things, separate chapters on certain subjects of obvious importance, such as photosynthesis and ionizing radiations. Moreover, in selecting specific topics and papers for detailed discussion, other interesting and significant contributions have had to be omitted, and some, no doubt, have been unintentionally overlooked. Our purpose, however, has been more to interpret than to review. No attempt has been made to cover the literature in a summary fashion, but we have undertaken to examine critically some of the important problems appropriate to the point of view adopted. In so doing we have worked out some previously unpublished treatments of existing data, while undertaking to provide a framework to aid in the interpretation of needed future data.

The book is intended to be useful both to biologists who are interested in the theoretical basis of rate processes and to chemists who are interested in biological reactions. Accordingly, certain aspects and backgrounds of various problems have been included which to the specialist will appear elementary and familiar, if not superfluous. To the specialist in a different, possibly remote, field, however, the same material may look strange and complex, if not forbidding. Obviously, it is not easy to attain an ideal solution to a situation of this kind. For the benefit of those who are not familiar with reaction rate theory, the general introduction given in Chapter 1 is supplemented by the barest essentials of thermodynamics and of classical, quantum, and statistical mechanics in Chapters 2 to 5, followed by the calculation of a simple reaction in Chapter 6. Although mastery of these subjects generally requires prolonged study, the fundamentals briefly presented in these chapters provide the inquiring reader a basis for understanding the background upon which reaction rate theory is built. On the other hand, one may readily pass directly from the introduction of Chapter 1 to the biological applications in Chapters 7 to 14, and take up the basic framework of the chemical theory at another time.

It is a distinct pleasure to acknowledge the aid we have received in the production of the manuscript. Although the original plan to write a book of this kind was conceived over ten years ago, most of the actual writing was accomplished during the academic years 1950–1952. In the interim a number of experimental studies by the authors and their associates at Princeton and the University of Utah, as well as elsewhere, contributed data of especial interest to a definitive solution of many of the problems discussed. These studies were aided by research grants from various sources, including the American Cancer Society. During several intervals, aggregating a total of two years between 1944 and 1951, opportunities for one of us (F. H. J.) to devote full time to research work related to the book, and directly to the writing of the book, were made possible in part by the tenure of a Fellowship of the John Simon Guggenheim Memorial Foundation. Most of the writing of the first ten chapters was done during 1950–1951 at the University of Utah in close collaboration between the first two authors, and under a contract with the Office of Naval Research. The next three chapters (11, 12, and 13) became possible through the cooperation of the third author, M. J. P., and his colleagues in the Biomechanics Group at the Medical School of the University of California in San Francisco, with the support of a grant from the National Foundation for Infantile Paralysis. On these three chapters collaboration has been limited by circumstances to relatively brief discussions as opportunity has allowed, and the exchange of views chiefly by mail. The final chapter (14) is the result of collaboration between Dr. Stephen Prager, Jowett Fellow at the University of Utah during 1951–1952, and H. E. The manuscript was brought to completion in 1952. We have not attempted to take into account results of more recent studies, except for the addition, in proof, of a brief addendum to Chapter 7, and a few references at the ends of some other chapters.

A number of authorities in different fields have had the kindness either to read critically certain parts of the manuscript, or to discuss informally one or more aspects of the work with the authors. Their comments, criticisms, and suggestions have been received, in each instance, with the utmost appreciation and, when followed, have been responsible for notable improvements through corrections, deletions, or revisions. To our colleagues, especially at the University of Utah, in Princeton, and in San Francisco, we gratefully acknowledge our indebtedness for assistance in various ways. Finally, to the many authors, editors, and publishers who have generously given us permission to use the previously published illustrations, referred to in the legends and listed in detail in the Appendix, we likewise make grateful acknowledgment.

F. H. J.
H. E.
M. J. P.

April, 1954

for · · ·
    because of · · ·
        and in spite of · · ·
        Our Students

Contents

Introduction

. . . it is physical chemistry which gives us the mighty
instrument for these investigations.

Arrhenius (1915)

The building stones of all nature, including the living world, are atoms and molecules. Each elementary process in living cells involves changes in 1, 2, or at most very few molecules at a time, and the whole multifarious activities of living organisms are, in fact, governed by the molecules which form the chromosomes, genes, and specific enzymes. Although an understanding of molecules is obviously not sufficient for an understanding of life, it is prerequisite to it. Accordingly, the first six chapters deal, for the most part, with the present knowledge of chemical reactions at the level of atoms and molecules, i.e., as more or less isolated systems. This introductory chapter will perhaps clarify the discussions which follow by giving at the start a brief account, largely in qualitative terms, of the nature of the chemical problem and of the approaches to its solution.

Absolute reaction rates

For a long time the goal of theoretical chemistry has been to predict, from first principles, the absolute rates of chemical reactions, i.e., to calculate the number of molecules reacting per second, knowing the physical properties of the molecules and the laws governing their behavior. To do this it is necessary to know not only the events that take place in the reaction itself but also those which lead up to it, as well as the forces responsible for stability of both reactants and products. Such detailed knowledge is not essential to account for the change from the initial to the final state of a thermodynamic equilibrium; fundamental laws of thermodynamics were successfully worked out without any detailed knowledge of atomic structure. It is impossible, however, for these laws alone to provide any clue to the length of time that will be required, under stated conditions, for equilibrium to be attained. They describe the quantitative relation between the rate of the forward direction and the rate of the backward direction of a reaction when the ratio of these reaction rates becomes constant and therefore equals the equilibrium constant. They also describe the relation between the equilibrium constant

1

and the relative concentration of reactants and products, the temperature, and the pressure. Only recently have the corresponding laws for rate processes been formulated. Rate processes proceed in an analogous way, through an activated complex which is in quasi-equilibrium with the reactants.

The notion of the activated complex attained a precise meaning in 1935, and it provides the basis of the modern theory of absolute reaction rates. No brief account can do justice to the many contributors in the fields of classical, quantum, and statistical mechanics, and chemistry as well as physics, whose work has made this theory possible, nor can a brief account give more than the basic ideas of the theory. In essence, however, the theory holds that every elementary rate process, whatever its nature—diffusion, solubility, oxidation, hydrolysis, many excitations, lubrication, etc.—can be treated as an unstable equilibrium between the reactants, in their normal state, and the activated complex, in the activated state. The activated complex is an intermediate molecule, with a lifetime of the order of 10^{-13} sec. Once formed, it decomposes with a universal frequency kT/h, which is the same for all reactions. In this expression T is the absolute temperature, h is Planck's constant, and k is the Boltzmann constant, i.e., R/N, the gas constant per molecule. The probability that the formation of the activated complex will lead to reaction is designated by the transmission coefficient κ, which is often equal to 1. Thus, in any reaction, the specific rate constant k' is accounted for on the basis of a quasi-equilibrium between the normal and the activated state (designated by the constant $K^{\ddagger}$) and the frequency of decomposition of the activated complex times the probability that the activated complex decomposes to the products:

$$k' = (\kappa kT/h)K^{\ddagger} \tag{1.1}$$

Since for all practical purposes $K^{\ddagger}$ behaves as an equilibrium constant, we will treat it as such. The conceptual differences will be considered presently (p. 19–20). Because the universal frequency kT/h is the same for all reactions and κ is usually equal to unity or very nearly so, differences in specific rates among different reactions depend upon the equilibrium constant $K^{\ddagger}$ between the normal and activated states of the atoms or molecules concerned.

The Arrhenius equation

The general notion of normal and activated states of reacting molecules goes back to Arrhenius (1889). The quantitative effect of temperature on the rate of hydrolysis of sucrose in the presence of various acids was too great to be accounted for in terms of the effect of temperature upon the kinetic energy of the molecules, or upon the amount of dissociation of the acids. Using the original notation, Arrhenius found that the relation between the velocity of reaction, Q_{t_0}, at one temperature t_0 and the velocity Q_{t_1} at a different temperature t_1 is described by the equation

$$Q_{t_1} = Q_{t_0} \cdot e^{A \cdot (T_1 - T_0) : T_0 T_1} \tag{1.2}$$

in which A is a constant, e is the base of natural logarithms, and T_0 and T_1 the absolute temperatures corresponding to t_0 and t_1, respectively. Arrhenius considered this equation in relation to van't Hoff's (1884) theoretically derived expression for the temperature dependence of equilibrium reactions. Thus, in a reversible reaction between A and B to give D and E, letting C represent the concentration of the reactant denoted by the subscript, we have

$$k_{,} C_A C_B = k_{,,} C_E C_D$$
$$k_{,,}/k_{,} = K = C_E C_D / C_A C_B \tag{1.3}$$

where $k_{,}$ and $k_{,,}$ are the specific reaction rate constants for the forward and backward reactions, respectively, and K is the equilibrium constant. The temperature relation of the k's is given by

$$\frac{d \log_{\text{nat.}} k_{,}}{dT} - \frac{d \log_{\text{nat.}} k_{,,}}{dT} = \frac{q}{2T^2} \tag{1.4}$$

where q is the heat in calories liberated per gram molecule when A and B are converted to D and E. Van't Hoff pointed out that, although equation (1.4) does not give the relation between temperature and the value of a single reaction rate constant k, this relationship has the form

$$(d \log_{\text{nat.}} k)/dT = (A/T^2) + B \tag{1.5}$$

in which A and B are constants.

To account for the large effect of temperature on the rate of sucrose hydrolysis, Arrhenius considered it necessary to introduce the new hypothesis of an activated state. This concept, although subsequently modified and made more precise, remains in modern rate theory. He suggested that *aktiven Rohrzucker* is very quickly formed at the expense of *inaktiven* as the temperature is raised, and that the rate of reaction depends upon the concentration of the active molecules. The rate increases about 12 per cent per degree, in contrast to the increase in kinetic energy of the system which, for gas molecules at ordinary temperatures, amounts to only about $\frac{1}{6}$ per cent per degree, according to the kinetic theory of gases. Arrhenius considered that at constant temperature the number of active molecules M_a must be proportional to the number of inactive molecules M_i:

$$M_a = k \cdot M_i \tag{1.6}$$

and hence from equation (1.5), omitting B as required by experiment, Arrhenius wrote

$$(d \log_{\text{nat.}} k)/dT = q/2T^2 \qquad (1.7)$$

which on integration becomes

$$k_{T_1} = k_{T_0} e^{q(T_1 - T_0)/2T_0 T_1} \qquad (1.8)$$

Equation (1.8) aside from notation is equation (1.2), $q/2$ being equal to A. Later, in treating complicated biological reactions, Arrhenius (1915) used the symbol μ in place of q, and referred to μ as "a constant." The later notation persists today, especially in studies of biological rates, the constant μ being variously referred to as the "critical thermal increment," "apparent activation energy," or "temperature characteristic."

Following Arrhenius, extensive work on both chemical and biological processes has shown that the rate is generally described with considerable accuracy by equation (1.8), provided that the range in temperature is not too large. Among biological reactions, including complicated physiological processes, the range in temperature over which the rate conforms to the Arrhenius equation is especially limited, the actual range depending upon not only the specific process but often also upon the specific chemical environment. At relatively low temperatures, familiarly between 35° and 40°C, the rates of biological reactions go through a maximum, or "optimum," with rise in temperature because of a reversible and also an irreversible inactivation of one or more protein catalysts upon which the process depends. The rate of the inactivating reaction itself often conforms to the Arrhenius equation. The quantitative rôle of protein denaturation in determining the temperature-activity curve of biological reactions is considered in some detail in Chapters 8, 9, and 10.

From equation (1.8) it is clear that a linear relation should result when the natural logarithm of the rate of reaction is plotted against the reciprocal of the absolute temperature, the slope of the line representing the value of $\mu/2$. Thus, when the data conform to the equation, the temperature dependence of the rate is given by the numerical value of μ. Among various reactions, however, it became apparent that in some instances the numerical value of μ was nearly the same for two different reactions, yet their rates at a corresponding temperature were far from the same; that is, the slopes of the lines obtained by plotting the logarithm of their rates against the reciprocal of the absolute temperature were parallel, but the intercepts of these lines on the ordinate were entirely different. Equation (1.8) was written as

$$v = Ae^{-E/RT} \qquad (1.9)$$

where v represents the observed velocity; R, the gas constant, has the present best value 1.98646 cal per deg per mole; and T is the absolute temperature. The constant E was obviously related to the energy of activation of the molecules in the system, but the meaning of A was still obscure.

With most reactions the Arrhenius equation proved to be successful in describing, often quite accurately, the relative rates at different temperatures. Deviations occurred when the temperature range was sufficiently extended, but the conformance of data to the equation was generally good within the range of temperatures that permitted convenient measurements of the rate. Even at temperatures convenient in this way, however, simple chemical reactions sometimes exhibit small but consistent deviations from the linearity required by constant values of A and of E in equation (1.9) (La Mer and Miller, 1935).

Early collision theory

Further development of the theory of reaction kinetics called for elucidation of the meaning of A and of E. The "collision theory," though incomplete, represented a notable advance in its statistical approach to the problem. Its origin, like that of other important theories, cannot be readily ascribed to a particular work (cf. discussions in Hinshelwood, 1933, 1940; Fowler and Guggenheim, 1939; Moelwyn-Hughes, 1932, 1933, 1947; Glasstone, Laidler, and Eyring, 1941; Laidler, 1950). Its basic assumption is that the rate of reaction depends upon the frequency with which two molecules collide with energy equal to or in excess of the activation energy. Strutt (1912) computed the number of successful collisions for certain reactions involving ozone and nitrogen, respectively, and found that at 100°C two molecules of ozone had to collide 6×10^{11} times, on the average, before the right sort of collision for chemical union occurred. At a silver oxide surface almost every collision with the surface resulted in destruction of the ozone, while an active nitrogen molecule had to collide 500 times, on the average, before being destroyed at an oxidized copper surface. Trautz (1916) was apparently the first to compare the computed and observed rates of bimolecular gaseous reactions, although Lewis (1918) independently arrived at the same results in a paper whose publication was delayed by World War I. Thus, on the basis of the kinetic theory of gases, the actual number Z of collisions between two species, A and B, of gaseous molecules is given by

$$Z = n_A n_B (r_A + r_B)^2 \left\{ 8\pi kT \left(\frac{1}{m_A} + \frac{1}{m_B} \right) \right\}^{1/2} \qquad (1.10)$$

in which n represents the concentration, r_A and r_B the mean collision radii, and m_A and m_B the mass of A and B, respectively, with k representing the Boltzmann constant and T the absolute temperature as usual.

The mean diameters were determined from viscosity studies and the masses from known molecular weights. With given concentrations of the reactants and the physical data concerning their radii and masses, the total number of collisions at a given temperature can be readily computed. The probability that the collision will be the right kind for reaction can be taken as exp $(- E/RT)$, but the value of E at this stage of the theory had to be determined empirically from the variation in specific rate with temperature. Replacing the constant A of equation (1.9) with Z of equation (1.10), we have for bimolecular reactions

$$v = Ze^{-E/RT} = n_A n_B (r_A + r_B)^2 \left\{ 8\pi kT \left(\frac{1}{m_A} + \frac{1}{m_B} \right) \right\}^{1/2} e^{-E/RT} \quad (1.11)$$

The relation given by (1.11) was successful in calculating the absolute rates of certain reactions within better than an order of magnitude of the observed values. In other instances the rates computed on the same basis are found to differ by several powers of 10 from the observed rates. Thus the theory was evidently incomplete in at least two respects: (1) the collision factor Z led to the approximately right result only in a restricted number of reactions, and (2) the activation energy E had no precise theoretical meaning.

Without inquiring further, for the moment, into the exact meaning of E, it is clear that equation (1.11) could be made to fit the data by multiplying Z by a factor P. It is reasonable to assume that, among reactions which proceed at rates much slower than would be expected from (1.11), there exists some sort of hindrance to the expected number of successful collisions. Thus, letting P represent a "probability" or "steric" factor, we have

$$v = PZe^{-E/RT} \quad (1.12)$$

For "slow" reactions the value of P varies from 10^{-1} to 10^{-8}, whereas in certain other instances the value of P is much greater than unity. Moreover, if P of equation (1.12) is taken to be constant, the observed variations in the value of E remain to be explained. The factor Z will change with temperature, since the expression for Z contains the term $T^{1/2}$, but this term has only a small influence, amounting to about 300 cal, on the numerical value of E.

In its early development, the shortcomings of the collision theory arose from a lack of understanding of the potential energies of molecules. Atoms were first treated as hard spheres, or points with mass, and to a large extent the same applied to molecules. The kinetic theory of gases sufficed to calculate the average kinetic energy of these hard spheres and the probability of their collisions at a given temperature. For monatomic gases the concept of a hard sphere is near enough; an atom has only three degrees of freedom, comprising motion in the x, y, and z directions. A diatomic gas molecule, however, has six degrees of freedom, viz., three of translation, two of rotation, and one of vibration, and in general any molecule has $3n$ degrees of freedom, n representing the number of atoms in the molecule. The total kinetic energy of the molecule is made up of motions in all its degrees of freedom, and, when this energy becomes equal to or greater than the activation energy, collision may result in reaction. The concept of the molecule as a hard sphere is not sufficient for interpretation of the activation energy E except in the most general way, namely, as the minimum energy required for reaction to take place. The number N_a of molecules that acquire this energy, by a series of successive collisions with other molecules or by any means such as radiation, among the total number N_t of the population is given by the Boltzmann-like expression

$$N_a/N_t = (\Sigma\omega_a/\Sigma\omega_t)e^{-E/kT} \tag{1.13}$$

where $\Sigma\omega_a$ and $\Sigma\omega_t$ are the weighted number of separate states corresponding to these respective energies. Assuming that the velocity of the reaction is proportional to the ratio N_a/N_t, it follows that the velocity will be given by an equation of the form of the Arrhenius equation (1.9). Moreover, other things such as $\Sigma\omega_a$ and $\Sigma\omega_t$ being equal, the velocity of different reactions at a given temperature will be determined by the value of E; the higher the value of E, the higher in general will be the temperature required for a given velocity of reaction. When proper examples are selected, reaction rates appear to depend almost wholly upon the value of E, but this is by no means invariably so. In general, however, the fraction of molecules which by chance attain an energy much greater than the average would be expected to be smaller than the fraction which attain an energy only slightly greater than the average. Raising the temperature has an exponential effect in increasing the number of molecules with sufficient activation energy E.

The early application of the collision theory to bimolecular reactions was successful only in those instances when, in effect, the molecules behaved essentially as hard spheres. Discrepancies between the calculated and observed rates (given the experimentally determined value of E) could be attributed to uncertainties in the exact diameters of the molecules. With advances in the understanding of the structure of atoms and of the forces which hold molecules together or which lead them to exchange partners, the whole picture became much clearer in outline and the detailed picture of potential energy became a fundamental consideration in reaction kinetics.

Energies of molecules

Viewed as hard spheres, the atoms of a monatomic gas could conceivably undergo changes in rotational energy on collision with another hard sphere of the same or of a different species, but this does not occur. The atoms of a monatomic gas move through space with only their three translational degrees of freedom, and they collide without changing their rotation. With a diatomic gas, however, while the molecule again has three degrees of translational freedom, the molecule moving as a whole through space, it has, in addition, two rotational degrees of freedom and one vibrational degree of freedom. The components of the rotational degrees of freedom consist in rotation about two of the three possible axes at right angles to each other; the third axis is along the line of attraction between the two atoms. Along this third axis lies the vibrational degree of freedom, the two atoms approaching and separating in the manner of simple harmonic motion. Momentarily, at the end of a single period of oscillation, the energy of this degree of freedom is entirely potential, whereas in the middle of a single period of oscillation the energy is purely kinetic. In Fig. 1.1 the potential energy is plotted as a function of distance. This type of relation, as we shall see, is an important aspect of modern rate theory.

Referring to Fig. 1.1, as the atoms come close together the potential energy rises sharply as would be expected from the very slight compressibility of the atoms. As they move apart, the potential energy decreases, passes through a minimum, and rises asymptotically to a limiting value corresponding to dissociation. The level in which the atoms of a molecule oscillate depends upon the total energy of the molecule, and it is only at the temperature of absolute zero that all the molecules are in the lowest level. It is interesting to picture, with the aid of Fig. 1.1, what happens as the temperature is raised.

Let us begin with a population of diatomic (gas) molecules at absolute zero. The molecules, all in the lowest level, have a "zero point" energy, $\frac{1}{2}h\nu$. This level, opposite the zero of Fig. 1.1, lies a half quantum above the potential minimum. At absolute zero the molecules crowd together to form a solid, in which the three translational degrees of freedom of the gas have been reduced to three vibrations. The rotations likewise change over into vibrations. Thus translational and rotational motion are restricted as if a box has closed in around each molecule so that it can only vibrate. Now, when energy is supplied to the system by radiation, any given molecule can absorb a portion of the energy only in a single lump, corresponding to $h\nu$, Planck's constant times the characteristic frequency of vibration of the particular species of molecules. As long as the molecule behaves as a simple harmonic oscillator, it will absorb only one quantum of energy at a time, and jump into the next higher quantum energy level. The situation may be compared to the strings on a violin. The frequency of vibration depends upon the tightness of the string. It can be set into vibration by sound waves from another instrument only when the frequencies are the same. When the frequencies are the same, the amplitude of the absorbing string increases; it vibrates at a higher level of energy. Similarly, when set into vibration by scraping or plucking,

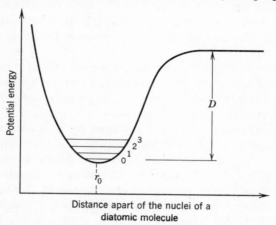

Fig. 1.1. Potential energy as a function of the distance between the nuclei of a diatomic molecule. The equilibrium distance between the atoms is represented at r_0, and the energy required for dissociation of the two atoms is indicated by the vertical length D. The horizontal lines represent successively higher quantum levels of energy.

the string vibrates always at its characteristic frequency, but with an amplitude that depends upon the force and duration of the mechanical stimulus.

The ammonia inversion reaction is measured by the absorption of microwaves. It is easily one of the most accurately measured of all rate processes, and it provides the basis for one of the most accurate measures of time known, the "ammonia clock" (cf. Clemence, 1952; Townes, 1952). Every second, the molecule "turns inside out" 23,870,090,000 times, i.e., the nitrogen atom becomes shifted from its position with respect to the plane made by the three hydrogen atoms to the symmetrical point on the opposite side of this plane. The frequency given is for the level $J = 3$, $K = 3$ (cf. Gordy, 1948). The corresponding frequency of radiation has a wavelength of about 1.25 cm; radio waves of this frequency are therefore absorbed by ammonia.

Although the quantum theory holds that increase in amplitude of vibration takes place in single jumps from one level to the next higher level for the harmonic oscillator, actual molecules differ more or less from simple harmonic motion and so occasionally emit quanta of nearly double and higher near multiples of the lower energy unit. Thus molecules are machines for changing the size of quanta. In the Compton effect, x-rays communicate a fraction of their quantum of energy to an electron in collision. In the Raman effect a fraction of a quantum of energy is absorbed. Furthermore, collisions between molecules excite them to new states and so increase or decrease the size of quanta which can be emitted. Energy quanta thus undergo all sorts of changes in energy content and therefore in color.

The absorption of energy, whether as a quantum of radiation or by collision with another molecule, takes place within such a short period of time that it is virtually instantaneous. The actual process occurs within a fraction of the period of a single vibration, i.e., in a time of the order of 10^{-13} sec. A quantum of energy acquired by a molecule in a lump becomes distributed among the various degrees of freedom of rotation and vibration. Translational levels have never been observed, but their positions are well known from theory. Rotational absorption falls in the far infrared, whereas the vibrational spectrum is in the near infrared. However, the energy spacing between these levels is ordinarily measured as an increment to an electronic transition usually falling in the ultra-violet. Fluorescence occurs when part of the absorbed energy is emitted; quenching occurs if the absorbed energy becomes distributed among vibrational degrees of freedom of the same or of different molecules.

With rise of temperature above absolute zero the individual molecules in a population increase their amplitude of vibration until the solid melts to a liquid, and the liquid vaporizes to a gas. Larger and larger numbers of molecules are driven into the higher quantum levels of energy. Whether or not an appreciable number of the gas molecules get into a level high enough to dissociate at a given temperature depends upon how tightly the atoms are held together. No diatomic gas dissociates to an appreciable extent at room temperature. Iodine molecules are among the most readily dissociating. At atmospheric pressure, 50 per cent dissociate at 1,370°C. Hydrogen fluoride at atmospheric pressure must reach about 6,000°C, the temperature of the surface of the sun, for 50 per cent or more of the molecules to dissociate. The dissociation energy for the H—F bond, 147.5 kilocalories (kcal) (Pauling, 1940a) is the highest known for any single bond. It is interesting that in aqueous solution the two atoms of H—F separate as ions with practically no activation energy. This follows from the fact that the reaction is immeasurably fast even at room temperature.

In Fig. 1.1 the lower part of the curve is very nearly a parabola.   The complete curve, however, is difficult to describe mathematically, and no exact equation has been derived.   Morse (1929) has proposed an equation (1.14) which is accurate enough for most purposes and provides a convenient means of finding the potential energy E of a diatomic molecule as a function of distance apart of the atoms:

$$E = D'[e^{-2a(r-r_0)} - 2e^{-a(r-r_0)}] \qquad (1.14)$$

Here D' is the heat of dissociation of the molecule plus the zero point energy (represented in Fig. 1.1 by the total vertical distance from the minimum of the curve to the plateau), r_0 is the equilibrium distance apart of the atoms, r is any other distance apart, and a is equal to $\pi v(2\mu/D')^{1/2}$ where μ, the "reduced mass," equals $m_1 m_2/(m_1 + m_2)$, m_1 and m_2 being the masses of the respective atoms.   Thus, knowing the masses of the atoms, the potential energy of the molecule can be plotted as a function of distance apart of the atoms on the basis of spectroscopic data and equation (1.14).   Since r_0 is never far from 1 Ångstrom unit (Å), it is usually sufficient to plot the Morse curve for distances of about 0.5 to 4.0 Å.

The collision process in a simple reaction

In a diatomic molecule BC the force which holds the two atoms B and C together is made up of two parts: (1) an electrostatic attraction, usually referred to as the "Coulombic" force, and (2) an "exchange" force resulting from the quantum-mechanical resonance of the valence electrons. When there is a reaction involving a change of partners, the exchange force is quantitatively much more significant than the Coulombic force. Let us consider, as a simple example, what happens when an atom A reacts with BC to give AB plus C.   For this reaction to occur, A and BC must collide with sufficient violence for the bond in BC to be broken while the bond in AB is strengthened.   Suppose that these reactants approach in such manner that each of the atoms falls along the same straight line.   With A initially at a great distance the attractive and repulsive forces between A and BC are negligible.   After reaction, the forces between AB and C are similarly very small.   During reaction the forces between each of the components are significant.   Diagrammatically we may picture these three stages as follows, r_0 representing the equilibrium distance of the molecule BC, and r_0' the equilibrium distance of AB:

(a)   A   B———r_0———C

(b)   A— — — — —B— — — — —C   (1.15)

(c)   A———r_0'———B   C

In the diagram (1.15) the sequence of events is as follows. In (a), A is approaching BC against a repulsive force arising from the attempt to crowd more than the two allowed electrons into a single bond. When A comes within sufficiently close range (b), the binding force in BC weakens, C being forced out to an average distance greater than r_0. In stage (b) of the diagram the three atoms are momentarily in the form of a single triatomic molecule with both of its two bonds slightly stretched to about 10 per cent beyond the equilibrium values. The intermediate configuration A— — —B— — —C is unstable and breaks into the products (c). Whenever A and BC approach with an energy equal to or greater than the activation energy and form the intermediate configuration, the result will be either that AB stays together and C goes off or the reactants are reconstituted. When the net rate of A plus BC going to AB plus C is equal to the rate of AB plus C going to BC plus A, the reaction is in equilibrium, and the ratio of the specific rates is the equilibrium constant.

Parenthetically, it is interesting to comment here on the stretching of bonds in stage (b) of the diagram (1.15) which results in a slight increase in the average bond lengths. In unimolecular reactions, where the stretching is the only effect, more space is occupied in the activated than in the normal state. Thus, by the Braun-Le Chatelier principle, pressure will decrease the concentration of activated states and slow the reaction, if, as we shall see is true, this principle applies to rates as it does to equilibria. In simple bimolecular reactions in the liquid state the expansion of volume accompanying bond stretching is more than offset by the contraction accompanying the overlap binding of additional atoms. In this case, where the total space occupied by the activated configurations is less than that occupied by the normal configurations, pressure should increase the reaction rate.

The germ of the modern rate theory is contained in the view of chemical reactions just discussed. The intermediate configuration is referred to as the "activated complex." Its general significance in chemical reactions was set forth in a complete theory of rate processes (Eyring, 1935a; Wynne-Jones and Eyring, 1935). This theory generalized an earlier paper by Pelzer and Wigner (1932). Some authors have preferred to give up the expression activated state, which was used by Arrhenius, and substitute the expression transition state. Polanyi and Evans (1935), besides developing the general theory, gave a particularly clear exposition of pressure effects from the modern viewpoint. The precise meaning of the activated complex is understandable only with extensive reference to quantum and statistical mechanics, the bare outlines of which are given in Chapters 4 and 5. With particular reference to terminology, however, there is one aspect which it is perhaps well to emphasize even in the course of this brief introduction, namely, that activated state and transition state are not altogether appropriate expressions. There are many possible activated states, according to the energy levels occupied by the activated complex, just as there are many possible normal states, according to the energy levels occupied by the normal molecules. The activated complex is a system at the top of the potential barrier with wide variation of other coordinates, like any other molecule. The nature of the activated complex requires a consideration of potential energy surfaces to make this notion clearer.

Potential energy surfaces

Referring back to the diagram (1.15), the variation in potential energy of the system with distance apart of the components is represented

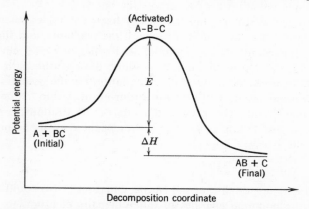

Fig. 1.2. Diagram illustrating the change in potential energy for the reaction $A + BC \rightleftharpoons AB + C$. The activation energy is represented by the vertical distance E, and the heat of reaction ΔH by the vertical distance between the level of heat content of $A + BC$ and of $AB + C$, respectively.

qualitatively by the curve of Fig. 1.2. As A approaches BC and comes within its reaction sphere, the distance between B and C increases to maintain the lowest potential energy. The potential energy rises and reaches a maximum when the distances A to B and B to C are momentarily greater than the equilibrium distance of either pair by about 10 per cent. In order for the reaction to proceed in either direction it is necessary for the reactants to go through this intermediate, critical configuration having a certain minimum energy, and the intermediate configuration is the same whether the reaction is proceeding from left to right or from right to left, except for direction of motion. The history of any one of the activated complexes differs according to the direction from which it has been formed, i.e., according to whether A———B———C (see Fig. 1.2) has been formed from A + BC or from AB + C, and quantum mechanics determines the extent to which the activated complexes formed from the left side proceed over to the right, and vice versa. In some reactions there is evidence that the top of the barrier has a more or less marked depression. In this case the activated complex may decompose to the products of the reaction, or reconstitute the reactants, according to a quantum-mechanical probability characterized by the transmission coefficient, κ. For the moment, the important thing to note is that between the initial and final states there exists a potential energy barrier which must be surmounted before reaction can occur in either direction. In general, although the energy barrier will be crossed in all possible ways, the number of crossings by the easiest way will be most probable. The favored route is the lowest way across the barrier.

The problem of calculating the energy barrier involves calculating the energies for all possible configurations of the reactants, and this involves as many dimensions as are required to fix the potential energy. The curve of Fig. 1.2 represents a section along the reaction path. London (1928, 1929) succeeded in deriving an equation for the potential energy E of a three-atom system and also for a four-atom system. For the three-atom system, letting Q represent the sum of the Coulombic energies of A, B, and C, and letting α, β, and γ represent the corresponding exchange energies, the energy E is

$$E = Q - \{\tfrac{1}{2}[(\alpha - \beta)^2 + (\beta - \gamma)^2 + (\gamma - \alpha)^2]\}^{1/2} \qquad (1.16)$$

Eyring (1930) suggested that the Morse equation (1.14) could be used to compute the potential energies of different pairs of atoms to put in the London equation (1.16). Eyring and Polanyi (1930, 1931) calculated a potential energy surface for the reaction $H + H_2 \rightarrow H_2 + H$, making the simplifying assumption that the Coulombic energy is a constant fraction of the total binding energy, as was suggested by the Heitler and London (1927) and Sugiura (1927) calculations for H_2.

Figure 1.3 illustrates a potential energy surface for the conversion of ortho to para hydrogen, taken from Eyring, Gershinowitz, and Sun (1935). When plotted on 60-degree coordinates rather than rectangular coordinates, a mass point sliding on the surface represents the distribution of the relative translational and vibrational energies. The respective curves at the top and at the right of the contour map illustrate the profile of the map at these cross sections; these sections are the Morse curves for H_2. Three-dimensional models have been constructed of potential surfaces according to the method used in plotting Fig. 1.3. A ball rolling on such a surface very nearly follows the path which a mass point follows

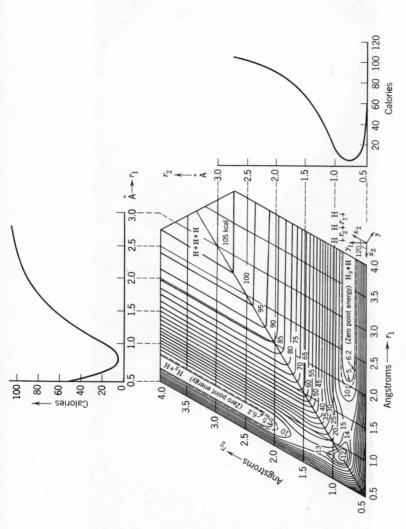

Fig. 1.3. Potential energy surface for three hydrogens in the ortho-para conversion, H + H₂ ⇌ H₂ + H, assuming 14 per cent Coulombic energy (Eyring, Gershinowitz, and Sun, 1935). The curves at the top and at the right of the figure are the Morse curves for H + H₂, showing the profile of the valley.

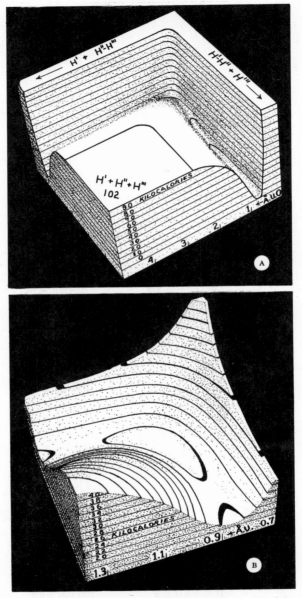

Fig. 1.4.   (A) Drawing made from a photograph of a model of the potential energy surface for the reaction $H + H_2 \rightleftharpoons H_2 + H$, constructed by Goodeve (1934) according to the contour lines calculated by Eyring and Polyani (1931). In this model, only the resonance forces are considered.   (B) Close-up of the saddle region of a model in which Coulombic as well as resonance forces have been taken into account.

theoretically, but deviates somewhat from the expected kinetic-potential energy changes because of friction which cannot be eliminated from the practical model and because the potential energy should be in the plane rather than be supplied by gravity acting vertically. The shape of a potential energy surface can be somewhat more clearly visualized in a three-dimensional model, as illustrated in Fig. 1.4. In more complicated reactions a model cannot be so readily constructed, because additional dimensions must be taken into account.

The potential energy surface under consideration (Fig. 1.3) consists of two valleys with a barrier or "pass" in between. Along the left side and

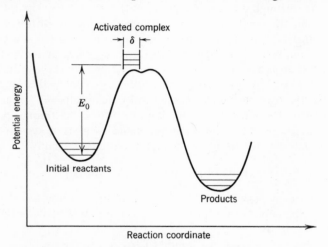

Fig. 1.5. Potential energy diagram for a surface such as the one illustrated in Fig. 1.3.

along the bottom side the walls are steep, corresponding to the rapid rise in potential energy as the distance between the two atoms of H_2 becomes less than the equilibrium value. The equilibrium distance is represented by the floor of the valley. In approaching the barrier the surface rises as the distances between all three hydrogen atoms affect the potential. The barrier itself is like a saddle, and inspection of Fig. 1.3 shows that in the saddle area occurs a basin of slightly lower potential energy. A cross section of the surface along the reaction path is illustrated in Fig. 1.5. The distance E_0 is the activation energy at the temperature of absolute zero. Although in principle this activation energy can be calculated, the accuracy of the value obtained depends upon the accuracy with which the potential surface is known. Even for the simplest reactions it is difficult to arrive *a priori* at a close value by means of the London equation.

Since the predicted rate will be off by a factor of 10 at room temperature for each 1.3 kcal that the activation energy is in error, it is not practical to rely on the value for activation energy calculated *a priori* by the approximate method outlined in the foregoing discussion. However, if the per cent Coulombic energy be chosen to cause E_0 to agree with experiment, the resultant surfaces are satisfactory.

Statistical calculation of reaction rates

Knowing the potential energy surface, the problem of calculating the rate of the reaction is simply that of calculating the rate at which mass points move through the saddle point over the barrier separating the products from the reactants. Since the reaction occurs through a continuous change of coordinates in passing from the normal states of the reactants in one valley, through the activated complex at the top of the barrier, to the products in the other valley, we consider a length δ at the top of the barrier, and an average velocity $\bar{v}$ of crossing this length. It follows that the reaction rate is then given by the number C^* of activated complexes in unit volume along the length δ times the frequency $\bar{v}/\delta$ of crossing and the quantum-mechanical chance κ that a system having crossed the barrier will continue through to reaction. Thus

$$\text{Rate of reaction} = C^*(\bar{v}/\delta)\kappa \tag{1.17}$$

Letting C_{AB} and C_C represent the concentration of reactants AB and C, respectively, the concentration of activated complexes in a length δ at the top of the barrier is

$$C^* = K^{\ddagger} \frac{(2\pi m^{\ddagger} kT)^{1/2} \delta}{h} C_{AB} C_C \tag{1.18}$$

where $K^{\ddagger}$ is an equilibrium constant for activated and reactant molecules, $m^{\ddagger}$ is the effective mass of the activated complex for motion along the reaction coordinate, k is the Boltzmann constant, h is Planck's constant, and T is the absolute temperature. The average velocity $\bar{v}$ in the forward direction along the length δ is

$$\bar{v} = \frac{\displaystyle\int_0^{\infty} (p/m^{\ddagger}) e^{-p^2/2m^{\ddagger}kT}\, dp}{\displaystyle\int_0^{\infty} e^{-p^2/2m^{\ddagger}kT}\, dp} = \left(\frac{kT}{2\pi m^{\ddagger}}\right)^{1/2} \tag{1.19}$$

where p is the momentum along the reaction coordinate, and the equation for velocity is the familiar one in statistical mechanics. Substituting from equations (1.18) and (1.19) into (1.17), we find

$$\text{Rate of reaction} = K^{\ddagger} \frac{(2\pi m^{\ddagger}kT)^{1/2}\delta}{h} \left(\frac{kT}{2\pi m^{\ddagger}}\right)^{1/2} \frac{1}{\delta} \kappa C_{AB}C_C$$

$$= K^{\ddagger}\kappa \frac{kT}{h} C_{AB}C_C \tag{1.20}$$

For the barrier diagrammed in Fig. 1.5, κ will be close to one-half, since the system is apt to get lost in the depression between the twin barriers. On the other hand, if there is but one barrier, $K^{\ddagger}$ will be smaller by one-half because of a symmetry factor for the activated complex and κ will exactly compensate this factor by becoming unity. Consequently, the same result is obtained with either a single or a twin barrier. When reactants and products are different we have in general a single highest barrier and take $\kappa = 1$.

Equation (1.20) is general for any reaction involving a barrier crossing, and it is basic in our subsequent considerations. The constant $K^{\ddagger}$ is like that for any equilibrium between reactants and products. In it we have taken the length δ along the barrier so that

$$\delta = h/(2\pi m^{\ddagger}kT)^{1/2} \tag{1.21}$$

This length usually lies between $\frac{1}{10}$ and 1 Å. Its precise value does not matter, since it cancels out of the final expression. Since $K^{\ddagger}$ is like an equilibrium constant, we can write

$$K^{\ddagger} = e^{-\Delta F^{\ddagger}/RT} = e^{-\Delta H^{\ddagger}/RT}e^{\Delta S^{\ddagger}/R} \tag{1.22}$$

Here $\Delta F^{\ddagger}$, $\Delta H^{\ddagger}$, and $\Delta S^{\ddagger}$, are the standard free energy, heat, and entropy of activation, respectively. Thus the methods of thermodynamics and statistical mechanics lie at our disposal in coping with reaction kinetics. The specific reaction rate k' may now be written

$$k' = \kappa(kT/h)K^{\ddagger} = \kappa(kT/h)e^{-\Delta F^{\ddagger}/RT} = \kappa(kT/h)e^{-\Delta H^{\ddagger}/RT}e^{\Delta S^{\ddagger}/R} \tag{1.23}$$

Furthermore, from thermodynamics, we have

$$(\partial F/\partial p)_T = V \tag{1.24}$$

and since $\Delta F^{\ddagger} = F^{\ddagger} - F_n$, we have

$$(\partial \Delta F^{\ddagger}/\partial p)_T = (\partial F^{\ddagger}/\partial p)_T - (\partial F_n/\partial p)_T = V^{\ddagger} - V_n = \Delta V^{\ddagger} \tag{1.25}$$

Here $F^{\ddagger}$ and F_n are the free energies for the activated and normal states, respectively, $V^{\ddagger}$ and V_n are the corresponding volumes, and p is the pressure. $\Delta V^{\ddagger}$ is the change in volume in passing from reactants to activated complex.

A true equilibrium constant is the ratio between specific rates of a given reaction in the forward and in the backward directions. Each of these rates is given by an equation of the form (1.20) or (1.23). The reaction comes to equilibrium when the concentration of reactants and of products is such that the backward balances the forward rate. In the quasi-equilibrium constant for activation, the reactants and the activated complex are not in equilibrium in the sense that they are constantly going directly from the one to the other, and it is a basic postulate of the modern theory that the number of activated complexes formed from the final states has no direct influence on the number of activated complexes formed from the initial states. It is true, of course, that $(1 - \kappa)$ is the chance that the initial reactants are reconstituted from the activated complex. This may be expected to occur especially when there is a depression at the top of the barrier. Thus, after the activated complex has crossed the first of twin barriers, the system may lodge in the depression, and when it decomposes it may do so in the direction from which it came, giving the original reactants, rather than going over the second barrier to products.

Partition functions

The constant $K^{\ddagger}$ is the ratio of the partition function of the activated complex to that for the reactants. The partition functions of any atom or molecule, including the activated complex, have the value $F = \Sigma e^{-\epsilon_i/kT}$, where ϵ_i is the energy of the ith state of the molecule and the summation is over all states. As the concentration of a species is always proportional to its partition function, we have an invaluable means of expressing equilibrium constants as ratios of the appropriate partition functions. Since the energy of a molecule can be written as the sum of energies for its degrees of freedom and this energy occurs in the exponent of the partition function, it follows that the overall partition function can be written as a product of partition functions for all the degrees of freedom. The partition function f_{tr} for three translational degrees of freedom is

$$f_{tr} = [(2\pi mkT)^{3/2}/h^3] V \tag{1.26}$$

in which V is the volume of the container and the other symbols are the same as in equations (1.18), (1.20), and (1.21). In those equations the partition function for translation for a length δ at the top of the barrier was considered, since this was involved in the expression for the probability of the occurrence of the activated complex at the top of the barrier. Expressions for the partition functions for the various other degrees of freedom, which must be taken into account in the complete calculation of reaction rates, are given in the following chapters. For the purposes of the present discussion, it is sufficient to remark that the appropriate expressions are derived from quantum- and statistical-mechanical theory.

Since the equilibrium constant for any system can be expressed in terms of the partition functions of the molecules concerned, equation (1.23) can be written

$$k' = \kappa(kT/h)(F^{\ddagger}/F_A F_B)e^{-E_0/RT} \tag{1.27}$$

Here $F^{\ddagger}$ is the partition function per unit volume of the activated complex, F_A, F_B are the partition functions of the reactants, and E_0 is the activation energy at absolute zero. The essential details concerning the calculation of the partition functions are given in the chapters which follow. For a particular system the physical data necessary for computing the nuclear, electronic, vibrational, and rotational energies can be obtained from spectroscopy, and data for computing the translational energies can be obtained from the mass and velocity.

From equations (1.22) and (1.23) it is apparent that the term $F^{\ddagger}/F_A F_B$ in equation (1.27) contains the entropy of activation, $\Delta S^{\ddagger}$. Frequently, especially for unimolecular reactions, the activated complex is a looser structure than the reactants and the entropy of activation is positive. In some reactions, however, the activated complex is a more rigid structure than the reactants, and the entropy of activation is negative. The specific rate in all cases, when the transmission coefficient κ is unity, depends upon the product of the exponential terms involving entropy and heats of activation, or, in other words, the free energy change in going from the normal states to the activated complex, the rate of decomposition of the activated complex always being equal to kT/h. For a reaction to proceed at a measurable rate at temperatures between about $0°$ and $50°C$ the free energy of activation must fall roughly between 20 and 30 kcal. This is the range of temperature which is of especial interest in biological processes. The activation energy for enzyme reactions frequently is of the order of 10 to 20 kcal, and, of course, T times the change in entropy of activation makes up the balance of $\Delta F^{\ddagger}$. In processes such as the denaturation of proteins, characterized by much higher activation energies, of the order of 100 kcal, the rate is measurable at temperatures as low as $50°$ only because of the large increase in entropy which compensates for the high heat of activation, bringing the free energy of activation again to a value that permits the reaction to proceed at the observable rate.

Interpretation of the Arrhenius and other theories

From equations (1.20) and (1.23) it is evident that the constant A of the Arrhenius equation (1.9) has the approximate equivalence

$$A \simeq \kappa(kT/h)e^{\Delta S^{\ddagger}/R} \tag{1.28}$$

The fact, referred to earlier, that deviations are observed to occur from the rates expected according to the Arrhenius equation, especially when the range of temperature is great, is to be attributed in part to the fact that A is slightly influenced by temperature, in the term kT/h, and in part by variation of $\Delta S^{\ddagger}$ with temperature. Much more significant for a changing A and energy of activation is a change in mechanism. The term $e^{-E/RT}$ of the Arrhenius equation is not identical with $e^{-E_0/RT}$ of equation (1.27). The E of Arrhenius has no simple significance, whereas E_0 is the activation energy at absolute zero, i.e., the difference at absolute zero between the energy per mole of activated complex and the sum of the energies of the reactants. The Arrhenius equation made no attempt to account for the relation between pressure and reaction rates. This relation, however, follows from the modern equilibrium theory (equation 1.25).

The inadequacy of the simple collision theory to elucidate the meaning of the A in the Arrhenius equation has been briefly considered. Other theories which bear on the development of the theory of absolute reaction rates are referred to in papers and monographs (e.g., Eyring, 1935a,b, 1938; Wynne-Jones and Eyring, 1935; Glasstone, Laidler, and Eyring, 1941) and need not be discussed in detail here. The work of Herzfeld (1919), however, calls for special mention, as follows.

If the absolute reaction rate theory is used to calculate the rate of unimolecular decomposition of a diatomic molecule of concentration C_3, we have

$$\frac{dC_3}{dt} = \kappa \frac{kT}{h} \frac{\dfrac{[2\pi(m_1 + m_2)kT]^{3/2}}{h^3} \dfrac{8\pi^2 I^* kT}{\sigma^* h^2} e^{-E_0/RT} C_3}{\dfrac{[2\pi(m_1 + m_2)kT]^{3/2}}{h^3} \dfrac{8\pi^2 IkT}{\sigma h^2} (1 - e^{-h\nu/kT})^{-1}}$$

$$= \kappa \frac{kT}{h} \frac{s^2}{d^2} (1 - e^{-h\nu/kT}) e^{-E_0/RT} C_3 \qquad (1.29)$$

The moments of inertia of the activated complex and of the original molecule are $I^* = [m_1 m_2/(m_1 + m_2)]s^2$ and $I = m_1 m_2 d^2/(m_1 + m_2)$, respectively, where s, d, m_1, and m_2 are the distances between the molecule in the activated and in the normal states and the masses of atom one and atom two, respectively. Aside from the factor κ this equation was obtained by Herzfeld in 1919. He used $Q = E_0$. This result is the Siamese twin of the collision theory. In fact, it was obtained by using the collision theory for combination of the atom pair, together with van't Hoff's result that the specific rate in the forward direction over the specific rate in the backward direction equals the equilibrium constant, which equilibrium constant Herzfeld then calculated from statistical mechanics.

The reason why Herzfeld's result was not more fruitful is that this example, involving two atoms, never proceeds by this mechanism and, if it did, it would involve an extraordinarily small value for the omitted factor κ. A third body is always necessary to supply the energy to cause decomposition, and for the bimolecular combination a third body must be present to stabilize the diatomic molecule by carrying off some of the extra energy. Thus there is no single example to which collision theory or this decomposition theory of Herzfeld's applies exactly. It was not until the nature of the activated complex involving more than two atoms was clearly understood that the theory of absolute reaction rates could be formulated.

Application of the modern theory to biological processes

In applying absolute rate theory to specific reactions, using established values for the properties of the reactants, the calculations necessary to predict the rate of even the simplest reactions are extensive and complicated. In biological reactions the rate is ultimately controlled by enzymes and other proteins having such complex structure and high molecular weight that it is not feasible to calculate the absolute rates from first principles. The same theory applies, however, to complicated as well as to simple reactions and can be used to gain a clearer insight into the mechanism of biological processes. In many cases, for example, it is profitable to visualize the biological process in terms of potential energy surfaces. In any case the quantitative variation in rate with such factors as temperature and pressure is to be interpreted on the basis of the modern theory.

Physiological processes represent a higher order of complexity than is encountered in the non-living world. Thus Schroedinger (1946) has considered it impossible for the statistical laws of chemistry and physics, as known at present, to account for the orderly and lawful behavior of the gene, which contains at most only a few million atoms. Actually nothing more unusual than templates, which serve as patterns to guide reactions, need be supposed. The extent to which the specific molecule —a given protein or enzyme—itself acts as a template, or is formed with the aid of some other type of template, possibly nucleic acids, cannot be stated with certainty at present. The fact that elementary biological compounds such as amino acids are predominantly levorotatory, whereas the chemical reactivity of levo- and dextrorotatory compounds is exactly the same, seems to require that, in the earliest beginning of life before more complex templates came into existence, a specific optically active compound acted as the master template. The predominance of the one type of optical isomer in living organisms argues in favor of the origin of life from one or at most very few molecules which set the pattern for all future development. The emergence of dextro isomers, either by independent origin or by Walden inversions of the corresponding levo isomer already in existence, would then be expected to survive in descendants only when such a compound was not a handicap in the competition for survival. An example of this kind is the occurrence of levopinene in European turpentine, and its dextro isomer in American turpentine (cf. Conant, 1936). To explain predominance of one isomer in one geographical region and the other in a second region, it may be supposed that the new pinene occurred as the result of a mutation in some plant. Since it is probably an end product in metabolism, the plant was probably neither helped nor penalized by the inversion and the two types of plants existed side by side. Later, some independent mutation having survival value occurred in the plant with inverted pinene and then such plants competitively won out over those with the uninverted variety.

Other special aspects of reaction rate control in biology arise from the restrictions imposed through the separation of the cell interior from its external environment by a membrane which allows the passage of different ions and molecules at different rates. As a result of the faster differential diffusion through the membrane of positive over negative ions formed inside the cell, either as new ions or ions solvated by metabolites, most cells (at "rest") are positively charged on their outer surface. In both plant and animal cells these potential differences may amount to as much as 80 to 100 millivolts (mv). Alterations in the membrane, in metabolism, or in the external environment may profoundly influence the ability of substances to penetrate in either direction. These and other factors are involved in the reversible changes that accompany every nerve impulse. Reaction rate theory is applicable to the general problems of diffusion, in membranes as well as in solutions, and to the phenomena of excitation and conduction in nerves as illustrated briefly in Chapter 14.

In spite of the patent complexity of physiological processes, they often behave kinetically in the manner of a simple reaction. Moreover, there are certain general features of biological reactions that are encountered throughout the living world. For example, the quantitative relation between the observed rate or activity with respect to such variables as pH and temperature invariably goes through a maximum, or "optimum." Although differing in detail among different processes, a thorough understanding of the phenomena in one specific process aids in the interpretation of the others. There is, as it were, a sort of "comparative biophysical chemistry" analogous to "comparative biochemistry" which Kluyver did much to establish in 1931 and which has been developed to advantage also by van Niel (1949a,b) and others. In the following paragraphs some general aspects of biological optima and other problems are briefly discussed.

Biological optima

Although loosely used in the sense of "most favorable," the biological optimum refers to a maximum in the curve relating a given process to a given variable. Complex phenomena such as longevity, intellectual efficiency, and amount of growth have optima with respect to temperature, pressure, *p*H, ionic concentration, etc. The same is true of isolated and purified enzyme systems, as is well known. It is not so well known how

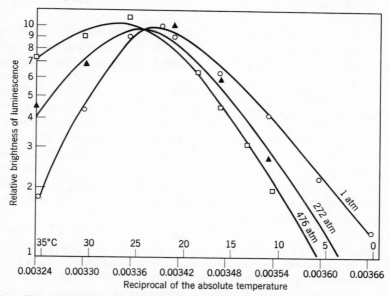

Fig. 1.6. The brightness of luminescence in *Photobacterium phosphoreum* as a function of temperature at three different hydrostatic pressures. The points represent data from experiments by Brown, Johnson, and Marsland (1942). The smooth curves were calculated by Eyring and Magee (1942) in accordance with equation (9.11) as discussed in Chapter 9 (cf. pages 308 to 320).

these optima are interrelated, and the mechanisms through which they may be reversibly altered by various factors. The study of bioluminescence has been particularly fruitful in advancing the understanding of the mechanisms and may be used here as a typical example that will be discussed in detail later, in Chapters 7–10.

In Fig. 1.6 the brightness of bacterial luminescence is plotted relative to dual parameters, temperature, and pressure. During short exposures to the different temperatures and pressures represented in Fig. 1.6 the changes in luminescence intensity are fully reversible. In simplest terms they are accounted for on the hypothesis of two reactions involving the same species of molecules: (1) a light-emitting reaction limited by the activity of an enzyme which we may call luciferase, and (2) an equilibrium between active and inactive forms of this enzyme. The two reactions proceed with a positive heat and volume change of activation and reaction, respectively, but the constants for heat and volume changes in the equilibrium are much larger than those in the catalytic reaction. The result is that the curves go through a maximum as the temperature is raised, and pressure has opposite effects on the observed rate at low and at high temperatures.

Although it is convenient to analyze the data of Fig. 1.6 in terms of two reactions (pp. 309–313), the situation may be viewed in a different way. In luminescence and temperature optima in general, the rate process simply measures the concentration of the activated complex. Now the activated complex is in equilibrium with its environment and is in fact composed of a species whose properties, in particular the heat content, are changing with temperature. So long as the activated complex represents a more energy-rich configuration for its constituents than their average value outside of the activated complex, just so long will a rise in temperature increase the rate. At the point where this ceases to be true the rate process will go through a maximum. At still higher temperatures the constituents of the activated complex are in equilibrium with more energy-rich configurations characterizing the reversibly inactive states of the enzyme. The slopes of the lines plotted in Fig. 1.6 are a measure of the activation energy, whether the slope is negative as at low temperatures, zero at the maximum, or positive as at higher temperatures. This holds for biological temperature curves whenever the rate is governed by a single species of activated complex. When several reactions involving different species of activated complex fix the rate, the situation is more complicated.

An exactly parallel situation exists with respect to pressure. So long as the volume of the activated complex exceeds the average volume of its constituents outside of the complex, just so long will pressure slow down the reaction. At the point where the volumes become equal there is no change in rate under pressure. When the volume of the activated complex is less than that of the reactants, pressure will speed up the rate.

The rate is always a measure of the concentration of activated complexes since the complexes always decompose at the same rate, kT/h. Thus, if we plot the equilibrium constant $K^{\ddagger} = k'h/\kappa kT$ against temperature, we are plotting the concentration of activated complexes when the reactants are at unit concentration. This equilibrium constant behaves in all respects like an ordinary equilibrium constant. For this reason it is interesting to examine the analogous equilibrium constants of certain simple reactions such as the dissociation of fatty acids. Here the relation between temperature and amount of dissociation shows a maximum near room temperature (Fig. 1.7). Harned and Embree (1934) showed that the curve is described by the equation

$$\log K - \log K_m = 1.15 \times 10^{-4}(T - \theta)^2 \tag{1.30}$$

Using ordinary thermodynamics, Magee et al. (1941) found the theoretical curve to be

$$\ln K - \ln K_m = \frac{(\Delta C_p)_\theta}{2R\theta^2}(T - \theta)^2 - \left\{\tfrac{2}{3}(\Delta C_p)_\theta - \tfrac{1}{6}\theta\left(\frac{\partial \Delta C_p}{\partial T}\right)\right\}\frac{(T - \theta)^3}{R\theta^3}$$

$$= 1.03 \times 10^{-4}(T - \theta)^2 + 3.72 \times 10^{-7}(T - \theta)^3 \tag{1.31}$$

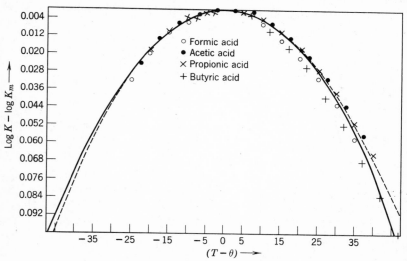

Fig. 1.7. Relation between temperature (abscissa) and amount of dissociation (ordinate) of some fatty acids (Magee et al., 1941).

At a temperature lower by $|T - \theta|$ degrees than the temperature θ of maximum dissociation, the un-ionized constituents have a lower heat content than the ionized, while the converse is true at temperatures $|T - \theta|$ degrees higher than θ.

The curve of Fig. 1.7 is of more than passing interest in relation to biological processes. Thus proteins in phosphate buffers undergo reversible dissociation in a manner that affects their catalytic activity as enzymes. In Fig. 1.7 the actual difference in amount of dissociation at the different temperatures is not great. In a protein, however, the effect of temperature on dissociation, and consequently on catalytic activity, is multiplied because of the relatively large number of ionizable groups. Fundamentally, the "reversible denaturation" of proteins involves, in part, the same mechanism as the one which applies to fatty acids.

An instructive rate process in inorganic chemistry that also shows a maximum with respect to temperature is the rate of causing DI molecules to jump from the jth to the $(j + 1)$th rotational level by absorption of microwaves. The number of molecules jumping per cubic centimeter per second, R, will have the value

$$R = bC_j = bC \frac{j(j + 1)e^{-[j(j+1)h^2]/8\pi IkT}}{8\pi^2 IkT/h^2} \tag{1.32}$$

Here C_j and C are the concentrations of molecules of DI per cubic centimeter in the jth state and in all states, respectively. If R is plotted against

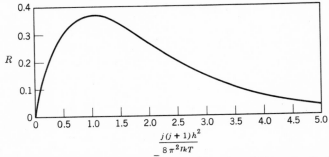

Fig. 1.8. Form of the curve for the rate of jumping of DI molecules from the jth to the $(j + 1)$th rotational level by absorption of microwaves, showing a maximum with respect to temperature.

$[j(j + 1)h_2]/8\pi^2 IkT$, the relation has the appearance shown in Fig. 1.8, since R takes the form $R = bxe^{-x}$.

The above examples (Figs. 1.6, 1.7, and 1.8) should serve to indicate that, whenever the properties of the activated complex have values of some extensive property such as heat content or volume, which equal those of the reactants at some value of temperature or pressure, respectively, this point will be a stationary point (maximum or minimum) for the rate process. Thus the heat or volume of activation may vary with temperature or pressure, respectively, actually going so far as to reverse their sign. It will usually be more convenient, however, to regard the reactants as existing in two or more forms with equilibrium constants relating them. This will lead to explicit expressions for the rate of the reaction which are comparatively simple, especially when multiple equilibria are established between active and inactive forms of an enzyme, as in the presence of inhibitors.

Enzyme inhibition

Enzymes are universally susceptible of thermal inactivation. The extent to which the change from active to inactive forms is reversible depends upon the stability of the product, and this stability may be modified by various factors. In the presence of drugs which reduce the catalytic activity of a given enzyme, the net rate of reaction is still governed by the concentration of activated complexes. Inhibitors ordinarily act by making inactive complexes with the enzyme. The total enzyme is then the sum of all these various species. The equation expressing this sum we will call a conservation equation. In the resulting rate equation (e.g., p. 383) the total enzyme, substrate, and specific reaction rate constant appear in the numerator, and the various equilibrium constants times the concentration of inhibitors to a power occur in the denominator. Here, however, two complications must be taken into account. First, when the enzyme-substrate compound accounts for an appreciable part of the total enzyme concentration it must be included in the conservation equation along with the enzyme inhibitor compounds. Second, certain types of inhibitors, when simultaneously present, are "antagonistic," i.e., they partially counteract each other's inhibitions, as if they combined with each other as well as with the enzyme. These phenomena are discussed at length in Chapter 10. Antagonism of two inhibitors arises when they combine with each other and so eliminate themselves, or when the two of them acting on an enzyme neutralize each other's effect. In the latter case we have a balancing of the effect of the inhibitors to give an intermediate state of the enzyme more active than the compound with either inhibitor alone. This notion of a more active intermediate state of the enzyme is important in various circumstances. For example, sulfanilamide and urethan antagonize each other's inhibition of bioluminescence. Similarly the active configuration of the enzyme is favored by the appropriate temperature and pressure. Thus, with particular reference to the luminescent enzyme, there is evidence that hydrogen ions, low temperatures, hydrostatic pressure, and sulfanilamide each stabilize the molecule in states characterized by relatively low heat content and small volume, whereas hydroxyl ions, high temperature, low pressure, and urethan each stabilize the molecule in states characterized by relatively high heat content and large volume, the catalytically active system being intermediate.

Apart from quantitative differences among different enzymes, the same concept of an intermediate configuration necessary for activity applies in general and is the basis for the optima that are found under the influence of various factors. When more than one parameter is varied, these optima may undergo some fancy changes.

Significance of molecular volume changes

With most small molecules, volume changes of activation or of reaction are small, amounting to only a few cubic centimeters per mole. In biological reactions the volume changes are sometimes quite large, of the order of 100 cc per mole, indicating that changes in a number of groups are concerned. With proteins, this is not surprising in view of the size and complexity of the system. These large volume changes can be interpreted according to at least two different mechanisms which are not mutually exclusive. The evidence is not sufficient as yet to evaluate their relative significance.

First, a large volume change might be expected to result from a drastic change in configuration of a large molecule, with the resultant exposure of groups with changed affinity for the solvent. The remarkable biological specificity of proteins has logically been attributed to the specific manner in which the polypetide chains are folded and held together by weak bonds, such as hydrogen bonds. The process of reversible denaturation has been pictured as consisting largely of a loosening of the native structure accompanied by an unfolding of the molecule. Large changes in entropy may be interpreted as a great increase in the number of accessible configurations. With this unfolding, hydrophobic groups are exposed and the water solubility of the molecule decreases. Because of the lesser attraction of hydrophobic than of hydrophilic groups to water, the molecule then occupies an effectively larger volume. The effects of pressure in reversing and retarding protein denaturation (Chapter 9), as well as the effects of various lipid soluble narcotics in catalyzing protein denaturation (Chapter 10), are consistent with this hypothesis. Moreover, when spread in films, proteins assume a thickness of about 10 Å, which proves a change in structure, in this case not ordinarily reversible.

Other phenomena also have been suggested as involving changes between folded and unfolded states of proteins. For example, the transformation of normal globulin into the chemically and physically indistinguishable antibody globulin possibly involves unfolding and refolding into a different specific configuration of polypeptide chains, without breaking primary covalent linkages (Pauling, 1940b). Reversible unfolding of proteins is possibly involved normally in various physiological processes, including muscle activity, amoeboid and other protoplasmic motion, nerve conduction, electric organ functioning, and osmotic processes (Meyer, 1929, 1951; Astbury, 1946, 1950; Szent-Györygi, 1947; Goldacre and Lorch, 1950; Pauling et al., 1951; Meyer and Mark, 1951). Furthermore, in biosynthesis, if any globular proteins act as templates they must unfold. This is a question of fundamental interest with reference to the mechanisms concerned in the synthesis of biologically specific molecules such as genes, viruses, enzymes, and proteins in general (cf. Troland, 1917; Muller, 1922, 1937; Delbrück, 1941; Eyring, Johnson, and Gensler, 1946; Haurowitz, 1950).

On the other hand, there is another mechanism which can equally well account for the volume changes, namely, the changes in electrostriction accompanying ionization or otherwise loosening of certain bonds. For example, the ionization of $H_2PO_4^-$ to HPO_4^{2-}, frequently present as a buffer, is accompanied by a volume decrease of 24 cc per mole (p. 339). The doubly ionized form draws the water molecules more tightly to itself with a volume decrease. Thus, in the denaturation of proteins in phosphate buffered solutions, the volume changes can at least partly be accounted for as the passage of protons from the proteins onto the HPO_4^- radicals. Moreover, the heat and entropy changes are understandable on the same basis. For example, the heat of reaction in the reversible denaturation of chymotrypsinogen at pH 2 in aqueous solution amounts to 99,600 cal, and the entropy to 316 cal per deg (Eisenberg and Schwert, 1951). Now the heat of fusion for water is 1435 cal per mole, and the entropy is 5.2 E.U. (entropy units, calories per degree). The entropy change in the denaturation of chymotrypsinogen could be accounted for by the melting of an average of 60.7 moles of water, and the heat of reaction by the melting of 69.4 moles of water per mole of protein. This would be explained if 60 to 70 molecules of water were "frozen" on the protein, and if denaturation involved the melting off of this water without pronounced changes in structure. Although the volume change of this reaction has not yet been analyzed, it could be accounted for in terms of the usual electrostriction, provided that there is a decrease in total solvation of ions accompanying the denaturation.

In addition to the foregoing observations, a spiral configuration of polypeptide chains in proteins has recently been proposed (Pauling and Corey, 1950, 1951a-g; Pauling, Corey, and Branson, 1951). This is supported by a number of theoretical considerations. The thickness of the spiral is about 10 Å. Since this is the same as the thickness of proteins spread in monofilms, the change in configuration accompanying spreading does not necessarily involve the type of "unfolding" which has been pictured earlier as free polypeptide chains with a predominance of hydrophilic groups directed below the surface and hydrophobic groups above.

Thus we know of no unequivocal evidence that proteins after synthesis ever reversibly unfold, even partially, into a one-dimensional chain or a two-dimensional network. The hypothesis of unfolding, however, provides a relatively simple and plausible interpretation of many observations on the behavior of proteins, especially with reference to viscosity changes (see, e.g., Simpson, Watson, Levedahl, Schellman, Frensdorf, and

Kauzmann, 1951).   We shall adopt this hypothesis, therefore, as a basis for discussions in subsequent chapters.

Ionizing radiations

The advent of ionizing radiations accompanying nuclear reactions has spurred the investigation of these radiations with reference to biological processes (as general references, cf. Lea, 1946; Barron, 1946; Allen, 1947; Barron, Dickman, Muntz, Singer, 1949; Nims, 1949; Edelmann, 1950a; Warren and Bowers, 1950; Curtis, 1951).

In general, wide differences in sensitivities to ionizing radiations exist not only among different organisms, but also among different tissues and cells.   Bacteria, for example, show little evidence of injury after a dosage of as much as 100,000 roentgen units (r), while only 155 r are sufficient to kill 50 per cent of the individuals (LD_{50}) in a population of *Drosophila* eggs.   Among mammals, guinea pigs succumb to 175 to 250 r, while rabbits require 800 r, with man intermediate, at about 450 r.   Within a given mammal, the lymphatic system appears to be most sensitive to injury, and brain and muscle are least sensitive; moreover, shielding of certain parts of the body such as the adrenal gland (Edelman, 1950b) or the spleen (Jacobson et al., 1949) during total body irradiation tends to reduce mortality or protect against damage to other parts of the body. When only the abdomen of rats is irradiated, the lethal dose is only half as much as that required when other parts of the body are irradiated (Bond et al., 1950).

There is as yet no known agent that will significantly ameliorate the injury resulting from irradiation, although certain "sulfhydryl" enzymes can be partially inactivated by x-radiation, and then partially reactivated by the addition of glutathione after irradiation (Barron, Dickman, Muntz, and Singer, 1949).   It is possible to reduce the mortality of rats by administering cysteine (but not cystine) prior to irradiation (Patt et al., 1948).   Cysteine or glutathione also partially protects against the inactivation of enzymes in solution by x-radiation, and the enzymes containing sulfhydryl groups appear to be most sensitive to radiation damage. Furthermore, some protection, even in animals, results from lowering of the oxygen tension (Dowdy et al., 1950).   Thus conditions favoring chemical reduction evidently lessen the damage by radiation.   The fact that the injury is lessened only if the reducing agent or a lowered oxygen tension exists prior to or during irradiation shows that the primary process of injury is completed rapidly and is not reversed easily.

At the molecular level the effects of radiation must occur either through the direct rupture of a bond in an essential molecule, or through the rupture of such a bond by reactions with radicals formed elsewhere by

the radiation.   The former mechanism is the basis of the "target theory."
The accumulating evidence indicates that quantitatively the more significant amount of injury results from the production of highly reactive
radicals from water.   In this sense the target mechanism concerns only
those particular instances when an essential molecule is struck directly,
while the same results also occur when an essential molecule is destroyed
or inactivated by radicals produced from water, or less frequently from
other molecules.

   Cells and tissues are about three-fourths water.   When water is subjected to x-rays, γ-rays, or α-particles, the following reactions occur
(Allen, 1947):

$$H_2O \xrightarrow{\text{radiation}} H_2O + e$$

$$H_2O + H_2O \longrightarrow H_3O + OH \qquad (1.33)$$

$$e + H_2O \longrightarrow H + OH^-$$

Theoretically, 15 electron volts (ev) are needed to get an ion pair, but
actually 30 ev are required, showing that excited molecules are also formed.

   The reactions (1.33) are primary processes.   When oxygen is present,
there is the additional reaction

$$O_2 + H \rightarrow HO_2 \qquad (1.34)$$

When proteins are present, as in all living cells, these molecules are struck
directly and likewise break into radicals.   Most of the damage to cells,
however, is attributable to the highly reactive H, OH, and, in the presence
of oxygen, HO_2.   Evidence from the mass spectrograph shows that
molecules when ionized by 75-volt electrons break down into a variety of
products.   First, hot ions are produced; the absorbed energy then
wanders through the molecule, and preferentially breaks the weaker
bonds.   Secondly, after a bond is broken, the molecule may break again,
since it still may be hot.   With biological molecules such as enzymes,
kinetic data indicate that they can continue to use up radicals after their
catalytic activity has been lost (cf. Alder and Eyring, 1952).

   The actual number of ions per cubic centimeter required for a lethal
dose in higher animals is small.   It is about the same as the number of
beryllium ions required for a lethal dose.   They must act, therefore, on
necessary constituents present only in small amounts.   Furthermore it
appears likely that one of the important causes of injury resides in damage
to the mechanisms of cell division.   Thus enormous doses of radiation
are required to produce immediately observable effects, and the sensitivity
of different tissues to irradiation are somewhat correlated with their
normal activity of cell division.   The state of the molecules at the time

of irradiation is evidently important, as judged by the facts that low temperature increases the survival time of frogs (Patt et al., 1948) and the configuration of enzyme molecules in a film influences their susceptibility to inactivation by radiation (Mazia and Blumenthal, 1948). The elementary processes in these and other aspects of the biological action of ionizing radiation are to be interpreted on the general framework of reaction rates with which the present work is concerned.

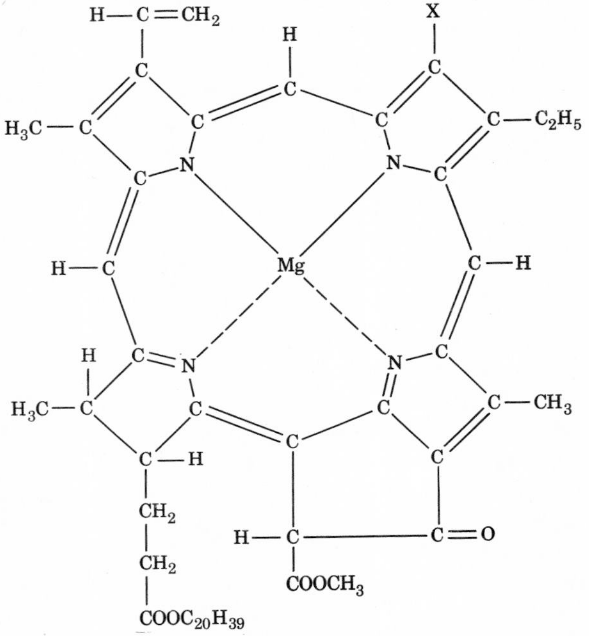

Fig. 1.9.   Structure of chlorophyll.   In chlorophyll a, $X = -CH_3$; in chlorophyll b, $X = -C\overset{\displaystyle O}{\underset{\displaystyle H}{\diagup}}$.

Photosynthesis

The present balance of life on the earth makes photosynthesis in green plants a key process in the cycle of organic matter.   Moreover, with the gradual depletion of the earth's storehouses of organic sources of energy, elucidation of the mechanism of photosynthesis is of increasing importance to the survival of civilization.   (As general references, cf. Rabinowitz, 1945, 1951; Franck and Loomis, 1949; Franck, 1951; Gaffron and Fager, 1951.)   The key molecule in photosynthesis is chlorophyll, whose structure is indicated in Fig. 1.9.

Although magnesium is necessary for photosynthesis, the absorption spectrum important in photosynthesis is only slightly changed by the presence or absence of magnesium.   The two important peaks of absorption in chlorophyll *a* supporting photosynthesis occur at 4,100 Å and 6,800 Å.   Chlorophyll *b* has nearly the same long wavelength absorption maximum, but the short wavelength maximum is shifted to about 5,000 Å. The longest wavelength effective in photosynthesis is about 7,100 Å, corresponding to 40 kcal of energy.   The chlorophyll molecules absorbing the energy-rich photons apparently lose their excess energy by internal conversion through which the excited electron drops down to the 40-kcal level.   In the meantime an excited molecule—probably the chlorophyll molecule—accepts an electron from water, transferring it to the vacated level and sending the denuded proton from water into solution.   The remaining OH radical is attached to an enzyme surface.   In photosynthesis by bacteria, which is not accompanied by the liberation of oxygen, the electron comes from a variety of substances, such as hydrogen sulfide or simple organic compounds, depending upon the biological species concerned.   The excited electron, raised into the 40-kcal level by the photon, can reduce a wide variety of substances, including $Fe^{3+}(CN)_6$ which goes to $Fe^{2+}(CN)_6$.   Hill (1937) first demonstrated that this photosynthetic reducing power could act upon added systems not involving carbon dioxide.   This reaction with added electron acceptors has become known as the Hill reaction.

Added benzoquinone is also reduced in the presence of illuminated chlorophyll, going to semiquinone.   The latter is then able to accept a second electron either from an adsorbed water molecule or from an adsorbed OH^- ion, or from some other source.   The result is that one photon can provide two electrons for a quinone, but only one electron for a $Fe^{3+}(CN)_6$.   This has been demonstrated in researches at the University of Utah (1951).   This evidence that the quantum efficiency in photosynthesis depends upon the substances reduced indicates a variability in quantum yields depending upon conditions.

It has been found by Spikes et al. (1950) that whole cytoplasm preparations of sunflower leaves contain a substance which is reduced by illuminated chloroplasts and is then re-oxidized in air when the light is turned off (Fig. 1.10).   It is reasonable to suppose that quinone-like substances accept an excited electron from chlorophyll in the intact leaf to become semiquinones.   These semiquinones then could well be the general reducing agents which move about in solution, either accepting a second electron and becoming a hydroquinone or else donating the first electron plus a proton and becoming quinone, in this way reducing in a series of steps the compounds made by the addition of carbon dioxide to

R—H to make R—COOH. The less active hydroquinone, which is unable to reduce many substances, nevertheless serves as a storehouse and presumably gets oxidized by O_2 back to active semiquinone.

A plausible scheme which fits what we know about the effect of light on chlorophyll and water may be written

$$(H_2O)_2\ EC + h\nu \rightarrow (H_3O_2)\ EC^- + H^+ \tag{1.35}$$

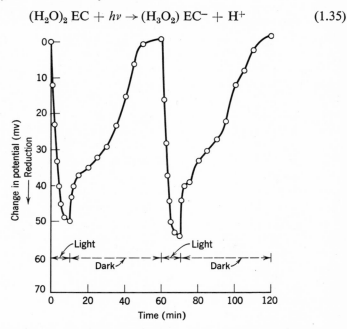

Fig. 1.10. Potential changes in light and in dark of cell-free, whole cytoplasm preparations plus chloroplasts of leaves of the wild sunflower, *Helianthus annus* L., without added electron acceptors (Spikes et al., 1950).

Here EC signifies the chlorophyll-enzyme complex, which probably holds two adsorbed water molecules. This is presumably followed by reactions of the type

$$(H_3O_2)\ EC^- + \text{quinone} + H^+ \longrightarrow (H_3O_2)\ EC + \text{semiquinone} \tag{1.36}$$

$$(H_3O_2)\ EC + 3\ \text{semiquinone} \longrightarrow O_2\ EC + 3\ \text{hydroquinone} \tag{1.37}$$

$$O_2\ EC \longrightarrow EC + O_2 \uparrow \tag{1.38}$$

$$4\ \text{hydroquinone} + O_2 \xrightarrow{\text{enzyme (?)}} 4\ \text{semiquinone} + 2\ H_2O \tag{1.39}$$

It should be emphasized that the nature of the "quinone-like" substances and their derivatives remains to be established. The course of the Hill reaction when an electron acceptor like $Fe^{3+}(CN)_6$ is added to remove electrons can be followed by measuring the rate of formation of $Fe^{2+}(CN)_6$, or by the pH change, or by the evolution of oxygen. Experiments show that these three products appear in the expected proportions simultaneously (Fig. 1.11).

The foregoing hypothesis of semiquinone-like intermediates accounts for the ability of green plants to carry on photosynthesis at light intensities

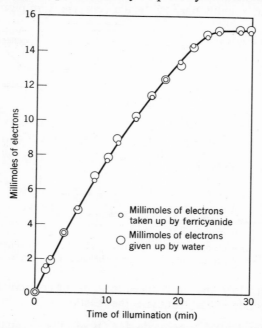

Fig. 1.11. Stoichiometry of the Hill reaction (Spikes, 1952).

so low that only one photon hits a chlorophyll molecule during the experiment, without having to invoke the concept of the "photosynthetic unit" in which some 2,000 chlorophyll molecules are postulated to pool their absorbed photons.

It is evident that the process of splitting water under the influence of light and chlorophyll can be separated from the process of reduction of carbon dioxide and synthesis of carbohydrate. The latter process brings up the problem of the probable nature of the R—H molecule which adds carbon dioxide and becomes reduced by the semiquinone-like substances. The partially proved scheme shown in Fig. 1.12 has been suggested by Benson et al. (1952). It is not supposed that this scheme is right in detail, but it summarizes the present status of the subject. The indicated

hydrogen atoms presumably come from the semiquinone-like intermediates. This cycle involving carbon dioxide is analogous to the
assimilation of carbon dioxide by heterotrophic bacteria through a
reversal of respiratory decarboxylation as observed by Wood and Werkman (1935, 1936; Werkman and Wood, 1942). In animals also, metabolic
processes in the liver result in the assimilation of free carbon dioxide.
Thus Vishniac and Ochoa (1951; cf. also Ochoa and Vishniac, 1952)
have shown that a highly purified "malic" enzyme from pigeon's liver, in

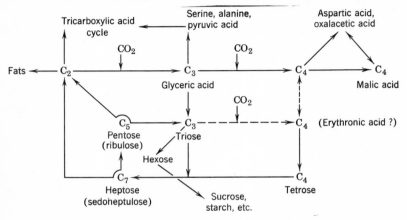

Fig. 1.12. Scheme of reactions in the reduction of carbon dioxide to yield
carbohydrate in photosynthesis (Benson et al., 1952).

the presence of Mn^{2+} and the reduced form of the coenzyme triphospho-
pyridine nucleotide (TPN), catalyzes the reaction:

$$\text{Reduced TPN} + \text{pyruvate} + CO_2 \rightarrow \text{TPN} + l\text{-malate} \qquad (1.40)$$

Furthermore, in the presence of illuminated, washed green grana of
spinach chloroplasts, plus the enzyme from pigeon liver plus carbon
dioxide, small amounts of l-malate are formed. In the dark, under
otherwise similar conditions, malate was not formed. Again, using
crystalline lactic dehydrogenase from rabbit muscle, which catalyzes the
reaction between reduced diphospyridine nucleotide (DPN) and pyruvate:

$$\text{Reduced DPN} + \text{pyruvate} \rightarrow \text{DPN} + \text{lactate} \qquad (1.41)$$

photochemical reduction of the DPN took place in the presence of
illuminated grana. It thus appears that illuminated chloroplasts can
catalyze the overall reaction:

$$H_2O + \text{TPN (or DPN)} \xrightarrow{\text{light}} \tfrac{1}{2}O_2 + \text{reduced TPN (or DPN)} \qquad (1.42)$$

This reaction can then be coupled with (1.40) or (1.41) to bring about the reductive carboxylation of pyruvate or malate, or its reduction to lactate. The photochemical synthesis of malate in these experiments was demonstrated by tracer studies with C^{14}. The method of adding carbon dioxide containing C^{14} and using chromatographic analysis has proved highly fruitful in determining the intermediates in carbon dioxide reduction.

In cell-free preparations great care must be taken to keep the enzymes active in photosynthesis. The enzymes responsible for carbon dioxide

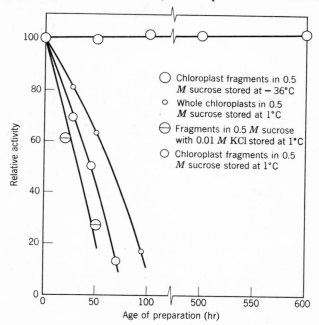

Fig. 1.13. Influence of conditions of storage on the activity of chloroplast preparations (Spikes, 1950–51).

fixation are destroyed when the leaf cells are broken up in a Waring blendor, although the enzymes promoting the photoreduction process of the Hill reaction remain active. In order to preserve the activity of the latter enzymes, however, the material must be kept chilled at around − 36°C (Fig. 1.13; cf. also Clendenning and Gorham, 1950).

Additional evidence of the sensitivity of chloroplast preparations to temperature is found in the kinetics of the Hill reaction. Thus the rate of oxygen production with either ferricyanide or quinone as acceptor goes through a maximum at about 35°C or less (Fig. 1.14). The curves of Fig. 1.14 are typical of enzyme reactions in showing an "optimum"

temperature, in this case at somewhat unusually low temperatures.   Low
temperature optima are also encountered in bioluminescence (Chapter 8).
Figure 1.14 also shows that the activation energy of the process is the same
with either ferricyanide or quinone as electron acceptor.   The actual rate
is approximately twice as fast with quinone as with ferricyanide at a given
temperature (at high intensity only).   This result indicates that the rate-

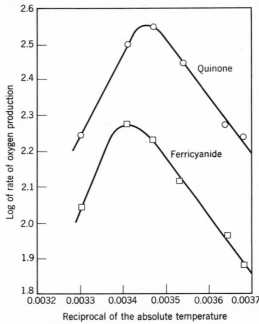

Fig. 1.14.   Influence of temperature on the rate of the Hill reaction
(Spikes, 1950–51).

limiting reaction is the making available of electrons.   The optimum
occurs at a slightly lower temperature with quinone probably because of
the inactivating effect of quinone on the enzyme, which effect is accelerated
at the higher temperatures in the manner of certain inhibitors discussed
in Chapter 10.
   Beyond the temperature of maximum rate, at about 35°C with
ferricyanide as electron acceptor, the rate of the Hill reaction shows a
progressive decrease with time (Fig. 1.15), although at lower temperatures
the rate is essentially uniform.   The decreasing rate with time is indicative
of irreversible destruction of one or more essential catalysts.   The
decreasing rates beyond the optimum temperature as shown in Fig. 1.14
are no doubt due in part, perhaps a large part, to such irreversible

destruction. Whatever measure of reversibility exists in the thermal diminution of rate remains to be determined.

Photosynthesis is a typical example of a complex physiological process, involving many reactions and many rate processes in achieving the end result. The intricate organization of cells, tissues, organs, and organisms in general obviously complicates attempts to interpret the rates of reactions

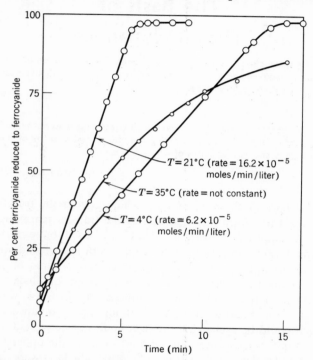

Fig. 1.15. Rate of the Hill reaction at three different temperatures, with ferricyanide as electron acceptor (Spikes, 1950, unpublished).

effective in maintaining normal structure and function, as well as those responsible for injury or death. In the following chapters we proceed from atoms and electrons to highly evolved organisms in an effort to interpret, so far as we are able at present, some of the fundamental mechanisms controlling reaction rates in the simplest and most complicated systems.

The Basis of
Thermodynamics

La chaleur n'est autre chose que la puissance motrice, ou plutôt,
que le mouvement qui a changé de forme.   C'est un mouvement
dans les particules des corps.

Carnot, 1824

The comprehension of the laws which govern any material system
is greatly facilitated by considering the energy and entropy of the
system in the various states of which it is capable.

J. Willard Gibbs, 1875

The basic laws of thermodynamics, which govern the transformation
of energy from one form into another, or the transfer from one body to
another, are empirical in origin.   They are based on experiments at
macroscopic levels with relatively large masses of matter and amounts of
energy, and do not depend upon the concept of atomic or molecular
structure.   Thus the second law, which in point of chronology was
recognized earlier than the one now known as the first law, was reached
at a time (Carnot, 1824) when heat was thought of as a substance, a sort
of fluid that could be exchanged between bodies or converted into work.
It was a natural consequence that, with advances in the understanding of
atomic and molecular structure, the thermodynamic laws were interpreted
on the basis of the motions and energies of these units, but again in a
purely statistical sense.   Thus temperature is directly proportional to the
average energy of particles in the system, and pressure is the average
momentum transfer per second to a square centimeter of surface.

When one or a very few molecules are considered, fluctuations from the
average values corresponding to the thermodynamic laws occur, as might
be expected.   The state of an individual molecule in a population is not
necessarily, and usually is not, equivalent to the average for the total
number.   Wide variations in energy exist.   Such fluctuations are, in fact,
of fundamental significance in reaction rates, since as already pointed out
(Chapter 1) reactions depend upon an improbable state, the activated
complex.   Also, in biological phenomena one or a very few molecules,

i.e., genes, may be thought of as governing a whole series of events leading to some readily observable end result.

Without exception, ensembles of atoms or molecules in statistically significant numbers are found to obey the laws of thermodynamics. Expressed in the form of equations, deductions based on these laws have been verified over and over in experience and no evidence has yet been found that they do not hold.

The first law of thermodynamics

The first law states that energy is conserved, i.e., that it may be neither created nor destroyed. This is a simple fact of experience with no known exception. The fact that matter and energy are interconvertible, as overwhelmingly demonstrated by the atomic bomb, deepens the meaning of this law and increases its generality; matter may be regarded as one of the forms of energy, with a quantitative equivalence to the other forms such as heat and electricity. This equivalence is given by Einstein's law, $E = mc^2$ (Einstein, 1905). Here the energy E is in ergs if mass m is taken in grams and the velocity of light, c, is expressed in centimeters per second. If any new form of energy, unknown or unrecognized at present, should be discovered, it would no doubt bear a quantitative equivalence to those already familiar, and the first law would continue to stand.

In algebraic form the first law may be stated

$$dQ = dE + dW \tag{2.1}$$

where dQ is the heat absorbed by a system, dE the increase in energy of the system, and dW the work done by the system. Heat and work are forms of energy and can be measured in the same units. Exact experiments like those first performed by Joule (1849) have established the equivalence of work and heat with great accuracy. Unlike the two laws which follow, the first law is applicable to single atoms or molecules, and in this sense may be considered more general.

The second law of thermodynamics

The only restriction imposed on energy changes by the first law is that of equivalence, i.e., the total amount of energy is the same at the start and at the finish, regardless of the forms into which it is transformed. It has nothing to say about direction. The second law is concerned with direction. It may be stated in a number of ways. Clausius (1850) expressed it simply: "Heat cannot of itself pass from a colder to a hotter body"; and Lord Kelvin (1853): "It is impossible by means of inanimate material agency, to derive mechanical effect from any portion of matter by cooling it below the temperature of the coldest of the surrounding objects." The first two laws immediately eliminate some devices that would be very handy: perpetual motion machines such as engines that would operate by extracting heat from a cold reservoir and so could run indefinitely.

The precise meaning of the second law can be clearly understood from a consideration of the Carnot cycle, named after the French engineer Carnot (1824), who studied the theoretical model of a heat engine operating in a reversible cycle. The engine consists of a cylinder and a frictionless

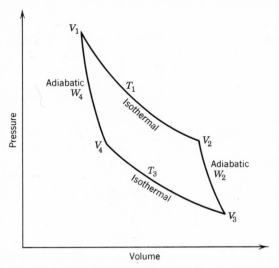

Fig. 2.1.   The Carnot cycle. V refers to volume, W to work, and
T to temperature.

piston which may exchange heat with a hot and a cold reservoir. The cylinder is filled with a perfect gas, exactly obeying the laws of Boyle and Charles:

$$pV = RT \qquad (2.2)$$

and $$(\partial C_v / \partial V)_T = 0 \qquad (2.3)$$

where p represents the pressure, V the volume of a mole of gas, R the gas constant, T the absolute temperature, and C_v the specific heat of the gas at constant volume. The piston first expands isothermally in contact with a heat reservoir, which furnishes a certain amount of heat to the system. Since a perfect gas expands at constant temperature and therefore at constant energy, all the heat absorbed is converted into work (Fig. 2.1, V_1 to V_2, with work $= W_1$). This isothermal expansion is followed by an adiabatic expansion from V_2 to V_3, with work W_2, accompanied by a drop in temperature from T_1 to T_3. No heat is absorbed or exchanged during this expansion. The work done comes from the internal energy of the gas. The next two stages involve compression. Stage three is an isothermal compression from V_3 to V_4, with work W_3 done by the gas, the pressure rising as the volume decreases, and the heat that is generated being given off to a cold reservoir. Finally the gas is further compressed adiabatically, from V_4 back to the starting point, V_1, at the original volume and temperature. In this, as in the second stage, there is no exchange of heat, the work done on the gas appearing as a rise in temperature from T_3 to T_1.

In this reversible cycle the heat absorbed, Q_1, in the isothermal expansion equals the work done W_1. Hence

$$Q_1 = W_1 = \int_{V_1}^{V_2} p\, dV = \int_{V_1}^{V_2} \frac{RT_1}{V}\, dV = RT_1 \ln \frac{V_2}{V_1} \tag{2.4}$$

Similarly, in the isothermal compression, heat Q_3 is absorbed by the system equivalent to the work W_3 done by the system:

$$Q_3 = W_3 = \int_{V_3}^{V_4} p\, dV = RT_3 \ln \frac{V_4}{V_3} \tag{2.5}$$

Actually in this compression Q_3 and W_3 are negative, corresponding to the fact that work is being done on the system and heat given off to the reservoir. In the adiabatic expansion, since $dQ = 0$, the change in internal energy dE of the system is equal to the temperature times the specific heat, and the work done dW equals the pressure times the change in volume, i.e., $dE = C_v\, dT$, and $dW = p\, dV$. Thus, from the first law,

$$dQ = dE + dW = C_v\, dT + p\, dV = 0 \tag{2.6}$$

From (2.6), the work done by the system in the adiabatic expansion,

$$W_2 = \int_{V_2}^{V_3} p\, dV = -C_v(T_3 - T_1) \tag{2.6a}$$

is just the same as the work done on the system, W_4, in the adiabatic compression, i.e.,

$$W_4 = \int_{V_3}^{V_1} p\, dV = -C_v(T_1 - T_3) \tag{2.6b}$$

$$W_2 + W_4 = 0 \tag{2.6c}$$

Thus, in operating around one complete cycle, the total work ΔW done by the system is $W_1 + W_3$. This may be expressed in terms of the changes in temperature and volume as follows.

Substituting from equation (2.2) for p in equation (2.6) and integrating over the adiabatic expansion from V_2 to V_3 gives

$$- C_v \int_{T_1}^{T_2} \frac{dT}{T} = R \int_{V_2}^{V_3} \frac{dV}{V} \qquad \text{or} \qquad - C_v \ln \frac{T_3}{T_1} = R \ln \frac{V_3}{V_2} \quad (2.7)$$

Integrating similarly over the adiabatic expansion, we obtain

$$- C_v \ln \frac{T_1}{T_3} = R \ln \frac{V_1}{V_4} \qquad (2.8)$$

From (2.7) and (2.8) we have

$$\frac{V_1}{V_4} = \frac{V_2}{V_3} \qquad (2.9)$$

Thus, substituting (2.9) in the expression for W_3 (equation 2.5), we obtain for the total work done in a Carnot cycle

$$\Delta W = W_1 + W_3 = (T_1 - T_3)R \ln \frac{V_2}{V_1} \qquad (2.10)$$

The efficiency η for a Carnot cycle is defined as the ratio of the work done to the heat absorbed:

$$\eta = \frac{\Delta W}{Q_1} = \frac{T_1 - T_3}{T_1} \qquad (2.11)$$

In addition to such properties as temperature, pressure, volume, and energy, any system may be considered to possess another property, namely, entropy, which unlike the first two is extensive, i.e., it depends upon the quantity of material in a system. Thus two moles of a gas under given conditions have twice the entropy of one mole. A verbal definition of entropy may be given in several ways; in general, it may be thought of as a measure of the degree of randomness, the amount of entropy increasing as the extent of restriction and organization of parts in a system decreases. Life processes superficially appear to be running contrary to the ultimate increase in entropy, accompanying the general "drift toward equilibrium" of the universe, inasmuch as life tends to decrease the total entropy by building highly ordered, complex systems. These systems, however, are always constructed at the expense of a part of the total free energy, in a manner strictly according to the thermodynamic laws, and the overall change in entropy continues incessantly in the direction of an increase.

A precise definition of entropy is simply the heat absorbed by the system in a reversible process divided by the temperature. Entropy changes may be either positive or negative, and they are usually indicated by the symbol ΔS in the units of calories per degree per mole, i.e., as entropy units, E.U. According to the third law zero entropy is reached by crystals at the absolute zero of temperature. In the Carnot cycle the reversible adiabatic expansion and compression involve no absorption of heat and, therefore, no change in entropy. Since heat is exchanged during the isothermal expansions and compression, these volume changes are accompanied by changes in entropy. Thus, in the isothermal expansion, entropy increases:

$$\Delta S_1 = \frac{Q_1}{T_1} = R \ln \frac{V_2}{V_1} \tag{2.12}$$

In the isothermal compression the entropy change is in the same amount, but in the opposite direction, i.e., the increase is negative, or a decrease:

$$\Delta S_3 = \frac{Q_3}{T_3} = R \ln \frac{V_4}{V_1} = - R \ln \frac{V_2}{V_1} \tag{2.13}$$

From (2.12) and (2.13) the general principle is apparent that the total entropy change for a perfect gas working around a Carnot cycle is zero.

The second law of thermodynamics may now be stated in another way: any other reversible heat engine working in a Carnot cycle will have the same efficiency as the perfect gas. Suppose, for example, that some other fluid could work reversibly around the cycle with less efficiency. In this case the engine could be operated in the reverse direction as a refrigerator rather than as a heat engine, and it could be driven with the more efficient perfect gas engine. The stroke of the refrigerator could be adjusted so that it delivers the same heat Q_1 to the high temperature reservoir as the perfect gas engine removes from it. When the compound system has gone through one complete cycle, each of the working fluids will have returned to the starting condition, and therefore the high temperature reservoir will have received the same heat from the refrigerator as it gave to the heat engine. The only change in the compound system is that the refrigerator removed more heat from the reservoir at temperature T_3 than the heat engine returned to it, and this difference in heat, by the first law of thermodynamics, must have appeared as work done. In other words, under this scheme, heat has been converted quantitatively into work with no other change whatever. But this is contrary to all experience. Had the working fluid been more, rather than less, efficient than the perfect gas, the operational scheme could simply be reversed, i.e., the perfect gas engine could be operated in the opposite direction, as a refrigerator, and the other fluid as a heat engine. By the same reasoning as before, it could be again shown that the compound system would change heat quantitatively into work, but, again, this is contrary to all experience.

Thus we are brought to the conclusion that any fluid proceeding reversibly in a Carnot cycle must have the same efficiency as the perfect gas. It follows that any system proceeding reversibly around the Carnot cycle can suffer no change in entropy.

Any sort of reversible cycle, however complex, for a working fluid can be broken up into a series of Carnot cycles, as illustrated in Fig. 2.2. The entropy change around the whole cycle is the sum of the entropy changes for the component cycles. Since the entropy change around each of the latter is zero, the sum is zero. Consequently, there is no entropy change

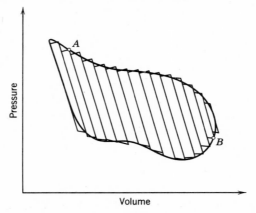

Fig. 2.2.   A complex reversible cycle considered as a series of
Carnot cycles.

for any fluid operating around any reversible cycle; in Fig. 2.2 the entropy change in proceeding clockwise from A to B must be the negative of the change in continuing clockwise from B to A. It follows that the entropy change in going reversibly from state A to state B is independent of the path followed and, therefore, depends only upon the initial and final states of the system. Thus, if the entropy is fixed for any one state of a system, it is fixed for all other states since the entropy change between states is fixed. In contrast, the heat dQ, which has been absorbed by a system depends upon the path in going from one state to another. The entropy is thus a property of the system, like volume, temperature, etc. Any state is usually specified by giving the composition and weight of the system, together with two of the three quantities, volume, temperature, and pressure.

The first and second laws may now be combined in one fundamental thermodynamic equation by replacing dQ of equation (2.1) with $T\,dS$:

$$T\,dS = dE + dW \qquad\qquad (2.14)$$

The third law of thermodynamics

The third law of thermodynamics grew out of the heat theorem proposed by Nernst in 1906 in regard to entropy at absolute zero. The heat theorem was based on experimental evidence and states that, at the absolute zero of temperature, the entropy of all condensed systems is the same. From a consideration of the fact that translational molecular motions cease at absolute zero, Planck deduced that the value of the entropy of every substance at 0°K is equal to zero. Subsequent evidence has shown that this generality does not hold in every instance, but it remains true that the entropy of crystalline solids at the temperature of absolute zero is zero; this fact constitutes a verbal statement of the third law of thermodynamics as given by G. N. Lewis (cf. Lewis and Randall, 1923). Experience has shown that the law may be expressed in a more general way by saying that the entropy of any solid or liquid at 0°K is finite and may be zero. It is apparent that, in taking a crystalline solid down to this lowest of temperatures, about all the heat that can possibly be squeezed out is out. Since entropy is defined as the heat absorbed in a reversible process divided by the temperature at which it is absorbed, a value of zero entropy is assigned to crystalline solids at absolute zero until some state is found, as is unlikely, with still lower entropy at this temperature.

Some useful thermodynamic functions

The foregoing principles can be extended by definitions and derivations. The following functions are particularly useful.

A property A of a system may be defined by the equation

$$A \equiv E - TS \tag{2.15}$$

from which
$$dA = dE - T\,dS - S\,dT$$

Subtracting (2.14),
$$T\,dS = dE + dW$$

gives
$$dA = -\,dW - S\,dT \tag{2.16}$$

From (2.16) it is apparent that, if some change in a system is carried through at constant temperature, the decrease in A is just the work done. Thus A is sometimes called the maximum work function, or the Helmholtz free energy (Helmholtz, 1882). When the only work done by a system is through the pressure it exerts in expanding against some external body, dW in equation (2.16) can be replaced by $p\,dV$:

$$dA = -\,p\,dV - S\,dT \tag{2.17}$$

whence
$$\left(\frac{\partial A}{\partial V}\right)_T = -\,p \tag{2.18}$$

and
$$\left(\frac{\partial A}{\partial T}\right)_V = -\,S \tag{2.19}$$

Equation (2.18) is the equation of state for the system, and (2.19) gives a method of calculating the entropy change.

Substituting (2.19) into (2.15), we obtain

$$E = A - \left(T\frac{\partial A}{\partial T}\right)_V = -T^2\frac{\partial}{\partial T}\left(\frac{A}{T}\right)_V \qquad (2.20)$$

In Chapter 5 it is seen that equation (2.20), when interpreted in terms of molecular structure, lies at the basis of equilibrium theory.

A function F may be defined by the equation

$$F = E - TS + pV$$

or
$$dF = dE - T\,dS - S\,dT + p\,dV + V\,dp \qquad (2.21)$$

Subtracting (2.14),

$$T\,dS = dE + dW$$

$$\overline{dF = -S\,dT + V\,dp - (dW - p\,dV)} \qquad (2.22)$$

From (2.22), for a change in dF at constant temperature and pressure,

$$dF = -(dW - p\,dV)$$

Thus $-dF$ is the total work that a system does at constant temperature and pressure, minus the work $p\,dV$ which the system does against the surrounding atmosphere. The function F is called the free energy, or the Gibbs free energy (Gibbs, 1874–1878). From (2.22), it is obvious that, when $dF = 0$ for a system, no external constraints, other than the encompassing pressure, are necessary to prevent it from changing. Under these circumstances the system is said to be at equilibrium.

The condition for equilibrium between two phases is of special interest. If at equilibrium some substance in the system, say the ith component, is transferred from phase one to phase two, there must be no change in the free energy. Thus, if F is the free energy of phase one, and F' is the free energy of a second phase,

$$\frac{\partial F}{\partial n_i}\,dn_i = \frac{\partial F'}{\partial n_i}\,dn_i \qquad (2.23)$$

The expression on the left in equation (2.23) is the work required to add dn_i moles of component i to phase one, and the expression on the right is the work required to add the same amount to phase two. The condition for equilibrium is that this relationship must hold for all components. In the literature the same quantity is symbolized in three different ways.

$$\frac{\partial F'}{\partial n_i} \equiv \bar{F}_i' \equiv \mu_i' \qquad (2.24)$$

Thus $\partial F'/\partial n_i$ is also called the chemical potential, μ_i', of the ith component in the primed phase or the partial molal free energy $\bar{F}_i'$ of this component.

Equilibrium constants

Following van't Hoff, let us consider a reaction chamber surrounded by a vacuum, and in the container a mixture of hydrogen, nitrogen, and ammonia at equilibrium, so that the equation

$$N_2 + 3H_2 = 2NH_3$$

is satisfied. The free energy change when the reactants, nitrogen and hydrogen, each at atmospheric pressure, are combined to form ammonia is calculated as follows.

We start with a mole of nitrogen at atmospheric pressure in a cylinder and reversibly introduce the cylinder into a vacuum without expansion of the gas. In this process an amount of work, $pV = RT$, is done by the atmosphere. Three moles of hydrogen, similarly introduced into a vacuum, have an amount of work $3RT$ done on them, since the three moles of hydrogen occupy three times the volume of the one mole of nitrogen. We next reversibly expand (or compress) the nitrogen to a pressure p_1 equal to its partial pressure in the reaction chamber. The work done by the gas is

$$\int_1^{p_1} p \, dV = RT \ln (1/p_1)$$

Here the nitrogen starts at one atmosphere and expands to the equilibrium pressure p_1. In the same way the expansion of the hydrogen from one atmosphere to its equilibrium pressure p_2 yields an amount of work $3RT \ln (1/p_2)$. Now we simultaneously introduce the one mole of nitrogen and the three moles of hydrogen reversibly into the reaction chamber and extract two moles of ammonia into a cylinder. In each case this is done through a semipermeable membrane which allows only the appropriate gas to pass between the cylinder and reaction chamber. In this process an amount of work, $p_1 V_1 = RT$, must be done on the nitrogen and an amount of work $3RT$ on the hydrogen, and the work done by the ammonia is $2RT$. If the ammonia is now expanded (or compressed) from its equilibrium pressure p_3 to one atmosphere and taken from the vacuum reversibly into the air, the work $2RT \ln (p_3/1)$ is done in the expansion and the work $2RT$ must be done against the atmosphere. All these work terms when added together give

$$RT \ln (p_3^2/p_1 p_2^3) = -\Delta F^0$$

This may also be written

$$e^{-\Delta F^0/RT} = K = p_3^2/p_1 p_2^3 \qquad (2.26)$$

When a substance does not obey the perfect gas law, it is still possible to represent the reversible work done in the expansion of n moles of the substance from state one to state two by the expression

$$nRT \ln (\alpha_1/\alpha_2) \tag{2.27}$$

Here $\alpha_1 = \gamma_1 p_1$ and $\alpha_2 = \gamma_2 p_2$, where the α's and γ's are called the activities and activity coefficients, respectively. At sufficiently low pressures the perfect gas law holds, and for these pressures it is convenient to take $\gamma = 1$. This fixes γ at other pressures. When this particular choice of activity coefficients is made, identifying activity with pressure in the range of low pressures, we follow Lewis in speaking of the activity as the fugacity. In the non-ideal range of pressures, equation (2.25) becomes

$$\Delta F^0 = - RT \ln (\alpha_3{}^2/\alpha_1\alpha_2{}^3) \tag{2.28}$$

For the general equilibrium

$$\sum_i n_i A_i = \sum_f n_f A_f \tag{2.29}$$

we have

$$\Delta F^0 = - RT \ln (\Pi\alpha_f{}^{n_f}/\Pi\alpha_i{}^{n_i}) = - RT \ln K \tag{2.30}$$

Here in each case n_i represents the number of reactant molecules A_i combining to give n_f molecules of product A_f. The α's in each case are the equilibrium activities. The symbols Σ and Π represent, as usual, the sum and products, respectively, over the various quantities following the symbol.

For reactions in solution, (2.30) still gives the free energy change for a process where the reactants at unit activity are changed over into products at unit activity. In this case it is convenient to take the activities equal to the concentrations in dilute solution, because in the low concentration range the work done by n moles of a substance in going from concentration c_i to c_j is $nRT \ln (c_i/c_j)$, and in any concentration this work is equal to $nRT \ln (\alpha_i/\alpha_j) = nRT \ln (\gamma_i c_i/\gamma_j c_j)$. We thus have a general equation connecting the standard free energy change for a reaction with the activities of the participating substances in their equilibrium state.

Using (2.21), (2.30), and remembering that the symbol Δ before a property signifies the difference between the initial and final values of the property, we have

$$K = e^{-\Delta F^0/RT} = e^{-(\Delta H^0 - T \Delta S^0)/RT} \tag{2.31}$$

When (2.31) is applied to liquids, it is of interest to calculate the effect on the equilibrium constant of changing the pressure from one atmosphere to a pressure p. Referring back to (2.22), we see that $\partial F/\partial p = - V$ for a system which is at constant temperature, working only against external pressure.   Hence

$$\frac{\partial \Delta F^0}{\partial p} = \frac{\partial F_f}{\partial p} - \frac{\partial F_i}{\partial p} = V_f - V_i = \Delta V \qquad (2.32)$$

Here the subscripts f and i refer to the final and initial states, respectively, whence

$$\Delta F_p{}^0 = \Delta F_1{}^0 + \int_{p=1}^{p} \Delta V \, dp = \Delta F_{p=1}{}^0 + \overline{\Delta V} \int_1^p dp = \Delta F_{p=1}{}^0 + \overline{\Delta V} P \qquad (2.33)$$

In (2.33) we have $P = p - 1$, and the subscripts on the ΔF's now indicate the hydrostatic pressure.   Thus, for reactions in solution, we can write

$$K = e^{-\Delta F_p{}^0/RT} = e^{-(\Delta F_1{}^0 + P\,\overline{\Delta V})/RT} \qquad (2.34)$$

The equilibrium constant is of universal importance in reactions. Its meaning is fundamentally the same, whether we are concerned with equilibria in the usual, thermodynamic sense, or whether we deal in the quasi-equilibrium between the normal and activated states in rate processes, as discussed in Chapters 1 and 6. Ordinarily, with reactions in solution at atmospheric pressure, the term ΔV is not taken into account, as it is practically never large enough, i.e., practically never more than a few cubic centimeters per mole, to make any difference in the value of $\Delta F_p{}^0$. Furthermore, with most ordinary reactions in solution, ΔV is so small that its influence becomes appreciable only at very high hydrostatic pressures of the order of several thousand atmospheres. In biological processes, however, which are likely to be under the control of large molecules, ΔV may be quite large, of the order of 100 cc per mole. Reactions that proceed with such large volume changes are readily influenced by moderate hydrostatic pressures of a few hundred atmospheres, such as occur in nature in the sea. Thus the influence of hydrostatic pressure on equilibria and reaction rates in biology becomes of distinct interest, and of importance in analyzing the reaction mechanism.

3

Fundamentals of
Classical Mechanics

In my opinion, the teaching of mechanics will still have to begin with
Newtonian forces, just as optics begins in the sensation of color, and
thermodynamics with the sensation of warmth, despite the fact that a more
precise basis is substituted later on.

Max Planck

Newton's laws

The laws governing the motions of bodies constitute the field of
mechanics; by classical mechanics we mean the developments which have
proceeded more or less directly from Newton's laws of motions. Like
the principles of thermodynamics they are the outgrowth of experience,
originally on a macroscopic level. They have also been found to hold,
within certain limitations, for atoms and molecules. In either case it is
apparent that the position of a body or of an infinitesimal particle can be
specified in space by means of rectangular, i.e., Cartesian, coordinates,
x, y, and z. Newton found that the relationship between the motion of
a natural body, its mass m, and forces X, Y, Z, acting upon it in the
direction of x, y, or z, respectively, may be expressed as

$$m\ddot{x} = X$$
$$m\ddot{y} = Y \tag{3.1}$$
$$m\ddot{z} = Z$$

in which the two dots over the coordinate represent the second derivative
with respect to time, that is, acceleration, along this coordinate. These
equations merely state the familiar principle that force equals the mass
times the acceleration. Where a single body is concerned, the problem
is relatively uncomplicated. When additional bodies are dealt with, each
one will have a set of equations like (3.1). Thus, if the total number is
$n/3$, there are n equations like (3.1), or we may say that each one has
3 degrees of freedom, corresponding to motion along each of the three
coordinates pertaining to that particular one. The ith one of these
equations may be written

$$m_i\ddot{x}_i = X_i \tag{3.2}$$

For atoms or molecules, a given system usually encompasses enormous numbers of particles. Predictions concerning the state of the system at any future time must be based on a knowledge of the positions and velocities of these particles at some earlier time. In attempting to make predictions with the aid of such knowledge and Newton's laws, it is frequently convenient to make use of a different set of coordinates, for, although the same result could be obtained with any set the treatment is not equally simple. For example, although rectangular coordinates could be used to describe the motion of a pendulum in one plane, it would be simpler to describe it in terms of the angle it makes with the vertical. Similarly polar coordinates, cylindrical, elliptical, parabolic, or other systems each simplify the appropriate problem.

Generalized coordinates

In order to describe at any instant a large number $n/3$ of individual particles, each having 3 degrees of freedom, a mass m, a kinetic energy T, and a potential energy V, the last named depending only upon the positions of the particle in space, generalized coordinates are advantageous because they allow the choice of the particular set that provides for the simplest solution of the differential equations. The ensuing argument is mathematical.

The set of equations (3.2) may be transformed to another set of coordinates, $q_1, q_2, q_3, \cdots, q_n$, where n is the number of degrees of freedom. Consider the set of transformations, $x_i = f_i(q_1, \cdots, q_n)$. Then

$$dx_i = \sum_{j=1}^{n} \frac{\partial x_i}{\partial q_j} dq_j$$

and

$$\dot{x}_i = \sum_j \frac{\partial x_i}{\partial q_j} \dot{q}_j \tag{3.3}$$

In these equations the partial derivative ∂ means that all the q's are kept constant except the one which is being varied. Now

$$\frac{\partial \dot{x}_i}{\partial q_k} = \sum_j \frac{\partial^2 x_i}{\partial q_k \, \partial q_j} \dot{q}_j \tag{3.4}$$

Furthermore,

$$d\left(\frac{\partial x_i}{\partial q_k}\right) = \sum_j \frac{\partial^2 x_i}{\partial q_j \, \partial q_k} dq_j$$

and

$$\frac{d}{dt}\left(\frac{\partial x_i}{\partial q_k}\right) = \sum_j \frac{\partial^2 x_i}{\partial q_j \, \partial q_k} \dot{q}_j \tag{3.5}$$

Comparing (3.4) and (3.5), we see that

$$\frac{\partial \dot{x}_i}{\partial q_k} \equiv \frac{d}{dt}\left(\frac{\partial x_i}{\partial q_k}\right) \tag{3.6}$$

From (3.3) we see also that

$$\frac{\partial \dot{x}_i}{\partial \dot{q}_k} = \frac{\partial x_i}{\partial q_k} \tag{3.7}$$

If we now consider our system of particles to be in a conservative field, i.e., one in which the energy is a function solely of the positions of the particles (a function solely of the "q's"), the work done in moving the system from one configuration to another depends only upon the initial and the final configurations and not on the particular path that is followed. Since the work done dW in this displacement is, as usual, force times distance, we can write, using Newton's equations (3.1) for the force, the expression

$$dW = \sum_i m_i \ddot{x}_i \frac{\partial x_i}{\partial q_k} dq_k \tag{3.8}$$

Here dW is the work done when the q's are kept constant except q_k, and when q_k changes from q_k to $q_k + dq_k$.

We next consider the identity

$$\ddot{x}_i \frac{\partial x_i}{\partial q_k} \equiv \frac{d}{dt}\left(\dot{x}_i \frac{\partial x_i}{\partial q_k}\right) - \dot{x}_i \frac{d}{dt}\left(\frac{\partial x_i}{\partial q_k}\right) \tag{3.9}$$

Substituting (3.6) and (3.7) in (3.9),

$$\ddot{x}_i \frac{\partial x_i}{\partial q_k} = \frac{d}{dt}\left(\dot{x}_i \frac{\partial \dot{x}_i}{\partial \dot{q}_k}\right) - \dot{x}_i \frac{\partial \dot{x}_i}{\partial q_k} \tag{3.10}$$

and substituting (3.10) in (3.8),

$$dW = \left(\frac{d}{dt}\sum_i m_i \dot{x}_i \frac{\partial \dot{x}_i}{\partial \dot{q}_k} - \sum_i m_i \dot{x}_i \frac{\partial \dot{x}_i}{\partial q_k}\right) dq_k$$

$$= \left[\frac{d}{dt}\frac{\partial}{\partial \dot{q}_k}\left(\sum_i \tfrac{1}{2}m_i \dot{x}_i^2\right) - \frac{\partial}{\partial q_k}\left(\sum_i \tfrac{1}{2}m_i \dot{x}_i^2\right)\right] dq_k \tag{3.11}$$

Remembering that the kinetic energy T is given by

$$T = \sum_i \tfrac{1}{2}m_i \dot{x}_i^2 \tag{3.12}$$

and that the work dW can be written as the product of a generalized force Q_k times the generalized distance dq_k, equation (3.11) becomes

$$Q_k \, dq_k = \left[\left(\frac{d}{dt} \frac{\partial}{\partial \dot{q}_k} T \right) - \frac{\partial T}{\partial q_k} \right] dq_k \qquad (3.13)$$

Now, for a conservative system we can write the generalized force Q_k as the negative of the rate of change of the potential V, with distance q_k:

$$Q_k = -\frac{\partial V}{\partial q_k} = \frac{d}{dt} \frac{\partial T}{\partial \dot{q}_k} - \frac{\partial T}{\partial q_k} \qquad (3.14)$$

Following Lagrange, we define the kinetic potential, $L = T - V$, and rewrite (3.14):

$$\frac{d}{dt} \frac{\partial L}{\partial \dot{q}_k} - \frac{\partial L}{\partial q_k} = 0 \qquad (3.15)$$

The last equation is correct because, in a conservative field, V is not a function of the q's. There is one equation of the set (3.15) for each q_k, i.e., for each degree of freedom of the system.

Theory of small vibrations

In addition to the energies associated with the translational motion of bodies as a whole, it is evident that they may vibrate about equilibrium. The foregoing development has been necessary in order to obtain a solution of the problem of small vibrations about stable and metastable equilibrium positions.

First, the kinetic energy of a system of particles can be written

$$T = \sum_{i, k} \tfrac{1}{2} a_{i, k} \dot{q}_i \dot{q}_k \qquad (3.16)$$

and the potential energy at a minimum or saddle point can be written

$$V = \sum_{i, k} \tfrac{1}{2} b_{i, k} q_i q_k \qquad (3.17)$$

Substituting (3.16) and (3.17) in equation (3.15) gives

$$\sum_i (a_{i, k} \ddot{q}_i + b_{i, k} q_i) = 0 \qquad (3.18)$$

In attempting to solve (3.18) we may try the solution

$$q_i = A_i e^{i \lambda t} \qquad (3.19)$$

which gives

$$\sum_i A_i (b_{i, k} - \lambda^2 a_{i, k}) = 0 \qquad (3.20)$$

This system of equations may be solved for A_1 giving:

$$A_1 = \frac{\begin{vmatrix} 0(b_{21} - \lambda^2 a_{21})(b_{31} - \lambda^2 a_{31}) & \cdots & \cdots & (b_{n1} - \lambda^2 a_{n1}) \\ 0(b^{22} - \lambda^2 a_{22})(b_{32} - \lambda^2 a_{32}) & \cdots & \cdots & (b_{n2} - \lambda^2 a_{n2}) \\ \vdots & & & \vdots \\ 0(b_{2n} - \lambda^2 a_{2n})(b_{3n} - \lambda^2 a_{3n}) & \cdots & \cdots & (b_{nn} - \lambda^2 a_{nn}) \end{vmatrix}}{\begin{vmatrix} (b_{11} - \lambda^2 a_{11})(b_{21} - \lambda^2 a_{21})(b_{31} - \lambda^2 a_{31}) & \cdots & (b_{n1} - \lambda^2 a_{n1}) \\ (b_{12} - \lambda^2 a_{12})(b_{22} - \lambda^2 a_{22})(b_{32} - \lambda^2 a_{32}) & \cdots & (b_{n2} - \lambda^2 a_{n2}) \\ (b_{1n} - \lambda^2 a_{1n})(b_{2n} - \lambda^2 a_{2n})(b_{3n} - \lambda^2 a_{3n}) & \cdots & (b_{nn} - \lambda^2 a_{nn}) \end{vmatrix}} \quad (3.21)$$

Since the numerator of (3.21) is zero, A can be different from zero only if the denominator is zero. The denominator is an equation of nth degree in λ^2, and so has n roots, $\lambda_1^2, \cdots, \lambda_n^2$. These correspond to n frequencies ν:

$$\nu_i = \frac{\lambda_1}{2\pi}, \cdots, \nu_n = \frac{\lambda_n}{2\pi} \quad (3.22)$$

Thus for any system of particles at stationary points, i.e., when the potential energy is homogeneous and quadratic in the coordinates, the system has n normal modes of vibration that can be calculated as indicated above. In Chapter 4 this method is applied to the calculation of the frequencies used in calculating the rate of a chemical reaction (Chapter 6).

The values of the A_i's of equation (3.19) that go with a given frequency ν_i may be found by substituting the corresponding λ_1 from equation (3.22) into equations (3.20). If any $n - 1$ of the n equations of (3.20), say the first $n - 1$, is divided by A_n, these equations can be solved for

$$\frac{A_1}{A_n}, \frac{A_2}{A_n}, \cdots, \frac{A_{n-1}}{A_n} \quad (3.23)$$

Now, if any arbitrary value is taken for vibrational amplitude A_n, all the other A's are determined both as to sign and to magnitude. It is then possible to draw arrows, as vectors, indicating the instantaneous direction and magnitude of the motion of each atom of a system as the system executes a particular normal mode of vibration.

Hamilton's equations

The generalized momenta p_i are defined by the set of equations

$$p_i = \frac{\partial T}{\partial \dot{q}_i} \quad (3.24)$$

When rectangular coordinates are employed, this reduces to the usual definition of momentum. The set of equation (3.24) is linear and homogeneous in the $\dot{q}$'s. Because T is homogeneous and quadratic, it follows that

$$\sum_i \dot{q}_i \frac{\partial T}{\partial \dot{q}_i} = 2T \tag{3.25}$$

Substituting (3.24) into (3.25) gives

$$\sum_i \dot{q}_i p_i = 2T \tag{3.26}$$

Now we can write

$$dT = \sum_i \left[\left(\frac{\partial T}{\partial q_i} \right)_{q, \dot{q}} dq_i + \left(\frac{\partial T}{\partial \dot{q}_i} \right)_{q, \dot{q}} d\dot{q}_i \right] \tag{3.27}$$

in which the subscript $q, \dot{q}$ indicates that all the q's and $\dot{q}$'s except the one with which you are taking the derivative are held constant. Similarly we may consider the relationship when the q's and p's are held constant:

$$\left(\frac{\partial T}{\partial q_k} \right)_{q, p} = \left(\frac{\partial T}{\partial q_k} \right)_{q, \dot{q}} + \sum_i \left(\frac{\partial T}{\partial \dot{q}_i} \right)_{q, \dot{q}} \left(\frac{\partial \dot{q}_i}{\partial q_k} \right)_{q, p} \tag{3.28}$$

Using (3.24), we can rewrite (3.28) as

$$\left(\frac{\partial T}{\partial q_k} \right)_{q, p} = \left(\frac{\partial T}{\partial q_k} \right)_{q, \dot{q}} + \Sigma p_i \left(\frac{\partial \dot{q}_i}{\partial q_k} \right)_{q, p} \tag{3.29}$$

and from (3.26) we obtain

$$2 \left(\frac{\partial T}{\partial q_k} \right)_{q, p} = \sum_i p_i \frac{\partial \dot{q}_i}{\partial q_k} \tag{3.30}$$

Subtracting (3.29) from (3.30) gives

$$\left(\frac{\partial T}{\partial q_k} \right)_{q, p} = - \left(\frac{\partial T}{\partial q_k} \right)_{q, \dot{q}} \tag{3.31}$$

Returning to (3.27), we see that

$$\left(\frac{\partial T}{\partial p_k} \right)_{q, p} = \sum_i \left(\frac{\partial T}{\partial \dot{q}_i} \right)_{q, \dot{q}} \left(\frac{\partial \dot{q}_i}{\partial p_k} \right)_{q, p} = \sum_i p_i \frac{\partial \dot{q}_i}{\partial p_k} \tag{3.32}$$

From (3.26) we obtain

$$2 \left(\frac{\partial T}{\partial p_k} \right)_{q, p} = \dot{q}_k + \sum_i p_i \frac{\partial \dot{q}_i}{\partial p_k} \tag{3.33}$$

Subtracting (3.32) from (3.33) gives

$$\left(\frac{\partial T}{\partial p_k} \right)_{q, p} = \dot{q}_k \tag{3.34}$$

If we now define the Hamiltonian as $H = T + V$, and remember that V depends only upon q, not upon $\dot{q}$ or p, equation (3.34) becomes

$$\left(\frac{\partial H}{\partial p_k}\right)_{q,\,p} = \dot{q}_k \tag{3.35}$$

Substituting (3.24) and (3.31) into (3.15) written in the form

$$\frac{d}{dt}\left(\frac{\partial T}{\partial \dot{q}_k}\right)_{q,\,\dot{q}} - \left(\frac{\partial T}{\partial q_k}\right)_{q,\,\dot{q}} + \frac{\partial V}{\partial q_k} = 0$$

gives

$$\frac{d}{dt}p_k + \left(\frac{\partial T}{\partial q_k}\right)_{q,\,p} + \left(\frac{\partial V}{\partial q_k}\right)_{q,\,p} = 0$$

or

$$\dot{p}_k = -\left(\frac{\partial H}{\partial q_k}\right)_{q,\,p} \tag{3.36}$$

The sets of equations (3.35) and (3.36) are known as Hamilton's canonical equations. They constitute an achievement of prime importance. Although it is now known that they by no means tell the whole story, they remain useful in the modern treatment of problems concerning the motions and energies of atoms and molecules.

Apart from their purely mathematical use, Hamilton's equations have a particularly interesting philosophical significance which for a time, especially during the seventeenth and eighteenth centuries, exerted considerable influence. Thus, if at some instant of time t, the positions $q_1, \cdots, q_n$ and the momenta $p_1, \cdots, p_n$ for some system of particles are all known, then at a time $t + dt$ they have the known values $q_1 + \dot{q}_1\,dt, \cdots, q_n + \dot{q}_n\,dt$ and $p_1 + \dot{p}_1\,dt, \cdots, p_n + \dot{p}_n\,dt$. Here numerical values for the $\dot{q}$'s and $\dot{p}$'s can be obtained from equations (3.35) and (3.36). Now, by repeating these calculations, starting each time with the new q's and p's, it is possible to find the position and momenta of any system, however complex, at any past or future time. This means that, for any system obeying Newton's mechanics, if the interaction potential and the position and momenta of all the particles were known at any instant of time, the state of the system at any time in the future could be calculated. The course of such a Newtonian world is completely determined, as Laplace enjoyed pointing out.

Atoms and molecules do not strictly obey Newton's laws, but obey instead the probability laws of quantum mechanics. This changes our world from a predestined Newtonian world to one which, at best, is highly predictable. The next chapter deals briefly with the essentials of quantum mechanics.

Principles of
Quantum Mechanics

Space sways and resounds;
space is filled with movement,
with forces and counter forces,
with tensions and functions,
with the tone of colors and light,
with life and rhythm,
and the dispositions of sublime divinity.

(Artist) Hans Hofmann, *Plastic Creation*

The origin of quantum theory

At the close of the last century Max Planck was busy with the problem of resolving a grave inconsistency in radiation theory. Classical theory shows that a volume V of empty space contains a number

$$dn = \frac{8\pi V v^2 \, dv}{c^3} \tag{4.1}$$

electromagnetic vibrational degrees of freedom lying between frequencies v and $v + dv$. In this expression c represents the velocity of light, as usual. Now, according to classical statistical mechanics, the average energy of each such oscillator is kT, the Boltzmann constant times the absolute temperature, giving for the corresponding energies of the dn oscillators the value

$$dE = kT \, dn = \frac{8\pi V k T v^2 \, dv}{c^3} \tag{4.2}$$

From equation (4.2) it is apparent that the theory predicts an ever-increasing energy density going up with the square of the frequency. The results of this equation are sometimes spoken of as "the ultraviolet catastrophe," since the idea of enormous energy densities in the high frequencies of ultraviolet radiation would have startling consequences.

Equation (4.2), however, is readily shown to be false simply by measuring the high frequency radiation emitted from an opening in a black body.   Planck (1901) found that kT in equation (4.2) must be replaced by

$$hv/(e^{hv/kT} - 1) \qquad (4.3)$$

which is the average energy that an oscillator would have if it could take up energy *only* in multiples of hv.   Planck's constant h has the measured value of 6.62×10^{-27} ergs per sec.   Multiplying the number of oscillational degrees of freedom (4.1) by the average energy per oscillator (4.3) gives

$$dE = \frac{8\pi V h v^3 \, dv}{c^3(e^{hv/kT} - 1)} \qquad (4.4)$$

This equation agrees exactly with experimental measurements.   At low frequencies equations (4.2) and (4.4) correspond exactly, and the frequencies for which there is agreement increase as the temperature is raised.

Thus was quantum theory born.   We conclude that radiation can be emitted only in multiples of hv, where v is the natural frequency of the oscillator.   It would be difficult to exaggerate the significance of this fundamental scientific advance.

The photoelectric effect

Six years later, in 1906, Einstein noted that the maximum kinetic energy E of electrons expelled by monochromatic light from a solid metal varied with the frequency of the incident light according to the equation

$$E = h(v - v_0) \qquad (4.5)$$

This, he concluded, showed that all the energy hv of a quantum of light was absorbed by the electron in a lump.   Of this energy the fixed amount hv_0 was required to free the electron from the metal, and the remaining portion of energy appeared as kinetic energy of the escaping electron. This left no doubt that light is absorbed in packets with energy hv.   In addition, the amount of energy in a packet is determined by the "color," or frequency v of the light, and is independent of the distance the light has traveled from its source.   Such packets of energy are called photons and have many of the properties of ordinary material particles.   Unlike the energy in a purely mechanical wave, however, the energy of a photon does not spread out with the square of the distance from the source.   The particulate nature of the energy of the photon, therefore, must somehow be reconciled with its wave-like properties which are revealed as interference patterns on a photographic plate when, for example, two neighboring narrow parallel slits are interposed between the light source and the photographic plate.   This particle-wave duality of light is also found to apply to matter.

The simple Bohr atom

In 1913 Nils Bohr was able to explain quantitatively the frequencies of the lines in the hydrogen spectrum which Rydberg had empirically fitted by the equation

$$\nu = R(1/n_1^2 - 1/n_2^2) \tag{4.6}$$

where n_1 and n_2 are integers. By ordinary mechanics the electrostatic attraction between electron and nucleus, e^2/r^2, must be balanced by the centrifugal force $\mu v^2/r$ of the electron revolving around the nucleus. Thus

$$e^2/r^2 = \mu v^2/r \tag{4.7}$$

Here e, r, μ, and v are the charge on the electron, distance between proton and electron, reduced mass, and velocity of the charge, respectively. The reduced mass μ has the value $Mm/(M + m)$, where M and m are the mass of the nucleus and electron, respectively. Since the potential energy of this system is $- e^2/r$, and the kinetic energy is $\frac{1}{2}\mu v^2$, it follows from (4.7) that the total energy E is given by

$$E = - e^2/r + \tfrac{1}{2}\mu v^2 = - e^2/2r \tag{4.8}$$

Bohr now assumed that the system occupied stationary states such that the angular momentum $\mu r^2 \omega$ of the system, multiplied by 2π, was an integer n times Planck's constant h. Expressed in the form of an equation, this gives

$$\mu r^2 \omega 2\pi = nh \tag{4.9}$$

The integer n is called a quantum number. If equation (4.9) is used to eliminate the angular velocity ω from (4.7), the latter gives for the radius of the Bohr orbit of hydrogen

$$r = n^2 h^2 / 4\pi^2 \mu e^2 \tag{4.10}$$

Substituting in (4.10) the numerical values of the constants, taking $n = 1$, gives $r = 0.537$ Å. This is the generally accepted value for the atomic radius of hydrogen in its lowest energy state. Combining (4.10) and (4.8) gives the energy E in one of these stationary states:

$$E = - (2\pi^2 \mu e^4/h^2)(1/n^2) \tag{4.11}$$

Bohr also assumed that when light was absorbed the molecule jumped from the state with quantum number n_1 to a state with quantum number n_2, absorbing the energy $h\nu = E_2 - E_1$. This gives

$$\nu = (2\pi^2 \mu e^4/h^3)(1/n_1^2 - 1/n_2^2) \tag{4.12}$$

The calculated value of the Rydberg constant $2\pi^2 \mu e^4/h^3$ in (4.12), when divided by c, the velocity of light, agrees exactly with the experimental value R in wave numbers defined by (4.6). This was another major advance in the understanding of atomic structure. The postulation of the existence of stable stationary states was especially difficult for a physicist to make in 1913, because classical theory showed that an electron undergoing acceleration in a circular path should radiate its energy and finally come to rest at the center of the atom. The assumption of these stationary states, however, gave a natural explanation of the discrete spectra regularly observed for many types of atoms and molecules.

If, instead of a hydrogen atom with nuclear charge e, we consider any atom with nuclear charge ze, all the arguments from equations (4.7) to (4.11) again apply exactly, provided that e^2 is replaced by ze^2. Thus, in general, the radius of such an atom becomes

$$r = n^2h^2/4\pi^2\mu e^2 z \tag{4.13}$$

and the energy is

$$E = -(2\pi^2\mu e^4 z^2/h^2)(1/n^2) \tag{4.14}$$

These results apply to a single electron attached to a nucleus of charge ze. If more than one electron is added to the nucleus, the problem of calculation of the radius and energy immediately goes beyond the methods developed here. However, by appropriately reducing z in accordance with the screening effect of the extra electrons on the central charge, and realizing that n must increase as electrons fill up the stationary states, equation (4.14) can be modified to give the energy of the multi-electron molecules.

The success of Bohr's calculation of the energy of hydrogen-like atoms led to a generalization of his method of calculating the energy of other stationary states in systems undergoing periodic motion. Thus, for any normal coordinate for which the generalized positional coordinate is q_i, the dynamically conjugate momentum is $p_i = \partial T/\partial \dot{q}_i$ (see Chapter 3, equation 3.24). The assumption Bohr made then was equivalent to

$$\oint p_i \, dq_i = nh \tag{4.15}$$

In (4.15) the circle on the integral sign means that the integral is over one period. A moment's consideration shows that (4.9) is indeed a straightforward application of (4.15). In the particular instance of the hydrogen atom, with its electron in a circular orbit, the angular momentum is constant and dynamically conjugate to the angular displacement. Thus, 2π times the constant angular momentum is the value of the integral in (4.15).

The energies of a particle in a box

Now suppose that we have a molecule in a rectangular box whose axes lie in the x, y, and z directions having lengths a, b, and c, respectively. The energy in the x direction is

$$E_x = \tfrac{1}{2}m\dot{x}^2 \tag{4.16}$$

But, according to (4.15), we have

$$n_1 h = \oint m\dot{x}\, dx = m\dot{x}\, 2a \tag{4.17}$$

or

$$\dot{x} = n_1 h/2ma \tag{4.18}$$

Substituting $\dot{x}$ from (4.18) into (4.16) gives

$$E_x = n_1^2 h^2/8a^2 m \tag{4.19}$$

Equation (4.19) gives correctly the allowed energy levels for the X-translational degree of freedom for a molecule, if n_1 takes the integral values from 1 to infinity. In the same way the allowed energy levels for the Y- and Z-translational degrees of freedom follow:

$$E_y = n_2^2 h^2/8b^2 m \tag{4.20}$$

$$E_z = n_3^2 h^2/8c^2 m \tag{4.21}$$

We next apply (4.15) in calculating the energy of a harmonic oscillator such as a diatomic molecule.

The energies of a harmonic oscillator

If the equilibrium distance between two atoms in a molecule is d and we represent by x the displacement from this equilibrium distance, the potential energy is

$$V = \tfrac{1}{2}fx^2 \tag{4.22}$$

The kinetic energy for the two atoms is

$$T = \tfrac{1}{2}m_1\dot{x}_1^2 + \tfrac{1}{2}m_2\dot{x}_2^2 \tag{4.23}$$

We next introduce the new coordinates

$$X = \frac{m_1 x_1 + m_2 x_2}{m_1 + m_2} \tag{4.24}$$

and

$$x + d = x_1 - x_2$$

Solving these for x_1 and x_2 gives

$$x_2 = X - \frac{m_1(x + d)}{m_1 + m_2}$$

$$\text{(4.25)}$$

and

$$x_1 = X + \frac{m_2(x + d)}{m_1 + m_2}$$

Taking the time derivatives and substituting (4.25) into (4.23) gives

$$T = \tfrac{1}{2}(m_1 + m_2)\dot{X}^2 + \tfrac{1}{2}\frac{m_1 m_2}{m_1 + m_2}\dot{x}^2 \equiv \tfrac{1}{2}M\dot{X}^2 + \tfrac{1}{2}\mu\dot{x}^2 \qquad \text{(4.26)}$$

Here M is the sum of the masses and μ is the reduced mass. Using Lagrange's equation,

$$\frac{d}{dt}\frac{\partial L}{\partial \dot{x}} - \frac{\partial L}{\partial x} = 0$$

where $L = T - V$ gives

$$\mu\ddot{x} + fx = 0 \qquad \text{(4.27)}$$

This is satisfied by the relation

$$x = A \sin (f/\mu)^{1/2}(t + \delta) \qquad \text{(4.28)}$$

This equation, with its two arbitrary constants A and δ, is the general solution of the second order differential equation (4.27). If we want x to equal zero when $t = 0$, then

$$x = A \sin (f/\mu)^{1/2} t \qquad \text{(4.29)}$$

where A is the maximum displacement of x. Since at the maximum displacement $\dot{x}$ is zero, making the kinetic energy zero, it follows that the total energy of the system is

$$E = V_{max} = \tfrac{1}{2}fA^2 \qquad \text{(4.30)}$$

From (4.29) it is clear that x repeats its value in a time τ where

$$(f/\mu)^{1/2}\tau = 2\pi$$

whence the frequency of vibration is

$$\nu = 1/\tau = (1/2\pi)(f/\mu)^{1/2} \qquad \text{(4.31)}$$

Now, from (3.24), (4.26), and (4.29),

$$p_x = \frac{\partial T}{\partial \dot{x}} = \mu\dot{x} = \mu A(k/\mu)^{1/2}\cos (k/\mu)^{1/2}t$$

whence

$$nh = \oint p_x \, dx = A^2 f \int_{t=0}^{2\pi(\mu/f)^{1/2}} \cos^2 \left(f/\mu\right)^{1/2} t \, dt$$

$$= \frac{A^2 f}{2} \int_{t=0}^{1/\nu} (1 + \cos^2 \left(f/\mu\right)^{1/2} t) \, dt$$

$$= f A^2 / 2\nu = E/\nu \tag{4.32}$$

Using (4.30) in (4.32), we see that

$$E = nh\nu \tag{4.33}$$

Specific heats and spectral measurements indicate that (4.33) gives the energy levels of the harmonic oscillator provided that n takes the half integral values $\frac{1}{2}, \frac{3}{2}, \frac{5}{2}$, etc. The fact that half quanta had to be arbitrarily postulated to fit experiment illustrates an inadequacy of our quantization scheme. The faultiness of these early methods is even more apparent in our next calculation.

The energy levels of the rotator

We take for the origin of a set of spherical coordinates the center of gravity of a diatomic molecule. The coordinates of the atom with mass m can be taken as a, θ, ϕ where a is the distance of this atom from the center of gravity. Then $- b$, θ, ϕ are the coordinates of the atom of mass, m_2, where b is the distance of this atom from the center of gravity. The kinetic energy of the first atom is then

$$T_1 = \tfrac{1}{2}m(\dot{x}^2 + \dot{y}^2 + \dot{z}^2) \tag{4.34}$$

Rectangular coordinates are readily expressed in spherical coordinates:

$$x = a \sin \theta \cos \phi$$
$$y = a \sin \theta \sin \phi \tag{4.35}$$
$$z = a \cos \theta$$

Taking the time derivative gives

$$\dot{x} = a \cos \theta \dot{\theta} \cos \phi - a \sin \theta \sin \phi \dot{\phi}$$
$$\dot{y} = a \cos \theta \dot{\theta} \sin \phi + a \sin \theta \cos \phi \dot{\phi} \tag{4.36}$$
$$\dot{z} = a \sin \theta \dot{\theta}$$

Thus the kinetic energy of atom 1 is

$$T_1 = \tfrac{1}{2}m_1 a^2(\dot{\theta}^2 + \sin^2 \theta \dot{\phi}^2) \tag{4.37}$$

By a completely analogous argument the kinetic energy of atom 2 is seen to be

$$T_2 = \tfrac{1}{2}m_2 b^2(\dot{\theta}^2 + \sin^2 \theta \dot{\phi}^2) \tag{4.38}$$

Thus the total kinetic energy T is the sum of T_1 and T_2:

$$T = \tfrac{1}{2}(m_1 a^2 + m_2 b^2)(\dot{\theta}^2 + \sin^2 \theta \dot{\phi}^2) = \tfrac{1}{2}I(\dot{\theta}^2 + \sin^2 \theta \dot{\phi}^2) \tag{4.39}$$

Using equation (3.24), we find

$$\frac{\partial T}{\partial \dot{\theta}} = I\dot{\theta} = p_\theta \tag{4.40}$$

Using (4.15), we obtain

$$nh = \oint p_\theta \, d\theta = \oint I\dot{\theta} \, d\theta = I\dot{\theta}2\pi \tag{4.41}$$

If the coordinates for the molecule are chosen so that $\dot{\phi} = 0$, then

$$E = \tfrac{1}{2}I\dot{\theta}^2 \tag{4.42}$$

Using (4.41) to eliminate $\dot{\theta}$ in (4.42) gives

$$E = \tfrac{1}{2}I(nh/2\pi I)^2 = n^2 h^2 / 8\pi^2 I \tag{4.43}$$

The measurement of the rotational spectrum as well as quantum mechanics indicates that n^2 must be replaced in (4.43) by $n(n+1)$ if this equation is to represent the energy spectrum correctly. Clearly some better way of finding energy levels is needed. To overcome such difficulties the quantum mechanics was developed.

We have already seen that light has the particle-like property of always keeping its energy localized no matter how far away from its source it is absorbed. On the other hand, photons passing through two closely placed slits develop a diffraction pattern even in light so dilute that only one photon is in the neighborhood of the slits at a time. Thus each photon shows wave properties.

The assumption that must be made about matter is that it, too, has this dual set of properties partaking both of the nature of particles and of waves. Davisson and Germer (1927) and Thompson (1928; Thompson and Reid, 1927) found that, when a beam of particles homogeneous with respect to velocity encountered crystalline matter, the particles showed the same kind of diffraction pattern shown by x-rays. De Broglie (1925) first predicted correctly that particles (electrons or atoms) would be diffracted as though they had the wavelength

$$\lambda = h/p \tag{4.44}$$

Here p is the momentum of the particles. This parallels earlier results for light. Thus, according to quantum theory and relativity, the energy of a photon is

$$E = h\nu = mc^2 \tag{4.45}$$

Dividing through by the velocity of light, $c = \nu\lambda$, gives

$$h(\nu/c) = h(1/\lambda) = mc = p \tag{4.46}$$

or

$$\lambda = h/p \tag{4.47}$$

Thus matter behaves as waves with a frequency given by the Einstein relation

$$\nu = E/h \tag{4.48}$$

and with a wavelength given by (4.44). Consequently for the wave velocity a of a particle we have

$$a = \lambda\nu = E/p \tag{4.49}$$

Now the total energy is

$$E = (p^2/2m) + V \tag{4.50}$$

where V is the potential energy. Using (4.50) in (4.49) gives

$$a = \frac{E}{[2m(E - V)]^{1/2}} \tag{4.51}$$

The equation for a wave with amplitude ψ and wave velocity a in three dimensions is

$$\frac{\partial^2\psi}{\partial x^2} + \frac{\partial^2\psi}{\partial y^2} + \frac{\partial^2\psi}{\partial z^2} = \frac{1}{a^2}\frac{\partial^2\psi}{\partial t^2} = -\frac{2m(E - V)}{E^2}\frac{\partial^2\psi}{\partial t^2} \tag{4.52}$$

For example, a function $\psi(lx + my + nz \pm at)$ represents a plane wave and satisfies (4.52) provided that the direction cosines l, m, and n satisfy the usual relation $l^2 + m^2 + n^2 = 1$. Here $(lx + my + nz \pm at)$ is the independent variable. For stationary states, i.e., solutions periodic in the time, we can write

$$\psi = \phi(x, y, z)e^{-2\pi i(E/h)t} \tag{4.53}$$

Substituting (4.53) in (4.52) gives

$$\left(\frac{\partial^2\phi}{\partial x^2} + \frac{\partial^2\phi}{\partial y^2} + \frac{\partial^2\phi}{\partial z^2}\right) e^{-2\pi i(E/h)t} = -\frac{4\pi^2 E^2 2m(E - V)}{h^2 E^2}\phi e^{-2\pi i(E/h)t}$$

or

$$\frac{\partial^2\phi}{\partial x^2} + \frac{\partial^2\phi}{\partial y^2} + \frac{\partial^2\phi}{\partial z^2} + \frac{8\pi^2 m}{h^2}(E - V) = 0 \tag{4.54}$$

This is Schroedinger's (1926) wave equation for a single particle.

The particle in a box

We first consider a particle in a box with axes along the x, y, and z axes and with the lengths a, b, and c parallel to these three axes. The potential energy V can be taken as zero except at the walls, where it becomes infinite. Putting $V = 0$ in (4.54), we now find it is satisfied by the wave equation

$$\psi = A \sin \frac{l\pi x}{a} \sin \frac{m\pi y}{b} \sin \frac{n\pi y}{c} \qquad (4.55)$$

providing

$$E = \frac{h^2}{8m} \left(\frac{l^2}{a^2} + \frac{m^2}{b^2} + \frac{n^2}{c^2} \right) \qquad (4.56)$$

Furthermore, the amplitude of the wave (4.55) must vanish at the walls. This happens if l, m, and n take integral values from 1 to infinity. In analogy to light waves the square of the amplitude (4.55) measures the probability of a particle being at the point with coordinates x, y, and z. This value (4.56) of the energy found from the wave equation agrees with the values in (4.19) et seq. obtained from the quantization condition (4.15). Combining the quantization condition (4.15) with the de Broglie wavelength relation gives

$$n = \oint (p/h) \, dq = \oint dq/\lambda \qquad (4.57)$$

Thus from (4.57) we see that the quantization condition requires that the allowed energies be so chosen as to give an integral number of wavelengths for the integral around the cycle. This parallels the requirement that the amplitude of the wave (4.55) vanish at the walls, which in turn requires that l, m, and n in (4.56) have integral values. Thus one sees a very close correlation between the old quantization condition and the modern wave-mechanical treatment. Chapters 5 and 6 of Q.C.[1] may be consulted for a detailed wave-mechanical derivation of the energy relations for the harmonic oscillator, for the rotator, and for the hydrogen atom.

The quantum-mechanical results for atoms carrying one electron are of especial interest since they give us the theory of atomic structure and explain Mendeleef's table. We substitute in (4.54) the potential energy $V = -ze^2/r$ for an atom with charge ze, where z is the atomic number and r is the distance between atom and electron. This gives

$$\frac{\partial^2 \phi}{\partial x^2} + \frac{\partial^2 \phi}{\partial y^2} + \frac{\partial^2 \phi}{\partial z^2} + \frac{8\pi^2 \mu}{h^2} \left(E + \frac{ze^2}{r} \right) \phi = 0$$

[1] *Quantum Chemistry* by Eyring, Walter, and Kimball (1944) is here abbreviated to Q.C.

We likewise replace the mass m of the electron by the reduced mass $\mu = mM/(m + M)$. Here M is the mass of the nucleus. The allowed energies are given by the equation

$$E = -\frac{2\pi^2\mu z^2 e^4}{n^2 h^2}$$

and the corresponding eigenfunctions φ are characterized by four quantum numbers $\varphi(n, l, m, s)$ where the principal quantum number n can take all possible integral values and determines the energy E of the electron; l measures the total angular momentum. The square of the total angular momentum is $l(l + 1)(h/2\pi)^2$. For a given n the quantum number l can take all integral values from 0 to $n - 1$. $mh/2\pi$ is the value found for the z component of angular momentum, and m can take the $2l + 1$ integral values between l and $- l$. The possible z components of spin of the electron on its axis is given by $sh/2\pi$, where s can take the two values $+ \frac{1}{2}$ and $- \frac{1}{2}$. An electron can take either value of s with any allowed value for the other quantum numbers. In actual atoms having several electrons, the energy of an electron depends upon the quantum number l as well as upon n. Thus, if l is a small number, the electron has a low angular momentum whence it can periodically plunge through the screening cloud of the other electrons and, as a consequence, be more tightly bound. High angular momentum, i.e., large values of l, prevent passages near the nucleus. We can specify the state of an electron by replacing the letters in the parentheses (n, l, m, s) by the corresponding numbers, much as a hotel guest is located by specifying the room number.

From the rules for allowed quantum numbers, we can see that the lowest states for an atom with one electron are $(100\frac{1}{2})$ and $(100\overline{\frac{1}{2}})$. This is the ground state of hydrogen. Helium houses its two electrons in the states $(100\frac{1}{2})$, $(100\overline{\frac{1}{2}})$. The bar over a number indicates a negative value. Lithium follows helium for its first two electrons, and the third goes into state $(200\frac{1}{2})$ or state $(200\overline{\frac{1}{2}})$. This filling up of the states in order continues until potassium, with 19 electrons, is reached. The nineteenth electron goes into state $(400\frac{1}{2})$ or state $(400\overline{\frac{1}{2}})$ instead of $(3, 2, m, s)$. Here m could take any of the values $(2, 1, 0, - 1, - 2)$ and s could be either $\frac{1}{2}$ or $- \frac{1}{2}$. In potassium the advantage of a low angular momentum which permits plunging through the cloud of the other 18 electrons more than makes up for the disadvantage of a larger principal quantum number. For the detailed assignment of the electrons, see the periodic table (Fig. 4.1).

From our discussion we see that the exact electronic energy equation when but one electron is present on an atom should be modified when many electrons are present. This can be done by replacing z by $z - s$ to give the energy

$$E = \frac{- 2\pi^2\mu(z - s)^2 e^4}{n^2 h^2}$$

Fig. 4.1. The periodic table of the elements. The six new elements, neptunium to berkelium, exhibit trivalence and behave like the rare earths and so have not been added. Iron can be taken as typical and used to explain the symbolism. The atomic number, 26, and the symbol Fe will be clear. The 5 means that it is a quintet state; i.e., in a magnetic field the lines split into 5 components. $^5D_4$ signifies the following. The 5 means that the two units of orbital angular momentum The D means that the total orbital angular momentum is two units. The subscript 4 shows that the two units of orbital angular momentum combine vectorially with the two units of spin to give a net spin angular momentum vector j of 4. The value 7.83 is the ionization potential in electron volts. $(3d)^6(4s)^2$ are just the outer partially filled shells. The deeper layers are full. The outer layers are empty.

1	2	3	4	5	6	7	8	9	10	11	12	13	14	15	16	17	18
1. H $^2S_{1/2}$ 13.527 $(1s)$																	2. He $^1S_0$ 24.46 $(1s)^2$
3. Li $^2S_{1/2}$ 5.363 $(2s)$	4. Be $^1S_0$ 9.28 $(2s)^2$											5. B $^2P_{1/2}$ 8.257 $(2s)^2(2p)$	6. C $^3P_0$ 11.217 $(2s)^2(2p)^2$	7. N $^4S_{3/2}$ 14.48 $(2s)^2(2p)^3$	8. O $^3P_2$ 13.55 $(2s)^2(2p)^4$	9. F $^2P_{3/2}$ 17.34 $(2s)^2(2p)^5$	10. Ne $^1S_0$ 21.45 $(2s)^2(2p)^6$
11. Na $^2S_{1/2}$ 5.12 $(3s)$	12. Mg $^1S_0$ 7.61 $(3s)^2$											13. Al $^2P_{1/2}$ 5.96 $(3s)^2(3p)$	14. Si $^3P_0$ 8.12 $(3s)^2(3p)^2$	15. P $^4S_{3/2}$ 10.9 $(3s)^2(3p)^3$	16. S $^3P_2$ 10.30 $(3s)^2(3p)^4$	17. Cl $^2P_{3/2}$ 12.95 $(3s)^2(3p)^5$	18. A $^1S_0$ 15.68 $(3s)^2(3p)^6$
19. K $^2S_{1/2}$ 4.318 $(4s)$	20. Ca $^1S_0$ 6.09 $(4s)^2$	21. Sc $^2D_{3/2}$ (6.7) $(3d)(4s)^2$	22. Ti $^3F_2$ 6.81 $(3d)^2(4s)^2$	23. V $^4F_{3/2}$ 6.71 $(3d)^3(4s)^2$	24. Cr $^7S_3$ 6.74 $(3d)^5(4s)$	25. Mn $^6S_{5/2}$ 7.41 $(3d)^5(4s)^2$	26. Fe $^5D_4$ 7.83 $(3d)^6(4s)^2$	27. Co $^4F_{9/2}$ 7.81 $(3d)^7(4s)^2$	28. Ni $^3F_4$ 7.61 $(3d)^8(4s)^2$	29. Cu $^2S_{1/2}$ 7.68 $(3d)^{10}(4s)$	30. Zn $^1S_0$ 9.36 $(3d)^{10}(4s)^2$	31. Ga $^2P_{1/2}$ 5.97 $(4p)$	32. Ge $^3P_0$ 8.09 $(4p)^2$	33. As $^4S_{3/2}$ 10.5 $(4p)^3$	34. Se $^3P_2$ 9.70 $(4p)^4$	35. Br $^2P_{3/2}$ 11.80 $(4p)^5$	36. Kr $^1S_0$ 13.93 $(4p)^6$
37. Rb $^2S_{1/2}$ 4.169 $(5s)$	38. Sr $^1S_0$ 5.667 $(5s)^2$	39. Y $^2D_{3/2}$ (6.5) $(4d)(5s)^2$	40. Zr $^3F_2$ 6.92 $(4d)^2(5s)^2$	41. Cb $^4D_{1/2}$ $(4d)^4(5s)$	42. Mo $^7S_3$ 7.35 $(4d)^5(5s)$	43. Ma	44. Ru $^5F_5$ $(4d)^7(5s)$	45. Rh $^4F_{9/2}$ 7.7 $(4d)^8(5s)$	46. Pd $^1S_0$ 8.3 $(4d)^{10}$	47. Ag $^2S_{1/2}$ 7.54 $(4d)^{10}(5s)$	48. Cd $^1S_0$ 8.96 $(4d)^{10}(5s)^2$	49. In $^2P_{1/2}$ 5.76 $(5p)$	50. Sn $^3P_0$ 7.30 $(5p)^2$	51. Sb $^4S_{3/2}$ $(5p)^3$	52. Te $^3P_2$ 8.96 $(5p)^4$	53. I $^2P_{3/2}$ 10.6 $(5p)^5$	54. Xe $^1S_0$ 12.08 $(5p)^6$
55. Cs $^2S_{1/2}$ 3.87 $(6s)$	56. Ba $^1S_0$ 5.19 $(6s)^2$	57. La $^2D_{3/2}$ $(5d)(6s)^2$ — 71. Lu $^2D_{3/2}$ $(4f)^{14}(5d)(6s)^2$	72. Hf $^3F_2$ $(6s)^2$	73. Ta $^4F_{3/2}$ $(6s)^2$	74. W $^5D_0$ $(5d)^4(6s)^2$	75. Re $^6S_{5/2}$ $(5d)^5(6s)^2$	76. Os $^5D_4$ (8,7) $(5d)^6(6s)^2$	77. Ir $^4F_{9/2}$ $(5d)^7(6s)^2$	78. Pt $^3D_3$ 8.88 $(5d)^9(6s)$	79. Au $^2S_{1/2}$ 9.18 $(5d)^{10}(6s)$	80. Hg $^1S_0$ 10.38 $(5d)^{10}(6s)^2$	81. Tl $^2P_{1/2}$ 6.07 $(6p)$	82. Pb $^3P_0$ 7.38 $(6p)^2$	83. Bi $^4S_{3/2}$ $(6p)^3$	84. Po $^3P_2$ $(6p)^4$	85.	86. Rn $^1S_0$ 10.69 $(6p)^6$
57.	88. Ra $^1S_0$ 5.252 $(7s)^2$	89. Ac	90. Th	91. Pa	92. U												

Here s is a screening constant giving the amount which other electrons screen the central nuclear charge z for the electron in question. For potassium, for example, the ionization potential for the outermost electron is 4.318 volts. If the inner 18 electrons screened completely effectively, s would be 18, giving $z - s = 1$, and E would equal the ionization potential of hydrogen, 13.527 volts, divided by 4^2. However, since $z - s = [(4.318 \times 4^2)/13.527]^{1/2} = 2.26$, we find $s = 16.74$ instead of 18. Electrons screen their competitors much less effectively if both have the same principal quantum number and so are at least roughly equidistant from the nucleus. Since the energy of an electron depends only upon the quantum numbers, n and l, it is usually sufficient to specify how many electrons a particular atom has with a given n and l. In this way one specifies the atomic "configuration." Instead of writing the numbers 0, 1, 2, 3, 4, 5, etc., specifying the l values, the letters s, p, d, f, g, h, etc., following the alphabet beyond f, are used instead. The number of electrons having a given configuration is written as a superscript on the right. Thus the configuration of hydrogen in its ground state is $(1s)$. The configurations of some of the other atoms are: $He(1s)^2$, $Li(1s)^2(2s)$, $Be(1s)^2(2s)^2$, $Al(1s)^2(2s)^2(2p)$, $C(1s)^2(2s)^2(2p)^2$, $N(1s)^2(2s)^2(2p)^3$, $O(1s)^2(2s)^2(2p)^4$, $F(1s)^2(2s)^2(2p)^5$, and $Ne(1s)^2(2s)^2(2p)^6$.

The screening of the hydrogen atom by its single $(1s)$ electron is so efficient that an extra electron is only bound by $\frac{2}{3}$ volt, whereas fluorine is so poorly screened that an extra electron is bound by 4 volts in spite of the principal quantum number having been increased from 1 to 2. In fact, fluorine is the most electronegative of all the elements because, with its five $2p$ electrons, it has the most ineffective screening together with the smallest possible principal quantum number a halogen can have. The alkali metals, on the other hand, readily lose their valence electron because the electrons below the outer electron screen the nucleus effectively.

Chemical bonds are simply the sharing of two electrons between two atoms and are stronger the less the electron pair is screened from the two nuclei and the lower the principal quantum number. The bond H—F is the strongest electron pair bond. Here we have low quantum numbers for the valence electrons and very incomplete screening on the fluorine. Both effects tend to make the bond strong. We now turn to some rather formal aspects of quantum mechanics.

Operators

One takes the first derivative of φ with respect to x by letting the operator $\partial/\partial x$ operate on φ to give $\partial\varphi/\partial x$. To get the second derivative of φ we operate twice with $\partial/\partial x$ to give $\partial^2\varphi/\partial x^2$. The quantity $x\varphi$ may be thought of as the operation of multiplying x into φ. When two or more operators are applied to φ, the order of operation may affect the result. Thus $x(\partial\varphi/\partial x)$ is different from

$$\frac{\partial}{\partial x}(x\varphi) = \varphi + x\frac{\partial\varphi}{\partial x}$$

Thus

$$\left[x\left(\frac{\partial}{\partial x}\right) - \left(\frac{\partial}{\partial x}\right)x\right]\varphi = -\varphi$$

The operators x and $\partial/\partial x$ are said not to commute. The difference of the two operators

$$\left[x\left(\frac{\partial}{\partial x}\right) - \left(\frac{\partial}{\partial x}\right)x\right] \qquad (4.58)$$

is called the commutator for these two operators. Operators are useful in a general formulation of quantum mechanics. We can write

$$(\partial/\partial x)(\varphi + \psi) = \partial\varphi/\partial x + \partial\psi/\partial x \qquad (4.59)$$

whereas

$$\ln(\varphi + \psi) \neq \ln\varphi + \ln\psi \qquad (4.60)$$

The operator $\partial/\partial x$ is said to be linear because the result of operating with $\partial/\partial x$ on a sum is the sum of the results of operating on the terms in the sum. Operations such as taking the logarithm, the sine, etc., are non-linear. Only linear operators are used in quantum mechanics.

The kinetic energy T for a particle is

$$T = \tfrac{1}{2}m(\dot{x}^2 + \dot{y}^2 + \dot{z}^2) = \frac{1}{2m}(p_x{}^2 + p_y{}^2 + p_z{}^2) \qquad (4.61)$$

where $p_x = m\dot{x}$ is the x component of momentum, and p_y and p_z are analogously defined. Thus the total energy H can be written

$$H = T + V = (1/2m)(p_x{}^2 + p_y{}^2 + p_z{}^2) + V \qquad (4.62)$$

Here V is the potential energy. If in H we replace p_x by $(h/2\pi i)(\partial/\partial x)$, p_y by $(h/2\pi i)(\partial/\partial y)$, and p_z by $(h/2\pi i)(\partial/\partial z)$ and then write

$$H\psi = E\psi$$

we obtain

$$-\frac{h^2}{8\pi^2 m}\left(\frac{\partial^2}{\partial x^2} + \frac{\partial^2}{\partial y^2} + \frac{\partial^2}{\partial z^2}\right)\psi + V\psi = E\psi \qquad (4.63)$$

This is just the wave equation for a particle derived previously. $|\psi|^2$, the square of the wave amplitude, as in physical optics, is proportioned to the probability of the system being located at each point.　The function ψ is said to have been normalized if

$$\int |\psi|^2 \, dx \, dy \, dz = 1 \tag{4.64}$$

The integral (4.64) is to be taken over the entire space accessible to the particle.　Such functions ψ must have special properties; this is indicated by saying that they belong to class Q.　Their absolute values squared for each configuration must be interpretable as the probability of occurrence of that configuration.　Thus the ψ's must belong to the set of functions Q which are single-valued and continuous (except at a finite number of points where the function may become infinite) and which give a finite result when the squares of the function is integrated over the entire range of the variables.

The operators met in quantum mechanics all belong to the class called Hermitian operators.　An operator α is Hermitian if

$$\int \varphi \alpha \psi \, d\tau = \int \psi \alpha^* \varphi \, d\tau \tag{4.65}$$

where φ and ψ belong to class Q.　As usual, the star on α means that, wherever the quantity $i = (-1)^{1/2}$ occurs in α, it is to be replaced by $-i$.　Suppose that

$$\alpha \psi = a \psi \tag{4.66}$$

where a is a constant.　Then a is said to be the eigenvalue associated with the eigenfunction ψ of the operator α.

Hermitian operators and real eigenvalues

We now prove that the eigenvalues of Hermitian operators are always real.　If we take the complex conjugate of equation (4.66) we obtain

$$\alpha^* \psi^* = a^* \psi^* \tag{4.67}$$

Multiplying both sides of (4.66) by ψ^* and integrating gives

$$\int \psi^* \alpha \psi \, d\tau = a \int \psi^* \psi \, d\tau \tag{4.68}$$

Multiplying (4.67) by ψ gives

$$\int \psi \alpha^* \psi^* \, d\tau = a^* \int \psi \psi^* \, d\tau \tag{4.69}$$

If we identify ψ^* with φ in (4.65), it follows that the left sides of (4.68) and (4.69) are equal.　Thus, subtracting (4.68) from (4.69) gives

$$0 = (a^* - a) \int \psi^* \psi \, d\tau \tag{4.70}$$

Thus, since the factor $\int \psi^* \psi \, d\tau \neq 0$, it follows that $a^* - a = 0$, that is, $a^* = a$.　Hence the eigenvalues of Hermitian operators are always real.

Orthogonality of eigenfunctions of a Hermitian operator

Next, let it be supposed that

$$\alpha\psi_1 = a_1\psi_1 \tag{4.71}$$

$$\alpha\psi_2 = a_2\psi_2 \tag{4.72}$$

where $a_1 \neq a_2$. Two eigenfunctions ψ_1 and ψ_2 are said to be orthogonal if

$$\int \psi_1^* \psi_2 \, d\tau = 0 \tag{4.73}$$

It can now be shown that two eigenfunctions ψ_1 and ψ_2 of the Hermitian operator α having different eigenvalues are orthogonal. Multiplying (4.71) by ψ_2^* and integrating, we obtain

$$\int \psi_2^* \alpha\psi_1 \, d\tau = a_1 \int \psi_2^* \psi_1 \, d\tau \tag{4.74}$$

Taking the complex conjugate of (4.72), multiplying by ψ_1, and integrating gives

$$\int \psi_1 \alpha^* \psi_2^* \, d\tau = a_2^* \int \psi_1 \psi_2^* \, d\tau = a_2 \int \psi_1 \psi_2^* \, d\tau \tag{4.75}$$

Since α is Hermitian, it follows from (4.65) that the left sides of (4.74) and (4.75) are equal. Subtracting the latter equation from the former gives

$$0 = (a_1 - a_2) \int \psi_2^* \psi_1 \, d\tau \tag{4.76}$$

Since $a_1 - a_2 \neq 0$, it follows that $\int \psi_2^* \psi_1 \, d\tau = 0$. Thus we see that two eigenfunctions of a Hermitian operator α having different eigenvalues are orthogonal.

This operator method for finding the wave equation can be generalized by stating a set of postulates. As always in science, the justification of the postulates must be that they lead to results in agreement with experiment.

The postulates of quantum mechanics

Postulate I. Any state of a system is described as fully as possible by a function $\psi(q_1 \cdots q_f, t)$ of the class Q. Here $\psi(q_1 \cdots q_f, t)$ is called the state function of the system and has the property that $\psi^* \psi \, d\tau$ is the probability that the variables lie in the f-dimensional volume element $d\tau$ at time t.

Postulate II. To every dynamical variable M there can be assigned a linear, Hermitian operator μ. The rules for finding these operators are: (a) If M is one of the position coordinates q or the time t, the operator is multiplication by the variable itself. (b) If M is one of the momenta p, the operator is $(h/2\pi i)(\partial/\partial q_i)$, where q_i is conjugate to p_i. Similarly, if M is the energy H it can be set equal to the operator $-(h/2\pi i)(\partial/\partial t)$. (c) If M is any dynamical variable expressible in terms of the q's, the p's, and t, the operator is found by substituting the operators for the q's, the p's, and t as defined above in the algebraic expression for M, and replacing the processes of ordinary algebra by those of operator algebra. If there is any ambiguity in the order, they must be arranged so that the resulting operator is Hermitian.

Postulate III. If the state function $\psi(q, t)$ is an eigenfunction of the operator μ corresponding to a dynamical variable M, i.e., if

$$\mu\psi = m\psi \tag{4.77}$$

then, in this state ψ, the variable M has the constant value m precisely. Such a state ψ is known as an eigenstate of M.

As an example of the working of these postulates, consider the system consisting of a particle of mass m moving in a potential field $V(x, y, z)$. The kinetic energy of the particle is

$$T = (1/2m)(p_x{}^2 + p_y{}^2 + p_z{}^2) \tag{4.78}$$

and the classical Hamiltonian function is

$$H = (1/2m)(p_x{}^2 + p_y{}^2 + p_z{}^2) + V(x, y, z) \tag{4.79}$$

According to Postulate II the Hamiltonian operator is

$$H = \frac{1}{2m}\left[\left(\frac{h}{2\pi i}\frac{\partial}{\partial x}\right)^2 + \left(\frac{h}{2\pi i}\frac{\partial}{\partial y}\right)^2 + \left(\frac{h}{2\pi i}\frac{\partial}{\partial z}\right)^2\right] + V$$

$$= -\frac{h^2}{8\pi^2 m}\left(\frac{\partial^2}{\partial x^2} + \frac{\partial^2}{\partial y^2} + \frac{\partial^2}{\partial z^2}\right) + V \tag{4.80}$$

From the last part of postulate II we have

$$H\psi = -\frac{h}{2\pi i}\frac{\partial\psi}{\partial t} \tag{4.81}$$

This is Schroedinger's time-dependent equation. For stationary states we can write

$$\psi(x, y, z, t) = \psi(x, y, z)e^{-2\pi i Et/h} \tag{4.82}$$

Substituting (4.82) in (4.81) gives

$$H\psi(x, y, z)e^{-2\pi i Et/h} = -\frac{h}{2\pi i}\frac{\partial}{\partial t}\psi(x, y, z)e^{-2\pi i Et/h}$$

$$= E\psi(x, y, z)e^{-2\pi i Et/h}$$

Dividing out $e^{-2\pi i Et/h}$ gives Schroedinger's time-independent equation:

$$H\psi = E\psi \tag{4.83}$$

Substituting from (4.80) for H in equation (4.83) gives exactly the wave equation (4.54).

The above postulates give a method for calculating the eigenstates for any property. The procedure is (a) to write down the expression for the property in classical mechanics; (b) to use postulate II to transform to the corresponding quantum-mechanical operator; (c) using postulate III, to find the eigenvalues going with the eigenfunctions.

Postulate IV. If ψ_1 and ψ_2 are eigenfunctions of the operator μ corresponding to the variable M with the eigenvalues m_1 and m_2, the state represented by $\varphi = c_1\psi_1 + c_2\psi_2$ is that state in which the probability of observing the value m_2 is $c_2^*c_2$. A starred quantity signifies its complex conjugate. Since the set of eigenfunctions $\psi_1, \psi_2, \cdots, \psi_i, \cdots$ of an operator μ can be taken as orthogonal (i.e., $\int \psi_i^* \psi_j \, d\tau = 0$) and can be taken as normalized (i.e., so that $\int \psi_i^* \psi_i \, d\tau = 1$), we may expand any normalized state function φ in terms of these ψ_i's:

$$\varphi = \sum_i c_i\psi_i$$

where
$$c_i = \int \psi_i^*\varphi \, d\tau$$

Consider now the integral $\int \varphi^*\mu\varphi \, d\tau$. Expanding φ in terms of the eigenfunctions of μ, we have

$$\int \varphi^*\mu\varphi \, d\tau = \int (\sum_i c_i^*\psi_i^*)\mu(\sum_j c_j\psi_j) \, d\tau$$

$$= \int (\sum_i c_i^*\psi_i^*)(\sum_j c_j m_j\psi_j) \, d\tau = \sum_j m_j c_j^* c_j$$

But $\sum_j m_j c_j^* c_j$ is merely the average value of M in the state φ, so that we have the important result that the average value of any dynamical variable M in any state φ is given by

$$\overline{M}_i = \int \varphi_i^*\mu\varphi_i \, d\tau \qquad (4.84)$$

where μ is the operator corresponding to M. In the next chapter we will see how to weight the average value $\overline{M}_i$ over all i states to get the average value for the system at equilibrium. We next consider the angular momentum **M** of a particle rotating about a fixed center. Boldface type will be used to indicate a vector quantity. Then

$$\mathbf{M} = \mathbf{r} \times \mathbf{p} \equiv (\mathbf{i}x + \mathbf{j}y + \mathbf{k}z) \times (\mathbf{i}p_x + \mathbf{j}p_y + \mathbf{k}p_z)$$

$$\equiv \mathbf{i}(yp_z - zp_y) + \mathbf{j}(zp_x - xP_z) + \mathbf{k}(xp_y - yp_x) \quad (4.85)$$

Here **r** is the vector distance from the center of rotation to the particle, and **p** is the vector for momentum of the particle. The cross between **r** and **p** means to take the vector product (Q.C., Appendix II).

Substituting $(h/2\pi i)(\partial/\partial x)$ in (4.85) for p_x, etc., in accordance with postulate II, we get for the corresponding quantum-mechanical operator for angular momentum:

$$\mathbf{M} = \mathbf{i}\,\frac{h}{2\pi i}\left(y\,\frac{\partial}{\partial z} - z\,\frac{\partial}{\partial y}\right) + \mathbf{j}\,\frac{h}{2\pi i}\left(z\,\frac{\partial}{\partial x} - x\,\frac{\partial}{\partial z}\right)$$

$$+ \mathbf{k}\,\frac{h}{2\pi i}\left(x\,\frac{\partial}{\partial y} - y\,\frac{\partial}{\partial x}\right) \equiv i\mathbf{M}_x + j\mathbf{M}_y + k\mathbf{M}_z \tag{4.86}$$

Carrying out the indicated operations in a straightforward manner gives

$$(M_x M_y - M_y M_x)\varphi = \frac{ih}{2\pi}\,M_z\varphi$$

or, omitting φ, we have for the operators the so-called commutation rules

$$M_x M_y - M_y M_x = \frac{ih}{2\pi}\,M_z$$

$$M_y M_z - M_z M_y = \frac{ih}{2\pi}\,M_x \tag{4.87}$$

$$M_z M_x - M_x M_z = \frac{ih}{2\pi}\,M_y$$

The operator

$$M^2 = M_x{}^2 + M_y{}^2 + M_z{}^2$$

may be shown to commute with M_x, M_y, and M_z by showing, for example, that

$$(M_z M^2 - M^2 M_z)\varphi = 0$$

by using the commutation rules.

We can then find a set of functions Y_{lm} which are simultaneously eigenfunctions for M_z and M^2. In Q.C. (p. 44) it is shown that

$$M^2 Y_{lm} = l(l+1)\left(\frac{h}{2\pi}\right)^2 Y_{lm} \tag{4.88}$$

and

$$M_z Y_{lm} = m\,\frac{h}{2\pi}\,Y_{lm} \tag{4.89}$$

From (4.89) we see the eigenvalue for the operator M_z going with the eigenfunction Y_{lm} is $m(h/2\pi)$. We now calculate the eigenvalue of the function

$$\{(M_x - iM_y)\,Y_{lm}\}$$

using the commutation rules (4.87). Thus

$$M_z\{M_x - iM_y)Y_{lm}\} = \left[M_xM_z + \frac{ih}{2\pi}M_y - i\left(M_yM_z - \frac{ih}{2\pi}M_x\right)\right]Y_{lm}$$

$$= (M_x - iM_y)\left(M_z - \frac{h}{2\pi}\right)Y_{lm}$$

$$= \frac{h}{2\pi}(m - 1)\{(M_x - iM_y)Y_{lm}\}$$

Thus

$$\{(M_x - iM_y)Y_{lm}\}$$

is an eigenfunction for M_z with an eigenvalue less by $h/2\pi$ than the value for Y_{lm}.   Therefore, starting with Y_{lm}, we can operate repeatedly with $(M_x - iM_y)$, each time getting a function whose eigenvalue has decreased by $h/2\pi$ until we get zero upon operating on the function whose eigenvalue for M_z has reached $lh/2\pi$.

Similarly

$$M_z\{(M_x + iM_y)Y_{lm}\} = (m + 1)\frac{h}{2\pi}\{(M_x + iM_y)Y_{lm}\}$$

Thus, starting with Y_{lm}, we can operate repeatedly with $(M_x + iM_y)$, getting each time an eigenfunction with eigenvalue greater by $h/2\pi$ until the eigenvalue $lh/2\pi$ is reached.   Thus we can derive from a single eigenfunction $2l + 1$ such functions, each an eigenfunction of M_z with eigenvalues differing by integral multiple of $h/2\pi$.

Furthermore, since M^2 commutes with M_x and M_y, we have

$$M^2\{M_x + iM_y)Y_{lm}\} = (M_x + iM_y)M^2Y_{lm}$$

$$= l(l + 1)\left(\frac{h}{2\pi}\right)^2\{(M_x + iM_y)Y_{lm}\}$$

Consequently $\{(M_x + iM_y)Y_{lm}\}$ is an eigenfunction for M^2 with the same eigenvalue as Y_{lm}.   Similarly $\{(M_x - iM_y)Y_{lm}\}$ has the same eigenvalue as Y_{lm}.   We have, therefore, a method to derive $(2l + 1)$ eigenfunctions for M^2 and M_z from a single eigenfunction of these operators.   The $2l + 1$ eigenfunctions all have the same eigenvalue for M^2 but differ in their eigenvalues for M_z by multiples of $h/2\pi$.   Thus l is either an integer or an integer plus $\frac{1}{2}$.   We will meet this latter case when electron spin is treated.

Also in Q.C. (p. 46) we find that

$$(M_x - iM_y)Y_{lm} = \frac{h}{2\pi}[l(l + 1) - m(m - 1)]^{1/2}Y_{l,\,m-1} \qquad (4.90)$$

and

$$(M_x + iM_y)Y_{lm} = \frac{h}{2\pi}[l(l + 1) - m(m + 1)]^{1/2}Y_{l,\,m+1} \qquad (4.91)$$

The results in the equations from (4.88) to (4.91) follow from the commutation rules (4.87). Any other operators which follow the same commutation rules will satisfy these same relations.

We are now ready to develop the theory of electron spins which is the basis of valence theory. Before quantum mechanics was discovered, it was only possible to explain about 10 per cent of the energy of binding of two such atoms as hydrogen. This 10 per cent was due to the mutual polarization of the atoms. The polarization binding is additive in a complex involving additional atoms. If all the binding were of this classical additive kind, the world as we know it could not exist. Atoms would all clump together in amorphous masses at low temperatures and distill into a vapor at high temperatures. The factor determining how many atoms would surround a central atom would be simply the available space. Activation energy, with all it means for persistence of molecular structure, would be non-existent, and any living thing would instantly change into a gas or into ashes. It becomes extraordinarily interesting and important to understand how valence bonds are formed. Before quantum mechanics, G. N. Lewis (1916, 1923) was able to show that electron pairing was of fundamental significance in the formation of valence bonds. Stable molecules containing an odd number of electrons are curiosities but not quite non-existent. Molecules such as NO and NO_2 have an expected penchant for pairing to satisfy their odd electron state. Pauling's book, *The Nature of the Chemical Bond* (1940a), does much to clarify stable structures in terms of valence theory. The unstable intermediates in chemical reactions, activated complexes, are like stable molecules in all their degrees of freedom except the one along the reaction coordinate. Thus the principles which govern stability and behavior of ordinary molecules operate for activated complexes. To provide the quantitative background for understanding valence and chemical stability, we must develop the theory of electron spin which was left out of classical molecular theory. Indeed valence can be understood in no other way.

In the early twenties it became clear that the state of electrons in atoms could not be completely described by assigning the three quantum numbers which fixed their translational degrees of freedom. There was an additional splitting of lines in a magnetic field which Uhlenbeck and Goudsmit (1925, 1926) first resolved by attributing a spin to the electrons. Such a spinning charge, like any solenoid, must have associated with it a magnetic moment μ proportional to the angular momentum S. Gerlach and Stern (1922a,b) measured this spin. They passed a beam of silver atoms through a strong inhomogeneous magnetic field and found the beam divided sharply into two beams. One beam was deflected as though each atom were a magnetic dipole of magnitude $eh/4\pi mc$ oriented along the field direction; the other atoms were deflected like a magnetic dipole of the same strength with its poles interchanged. A monovalent atom like silver has only one unpaired electron, and, as this atom is in a state without orbital angular momentum, the measured magnetic moment is to be attributed to the spin of the valence electron.

S_x, S_y, and S_z, the x, y, and z components of electron spin angular momentum, are assumed to obey the same commutation rules (4.87) as the components of orbital angular momentum. Hence all the relations (4.87) through (4.91) can be written over again simply by replacing M, wherever it occurs, by S. The Stern-Gerlach experiment shows that the electron has only two states. Hence $2l + 1 = 2$ or $l = \frac{1}{2}$. If we call our state with the highest z component of spin α and the other function β, we have [using (4.90) and remembering that $l = \frac{1}{2}$ and $m = \frac{1}{2}$ for the state α, while $l = \frac{1}{2}$ and $m = -\frac{1}{2}$ for the state β] the following results:

$$(S_x - iS_y)\alpha = (h/2\pi)[\tfrac{1}{2}(\tfrac{1}{2} + 1) - \tfrac{1}{2}(\tfrac{1}{2} - 1)]^{1/2} \beta = (h/2\pi)\beta \quad (4.92)$$

Similarly,
$$(S_x - iS_y)\beta = 0 \quad (4.93)$$

$$(S_x + iS_y)\alpha = 0 \quad (4.94)$$

$$(S_x + iS_y)\beta = (h/2\pi)[\tfrac{1}{2}(\tfrac{1}{2} + 1) + \tfrac{1}{2}(-\tfrac{1}{2} + 1)]^{1/2} \alpha = (h/2\pi)\alpha \quad (4.95)$$

By adding and subtracting the above four equations appropriately, we find
$$S_x\alpha = (h/4\pi)\beta$$
$$S_y\alpha = i(h/4\pi)\beta$$
$$S_x\beta = (h/4\pi)\alpha \quad (4.96)$$
$$S_y\beta = -i(h/4\pi)\alpha$$

also
$$S_z\alpha = (h/4\pi)\alpha$$
$$S_z\beta = (h/4\pi)\alpha$$

Furthermore, from (4.88) or from the above relations,
$$S^2\alpha = \tfrac{1}{2}(\tfrac{1}{2} + 1)(h/2\pi)^2\alpha = \tfrac{3}{4}(h/2\pi)^2\alpha \quad (4.97)$$
$$S^2\beta = \tfrac{3}{4}(h/2\pi)^2\beta$$

The variation method. An arbitrary normalized function φ can be expanded in terms of the orthogonal set of eigenfunctions ψ_i of an operator α with corresponding eigenvalues a_i in the form

$$\varphi = \sum_i c_i\psi_i \quad (4.98)$$

where
$$c_i = \int \psi_i^*\varphi \, d\tau \quad (4.99)$$

Hence
$$\alpha\varphi = \alpha\sum_i c_i\psi_i = \sum_i c_i a_i\psi_i \quad (4.100)$$

Multiplying through by φ^* and integrating gives the average value

$$\bar{a} = \int \varphi^* \alpha \varphi \, d\tau = \int \sum_j c_j^* \psi_j^* \sum_i c_i a_i \psi_i \, d\tau = \sum_i c_i^* c_i a_i \qquad (4.101)$$

We call the lowest of all eigenvalues a_1, and the integral subscripts are assigned so that they increase with the eigenvalues. Clearly the lowest possible value $\bar{a}$ which any state of the system φ can lead to arises when

$$\sum_i c_i^* c_i = 1 = c_1^* c_1$$

In this case $\bar{a} = a_1$ and $\varphi = \psi_1$. This suggests a procedure for finding the eigenfunctions and eigenvalues for any operator. We choose a set of trial functions $\varphi_1, \varphi_2, \cdots, \varphi_n$ and ask what linear combination of them will give the lowest value for the property $\bar{a}$ corresponding to the eigenfunction α. We are led to the relation

$$\delta \int \sum_i c_i^* \varphi_i^* (\alpha - a) \sum_j c_j \varphi_j \, d\tau = 0 \qquad (4.102)$$

Here the variation is on the c^*'s and c's, so we are led to the equations

$$\sum_j \sum_i \delta c_i^* c_j \int \varphi_i^* (\alpha - a) \varphi_j \, d\tau + \sum_i \sum_j c_i^* \delta c_j \int \varphi_i^* (\alpha - a) \varphi_j \, d\tau = 0 \qquad (4.103)$$

It is convenient to substitute

$$\int \varphi_i^* \alpha \varphi_j \, d\tau = a_{ij}$$

and

$$\int \varphi_i^* \varphi_j \, d\tau = s_{ij}$$

To satisfy (4.103) the coefficient of each δc_i^* and δc_j must equal zero. Because α is Hermitian it follows that if we satisfy the equations

$$\sum_j c_j(a_{ij} - s_{ij}a) = 0 \qquad (4.104)$$

the coefficients of δc_j will automatically vanish.

Solving (4.104) for c_1 gives

$$c_1 = \frac{\begin{vmatrix} 0(a_{12} - s_{12}a) & \cdots & \cdots & (a_{1n} - s_{1n}a) \\ 0 & \cdots & \cdots & \cdots \\ \cdots & \cdots & \cdots & \cdots \\ 0(a_{11} - s_{11}a)(a_{12} - s_{12}a) & \cdots & (a_{1n} - s_{1n}a) \end{vmatrix}}{\begin{vmatrix} (a_{11} - s_{11}a)(a_{12} - s_{12}a) & \cdots & (a_{1n} - s_{1n}a) \\ \cdots & \cdots & \cdots & \cdots \\ \cdots & \cdots & \cdots & \cdots \\ (a_{n1} - s_{n1}a) & & & (a_{nn} - s_{nn}a) \end{vmatrix}} \qquad (4.105)$$

Since the numerator of (4.105) is zero, the denominator must be zero also if there are to be non-vanishing values of c_1. A non-zero value for any other c requires the vanishing of this same denominator. As the denominator is of nth degree in the quantity a, it vanishes for n values $a_1, a_2, \cdots, a_n$. Having solved for the n values of a, we can then substitute any one of these values, say a_i, back into the set of equations (4.104). If we use, say, the first $n - 1$ equations, dividing each equation through by c_n, it is possible to find numerical values for the $n - 1$ ratios for $c_1/c_n, c_2/c_n, \cdots, c_{n-1}/c_n$. If we combine these results with the condition

$$1 = \int \sum_i c_i{}^* \varphi_i{}^* \sum_j c_j \varphi_j \, d\tau$$

the c's are completely determined. All the c's may be chosen real. This process of finding c's can be repeated for each of the n values of a in turn. Thus the variation method leads us to the best set of n eigenfunctions, with n corresponding eigenvalues, that can be made from a linear combination of n starting functions. If this set of functions is sufficiently extensive—a complete set—the a's determined are the exact values.

The Pauli exclusion principle

Pauli (1925) observed that no two electrons, or more generally no two elementary particles, can ever occupy a state for which all four quantum numbers are equal. On the other hand, the square of the absolute value of an eigenfunction for a set of particles must remain unchanged when two identical particles interchange positions, since this quantity measures the probability of the two equally likely configurations. An eigenfunction which is a function of the three spatial coordinates of a single particle is called an orbital. The three quantum numbers n, l, and m in general specify such an orbital. It will be convenient to specify electron orbitals by the letters of the alphabet, a, b, c, etc. To specify completely the state of an electron, the z component of its spin must be specified as α or β corresponding to plus or minus $\frac{1}{2}(h/2\pi)$, respectively. Thus the assignment for four electrons

$$(a\alpha)_1 \qquad (b\beta)_2 \qquad (c\alpha)_3 \qquad (d\alpha)_4 \qquad (4.106)$$

specifies that electron 1 is in the state with orbital a and with spin α, whereas electron 2 is in orbital b with spin β, etc. Actually, any permutation of the electrons among these four spin-orbital states is just as likely as the above assignment. It turns out that there is no way of being sure how the electrons are assigned.

The requirements that no two electrons can have the same four quantum numbers and that the square of the overall eigenfunction be unchanged in value when two identical particles are interchanged are fulfilled if the four electrons are assigned to the determinantal eigenfunction:

$$\varphi = \frac{1}{(4!)^{1/2}} \begin{vmatrix} (a\alpha)_1 & (b\beta)_1 & (c\alpha)_1 & (d\alpha)_1 \\ (a\alpha)_2 & (b\beta)_2 & (c\alpha)_2 & (d\alpha)_2 \\ (a\alpha)_3 & (b\beta)_3 & (c\alpha)_3 & (d\alpha)_3 \\ (a\alpha)_4 & (b\beta)_4 & (c\alpha)_4 & (d\alpha)_4 \end{vmatrix}$$

$$\equiv \frac{1}{(4!)^{1/2}} \sum_{\nu} (-1)^{\nu} P_{\nu} (a\alpha)_1 (b\beta)_2 (c\alpha)_3 (d\alpha)_4$$

$$\equiv \begin{pmatrix} abcd \\ \alpha\beta\alpha\alpha \end{pmatrix} \tag{4.107}$$

Such determinants were used early by Slater (1931) in treating molecular problems. P_{ν} means any permutation of the four subscripts 1, 2, 3, 4. If the particular permutation is equivalent to an even number of transpositions of pairs, it is said to be even; if it is equivalent to an odd number of transpositions, it is said to be odd. The symbol ν is assigned an even value for even and an odd value for odd permutations. The last notation for the determinant φ in (4.107) will be found useful.

Now, for example, when $a = c$, we see that the first and third columns are equal; therefore by the property of determinants φ vanishes. It is thus clear that the determinantal form φ precludes assigning two like particles to two identical states. Interchanging two numbers such as 1 and 2 corresponds to interchanging these two particles, and from the rules of determinants we see that φ changes sign. φ^2 is unaffected by interchanging any pair of numbers. Thus φ^2 weights the probability of these two like configurations equally.

Chemical bonds

We suppose that two atoms A and B are held together by sharing electrons 1 and 2 in two overlapping orbitals a and b situated on A and B, respectively. The four possible φ's are

$$\varphi_1 = \begin{pmatrix} ab \\ \alpha\alpha \end{pmatrix} \qquad \varphi_2 = \begin{pmatrix} ab \\ \alpha\beta \end{pmatrix} \qquad \varphi_3 = \begin{pmatrix} ab \\ \beta\alpha \end{pmatrix} \qquad \varphi_4 = \begin{pmatrix} ab \\ \beta\beta \end{pmatrix} \tag{4.108}$$

Here the notation $\begin{pmatrix} ab \\ \alpha\alpha \end{pmatrix}$ is shorthand for the determinant $\begin{pmatrix} ab \\ \alpha\alpha \end{pmatrix} = [1/(2)^{1/2}[(a\alpha)_1(b\alpha)_2 - (a\alpha)_2(b\alpha)_1]$. Using these four φ functions in the variation method, we are led to the following four-rowed determinant for the denominator of (4.105).

$$
\begin{vmatrix}
(H_{11} - S_{11}E) & 0 & 0 & 0 \\
0 & (H_{22} - S_{22}E) & (H_{23} - S_{23}E) & 0 \\
0 & (H_{32} - S_{32}E) & (H_{33} - S_{33}E) & 0 \\
0 & 0 & 0 & (H_{44} - S_{44}E)
\end{vmatrix} = 0 \quad (4.109)
$$

Here

$$
H_{11} = \tfrac{1}{2}\int\{(a\alpha)_1(b\alpha)_2 - (a\alpha)_2(b\alpha)_1\}H\{(a\alpha)_1(b\alpha)_2 - (a\alpha)_2(b\alpha)_1\}\,d\tau_1\,d\tau_2 \tag{4.110}
$$

The integration over spin eigenfunctions for an electron always yields unity if the spin eigenfunctions are alike; otherwise zero is obtained. If we call the integral

$$
\int a_1 b_2 H a_1 b_2\, dx_1\, dy_1\, dz_1\, dx_2\, dy_2\, dz_2 = A
$$

and

$$
\int a_1 b_2 H a_2 b_1\, dx_1\, dy_1\, dz_1\, dx_2\, dy_2\, dz_2 = \alpha
$$

we obtain

$$
H_{11} = A - \alpha
$$

Similarly, S_{11} is exactly the same as H_{11} in (4.110) except that the operator H is replaced by 1. Thus

$$
S_{11} = 1 - S^2
$$

where

$$
S^2 = \int a_1 b_2 a_2 b_1\, dx_1\, dy_1\, dz_1\, dx_2\, dy_2\, dz_2
$$

Equation (4.109) is satisfied for four values of E. Three of these roots have the same value,

$$
E = \frac{A - \alpha}{1 - s^2}
$$

and correspond to the triplet state; the fourth root is

$$
E = \frac{A + \alpha}{1 + s^2}
$$

The last state is the low-lying singlet state in which molecules are found at ordinary temperatures. Heitler and London (1927) and Sugiura (1927) solved the integrals for the H_2 molecule; they used hydrogen atomic orbitals for a and b in (4.108). These results give a binding energy of 72.4 kcal to be compared with 108.8 found experimentally. James and Coolidge (1933), using extremely elaborate eigenfunctions, found energy values very close to the experimental ones. For more complex molecules only approximate methods are available. The best calculation of bond energies between atom pairs reveals that the atomic orbitals are displaced toward the bond centers both by displacement of their centers of gravity and by distortion.

If exactly this same procedure is carried through for four monovalent atoms with orbitals a, b, c, and d, one gets a secular equation involving $2^4 = 16$ determinants corresponding to assigning either spin eigenfunction α or β with each of the four orbitals. This leads, as in the case of two atoms (see Q.C., p. 245), to London's equation for the lowest energy for the system:

$$E = A + B + C \pm [\tfrac{1}{2}\{(\alpha - \beta)^2 + (\alpha - \gamma)^2 + (\beta - \gamma)^2\}]^{1/2} \quad (4.111)$$

Here
$$A = A_1 + A_2 \qquad \alpha = \alpha_1 + \alpha_2$$
$$B = B_1 + B_2 \qquad \beta = \beta_1 + \beta_2$$
$$C = C_1 + C_2 \qquad \gamma = \gamma_1 + \gamma_2$$

The Latin letters stand for the coulombic binding, and the Greek letters represent exchange binding. As the distances between the atoms vary, the bindings between pairs vary, of course, and with them the total binding energy E. The numbers at corners in the figure indicate the four atoms. If atom 2, for example, is moved to infinity, all bonds involving the subscript 2 become zero. Thus (4.111) is still the equation for the energy, but the letters now stand for single bonds instead of the sums of pairs of bonds. In Chapter 6 we apply London's formula to the calculation of potential surfaces. Formulas for any number of atoms can be readily set up. Methods of calculating such energy relations for more electrons are available (Slater, 1931; Eyring and Kimball, 1933; Pauling, 1933).

5

Essentials of
Statistical Mechanics

. . . any possible mechanism, left to act by itself, must set
up and preserve the laws of statistical equilibrium.

Fowler, 1936

Introduction

With a fixed amount of energy in an atomic system, the energy possessed
by individual atoms or molecules fluctuates about a mean value according
to well-understood laws of chance. There is an imperfect analogy
between this situation and that existing in a human economy where
individuals chosen at random have wealth clustering around the average
value for the community.

To specify the position of an atom in space it suffices to know its
coordinates along three mutually perpendicular axes. Thus the atom is
said to have 3 degrees of freedom which cannot disappear even when it
combines with other atoms to form a molecule. A molecule containing
n atoms thus has $3n$ degrees of freedom. Associated with each degree of
freedom is a velocity and therefore also a momentum and an energy.
The energy of any system of atoms and molecules is the sum of the energies
associated with its various degrees of freedom.

To develop our statistical treatment we will consider the following
simple model. Consider any system A, such as a benzene molecule or
a group of molecules enclosed in a metallic container B, composed of
$s/3$ atoms which consequently possess s oscillational degrees of freedom.
We suppose the system A plus B has a total energy E and ask what the
chance is that system A has some amount ϵ of this energy distributed in
a unique way in its degrees of freedom. In our particular example of a
benzene molecule ϵ is to be partitioned in a unique way among the 36
degrees of freedom. This means that the remaining energy $(E - \epsilon)$ can
be distributed in any of a number N_{ns} of ways among the s oscillators.
We assume that each oscillator can take up energy in integral multiples
of $h\nu$. Thus N_{ns} is the number of ways that n quanta of energy, where
$n = (E - \epsilon)/h\nu$, can be distributed among the s oscillators.

Before going further with our calculation we need to introduce a postulate which is in effect a quantum-mechanical version of the famous ergodic hypothesis. We postulate that any unique allowed way of distributing the total energy E in the system $A + B$ is exactly as likely to occur as any other unique allowed way of distributing the energy. Thus, if we want to know how likely it is any particular situation will arise, we calculate how many possible ways of distributing the energy this situation corresponds to. This number of ways is next divided by the sum of all possible ways of distributing the energy. The ratio then gives the probability of the system being in the situation described. We now proceed to calculate N_{ns} for a particular value of ϵ. This problem then involves the simple question: how many ways may n quanta be distributed among s oscillators? If n is zero, for example, clearly a zero amount of energy can be given to s oscillators in but one way. If n is one quantum, this quantum can be distributed in s ways since each oscillator in turn can have the energy. To calculate the general case it will be convenient to consider the n quanta and s oscillators arranged in a linear array with at least one oscillator always on the extreme right. We shall assume that all the quanta lying between two oscillators belong to the oscillator on the right. A typical situation will have the appearance

$$[\bigcirc\bigcirc\bigcirc\times]\,[\bigcirc\times]\,[\times]\,[\bigcirc\bigcirc\times]\,[\bigcirc\bigcirc\bigcirc\times]$$

where quanta are represented by circles and oscillators by crosses, and the brackets indicate which quanta go with each oscillator. Keeping one oscillator on the extreme right, the remaining $(n + s - 1)$ quanta and oscillators can be arranged along the line in $(n + s - 1)!$ ways. This procedure overestimates the number of distinct configurations in two ways. First, we cannot distinguish between the quanta so we must divide by a factor $n!$ Second, any interchange of the groups set off by brackets gives no new configuration, so we should divide by $(s - 1)!$ The bracket on the extreme right is not permuted since it contains the oscillator always held on the extreme right in accord with our argument. The result is

$$N_{ns} = \frac{(n + s - 1)!}{n!(s - 1)!} \tag{5.1}$$

Thus the probability of the system A having the energy ϵ assigned to it in a unique way is

$$p = \frac{(n + s - 1)!}{n!(s - 1)!} \Big/ \sum_{m} \frac{(m + s - 1)!}{m!(s - 1)!} \tag{5.2}$$

where the summation is over all possible ways of assigning the energy to system A. Like n, m refers to the number of quanta distributed among the s oscillators. Three mathematical relations help in the reduction of (5.1) to a more tractable form for large values of n and s. They are: (1) Stirling's approximation,

$$x! = (2\pi x)^{1/2} x^x e^{-x} \tag{5.3}$$

(2) the binomial theorem,

$$(a + b)^n = a^n + na^{n-1}b + \cdots \frac{n!}{(n-r)!r!} a^{n-r}b^r + \cdots \tag{5.4}$$

(3) and the exponential expansion,

$$e^x = 1 + x + \cdots + x^n/n! + \cdots \tag{5.5}$$

Applying (5.3) gives

$$N_{ns} = (2\pi)^{-1/2} \frac{(n+s-1)^{n+1/2}}{n} \frac{(n+s-1)^{s-1}}{(s-1)^{s-1/2}} \tag{5.6}$$

The probability of an isolated molecule or group of molecules being in a particular energy state, as a matter of experiment, is independent of the material of the walls of the vessel with which it occasionally collides so long as the whole system is maintained at constant temperature. In our case it will be convenient to consider a large vessel so that s will be large. Furthermore, we make the vessel out of a material such that $h\nu$ will be very small. In this case n is very large. Thus we suppose that $n \gg s$. Using the binomial theorem, we have

$$\left(\frac{n+s-1}{n}\right)^{n+1/2} = \left(1 + \frac{s-1}{n}\right)^{1/2}\left(1 + \frac{s-1}{n}\right)^n$$

$$= \left(1 + \frac{s-1}{n}\right)^{1/2}\left\{1 + n\left(\frac{s-1}{n}\right) + \frac{n(n-1)}{2!}\left(\frac{s-1}{n}\right)^2\right.$$

$$\left. + \frac{n(n-1)(n-2)}{3!}\left(\frac{s-1}{n}\right)^3 + \cdots\right\}$$

$$\cong e^{s-1}$$

The final step here uses the exponential expansion and becomes strictly correct as n/s becomes very large. Of course, since $s \gg 1$ it follows that $s - 1 \approx s$. Returning to the last factor in (5.6), we have

$$(n + s - 1)^{s-1} = \left(\frac{E - \epsilon}{h\nu} + s - 1\right)^{s-1}$$

$$= \left(\frac{E + (s-1)h\nu}{h\nu}\right)^{s-1}\left\{1 - \frac{\epsilon}{E + (s-1)h\nu}\right\}^{s-1}$$

If the average energy per oscillator is γ, we can write

$$E + (s - 1)h\nu = s\gamma + g$$

where

$$g = \epsilon + (s - 1)h\nu$$

will be negligible compared with $s\gamma$ if, as we suppose, n is large compared with s and ϵ is much smaller than E. In this case

$$(n + s - 1)^{s-1} = \left(\frac{E + (s - 1)h\nu}{h\nu}\right)^{s-1} \left(1 - \frac{\epsilon}{s\gamma + g}\right)^{s-1}$$

$$= \left(\frac{E + (s - 1)h\nu}{h\nu}\right)^{s-1} \left\{1 - (s - 1)\frac{\epsilon}{s\gamma + g}\right.$$

$$\left. + \frac{(s - 1)(s - 2)}{2!}\left(\frac{\epsilon}{s\gamma + g}\right)^2 + \cdots\right\}$$

$$\cong \left(\frac{E + (s - 1)h\nu}{h\nu}\right)^{s-1} \left\{1 - \frac{\epsilon}{\gamma} + \frac{\epsilon^2}{2!\gamma^2} - \frac{\epsilon^3}{3!\gamma^3} + \cdots\right\}$$

$$\cong \left(\frac{E + (s - 1)h\nu}{h\nu}\right)^{s-1} e^{-\epsilon/\gamma}$$

Therefore

$$N_{n,\,s} \cong \frac{(2\pi)^{-1/2} e^{s-1}}{(s - 1)^{s-1/2}} \left(\frac{E + (s - 1)h\nu}{h\nu}\right)^{s-1} e^{-\epsilon/\gamma} = C e^{-\epsilon/\gamma} \qquad (5.7)$$

where C is a constant independent of ϵ. Substituting in (5.2), we see that

$$p_i = \frac{C e^{-\epsilon_i/\gamma}}{\sum\limits_i C e^{-\epsilon_i/\gamma}} = \frac{e^{-\epsilon_i/\gamma}}{\sum e^{-\epsilon_i/\gamma}} \qquad (5.8)$$

The denominator of (5.8) is to be summed over all possible states of the system A. The parameter γ in (5.8) can be evaluated by calculating some property of the system A (such as the pressure if we let A be a perfect gas) and comparing with the experimental results. The result is $\gamma = kT$. This may be seen directly. Thus the Dulong and Petit rule for the specific heat of a mole of metal atoms, at temperatures where it has reached its limiting high temperature value, is 6 cal. When this is expressed in calories, we have $k = 6/3N$, since the 6 cal are for $3N$ oscillators. If we choose oscillators with arbitrarily small values of $h\nu$, the temperature interval near absolute zero over which the specific heat per oscillator falls below k is made arbitrarily small so that the average energy of the oscillator approaches $\gamma = kT$ to any desired degree of approximation.

Rewriting (5.8) with $\gamma = kT$ gives

$$p_i = \frac{e^{-\epsilon_i/kT}}{\Sigma e^{-\epsilon_i/kT}} \tag{5.9}$$

Thus we have an explicit expression for the probability that any arbitrary system is in one of its unique states i having the energy ϵ_i.

Now, if $\overline{M}_i$ is the average value of a property of any system A when it is in the ith state, the thermodynamic average value of this property is

$$\overline{M} = \Sigma \overline{M}_i p_i = \frac{\Sigma \overline{M}_i e^{-\epsilon_i/kT}}{\Sigma e^{-\epsilon_i/kT}} \tag{5.10}$$

In equation (4.84) we saw that quantum mechanics enables us to calculate $\overline{M}_i$ for any dynamical property. Statistical mechanics provides, by means of (5.10), the overall average for the property.

Using (5.10), the average energy E of a system is

$$E = \sum_i \epsilon_i p_i = \frac{\Sigma \epsilon_i e^{-\epsilon_i/kT}}{\Sigma e^{-\epsilon_i/kT}} \equiv kT^2 \frac{\partial \ln}{\partial T} (\Sigma e^{-\epsilon_i/kT}) \tag{5.11}$$

The partial derivative with respect to temperature in (5.11) signifies that any dependence of ϵ_i on volume or such things as electric, magnetic, or gravitational fields are not allowed to change during the operation. The quantity $f = \Sigma e^{-\epsilon_i/kT}$ is called the partition function for the system. Equation (2.14) can be rewritten

$$\int_{T=0}^{T} dS = \int_{T=0}^{T} \frac{1}{T} \left(\frac{\partial E}{\partial T}\right) dT \tag{5.12}$$

for a process where the volume is held constant. Introducing (5.11) into (5.12) and integrating by parts gives

$$S - S_{T=0} = \int_{T=0}^{T} \frac{1}{T} \frac{\partial}{\partial T} \left(kT^2 \frac{\partial}{\partial T} \ln \sum_i e^{-\epsilon_i/kT}\right)$$
$$= \left[\frac{1}{T}\left(kT^2 \frac{\partial}{\partial T} \ln \sum_i e^{-\epsilon_i/kT}\right)\right]_{T=0}^{T} + \left[k \ln \sum_i e^{-\epsilon_i/kT}\right]_{T=0}^{T} \tag{5.13}$$

The summation in the partition function, $\Sigma e^{-\epsilon_i/kT}$, is over all possible levels. Let us suppose that there are ω_j levels with the same energy ϵ_j, where ω_j may be an integer greater than unity. The factor ω_j is called the degeneracy factor. Making the substitution $\sum_i e^{-\epsilon_i/kT} \equiv \sum_j \omega_j e^{-\epsilon_i/kT}$ in (5.13), we note that at the lower limit the two brackets cancel except for the term $- k \ln \omega_1$ and we have

$$S_{T=0} = k \ln \omega_1 \tag{5.14}$$

Here ω_1 is the degeneracy of the lowest state of the system. We state the third law of thermodynamics in statistical mechanical language as follows: For crystalline systems ω_1 is not changed to a new value by any chemical reaction. In so far as the third law, based on experience, is true, we will make no error in chemistry in dividing out of every ω in (5.13) any factor (as, for example, possible nuclear degeneracy) which makes ω_1 differ from unity, and so we may assume that a crystalline system has zero entropy at absolute zero. Now from (5.13) and (2.15) we have

$$S = \frac{1}{T}\left(kT^2 \frac{\partial \ln}{\partial T}\sum_i e^{-\epsilon_i/kT}\right) + k \ln \sum e^{-\epsilon_i/kT}$$

$$= \frac{E}{T} - \frac{A}{T} \tag{5.15}$$

Hence
$$A = -kT \ln \Sigma e^{-\epsilon_i/kT} \tag{5.16}$$

This result may be seen even more directly. From thermodynamics,

$$E = -T^2(\partial/\partial T)(A/T)$$

Combining this with (5.11) gives

$$-T^2(\partial/\partial T)(A/T) = kT^2(\partial \ln/\partial T)\Sigma e^{-\epsilon_i/kT}$$

Hence $A = -kT \ln \Sigma e^{-\epsilon_i/kT} + CT$. Since by the third law A at the absolute zero becomes equal to ϵ_1, the energy of the system in its lowest state, and the entropy approaches zero, we must take $C = 0$. In Chapter 2 it was seen that all thermodynamic properties may be calculated from a suitable expression for A. Thus, if from quantum mechanics, spectroscopy or otherwise we can get the energy levels which go into the partition function, we have a great body of knowledge at our disposal. Using (5.16) for A and (2.18) for p, we can calculate $F = A + pV$ in terms of partition functions. Substituting this in (2.26), we can readily get the equilibrium constant in terms of partition functions. It is instructive, however, to proceed differently.

Equilibrium constants from partition functions

Consider as a typical example the reaction $H_2 + I_2 = 2HI$. We can draw the schematic potential diagram for this reaction as in Fig. 5.1. Each energy level in the diagram is a sum of twelve contributions, one from each of the twelve degrees of freedom. A representative of the final state of the system is any pair of HI molecules. There are thus $\{m_{HI}(m_{HI} - 1)\frac{1}{2}\}$ such representatives of the system where m_{HI} is the number of HI molecules. The symmetry factor $\sigma = \frac{1}{2}$ takes care of the fact that otherwise each pair is counted twice. Similarly, for the number of representations of initial states we have $\{m_{H_2} m_{I_2}\}$. Summing equation (5.9) over final states and dividing this by the sum over initial states of the system, and realizing that the denominator in (5.9) is over all states initial and final, we obtain the equation

$$\frac{\{m_{HI}(m_{HI} - 1)\tfrac{1}{2}\}}{m_{H_2} m_I} = \frac{1}{2} e^{-E_0/kT} \frac{\sum_f e^{-\epsilon_f/kT}}{\sum e^{-\epsilon_i/kT}} \qquad (5.17)$$

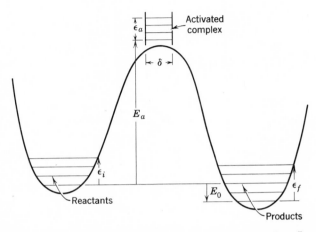

Fig. 5.1. Schematic potential diagram for the reaction $H_2 + I_2 = 2HI$. Energies of the various levels are represented by ϵ_i for the initial, ϵ_a for the activated, and ϵ_f for the final states; E_a represents the activation energy at absolute zero temperature, and E_0 the energy of two HI molecules at absolute temperature referred to an H_2 and an I_2 molecule in their lowest state as the zero of energy.

Canceling out the $\tfrac{1}{2}$ from both sides of (5.17) and remembering that for large numbers such as Avogadro's $m_{HI} - 1 \approx m_{HI}$, and finally changing numbers of molecules into concentration by dividing through by V, we get

$$\left(\frac{m_{HI}}{V}\right)^2 \bigg/ \left(\frac{m_{H_2}}{V}\right)\left(\frac{m_{I_2}}{V}\right) \equiv \frac{(HI)^2}{(H_2)(I_2)} = e^{-E_0/kT} \frac{\sum_f e^{-\epsilon_f/kT} V^{-2}}{\sum_i e^{-\epsilon_i/kT} V^{-2}} \qquad (5.18)$$

In the general case with the equilibrium $n_1 A_1 + n_2 A_2 + \cdots = m_1 B_1 + m_2 B_2 + \cdots$ we obtain

$$K = \frac{(B_1)^{m_1}(B_2)^{m_2} \cdots}{(A_1)^{n_1}(A_2)^{n_2} \cdots} = e^{-E_0/kT} \frac{\sum_j e^{-\epsilon_j/kT} V^{-(m_1+m_2+\cdots)}}{\sum_i e^{-\epsilon_i/kT} V^{-(n_1+n_2+\cdots)}} \qquad (5.19)$$

Explicit expression for partition functions

If we indicate the degrees of freedom of a system by Roman numerals and the state they are in by letters, we can write for their total energy

$$\epsilon_j = \epsilon_a{}^{\mathrm{I}} + \epsilon_b{}^{\mathrm{II}} + \epsilon_c{}^{\mathrm{III}} + \cdots \qquad (5.20)$$

It is frequently accurate enough to assume that the energy in one degree of freedom is unaffected by the particular quantum level which is occupied in some other degree of freedom. In that case

$$\begin{aligned} \sum_j e^{-\epsilon_j/kT} &= \sum e^{-(\epsilon_a{}^{\mathrm{I}} + \epsilon_b{}^{\mathrm{II}} + \epsilon_c{}^{\mathrm{III}} + \cdots)/kT} \\ &= \sum_a e^{-\epsilon_a{}^{\mathrm{I}}/kT} \sum_b e^{-\epsilon_b{}^{\mathrm{II}}/kT} \sum_c e^{-\epsilon_c{}^{\mathrm{III}}/kT} \cdots \end{aligned} \qquad (5.21)$$

Thus the partition function for a system is the product of the partition functions for the individual degrees of freedom.

Translational partition functions

In equation (4.19) the energy of a degree of translation is given as $E = n^2h^2/8a^2m$. Thus for the partition function, f_t for a degree of translation freedom we have

$$f_t = \sum_{n=1}^{\infty} e^{-n^2h^2/8a^2mkT} \approx \int_0^{\infty} e^{-n^2h^2/8a^2mkT} \, dn = \frac{(2\pi mkT)^{1/2} a}{h} \qquad (5.22)$$

Here a is the length of the container in the direction of the motion. The partition function f_{3t} for three degrees of freedom in a rectangular box of volume V is therefore

$$f_{3t} = \frac{(2\pi mkT)^{3/2} V}{h^3} \qquad (5.23)$$

Vibrational partition functions

In equation (4.33) we found that the energy of an oscillator is $E = (n + \tfrac{1}{2})h\nu$, where n takes integral values from zero to infinity. Consequently, the vibrational partition function f_v' has the value

$$\begin{aligned} f_v' &= \sum_n e^{-(1/2+n)(h\nu/kT)} \\ &= e^{-h\nu/2kT}(1 + e^{-h\nu/kT} + e^{-2h\nu/kT} + \cdots) = \frac{e^{-(1/2)(h\nu/kT)}}{1 - e^{-h\nu/kT}} \end{aligned} \qquad (5.24)$$

If the zero energy for the oscillator is chosen at the half quanta value rather than at the zero of potential, as is usually more convenient, we have for the partition function of a degree of vibration

$$f_v = \frac{1}{1 - e^{-h\nu/kT}} \qquad (5.25)$$

Partition functions for rotation

The energy of a two-dimensional linear rotator is found to have the value

$$E = \frac{J(J+1)h^2}{8\pi^2 I}$$

with a $(2J+1)$-fold degeneracy. The partition function for a two-dimensional unsymmetrical rotator is therefore

$$f_{2r} = \sum_{J=0}^{\infty} (2J+1)e^{-J(J+1)h^2/8\pi^2 I k T}$$

$$= \int_{J=0}^{\infty} (2J+1)e^{-J(J+1)h^2/8\pi^2 I k T}\, dJ = \frac{8\pi^2 I k T}{h^2} \quad (5.26)$$

If the molecule is symmetrical, only half the J values are allowed, either the odd or the even values occurring, depending upon the spin of the nuclei. Thus the partition function will be only half as large. For any linear molecule, then, we have

$$f_{2r} = \frac{8\pi^2 I k T}{\sigma h^2} \quad (5.27)$$

where σ is 1 or 2 depending upon whether the linear molecule is unsymmetrical or symmetrical.

Similar but more complicated considerations (Fowler, 1936) lead to the expression

$$f_{3r} = \frac{8\pi^2 (8\pi^3 ABC)^{1/2}(kT)^{3/2}}{\sigma h^3} \quad (5.28)$$

for the three-dimensional rotator. Here the symmetry number σ is the number of different configurations which look exactly the same. Thus σ equals 12 for benzene and for methane, and 2 for water. A, B, and C are the three moments of inertia of the molecules. k, T, and h are as usual the Boltzmann constant, the absolute temperature, and Planck's constant, respectively.

Upon substituting the partition functions into (5.19), the equilibrium constant for the hydrogen, iodine, hydrogen iodide equilibrium becomes

$$K = \frac{\left(\dfrac{(2\pi m_3 kT)^{3/2}}{h^3}\dfrac{8\pi^2 I_3 kT}{h^2}\dfrac{1}{1-e^{-h\nu_3/kT}}\right)^2 e^{-E_0/kT}}{\dfrac{(2\pi m_1 kT)^{3/2}}{h^3}\dfrac{8\pi^2 I_1 kT}{2h^2}\dfrac{1}{1-e^{-h\nu_1/kT}}\dfrac{(2\pi m_2 kT)^{3/2}}{h^3}\dfrac{8\pi^2 I_2 kT}{2h^2}\dfrac{1}{1-e^{-h\nu_2/kT}}}$$

$$(5.29)$$

Subscripts 1, 2, and 3 refer to hydrogen, iodine, and hydrogen iodide, respectively. E_0 is the energy of two HI molecules at the absolute zero of temperature referred to an H_2 and an I_2 molecule in their lowest state as the zero of energy.

If we represent by ΔH the readily measurable heat of combustion of the products of a reaction minus the heat of combustion of the reactants we have

$$\Delta H = \Delta(pV) + RT^2 \left(\frac{\partial \ln K}{\partial T}\right)_V \tag{5.30}$$

For a gas we have in addition

$$\Delta(pV) = \Delta nRT \tag{5.31}$$

Here the Δ in $\Delta(pV)$ and in Δn represents the increase in these properties for the final state over the value for the initial state. Thus Δn is the total number of moles of final molecules minus moles of initial molecules. All the masses, moments of inertia, and frequencies appearing in equation (5.29) are available in the literature. Equation (5.30) makes it possible to calculate E_0 from these quantities and the heats of combustion. The equilibrium constant is thus readily calculated at all temperatures for many equilibria. In the solid or liquid state, the translational degrees of freedom may be replaced by vibrational partition functions. Rotational degrees of freedom sometimes become vibrations in condensed phases.

The theory of rate processes

The fundamental conception in reaction rates is that reactants combine to form a critical intermediate called the activated complex to which equilibrium theory can be applied. If one plots on independent co-ordinates all the distances which must be specified to fix the potential energy of the activated complex, and in an independent direction measures the corresponding energy, a potential surface in configuration space is obtained which is much like an ordinary landscape. These potential surfaces in configuration space are in $3n - 5$ and $3n - 4$ dimensions for non-linear and linear activated complexes, respectively. On such a surface, basins correspond to compounds and the saddle points in the passes between the low regions correspond to the activated complex. If, from an initial low region, one climbs to the pass along what would be the water course of an ordinary landscape and then descends by the water course into the adjoining region, this path corresponds to the reaction coordinate here. A plot of energy against distance along the reaction coordinate for any reaction has the general appearance of Fig. 5.1.

In Fig. 5.1 the various initial energy levels have energies ϵ_i, and those for the activated state have energies ϵ_a. Each of these energies is a sum of $3n$

components, one for each degree of freedom. We represent the rate process by the equation $A + B \cdots \rightarrow M^{\ddagger} + N + \cdots \rightarrow X + Y \cdots$. Here A, B, etc., represent the initial species. $M^{\ddagger}$ represents the activated complex, and N, etc., are molecules formed with the activated complex. X, Y, etc., represent final products. Now, just as for an ordinary equilibrium, we can write for the probability of the activated over the normal state

$$\frac{n_{M}^{\ddagger} n_{N} \cdots}{n_{A} n_{B}} = \frac{\sum_{a} e^{-\epsilon_a/kT} e^{-E_a/kT}}{\sum_{i} e^{-\epsilon_i/kT}} \tag{5.32}$$

or

$$\frac{[M^{\ddagger}][N] \cdots}{[A][B] \cdots} = \frac{\sum_{a} e^{-\epsilon_a/kT}/V^r \, e^{-E_a/kT}}{\sum_{i} e^{-\epsilon_i/kT}/V^s} = K^* \tag{5.33}$$

In (5.33) $[M^{\ddagger}]$ means the number of molecules per cubic centimeter of the activated complex; the other parenthetic expressions have similar meanings. r and s are the number of molecules in an example of the activated and normal states, respectively. The velocity of reaction of an activated molecule will now be calculated. At equilibrium, half of the activated complexes will be proceeding toward the right and half toward the left. From the equation

$$\frac{1}{2} m^{\ddagger} u^2 = \frac{n^2 h^2}{8\delta^2 m^{\ddagger}} \tag{5.34}$$

which equates two expressions for the kinetic energy of a translational degree of freedom, we find for the velocity u of a system in the level with quantum number n the value

$$u = \frac{nh}{2\delta m^{\ddagger}} \tag{5.35}$$

The average value of the velocity of an activated complex across the barrier is

$$\bar{u} = \frac{\int_0^\infty (nh/2\delta m^{\ddagger}) e^{-n^2 h^2/8\delta^2 m^{\ddagger} kT}}{\int_0^\infty e^{-n^2 h^2/8\delta^2 m^{\ddagger} kT}} = \left(\frac{2kT}{\pi m^{\ddagger}}\right)^{1/2} \tag{5.36}$$

The transmission coefficient κ is the chance that a barrier crossing will result in reaction. For a thin barrier the leakage through the barrier should be added to the rate of passage over the barrier. It would be necessary to take κ greater than unity to account for such an effect. If the barrier crossing is accompanied by an electronic reorganization such as a change of multiplicity, κ may be considerably less than unity. The available evidence indicates that κ is usually very close to 1, and, unless there is evidence to the contrary, we assume $\kappa = 1$. Any approximation in this assumption is reflected in a compensating change in the entropy of activation. Now the velocity of reaction can be written

$$v = [M^{\ddagger}]\frac{1}{2}\frac{\bar{u}}{\delta}\kappa = \frac{[A][B]\cdots}{[N]\cdots}K^*\frac{1}{2}\frac{u}{\delta}\kappa \tag{5.37}$$

The partition function for the degree of freedom along the reaction coordinate at the top of the barrier is well approximated by the translational degree $[(2\pi m^{\ddagger}kT)^{1/2}/h]\delta$. Returning to (5.33), we write

$$K^* \equiv K^{\ddagger}\frac{(2\pi m^{\ddagger}kT)^{1/2}}{h}\delta \tag{5.38}$$

Equation (5.38) constitutes a definition of $K^{\ddagger}$. If $\delta = h/(2\pi m^{\ddagger}kT)^{1/2}$, we have $K^{\ddagger}$ becoming equal to K^*. Thus $K^{\ddagger}$ is the equilibrium constant for activated complexes against reactants for the length $\delta = h/(2\pi m^{\ddagger}kT)^{1/2}$. This value for δ is of the order of 1 Å, and it varies with the reduced mass $m^{\ddagger}$. Since δ cancels out of the equation for the velocity of reaction, its exact value has no significance for the theory of absolute reaction rates. Substituting (5.38) into (5.37) gives

$$v = \frac{[A][B]\cdots}{[N]\cdots}\kappa K^{\ddagger}\frac{kT}{h} \tag{5.39}$$

Thus we have for the specific rate constant

$$k' \equiv \kappa K^{\ddagger}\frac{kT}{h} \tag{5.40}$$

The specific rate constant is the velocity of reaction at unit concentration of the constituents of reaction. It should be emphasized that (5.39) and (5.40) are equally applicable to reactions in either the solid, liquid, or gaseous states. The state of the system, of course, determines the expressions to be used for the partition functions for the various degrees of freedom of the normal and activated states, which go to make up $K^{\ddagger}$.

For the reaction $H_2 + I_2 \rightarrow H{-}H \rightarrow 2HI$ we have

$$
v = \frac{[H_2][I_2]\dfrac{(2\pi m_3 kT)^{3/2}}{h^3}\dfrac{8\pi^2(8\pi^3 A_3 B_3 C_3)^{1/2}(kT)^{3/2}}{2h^3}\displaystyle\prod_{i=1}^{5}\dfrac{1}{1-e^{-h\nu_i/kT}}e^{-E_a/kT}}{\dfrac{(2\pi m_1 kT)^{3/2}}{h^3}\dfrac{8\pi^2 I_1 kT}{2h^2}\dfrac{1}{1-e^{-h\nu_1/kT}}\dfrac{(2\pi m_2 kT)^{3/2}}{h^3}\dfrac{8\pi^2 I_2 kT}{2h^2}\dfrac{1}{1-e^{-h\nu_2/kT}}}
$$
$$\times\;\kappa\,\frac{kT}{h} \tag{5.41}$$

Here the subscripts 1, 2, and 3 refer to hydrogen, iodine, and the activated complex H_2I_2, respectively. For the detailed calculation in this and many other cases see Glasstone, Laidler, and Eyring (1941).

As for any other equilibrium constant, we can write

$$K^{\ddagger} = e^{-\Delta F^{\ddagger}/RT} \tag{5.42}$$

As the free energy of activation $\Delta F^{\ddagger}$ behaves like any other free energy change, we now have at our disposal all the methods of thermodynamics for treating rate processes. We suppose that for some rate process an external potential or stress does an amount of work W_1 in helping reactants to reach the activated state, and an amount of work W_2 is done on products returning over the barrier top. We can then write for the forward specific rate

$$k_f = k_1 e^{W_1/kT} \tag{5.43}$$

and for the specific backward rate

$$k_b = k_2 e^{-W_2/kT} \tag{5.44}$$

The difference of these two specific rates multiplied by the concentrations gives the net rate of passage over the barrier. Such relations are important in theories of viscosity, plastic flow, muscle contraction, and electrolysis, etc. Our theory of elementary reaction rates thus has reached the same degree of completion as the thermodynamic theory of equilibrium. The available evidence indicates that the application of equilibrium theory to the activated complex concentration introduces a negligible error. Any energy states, out of equilibrium with the initial state, must be treated as separate entities in the rate equations. This is illustrated in the complex series of reactions often associated with chain reactions.

Calculation of
Absolute Rates;
Four-Atom Reactions

Interdependence absolute, foreseen, ordained, decreed,
To work, Ye'll note, at any tilt an' every rate o' speed.

Kipling, "M'Andrews Hymn"

Most chemical bonds can be broken and other bonds formed by the enzymes present in living systems. There are organisms whose enzymes can cause hydrocarbons and even hydrogen to react with oxygen to provide the necessary energy source for metabolism. However, in the absence of catalysts, these reducing agents may be heated with oxygen to several hundred degrees without reacting. Nitrogen-fixing bacteria are able to join atmospheric nitrogen to hydrogen taken from sugars to make amines, whereas ammonia cannot be formed from nitrogen and hydrogen outside of living things, except in the presence of some catalyst such as iron oxide at elevated temperatures and at high pressures. There are bonds which apparently no enzyme can sever, even though thermodynamics favors their dissolution. The pure single electron pair, carbon-to-carbon bonds in diamond, apparently belong in this category.

The increase in potential energy which hinders the reaction of colliding saturated molecules puts in an appearance as the filled electronic orbitals start overlapping. The reason is that the electrons must be promoted into higher states in such a manner as never to leave more than two electrons in any one orbital. These two electrons in an orbital necessarily have opposed spins. On the other hand, an atom, radical, or ion, possessing an unfilled orbital, can attach itself to a saturated molecule with relatively little promotional energy. Thus, although an iodine molecule with its electron pair requires 40 kcal of activational energy before it can successfully split a hydrogen molecule to give two HI molecules, a free hydrogen atom with a half-empty orbital can split a hydrogen molecule with only 8 kcal of activational energy. Ionic crystals, such as sodium chloride, as well as metal crystals possess surfaces of unsaturated positive ions in the one case, and unsaturated atoms in the other, which adsorb saturated molecules. The adsorbed molecules frequently break into two or more parts. These adsorbed fragments may then reassemble in other ways to give new molecules. Thus deuterium can react slowly with hydrogen on a chromium oxide surface even at $-185°C$. The rate of reaction goes up with the temperature, as would be expected. This sort of catalysis by solid surfaces is not important in living things. However, ions in solution form critical parts of enzymes and are then called coenzymes. Because ions of the transition elements are capable of existing in more than one valence state, they can become a depository for extra electrons which may then be returned after the reorganization. Illustrating this process is the oxidation of secondary propyl alcohol to acetone in the presence of chromic ions. The following mechanism has been shown by Westheimer to occur in dilute acid solution:

$$HCrO_4^- + CH_3CHOHCH_3 + H^+ \overset{rapid}{\rightleftharpoons} (CH_3)_2CHOCrO_3H + H_2O$$

$$B + (CH_3)_2CHOCrO_3H \xrightarrow[determining]{rate} BH^+ + (CH_3)_2CO + HCrO_3^-$$

Here B represents a molecule of water or some other base.

Positive ions like the alkalis and alkaline earths, dissolved in water regularly, coordinate several water molecules. In certain enzymes these coordinated water molecules are more or less completely replaced by proteins or prosthetic groups and by substrate to form the activated complex. The process of coordination is through an electron pair provided by the coordinated molecules. This partial loss of an electron pair lessens the electronic congestion in adjacent bonds, and so lessens the promotional energy in the activated state when these bonds are involved in reaction with saturated molecules. The size and charge of an ion will influence how snugly a coordinated molecule fits into the space left for it, and so decides how effective it is in promoting a particular activated state involving a particular enzyme and substrate. Thus we find specific ions playing special rôles in promoting the various types of physiological reactions by lowering the activation energy in this way. In fact, any ion, positive or negative, may turn out to be of importance in promoting the formation of the activated complexes for some critical reaction. Similarly, any substance, ionic or otherwise, is a poison if it compounds with some necessary constituent in such a way that this constituent becomes less available for forming a critical activated complex. Physiological structures such as membranes, which pass through a sequence of states, for example, during the excitation of a nerve, require a nice balance between ions and the other molecules which enter into the various complexes arising during the cycle of changes.   In fact, whether one is interested in the activated complexes controlling reaction rates or in the stable molecular arrangement of equilibrium, the problem is always that of structure and of the factors which increase or decrease molecular stability.   Until a few years ago structural organic chemistry was essentially a shorthand to explain the observed reactions which a molecule undergoes.   The fact that modern methods of establishing structure correlate with the older theories indicates that if we know structure we can predict reactivity.   Many systems require a polar solvent such as water to catalyze chemical reaction.   A crystal of potassium chloride exchanges ions with crystalline sodium bromide slowly, if at all, unless water is present, in which case the ions change partners easily.   Reaction by way of ions avoids the effort to crowd more than two electrons into an orbital with the accompanying promotional activation energy.   Many organic reactions proceed by an ionic mechanism in spite of the fact there is no measurable concentration of ions by the usual tests.

In spite of the fact that the London equation (4.111) yields only very approximate values for activation energies, it is instructive to use it in calculating a potential surface which is then made the basis for a calculated rate of reaction.   We follow here, almost exactly, the paper of Altar and Eyring (1936) on the reaction $H_2 + ICl \rightarrow HI + HCl$.

The simultaneous interaction of more than two atoms with each other is a complicated theoretical problem.   In so far as it manifests itself in chemical exchange reactions it can be described on the following four assumptions:

1. When an atom is joined by at least sufficiently many bonds to saturate its valence, the lower potential energies will correspond to configurations, making additional bonds to this atom as small as possible without weakening the main bonds.

2a. The energy of interaction of more than two atoms can be expressed as a function of single bond additive and exchange energies.   Here we are using the word "bond" in a somewhat wider sense than usual, meaning electron pair energy which two atoms at any particular distance would exhibit in the absence of other atoms.

2b. The interaction energy a of a pair of atoms consists of two parts: one part A arising from "classical" forces, which is purely additive, and a second α arising from quantum-mechanical electron exchange.   The latter part is not simply additive and is responsible for the valence properties of atoms..

3. In the approximation considered here, the addition law for the latter type of binding is taken to be that following from perturbation theory

calculations. For the case of three and four atoms the following well-known formula is obtained (London, 1929; Eyring and Polanyi, 1931):

$$E = A + B + C - \{\tfrac{1}{2}[(\alpha - \beta)^2 + (\beta - \gamma)^2 + (\gamma - \alpha)^2]\}^{1/2} \quad (6.1)$$

where $a = A + \alpha$, $b = B + \beta$, $c = C + \gamma$ are the bonds in the case of three atoms, while for four atoms (see Fig. 6.1)

$$a = a_1 + a_2 \qquad b = b_1 + b_2 \qquad c = c_1 + c_2$$

$$A = A_1 + A_2 \qquad B = B_1 + B_2 \qquad C = C_1 + C_2$$

$$\alpha = \alpha_1 + \alpha_2 \qquad \beta = \beta_1 + \beta_2 \qquad \gamma = \gamma_1 + \gamma_2$$

4. The actual amounts of additive and of exchange energy for each pair are taken to be constant fractions of the total interaction energy as represented by its Morse curve:

$$A_1 = \lambda a_1 \qquad \alpha_1 = (1 - \lambda)a_1$$

$$B_1 = \lambda b_1 \qquad \beta_1 = (1 - \lambda)b_1 \qquad\qquad (6.2)$$

$$C_1 = \lambda c_1 \qquad \gamma_1 = (1 - \lambda)c_1$$

The assurance with which these four assumptions can be accepted probably decreases in the order in which they are quoted. It will naturally be very interesting to see to what extent these assumptions, taken

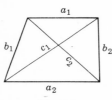

Fig. 6.1

separately, can be justified or improved upon by comparison with experiment. Even the most specific assumption (4) has not been shown to be in disagreement with experiment for configurations near the activated state, though for interatomic distances less than the equilibrium distance of two atoms the fraction λ certainly decreases with decreasing distance. When more experimental information is available, we may find it desirable to replace by more general relations the assumption of a percentage λ not varying with distance. There is nothing in our present procedure that would not be equally well adapted to such a generalization. We shall find that assumptions 1 and 2, together with very much less specific assumptions than 3 and 4, permit us to draw conclusions based only on the potential curves of the atom pairs and on geometrical relations. In view of the semi-empirical basis of equation (6.1) it is desirable to carry the more firmly established assumptions to their farthest logical conclusions before making more specific assumptions about (6.1). For example, the conclusions that activated complexes for three monovalent atoms should be linear and that activated complexes of four monovalent atoms are planar, or more generally that configurations are more stable the smaller the exchange binding between the atoms not paired in the ordinary chemical sense, rest on a more general basis than 3 and 4, and yet these conclusions are sufficient to enable us to find the "best reaction surface" in bond space, as we shall see.

We describe the potential function E of a three- or four-particle system in bond space instead of the usual configuration space.   That is, we shall represent our system by using the three bond energies a, b, c as orthogonal coordinates.   That this is possible for four atoms depends upon the fact that the three pairs of bonds a_1 and a_2, b_1 and b_2, c_1 and c_2 enter into (6.1) only through their sums.   Apparently it is generally true that the interaction energy of an even-numbered particle system $2n$ involves no more linearly independent combination of bonds to express the energy than does the one for $2n - 1$ atoms.

By abandoning the configuration space one sacrifices the foremost advantage of that treatment, i.e., that the configuration changes of the system in a reaction may be represented by a mass point subjected to the known potential E and obeying the laws of ordinary mechanics.   But such a representation turns out to be not feasible for more than three particles, quite apart from the complications in visualizing which arise from the many dimensions.

The success and the simplicity of the new treatment depend upon the following fact: In general, of the six parameters specifying a configuration of four particles in space, only two, say a and b, need be considered as actually independent and as determining a surface B which will include the best reaction path.   This surface will be considered in detail later. A reaction may be described by saying that the system starts from a configuration where a has its maximum value and $b = c = 0$, and proceeds to a final state where b is a maximum and $a = c = 0$.   By the "best reaction path" is meant that sequence of configurations by which this transition is accomplished in a way most economical of potential energy.   Thus each of these configurations must have a minimum potential energy in all directions except the one in which the reaction proceeds.   The point of highest potential energy along this path represents the activated configuration.   It is clearly true that for this point—a saddle point—the energy is stationary in all directions, a fact of fundamental importance in that it allows us to use the theory of small vibrations for setting up the partition function of the activated state.   Mathematically, the activated configuration is thus determined as the point with the highest potential along the best reaction path for which $dE = 0$.

It is characteristic of the theory of reaction rates that the original and the activated configurations are the only ones whose physical properties determine the rate of reaction. Only in the case of two saddle points of nearly equal heights is it necessary to consider both.

Since we propose to describe the progress of a reaction in bond space, we must consider how points in bond space and in configuration space correspond to each other. In the case of three atoms, the three bonds are just sufficient to determine the configuration, except for a certain ambiguity which is readily disposed of.[1] In the case of four atoms, however, the situation is complicated by the fact that it takes six parameters to determine a configuration so that there exist in general ∞^3 configurations for a point (a, b, c). On the other hand, there are regions in bond space which are not attainable by a particular system, owing to the obvious restriction on the greatest absolute value a bond can take, and also owing to the geometrical restrictions which prevail among the six distances between four atoms. It so happens that in spite of this general situation the best reaction path, because of the conditions on c, always lies on the boundary surface between the physically attainable and the unattainable region, and for this surface B there does exist a point-to-point correspondence between bond and configuration space.

We now show that the best reaction path lies completely on the boundary surface. We start out by finding for every given pair of values a, b the smallest possible value of $|c|$ which is attainable by our system under its geometrical restrictions. The surface so defined in bond space will clearly be a boundary surface for the attainable region. Its equation can be set down as

$$d(c_1 + c_2)_{a,b} = 0 \tag{6.3}$$

On the other hand, if we restrict our attention to all those points a, b, c which for given values a, b have their minimum value of E, the surface so obtained must completely contain the best reaction path. But this condition can be written

$$(dE)_{a,b} = (\partial E/\partial c)(dc_1 + dc_2) = 0 \tag{6.4}$$

It should be borne in mind that the differentials dc_1 and dc_2 occurring in (6.3) and (6.4) are related to each other in a way depending upon the geometry of the system, i.e., on the specific values assigned to a_1, a_2, b_1, b_2 and also involve the Morse curves of the individual atom pairs. But from (6.4) it follows that a stationary value of E corresponds to a

---

[1] This ambiguity arises in the case of four, three, and even two-atom systems, because two different distances are always associated with every negative value of E occurring in the diatomic potential curve. No complication arises from this fact since the reaction path never involves configurations where an interatomic distance is contracted beyond the equilibrium distance for that pair.

stationary value of c, the unimportant singular cases where $\partial E/\partial c = 0$ being ignored. Whether a minimum of E corresponds to a minimum or a maximum of c is determined by the sign of $\partial E/\partial c$, which in the particular case of the London formula can be written

$$\partial E/\partial c = \lambda - [(1 - \lambda)(c - \tfrac{1}{2})(a + b)]$$
$$\times [\tfrac{1}{2}((a - b)^2 + (a - c)^2 + (b - c)^2)]^{-1/2} \quad (6.5)$$

This is negative if $|c|$ is the smallest of the bonds, as it is for the comparatively small values which λ assumes for non-metallic elements. Thus we have shown that, to make E as low as possible for a given a and b, the value $|c|$ must be made a minimum, and thus the best reaction path lies in the boundary surface. Equations exactly similar to (6.3) and (6.4) can be discussed for a and b. If $|a|$ happens to be the largest of the three, $\partial E/\partial a$ is positive; therefore a minimum value of E will now go with a maximum value for $|a|$. In some cases it is found more convenient to use the latter relationship. In the intermediate case where $|b|$, say, is neither the largest nor the smallest of the three, $|b|$ should be made a minimum or a maximum depending upon whether $\partial E/\partial b \lessgtr 0$. A mechanical device which enables one easily to satisfy condition (6.3) will be described in a later section.

A vector addition rule for bond energies

From this more or less kinematical discussion of configurations in bond space we now turn to the question of the interaction energy of a system of atoms. In particular we shall consider the nature of the equipotential surfaces defined by (6.1) and (6.2). We now prove that the law of combination of exchange energies as expressed by the square root in (6.1) is equivalent to the simple vector addition

$$E_{ex} = \{\tfrac{1}{2}[(\alpha - \beta)^2 + (\beta - \gamma)^2 + (\gamma - \alpha)^2]\}^{1/2} = |\alpha + \omega\beta + \omega^2\gamma| \quad (6.6)$$

where ω and ω^2 are third roots of unity. This situation is also represented by the vector diagram, Fig. 6.2, in terms of which the following simple proof can be given: If we plot the bond energies α, β, γ end-on, making angles of 60° with each other as in Fig. 6.2, the resultant has the horizontal and vertical components $[\beta - \tfrac{1}{2}(\alpha + \gamma)]$ and $\tfrac{1}{2} \times 3^{1/2}(\alpha - \gamma)$. Thus its length turns out to be just E_{ex}. The existence of such a simple vector addition rule for bonds in three- and four-particle systems is significant and suggests the possibility of similar relations in more complicated cases. Its practical importance lies in the avoidance of practically all calculations in obtaining potential energies from the individual bonds, especially since the 60° triangular paper on the market is ideally suited for such purposes.

The equipotential surfaces in bond space likewise turn out to be strikingly simple.   Transforming to new orthogonal coordinates by means of a rotation of the a, b, c axes,

$$x = 2^{-1/2}(a - b)$$
$$y = 6^{-1/2}(a + b - 2c) \tag{6.7}$$
$$z = 3^{-1/2}(a + b + c)$$

and using (6.1) and (6.2) we find that the expression for the energy of the system becomes

$$E = 3^{1/2}\{\lambda z - (1 - \lambda)[\tfrac{1}{2}(x^2 + y^2)]^{1/2}\}$$
$$= 3^{1/2}[\lambda z - (1 - \lambda)/2^{-1/2}r] \tag{6.8}$$

Thus it is seen that the equipotential surfaces are circular cones with their axes along the z axis, and with their apex angle $2\tan^{-1}\lambda/(1 - \lambda)$ depending only upon the ratio of additive to exchange binding.   The relation

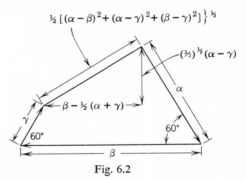

Fig. 6.2

exhibited by (6.8), that E_{ex} is simply proportional to the distance r from the z axis, provides an alternative proof of our previously given vector addition rule, since the three valence bonds α, β, γ, when plotted along their axes, a, b, c, appear to make just the angles used in Fig. 6.2 to an observer looking down the z axis.   The equipotential surfaces in bond space, together with the boundary surface B, determine completely the best reaction path: The intersection of the equipotentials with B traces a system of equipotential lines on B of much the same character as the system of equipotential lines found in the usual plots of a potential surface in configuration space for a three-atom problem.

In many triatomic reactions the smallest bond c remains very small throughout, so that the surface B can be approximated by the plane $c = 0$.   In this case the equipotential curves on B are simply a system of confocal ellipses generated by the intersection of the ab plane with the cones.   The reaction path is then the line where either a or b has its most negative value, c being zero.

The other extreme, where $|c|$ assumes comparatively large values for three-atom reactions, is typified by the case of three H atoms.   In Fig.

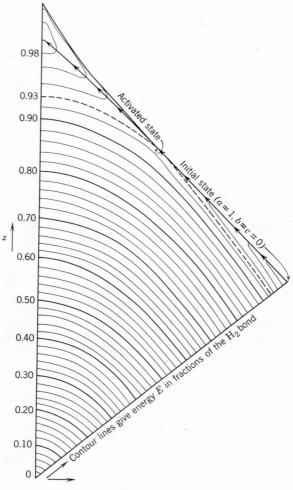

Fig. 6.3

6.3 we have given the equipotential curves plotted on the B surface as they appear looking along the y direction in bond space.   This particular projection was chosen because of the ease with which the construction can be carried out.

The potential diagram for $c = 0$ is practically identical with the one for three H atoms in the region lying below the best reaction path indicated by arrows in Fig. 6.3.[1] It has seemed desirable to give this brief discussion of two typical three-atom cases since the general features are just the same as for four-atom reactions.

Locating the activated configuration of four atoms

It is in the application to four-atom reactions that the use of bond space instead of configuration space proves to be of real advantage. Even in the presentation of a symmetric case such as $H_2 + I_2$, the method of finding the activated state as well as the representation of the potentials in configuration space becomes extremely laborious. With the present method, a four-atom system with no symmetry at all such as $H_2 + ICl$ has been investigated and the reaction rate calculated with no unreasonable hardships.

A mechanical device for selecting a configuration, which for a given pair of values a, b has the smallest possible $|c|$ to go with it, is pictured in Fig. 6.4. Scales are provided on which the six interatomic distances between four atoms H, H, I, Cl are marked with their respective bond energies and the scales so obtained are attached to each other so as to present a model of the plane configurations of these four atoms. The scales are hinged by means of thumbtacks in such a way that, without varying four of the six distances, the remaining two, let us say the diagonal ones, can be adjusted until the sum of their energies (absolute values) as read directly from their scales is a minimum. In doing this one must of course try various combinations of a_1 and a_2 which add up to the same a, and also various combinations for b, until an absolute minimum for $|c|$ is obtained. By way of emphasis we should like to point out that this method of variation leads to a unique configuration for fixed values of a and b, thus establishing our previous statement that there exists a point-to-point correspondence between those points in three-dimensional bond space which lie on the surface B and the points on the corresponding surface in six-dimensional configuration space.

A point on the B surface can be found in a few minutes with the use of this device. A sufficient number of such combinations (a, b, c) must be found to map out the potential diagram on the B surface. A very pleasant

---

[1] As pointed out in the footnote on p. 106, we are ignoring throughout configurations involving "contracted" bonds. However, extending the B surface into this region results in making multiple-valued the present allowed portion of the B surface in the case $c = 0$. In the case $c \neq 0$, the extended B surface bends over completely in the direction of the z axis, crosses it, and finally departs in the direction of infinite positive z.

feature of this procedure is that it enables us to describe the essential aspects of the potential surface in two-dimensional diagrams in spite of the fact that the number of parameters of the dynamical problem is six. The plot for the reaction, $H_2 + ICl \rightarrow HI + HCl$ is given in Fig. 6.5, which shows the projection on the ab plane of the intersections of the

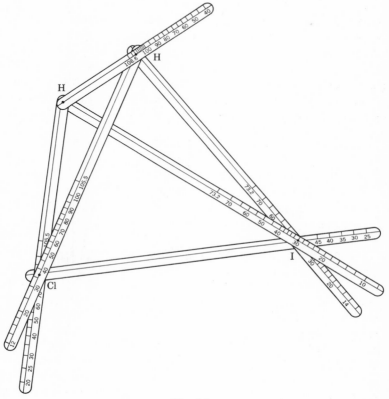

Fig. 6.4

boundary surface with the equipotential curves.   An alternative way which is sometimes more satisfactory is to plot the xy projection.

Since the B surface does not depend upon a particular potential law, the points a, b, c determined in the way described may be used for different fractions λ of additive binding and indeed for different laws of interaction, and the results may be compared with experiment.   In this particular case we have located the activated point and determined the activation energy for 14, 17, and 20 per cent of additive binding; the results appear in Table 6.2.

The constants used in the Morse curves for the various bonds are given in Table 6.1, where the Morse curve is given by

$$E = D'[e^{-2a(r-r_0)} - 2e^{-a(r-r_0)}]$$

Table 6.1

	r_0(Å)	ω_0(cm^{-1})	D (kcal)	D' (kcal)	a
H—H	0.74	4,375	102.4	108.6	1.941
I—Cl	2.310	384.6	49.4	49.95	1.871
H—Cl	1.282	2,840.8	101.5	105.5	1.781
H—I	1.616	2,233	70.0	73.2	1.700

There is nothing in our procedure which limits us to the constant percentage rule as expressed by the constant λ in equation (6.2). We might equally well have replaced each of the energy scales in our model

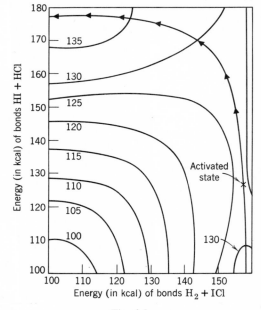

Fig. 6.5

by a double scale giving the additive and the exchange part of the bond as separate functions of the distance.

The accuracy with which the activated configuration can be found by using this easily improvised mechanical model (of a size no larger than is convenient) is more than sufficient for all practical purposes. But, if greater accuracy is required, a rapidly converging mathematical procedure can be devised which renders the question of attainable accuracy merely one of how much numerical computation we are willing to bestow on the solution. Suppose that from the mechanical model we have obtained a configuration close enough to the activated one to make all the first derivatives $\partial E/\partial q_i$ small, and suppose that we are in possession of a complete set of second derivatives $\partial^2 E/\partial q_i \partial q_k$, taken with respect to all five "plane" coordinates q_i, for this configuration. Knowledge of these second derivatives is necessary anyway for the calculation of the characteristic vibrations, and the method for obtaining them will be described later in that connection. Denoting by Δq_i the differences of the coordinates of the true activated configuration minus those for the approximate one which was found, we can expand the first derivatives $\partial E/\partial q_i$ in the neighborhood of the activated point where $(\partial E/\partial q_i)_{q_{i_0}} = 0$ as follows:

$$(\partial E/\partial q_i)_{q_{i_0} - \Delta q_i} = \sum_k (\partial^2 E/\partial q_i \partial q_k)(-\Delta q_k) \qquad (6.9)$$

Solving this set of inhomogeneous linear equations for the quantities Δq_k and using five arbitrary quantities λ_k as multipliers, we can express our solution in a particularly condensed form as follows:

$$D \equiv \begin{vmatrix} -\sum \lambda_k \Delta q_k & \partial E/\partial q_1 & \partial E/\partial q_2 & \cdots & \partial E/\partial q_5 \\ \lambda_1 & \partial^2 E/\partial q_1 \partial q_1 & \partial^2 E/\partial q_1 \partial q_2 & \cdots & \partial^2 E/\partial q_1 \partial q_5 \\ \lambda_2 & \cdot & \cdot & & \cdot \\ \cdot & \cdot & \cdot & \cdot & \cdot \\ \cdot & \cdot & \cdot & \cdot & \cdot \\ \lambda_5 & \partial^2 E/\partial q_5 \partial q_1 & \cdot & \cdots & \partial^2 E/\partial q_5 \partial q_5 \end{vmatrix} = 0 \quad (6.10)$$

From (6.10) a particular Δq_ρ is determined by putting the corresponding $\lambda_\rho = 1$ and all the other λ's equal to 0. For practical computation it is very convenient to first reduce the determinant D to diagonal form except for the first row and the first column, thus obtaining all quantities Δq_i at once. These five quantities define a certain change in the originally assumed configuration, a change which can be carried out graphically with great ease and precision. For this new configuration the first derivatives $\partial E/\partial q_i$ may be recalculated, and the improvement obtained in locating the activated point may be judged by the decreases simultaneously obtained in all five derivatives. The process has been applied to the activated configurations of $H_2 + ICl$ both for $\lambda = 17$ per cent and 20 per cent, with results tabulated in Table 6.2. The simultaneous decrease of all five derivatives by a factor of approximately 0.10 must be very striking to anyone who tries to improve the approximate configuration in a less systematic fashion. The activation energies E_c (see Fig. 6.6) for 14 per cent and for 20 per cent were found to be 41.2 and 24.9 kcal, respectively. By linear interpolation a percentage of 17 was indicated as giving $E_c = 33$.

Table 6.2

Per Cent	Config.*	H—H r_1	I—Cl r_2	H—Cl r_3	H—I r_4	H—Cl r_5	H—I r_6	$\partial E/\partial q_1$	$\partial E/\partial q_2$	$\partial E/\partial q_3$	$\partial E/\partial q_4$	$\partial E/\partial q_5$
17	1	0.8033	2.335	1.597	2.264	2.214	2.475	2.966	−4.022	−3.831	−1.519	0.795
	2	0.8048	2.354	1.597	2.200	2.195	2.460	0.395	−0.399	0.158	0.200	−0.513
20	1	0.791	2.346	1.564	2.372	2.166	2.548	1.071	0.229	−1.050	−4.143	−1.415
	2	0.792	2.345	1.564	2.330	2.190	2.508	0.037	−0.06	0.80	0.48	0.06
14	1	0.830	2.39	1.61	2.08	2.24	2.41					

* 1 and 2 refer to the preliminary and the improved configuration. Distances are given in Angstrom units.

The experimental value of E is approximately 34 kcal (Bonner, Gore, and Yost, 1935). The activated point for 17 per cent was then actually determined; it gave an activation energy $E_c = 32.8$ kcal. The activated configuration for 14 per cent was not determined with the same accuracy

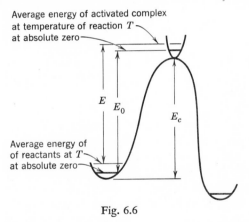

Fig. 6.6

as for the other two cases. Sherman and Li (Sherman and Li, 1936) have calculated a value of 24.6 kcal; they used 14 per cent additive binding in agreement with the value given here.

The vibrations of the activated state (vibrations of plane configurations of four unlike atoms)

Six of the twelve modes of motion of four atoms arranged in a plane involve a change in the relative positions of the atoms, while the other six amount to rigid translations or rotations of the whole molecule and proceed without change in the potential energy. Of the "internal" motions, five preserve the plane arrangement of the four atoms, whereas the sixth involves displacements different in sign for adjacent atoms and at right angles to the plane of equilibrium. Since this plane is obviously a plane of symmetry for the molecule, the last mode belongs to a symmetry class different from the rest, and the secular equation splits into two factors of first and fifth degree, respectively. No other symmetry conditions are imposed on the activated configuration like those for reactions

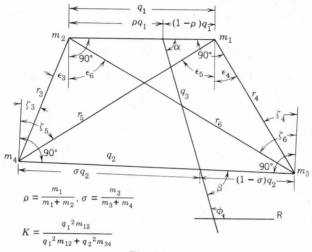

$$\rho = \frac{m_1}{m_1 + m_2}, \sigma = \frac{m_3}{m_3 + m_4}$$

$$K = \frac{q_1{}^2 m_{12}}{q_1{}^2 m_{12} + q_2{}^2 m_{34}}$$

Fig. 6.7

of the type $H_2 + I_2 \rightarrow 2HI$, where the secular equation decomposes into $1 + 2 + 3$ degrees of freedom (Wheeler et al., 1935).

We consider first the vibrations where the plane arrangement is preserved but ignore translational motions in this plane by keeping the center of gravity fixed at the origin. Tentatively we introduce six parameters the meaning of which is apparent from Fig. 6.7 and the following remarks: q_3 is the distance between the two centers of gravity of m_1 with m_2 and m_3 with m_4. One of these centers of gravity separates q_1 into two parts in the ratio $\rho : (1 - \rho)$, and the other separates q_2 in the ratio $\sigma : (1 - \sigma)$. These six coordinates describe not only the relative positions of the four particles but also the angular position φ of the whole system relative to a reference line R fixed in the plane. Thus the kinetic energy, when expressed in all six parameters, includes a part arising from rotations in the plane which can be separated from the rest because such a motion involves no changes in the potential energy.

The final coordinates were chosen in such a manner as to give a sum of square terms for the kinetic energy. This determines the coordinates, of course, only to within an orthogonal transformation, but the rotational coordinate Φ is uniquely determined by the requirement that it be normal to all the other coordinates none of which can involve the parameter φ.

The expression for the kinetic energy in terms of the parameters defined in Fig. 6.7 is easily calculated to be:

$$2K = m_{12}\dot{q}_1{}^2 + m_{34}\dot{q}_2{}^2 + m_{1234}\dot{q}_3{}^2 + a\dot{\varphi}^2 + b(2\dot{\varphi}\dot{\alpha} + \dot{\alpha}^2) + c(2\dot{\varphi}\dot{\beta} + \dot{\beta}^2) \quad (6.11)$$

where m_{12}, m_{34}, and m_{1234} are reduced masses of m_1 with m_2, m_3 with m_4, $m_1 + m_2$ with $m_3 + m_4$, respectively, and where a, b, c stand for

$$a = \sum_1^4 m_i R_i{}^2 \qquad b = q_1{}^2 m_{12} \qquad c = q_2{}^2 m_{34}$$

The R's measure distances from the center of gravity of the system. The last three terms of (6.11) are easily transformed into a sum of squares if we substitute

$$\dot{u} = \dot{\varphi}(a - b - c)^{1/2} \qquad \dot{v} = b^{1/2}(\dot{\alpha} + \dot{\varphi}) \qquad \dot{w} = c^{1/2}(\dot{\beta} + \dot{\varphi})$$

which property is preserved under any orthogonal transformation, in particular the following one:

$$U = a^{-1/2}[(a - b - c)^{1/2}u + b^{1/2}v + c^{1/2}w]$$

$$V = \{(a-b-c)/[a(b+c)]\}^{1/2}[-(b+c)/(a-b-c)^{1/2}u + b^{1/2}v + c^{1/2}w] \quad (6.12)$$

$$W = (b + c)^{-1/2}(c^{1/2}v - b^{1/2}w)$$

Substituting for these variables in terms of the original parameters φ, α, β and also for a, b, c, we obtain

$$2K = m_{12}\dot{q}_1{}^2 + m_{34}\dot{q}_2{}^2 + m_{1234}\dot{q}_3{}^2$$

$$+ \left[q_1{}^2 m_{12} + q_2{}^2 m_{34} - \frac{(q_1{}^2 m_{12} + q_2{}^2 m_{34})^2}{\Sigma m_i R_i{}^2} \right] \dot{q}_4{}^2$$

$$+ \frac{q_1{}^2 q_2{}^2 m_{12} m_{34}}{q_1{}^2 m_{12} + q_2{}^2 m_{34}} \dot{q}_5{}^2 + \frac{\dot{\Phi}^2}{\Sigma m_i R_i{}^2} \qquad (6.13)$$

where $q_4 = k\alpha + (1 - k)\beta = (q_1{}^2 m_{12}\alpha + q_2 m_{34}\beta)(q_1{}^2 m_{12} + q_2{}^2 m_{34})^{-1}$, $q_5 = \alpha - \beta$;

$$\dot{\Phi} = \Sigma m_i R_i{}^2 \dot{\varphi} + q_1{}^2 m_{12}\dot{\alpha} + q_2{}^2 m_{34}\dot{\beta} \qquad (6.14)$$

The newly defined coordinates q_4 and q_5 do not involve the angle φ and are thus orthogonal to the rotations of the system as a whole. The rotational coordinate is thus Φ; since it does not enter into the potential function for the system, it may be omitted from further consideration.

As stated previously, there exists but one internal degree of freedom which carries the four particles out of their plane of equilibrium $z = 0$. Indeed, of the four independent motions involving displacements z_i at right angles to the equilibrium plane, we may choose two as the rotations r_x and r_y, and a third as the translation t_z, and represent them by the coordinates

$$r_x = \Sigma m_i z_i x_i = q_1 m_{12} \sin \alpha (z_1 - z_2) + q_2 m_{34} \sin \beta (z_3 - z_4)$$

$$r_y = \Sigma m_i z_i y_i = (q_3/\Sigma m_i)[-(m_3 + m_4)(m_1 z_1 + m_2 z_2)$$
$$+ (m_1 + m_2)(m_3 z_3 + m_4 z_4)]$$

$$t_z = \Sigma m_i z_i$$

The internal motion is then completely determined by the requirement that its coordinate q_6 be orthogonal to r_x, r_y, t_z. Let q_6 be a linear function of the z displacements $q_6 = \sum_i \sigma_i z_i$; then the following relations must hold among the σ's:

$$\sum_{i=1}^{4} m_i \sigma_i x_i = 0 \qquad \sum_{i=1}^{4} m_i \sigma_i y_i = 0 \qquad \sum_{i=1}^{4} m_i \sigma_i = 0$$

Thus we find by a simple elimination process that q_6 is proportional to

$$q_6 \sim$$

$$\begin{vmatrix} z_1 & z_2 & z_3 & z_4 \\ q_1 m_{12} \sin \alpha & -q_1 m_{12} \sin \alpha & q_2 m_{34} \sin \beta & -q_2 m_{34} \sin \beta \\ q_1 m_{12} \cos \alpha - m_1 q_3 \frac{m_3 + m_4}{\Sigma m_i} & -q_1 m_{12} \cos \alpha - m_2 q_3 \frac{m_3 + m_4}{\Sigma m_i} & q_2 m_{34} \cos \beta + m_3 q_3 \frac{m_1 + m_2}{\Sigma m_i} & -q_2 m_{34} \cos \beta + m_4 q_4 \frac{m_1 + m_2}{\Sigma m_i} \\ m_1 & m_2 & m_3 & m_4 \end{vmatrix}$$

One possible way of describing the internal motion connected with q_6 is the following:

$$\Delta z_1 = \Delta q_6 \left[\frac{\cot \alpha - \cot \beta}{q_3(m_1 + m_2)} + \frac{1}{q_1 m_1 \sin \alpha} \right]$$

$$\Delta z_2 = \Delta q_6 \left[\frac{\cot \alpha - \cot \beta}{q_3(m_1 + m_2)} - \frac{1}{q_1 m_2 \sin \alpha} \right]$$

$$\Delta z_3 = \Delta q_6 \left[\frac{-\cot \alpha - \cot \beta}{q_3(m_3 + m_4)} - \frac{1}{q_2 m_3 \sin \beta} \right]$$

$$\Delta z_4 = \Delta q_6 \left[-\frac{\cot \alpha - \cot \beta}{q_3(m_3 + m_4)} + \frac{1}{q_2 m_4 \sin \beta} \right]$$

(6.15)

The displacements (6.15) comply with the three conditions:

$$\Sigma m_i x_i \Delta z_i = 0 \qquad \Sigma m_i y_i \Delta z_i = 0 \qquad \Sigma m_i \Delta z_i = 0$$

as can be readily established. Thus they are orthogonal to the three rigid motions (Δr_x, Δr_y, Δt_z) and of course also to the other modes which do not involve z_i. Using (6.15), the kinetic energy K_6 associated with q_6 is then

$$2K_6 = \dot{q}_6{}^2 \left[\left(\frac{\cot \alpha - \cot \beta}{q_3} \right)^2 \left(\frac{1}{m_1 + m_2} + \frac{1}{m_3 + m_4} \right) \right.$$
$$\left. + \left(\frac{1}{q_1 \sin \alpha} \right)^2 \frac{1}{m_{12}} + \left(\frac{1}{q_2 \sin \beta} \right)^2 \frac{1}{m_{34}} \right]$$

The next problem is the computation of the force constants of the activated configuration. Since the activated configuration, like a stable configuration of atoms, has a stationary value of the interaction energy,

Table 6.3

$$E = \lambda(a + b + c) - (1 - \lambda)R$$

Here

$$R = \{\tfrac{1}{2}[(a - b)^2 + (b - c)^2 + (c - a)^2]\}^{1/2} \quad \text{and} \quad a = a_1 + a_2, \quad b = b_1 + b_2, \quad c = c_1 + c_2$$

$$\frac{\partial^2 E}{\partial q_\alpha \, \partial q_\beta} = \sum_i \frac{\partial E}{\partial r_i} \frac{\partial^2 r_i}{\partial q_\alpha \, \partial q_\beta} + \sum_{ik} \frac{\partial^2 E}{\partial r_i \, \partial r_k} \frac{\partial r_i}{\partial q_\alpha} \frac{\partial r_k}{\partial q_\beta} \qquad \frac{\partial E}{\partial a_1} = \frac{\partial E}{\partial a_2} = \lambda - \frac{3}{2} \frac{(1 - \lambda)}{R} a + \frac{1}{2} \frac{(1 - \lambda)}{R} (a + b + c)$$

$$\frac{\partial E}{\partial r_i} = \frac{\partial E}{\partial \alpha_i} \frac{d\alpha_i}{dr_i} = \frac{\partial E}{\partial a_i} \frac{da_i}{dr_i} \qquad \frac{\partial^2 E}{\partial a_1{}^2} = \frac{\partial^2 E}{\partial a_2{}^2} = \frac{\partial^2 E}{\partial a_1 \, \partial a_2} = -\frac{3}{4} \frac{1 - \lambda}{R^3} (b - c)^2$$

$$\frac{\partial^2 E}{\partial r_i \, \partial r_k} = \frac{\partial^2 E}{\partial a_i \, \partial a_k} \frac{da_i}{dr_i} \frac{da_k}{dr_k} + \delta_{ik} \frac{\partial E}{\partial a_i} \frac{\partial^2 a_i}{\partial r_i \, \partial r_k} \qquad \frac{\partial^2 E}{\partial a_i \, \partial b_i} = -\frac{3}{4} (1 - \lambda) \left[\frac{(a - b)^2}{R^3} - \frac{1}{R} \right] = \frac{\partial^2 E}{\partial c_i{}^2} + \frac{3}{4} \frac{(1 - \lambda)}{R}$$

where $i = 1, 2$.

it is actually in stable equilibrium in all degrees of freedom except the one along which the reaction proceeds. That means that all first derivatives $\partial E / \partial q_\alpha$ are 0, and that for small displacements from the activated configuration the energy function can be expanded:

$$dE = \sum_{\alpha\beta} (\partial^2 E / \partial q_\alpha \, \partial q_\beta) \, dq_\alpha \, dq_\beta \tag{6.16}$$

The second derivatives in (6.16) are force constants for small displacements from equilibrium. When transformed into a sum of squares, only one force constant in (6.16) will exhibit a negative sign.

It has been preferable here to follow an explicit analytical procedure in deriving numerical values for the force constants rather than the previously followed methods which, though applicable in simpler cases, become excessively laborious for more degrees of freedom. One other fact should be borne in mind. The present method of second derivatives gives the force constants for infinitesimal vibrations so that in case of considerable anharmonicities they may not give the correct frequencies of finite vibrations.

Formulas necessary for the calculation of the second derivatives are presented in Tables 6.3, 6.4, and 6.5. Formulas in Tables 6.4 and 6.5 are of course perfectly general and depend only upon the geometry of

Table 6.4. Formulas $\partial r_i / \partial q_j$ Valid for Any Configuration of Four Atoms in a Plane

(Notation as in Fig. 6.7)

	q_1	q_2	q_3	q_4	q_5
r_1	1	0	0	0	0
r_2	0	1	0	0	0
r_3	$-\rho \sin \epsilon_3$	$\sigma \sin \zeta_3$	$\sin(\alpha - \epsilon_3)$	$q_3 \cos(\alpha - \epsilon_3)$	$-\rho(1-k)r_1 \cos \epsilon_3 - \sigma k r_2 \cos \zeta_3$
r_4	$-(1-\rho) \sin \epsilon_4$	$(1-\sigma) \sin \zeta_4$	$\sin(\alpha + \epsilon_4)$	$q_3 \cos(\alpha + \epsilon_4)$	$(1-\rho)(1-k)r_1 \cos \epsilon_4 + (1-\sigma)k r_2 \cos \zeta_4$
r_5	$(1-\rho) \sin \epsilon_5$	$\sigma \sin \zeta_5$	$\sin(\alpha - \epsilon_5)$	$q_3 \cos(\alpha - \epsilon_5)$	$(1-\rho)r_1(1-k) \cos \epsilon_5 - \sigma k r_2 \cos \zeta_5$
r_6	$\rho \sin \epsilon_6$	$(1-\sigma) \sin \zeta_6$	$\sin(\alpha + \epsilon_6)$	$q_3 \cos(\alpha + \epsilon_6)$	$-\rho(1-k)r_1 \cos \epsilon_6 + (1-\sigma)k r_2 \cos \zeta_6$

Table 6.5. Derivatives of ϵ_i, α, and β with Respect to the Coordinates q_k

	q_1	q_2	q_3	q_4	q_5
ϵ_3	$-\dfrac{\rho}{r_3} \cos \epsilon_3$	$\dfrac{\sigma}{r_3} \cos \zeta_3$	$-\dfrac{1}{r_3} \cos(\alpha - \epsilon_3)$	$\dfrac{q_3}{r_3} \sin(\alpha - \epsilon_3)$	$\dfrac{1}{r_3}[\rho r_1(1-k)\sin \epsilon_3 + \sigma r_2 k \sin \zeta_3] + 1 - k$
ϵ_4	$-\dfrac{1-\rho}{r_4} \cos \epsilon_4$	$\dfrac{1-\sigma}{r_4} \cos \zeta_4$	$\dfrac{1}{r_4} \cos(\alpha+\epsilon_4)$	$-\dfrac{q_3}{r_4} \sin(\alpha+\epsilon_4)$	$-\dfrac{1}{r_4}[(1-\rho)r_1(1-k)\sin \epsilon_4 - (1-\sigma)r_2 k \sin \zeta_4] - 1 + k$
ϵ_5	$\dfrac{1-\rho}{r_5} \cos \epsilon_5$	$\dfrac{\sigma}{r_5} \cos \zeta_5$	$-\dfrac{1}{r_5} \cos(\alpha - \epsilon_5)$	$\dfrac{q_3}{r_5} \sin(\alpha - \epsilon_5)$	$\dfrac{1}{r_5}[(1-\rho)r_1(1-k)\sin \epsilon_5 + \sigma r_2 k \sin \zeta_5] + 1 - k$
ϵ_6	$\dfrac{\rho}{r_6} \cos \epsilon_6$	$\dfrac{1-\sigma}{r_6} \cos \zeta_6$	$\dfrac{1}{r_6} \cos(\alpha+\epsilon_6)$	$-\dfrac{q_3}{r_6} \sin(\alpha+\epsilon_6)$	$\dfrac{1}{r_6}[\rho r_1(1-k)\sin \epsilon_6 - (1-\sigma)r_2 k \sin \zeta_6] - 1 + k$
α	0	0	0	1	$1 - k$
β	0	0	0	1	$1 - k$

The corresponding derivatives for the angle ζ_i follow from the same table as the ϵ_i by use of the identities: $\epsilon_i - \zeta_i = \pm (\alpha - \beta)$, $i = 3, 4, 5, 6$, where the plus sign goes with $i = 3, 5$ and the minus sign goes with $i = 4, 6$. The geometrical significance of the symbols is given in Fig. 6.7.

the quadrilateral (Fig. 6.7). They give only first derivatives because tabulation of all second derivatives would require too much space; however, calculation of the second derivatives $\partial^2 r_i / \partial q_\alpha \partial q_\beta$ from Tables 6.4 and 6.5 requires no further consideration of Fig. 6.7.

The second derivative $\partial^2 E / \partial q_6{}^2$ remains to be calculated. We have

$$\frac{\partial^2 E}{\partial q_6{}^2} = \sum_{ij} \frac{\partial^2 E}{\partial r_i \partial r_j} \frac{\partial r_i}{\partial q_6} \frac{\partial r_j}{\partial q_6} + \sum_i \frac{\partial E}{\partial r_i}\left[\frac{\partial^2 r_i}{\partial z_i{}^2}\left(\frac{\partial z_i}{\partial q_6}\right)^2 + \frac{dr_i}{dz_i} \frac{\partial^2 z_i}{\partial q_6{}^2}\right] \quad (6.17)$$

which reduces to

$$\frac{\partial^2 E}{\partial q_6{}^2} = \sum_i \frac{\partial E}{\partial \alpha_i} \frac{\partial \alpha_i}{\partial r_i} \frac{1}{r_i}\left[\frac{d}{dq_6}(z_{i2} - z_{i1})\right]^2 \quad (6.18)$$

since all the derivatives $\partial r_i/\partial q_6$ are zero on account of the symmetry character of this mode of motion (all the r's are minima in the plane arrangement) and since

$$\frac{\partial^2 z_i}{\partial q_6^2} = 0 \quad \text{and} \quad \frac{\partial^2 r_i}{\partial z_i^2} = \frac{1}{r_i}$$

Here the z_i in (6.17) refer to the z projections of the distances r_i, and the quantities z_{i1} and z_{i2} in (6.18) refer to the two end points of the interatomic distances r_i. Thus the force constant is given by (6.18), and all the mixed derivatives involving q_6 vanish identically.

The vibration frequencies for the reaction $H_2 + ICl \rightarrow HI + HCl$

In evaluating the terms for the kinetic and the potential energy (using 17 per cent additive binding) we are led to the following secular equations for the five normal vibrations in a plane:

$$\begin{vmatrix} (402.82 - 0.25X) & 5.29 & 93.30 & 107.33 & 0.87 \\ 5.29 & (246.10 - 13.86X) & 5.72 & 34.54 & 7.78 \\ 93.30 & 5.72 & (-62.70 - 0.9879X) & -78.64 & -20.12 \\ 107.33 & 34.54 & -78.64 & (112.37 - 3.99X) & 39.50 \\ 0.87 & 7.78 & -20.12 & 39.50 & (29.86 - 0.161X) \end{vmatrix} = 0$$

The twisting vibration out of the plane is given by the equation $272.88 - 1.5788X = 0$. Here the force constants are in units of kilocalories per mole A^{-2}, and in the kinetic energy mass is expressed in molecular weights and distance in Ångstroms (where distance occurs).

Table 6.6

Activated Configuration for	Moments of Inertia (gram atom, A^2)			Frequencies of Characteristic Vibrations				(cm⁻¹)		Activation Energy E_c (kcal)
	A_3	B_3	C_3	ν_1	ν_2	ν_3	ν_4	ν_5	ν_n	
17% additive binding	152.95	5.81	158.76	4,391.0	1,580.0	1,426.0	481.0	435.0	i1128	32.8
20%	158.54	6.00	164.54	4,696.0	1,522.0	1,344.0	550.0	442.0	i933	24.9

The six characteristic frequencies ν_i for 17 per cent additive binding are given in Table 6.6 in wave numbers. They are obtained from the six roots X_i of the secular equations by the simple relationship $\nu_i = 108.46X^{1/2}$.

The corresponding secular equations for 20 per cent additive binding are

$$\begin{vmatrix} (465.07 - 0.25X) & -2.48 & 76.26 & 81.46 & -2.11 \\ -2.48 & (252.68 - 13.86X) & 11.65 & 38.50 & 6.60 \\ 76.26 & 11.65 & (-47.14 - 0.9878X) & -46.41 & -19.00 \\ 81.46 & 38.50 & -46.41 & (148.57 - 3.99X) & 34.62 \\ -2.11 & 6.60 & -19.00 & 34.62 & (26.96 - 0.1565X) \end{vmatrix} = 0$$

and $250.08 - 1.631X = 0$.

The rate of reaction

The general expression for the rate of a reaction of this type has been given by Eyring (1935a). Thus we have the equation

$$k_1 = \kappa \left(\frac{m_3'}{m_1' m_2'}\right)^{3/2} \frac{\sigma_1 \sigma_2}{\sigma_3} \frac{5.785 \times 10^{14}}{T} \frac{(A_3' B_3' C_3')^{1/2}}{I_1' I_2'} \frac{\left(2 \sinh \dfrac{h\nu_1}{2kT}\right)\left(2 \sinh \dfrac{h\nu_2}{2kT}\right)}{\displaystyle\prod_{i=1}^{5}\left(2 \sinh \dfrac{h\nu_i}{2kT}\right)}$$

$$\times \left[1 - \frac{1}{24}\left(\frac{h\nu_n}{kT}\right)^2\right] \exp\left(-\frac{E_c}{kT}\right) \quad (6.19)$$

Here the subscripts 1 and 2 refer to the hydrogen and iodine chloride molecules, respectively, and 3 to the activated complex. κ, m_i', σ_i, and ν_i refer to the transmission coefficient which we take equal to unity, the mass of the ith molecule, the rotational symmetry number, and the frequency, respectively. $A_3 B_3 C_3$ are the three principal moments of inertia of the activated complex, and I_1' and I_2' the moments of inertia of the hydrogen and iodine chloride molecules, respectively. ν_n is the imaginary mode of vibration normal to the barrier. The primes indicate that masses are to be taken in molecular weights units and lengths in Ångstroms, in which case k_1 is given in the units cc moles^{-1} sec^{-1}.

If, as is usual, we define the energy of activation as

$$E = kT^2 \, d \log (k/T^{1/2})/dT$$

we have

$$E = E_0 + \sum_{i=1}^{5} \frac{h\nu_i}{\exp(h\nu_1/kT) - 1} - \frac{h\nu_1}{\exp(h\nu_1/kT) - 1}$$

$$- \frac{h\nu_2}{\exp(h\nu_2/kT) - 1} - \frac{3}{2}kT$$

and

$$E_0 = E_c + \sum_{i=1}^{5} \tfrac{1}{2} h\nu_i - \tfrac{1}{2}(h\nu_1 + h\nu_2)$$

We thus obtain for 17 per cent additive binding $E_c = 32.8$, $E_0 = 37.85$, and $E = 36.62$ at $503.2°$. For 20 per cent additive binding $E_c = 24.9$, $E_0 = 30.29$, $E = 29.04$. Now defining three A's by the equations

$$k = A_c e^{-E_c/kT} = A_0 e^{-E_0/kT} = A e^{-E/kT}$$

we obtain Table 6.7.

These values are to be compared with the experimentally obtained specific reaction rate of Bonner, Gore, and Yost (1935). We change k

from their units to cc mole^{-1} sec^{-1} and so obtain $k = 0.52 = 1.64 \times 10^{15} e^{-33,900/k478.2}$; $2.8 = 1.49 \times 10^{15} e^{-33,900/k503.2}$; and $5.8 = 1.60 \times 10^{15} e^{-33,900/k513.2}$.

By inspection of Table 6.7 we see that A is independent of whether 20 per cent or 17 per cent additive binding is used. This is important because it means that it is uniquely fixed by the potential function and depends upon no arbitrary constant. If the percentage additive binding were raised to a fraction over 20 per cent, E would be lowered by a calorie to 28 kcal and k would then agree rather well with the experimental values.

Table 6.7

% Additive	T	k	$A_c \times 10^{10}$	$A_0 \times 10^{13}$	$A \times 10^{12}$
17	478.2	7.44×10^{-5}	7.36	1.50	4.11
	503.2	5.12×10^{-4}	9.06	1.46	4.16
	513.2	1.03×10^{-3}	9.64	1.37	4.09
20	478.2	2.28×10^{-1}	5.51	1.60	4.30
	503.2	1.01	6.61	1.46	4.17
	513.2	1.79	7.26	1.43	4.21

The theoretical k would, however, not increase with temperature as fast as the experimental value does. Thus, if Bonner, Gore, and Yost are, as they believe, actually measuring the reaction rate here calculated and if their values of k are dependable, our calculated A is too small by a factor of ≈ 350. A will be increased by this amount if the three lowest frequencies are actually around 50 wave numbers instead of the calculated values. Such a change would also reduce the excess $(E_0 - E_c)$ of the zero point energy in the activated state over that in the initial state to practically zero. More experiments seem necessary before any of these quantities can be assigned from experiment with assurance. The corresponding isotopic reactions will also be useful in calculating $E_0 - E_c$. Extensive accurate data on reactions of this type will be particularly valuable in determining the accuracy and in suggesting methods for improving the calculation-of potential functions of activated complexes.

More exact surfaces for this reaction will be calculated in the future with an accompanying change in the activation energy, frequencies, and moments of inertia but not in the general procedure for theoretically estimating a rate of reaction. The Theory of Rate Processes (Glasstone, Laidler, and Eyring, 1941) gives many other examples which should prove instructive to the reader.

Luminescence

Where is the way where light dwelleth? and as for darkness,
where is the place thereof?

Job, 38: 19

Biological rate processes

The theory of chemical reactions, whose main essentials have been briefly outlined in the preceding pages, applies to every rate process, wherever there is an orderly, progressive change with time. In living cells, however, the problem is the most involved because a higher order of complexity is encountered here than anywhere else. Processes which were once looked upon as a simple reaction, under the control of some particular catalyst, e.g., the fermentation of sugar by "zymase," have long since been shown to involve a series of consecutive and cyclic reactions with as many specific catalysts. Even with extracted and crystallized single enzymes, it is not yet possible to calculate absolute rates of a specific reaction in the manner illustrated in Chapter 6, but the usefulness of the theory in the interpretation of biological mechanisms, as in many other connections, does not depend upon such theoretical calculations from basic data.

Under "biological rate processes" we would include phenomena of a broad gradation of complexity, from those which depend chiefly upon simple diffusion or solubility to such familiar but immensely complicated processes as reproduction, growth, and differentiation. Inasmuch as the very complicated processes undoubtedly depend upon a multitude of individual, consecutive, and interlinked reactions, it would seem logical, before undertaking any analysis of the whole as an overall rate process, first to consider single, isolated enzyme systems. The fact is, however, that the study of processes in living cells has contributed a great deal to the knowledge of distinct catalytic systems; Warburg's *Atmungsferment*, for example, was discovered in intact cells, and for a long time more was learned of its nature from this approach than from studies of extracts. Of particular significance, from the present point of view, have been the studies of bioluminescence, for no other process has been analyzed as fully with respect to the action of temperature and hydrostatic pressure as well as certain other factors, and much of this work has been based on the luminescence of living bacteria. The results have revealed some fundamental mechanisms which potentially influence the observed rate of enzyme reactions generally. Subsequent evidence, obtained with other more and less complicated systems, has revealed parallel mechanisms, thereby furnishing support for the conclusions arrived at in kinetic studies of luminiscence. Since the characteristics of the luminescent system are in many respects typical of biological oxidations and of more complex processes, it provides a useful "model" for interpreting the mechanism of various influences in other connections. Thus it is convenient and appropriate to discuss bioluminescence as an approach to the solution of basic problems in the kinetics of both simpler and more complex processes.

Bioluminescence in general

The general subject of bioluminescence has been treated extensively by Harvey (1920, 1924, 1927, 1935, 1940, 1941, 1951, 1952), and only those aspects which bear on the kinetics will be considered here. The biological production of "cold light" occurs only in the presence of molecular oxygen, with a few exceptions of unknown meaning (Harvey, 1926; Harvey and Korr, 1938). The necessity of oxygen for luminescence was first indicated in some classic experiments by Robert Boyle (1667), who found that "air," and a very small amount of air indeed, was required to maintain the glow of "shining meat" and other naturally occurring materials which, as we now know, were overgrown with luminous micro-örganisms. The precise minimum amount of oxygen necessary for visible luminescence is uncertain, but modern experiments have shown that it is almost incredibly small; Meyer has reported (1942) that 1 part of oxygen in 10^{10} parts of nitrogen at atmospheric pressure is sometimes sufficient. Harvey (1940; cf. also Harvey and Morrison, 1923) places the minimum for bacteria at a partial pressure of oxygen of about 0.0007 mm of mercury, with a somewhat less amount for certain extracts (*Cypridina*). With other things the same, the amount of oxygen needed for maximum brightness of bacterial luminescence is also small, of the order of 1 or 2 mm of mercury (Shoup, 1929; Shapiro, 1934), above which the reaction becomes zero order with respect to oxygen over a wide range of pressures. Luminescence in some of the higher fungi (*Panus stipticus, Armillaria mellea*, and *Clitocybe illudens*) is much more sensitive to a decrease in the partial pressure of oxygen below 150 mm of mercury (Hastings, 1952).

The dependence of bioluminescence on oxygen is shared by numerous examples of chemiluminescence, wherein light production accompanies the oxidation of various unrelated compounds in solution, at relatively low temperatures. Thus it is natural to assume that in living organisms or in their products the emission of cold light accompanies the aerobic oxidation of some particular substance.   The chemical identity of such a substance has not yet been established in any organism, or its extracts, and profound differences in the spectral distribution of emitted light suggest that the same substance could scarcely be the source of light in all instances.   On the other hand, among the luminous bacteria, although they comprise a group that would be considered bacteriologically to include very distantly related representatives, the spectrum of emitted light is so nearly the same that the substance concerned in their luminescence is probably closely related, or perhaps in some cases is identical (Eymers and van Schouwenburg, 1937b; van der Burg, 1943).

Evidence of enzyme-subtrate systems ("luciferase" and "luciferin") in bioluminescence

From only a very few, about half a dozen, of the great many living organisms endowed with the property of luminescence has it been possible to obtain luminous extracts.   The first were obtained by Dubois (1885) from the elaterid beetle, *Pyrophorus*, in a very simple experiment which has provided the basis for subsequent approaches to the problem with different organisms.   Dubois showed that boiling water quickly and permanently destroys luminescence of the light organ of *Pyrophorus*. When the same organ is ground up in cold water, the light gradually disappears.   If, however, the boiling water extractives are mixed with the non-luminous, triturated organ at room temperature, luminescence reappears at once, then gradually subsides.   Thus it is evident that the luminescent system from this source includes heat-stable as well as heat-labile components.   Dubois (1887) carried out a similar experiment with the luminescent clam, *Pholas dactylus*, and came to the conclusion that light emission resulted from the oxidation of a heat-stable substrate, "luciférine," by an enzyme, "luciférase."   His terminology has persisted and is still applied to bioluminescent systems in general, even though the chemical identities and relationships of "luciferins" in different organisms are still unknown, and the presence of luciferase in the vast majority is largely a matter of presumption.   Dubois' terminology, in its anglicized form, was adopted by Harvey, who found evidence of such a system in American fireflies, *Photinus* and *Photuris*, the Japanese firefly, *Luciola*, and the Japanese ostracod crustacean, *Cypridina*.   The material from *Cypridina* has proved especially favorable for studies of the light-emitting system, and investigations chiefly by Harvey and his associates since 1916 (cf. Harvey, 1940, 1952) leave no doubt that the heat-labile component from this source has the characteristics of an enzyme, which in the presence of water and molecular oxygen will catalyze the oxidation of the relatively heat-stable component with emission of visible light.   The latter component is usually referred to as the substrate, in the usual sense of the word, although it remains possible that, in some cases at least, it functions as a coenzyme and actually belongs in the category of such catalysts of cellular metabolism. As far as the mechanism of the reaction is concerned, the distinction is not very meaningful.

Partial purification of *Cypridina* luciferase

Most of the efforts toward purification of the luminescent system have been directed at isolation of the substrate, luciferin, whose dialyzability and relative heat stability allow a more ready application of organic chemical procedures. The cold water extractives containing active luciferase also contain an undetermined number of other substances, probably including other active enzymes, although the catalytic activity of such extracts toward substrates other than those involved in light emission has not been systematically tested. The elimination of a considerable amount of inert materials has been accomplished, however, in the following manner (Giese and Chase, 1940). The dried and ground-up whole organisms are usually extracted first with benzene. The residue is taken up in distilled water and dialyzed through cellophane against repeated changes of distilled water in the refrigerator. The dialyzate includes some highly colored solutes, most of the oxidized and unoxidized luciferin, and inorganic salts. At the same time, a very considerable amount of precipitate forms, possibly a globulin, practically devoid of luciferase activity. The precipitate is eliminated by centrifugation. The nearly clear and almost colorless supernatant retains its luciferase activity during long storage in the refrigerator, even if molds and bacteria develop in it. Preliminary electrophoretic studies at pH 7.6 (Chase, Schryver, and Stern, 1948) have shown that it contains three components, one of which is stationary and inactive. The other two components have mobilities of the order of 10 and 17×10^{-5} cm^2 sec^{-1} volt^{-1}, respectively. In the experiments described, luciferase activity migrated with the more slowly moving component, which was present in a higher concentration than the stationary substance. The faster moving component represented less than 10 per cent of the total protein. No evidence is yet available as to the proportion of luciferase in the more slowly moving fraction. A method of fractional precipitation followed by adsorption on calcium phosphate has yielded luciferase preparations with an estimated purity of some 200 times that of the crude extracts (McElroy and Chase, 1952).

A molecular weight of 20,000 for *Cypridina* luciferase was estimated by Kauzmann et al. (1949) as a figure which gave reasonable results in calculating the thermodynamic constants for the formation and decomposition of the enzyme-substrate complex. There is reason to believe, on other grounds, that luciferase in bacteria (not yet separated from the living cells) has approximately this molecular weight. Thus the bacterial luminescent system undergoes a reversible thermal inactivation with a heat (ΔH) of 55,260 cal, and entropy (ΔS) of 184 E.U. (entropy units or cal per deg) (Eyring and Magee, 1942). These values correspond closely to those of 57,380 cal and 180 E.U., in the reversible denaturation of crystalline soybean trypsin inhibitor (Kunitz, 1948) which has a molecular weight of about 24,000 (Kunitz, 1947a). The similarity in both heat and entropy indicates a similarity in molecular weight.

Partial purification and properties of *Cypridina* luciferin

The luciferin of dried and ground-up whole *Cypridinae* has been concentrated by about 2,000 times, relative to the dry material, and has been obtained in an estimated purity of about 50 per cent through the methods of Anderson (1933, 1935). Purification methods have also been devised by Kanda (1924, 1929). Anderson's procedure consists in extraction first with methyl alcohol, followed by extraction with butyl alcohol. The butyl alcohol extract is benzoylated, yielding products that are inactive in light production with luciferase. These products are transferred to ether, in which they (but not active luciferin) are soluble. The ether is removed and the residue suspended in 0.55 N hydrochloric acid, which is then heated in an atmosphere of hydrogen for 1 hr at 100°C, thereby regenerating active luciferin. Since the purified luciferin has been found to decompose fairly rapidly in the presence of oxygen, the hydrolysis in acid must be carried out under anaerobic conditions. By repeating the benzoylation-hydrolysis procedure, greater purity is obtained. The product is light yellow in color and remains stable for years in solution in butyl alcohol from which all the dissolved oxygen has been removed by pure hydrogen. Mason has worked out a somewhat faster procedure for purification and has obtained a product that is chromatographically homogeneous with respect to two components, α- and β-luciferin, each of which is active for light emission in the presence of luciferase (Mason and Davis, 1952).

Evidence regarding the chemical nature of *Cypridina* luciferin is incomplete, largely because such small quantities of the crude material have been available to investigators of the problem that a fully purified material has not yet been obtained. Microanalysis by Chakravorty and Ballentine (1941) of the partially purified material seemed to indicate that carbon, hydrogen, and oxygen were the only constituents; no nitrogen, sulfur, halogens, or ash was detected. Subsequent analyses by Chase and Gregg (1949), however, showed that about 8 per cent of nitrogen was present in material of the same degree of purity. Mason (1952a) has confirmed the presence of nitrogen in about this proportion in highly purified luciferin, and has found a small amount of ash in the same material. Indirect evidence, based on the quantitative relations between the relative amount of luciferin that combines with known amounts of ferricyanide (the uncombined proportion of luciferin being estimated in terms of the amount of light quickly emitted on addition of luciferase) has provided reason to believe that the combining and molecular weights of luciferin are between 250 and 570 (Chase, 1949a).

The partially purified luciferin combines irreversibly with cyanide at concentrations as low as 0.000033 M (Giese and Chase, 1940). In crude extracts, however, high concentrations have no effect on the light-emitting reaction (Harvey, 1917a; van Schouwenburg, 1938). It follows that the crude extracts either contain considerable quantities of substances, other than luciferin, which avidly bind cyanide, or else the luciferin is considerably modified in the process of purification. The latter interpretation is favored by some marked differences in the solubility of luciferin contained in the dried, whole *Cypridina*, and in purified extracts, respectively, as judged by the relative amounts that dissolve in various alcohols and other solvents (Chase, 1948a).

Studies by Anderson (1936) of the rate and total amount of light emission from given amounts of luciferin after treatment with oxidizing and reducing agents have established another important property of the molecule in partially purified extracts. In the presence of molecular oxygen, or of such agents as ferricyanide or cerium sulfate, it undergoes a non-luminescent, or "dark" oxidation. The product will not react with luciferase to give luminescence, but it may be reduced with hydrosulfite, after which it will react with the enzyme to give luminescence. Anderson refers to the oxidation product of the dark reaction with potassium ferricyanide, which takes place in the absence of luciferase, as "oxidized luciferin." Previously Harvey had referred to the oxidation product of luciferin, whether catalyzed by luciferase or not, as "oxyluciferin." Although the relation between the products of oxidation under different conditions, or by different agents, is not yet clear, there is some justification for believing that they are not all identical.

The reaction of luciferin to oxidized luciferin appears to be a mobile equilibrium, but the product is not stable and decomposes fairly fast at room temperature. Consequently, within a short time after oxidation by ferricyanide, it is no longer possible to obtain active luciferin by reduction with hydrosulfite. The oxidation-reduction potential E_0' for the reversible reaction has been estimated as $+ 0.026$ volt at pH 7.0, which would be only slightly negative to that of the quinhydrone system, suggesting a relation of the luciferin molecule to some naturally occurring hydroxy-benzene derivatives (Anderson, 1936; Korr, 1936).

In contrast to the results obtained with ferricyanide-oxidized luciferin, Anderson (1936) found that, after the light-emitting oxidation of luciferin in presence of luciferase, the addition of hydrosulfite did not restore any very considerable amount of the reduced form that could be oxidized again with light emission. Anderson pointed out explicitly that this

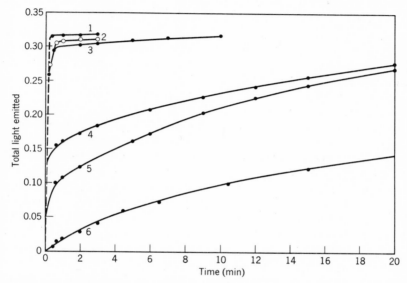

Fig. 7.1. Total light emitted as a function of time after mixing *Cypridina* luciferin and luciferase. The amounts of enzyme and substrate were the same in each case, but curves 4, 5, and 6 were obtained with a considerable fraction of the luciferin in a reversibly oxidized state at the start of the reaction (Anderson, 1936).

observation does not justify the conclusion that the light-emitting oxidation cannot be reversed; it does show that no large amount of the initial form of luciferin is restored by the action of ordinary reducing agents after the luminescent reaction in the extracts employed.

The precise significance of this "irreversible" reaction is open to several possible interpretations and will probably remain unsettled until more biochemical evidence becomes available. From the point of view of kinetics, it is evidently partly responsible for the progressive decline in intensity of luminescence following the mixing of luciferin and luciferase solutions, in either crude or purified extracts. The rate of this decline during the early part of the reaction is first order with respect to luciferin, i.e., the luminescence intensity decreases exponentially with time, in the same manner as the amount of substrate would ordinarily decrease during many enzyme reactions. Subsequently there is nearly always a dim but visible glow that may persist for a long time; it probably represents the oxidation of luciferin which is being gradually reduced, through the action of unknown agents in the extracts, from a reversibly oxidized state. By deliberately varying the proportion of fully reduced and reversibly oxidized luciferin at the start, the rate of light emission can be varied enormously, and the ordinarily dim afterglow can be made either wholly negligible (in a rapid reaction, with essentially all the luciferin in a reduced state at the start) or quite conspicuous and bright (in a reaction which takes much longer to complete), with the same concentration of enzyme in both cases. Figure 7.1 illustrates these relationships.

Hypothetical structure of luciferin

Hypothetical models of an unknown molecule, based on fragmentary evidence of the sort discussed above, sometimes lead to astonishing results. In the present instance, one hypothesis in particular, viz., that of a quinone compound, has given rise to both useful experimentation and extensive discussion. For this reason, and also because it provides a model that facilitates the picturing of such kinetics as are illustrated in Fig. 7.1, it deserves special mention, however closely or remotely correct it ultimately turns out to be.

First, it was suggested in informal discussions (F. H. J., 1939) that the luciferin molecule might be pictured as a hydroquinone with a primary alcohol side group (Fig. 7.2A), the reversible dark oxidation consisting of the removal of two hydrogens to give the corresponding quinone, and the light-emitting oxidation involving the degradation of the alcohol to a carboxyl group. The quinone structure was assumed on the basis of the redox potential data of Anderson and Korr, and the alcohol group was assumed merely as a common type of not readily reversible biological oxidation. Although the possibility that the two oxidations might involve different groups on the same molecule was pointed out by Johnson, van Schouwenburg, and van der Burg (1939),the above-mentioned model seemed too hypothetical at the time to justify more specific mention.

A short time later, Chakravorty and Ballentine (1941) arrived at very nearly the same hypothetical model (Fig. 7.2B), differing only in that they postulated a ketone group next to the alcohol in order to account for the irreversible combination of cyanide with purified luciferin, which had been discovered by Giese and Chase (1940) in the meantime. Chakravorty and Ballentine undertook to test the hypothesis in two ways. First they added hydroxylamine acetate to a partially purified luciferin solution and obtained a microcrystalline precipitate, a result that is in keeping with the presence of a ketone group. Mason (1952a) could not confirm this result. Secondly, they carried out a procedure with "irreversibly oxidized" luciferin that should resynthesize a ketohydroxy side group, by

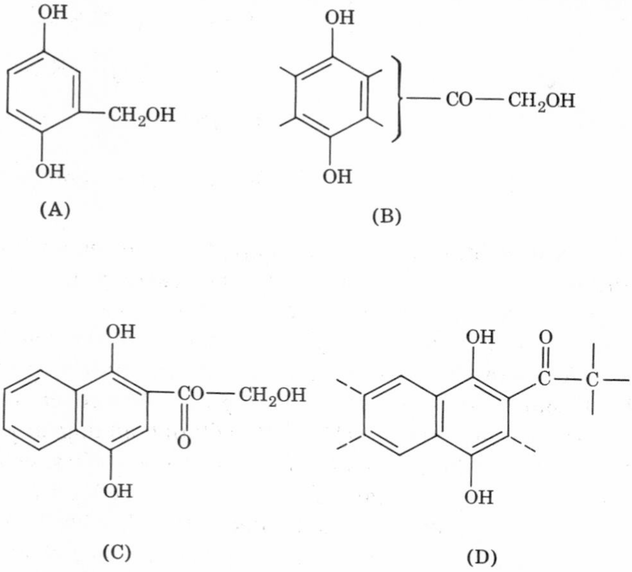

Fig. 7.2. Evolution of a hypothetical structure of *Cypridina* luciferin. (A) Model suggested by Johnson (1939, unpublished) to account for the readily reversible, dark oxidation by ferricyanide, etc., with an apparent redox potential close to that of the quinone-hydroquinone system, and for the not readily reversible, light-emitting oxidation with luciferase (oxidation of the alcohol side group to an acid). (B) Partial structure independently proposed by Chakravorty and Ballentine (1941), based on qualitative results obtained in a chemical procedure for resynthesis of a ketohydroxy group, hypothetically present on luciferin before degredation presumably to a carboxyl group during luminescent oxidation. (C) Structure deduced by Kluyver, van der Kerk, and van der Burg (1942), in accordance with the results of Chakravorty and Ballentine, and supported by the action specturm of extinction of bacterial luminescence by radiation with strong visible and ultraviolet light. (D) Partial structure proposed by Spruit (1949) after further studies of substituted naphthohydroquinones.

treating the spent product of the luminescent oxidation with sulfuroxychloride, followed by diazomethane and hydrolysis with sulfuric acid. The product, according to qualitative tests, gave rise to a bright flash of luminescence when mixed with luciferase, whereas a corresponding specimen that had not been carried through the same procedure gave only a weak flash.   The presumed reactions may be represented essentially as follows:

(1) $R—CO—CH_2OH \xrightarrow[\text{oxygen}]{\text{luciferase}} R—COOH$ + luminescence

(2) $R—COOH + SOCl_2 \longrightarrow R—COCl + SO_2HCl$

(3) $R—COCl + CH_2N_2 \longrightarrow R—COCHN_2 + HCl$

(4) $R—COCHN_2 + H_2SO_4 \longrightarrow R—COCH_2OH + N_2$

(5) $R—CO—CH_2OH \xrightarrow[\text{oxygen}]{\text{luciferase}} R—COOH$ + luminescence

There seems to be little reason to doubt that, given the postulated product of the luminescent oxidation in (1), the reactions (2), (3), and (4) would result in restoring the ketohydroxy group in place of the carboxyl. It does not follow, however, that either of these groups belongs to the luciferin molecule, inasmuch as the luciferin preparation used at the start was probably not better than 50 per cent pure.   Moreover, it has been shown (Johnson and Eyring, 1944) that, without adding any luciferin, luminescence may be obtained from old solutions of luciferase which had been subjected to prolonged dialysis and stored in a refrigerator for some two years, if such solutions were first treated with either $Na_2S_2O_4$, reduced coenzyme I, reduced riboflavin, hydrogen and platinized asbestos, or glucose and washed cells of bacteria, and then aerated with oxygen.   It seems possible, therefore, that reactions (2), (3), and (4) above may merely have provided a suitable reducing compound for reducing some reversibly oxidized luciferin to a form that would react with luciferase and oxygen to produce more light than a control not so treated.   Further purification of the luciferin would be necessary to prove that some compound such as pyruvic acid, $CH_3COCOOH$, was not decarboxylated during the luminescent reaction to CH_3COOH, and then synthesized to CH_3COCH_2OH, which then acted as a hydrogen donor to the luciferin or luciferin-luciferase complex as in the experiment with old, dialyzed luciferase.   This possibility is made more plausible by the facts that pyruvic acid is a common intermediate in oxidative metabolism and neither the substrate nor enzyme preparations used in the luminescent reaction were anything like pure.   Furthermore, if this acid is present in such extracts in the form of phosphopyruvic acid, it is reasonable to expect that inorganic phosphate might be liberated, through the action of one of the catalysts in the probably mixed-enzyme preparation containing luciferase, simultaneously with the luminescent reaction.   The liberation of phosphate has been reported by McElroy and Ballentine (1944), who regarded it as evidence that luciferin contains "energy-rich" phosphate as a source of energy for light emission.

The above considerations show that the observations described are open to more than one reasonable interpretation. The significance of Chakravorty and Ballentine's experiments (1941), as well as McElroy and Ballentine's experiments (1944), becomes less clear in view of more recent analyses of highly purified luciferin preparations which have revealed the presence of a considerable proportion of nitrogen and the absence of phosphorus (Chase and Gregg, 1949; Mason, 1952a).

From a different line of investigation, evidence has been obtained that is at least consistent with the hypothesis of a naphthoquinone structure in luciferin. In a study of the extinction spectrum of bacterial luminescence, under the influence of strong radiation in the visible and ultraviolet, Kluyver and associates (Kluyver et al., 1942; van der Kerk, 1942) found some important similarities to the absorption spectrum of derivatives of 1,4-naphthoquinone. On the basis of their results and of other data, they suggested that luciferin (presumably of both bacteria and *Cypridina*) is closely related to and perhaps identical with 1,4-dihydroxy-2-naphthylhydroxymethylketone (Fig. 7.2C). Later, Spruit (1946, 1947, 1948, 1949) synthesized and measured the absorption spectra of a number of hydro-, benzo-, naphtho-, and anthraquinone derivatives, including the compound diagramed in Fig. 7.2C. The absorption spectrum of this particular compound (Fig. 7.3, curve I) closely resembles the extinction spectrum of bacterial luminescence after the latter spectrum has been corrected for the absorption of incident radiation by inert constituents of bacterial protoplasm (Fig. 7.3, II; Spruit, 1946, 1949). The same compound (Fig. 7.2C) was independently synthesized by Rexford, and was tested for luminescence in the presence of *Cypridina* luciferase with negative results (Johnson, Rexford, and Harvey, 1949). Spruit (1949) also obtained negative results in a corresponding test and found that this compound, in common with other naphthoquinone derivatives (vide infra) exerted an inhibitory effect on bacterial luminescence. Thus it is clear that the compound in question (Fig. 7.2C) is not identical with *Cypridina* luciferin, although the two could still be closely related, inasmuch as the meticulous specificity of certain oxidative enzymes could easily account for a failure of the enzyme to catalyze the oxidation of molecules differing only slightly from the natural substrate. Spruit (1949) has suggested the partial structure shown in Fig. 7.2D, for bacterial luciferin and for the substance responsible for the photochemical inactivation of bacterial luminescence.

If bacterial luciferin is closely related in structure to the compounds suggested (Fig. 7.2, C or D), but not identical with them, a competitive

inhibition might be expected to occur when compounds of this type are
added to a suspension of luminescing cells.   An inhibition by naphthoquinones does indeed take place (Spruit and Schuiling, 1945; McElroy
and Kipnis, 1947), but the amount of inhibition is related to the density
of the cell population, and appears to involve an essentially irreversible

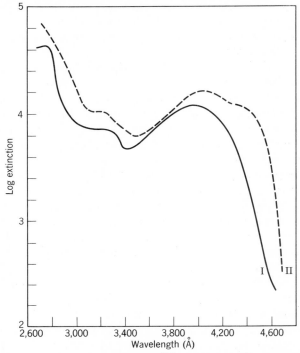

Fig. 7.3. I. Absorption spectrum of 1,4-dihydroxy-2-naphthylhydroxy-
methylketone (Fig. 72.C). II. Photochemical inactivation spectrum of
luminescence in *Photobacterium phosphoreum*, after corrections for the
absorption of incident radiation by inert constituents of the bacterial
protoplasm. This curve is shifted along the vertical axis to avoid intersection of the two curves (Spruit, 1949).

combination with cellular constituents.   Furthermore, the effects on
luminescence apparently do not result, in the manner anticipated, from a
competition between the naphthoquinone and luciferin for bacterial
luciferase, but rather from the action of the naphthoquinones as redox
systems which influence the state of oxidation of the luciferin.

Pursuing the idea (McElroy and Ballentine, 1944) that *Cypridina*
luciferin contains "energy-rich" phosphate groups, McElroy has carried
out numerous experiments with material from the light organ of fireflies

and has obtained crude and partially purified extracts which luminesce repeatedly on addition of adenosine triphosphate (ATP) (McElroy, 1947; McElroy and Strehler, 1949). This luminescence is dependent upon, or strongly favored by, the presence of certain divalent cations, including Mg^{2+}, Co^{2+}, and Mn^{2+}, which also increase the activity of certain adenosine triphosphatase enzyme preparations. Some of the partially purified extracts luminesce on addition of adenosine diphosphate (ADP) (McElroy, 1951). Extracts from different species of American and Jamaican fireflies differ in their response to the addition of ATP. In some instances, ATP plus firefly "luciferin" must be added in order to elicit luminescence, while in at least one instance the addition of neither of these preparations alone, nor of the two together, is sufficient (McElroy and Harvey, 1951). Cold water extracts of *Cypridina* and some other luminescent organisms do not luminesce on addition of ATP (Harvey and Haneda, 1952).

Although the amount of light emitted on addition of ATP to the appropriate firefly extracts is quantitatively related to the amount of ATP added, it has not been possible to demonstrate by ordinary methods any decrease in labile phosphate when 1 cc of 0.0015 M ATP solution is added to a 9-cc reaction mixture of a considerably purified luminescent system of the firefly *Photinus pyralis* (McElroy, 1951). In this case light emission results when the ATP is added, and after it has subsided, with the ATP still present, it will result again on a second addition of ATP. Moreover, after the first addition of ATP, luminescence occurs a second time if any one of a number of different inorganic or organic compounds is added. The interpretation of the effects of ATP in bringing about luminescence of firefly extracts remains to be clarified.

A second hypothesis concerning the nature of luciferin is that it is a flavin, or is closely associated with a flavin compound. Eymers and van Schouwenburg (1937b) noted certain similarities in the bioluminescence of several species of bacteria, in *Cypridina* extracts, and in the fluorescence of lactoflavin. In subsequent studies (van der Burg, 1943; Spruit-van der Burg, 1950) it has been shown that the density of the bacterial cell suspension influences the spectral characteristics of the luminescence, i.e., beyond a certain maximum density the emitted light appears to be shifted toward the red, and the precise significance of the earlier observations is uncertain. Other facts, however, such as the following, suggest a relationship between luminescence and flavin, or flavin-like substances.

Addition of lactoflavin to dark variants of luminous bacteria appears to favor a recovery of luminescence (Doudoroff, 1938). The light organs of fireflies have been shown to be comparatively rich in flavin (Brooks, 1940; Ball and Ramsdell, 1944), and likewise a species of luminous bacteria (*Photobacterium phosphoreum*; Rottier, 1942). A marked yellow color is associated with the light organs of numerous luminescent animals (Harvey, 1940), but, while this could be due to the presence of flavoprotein, other substances, including derivatives of naphthoquinones, could be responsible for the color. In experiments already referred to (p. 132) Johnson and Eyring (1944) obtained luminescence from long-dialyzed, old preparations of luciferase, after adding reduced coenzyme I, reduced riboflavin, or certain other reducing agents, followed by aeration with air or oxygen. Presumably, small amounts of luciferin remained in this enzyme preparation in a reversibly oxidized state. Almost incredibly small amounts, in fact, are needed for visible luminescence; Harvey (1923) has estimated the minimal amount as of the order of 1 part of luciferin in 40,000,000,000 of water. By way of comparison, it is interesting to note that, among the known chemiluminescent substances, dimethyl-diacridinium nitrate has been observed to luminesce visibly when diluted to 1 part in 20,000,000,000 (Gleu and Petsch, 1935). This substance has a molecular weight of about 500, which is not very different from the probable molecular weight of *Cypridina* luciferin.

Data on the absorption spectrum of partially purified luciferin, which are discussed in the following paragraph, indicate some similarities to coenzyme-riboflavin systems, although the changes in absorption accompanying oxidation and reduction do not entirely conform. Thus, both reduced luciferin (Chase, 1943, 1945) and codehydrogenase (Warburg and Christian, 1936) absorb at 320 mμ (millimicrons), and this absorption decreases on oxidation; reduced luciferin absorbs at 435 mμ, whereas oxidized riboflavin absorbs at 445 mμ, these peaks disappearing as the luciferin is oxidized and the riboflavin is reduced, respectively; and both oxidized luciferin and flavin-adenine dinucleotide as well as the "old yellow enzyme" have absorption maxima at 465 mμ. Unlike the free flavins, luciferin does not ordinarily exhibit fluorescence, although a moderately strong, greenish yellow fluorescence of highly purified *Cypridina* luciferin in concentrated ammonium hydroxide has been observed (Mason and Davis, 1952). The fact that luciferin gives rise to chemiluminescence shows that it is transformed into a fluorescent substance. Moreover, the fluorescence of molecules may be eliminated through various mechanisms; for example, the fluorescence of riboflavin is abolished by substituents on the 3-imino group (Kuhn and Rudy, 1936). It disappears also in the presence of certain purines which form a complex with it (Weber, 1950) and which at the same time cause the absorption spectrum to resemble that of the flavin-adenine dinucleotide. There are certain structural points in common between the flavin compounds, which are of virtually universal occurrence in living cells, and the synthetic cyclophthalhydrazides (cf. Fig. 7.7, p. 142), which exhibit brilliant luminescence on oxidation by various agents in solution at room temperature (Albrecht, 1928; Tamamushi and Akiyama, 1938; Drew, 1939; van der Burg, 1943).

The significance of hydrogen peroxide in known chemiluminescent reactions (pp. 159–160; 165–169), and the fact that the aerobic oxidation of certain natural substrates in cellular metabolism is catalyzed by coenzyme-flavoprotein systems with the production of hydrogen peroxide (cf. Baldwin, 1948), suggest that the function of bioluminescence may be closely associated with such systems.

The most recent studies of highly purified concentrates of *Cypridina* luciferin indicate that the α- and β-forms are composed, in part at least, of amino acids (Mason, 1952b). The infrared absorption of α-luciferin is strong at 3,250, 2,825, 1,680, 1,625, and 1,510 cm^{-1}, corresponding to amide bonds as in peptides or in cyclic ureides. β-Luciferin does not give a ninhydrin test for free amino groups, but on hydrolysis in 4 N acid in the absence of molecular oxygen there are released ninhydrin positive substances which have been tentatively identified, by two-dimensional paper chromatography, as glycine, threonine, proline, lysine, aspartic acid, glutamic acid, leucine, isoleucine, or phenylalanine. The hydrolyzate also contains an unidentified ninhydrin positive substance and a yellow pigment readily separated from the amino acid fraction. Luminescent activity is identified in chromatograms with the active, yellow polypeptide. These observations suggest that *Cypridina* luciferin is related to the class of pigmented polypeptides produced by actinomycetes (Waksman and Tishler, 1942; Lehr and Berger, 1949).

Absorption and emission spectra of *Cypridina* extracts

Although the absorption and emission spectra of the partially purified extracts of *Cypridina* luciferin have not provided conclusive evidence about the structure of the molecule, they have indicated certain significant changes that take place on oxidation, and they furnish a means of specifying, with some assurance, which molecule, i.e., enzyme or substrate, it is that emits. Reduced luciferin can be identified with a substance that has an absorption maximum at 435 mμ in the visible (Chase, 1943, 1945; Chase and Brigham, 1951). On addition of oxygen, this peak shifts rapidly to one at 465 mμ and then gradually disappears, leaving a practically colorless solution (Fig. 7.4A). Under these conditions, i.e., auto-oxidation, no visible luminescence is produced. If luciferase as well as oxygen is added to the reduced luciferin, light emission occurs and the same changes take place in the absorption spectrum of the mixture, but at a rate some 100 times faster than without the enzyme (Fig. 7.4B). The concentrations of luciferin, as judged by the total amount of light emitted, correspond to the labile color of the solutions used in these experiments, making it highly likely that it is indeed the luciferin whose absorption is recorded. Moreover, the correspondence between the

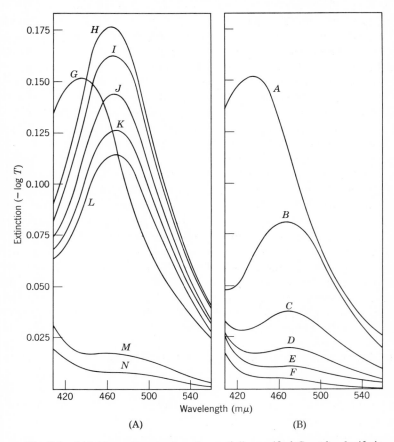

Fig. 7.4. (A) Absorption spectra of a partially, purified *Cypridina* luciferin solution; G, immediately after exposure to air and H, I, J, K, L, M, N, after 9, 20, 30, 39, 49, 455, and 1,140 min, respectively. (B) Absorption spectra of a luciferin solution to which luciferase has been added and the luminescent reaction is taking place; A, immediately after dissolving the luciferin; B, 1 min after adding luciferase; and C, D, E, F, after 12, 22, 40, and 457 min, respectively (Chase, 1943).

maximum absorption at 465 mμ, and the maximum emission at 475 or 480 mμ (Coblentz and Hughes, 1926; Eymers and van Schouwenburg, 1937b) indicate that luciferin is the molecule that emits.

The spectrographic data indicate that the same changes take place during the dark auto-oxidation and during the light-emitting reaction catalyzed by luciferase. Luminescence occurs with the enzyme, not necessarily because different hydrogens are removed, but because the reaction proceeds by a different mechanism. Whether or not these oxidations remove the same hydrogens as in the ferricyanide oxidation is not yet established, inasmuch as spectral changes in the presence of ferricyanide have not been studied. The reaction of oxygen with hydroquinone to give quinone and water provides insufficient energy for radiation at the wavelengths observed. Emission at 475 mμ requires 60,700 cal. This amount of energy could be furnished by the oxidation of a keto-hydroxy to a carboxyl group, in accordance with the hypothetical molecules shown in Fig. 7.2, although it is not essential, in such event, that the group whose oxidation furnishes the energy be a part of the luciferin molecule itself. The destruction of luciferin, as judged by the disappearance of color in the presence of oxygen, could scarcely be due to degradation of this side group, which does not itself absorb in the visible but probably involves the breakdown of a ring structure.

Light-emitting molecules

Although in no case has the structure been established for the molecules directly responsible for bioluminescence, there are numerous examples both of naturally occurring and of synthetic substances which exhibit chemiluminescence during oxidation under appropriate conditions. These same substances, e.g., the cyclophthalhydrazides, are generally also fluorescent. The energy for fluorescent and chemiluminescent radiation, respectively, is supplied in a different manner, but the electronic mechanism of light emission is fundamentally the same. Before discussing the mechanism, it is profitable to consider briefly some of the structural aspects of known molecules which emit cold light, with particular reference to points of possible significance in bioluminescence.

Among the myriad types of luminous organisms, the color of light that is characteristic of the different light organs or tissues extends from a clear blue to a pronounced red. The latter color is unusual, for, in most cases, the luminescence is blue, blue-green, or yellowish. In the "railroad worm" the single red light at the front of the animal is a true luminescence, since it has been shown (Harvey, 1944) that this radiation in the longer wavelengths does not result from the possible alternative mechanism of absorption of shorter wavelengths, more commonly encountered, by a color-filtering substance or one that fluoresces in the red. Thus it is obvious that different molecules are responsible for light emission among some of the different organisms. On the other hand, since the essential molecules responsible for a given phenomenon in the living world are often related and sometimes identical (e.g., among the coenzymes of oxidative systems in different organisms), one would not expect nature to be so extravagant as to use totally different types of light-emitting molecules for luminescence in various organisms. It is logical to seek a fundamental unit that could provide the basis of bioluminescence in general, and which by minor modifications of substituents would give rise to light whose maximum intensity would occur in different regions of the visible spectrum in accordance with the nature of the substituents. Analogous "variations on a theme" are especially abundant among plant products, including alkaloids, pigments, and other types of compounds.

Table 7.1. Influence of Substituents in the Benzene Ring of Phthalic Hydrazide on the Wavelength (λ_{max}) of Maximum Chemiluminescent Intensity, Relative Intensity of Emitted Light (van der Burg, 1943), and Apparent Color (Drew and Pearman, 1937)

Derivative	Substituent	λ_{max}	Apparent Color of Light	Relative Intensity of Chemi-luminescence	Relative Intensity of Fluorescence in:	
					Acid Solution	Alkaline Solution
3-Amino	NH_2	4,240	Blue	100.0	100.0	0.3
3-Methylamino	CH_3NH	4,510	Greenish blue	60.0	100.0	00.0
3-Hydroxy	OH	4,160	Bluish violet	20.0	20.0	0.2
4-Amino	NH	4,175	Blue	4.0	20.0	0.3
3-Acetylcarbamino	$CH_3CONHCONH$	4,625		2.0	1.0	0.6
3-Brom	Br	4,170		1.0	20.0	0.1
3-Acetamido	CH_3CONH	4,240	Greenish blue	1.0		
Pyromellitic acid		5,400	Yellow	0.2		
Na 3-hydrazino-β-sulfonate	$NaSO_3NHNH$	4,240	Whitish blue	0.2	0.2	
Unsubstituted	None	4,125	Whitish blue	0.02		0.2
3-Nitro	NO_3	4,020	Whitish yellow	0.01	0.2	

Among the molecules of known structure, the cyclophthalhydrazides furnish very tempting models, in spite of the fact that, as far as we know, they do not include naturally occurring compounds. Among the characteristics which they share with bioluminescence are the following. First, of course, is the fact that they are easily oxidized in aqueous solution at physiological temperatures with the production of vivid luminescence. Moreover, various substituents influence the color as well as the intensity of the emitted light (Table 7.1) and the spectral distribution of the light from different derivatives resembles the spectral distribution of bioluminescence among different organisms (Figs. 7.5 and 7.6). As in bioluminescence, the production of light accompanies an oxidation, usually in the presence of molecular oxygen or hydrogen peroxide and a suitable catalyst. Although inorganic catalysts such as potassium ferricyanide will do, organic catalysts such as hemoglobin or vegetable peroxidases, which aid the decomposition of peroxides, will also function. Depending upon the conditions, the luminescent oxidation may or may

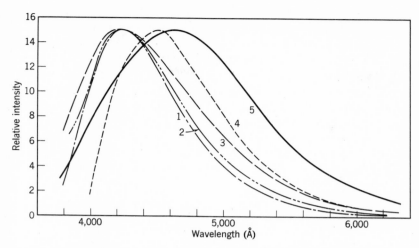

Fig. 7.5. Chemiluminescent spectra of phthalhydrazide derivatives (van der Burg, 1943): 1, 3-aminophthalhydrazide; 2, sodium 3-hydrazinosulfonate-phthalhydrazide; 3, 3-Acetamidophthalhydrazide; 4, 3-methylaminophthal-hydrazide; 5, 3-acetylcarbamidophthalhydrazide.

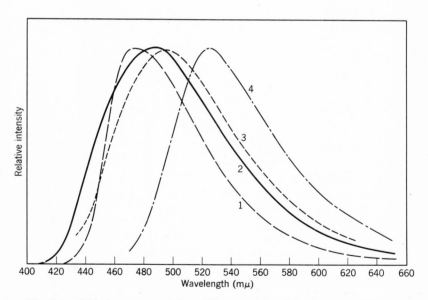

Fig. 7.6. Emission spectra of three different species of luminous bacteria and a luminescent fungus (Spruit-van der Burg, 1950): 1, *Photobacterium phosphoreum;* 2, *P. splendidum;* 3, *P. fischeri (Achromobacter fischeri);* 4, *Armillaria mellea.*

not involve the destruction of considerable amounts of the hydrazide (Drew, 1939). Finally, the basic structure of the molecule resembles, in certain respects, that of naturally occurring flavin compounds (Fig. 7.7).

Because of its virtually universal significance in the oxidative metabolism of living cells, riboflavin (A) is the most generally familiar of the substances

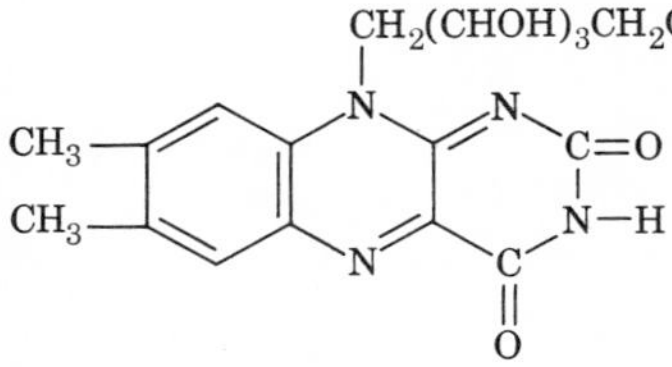

(A) Riboflavin (vitamin B$_2$) 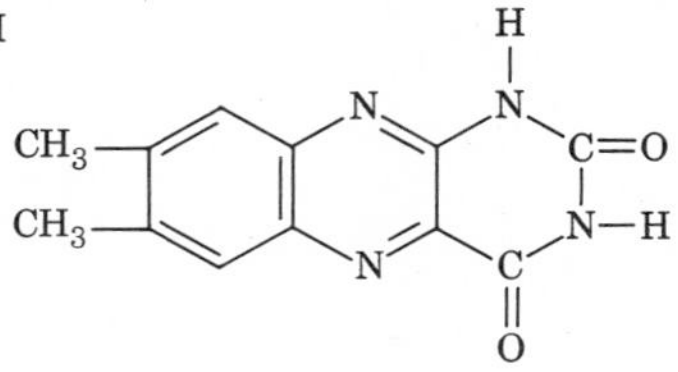　　　　　　(B) Lumichrome

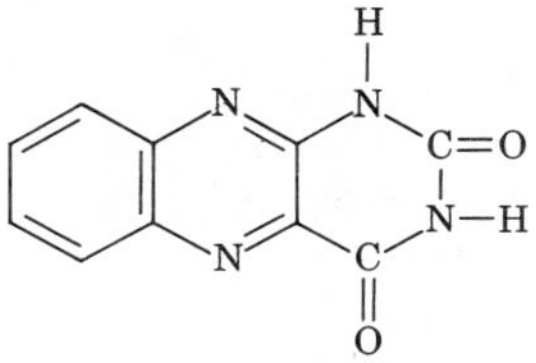

(C) Alloxazine 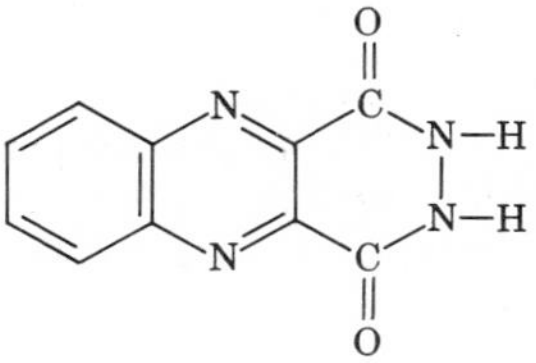　　　　　　(D) Quinoxalinic hydrazide

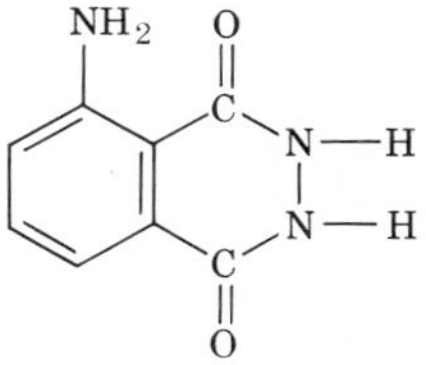

(E) 3-Aminophthalhydrazide 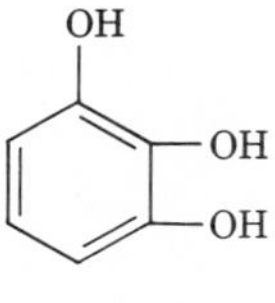　　　　　　(F) Pyrogallol

Fig. 7.7. Some light-emitting molecules. *A, B, C, D,* and *E* are strongly fluorescent in acid solution; *D, E,* and *F* may be oxidized with chemiluminescence.

shown in Fig. 7.7. By irradiation in alkaline solution, it is converted to lumichrome (B), which differs from the synthetic compound alloxazine (C) only by the presence of the methyl substituents in the 6,7 positions. Compound (C) was known to the organic chemistry field long before any relationship to vitamin B$_2$ was suspected. None of these three compounds has been shown to oxidize with chemiluminescence, although there is no obvious reason why they should not, inasmuch as they fluoresce in the visible region of the spectrum. Of the remaining three compounds, quinoxalinic hydrazide (D) most nearly resembles alloxazine, differing only in that the nitrogens in the first ring are adjacent to each other, rather than alternating with the carbons. It has been found to exhibit chemiluminescence, by Wegler (1937) and W. S. Johnson (1937; cf. Drew, 1939). The most brilliantly chemiluminescent compound among the three is 3-aminophthalhydrazide (E), commonly known as "luminol." The 3-amino group is not essential for chemiluminescence, but the unsubstituted compound, under similar conditions of oxidation, gives rise to light only 1/5,000 as bright as the 3-amino compound, and the light from the 3-nitro compound is even less intense, amounting to only 1/10,000 that of the 3-amino compound.

Pyrogallol (F) is the simplest of the chemiluminescent substances shown in Fig. 7.7, and it is of interest that its aerobic oxidation is catalyzed, though without visible light production, by naturally occurring enzymes, e.g., tyrosinase (Raper, 1932) or laccase (Yakushiji, 1940). Unlike the other compounds, pyrogallol has no nitrogens in the ring, although it does have conjugate double bonds. It is unlike the other compounds in the additional respect that it does not fluoresce in the visible. Many substances of even simpler structure, also showing no fluorescence in the visible, have been found to luminesce under appropriate conditions, e.g., formaldehyde, methyl or higher alcohols, and sodium acetate (Trautz, 1905). We cannot account for the luminescence of these simpler substances without assuming that they are first converted, under the conditions required for luminescence, to quite different compounds, and that it is the latter which are responsible for light emission. Because of the lack of information in this regard, it is not profitable to discuss here the possible mechanisms involved in their luminescence.

There is sufficient evidence, however, to arrive at a theoretically plausible mechanism, whether it is fully correct or not, with reference to the cyclophthalhydrazides, pyrogallol, and related compounds containing benzene or other ring structures. In doing so, it is necessary to take into account (1) the established facts and theory of absorption and emission of light by molecules in general as well as by chemiluminescent compounds in particular, (2) the conditions of oxidation which give rise to chemiluminescence, and (3) the energy relationships of the transitions. As in all other reactions, potential energy diagrams constitute the fundamental basis for understanding the mechanisms.

Light absorption and emission

In the simplest example, that of a monatomic substance or single ion, absorption and emission take place at the same frequencies. Absorption

of the energy of a given frequency raises an electron to a higher energy
level, and radiation occurs when this energy is released with the return of
the electron to its former level.   Quenching may occur if the excited atom
or ion collides with another one and the energy is dissipated in vibration.

With a di- or polyatomic molecule, the absorption spectrum depends
upon possible stable electronic configurations of the molecule and upon
the relation of the potential energy surfaces of the excited to the normal

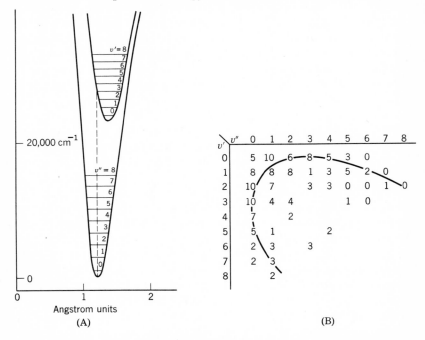

Fig. 7.8.   Potential energy curves (A) and distribution of intensities (B) for the
alpha-bands of BO (Gaydon, 1950).

state.   In general, some of the energy of excitation will be dissipated in
vibration, with the result that fluorescence will occur at longer wavelengths
than the absorption.   Let us consider a specific example: that of boron
oxide (Gaydon, 1950).   Figure 7.8A shows potential energy curves for the
normal and excited states of the alpha system.   Diagram 7.8B gives the
estimated intensity of emission (Mulliken, 1925) for the various transitions
$v' \rightarrow v''$ plotted on the sides of the diagram.

By the Franck-Condon principle the transitions from one surface to the
other may be represented by vertical lines drawn from the end of a given
level to the point where the line intersects the other surface.   The reasons

underlying this principle are essentially two: first, the electronic transitions, because of the small electronic mass, take place within an interval of time (ca. 10^{-15} sec) short in comparison to the change in distance apart of the nuclei of the atoms, vibrating at a frequency of about 10^{13} per sec at room temperature, and, second, the vibration of the molecule at a given level is very similar to a simple harmonic motion, with the result that the molecule spends most of the time at the limits of the level and the transition will therefore be most likely to occur from these points.

Although the data given in Fig. 7.8B were obtained (Mulliken, 1925) by a visual estimation of the relative intensities of the emission lines on a photographic plate, it is instructive to see how these data can be used to construct the intensity curves for absorption as well as for emission.

The intensity $I(v', v'')$ of an emission line satisfies the equation

$$I(v', v'') = bN_{v'}k(v', v'') \tag{7.1}$$

where $N_{v'}$ is the population of molecules in the state v'; $k(v', v'')$ is the frequency of transition from v' to v''; and b is a proportionality constant. The population of molecules in the state v' is

$$N_{v'} = N_0' \exp\left(-v'hv'/kT'\right) \tag{7.2}$$

where N_0' is the population of the state, $v' = 0$. The characteristic frequency of the excited state is v'. The intensity of an absorption line is, similarly,

$$I(v'', v') = b''N_{v''}k(v', v'') \tag{7.3}$$

in which all the terms are analogous to those in equation (7.2). Dividing equation (7.3) by (7.1) and using (7.2),

$$\begin{aligned} I(v'', v') &= b''N_{v''}/b'N_{v'}I(v', v'') \\ &= bI(v', v'') \exp\left(-v''hv''/kT'' + v'hv'/kT'\right) \end{aligned} \tag{7.4}$$

Since we are undertaking to calculate only the relative intensities, b can be tentatively chosen equal to unity. We have then

$$I(v'', v') = I(v', v'') \exp\left[-hv''/kT''(v'' - gv')\right] \tag{7.5}$$

where
$$g = (hv'/kT')(kT''/hv'') \tag{7.6}$$

Thus each entry in Fig. 7.8B gives a value for $I(v', v'')$ for emission, and by means of equation (7.5) we can get the corresponding entries $I(v'', v')$ for an absorption table, from which an absorption curve, in relative units, may be plotted. The curve may be expressed in absolute units by multiplying by the appropriate value of b.

The same data (Fig. 7.8) provides the basis for estimating the effective temperature of the emitting BO molecules. Assuming that the sum of the line intensities, S_i, from a particular level $v' = i$, is proportional to the population N_i in the v' level, we have

$$\frac{S_i}{S_j} = \frac{N_i}{N_j} = e^{-(E_i - E_j)/kT} \tag{7.7}$$

From Fig. 7.8, we find that $S_0 = 37$, $S_1 = 36$, and $S_2 = 29$. Mulliken (1925) gives for the energy difference between the states $v' = 0$ and $v = 1$ the value 1,261 cm^{-1}, and between $v' = 0$ and $v' = 2$ the energy 2,499 cm^{-1}. If we use the values for $v' = 0$ and 1 in equation (7.7), we get an impossibly high value for the effective temperature T. The values for $v' = 0$ and 2 give $T = 8,900°C$, which still seems much too high. Although the inaccuracy of the data associated with the visual estimation of line intensities is relatively small, there is a serious source of error in the fact that only the transitions corresponding to band heads have been included in Fig. 7.8B. This leads to error because the sum of the transition probabilities of a system from a single upper state to all possible lower states is a number that is nearly independent of the upper state chosen. No such sum rule applies, however, if only a part, instead of all, of the receiving states is included.

From the above it is evident that the detailed procedure of predicting the absorption spectra of molecules is possible in principle but is rarely feasible. Equation (7.4), however, shows us that at ordinary temperatures, e.g., with molecules which absorb and fluoresce in solution, the effect of the Boltzmann factor in weighting the molecular population will insure that the maximum in the absorption curve will correspond closely to the energy E_a in Fig. 7.10, while in emission the maximum will fall at the longer wavelength corresponding to energy E_b. Consequently, a molecule absorbing in the near ultraviolet may fluoresce in the visible, as is frequently observed. Moreover, the fluorescence curve will be very nearly the mirror image of the absorption curve taken by reflection about the ordinate lying midway between the two maxima. This relationship, for which the foregoing discussion provides the theoretical basis, is illustrated by the data of van der Burg (1943) for the absorption and fluorescence of luminol (Fig. 7.9).

The intensity of fluorescence is determined by the frequency of electronic transitions from the upper to the lower potential surface. Any dipole transition frequency has the value (Eyring, Walter, and Kimball, 1944, p. 115)

$$A_{m \to n} = \frac{32\pi^3 \nu_{mn}{}^3}{3c^3\hbar} |R_{mn}|^2 \tag{7.8}$$

where $\qquad\qquad R_{mn} = \int \psi^*{}_m \Sigma e_i \mathbf{r}_i\, \psi_n\, d\tau \tag{7.9}$

The quantities ν_{mn}, c, and $\hbar$ signify the emitted frequency, velocity of light, and Planck's constant divided by 2π, respectively. R_{mn} is called the matrix component of the electric moment between the initial and final states. It is usually some fraction of the charge on the electron multiplied by a distance of the order of 10^{-8} cm. Taking $\nu_{mn}/c = 23,600$ cm^{-1} (the value for the $v' = 0$ to $v'' = 0$ transition for the alpha-band of BO) and $R_{mn} = 4.8 \times 10^{-1}$ in equation (7.8) gives $A = 0.97 \times 10^8$. This rate of emission of about 10^8 per sec, however, is in competition with the various quenching mechanisms. On the other hand, it may be increased or

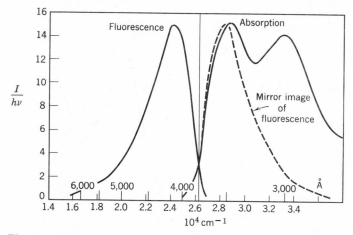

Fig. 7.9. Relation between the spectral distribution for absorption and fluorescence of luminol (3-aminophthalhydrazide) in 0.01 N potassium hydroxide (van der Burg, 1943).

decreased by certain factors, such as an appropriate substituent in the molecule, which tend to change the electric dipole moment matrix component. If the initial and final states of an electronic transition correspond to a different type of spin coupling of the electrons (i.e., transition between a triplet and singlet state), R_{mn} may become exceedingly small but not zero. Such forbidden triplet-singlet transitions have been studied by Lewis and Kasha (1944) and others for substituted ethylene and related molecules. The color of light emitted is very near that of the substituted phthalhydrazides under discussion here. The fact that triplet oxygen is formed from singlet peroxide in the processes under discussion suggests that the catalytic phthalhydrazide may be left in an excited triplet state by the departing triplet oxygen.

The general mechanisms of fluorescence and of quenching are illustrated by the simplified diagrams of Fig. 7.10, indicating three mechanisms for

the disappearance of excited molecules: (1) by radiation, with rate
constant k_b, (2) by internal quenching with rate constant k_c, and (3) by
external quenching, which may involve collision with any of a variety of
molecules, M_α, with rate constants that may be collectively designated
by k_α.

Referring to Fig. 7.10, excitation as a result of radiation occurs by
passage of the system from region A to region B, and fluorescence by
passage from B to A, as indicated by the vertical lines.   From region B

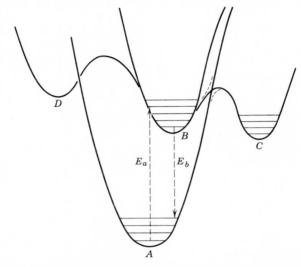

Fig. 7.10.   Diagram to illustrate the mechanisms of excitation, fluorescence,
and quenching.   The various curves represent simplified cross sections of
different potential energy surfaces which are usually not in the same plane.
Absoption, a; emission, b.

the molecule may go over to another stable configuration represented by
C (not ordinarily in the same plane) from which it may later return to B
and radiate by dropping to C, thus giving rise to phosphorescence.   On
the other hand, it may cross in the region of the dotted lines from either
B or C to A and lose its excitation energy in vibration, without radiating,
i.e., by internal quenching.   This is the usual mechanism involved when
molecules, such as pigments in general, absorb but do not radiate.   Finally,
the excited molecule may collide with some other molecule, in a rate
process involving an activation energy, and attain a different stable
configuration, without radiation, on still another surface which for simplicity may be again represented by C.   This is the process of external
quenching.

The net rate of formation of excited molecules, with concentration N^*, equals the rate of formation minus the rates of disappearance of the excited molecules. Thus

$$\frac{dN^*}{dt} = k_a N - k_b N^* - k_c N^* - \sum_\alpha (k_\alpha M_\alpha) N^* \qquad (7.10)$$

In this equation $k_a N$ equals the rate of excitation of molecules, $k_b N^*$ is their rate of emitting light, and $k_c N^*$ gives the rate of internal quenching. It will be recalled that M_α represents either a molecule of the same type as the excited molecule or a different species, and the term $k_\alpha M_\alpha N^*$ gives the rate of quenching due to molecules of type α. For simplicity, we omit, in the general formulation, the possibility that more than one molecule of M combines with N^*.

In the steady state $dN^*/dt = 0$, which then gives

$$N^* = \frac{k_a N}{k_b + k_c + \sum_\alpha k_\alpha M_\alpha} \qquad (7.11)$$

Since the intensity of emission, I_{em}, is equal to the rate at which N^* molecules disappear with radiation, it follows (introducing a proportionality constant b to allow for different units of measurement) that

$$I_{em} = b k_b N^* = b(k_a N) \left\{ \frac{k_b}{k_b + k_c + \sum_\alpha k_\alpha M_\alpha} \right\} \qquad (7.12)$$

The braces in (7.12) give the fraction f of the molecules which are excited and which then emit. This efficiency factor f may also be written

$$f = \left(\frac{k_b}{k_b + k_c + k_1 M_1 + k_2 M_2} \right) \frac{1}{1 + \sum\limits_{\alpha=2}^{r} \dfrac{k_\alpha M_\alpha}{k_b + k_c + k_1 M_1 + k_2 M_2}}$$

$$\equiv \frac{K'}{1 + \sum\limits_{\alpha=2}^{r} k_\alpha' M_\alpha} \qquad (7.13)$$

where

$$K' = \frac{k_b}{k_b + k_c + k_1 M_1 + k_2 M_2} \quad \text{and} \quad k_\alpha' = \frac{k_\alpha}{k_b + k_c + k_1 M_1 + k_2 M_2}$$

Here $k_1 M_1$ represents the rate of self-quenching of an excited molecule, and $k_2 M_2$ represents the rate of quenching by the solvent. The subscripts 2 to r represent the other quenching species. The emission efficiency in the absence of species 2 to r is K', and approximately 20 per cent is not an unusual value for this efficiency. For fluorescence the rate of excitation of molecules is given by $k_aN = (I\alpha)N$, where I is the intensity of the exciting radiation and α is the absorption coefficient in appropriate units.

In Fig. 7.10 region D (again in a different plane from that of A and B as well as C) is intended to represent the initial state of a reactant which crosses to an excited state B in a reaction such as oxidation, and gives rise to chemiluminescence or, in biological materials, to bioluminescence. We shall consider the electronic mechanisms presently. First it is necessary to discuss briefly some of the established facts concerning the reactions which lead to chemiluminescence, starting with known compounds.

Efficiency of fluorescence and chemiluminescence

Table 7.1 shows that among the various members of the substituted phthalhydrazides there is approximate parallelism between the intensity of fluorescence in acid solution and the intensity of chemiluminescence in alkaline solition. From equation (7.12) the efficiency factor (in braces) for light emission by excited molecules is the same for chemiluminescence and fluorescence. On the other hand, the specific rate k_a of excitation for fluorescence is proportional to the intensity of the incident radiation, and to the absorption coefficient, whereas for chemiluminescence k_a in equation (7.12) will have the usual form of a specific rate constant as given by equation (1.23), p. 19 (or equation 7.16 below). In excitation by radiation of a given density ρ, as in fluorescence (Eyring, Walter, and Kimball, 1944, p. 113),

$$k_a = \rho \frac{2\pi}{3\hbar^2} \left| \int \psi^*_m \Sigma e_j \mathbf{r}_j \psi_n \, d\tau \right|^2 \tag{7.14}$$

Although there is no reason to expect that k_a for chemiluminescence and for fluorescence will be parallel among different derivatives of the phthalhydrazides, the emission efficiency, as given by the expression in braces in equation (7.12), should be independent of the mechanism of excitation. The rate of disappearance of excited molecules by radiation, k_b, is given by

$$k_b = \frac{32\pi^3 \nu_{mn}^3}{3c^3\hbar} \left| \int \psi^*_m \Sigma e_j \mathbf{r}_j \psi_n \, d\tau \right|^2 \tag{7.15}$$

The rate constant of internal quenching, k_c, is of the form

$$k_c = \kappa \frac{kT}{h} e^{-\Delta F^{\ddagger}/RT} \tag{7.16}$$

where
$$\kappa = \frac{1 - \gamma}{1 - (\gamma/2)} \tag{7.17}$$

and
$$\gamma = e^{-4\pi^2 \epsilon_{12}^2 / hV|S_1 - S_i|} \tag{7.18}$$

It is apparent that equations (7.17) and (7.18) are concerned with the transmission coefficient κ, which, though ordinarily about equal to unity for most reactions, may change for reactions in which the proximity of two surfaces gives rise to a chance that the system will cross from the one

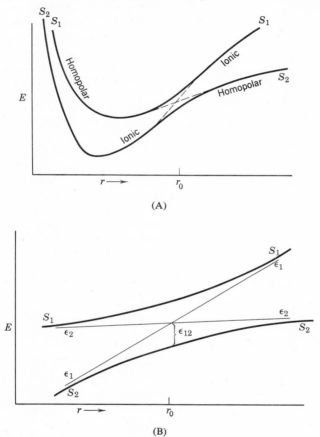

(A)

(B)

Fig. 7.11. (A) Diagram to illustrate the crossing of potential energy surfaces (Eyring, Walter, and Kimball, 1944, p. 327). (B) Energy relations at the point of "crossing."

surface to the other. The meaning of the terms in equation (7.18) is made clear from the diagram in Fig. 7.11A, in which the dotted lines between the surfaces correspond to those in Fig. 7.10.

Referring to equation (7.18) and Figs. 7.11A and 7.11B, γ is the chance that the system will follow the line from surface 1 across to surface 2, while $(1 - \gamma)$ is the chance that on the return vibration the system will stay on surface 2 and so pass by a radiationless transition to the lowest minimum. S_1 and S_2 are the energy gradients of the two dotted lines at the intersection, and ϵ_{12} is the perturbation energy indicated by the short line normal to surface 2, extending to the point of intersection. This perturbation energy is calculable from quantum mechanics. V is the velocity with which the system traverses the intersection and has the average value $V = (2kT/\pi\mu)^{1/2}$, where μ is the reduced mass for the reaction coordinate at the intersection. A numerical value for γ may be readily computed by taking the reasonable value of 100 kcal per Å per mole for $|S_1 - S_2|$, and taking $\mu = 2.4 \times 10^{-23}$ grams per molecule.

Table 7.2.   The Transition Probabilities for the $\lambda = 2,700$ Å
Band of Substituted Benzenes

Molecule	Theoretical f	Observed f
C_6H_5CH	0.0005	0.0013
$C_6H_5NH_2$	0.0140	0.0246
C_6H_5OH	0.0060	0.0197
C_6H_5F	0.0003	(0.0010)

This μ corresponds to the reduced mass of an oxygen molecule vibrating against 3-aminophthalhydrazide. If we take $\epsilon_{12} = 1$ kcal per mole as a reasonable value, with the calculated velocity at 300°K, $V = (2kT/\pi\mu)^{1/2}$ $= 3.3 \times 10^4$ cm per sec, we obtain $\gamma = 0.28$. If ϵ is doubled, then γ, instead of being approximately 1/4 is 1/256. Conversely, for $\epsilon = 0.5$ kcal, $\gamma = 0.707$. A useful approximate formula is

$$\gamma = (0.28)^{\epsilon^2} \approx (\tfrac{1}{4})^{\epsilon^2} \tag{7.19}$$

where ϵ is the interaction energy in kilocalories per mole.

The transition probabilities f for substituted benzenes are given in Table 7.2, from Mulliken and Rieke (1941). Aside from minor changes, Table 7.2 is originally due to Sklar (1939). The observed value of 0.0010 in parentheses for C_6H_5F is really the value for C_6H_5Cl. The summation of the f values from a particular state to all possible states adds up to the number of electrons in the molecule. Our k_b might be expected to be roughly proportional to f, even though we are concerned with a different molecule. There is a rough parallelism between the effect of substituents in Table 7.2 and their effect on chemiluminescence of the phthalhydrazides as given in Table 7.1. Because of quenching effects, the parallelism would be expected to be only rough.

Efficiency of bioluminescence *in vitro*

Because *Cypridina* luciferin has been shown to undergo a dark oxidation in absence of the enzyme (Anderson, 1936; cf. p. 128), it is to be expected that the efficiency of luminescence, in the presence of the enzyme, will be affected by the rate of the dark oxidation occurring simultaneously with the light-emitting reaction. The total amount of light produced with a given initial amount of luciferin will thus vary not only with factors that influence the proportion of molecules which, having already become excited, release their energy by radiation (expression in braces in equation 7.12) but also with factors which influence the proportion of molecules that attain the excited state in the oxidative reactions involved. In these circumstances the rate constant for excitation, k_a of equation (7.12), is obviously not a simple rate constant but embodies at least two rate

Table 7.3. Total Light Emitted by Corresponding Amounts of Partially Purified *Cypridina* Luciferin in the Presence of Different Salts at a Concentration of 0.0095 M Each

(From Anderson, 1937)

Salt	Total light (arbitrary units)	Salt	Total light (arbitrary units)
NaCl	2.3	$K_2C_2O_4$	1.2
KCl	2.2	K_2SO_4	1.1
NaBr	1.9	(No salt)	1.0
KBr	2.0	KCNS	0.12
KF	1.4	KI	0.08
KNO$_3$	1.3		

processes, which, following the notation employed by Chase and Lorenz (1945) in their study of temperature effects, we shall designate k_1 for the enzyme-catalyzed reaction leading to light emission, and k_2 for the dark, auto-oxidation. Letting a stand for the initial amount of luciferin, and b for a proportionality constant taking into account the units of measurement, equation (7.12) becomes

$$\text{Total light} = b(a)\left(\frac{k_1}{k_1+k_2}\right)\left[\frac{k_b}{k_b+k_c+\sum_\alpha k_\alpha M_\alpha}\right] \quad (7.20)$$

This equation provides a quantitative basis for the interpretation of the effects of temperature, quenching agents, etc., on the total light, or efficiency of *Cypridina* luminescence. We shall consider first the influence of specific anions, which is of interest in connection with the influence of substituents considered in the preceding discussion.

At constant temperature the addition of chloride in concentrations up to approximately half molar increases the total light by as much as 3.4 times, as compared with salt-free solutions (Anderson, 1937). At a concentration of 0.0095 M, bromide, fluoride, nitrate, oxalate, and sulfate, in this order, are less effective than chloride, whereas thiocyanate and iodide reduce the total light by about 90 per cent (Table 7.3).

The experimental data are not sufficient to determine with certainty which of the terms in equation (7.20) is most altered by the presence of the salts listed in Table 7.3, but Anderson presented evidence that the dark oxidation was not a significant factor in the effects observed. Thus the results may be accounted for on the assumption that in each case the total number of luciferin molecules that get excited during the course of the reaction is the same, i.e., that the expression outside the brackets of equation (7.20) is constant, while the efficiency varies under the influence

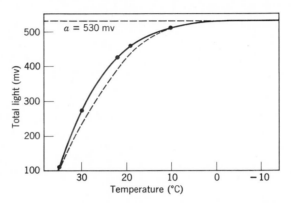

Fig. 7.12. Total light of partially purified extracts of *Cypridina* as a function of temperature (Chase and Lorenz, 1945). The points and solid line represent the data from experiments. The added broken line was calculated on the basis of a different mechanism as described in the text.

of the different ions according to the proportion of excited molecules which radiate in comparison to those which are internally and externally quenched $(k_c + \sum_{\alpha} k_\alpha M_\alpha)$.

Considering only the expression in backets in equation (7.20), for purposes of illustration we may take k_b, in the absence of salt, as equal to one times some factor 10^x, where x is probably in the neighborhood of 5 to 8. The other rate constants, k_c and k_α, will be multiplied by the same factor, but for simplicity we may omit this factor in the following treatment. Now let us suppose that the sum of the constants k_c and $\sum_{\alpha} k_\alpha M_\alpha$, in the absence of salt, equals 6. The efficiency, on a relative scale, would then equal $1/(1 + 6) = 0.143$. Assuming that 0.0095 M sodium chloride increases the value of k_b to 3, we would have $3/(3 + 6) = 0.333$; and assuming that 0.0095 M potassium iodide increases the other constants (in the absence of salt) to 87, we would have $1/(1 + 87) = 0.0113$. The ratio of 0.143 : 0.333 : 0.0113 corresponds to that of 1 : 2.3 : 0.08 on the arbitrary scale of Table 3 for the relative influence of these ions on the amount of total light.

Anderson (1937) noted that the potent quenching effect of thiocyanate or iodide may be strongly opposed by the addition of chloride. The action of the two ions when simultaneously present thus appears to be competitive.

The influence of temperature on the effects of ions such as those listed in Table 7.3 has not been studied, but data are available with respect to the influence of temperature on the total light of *Cypridina* extracts in solutions of constant ionic composition and pH (Chase and Lorenz, 1945). Using reaction mixtures containing a final concentration of 0.01 M sodium chloride, buffered at pH 6.8 by 0.05 M phosphate buffer, the relation shown in Fig. 7.12 was observed.

On the assumption that the reduction in total light with increase in temperature resulted entirely from an increasing significance of the dark auto-oxidation of the substrate, Chase and Lorenz obtained rate constants for the two reactions, k_1 (luminescent, enzyme catalyzed) and k_2 (dark), and on this basis arrived at apparent activation energies for each. Their method was essentially as follows. Let $x =$ amount of luciferin consumed in the luminescent reaction; $y =$ amount of luciferin consumed in the dark oxidation; $a =$ initial amount of luciferin (the same at each temperature); $K =$ the apparent (i.e., the measured) velocity constant (actually $K = k_1 + k_2$); $A =$ value approached by x when the reaction was nearly complete. It is assumed that the two reactions occur simultaneously.

$$\frac{dx}{dt} = k_1(a - x - y) \tag{7.21}$$

$$\frac{dy}{dt} = k_2(a - x - y) \tag{7.22}$$

From (7.21) and (7.22), $dy/k_2 = dx/k_1$, and, since y and x both equal 0 when t equals 0, $y = (k_2/k_1)x$. Substituting for y in (7.21),

$$\frac{dx}{dt} = k_1\left(a - x - \frac{k_2}{k_1}x\right)$$

$$= k_1 a - (k_1 + k_2)x \tag{7.23}$$

Integrating,
$$\int \frac{dx}{a + bx} = \frac{1}{b}\ln(a + bx) \tag{7.24}$$

$$t = -\frac{1}{k_1 + k_2}\ln[k_1 a - (k_1 + k_2)x] + c \tag{7.25}$$

In (7.25) the integration constant c becomes $1/(k_1 + k_2) \ln k_1 a$ for the condition $t = 0$, $x = 0$; hence

$$x = \frac{k_1 a}{k_1 + k_2} (1 - e^{-(k_1 + k_2)t}) \qquad (7.26)$$

Equation (7.26) is equivalent to the usual equation for a first order reaction, $\ln A/(A - x) = Kt$, when K represents $k_1 + k_2$, and A equals $ak_1/(k_1 - k_2)$.

In analyzing the data of Fig. 7.12, the value of a was obtained by extrapolation of the curve to lower temperatures, where the dark reaction was assumed to be negligible in comparison with the luminescent reaction.

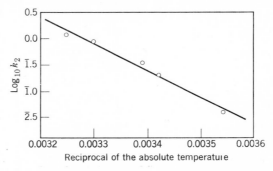

Fig. 7.13.   Analysis of the temperature dependence of the velocity constant k_2 for the dark oxidation of *Cypridina* luciferin, according to Chase and Lorenz (1945).

In terms of millivolts, the units of total light recorded on the apparatus used, (a in these experiments) was found to be asymptotic to 530 mv. At all temperatures, when the reaction approaches completion, A (the observed total light) approaches x, and a value for y may be obtained, since $y = a - x \simeq a - A$. From these values the apparent velocity constant K may be resolved into values for k_1 and for k_2.

When the logarithm of k_2 is plotted against the reciprocal of the absolute temperature, the relationship appears to be linear (Fig. 7.13) and the slope of the line indicates an activation energy of about 25,000 cal.

A similar plot of k_1/k_2, or of k_1 alone, does not result in a straight line because the enzyme-catalyzed reaction goes through a maximum observed rate as a result of the thermal inactivation of the catalyst (cf. Chapter 8) in the higher temperature range.   The data, however, permit an estimate of the activation energy for k_1 as 5,000 cal, and for the thermal inactivation, probably to a large extent reversible, a heat of reaction of some 50,000 cal.

Although the treatment described above is fundamentally sound, it is interesting to note that the observed data are roughly described on the basis of a different mechanism, corresponding to the one responsible for Anderson's (1937) results with various anions. On this basis, reduction in total light with rise in temperature is assumed to occur entirely through the internal and external quenching reactions (k_e and $\sum_\alpha k_\alpha M_\alpha$ in the brackets of equation 7.20), and k_2 is neglected in the expression $k_1/(k_1 + k_2)$. There is no reason to expect an influence of temperature on k_b for the radiation of excited molecules. Numerical values which result in the broken line shown in Fig. 7.12 are as follows.

Using equation (7.12) and considering only the terms inside the braces, the radiationless transitions of quenching may be represented as a single rate. Total light, T.L., is proportional to efficiency, Eff.:

$$\text{T.L.} \propto \text{Eff.} = \frac{k_b}{k_b + (kT/h)e^{\Delta S^\ddagger/R}e^{-\Delta H^\ddagger/RT}} \qquad (7.27)$$

The following values were used for the various constants in (7.27) to give the broken line in Fig. 7.13: $k_b = 1.546 \times 10^5$, $\Delta S = 70$ E.U., and $\Delta H = 31,500$ cal, with the usual values for the other constants, $k = 1.372 \times 10^{-16}$ erg per degree, $h = 6.547 \times 10^{-27}$ erg-sec, and $R = 1.98$ cal per °C per mole. At temperatures of 10°, 25°, and 35°C, the efficiency then amounts to 0.963, 0.598, and 0.2045, respectively. Multiplying Chase and Lorenz's value of 530 mv, their theoretical total light, by these efficiencies, we obtain 509.4, 316.9, and 108.4, as compared with their values of 510, 380 (estimated from their smooth curve, Fig. 7.12), and 110, respectively.

It will be noted that the value of 1.546×10^5 for k_b is quite reasonable for the lifetime of an excited molecule in this reaction and is consistent with the results of the flow-method studies of the *Cypridina* reaction by Chance et al. (1940), discussed later (p. 172). The entropy is high, and to the extent that the hypothesis is correct, would indicate that a protein, perhaps the enzyme itself, is involved in the quenching mechanisms. On this hypothesis, the entropy would have t˜ be high, in order for the rate of quenching to be appreciable.

The analysis by Chase and Lorenz would seem to indicate that the influence of temperature on quenching reactions, as discussed above, is negligible, but this is unlikely. The decrease in total light with rise in temperature undoubtedly involves a temperature dependence in both the dark oxidation and the quenching mechanisms, and the relative importance of the two remains to be established. Frequently, as analyses are extended, apparently single rate constants of relatively simple reactions are found to comprise a number of more elementary processes. On the other hand, even with complex processes taking place in cells and tissues, the controlling principles are not necessarily obscured by the multiplicity of reactions. Fundamental advances toward an ultimately complete understanding are often made while awaiting the elucidation of subsidiary mechanisms.

The efficiency of *Cypridina* luminescence in relation to hydrogen or hydroxyl ion concentration (Anderson, 1933; Chase, 1948b), at constant temperature, has been studied in somewhat more detail than in relation

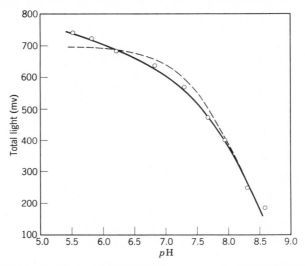

Fig. 7.14. Total light of *Cypridina* extracts as a function of *p*H (Chase, 1948b). The solid line was drawn through the observed points, and the added broken line was calculated as described in the text.

to ions in general. Here again, however, the data are not sufficient for a final analysis. Figure 7.14 illustrates the total light as a function of *p*H at 24° to 26°C in a reaction mixture containing a final concentration of 0.01 M NaCl, 0.067 M each of KH_2PO_4, Na_2HPO_4, and butyl alcohol.

In interpreting the data shown in Fig. 7.14, this question at once arises: How much of the decrease in total light at the higher *p*H might be caused by the dark oxidation of luciferin discussed above? Experiments designed to test this point revealed that, at *p*H 8.0, essentially none of the observed decrease could be attributed to the dark oxidation. Similar experiments were apparently not carried out in a more acid range.

The earlier study of total light in relation to temperature (Chase and Lorenz, 1945), however, indicated that, at *p*H 6.8 and 25°C, under almost identical conditions, about 30 per cent of the luciferin (estimated from the smooth curve, Fig. 7.12) should be consumed in the dark oxidation. It would thus appear that the dark oxidation proceeds more rapidly at pH 6.8 than at pH 8.0 and, therefore, that there is a range of pH, toward the acid side, within which the dark oxidation contributes significantly to the decrease in efficiency.   In a still earlier study (Chase, 1940), it was concluded that the rate of the spontaneous, dark oxidation of luciferin increases rapidly as the solution is made more alkaline, and it was estimated that the rate increases roughly in proportion to the fifth root of the hydroxyl ion concentration between pH 5 and 8.   Thus the evidence regarding the relation between pH and the dark, auto-oxidation of luciferin is not clear.

The data of Fig. 7.14 can be approximately accounted for without assuming a pH dependence of either the luminescent oxidation (k_1 of equation 7.20) or of the dark oxidation (k_2 of equation 7.20), and by assuming that the decrease in total light with increase in pH results from a drop in efficiency due to the factor in the brackets of equation (7.20). The total light may then be written

$$\text{Total light} = 750 \, \frac{1}{1 + (k_c'/k_b) + (k_\alpha/k_b)(\text{OH}^-)} \tag{7.28}$$

If we take $k_c'/k_b = 0.07$ and $k_\alpha/k_b = 10^{-8}$, we obtain for total light

$$\text{Total light} = 750 \left[\frac{1}{1.07 + 10^{-8}(\text{OH}^-)} \right] \tag{7.29}$$

Equation (7.29) gives the broken curve in Fig. 7.14.

Chemiluminescent reactions

Although the most brilliant chemiluminescences appear to take place in the presence of oxygen, and especially of hydrogen peroxide, neither of these agents is uniformly essential.   Moreover, although oxidizing agents appear to initiate the luminescent reaction in some instances, reducing agents are required in others.   Among the best known examples, viz., the cyclophthalhydrazides, dimethyldiacridiniun nitrate, and pyrogallol, the important facts are as follows.

The 3-amino substituted phthalhydrazide ("luminol") in alkaline solution emits a bright and lasting luminescence in an atmosphere of pure hydrogen on addition of potassium ferricyanide.   This observation was made by Harvey in 1928, and, although it is referred to in his monograph (1940), the details of the experiment have not been published.   We have recently confirmed the experiment.   The addition of ferricyanide in the presence of oxygen also results in luminescence, which is brighter if hydrogen peroxide is also added.   With the latter compound, organic catalysts that decompose peroxide, e.g., hemoglobin or catalase, may be used instead of ferricyanide or similar inorganic oxidizing agents.

In contrast to the above the luminescence of dimethyldiacridinium nitrate takes place only in the presence of molecular oxygen or hydrogen peroxide, and is augmented in alkaline solutions by the addition of osmium tetroxide or of reducing agents such as sulfites or stannites (Gleu and Petsch, 1935; Tamamushi and Akiyama, 1939; Tamamushi, 1943).

With pyrogallol a faint flash of luminescence results on addition of sodium hypochlorite or of hydrogen peroxide plus potassium ferricyanide,

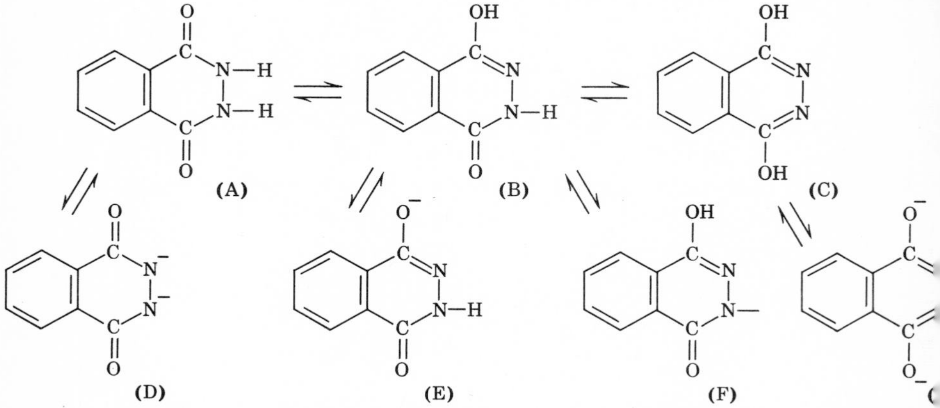

Fig. 7.15. Tautomeric and ionized forms of phthalic hydrazide.

but a bright luminescence results on addition of hydrogen peroxide plus potassium ferrocyanide (Harvey, 1917c). Numerous catalysts may be used for the pyrogallol luminescence, but light emission, in almost every instance, is dependent upon the addition of hydrogen peroxide; luminescence following the addition of sodium hypochlorite without adding hydrogen peroxide is the only known exception.

In regard to possible reaction mechanisms the most extensive of the available chemical and spectroscopic evidence pertains to the cyclophthalhydrazides. In solution they undergo tautomerization from the diketo to the dienol form, with the monoenolic form as a highly unstable intermediate. Each of these forms may undergo ionization. Thus, for the unsubstituted molecule, there are seven possible forms (Fig. 7.15), and, for derivatives in which substituents in the benzene ring confer asymmetry, additional monoenolic forms are possible. Drew (1939) has shown that methylation either of an imino nitrogen or of the enol groups results in the loss of chemiluminescence. It seems, therefore, that the property of luminescence depends upon not only the dilactim structure, but also upon the ability to produce the dilactimic ion.   From these facts it does not follow that the radiating form is the dilactimic ion, but spectroscopic data provide evidence as to which of the possible forms probably emits light.

The 3-amino and several other substituted compounds in mildly acid or alkaline solution (0.01–0.025 N) have two absorption maxima in the ultraviolet (Fig. 7.16) at about 290 and 350 mμ, respectively (Zelinsky and Sveshnikov, 1942;   van der Burg, 1943).   In concentrated acid (10 per cent HCl) the peak at 350 mμ disappears, while that at 290 mμ remains.   In concentrated alkali (50% sodium hydroxide) the reverse is

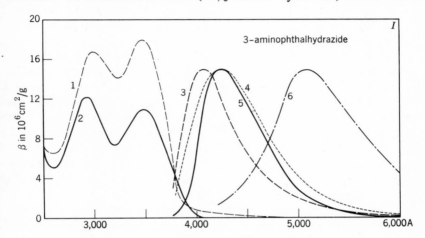

Fig. 7.16. Absorption, fluorescent, and chemiluminescent spectra of 3-aminophthalhydrazide (van der Burg, 1943): 1, absorption, alkaline solution; 2, absorption, acid solution; 3, fluorescence, in 0.01 N KOH; 4, chemiluminescence; 5, fluorescence, in acid solution; 6, fluorescence, in 0.1 N KOH.

true.   Two forms of the molecule are evidently present in the mildly acid or alkaline solutions.   Since the degree of acidity influences ionization but not tautomerization, we must conclude that the form of the molecule in strong acid is one with the hydrogens un-ionized, and in alkali it is one with the hydrogens ionized, without being able to distinguish, on these grounds, whether the site of ionization is the enol or imino group.   Other evidence, however, permits the following probable distinction to be made.

The chemiluminescence of 3-amino- or 3-methylaminophthalhydrazide has very close to the same spectral distribution as the fluorescence of these compounds in acid solution (Fig. 7.16).   This correspondence indicates that the molecule which emits is one which predominates in acid solution, i.e., which does not have its hydrogens ionized off and, therefore, is not the dilactimic ion itself.   But, since the ability to form the dilactimic ion appears essential for chemiluminescence (Drew, 1939), we conclude that it is required in the chemical reactions leading up to the excited molecule. Although the available evidence is not conclusive, we suppose that structure (C) of Fig. 7.15 is the chief constituent and fluorescent molecule in acid solutions, and that (G) is the chief constituent in strongly alkaline solutions.   It is necessary to assume that in alkaline solutions the chemical excitation of luminol leaves it in the acid stable form (C).   The beneficial influence of the hydroxyl ion on the intensity of chemiluminescence, therefore, is to be interpreted not on the basis of aiding the ionization of the enolic hydrogens, since this process reduces the amount of potentially luminescent molecules, but rather as an aid to intermediate steps of electron rearrangement and transfer.

The data of van der Burg (1943) show that, although the respective chemiluminescent spectra correspond more or less closely to those of fluorescence in acid solutions of the 3-amino-, 4-amino-, 3-methylamino-, sodium 3-hydrazino-β-sulfonate-, and 3-acetamidophthalhydrazides, it is apparently the alkaline structure of 3-acetylcarbamidohydrazide that chemiluminesces. With the 3-nitro substituted compound the chemiluminescence occurs at shorter wavelengths than the fluorescence of acid solutions, suggesting that this compound suffers considerable modification before emission of light, since in general it is to be expected that the chemiluminescent spectrum of a molecule will be the same, or very nearly the same, as the fluorescent spectrum.   If the two are different, it can only mean that the structure of the emitting molecules is different.   It is not surprising that the chemical reactions which furnish the relatively high energy necessary for visible radiation should sometimes so alter the molecule that the spectral distribution of the light is altered from that of fluorescence, or even abolished.   Factors other than alteration of the molecule also influence the amount of emitted light, e.g., through the several mechanisms of quenching, as already discussed, or through the effects of various simple substituents that may cause as much as a 10,000-fold difference in intensity of the light under similar conditions of oxidation (Table 7.1).   These substituents act to modify R_{mn}, the matrix component of the electric moment between the initial and final state of a transition (Fig. 7.8).   Of the numerous examples of fluorescent substances, relatively very few have been found to exhibit chemiluminescence.   Among those which do not exhibit it, chemical means of excitation must be lacking, since fluorescence shows that the excited molecule will luminesce.

Energies of visible luminescence

From Figs. 7.5 and 7.6 it is apparent that the emission spectra in chemiluminescence of cyclophthalhydrazides and in bioluminescence extend into or beyond the blue, i.e., to wavelengths of 4,000 and 4,400 Å or shorter, respectively.   The energies of these transitions may be readily computed as follows.

The energy in ergs per molecule at any wavelength is equal to $h\nu$. Avagadro's number N times $h\nu$ gives the energy in ergs per mole, which may be converted to calories per mole by dividing by 4.18×10^7, i.e., by the number of ergs per calorie:

$$E = \frac{h\nu N}{4.18 \times 10^7} \tag{7.30}$$

Usually it is convenient to make use of the conversion factor of 2.86 which, multiplied by the wave number, results directly in energy in calories per mole.   The wave number is the reciprocal of the wavelength in centimeters.   Thus, for the wavelength of 4,000 Å,

$$\text{Wave number} = \frac{1}{4,000 \times 10^{-8}} = 25,000 \text{ cm}^{-1}$$

$$E = 25,000 \times 2.86 = 71,500 \text{ cal per mole}$$

The conversion factor of 2.86 is derived from equation (7.30).   Since $\nu = c/\lambda$,

$$E = \frac{1}{\lambda}\left(\frac{chN}{4.18 \times 10^7}\right) = \frac{1}{\lambda}\left(\frac{3 \times 10^{10} \times 6.547 \times 10^{-27} \times 6.02 \times 10^{23}}{4.18 \times 10^7}\right) = \frac{1}{\lambda} \text{ (2.86)} \tag{7.31}$$

The energy equivalent to the wavelength of 4,400 Å amounts to 22,727 $\times$ 2.86, or practically 65,000 cal per mole.

These energies impose certain restrictions upon any hypothetical mechanisms for the luminescences involved, since any postulated chemical reaction, or series of chemical reactions, which on purely thermodynamic grounds could not provide sufficient energy, cannot be responsible for the luminescence.   There seems to be no way, for example, that luminol plus ferricyanide can react anaerobically in a manner to give sufficient energy for luminescence without destruction of some of the luminol.   In the presence of hydrogen peroxide, on the other hand, the energy requirements may be met and light emission may take place without destruction of the luminol.   Bearing in mind these energy requirements, the conditions of oxidation, and other facts, we are led to propose the following mechanisms.

Electronic and chemical changes in chemiluminescence

The influence of substituents on the fluorescent and chemiluminescent intensities of different cyclophthalhydrazides (Table 7.1) indicates that luminescence is enhanced by those groups which direct the nitration of similarly substituted benzene to ortho-para positions. Meta-directing groups cause little change in the efficiency of emission over that of the unsubstituted compound. It seems likely that the ortho-para-directing groups act by promoting the quinone type of electronic structure, in which there is a double bond between the ortho-para-directing group and the ring carbon to which it is attached. This tends to pile up two pi electrons on the carbon para or ortho to the substituent. It is reasonable to believe that the excited state consists of a quinone-like type of electronic structure which has a higher energy than the freely resonating structure. Light emission would occur on electronic rearrangement from the former to the latter. The problem thus becomes in part a question of how the excited quinone type of structure can be chemically induced.

Let us consider first the anaerobic, chemiluminescent reaction of luminol and potassium ferricyanide. Since the necessary energy must come from the destruction of a part of the luminol, it seems most reasonable to suppose that structure (G) of Fig. 7.16 loses its charges by transfer of two electrons to the ferricyanide radical, and then hydrolyzes to phthalic acid plus the unstable substance, di-imine, N_2H_2, somewhat according to Albrecht (1928; cf. also Tamamushi and Akiyama, 1938; Drew, 1939).

$$(7.32)$$

The highly reactive di-imine would be expected, in water solution alone, to decompose probably to N_2 and hydrazine, N_2H_4. Hydrazine is such a powerful reducing agent that, if present in sufficient amounts, it would reduce all the Fe^{3+} in a solution virtually at once. We might expect undecomposed luminol to catalyze the reduction of di-imine by Fe^{3+} as follows:

$$(7.33)$$

In this reaction, four pi electrons are removed from the benzene ring by four Fe^{3+}, allowing two $N{=}N$ groups of di-imine to go on the ring and four protons to go into solution.   Both this and the preceding reactions are obviously favored by an excess of hydroxyl ions, in conformance with the facilitation of chemiluminescence by alkalinity of the solution.   Also, the molecule undergoing excitation has the structure that predominates in acid solution, as demanded by the spectroscopic data discussed earlier. However, the Fe^{3+} may be supposed to extract its electrons from luminol from the oxygen negatively charged by previous ionization of an H atom. The excited state would presumably result as the nitrogens spontaneously leave the ring:

$$+2N_2 \qquad (7.34)$$

$$+h\nu \qquad (7.35)$$

The step (7.34) would be favored by the un-ionized state of the luminol. The overall reaction may thus be represented as

$$8OH^- + 2 \quad \cdots \quad +8Fe^{3+} \longrightarrow 2 \quad \cdots \quad +8Fe^{2+} + 4H_2O + 2N_2$$

$$(7.36)$$

wherein the available free energy is more than adequate for the observed luminescence.   Moreover, the distance between $N{=}N$ is 1.20 Å (Pauling, 1940a), which is about right for combination with the two carbons $C{=}C = 1.39$ Å apart on the benzene ring.

We assume that, in the presence of hydrogen peroxide, the mechanism is very much the same, with the difference that oxygen rather than nitrogen is liberated, and no destruction of the luminol is essential. The distance between the oxygens of hydrogen peroxide is 1.32 Å, which is approximately the $N \!=\! N$ distance given above. Since the decomposition of each peroxide yields 25,090 cal of free energy, two molecules of peroxide are not enough to provide the more than 70,000 cal required for the emitted light; and, since three molecules are difficult to fit into a reasonable reaction mechanism, we assume that four are involved.

$$2 \; [\text{luminol}] + 4Fe^{2+} + 4H_2O_2 \longrightarrow 2 \; [\text{product}] + 4Fe^{3+} + 4OH^- \tag{7.37}$$

$$[\text{product}] + 4Fe^{3+} \longrightarrow [\text{product}] + 4Fe^{2+} + 4H^+ \tag{7.38}$$

$$[\text{product}] \longrightarrow [\text{product}] + 2O_2 \tag{7.39}$$

After (7.39) light emission occurs by the same mechanism as in (7.35). The overall reaction is

$$4H_2O_2 \rightarrow 4H_2O + 2O_2 \qquad \Delta F = -100 \text{ kcal} \tag{7.40}$$

Hydrogen peroxide acts as a reductant, while its decomposition is catalyzed by luminol and by the ferri-ferro system.

It will be noted that in the first reaction (7.37) of this series, the reduced form of the iron catalyst reacts with luminol, although the oxidized form, i.e., potassium ferricyanide, is added. If essentially none of the reduced form is present in the ferricyanide solution before it is added, it will be readily produced by reaction (7.32), which, itself, leads to luminescence at the expense of some of the luminol. Subsequently, although both types of reactions, (7.32) and (7.37), may be assumed to occur simultaneously in the presence of hydrogen peroxide, a large amount of chemiluminescence could easily result from (7.37) and those following, without destruction of the luminol.

Thus, with hydrogen peroxide, the excited state is the same as assumed before, but more luminescence might be expected because the hydrazide is not necessarily destroyed.   Under appropriate conditions of oxidation, in fact, light emission may occur without considerable loss of luminol (Drew, 1939).   On the other hand, after some 100,000 cal of energy have been absorbed in reaching the excited state, it is likely that some of the excited molecules will be destroyed, the relative amount depending, as would be expected, upon the conditions.

With pyrogallol the initiation of luminescence by reducing agents plus hydrogen peroxide is understandable along the lines of a mechanism resembling the one above.   An energy equivalent to the decomposition of four peroxide molecules is again needed.

$$+4Fe^{2+}+4H_2O_2 \longrightarrow +4OH^-+4Fe^{3+} \tag{7.41}$$

$$+4Fe^{3+} \longrightarrow +4H^++4Fe^{2+} \tag{7.42}$$

The remaining steps, i.e., liberation of oxygen (leaving the molecule in the excited state), followed by radiation and return to the normal state, are the same as in the luminol example; the overall reaction may be represented as in (7.40).

With dimethyldiacridinium nitrate we suppose that the electronic mechanisms involved in chemiluminescence are fundamentally similar to those in the examples discussed above.   Molecular oxygen seems to be necessary for light emission, unless hydrogen peroxide is added.   The rôle of oxygen is presumably that of giving rise to hydrogen peroxide or to some other reactant which takes part in the process of excitation, but in neither the pyrogallol nor the dimethyldiacridinium nitrate luminescences have the intermediate reactions been established, and it would not seem profitable for the time being to speculate at length upon their nature.

In support of the above mechanisms, it is of particular interest and significance that $^3\Sigma$ oxygen can scarcely leave a benzene ring without leaving it in an excited state, nor can free oxygen readily combine with benzene unless the ring is in an excited state. In the normal state of freely resonating, lowest energy, a typical arrangement of electrons is as

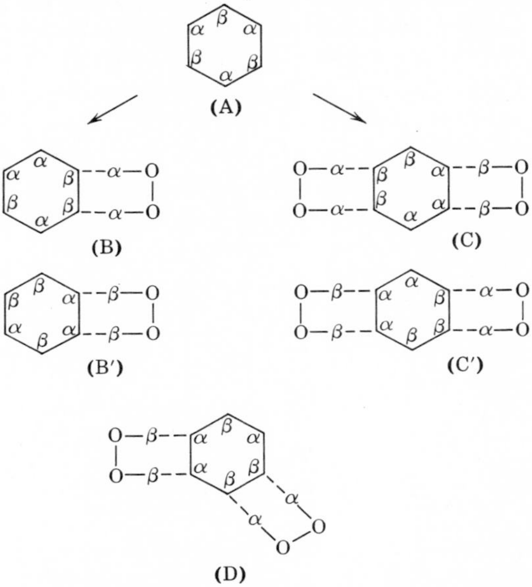

Fig. 7.17.   Possible resonating structures of benzene, and possible ways of combination of the excited states and O_2.

represented in Fig. 7.17A, where the eigenfunction α represents a positive spin, and β a negative spin.   There are twenty ways of assigning three α's and three β's to the six ring positions of benzene.   Oxygen molecules are normally in the triplet state, the electron spins being in the same direction, i.e., α, α or β, β.   To combine with a benzene molecule, the oxygen molecule must share its pair of electrons with another pair of opposite spin.   It can only do this with benzene in one of the excited states (B), (B'), (C), unless it comes up with an enormous energy (Fig. 7.18).   In Fig. 7.17, (C') is the same as (C).   (D) represents a benzene-two O_2 configuration, where the benzene might be left by the two departing O_2 molecules in a low energy state.   Nevertheless, once having combined with an excited benzene molecule, it is difficult for oxygen to leave without leaving the benzene in an excited state, since it tends to leave two like spins adjacent to each other.   A rigorous discussion of this question is rather complicated.   The probability of jumping from the excited to the normal surface involves the same expressions κ and γ (equations 7.17 and 7.18) discussed earlier for internal quenching.

The reactivity of excited molecules is the basis for some well-known polymerization reactions (e.g., Mark and Tobolsky, 1950).   The polymerization of pyrogallol is of especial interest in connection with luminescence, inasmuch as it has been noted (Harvey, 1917b) that chemiluminescence does not occur in concentrated solutions of this compound

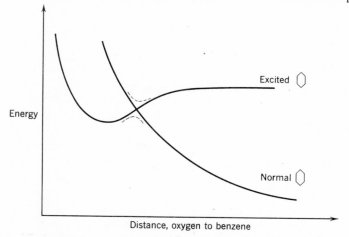

Fig. 7.18.   Potential energy diagram for the combination of O_2 with benzene in the normal and excited states, respectively.   Oxygen cannot get very close to normal benzene except with a very high energy.

under the same conditions that favor light emission in dilute solutions. The mechanism is one of external quenching, leading to the formation of complex polymers that make the solution a murky black.   It involves the reaction of excited molecules with each other, occurring with increasing readiness as the concentration of pyrogallol is increased.   It would be anticipated, on the other hand, that, by raising the viscosity of the solution with some inert agent, this external quenching might be reduced sufficiently to permit chemiluminescence in the more concentrated solutions.   At higher viscosities diffusion is slower and the interaction of the excited molecules correspondingly less probable.   The effect of a rise in viscosity is generally to increase fluorescence in this manner.

There are other more or less familiar reactions which may involve external quenching by the interaction of excited molecules; for example, the formation of the dark pigment, melanin, which takes place at cut surfaces of apples, potatoes, mushrooms, etc., when exposed to air, and in the skins of animals when exposed to strong sunlight. The initial reactions involve the oxidation of polyphenols by the enzyme tyrosinase (cf. Raper, 1932), but the final steps apparently proceed without a catalyst and lead to products that have not as yet been fully identified. These final steps possibly involve the interaction of molecules excited either by oxidation or by radiation. It has been suggested (Gould, 1939; Sizer, 1943) that the unusually low activation energy of the enzyme tyrosinase, apparently 2,700 cal (Gould, 1939), is due in part to the participation of a photochemical process.

Electronic mechanisms in efficiency

From the foregoing discussions it is apparent that the efficiency of luminescence may be affected by ions or by substituents in the light-emitting molecule in three distinct ways: by influencing the probability of transitions from the excited to the normal state (k_b of equation 7.12); by influencing the probability of crossing a radiationless transition from the excited to the normal potential surface (γ in equations 7.17 and 7.18; cf. Figs. 7.10, 7.11, and 7.17), and also by changing the surface so that the free energy of activation for quenching is altered. Although there are data with respect to the quantitative effects of substituents on the luminescence of the cyclophthalhydrazides, and of ions in solution on the luminescence of *Cypridina* extracts, data on the effects of both factors are not yet available with respect to either of these luminescences. In line with the theory that has been set forth, however, it is possible to arrive at a reasonable picture of the electronic mechanisms involved in efficiency, as follows.

It has been pointed out (p. 163) that, among the derivatives of phthalic hydrazide, the substituents which intensify fluorescence and chemiluminescence are those which direct nitration to the ortho and para positions of the correspondingly substituted benzene ring (cf. Table 7.1, p. 140). The interpretation expressed for this relationship is that it reflects the tendency for ortho-para-directing groups to promote the quinone type of electronic structure of the excited state by piling up two pi electrons on the carbon ortho or para to the substituent. This results in an increase in the matrix component for the electric dipole moment in equation (7.9) and, therefore, an increase in luminescence. The substitution, in the 3 position of cyclophthalhydrazide (Fig. 7.15), of an electron-contributing group, such as NH_2, would clearly favor the migration of a pi electron to the opposite end of the ring (Fig. 7.19A). On the other hand, the presence of a highly electron-removing group, such as NO_2, in the same position would have the reverse influence of holding the electron at that end of the ring (Fig. 7.19B). As shown in Table 7.1, the intensity of luminescence of these respectively substituted phthalic hydrazides differs by a factor of 10,000.

The influence of chloride ions in solution on the luminescence of *Cypridina* extracts (Anderson, 1937) may be pictured as similar to that of the NH_2 substituent of luminol (Fig. 7.19C). Since the closely related halogen ion, iodide, greatly reduces the efficiency of *Cypridina* luminescence, we must conclude that it acts through a mechanism different from that of the chloride ion, which increases the efficiency. Inasmuch as

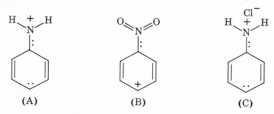

(A)   (B)   (C)

Fig. 7.19. Diagram illustrating the possible electronic mechanism of the influence of substituents and ions on the efficiency of luminescence. The dots represent pi electrons of the benzene ring. Luminescence is favored by (A) and (C), and interfered with by (B).

chloride and iodide ions are competitive in their effects, as noted earlier (p. 155), they must combine with the luciferin at the same site. Each ion has at least two effects: one on k_b, the other on quenching. For chloride ion, the first effect is most notable; iodide is a more efficient quencher either through decreasing γ or through decreasing the free energy of the quenching reaction. Anderson showed that the increased efficiency of luminescence is not due to a relative weakening of the dark oxidation. This follows from the fact that the efficiency was not affected by more than 10 per cent by a fourfold change in luciferase concentration. Our discussion here is in substantial accord with Anderson's conclusions.

Rate-limiting reactions in *Cypridina* extracts

Although the structure of *Cypridina* luciferin has not been established, it seems safe to conclude, on the basis of the foregoing considerations, that it is a ring compound, possibly including heterocyclic nitrogens, and that excitation and radiation occur through mechanisms not fundamentally different from those discussed in relation to luminol or pyrogallol. Moreover, it is clear that light emission involves an enzyme-catalyzed reaction with the reduced form of a reversibly oxidizable substance, accompanied by the destruction of a molecule or group of a molecule which supplies at least part of the energy necessary for excitation. On the other hand, it is not certain (1) that the required energy is furnished by destruction of part of the luciferin itself (as, e.g., in the anaerobic chemiluminescence of luminol in the presence of ferricyanide), or (2) that the hydrogens removed in the reversible, dark oxidation of *Cypridina* luciferin are the same as, or different from, the hydrogens removed in the luminescent reaction. In general terms, we know that, in the presence of oxygen, some reactant R combines with the luciferin L, bringing it into an excited state. The reactant R might be oxygen itself, or it might be hydrogen peroxide or some other substance. It might be produced by a reaction with a substance X, possibly a side group on the luciferin molecule, or a totally different substance. We also know that luciferin and luciferase may be separated and recombine with each other. Schematically, the known reactions may be represented as follows:

(1) $$X + O_2 \rightarrow Y + R \tag{7.43}$$

(2) $$A + L \rightleftharpoons AL \tag{7.44}$$

(3) $$AL + R \rightarrow AL' + Z \tag{7.45}$$

(4) $$AL' \rightarrow AL + h\nu \tag{7.46}$$

(5) $$L + Fe^{3+} \rightleftharpoons L_0 + Fe^{2+} \tag{7.47}$$

where Y, Z, and L_0 are unknown products, and the prime indicates the excited state of luciferin. In this scheme the ferricyanide reaction is assumed to take place with L, although it might occur with X, giving an oxidized product, X_0.

By means of the flow method for measuring rapid reactions, it has been possible to distinguish with some assurance which of the series, (7.43) to (7.46), is relatively slow (Chance et al, 1940). Using crude extracts of *Cypridina*, the time required for the intensity of the light to reach a maximum was measured when luciferin plus oxygen was mixed with luciferase plus oxygen, and when a solution of luciferin plus luciferase, without oxygen, was mixed with oxygenated water. The results indicated that the combination between the enzyme and substrate (7.45) reached half completion in 0.004 sec. The reaction with oxygen, and the subsequent ones leading to light emission, when the enzyme and substrate were already in equilibrium, required only about 0.001 sec for half completion. Evidently (7.45) is ordinarily the slowest and therefore the rate-limiting step. Reaction (7.47) becomes limiting only when the luciferin solution contains a significant amount of L_0 which goes back to L during the course of the luminescent reaction, as indicated by the results of Anderson's (1936) study (Fig. 7.1).

When the luciferin is essentially all in the form L at the start, and a sufficient concentration of luciferase is employed for the reaction to go

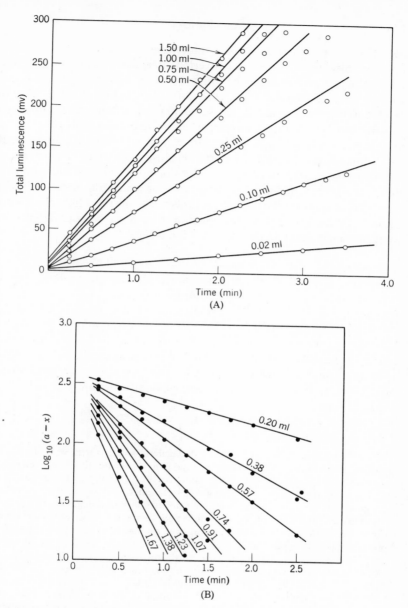

Fig. 7.20. (A) Total light emitted as a function of time after mixing a constant small amount of luciferase with various amounts of luciferin, as indicated in the figure, in a constant final volume (Chase, 1949b). (B) First order rates of the luminescent reaction with a constant initial amount of luciferin and various amounts of luciferase, indicated on the figure, in a constant final volume of reaction mixture (Chase, 1950).

essentially to completion within a short time, i.e., short enough that no considerable amount of L is converted to a form such as L_0 by dark auto-oxidation, the kinetics conform to those of a reaction first order with respect to the luciferin concentration; light intensity decreases exponentially with time, in the same manner as the concentration of substrate in any ordinary enzyme reaction decreases with time. Thus, with a given concentration of luciferase, a straight line results when the logarithm of light intensity is plotted against time after the reactants are mixed. Under optimal conditions the slope of the line is determined by the concentration of luciferase times the concentration of luciferin (Fig. 7.20) in the manner that would be expected from the Michaelis-Menton Theory (Chase, 1949b).[1] These relationships must be considered somewhat further because of their kinetic significance.

The Michaelis-Menton formulation in *Cypridina* luminescence

The theory of Michaelis and Menton (1913) for determining the dissociation constant of the enzyme-substrate complex has been employed with reference to numerous enzyme systems (cf. Haldane, 1930) and to the reaction with partially purified extracts of *Cypridina* (Chase, 1949b). The theory, originally applied to the rates of hydrolysis of sucrose by invertase, is briefly as follows. Letting E represent the enzyme combining with substrate S to give an intermediate complex ES that breaks down into the products P and the enzyme, the overall reaction is

$$E + S \underset{k_2}{\overset{k_1}{\rightleftharpoons}} ES \overset{k_3}{\rightarrow} E + P \qquad (7.48)$$

[1] With unpurified extracts, dilution of the luciferin solution with water results in a marked increase in the velocity constant of the luminescent reaction at a given concentration of luciferase (Amberson, 1922; Stevens, 1927; Harvey and Snell, 1931). If the dilution is made with a corresponding solution containing luciferin which has undergone non-luminescent oxidation, the velocity constant remains the same. With purified extracts and constant concentration of luciferase, the velocity constant remains independent of the luciferin concentration over a range in concentration as great as those studied with unpurified extracts (Chase and Harvey, 1942). The anomalous kinetics in crude solutions have not been satisfactorily explained. The simplest interpretation is that these solutions, containing all the heat-stable extractives of the dried organisms, include inhibitors of luciferase activity; the effect of the inhibitor decreases on dilution with water but remains the same on dilution with oxyluciferin solution where the concentration of the inhibitor remains the same. The erratic results obtained by Amberson (1922), when he diluted the luciferin solutions with oxyluciferin solutions whose concentration he had adjusted to match the color of the luciferin solution, are understandable on the same basis. The fact that the total light does not decrease as much as expected, i.e., does not decrease in proportion to aqueous dilution of unpurified luciferin (Stevens, 1927), also favors the interpretation of dilution of inhibitors and probably of quenching agents as well.

The rate of the reaction is proportional to the amount of ES. Also,

$$\frac{d(\text{ES})}{dt} = k_1(\text{E})(\text{S}) - k_2(\text{ES}) - k_3(\text{ES})$$

$$= k_1(\text{E})(\text{S}) - (k_2 + k_3)(\text{ES}) \tag{7.49}$$

At steady state, $d(\text{ES})/dt = 0$, and therefore

$$(\text{ES}) = \frac{k_1(\text{E})(\text{S})}{k_2 + k_3} \tag{7.50}$$

The velocity V of formation of products is

$$V = \frac{d\text{P}}{dt} = k_3(\text{ES}) = \frac{k_3 k_1(\text{E})(\text{S})}{k_2 + k_3} \tag{7.51}$$

Letting E_0 represent the total amount of enzyme, $E + ES$,

$$(\text{E}_0) = (\text{E}) + \frac{k_1(\text{E})(\text{S})}{k_2 + k_3} = (\text{E})\left(1 + \frac{k_1(\text{S})}{k_2 + k_3}\right) \tag{7.52}$$

Using (7.52) to replace E in (7.51) gives

$$V = \frac{k_3 k_1(\text{S})(\text{E}_0)}{k_2 + k_3 + k_1(\text{S})} \tag{7.53}$$

When the concentration of the substrate is increased sufficiently, k_2 and k_3 will be negligible compared to $k_1(\text{S})$ in the denominator of (7.53), and hence $V_{\max} = k_3(\text{E}_0)$. The ratio between the velocity at a given substrate concentration to the maximum velocity is then

$$\frac{V}{V_{\max}} = \left(\frac{k_3 k_1(\text{S})(\text{E}_0)}{k_2 + k_3 + k_1(\text{S})}\right)\left(\frac{1}{k_3(\text{E}_0)}\right) = \frac{(\text{S})}{\dfrac{k_2 + k_3}{k_1} + (\text{S})} = \frac{(\text{S})}{K_m + (\text{S})} \tag{7.54}$$

The Michaelis-Menton constant K_m is defined as $(k_2 + k_3)/k_1$, in accordance with equation (7.54), and it is apparent that, with concentrations of substrate that give just half the maximum velocity, $K_m = (\text{S})$.

Ordinarily K_m is measured by obtaining the substrate concentration that results in half the maximum velocity with a given concentration of enzyme. With the luminescent system, however, the limited supply of purified luciferin available for the experiments has made it impossible to determine the precise maximum velocity at very high substrate concentrations directly. Instead, this datum has been determined graphically, by the method of Lineweaver and Burk (1934), who pointed out that, if the reciprocal of equation (7.54) is multiplied through by (S), a linear equation is obtained:

$$\frac{(S)}{V} = \frac{(S)}{V_{max}} - \frac{K_m}{V_{max}} \qquad (7.55)$$

When this equation is satisfied, a straight line results in the plot of $(S)/V$ against (S), the slope of the line being equal to the reciprocal of the maximum velocity, and the intercept equal to the value of K_m/V_{max}.

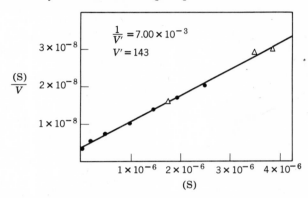

Fig. 7.21. The data of Fig. 7.20A plotted according to equation (7.55). The substrate concentration on the abscissa is expressed as molarity, with an estimated molecular weight of 500 for luciferin. This value can scarcely be in error by more than a factor of 2, which would not affect the order of magnitude of the value computed for K_m. (Chase, 1949b.)

The data of Fig. 7.20A have been plotted in this manner in Fig. 7.21, which indicates satisfactory agreement with the equation and gives a value of 5.95×10^{-7} for K_m.

Data similar to those illustrated in Figs. 7.20A and 7.21, but obtained with a different concentration of luciferase, gave a value for K_m of 6.03×10^{-7}, in substantial agreement with the previous value. A number of other oxidative systems have been found to have a K_m of this order of magnitude (Haldane, 1930), whereas for many hydrolytic enzymes K_m seems to be of the order of 10^{-2}. The fact that only a small amount of substrate appears necessary in order to saturate the luminescent enzyme system is of interest in connection with intracellular luminescence, e.g., of bacteria, to be discussed presently.

Further analysis of K_m requires data with respect to temperature and an interpretation of the precise meaning of K_m (Briggs and Haldane, 1925; Kauzmann et al., 1949). Ordinarily it is assumed that the rate of dissociation of the complex ES is fast in comparison to its rate of decomposition into products, i.e., that $k_2 \gg k_3$, in which case $K_m = k_2/k_1$ to a close approximation; the usual thermodynamic analysis will yield values for the heat and entropy of dissociation of the complex.   On the other hand, if the complex decomposes into products much faster than it is formed by combination of the enzyme and substrate, i.e., if $k_3 \gg k_2$, then $K_m \cong k_3/k_1$.   In this event the significance of K_m is that of a ratio of rate constants, and the analysis of temperature data yields values for the difference in heats and entropies of activation of the two reaction rates in the forward direction:

$$K_m = \frac{\kappa_3(kT/h)K_3^\ddagger}{\kappa_1(kT/h)K_1^\ddagger} = \frac{\kappa_3}{\kappa_1}\, e^{-(\Delta H_s^\ddagger - \Delta H_1^\ddagger)/RT}\, e^{(\Delta S_s^\ddagger - \Delta S_1^\ddagger)/R} \qquad (7.56)$$

By assuming 20,000 as a reasonable value for the molecular weight of luciferase (cf. also p. 127 and pp. 243–250), and assuming 300 for the molecular weight of luciferin, Kauzmann et al. (1949) arrived at a maximum velocity for k_3, in absolute units, of 0.58 sec^{-1} at 15°C, and 1.17 sec^{-1} at 22°C.   These values would indicate an energy of activation of 17,000 cal per mole, and an entropy of activation of -0.5 E.U.   For the Michaelis constant a heat of reaction was estimated as 8,200 cal per mole, with an entropy of 0.8 E.U.   Depending upon whether the constant K_m actually represents k_2/k_1 or k_3/k_1, this value for the entropy represents the entropy increase in the dissociation of 1 mole of the enzyme-substrate complex to give 1 mole of luciferin in the solution, or it represents the difference between the entropies of activation of k_3 and k_1.   If the former alternative is correct, the value of 0.8 E.U. may be corrected for the entropy of mixing of luciferin with water $[= -R \ln$ (mole fraction luciferin in molal solution)], amounting to -8 E.U., giving a value of -7.2 E.U. for the "inherent" entropy of dissociation of the luciferin-luciferase complex.

In connection with the above heats and entropies, it will be recalled that there is evidence from kinetic analyses of _Cypridina_ luminescence at temperatures of 10° to 35°C (Chase and Lorenz, 1945, p. 156) that the light-emitting oxidation has an apparent activation energy of around 5,000 cal.   Since the Michaelis-Menton constant, according to Kauzmann et al., has a heat of reaction (depending on whether it is interpreted as representing k_2/k_1 or as k_3/k_1) amounting to around 8,200 cal, whereas k_3 is characterized by 17,000 cal, it seems that the 5,000 cal for the overall reaction is to be attributed to k_1.

If we assume $k_1 < k_3$ in keeping with the observation that the combination of substrate and enzyme is slower than the subsequent decomposition, it follows that $k_3 > k_2$ (Chance et al., 1940).   Hence, $K_m = k_3/k_1$, whence $\Delta H_3^\ddagger - \Delta H_1^\ddagger = 8,200$.   Putting these results together, we obtain Fig.

7.22. If Fig. 7.22 correctly pictures the actual situation, the rate k_3 must have an entropy more than 52 E.U. more positive than that for k_1.

The Michaelis-Menton theory is considered again in a later discussion of bacterial luminescence (p. 182).

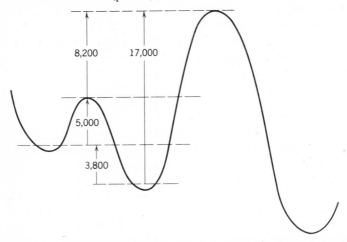

Fig. 7.22.   Potential energy diagram to illustrate the possible relationship between activation energies in the luminescent reaction of *Cypridina*, as discussed in the text.

The luminescent system in bacteria

Since various attempts to obtain luminescent extracts from bacteria have not yet been successful (cf. Korr, 1935; van der Kerk, 1942), the presence of a luciferin-luciferase system in these organisms, comparable to that in *Cypridina*, has been only inferred, not proved.   Bioluminescence, however, is certainly an example of chemiluminescence, requiring some specific molecule which undergoes a transition to an excited state and then radiates.   The same species of molecules might be significantly involved as an intermediary in the overall hydrogen transfer of oxidative metabolism of the cell, and these molecules might be very nearly identical with one of the more or less familiar coenzymes, such as a flavin or pyridine nucleotide, which fluoresce in the visible region of the spectrum.   On the other hand, it remains possible that luciferin in bacteria is a metabolic by-product, perhaps comparable to some of the microbial pigments or antibiotic compounds.   In this event, light emission would still require a chemical means of excitation, by reaction between the luciferin and some other reactant, such as hydrogen peroxide, or by auto-oxidation.   Although there is no unequivocal evidence as to which of these conceivable alternatives is correct, it is clear that bacterial luminescence is also governed by enzyme activity, whether this activity is involved, as two extremes of possible interpretations, in the production of a luciferin which auto-oxidizes with light emission, or in specifically catalyzing the oxidation of a luciferin in the same manner as in extracts of *Cypridina*. Numerous considerations favor the latter interpretation. Among them are the similarities in emission spectra and in the influence of factors such as temperature, hydrogen ions, and inhibitors, which are taken up in the discussions that follow.

Unlike the situation in extracts, however, the intensity of luminescence in a population of non-reproducing bacterial cells, under favorable physiological conditions, may remain at a constant level for considerable periods of time—for an hour or longer. From the point of view of investigating the rate-controlling mechanisms of a process in living cells, this normally uniform intensity has certain advantages. Luminescence, itself, has unique advantages for kinetic studies, inasmuch as the brightness of the emitted light, under given conditions, is evidently proportional to the velocity of the reaction supplying the energy for excitation. The interpretation of the uniformity of intensity as a function of time can only be that the reactants, in effect, remain constant, the luciferin being replenished at the rate at which it is consumed. The same results might be expected to obtain, over short periods of time, either by the steady production of luciferin from a precursor (as, e.g., the steady rate of carbon dioxide production during uniform rate of respiration), followed by destruction in the luminescent reaction, or by alternate oxidation and reduction of the same molecules, without destruction in the luminescent reaction. The latter possibility might easily be the case, if excitation were brought about by hydrogen peroxide which had been produced by some other system; this situation would be comparable to the mechanism for the chemiluminescence of luminol or pyrogallol discussed on pp. 166 and 167.

Indirect evidence that bacteria possess a luciferase that is distinct from the catalyst responsible for by far the larger fraction of oxygen consumed in aerobic respiration derives from experiments with inhibitors. Luminescence has long been known to be especially sensitive to narcotics, particularly those of the lipid-soluble series such as alcohol, ether, chloroform, urethan, and these agents are capable of reversibly diminishing the brightness of luminescence without a correspondingly great effect on the rate of total oxygen consumption (Harvey, 1917a; Taylor, 1934, 1936; van Schouwenburg, 1938). Conversely, small concentrations of cyanide greatly diminish the rate of total oxygen consumption without greatly affecting the brightness of luminescence. It follows that, of the total oxygen consumed, only a small fraction is responsible for light production, and the simplest interpretation is that two different enzymes are responsible for most of the oxygen consumption and for luminescence, respectively.

Additional evidence for the distinction between these enzymes, as well as for the probability that both are auto-oxidizable by molecular oxygen, has been obtained by van Schouwenburg (1938). At low oxygen tensions the rate of oxygen consumption and brightness of luminescence may be reduced, the former much more readily than the latter. Under these conditions two auto-oxidizable enzymes, with somewhat different affinities for oxygen, would be expected to be thrown into competition for the oxygen. If now the one responsible for most of the oxygen consumption, known to be more sensitive to cyanide, is eliminated from activity by the addition of a small amount of cyanide, the enzyme responsible for luminescence should increase in activity. These results were, in fact, realized in the experiment.

Although bacterial luminescence may be reversibly inhibited by relatively high concentrations of cyanide, and the already much reduced rate of oxygen consumption proportionately inhibited (van Schouwenburg, 1938), whereas cyanide combines irreversibly with partially purified *Cypridina* luciferin and has no apparent effect on the reaction in crude extracts, the systems in bacteria and in *Cypridina* appear otherwise to be fundamentally similar. Analyses of the kinetics are consistent with the view that they are similar, and in further discussions we shall assume that they are.

Relation of bacterial luminescence to the general respiration

In suspensions of luminous bacteria deficient in nutrient substrates, and especially in washed cell suspensions, the rate of oxygen consumption and the brightness of luminescence are submaximal. Addition of glucose to the suspension medium causes a virtually immediate increase in rate of oxygen consumption and in intensity of luminescence (Johnson, 1939; cf. also Johnson, 1938), although not necessarily proportionately. Peptone likewise leads to an increase in both processes, much too rapidly to be accounted for in terms of an increase in number of cells (van Schouwenburg, 1938). On the basis of the influence of adding hydrogen donators, as well as the influence of inhibitors and other considerations, van Schouwenburg proposed the first definite scheme for the relation of the luminescent system to the general respiratory pathway of hydrogen transfer in luminous bacteria (arrows indicate the direction of hydrogen or electron transfer):

$$\text{Substrate} \rightarrow \text{dehydrogenation system} = \begin{cases} \rightarrow \text{luciferin} \rightarrow \text{luciferase} \rightarrow O_2 \\ \quad \longrightarrow O_2 \quad (7.57) \\ \rightarrow \text{heme enzyme} \longrightarrow O_2 \end{cases}$$

The direct oxidation of bacterial luciferin by oxygen, suggested by Anderson's (1936) experiments with *Cypridina* luciferin, is problematical. Exhaustive analyses of the influence of cyanide, urethan, and oxygen tension, separately and in combination, provided evidence that, although low concentrations of cyanide no doubt act on an iron-containing heme catalyst responsible for most of the aerobic respiration, higher concentrations are required to act appreciably on the luciferin. It was concluded that narcotics such as urethan, however, act primarily upon the luciferase. The fact that urethan acts directly and reversibly on luminescence has been demonstrated with the partially purified *Cypridina* system (Johnson and Chase, 1942), although it is not possible to distinguish, on the basis of the kinetic data obtained, whether the inhibition occurred through a reversible combination between urethan and luciferin or between urethan and luciferase (cf. p. 373).

The above scheme is consistent with the established facts concerning the action of inhibitors, and it accounts, in a general way, for the influence of glucose and peptone on the brightness of luminescence. In this connection it is perhaps significant that the average free energy of the oxidative removal of two hydrogens from glucose amounts to 57,300 cal, which is close to the free energy corresponding to the wavelength of maximum intensity of emitted light, or 60,700 cal. Moreover, although experiments have not been made with a large number of possible substrates, none has been found to increase luminescence so much as glucose. The possibility is not excluded that substrates other than glucose (e.g., among the mixture of substances, probably including small amounts of glucose, in peptone) are dehydrogenated with sufficient free energy change to give rise to luminescence via the luciferin-luciferase system, especially if they lead to the formation of hydrogen peroxide. If glucose is directly involved, it would not seem possible that its stepwise degradation through the system of respiratory catalysts could proceed far and still leave sufficient energy for the observed wavelengths of radiated light.

The van Schouwenburg scheme (7.57) has been variously modified and extended (Johnson, Eyring, Steblay, Chaplin, Huber, and Gherardi, 1945; Spruit and Schuiling, 1945; Spruit, 1946; McElroy and Kipnis, 1947), but for present purposes it is perhaps most useful in its original form, unadorned by further details adduced from subsequent and not completely certain evidence. With reference to the scheme of reactions on p. 172, the rôle of glucose in increasing luminescence might be interpreted either as providing an increase in the amount of reactant R in reaction (7.43), or as increasing the amount of L in the reduction of L_0 in reaction (7.47) with the Fe^{3+} replaced by glucose and enzyme systems; the latter alternative is more directly in line with the van Schouwenburg scheme.

The influence of redox indicators, including naphthoquinones (Spruit and Schuiling, 1945; Spruit, 1946; McElroy and Kipnis, 1947) is presumably mediated through a reaction similar to (7.47).

Efficiency of bacterial luminescence

There is no good reason to doubt that the Michaelis-Menton theory applies in bacterial luminescence in essentially the same manner as it does in *Cypridina* luminescence, but, since the luminescence of bacteria appears to be inextricably bound to the integrity of living cells, it does not lend itself to analysis in the same manner. The formulation for the velocity of formation of excited molecules, in accordance with equations (7.12) and (7.51), is

$$V = \frac{k_1 k_3 (L)(A)}{k_2 + k_3} = k_a L \tag{7.58}$$

Taking account, also, of emission and quenching, we obtain for the net rate of formation of excited molecules

$$\frac{dL^*}{dt} = \frac{k_1 k_3 (L)(A)}{k_2 + k_3} - k_b L^* - k_c L^* - \sum_\alpha (k_\alpha M_\alpha) L^* \tag{7.59}$$

Any attempt to analyze the influence of factors such as ions on the efficiency of bacterial luminescence, in the manner illustrated for *Cypridina* extracts (pp. 152 to 155) is complicated by the uncertainty about how much the observed results should be attributed to the luminescent system itself and how much to the cell as a whole. Iodide, for example, might be expected to extinguish luminescence by killing the cells. Moreover, the influence of ions cannot be considered apart from osmotic pressure of the solution, inasmuch as most of the species of luminous bacteria are marine in origin and for optimal function require a medium that is approximately isotonic with sea water. Viability, luminescence, and respiration of cell suspensions are maintained in isotonic solutions of non-penetrating non-electrolytes, such as sucrose; therefore external salt does not have to be supplied (Johnson and Harvey, 1938). On the other hand, growth in nutrient media fails to take place unless minimal concentrations of salt are added and cultures developing in the minimal concentrations of salt needed for growth do not luminesce (Johnson, 1947). As the concentration of sodium chloride is increased beyond such minimal amounts, luminescence of growing cultures becomes brighter and lasts longer, though at high concentrations both growth and luminescence are again inhibited (cf. Warren, 1945). The influence of the sodium chloride concentration in the medium of developing cultures calls for further study; it may well act, in part, on the efficiency of bacterial luminescence in the same manner as on that of *Cypridina* extracts.

The influence of hydrogen ions, temperature, pressure, and inhibitors is also complicated to some extent by the general influence of these factors on systems other than the luminescent system and on the cell as a whole, but under appropriate conditions their effects are readily reversible and kinetic analyses have been found to conform to relatively simple, theoretical mechanisms involving primarily the activity of the enzyme. The theory and evidence are discussed in later chapters.

Rate control in bacterial luminescence

The constant level of bacterial luminescence, under favorable conditions, shows that all the terms in equation (7.59) are constant for those conditions. By the same token, the intensity of luminescence varies with any factor that changes any of the terms in this equation. There is reason to believe, however, that under optimal conditions of salt concentration, with an excess of glucose and oxygen in the medium, the rate of the luminescent reaction and, therefore, the brightness of luminescence, is limited primarily by the amount and activity of the enzyme A. The amount of L thus appears to be in excess. In terms of the Michaelis-Menton theory, the substrate concentration is so high relative to that of the enzyme that the enzyme is practically saturated, with the result that the overall reaction proceeds as if governed by a single specific reaction rate constant k':

$$I \propto V = bk'(L)(A) \tag{7.60}$$

where b is a proportionality constant and L is constant. When the amount of L is sufficiently reduced by decreasing the amount of oxidizable substrate in the medium, the velocity is decreased. Or, if hydrogen transfer is drained through other systems, the light is relatively low unless the hydrogen transfer can be shunted through the luminescent system. The effect of cyanide in increasing the luminescence of dim variants of luminous bacteria (Spruit and Schuiling, 1945; Spruit, 1946) possibly takes place by such a mechanism; likewise the effect of cyanide on luminescence at low oxygen tensions (p. 180) and the effect of carbon monoxide at certain ratios with respect to the partial pressure of oxygen (van Schouwenburg and van der Burg, 1940).

Under conditions of steady state luminescence the intensity may be momentarily increased to several times its constant level if the cells are brought under conditions of anaerobiosis and are then suddenly aerated (Harvey, 1932). The "flash" of luminescence that occurs with the introduction of oxygen has been studied at some length (Johnson, van Schouwenburg, and van der Burg, 1939; Schoepfle, 1940; 1941). It never lasts for more than a few seconds, and the total excess luminescence is always small. Both the constant level intensity and the brightness of the flash, however, are much greater with an excess of glucose in the medium than in corresponding suspensions of washed cells alone. Unlike

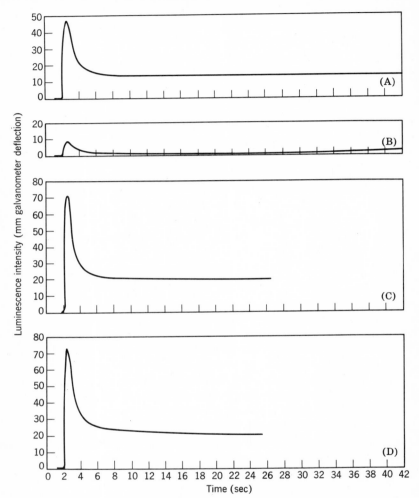

Fig. 7.23. The flash of luminescence following addition of oxygen to a suspension of luminous bacteria (*Achromobacter fischeri*): (A) after 2 min and (B) after 50 min of anaerobiosis with glycerol as exogenous substrate; (C) after 3 min and (D) after 82 min of anaerobiosis with glucose as exogenous substrate. (Johnson, van Schouwenburg and van der Burg, 1939.)

the phenomenon of "oxygen debt," e.g., in muscle and other tissues, which increases with the duration of anaerobiosis, the flash of luminescence reaches a maximum after only momentary lack of oxygen. In fact, during long periods without oxygen, unless the medium contains a fermentable substrate such as glucose, the flash that would ordinarily occur on addition of oxygen is all but eliminated and there follows a gradual rise in luminescence which lasts for a minute or longer. The presence of an adequate amount of glucose prevents this reduction in the flash, whereas the presence of glycerol, which can be oxidized aerobically but not anaerobically in the organisms studied, does not have such effect (Fig. 7.23).

The general interpretation of the flash is that during anaerobiosis there is an accumulation, through an equilibrium reaction, of reactants concerned with luminescence. Since these reactants obviously are not formed by the action of molecular oxygen (e.g., in reaction 7.43) during the period of oxygen lack, it seems probable that they consist of luciferin and luciferase. Thus the amount of the luciferin-luciferase complex increases under anaerobiosis to an extent governed by the amount of L, which is in turn governed by amount of reducing compounds, such as glucose, which influence a reaction similar to (7.47).

The interpretation of the reduction in flash after long periods of anaerobiosis and the influence of fermentable substrate in preventing this reduction are of particular interest in relation to mechanisms which control the luminescence reaction primarily through influencing the amount of active enzyme A. Because of the known activation of proteolysis in aerobic cells deprived of oxygen (Grassman, 1932; Grassman and Schneider, 1936) it is reasonable to suppose that the reduction of the flash, under the conditions described, is caused by a reversible proteolysis of the enzyme (Johnson, van Schouwenburg and van der Burg, 1939). This explanation is of more than incidental interest here, not only because it is possibly involved in numerous analogous effects in other cells, e.g., the protection of functional activity of the central nervous system against damage by oxygen lack, and the "induction period" of photosynthesis following anaerobiosis, but also because it has emphasized the importance of a reversible change in the protein structure of the luciferase. Other reversible changes that evidently take place in the protein structures of this enzyme, in ways that affect its catalytic activity under the influence of temperature, hydrostatic pressure, and certain inhibitors, are discussed in the following chapters.

ADDENDUM

A fundamental advance in the study of bacterial luminescence has been reported by Strehler (1953) since the manuscript of this book was submitted to the publishers. Strehler succeeded in obtaining easily visible luminescence in cell-free water extracts of acetone-dried luminous bacteria (*A. fischeri* and other species). After the initial light emission had ceased, luminescence could be restored by adding (a) boiled extracts of the acetone-dried bacteria, or (b) diphosphopyridine nucleotide (DPN), or better (c) reduced DPN ($DPNH_2$). In further studies (Strehler and Cormier, 1953), it was found that luminescence of extracts after long dialysis could be restored by $DPNH_2$ or by DPN plus malic acid, whereas DPN plus various other intermediates of the Krebs and Embden-Meyerhof cycles were ineffective. Luminescence of extracts was not supported, or was actually inhibited, by numerous other substances, including adenosine triphosphate, alone or in combination with $DPNH_2$. Flavin mononucleotide (FMN), however, increased the luminescence. An enormous increase in luminescence resulted from the addition of a factor, identified as palmitic aldehyde (Cormier and Strehler, 1953), from hog kidney cortex. A study of the pressure-temperature-inhibitor relationships of the luminescence of extracts (Strehler and Johnson, 1954) has yielded results remarkably similar to those obtained previously with intact cells.

Partially purified luminescent extracts have been obtained from distilled water cytolysates of *A. fischeri* (McElroy et al., 1953). Luminescence of these extracts apparently requires $DPNH_2$, FMN and an additional factor, which, it was suggested, is bacterial luciferin, present in fresh, boiled enzyme preparations. Other evidence, however, indicates that this factor may be analogous to palmitic aldehyde. Moreover, the addition of either reduced FMN or reduced riboflavin alone to Strehler's bacterial extracts results in luminescence, and there is justification for considering reduced FMN as bacterial luciferin (Strehler, Harvey, Chang and Cormier, 1954).

Strehler and Shoup (1953) have observed the chemiluminescence of flavin in the presence of peroxide plus iron, copper, or osmium catalysts.

Temperature

......................the parching Air
Burns frore, and cold performs th' effect of Fire.

Milton, *Paradise Lost*

It has been estimated that, if the average daily temperature on the face of the earth as a whole were suddenly raised or lowered by only 20 degrees, all life would perish. This estimate may not be fully correct, but neither is it far wrong, since disastrous consequences to most forms of life would surely follow a sudden change of this sort by seemingly few degrees. Moreover, it bears eloquent witness to the narrow range of temperatures through which life can successfully operate. Even by changes so gradual as to allow the various devices of migration, mutation, and evolution to favor survival, the range of temperatures would not be greatly extended. The diversity of life depends upon intricate links between the activities of different organisms, and in each organism there are limitations at both ends of the scale beyond which it is difficult to conceive how reproduction, growth, or metabolism could proceed at a significant rate.

Survival itself, however, varies enormously at extremes of temperature according to the degree of specialization and complexity of the organism. Many primitive organisms retain their viability in a state of suspended activity at almost incredibly low temperatures and show no apparent injury when restored to their normal environmental conditions. Thus various species of bacteria have been subjected, in some cases for months at a time, to liquid air temperatures of $-182°$ to $-190°C$ (Macfadyen, 1900; Macfadyen and Rowland, 1900a; Paul and Prall, 1907; Dewar, 1910; Harvey, 1913; Winchester and Murray, 1936); bacteria, yeasts, and spores of higher fungi have survived the temperature of liquid hydrogen, $-253°C$ (Macfadyen and Rowland, 1900b; Paul and Prall, 1907; Beijerinck and Jacobsen, 1908; Becquerel, 1910; de Jong, 1922); and a remarkable array of living forms have recovered their normal activity after exposure to the temperature of liquid helium, within only a couple of degrees of absolute zero, including luminous bacteria (Zirpolo, 1933), moss spores (Becquerel, 1932), pollen grains (Becquerel, 1929), seeds of higher plants (Becquerel, 1925; Lipman, 1936), some lower animals (Rahm, 1923; Becquerel, 1936), and others (cf. Luyet and Gehenio, 1940).[1] Primitive but highly specialized organisms, e.g., certain pathogenic bacteria such as meningococci and gonococci, which are parasitic on warm-blooded animals, readily succumb to the slight cold of an ordinary refrigerator (Topley and Wilson, 1936), although, paradoxically, gonococci have been found to recover after exposure to liquid air temperatures (Lumière and Chevrotier, 1914). Highly evolved, complex animals such as mammals succumb to any considerable lowering of their normal body temperature, although recent studies (cf. Hardy, 1950) have indicated that they are better able to survive abnormal cold than had been assumed previously; e.g., young white rats recovered after cooling to 3°C, at which all perceptible signs of life, including heart beat and circulation of the blood, ceased (Fairfield, 1948). It is only because of the decrease in chemical (metabolic) reaction rates at low temperatures that they can survive. Irreparable damage to the central nervous system, · for example, quickly follows any cessation of oxygen supply through stoppage of the circulation at normal temperature.

In all organisms it is likely to be more disastrous to raise than to lower the temperature by a given amount from the normal "optimum," for the most destructive processes have a high temperature coefficient, and their effects become increasingly irreversible as the temperature is raised. The higher animals, including man, normally function at virtually constant body temperature, controlled by subtle physiological mechanisms against fluctuations in the environment and scarcely ever varying by more than three or four degrees. The unpleasantness of chills and fever is probably due, in part, to the variations from normal body temperatures, although in disease there are unpleasant changes in metabolism arising from factors other than increased temperature alone.

For biological activity the vast majority of organisms are confined to temperatures between somewhat above 0°C and somewhat below 50°C, with varying degrees of sensitivity to temperature changes within this range. The most sensitive activity seems to be the movement of pseudopodia in slime molds, which responds noticeably to an estimated difference of 0.0005°C (Bonner, Clark, Neely and Slifkin, 1950). In rare instances lower organisms have been found carrying on apparently normal activities at 0°C, e.g., the Alaskan stonefly, *Namoura columbiana* (Sailer, 1950), or growing slowly at temperatures as low as − 4 to − 6.7°C, e.g., certain bacteria and molds (Berry and Magoon, 1934). Among vertebrates the polar codfish (*Boreogadus saida*) remains active at environmental temperatures between − 1.5° and + 2.0°C, and has been maintained in the

---

[1] The survival of cells, tissues, organs, and organisms after ultra-rapid freezing at very low temperatures is reviewed by Luyet (1952).

laboratory at $-1°$ to $0°C$ (Peiss and Field, 1950). Cold-blooded animals from temperate regions do not evidence such adaptation to cold habitats; fish, amphibia, and reptiles in the temperate zones undergo a general anesthesia when placed in cracked ice, then recover at room temperature (Parker, 1939). Birds and mammals in arctic and tropical habitats, respectively, have various adaptive mechanisms, including specific sensitivities in rate of general metabolism to environmental temperature, for maintaining constant body temperatures (Scholander et al., 1950).

At the other end of the scale, there are some grounds for believing that bacteria indigenous to deep oil well brines may normally exist at temperatures of $100°C$ or above, probably aided by the relatively high hydrostatic pressure (ZoBell and Johnson, 1949).

The purpose of this chapter is to examine and, in so far as we are able, to interpret at the molecular level some of the general and specific mechanisms through which temperature exercises a controlling influence on biological reactions. Temperature is certainly one of the most fundamental of all factors that affects the rate and, especially in biology, the net result of chemical reactions.

Because of the relation of every chemical reaction to both temperature and pressure (equations 1.21 and 1.24), and also because changes in pressure may quite offset the effects of changes in temperature, it would be logical to consider these two variables together.   It is more convenient, however, to begin with temperature, and here again the phenomenon of bioluminescence has proved to have unusual advantages as a research tool.   The action of pressure is taken up in Chapter 9.

The "optimal temperature" of biological processes

Implicit in the familiar fact that, at either the hot or cold limits of a relatively narrow range of temperatures, all biological processes practically cease is the consequence that some intermediate range of temperature must be the most favorable.   For a long time, the "most favorable" intermediate temperature has been called the "optimum," although this term has frequently been used without a precise meaning.   Thus it is not uncommon to find reference to the optimal temperature of a whole organism—a species of bacteria, a tropical or arctic plant, a type of fish or other poikilothermic animal.   In a general way, there are wide differences in this so-called optimum among different organisms, and these differences are often correlated with the natural habitat (Figs. 8.1 and 8.2). In a single species, however, the optimal temperature is not necessarily the same for different aspects of its life phenomena, such as rate of growth, maximum size of body, respiration, pigmentation, individual

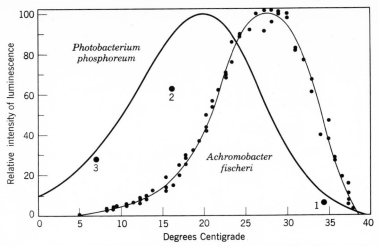

Fig. 8.1. Temperature-activity curves for brightness of luminescence in suspensions of two species of bacteria: *Photobacterium phosphoreum*, isolated from the cold waters of the North Sea, and *Achromobacter fischeri*, isolated from a dead squid during summer months at Woods Hole, Massachusetts (Brown, Johnson, and Marsland, 1942). The large, solid circles numbered 1, 2, and 3, respectively, represent the intensity of luminescence of the suspension of *Photobacterium phosphoreum* during cooling from about 35°C.

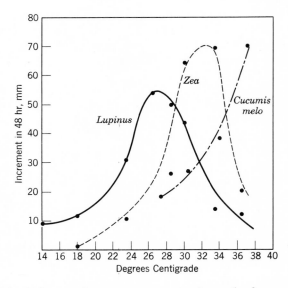

Fig. 8.2. Influence of temperature on rate of growth of common plants indigenous to temperate (*Lupinus*) and warmer climates (*Zea* and *Cucumis melo*). From D'Arcy Thompson (1942); data of Sachs.

190

enzyme activity, and longevity.   Some of these relationships are illustrated by the following examples.

The rate of reproduction of a culture of bacteria may be increased by a rise in temperature at the expense of the maximal number of cells finally

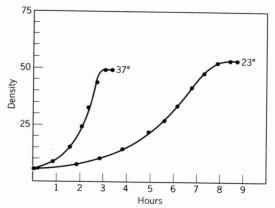

Fig. 8.3.   Density of cells in a bacterial culture, as a function of time after inoculation, at two different constant temperatures (Monod, 1942).

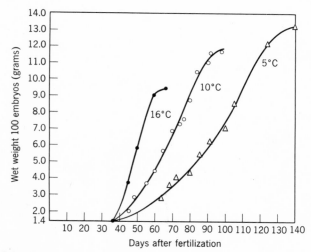

Fig. 8.4.   Rate of growth and final size of trout larvae raised at different constant temperatures (Gray, 1928).

attained in the population (Fig. 8.3; cf. also Graham-Smith, 1920; Gray, 1929); similarly, the influence of temperature upon the rate of growth and upon the final size of trout larvae (*Salmo fario*) is in opposite directions (Fig. 8.4). Among lower animals it is not unusual to find larger body sizes associated with cold habitats; many arctic species grow to larger size than their near relatives in warm climates, and flies are larger in winter than in summer broods (Thompson, 1942). Within a single day the body size and nuclear volume in a culture of protozoa undergo an increase at cool temperatures and a decrease at warm temperatures (Popoff, 1908). On the other hand, size is not always

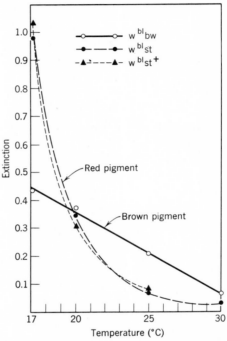

Fig. 8.5. Amount of red and brown pigment produced by mutant strains of *Drosophila* when raised at different temperatures (Ephrussi and Herold, 1945).

decreased at the higher temperatures. When cultivated at temperatures above their normal optimum for rate of cell division, bacterial cells may become enormously larger than usual; e.g., the cells of *Acetobacter*, in cultures incubated at 40°C, may increase to as much as 150 times their familiar size (Hansen, 1894), reflecting a difference in the effects of temperature on the rate processes of cell division and of growth.

Variations in the production of a red and brown pigment in mutant strains of the fruit fly, *Drosophila*, when raised at different temperatures, are illustrated in Fig. 8.5 (Ephrussi and Herold, 1945). The kinetics of the net result is obviously different for the two pigments, but the amount of each decreases with rise in temperature. An opposite effect of temperature on pigmentation occurs in nature during seasonal variations; one of the best known examples is that of the several species of grouse, known as ptarmigans, which inhabit northern regions. In summer their plumage is dark and harmonizes with the rocky barrens where they feed on mosses, lichens, etc.; in winter the feathers become white, harmonizing with the deep snow of their habitat at that season.

Longevity is another aspect of the temperature parameter, not only among microörganisms, but also among higher forms of life (Fig. 8.6; cf. also Loeb and Northrop, 1917). As in many other complex biological processes, length of life, as a whole, has an optimal temperature, other

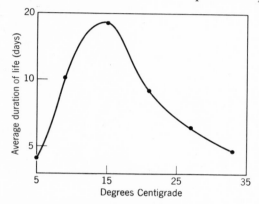

Fig. 8.6.   Length of life of the water flea, *Moina*, as a function of temperature (Terao and Tanaka, 1930).

factors being the same.   Among the "warm-blooded" animals, birds and mammals, including man, a relationship qualitatively similar to that illustrated in Fig. 8.6 no doubt exists, although the quantitative data are understandably more difficult to obtain and the range in temperature is more restricted on either side of the maximum of the curve. There is nothing unique about such a restricted range, nor is it associated only with complex organisms; it is found, for example, with respect to the rate of growth of bacteria, among the hemophilic pathogens.   Furthermore there is no *a priori* reason to conclude that the normal body temperature of the homoithermic animals is the optimal for longevity, although it appears to be optimal for general physiological activity.

The above examples are a few from the multitude that could be cited with reference to optimal temperatures in biology, and they illustrate in a small measure the diversity of temperature relationships which one would like to interpret on a precise, albeit not always a simple, theory.

General interpretation of the temperature optimum

It is clear that the rate of no single chemical reaction could well go through so great a change on either side of a pronounced maximum within the short range of temperatures characteristic of biological processes. A minimum of two reactions is essential: one accelerating, the

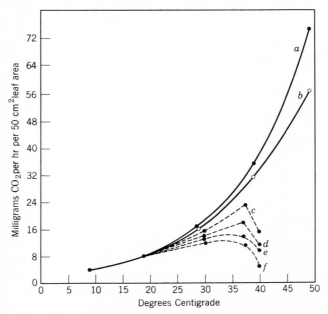

Fig. 8.7. Observed rates (broken lines) of carbon dioxide assimilation in leaves of the cherry laurel, as a function of the duration of the experiment. The uppermost broken-line curve is for observations lasting 2.5 hr, and the successively lower curves for 3.5, 4.5, and 5.5 hr, respectively. The upper solid line represents the rate which would be predicted when a single reaction with a Q_{10} of 2.1 is assumed, and the lower solid line on a similar assumption of a reaction with a μ of 12,230 cal. (After Blackman, 1905, data of Matthaei, 1905, and after Buchanan and Fulmer, 1930.)

other diminishing, the process, and both increasing, though to different extents, with rise in temperature. The full mechanism responsible for the maximum in the curve, i.e., the optimal temperature, might be expected to depend upon the complexity of the process, and many more than two reactions are no doubt concerned in the temperature-activity curve of complicated phenomena, considered as a whole, in living cells.

The earliest, somewhat qualitative, interpretations recognized the necessity of at least two reactions having opposite effects on the overall process; e.g., Tammann (1895) assumed that enzymatic processes undergo acceleration with rise in temperature, but then decrease beyond the maximum because of a thermal destruction of the catalyst. On this hypothesis the optimal temperature should be a function of the duration of the experimental measurements, i.e., the optimum should occur at higher temperatures, the shorter the duration of the measurements. Evidence that this phenomenon indeed occurs in living cells was found in studies on the rates of carbon dioxide assimilation through photosynthesis in leaves of the cherry laurel (Matthaei, 1905; Blackman and Matthaei, 1905). The data were used in theoretical considerations by Blackman (1905) and are illustrated in Fig. 8.7.

In Fig. 8.7, the theoretical rate of the process as a whole, apart from the influence of any reactions which would diminish its rate at the higher temperatures, is calculated on the basis that the temperature coefficient Q_{10} for the process is 2.1, as well as on the basis of an activation energy of 12,230 cal (Buchanan and Fulmer, 1930). Although the Q_{10}, or ratio between the rate of a reaction at one temperature and the rate of the reaction at a temperature 10°C higher, has no rational basis, it has been widely used, especially in biology (cf. Przibram, 1923), as a quantitative basis for the comparison of the effects of temperature, and it is still useful.

In Fig. 8.7 the lowering of the optimal temperature with increasing periods of exposure is very probably due to a rate process of irreversible destruction of one of the essential catalysts, as Blackman assumed. On the other hand, it is conceivably caused by a reversible mechanism, such as that involved in the effects of urethan on bacterial luminescence discussed later (p. 409), inasmuch as a rate process of liberation of substances having effects similar to those of urethan might occur in living tissues at the higher temperatures.

Blackman's interpretations were only partially quantitative and were incomplete (cf. also Chick and Martin, 1910, 1911). They were concerned with the chief factors, when others were certainly involved. Although they undoubtedly contained a large element of truth, they did not account for, among other things, the fact, pointed out by Kanitz (1915), that there is a progressive decrease in Q_{10} with rise in temperature. This decrease is much greater than can be attributed to the empirical formulation of the Q_{10}, which would be expected to yield slightly lower values as the temperature is raised, for a reaction with a constant μ value. The data of Fig. 8.7 show that the value of μ, itself, becomes less for successively higher temperature intervals, up to the maximum of activity where it becomes zero. Moreover, up to this maximum (with short periods of observations), the effects of temperature on the rate of a biological process are usually quite reversible. Experiments concerning the reversibility of the thermal diminution in activity by brief exposures to temperatures higher than the usual optimum seemed rather pointless at that time and for years afterwards. The idea that there was only an irreversible destruction of the systems at these temperatures was too firmly entrenched in the minds of those who sought to explain the data. The real significance of the relatively few scattered observations and experiments on the reversibility of seemingly destructive effects of high temperatures has been appreciated only recently. It had to await progress in protein chemistry, which demonstrated that drastic but reversible changes in these large molecules may take place in a manner affecting the catalytic activity of enzymes, and accompanied by large heats, entropies, and volume changes of reaction. The importance of such reactions at temperatures below, as well as above, the optimum will be discussed presently.

Accepting the destruction of catalysts at relatively high temperatures and the acceleration of their action by heat at the lower temperatures, the problem resolves itself into the question of the mechanisms responsible for the change in rate at intermediate temperatures. Here, again, some general ideas were advanced long before they were tested by precise formulations in specific application to experimental data. At the same time, efforts toward rational, quantitative interpretations were made. From these roots sprang hypotheses which, partially correct or erroneous, are still widely held and therefore require critical examination.

From the point of view of its effect on subsequent thought, perhaps the most influential idea was that of Blackman (1905) and Pütter (1914), sometimes called the Blackman-Pütter principle. In essence, this principle states that every biological process depends upon a series of consecutive and other reactions, each characterized by a definite temperature coefficient, and each becoming the limiting factor or the master process at a definite temperature. There is no denying that many biological processes do depend upon a series of reactions and may be considered largely limited at certain temperatures by some particular one more than by the others. To designate one as the master process, however, is a matter of definition, since the net results at all temperatures remain dependent upon the other contributory reactions. Strictly speaking, it is more appropriate to say that certain reactions have a more significant influence at some temperature ranges than at others; e.g., any reaction with a very high heat and entropy of reaction or of activation that is completely negligible at room or body temperature may at somewhat higher temperatures become suddenly important. At these higher temperatures, however, the other reactions are still influenced in exactly the manner determined by their own thermodynamic or rate constants.

With isolated enzyme systems the number of reactions contributing to the measured result would be expected to be much fewer than in the more complicated processes of living cells.   Yet the kinetics of specific enzyme reactions *in vitro* are subject to modification by many factors, including the influence of products of the reactions, impurities in the preparation (sometimes in incredibly small amounts), and the chemical environment (salts, *p*H, etc.) which may not only alter stability and activity of the catalyst but also, in some instances, the reactivity of the substrate.   On the other hand, within the highly organized and well-regulated environment of a living cell, complex processes often proceed at a steady state with close conformity to the kinetics of a single reaction.   These relationships will be discussed in more detail presently.   For the moment, it is interesting to note that the idea of a series of "master processes" in biological temperature relationships was advanced by some of the first investigators of the problem.

In contrast to those who have sought a physical-chemical interpretation of biological rate processes, a considerable number of investigators have concluded that the usual laws governing the temperature relations of chemical reactions do not hold in biology (cf. discussions in Bělehrádek, 1930).   This conclusion smacks of vitalism and need not be considered in detail.   To the extent that the complexity of the process leads to apparent deviations from these laws, the conclusion might seem to follow. Such deviations are to be expected, and there is no justification for assuming that they result from anything other than the participation in the process of a number of individual reactions, each of which proceeds in strictest accordance with the same physical-chemical laws which would apply to them in a test tube.   The problem is merely one of adequate analysis, which for most biological processes is still far from complete.

Arrhenius (1907, 1908) was apparently the first to apply his formulation for the influence of temperature on chemical reactions to the rates of biochemical phenomena, and to point out that the value of μ in the thermal destruction of enzymes is several times higher than that of the specifically catalyzed reaction; an optimal temperature is the inevitable consequence of such a difference.   Figure 8.8 shows the data of Kjeldahl (1881) on the rate of inversion of sucrose by invertase, as treated by Arrhenius (1915).   Although Arrhenius' theory calls for using the reciprocal of the absolute temperature rather than degrees Centigrade on the abscissa, to reveal linearity, the shape of the curve is not appreciably different over the relatively short range of temperature concerned.   The value of μ for the enzyme-catalyzed reaction was computed to be 9,080 cal from the formula

$$K_1 = K_0 e^{\frac{\mu}{2}\left(\frac{T_1 - T_0}{T_0 T_1}\right)} \tag{8.1}$$

where K_0 is the velocity of the reaction at absolute temperature T_0, K_1 is the velocity at T_1, and e is the base of natural logarithms.   The approximate value of 2 is taken for the gas constant in the denominator of the exponent of e.

The rapid decrease in rate of inversion at temperatures above about 52.5°C (Fig. 8.8) is evidence of the high value of μ in the reaction, which Arrhenius interpreted as "spontaneous destruction" of the enzyme, responsible for the reduction in rate.   Arrhenius noted that the high values of μ characteristic of the spontaneous destruction of enzymes apply also to such biological materials as antibodies, and to the coagulation of

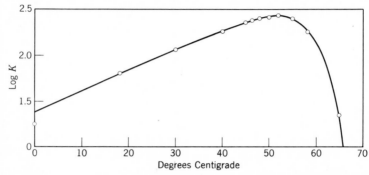

Fig. 8.8.   The rate of inversion of sucrose by invertase as a function of temperature, plotted by Arrhenius (1915) from the data of Kjeldahl (1881).

proteins by heat.   In the presence of acids and alkalies, however, the value of μ in these processes is much lower.   Table 8.1 lists some of the data from Arrhenius (1907, 1915).

In the present discussion the precise numerical values of μ listed in Table 8.1 are not of primary importance.   They are subject to various influences, including in some instances the purity or the past history of the preparations, as well as the particular range of temperature for which the μ was computed.   Some general relationships noted by Arrhenius, however, are manifestly clear; particularly, the much lower μ values for enzyme-catalyzed reactions than for the "spontaneous destruction" of enzymes and other large molecules, and the similarity of the μ values for both specific enzyme reactions and complex processes (heart beat, respiration, etc.) in living cells to those of ordinary chemical reactions.   It is also apparent that a given reaction catalyzed by an enzyme, e.g., the hydrolysis of sugar, has a much lower μ than when catalyzed by non-specific agents, such as hydrogen ions.   Furthermore, the apparent activation energy for the coagulation or precipitation of proteins is enormously decreased by acid.

Following the example of Arrhenius, the investigation of an immense number of enzyme reactions and more complex processes has resulted in the accumulation of useful data. In many instances there has appeared to be a linear relationship between the logarithm of the rate or activity and the reciprocal of the absolute temperature, from temperatures well

Table 8.1. Some Values of μ, as Computed by Arrhenius (1907, 1915) for Biochemical and Biological Processes

Process	μ
Spontaneous destruction	
Tetanolysin	162,000
Vibriolysin	128,000
Rennet, 2% solution	90,000
Pepsin, 2% solution	75,600
Trypsin, 2% solution	62,000
Emulsin, 0.5% solution	45,000
Emulsin, dry	26,300
Yeast invertase	72,000
Dibromsuccinic acid	22,200
Coagulation or precipitation	
Egg white by heat	135,600
Hemoglobin by heat	60,100
Milk by rennet	20,650
Egg white by sulfuric acid	11,000
Digestions	
Casein by trypsin	37,500
Powdered casein by trypsin	7,400
Gelatin by trypsin	10,570
Gelatin by pepsin	10,750
Egg white by pepsin	15,570
Various processes	
Hydrolysis of cane sugar by acids	25,600
Hydrolysis of cane sugar by invertase (Kjeldahl)	9,080
Hydrolysis of cane sugar by invertase	11,000
Alcoholic fermentation by yeast cells	15,600
Respiration by plants	14,800
Cell division in eggs (mean value)	14,100
Heart beats of pacific terrapin	16,060

below to those approaching the optimum, while in many others the relationship has been more or less obviously a curve showing progressive decrease in μ with rise in temperature. Generally, the effects of raising the temperature have been quantitatively reversible on cooling, provided that the material has not been maintained for any considerable period of time at or above the temperature of maximal activity.

The Crozier theory

In undertaking to interpret further the temperature relationships of biological activity, Crozier and his collaborators (1924–26) carried out a series of studies and proposed a theory embodying the following chief points: (1) a catenary series of reactions, each with a definite μ value, temperature characteristic, or critical thermal increment, underlies every physiological process; (2) the overall process is limited, within definite

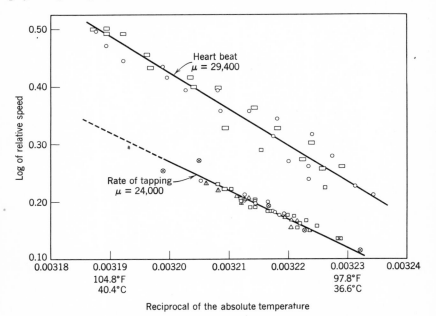

Fig. 8.9. Upper line, rate of heart beat in two diathermy experiments on human subjects; lower line, rate of tapping, estimated to represent 1-sec intervals, by subjects in whom fever was raised by diathermy or by influenza (Hoagland and Perkins, 1934–35).

ranges of temperature, by a slowest step or master reaction; (3), at a certain critical temperature a different master reaction may assume control, and a sharp "break" will be apparent in the slopes of lines in an Arrhenius plot of the data; and (4) it might be possible to identify corresponding master reactions in different physiological processes (e.g., heart beat, locomotion, respiration) by correspondence in their measured μ values.   The first two of these postulates are essentially the same as the Blackman-Pütter principle.   The latter two have been the subject of so much discussion and controversy that they call for further comment. We shall consider the third one first.

A few typical examples of data from the work of Crozier and others are illustrated in Figs. 8.9 to 8.23.   Examination of many diverse processes reveals that, no matter how complex, there is practically always some considerable range of temperature over which the relation between temperature and activity conforms to the Arrhenius equation.   The functioning of the human brain in consciousness is perhaps as complex a process as one can find in biology, yet there is evidence (Fig. 8.9) that the activity here bears a simple relation to temperature.   Hoagland (1936a, c) has pointed out that, if our sense of time depends upon the

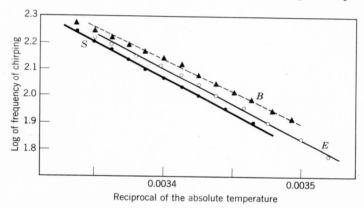

Fig. 8.10.   Temperature dependence of the rate of chirping of the tree cricket, *Oecanthus* (Crozier, 1924–25b;   data of Bessey and Bessey, 1898, curve *B*;   data of Edes, 1899, curve *E*;   and data of Shull, 1907, curve *S*. Additional data have been reported by Matthews (1942).

velocity of chemical events in the brain, time should seem to pass more slowly during a fever, since the acceleration of chemical events in the brain by the higher temperature would cause more physiological time to pass per unit of the solar time to which we are accustomed at normal temperature.   Furthermore, if the velocity of chemical events is limited largely by a single, slowest reaction, conformity in the rate of the overall process to the Arrhenius equation would be logically anticipated.   Such conformity is indicated by the data of Fig. 8.9, which for comparison includes data with respect to another complex process, the rate of heart beat.   Unfortunately, the range in temperature over which these processes can be measured (about 4 degrees Centigrade in Fig. 8.9) is limited by the complaisance of the subjects.   Among lower animals, however, rhythmic processes paced by nervous activity conform to the Arrhenius relation over a wider range of temperatures, e.g., the rate of chirping by crickets (Fig. 8.10) extending over about 12°C.   Data with respect to a somewhat

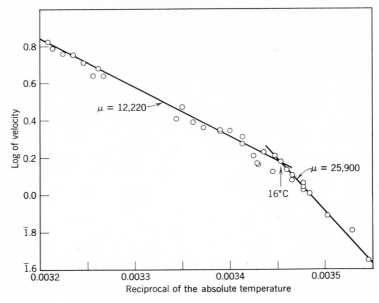

Fig. 8.11. Temperature dependence of the velocity of creeping of the ant, *Liometopum apiculatum* (Crozier, 1924–25a; data of Shapley, 1920).

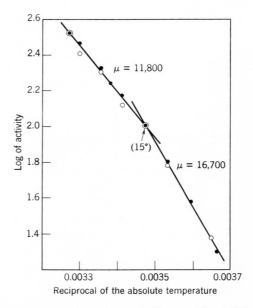

Fig. 8.12. Temperature dependence of ciliary activity (solid circles) and oxygen consumption (open circles) of the gill epithelium of the clam, *Mytilus* (Crozier, 1924–25a; data of Gray, 1923).

wider range in temperatures usually reveal departures from the purely
linear relationship apparent in Figs. 8.9 and 8.10.   Thus Fig. 8.11 shows
another example of biological activity under nervous control, the rate of
creeping of ants, between about 10° and 27°C, and illustrates what Crozier
has interpreted as a break at a critical temperature, in this case at 16°C.
The two straight lines were drawn by inspection and interpreted to indicate

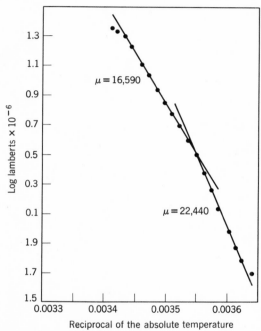

Fig. 8.13.   Brightness of luminescence in a suspension of *Bacterium phosphorescens* as a function of temperature, below that of the maximum
(Morrison, 1924–25).   Root (1932) has similarly treated data referring to a
different species.

master reactions with temperature characteristics of 25,900 cal below
16°C, and 12,220 cal above 16°C.   A smooth curve could also be drawn
by inspection, however, to fit the observed data equally well; in this, as
in so many experiments with living material, the measured points are
somewhat scattered.

It is not unusual to find relatively little difference in slopes of two such
lines drawn by inspection (Figs. 8.12 and 8.13), and to find the position
of the "critical temperature" correspondingly indefinite.   The difference
in the values of μ is sensitive to slight differences in slopes.   In these

instances it seems even more likely that the data actually represent smooth curves.   The subjective element is difficult to eliminate where no precise formulation is available to apply as a test for the presumed discontinuities and changes in slope.   Buchanan and Fulmer (1930) have pointed out how readily a continuous variation in μ may be misconstrued as successive

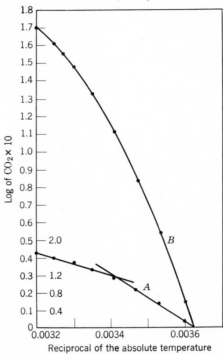

Fig. 8.14.   The rate of carbon dioxide production in alcoholic fermentation by yeast as a function of temperature (Slator, 1911), plotted on two different scales of the ordinate by Buchanan and Fulmer (1930).   The two linear portions seemingly present in curve A are revealed as a continuous variation in B, when the same data are plotted on the wider scale of the ordinate.

linear relations, when the units on the ordinate are relatively close together (Fig. 8.14).

Figures 8.15 and 8.16 illustrate data which extend from temperatures only slightly above 0°C up to and beyond the optimum.   In Fig. 8.15 three linear portions and two critical temperatures have been indicated. The slopes of the three lines become successively less with rise in temperature.   By inspection alone, however, a smooth curve seems equally appropriate.   In Fig. 8.16 two critical temperatures have again been indicated.   Two straight lines have been drawn and, contrary to the usual experience, the slope of the one at lower temperatures is less, instead of greater, than the one at the next higher temperatures.

Under some conditions enormous changes in slope may occur within a narrow range of temperature, e.g., with processes which have a sharp optimum temperature, approached from low temperatures by a nearly

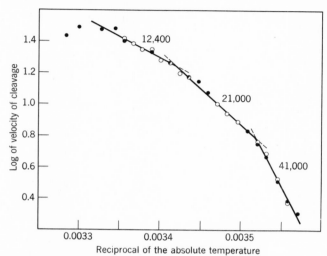

Fig. 8.15.   Rate of cell division of sea urchin (*Arbacia*) eggs as a function of temperature (Crozier, 1924–25b; data of Loeb and Wasteneys, 1911, solid circles; data of Loeb and Chamberlain, 1915, hollow circles).

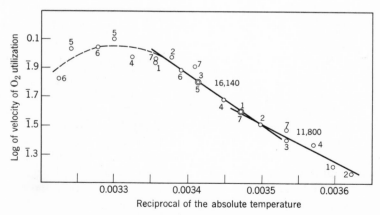

Fig. 8.16.   Rate of oxygen consumption of *Arbacia* (sea urchin) eggs as a function of temperature (Crozier, 1924–25b; data of Loeb and Wasteneys, 1911).

straight line on an Arrhenius plot, then dropping precipitously just beyond the optimum.   Moreover, very marked changes in slope may be associated with changes in state or structure of the system, e.g., in the activity of hydrolytic enzymes, such as lipase or invertase, in the neighborhood of 0°C (Figs. 8.17 and 8.18; Sizer and Josephson, 1942).   With lipase it is apparent that the change in slope occurs at about the same temperature whether the reaction mixture contains sufficient glycerol to keep it in a fluid state, or does not contain glycerol and exists in a frozen, solid state

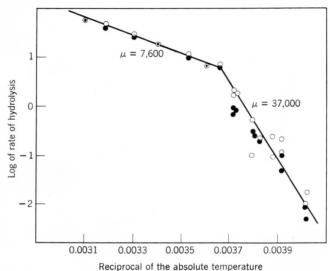

Fig. 8.17.   Temperature activity curve for the hydrolysis of tributyrin by pancreatic lipase, in the presence of about 36% glycerol (hollow circles) and without glycerol (solid circles) (Sizer and Josephson, 1942).

at temperatures below the "break."   Consequently the change in slope evidently does not result from the change in state alone, and in the presence of large amounts of glycerol it must be attributed to the influence of temperature on other factors, including the influence of temperatures below zero on viscosity and diffusion.   Kavanau (1950) has worked out an empirical formulation which fits the increase in apparent activation energy of biological processes at low temperatures.   Although its theoretical significance is not fully clear, the suggestion that the mechanism involves changes in molecular configuration which affect the catalytic properties of the enzyme is plausible.   Furthermore, it is reasonable to believe that the activation energy is higher at low temperatures, and that this circumstance is partially responsible for the change in μ value encountered in various biological reactions.

Under these circumstances (Figs. 8.17 and 8.18) the "breaks" in the curve may be interpreted as arising from a change in relative importance of rate-limiting reactions, though not necessarily in the original sense of different pace-setting reactions in a catenary series essential to the observed result. The reality of sharp breaks in the preceding figures is questionable on various grounds, some of which have been briefly indicated. In addition, it is difficult to arrive at a quantitative and reasonable theoretical mechanism which would give similar breaks at "critical temperatures." Burton (1939) concluded that, for one of two consecutive reactions to

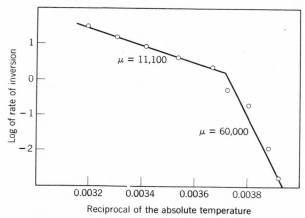

Fig. 8.18. Temperature-activity curve for the hydrolysis of sucrose by yeast invertase, without glycerol (Sizer and Josephson, 1942).

assume mastery, within 10 per cent, at some particular temperature, its activation energy would have to be at least seven times that of the other. Morales (1947) has shown, however, that the difference need not be so great and would actually amount to 2.7 times, rather than the 7 times estimated by Burton. Booij and Wolvekamp (1944), in an exhaustive critique, have examined a number of conceivable mechanisms and concluded that the notion of the master reaction in Crozier's sense cannot hold. Stearn (1949) has also discussed this problem on the basis of theoretical formulations for consecutive and simultaneous reactions in the steady state. Without entering here into the details of the arguments of these several authors, which may be found in the original papers, it seems evident that sharp breaks at critical temperatures, on the basis postulated by Crozier, are not real, although changes in slope undeniably occur, and in some instances more gradually than in others. The extent to which differences in temperature characteristics of catenary reactions contribute to the changes in slope cannot be accurately determined without some definite formulation, which the Crozier theory does not attempt to provide, and which in physiological processes may become exceedingly complicated.

The fourth point listed on p. 200, viz., the possibility of recognizing similar master reactions in diverse processes by means of their μ values, obviously depends, first on the existence of a single rate-determining step. Secondly, it depends upon an essentially constant μ for the limiting system in different cellular and chemical environments. Of the two conditions, both of which are necessary to justify the postulate, the first is supported by, or is at least consistent with, the fact that so many physiological processes as a whole show a close conformity to the Arrhenius equation over a significant range of temperature. The second is supported by some facts and rendered unlikely by others. The following evidence has been cited in support of the postulate.

The activity of a few enzymes (invertase, urease) has been found to have the same μ value within living cells and in extracts (Sizer, 1943). Furthermore, there are data (Sizer, 1943) indicating that the μ value for certain enzyme activities *in vitro* is independent of the purity of their extracts, of pH, of electrolyte concentration, and of the relative concentrations of enzyme and substrate. These relationships, however, certainly do not hold in general. Another line of evidence which has been taken as support for a really characteristic μ for a given process is the close similarity of μ values for the dehydrogenation of various substrates by *Escherichia coli* (Gould and Sizer, 1938). A μ of 19,400 cal was found for the rate of anaerobic reduction of methylene blue with the bacteria plus each of various substrates: acetate, galactose, glucose, glutamate, glycine, lactate, mannitol, succinate, sucrose, and xylose. The significance of the same μ value here, however, is uncertain, inasmuch as more than one specific enzyme was undoubtedly concerned; it might be a coincidence or it might indicate a similar pace-setting reaction in the process of reduction of the dye. Moreover, other values of μ have been reported for the dehydrogenation of some of the same substrates by the same organism, e.g., 16,700 for succinate (Crozier, 1924–25b, data of Quastel and Whetham, 1924) and 13,000 to 14,600 with glucose; they vary slightly with the amount of added coenzyme (Johnson and Lewin, 1946a). By using the same technique but a different organism, the μ value for dehydrogenation of glucose by *Rhizobium trifolii* was found to be 13,600 cal (Koffler, Johnson, and Wilson, 1947). These discrepancies from the values reported by Gould and Sizer (1938) as well as other inconsistencies relative to the conformance of the hypothesis to the data given by Sizer (1943) are sufficiently large to question the usefulness of the hypothesis at issue, regardless of whether the discrepancies arise from minor differences in experimental conditions, or from specific differences in the strains and species of organisms studied. In addition, such discrepancies add to the uncertainty of the meaning of a somewhat rough correspondence between the statistical distribution (Fig. 8.19) of μ values in physiological processes (Crozier, 1926) and in individual enzyme systems (Sizer, 1943; Morales, 1947).

Finally, changes in the observed μ both in physiological processes and in individual enzyme systems have been found to occur under the influence

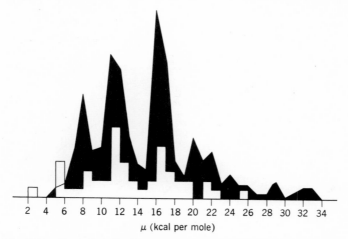

μ (kcal per mole)

Fig. 8.19. Statistical distribution of 360 μ values for various physiological processes (solid areas, data of Crozier, 1926) and of some 48 individual enzyme systems (hollow areas, data of Sizer, 1943) showing a rough overlapping of ranges and similarity of modes (Morales, 1947).

of various factors. For example, the temperature characteristics for the hydrolysis of urea by urease of *Proteus vulgaris* (Sizer, 1941) vary markedly with constituents of the culture medium and age of the culture (Fig. 8.20; cf. also Sizer, 1941, Table 1). Likewise, the μ for the activity of either crude extracts or crystallized urease preparations from jack bean meal varies, usually reversibly, in the presence of oxidizing-reducing substances (Fig. 8.21) and certain other agents (Sizer, 1939).

From Sizer's data it is clear that the measured μ value of individual enzyme systems may be readily modified by the chemical environment and furthermore that typical "breaks" in the Arrhenius curves for such simple systems may seem to appear, just as in physiological processes. Here, however, there is no reason to attribute changes in slope to the participation of a series of reactions which would be expected in living cells; they are to be attributed rather to an effect on the catalytic properties of the enzyme. Although we are not in accord with the view of definite μ values above and below "critical temperatures" (Fig. 8.21, curves 3, 4, and 5), Sizer's general interpretation of changes in slope under the influence of oxidizing and reducing agents seems essentially correct, namely, that these agents affect the catalytic activity of the enzyme, possibly by acting on

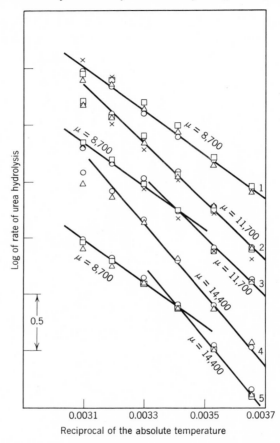

Fig. 8.20. Temperature dependence of urea hydrolysis by urease in bacterial cells (*P. vulgaris*). The individual curves are arbitrarily placed with respect to the ordinate. Age of culture and composition of medium as follows: 1, 19 hr, 1% peptone and 1% glucose; 2, 18 hr, 1% tryptone, 1% glycerol, 0.2% urea; 3, 23 hr, 1% peptone, 0.2% urea, 0.03% tyrosine; 4, 12 hr, 1% peptone, 1% glycerol, 0.2% urea; 5, 20 hr, 1% peptone, 1% mannitol, 0.2% urea. The different symbols refer to additions to the reaction mixture of 2 ml of urea-phosphate and 1 ml of bacterial suspension: circles, 1 ml H_2O; crosses, 1 ml 0.2 M KCN; squares, 1 ml 0.01 M Na_2SO_3; and triangles, 1 ml 0.2 M $Na_2S_2O_3$ (Sizer, 1941).

the sulfhydryl groups (cf. Barron, 1951) of the protein (cf. also Sizer and Tytell, 1941; Sizer, 1942a, b). Additional examples of the influence of agents which alter reversibly the observed μ of various processes, evidently by equilibrium combinations with an enzyme, are discussed in Chapter 10 on the basis of a quantitative theory stemming from investigations of

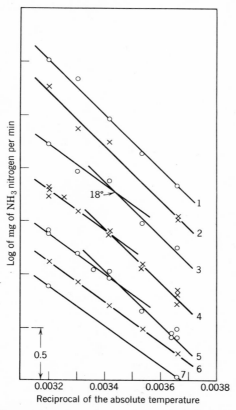

Fig. 8.21. Temperature dependence of urea hydrolysis by crystallized urease in solutions containing 0.068 M $K_3Fe(CN)_6$ (curve 1), 0.068 M $K_4Fe(CN)_6$ (curve 7), and mixtures of the two in ratios of $\frac{3}{1}$, $\frac{2}{1}$, $\frac{1}{1}$, $\frac{1}{2}$, and $\frac{1}{3}$ (curves 2, 3, 4, 5, and 6, respectively) (Sizer, 1939).

bioluminescence. A more recent study of the urease system in particular (Kistiakowsky and Lumry, 1949) is in substantial accord with the same theory.

Changes in the μ value for an oxidative process dependent upon consecutive enzyme reactions, *in vitro*, have been observed through the action of specific inhibitors (Hadidian and Hoagland, 1940, 1941). The aerobic oxidation of succinate by the succinodehydrogenase, cytochrome, and cytochrome oxidase, in the absence of added inhibitors, had a μ of 11,200 cal. In the presence of 2.4×10^{-7} M cyanide, which reduces the amount of catalytically active oxidase, the μ for this oxidation was changed to 16,000 cal (Fig. 8.22). On the other hand, the addition of selenite, which selectively poisons the dehydrogenase, did not change the μ of 11,200. With the system first poisoned by cyanide, it was possible to change the μ from 16,000 back to 11,200 by the addition of a critical amount of selenite.

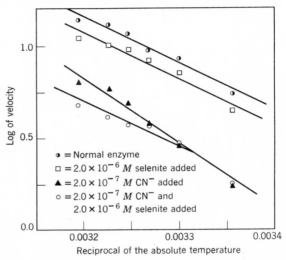

Fig. 8.22. Temperature dependence of the rate of oxidation of succinate by the dehydrogenase, cytochrome-cytochrome oxidase enzyme system extracted from beef heart, and the influence of selenite and cyanide, separately and together, on the temperature dependence. These data are from a single experiment (Hadidian and Hoagland, 1940).

It thus appears that the rate of the overall oxidation is normally limited by the dehydrogenase, in a first step characterized by a μ of 11,200 cal, while the last step, which becomes limiting in the presence of cyanide, has a μ of 16,000 cal. Actually, more data would be necessary to conclude that oxidation of cytochrome by cytochrome oxidase has a μ of 16,000 cal, since the action of an inhibitor may profoundly affect the observed value (cf. Chapter 10).

The data of Hadidian and Hoagland are of particular interest, however, since they are paralleled to some extent by phenomena of brain activity under normal and pathological conditions and can be correlated with changes in brain iron, presumably of the cytochrome system. Electro-encephalography of the occipital cortex in man has revealed the normal

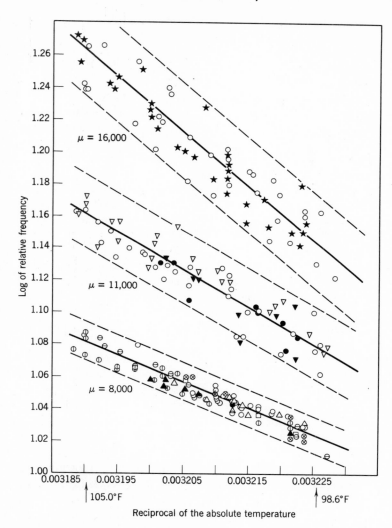

Fig. 8.23.   Frequency of the alpha rhythm in the occipital cortex of man, as a function of temperature.   Lowest curve, data from three normal individuals; middle curve, from a patient with multiple sclerosis and two of the least affected general paretics; uppermost curve, from two patients who were worst affected by paresis.   The intercepts on the ordinate are arbitrary. Solid points were obtained during decrease, and hollow points during increase of fever (Hoagland, 1936c).

occurrence of spontaneous, rhythmic variations of potential, which, with the aid of suitable amplifiers, may be detected through pad electrodes placed on the head. The alpha rhythm, constituting variations of 50 to 100 mv, with a usual frequency of about 10 per sec (Berger, 1929 and later; Adrian and Yamagiwa, 1935; Kornmuller, 1935), are accelerated by a rise in temperature to different extents in normal individuals and those with paresis (Hoagland, 1936b, c).

Figure 8.23 shows the changes in frequency of the alpha rhythm in ten normal or diseased subjects whose temperature was varied by means of diathermy. The range in temperature (slightly more than 6°C) was necessarily limited in this study, and the increase in frequency of the rhythm during fever was less than double. Although each point in Fig. 8.23 represents the mean of about 500 alpha cycles, the points are somewhat scattered because of difficulty in obtaining precise values and because of variations in the rhythm. Despite these facts, the data are essentially in accord with the Arrhenius equation, and it is clear that the numerical value of the observed μ in patients with advanced stages of the disease is approximately double that in normal individuals.

With reference again to the Crozier theory, the evidence considered in the foregoing discussions is against the view that the nature of normally limiting reactions can, in general, be recognized by their measured μ values. These values are subject to as much variation as a result of differences in chemical environments, including the presence of inhibitors, as the variation among different well-defined systems under similar conditions. Variations not only with disease but also with age of organism and other complex factors (cf. Bělehrádek, 1930, 1935) are difficult to interpret in specific terms; they could result from a change in the limiting reaction in a catenary series, or they could result from the presence of substances that affect the catalytic activity of the same system. On the other hand, the conformity of many rates to the Arrhenius relation provides justification for the assumption that the process is limited largely by one reaction, even though the slope of the line in an Arrhenius plot of the process may be influenced by agents which affect the catalytic activity of the system, and even though the slope changes with rise in temperature. Justification for these remarks resides partly in the foregoing discussions, and partly in those which follow in this and the next two chapters.

Reversible denaturation of enzymes

One of the mechanisms, which seems to be of widespread importance, through which the μ value of both individual enzyme reactions and physiological processes is influenced either gradually with rise in temperature, or more or less suddenly, is an equilibrium between native, active and denatured, inactive forms of the catalyst. The influence of this equilibrium upon the observed rate may be manifested at temperatures well below the normal optimum. Evidence that it is significant in the thermal diminution of observed rate far beyond the optimum (as well as near it or slightly below) has been found, in certain instances, in a quantitative reversibility of the diminished rate when the system is cooled. The complete reversibility depends upon very brief exposures to the high temperatures, inasmuch as a rate process of destruction of the system, as recognized early by Tammann, Blackman, Arrhenius, and others, always takes place also.

The quantitative significance of the denaturation equilibrium as a controlling factor in physiological processes of living cells was first demonstrated in connection with bacterial luminescence (Johnson, Brown, and Marsland, 1942a; Brown, Johnson, and Marsland, 1942; Eyring and Magee, 1942; Johnson, Eyring, and Williams, 1942). Thus the net rate of the process under given conditions can be quantitatively accounted for, to a large extent, on the basis of three reactions involving the same species of molecules, i.e., a single enzyme. They are (1) the catalytic reaction itself, with an activation energy corresponding to those of ordinary chemical reactions and enzyme-catalyzed processes in general; (2) the reversible thermal inactivation of the enzyme, with a high heat and entropy of reaction characteristic of large molecules such as proteins; and (3) the rate process of destruction of the enzyme, with high heats and entropies of activation, also characteristic of such large molecules (Eyring and Stearn, 1939). These reactions can be readily formulated according to a definite and precise theory as described presently. First, it is interesting to consider briefly some of the earlier observations which have been either suggestive or explicitly indicative of the reversibility, simply by cooling, of thermal inactivation of enzymes and related phenomena.

A partial reversibility of heat rigor in frog muscle was described in 1893 by Gotschlich, and a reversible "heat rigor" of plant protoplasm by Sachs in 1864. Among enzymes, Gramenizky (1910, 1913) found that the saccharifying power of takadiastase solutions, after diminution by heating, recovered slowly when the solutions were allowed to stand at temperatures below 40°C. Miyake and Ito (1923, 1924) confirmed Gramenizky's results and showed that solutions of this enzyme could be heated to quite high temperatures, of 100°C and above, followed by subsequent recovery of activity at room temperature. At 140°, the "lethal temperature," however, the activity was quickly and permanently destroyed. Trypsin, in acid solutions, was found some time ago to be surprisingly heat stable (Mellanby and Woolley, 1913; Edie, 1914), retaining proteolytic activity after heating almost to boiling, although in neutral or alkaline solutions

it was readily destroyed.   The enzyme preparations used in these studies
were necessarily crude, and the stability of the enzymes was undoubtedly
influenced by the impurities that were present.

More recent and precise studies of crystalline trypsin (Northrop, 1932;
Kunitz and Northrop, 1933–34) have demonstrated that the catalytic
activity of solutions at pH 1 to 7, with low salt concentration, is not
decreased after they are subjected to 100°C for 1 to 5 min and then cooled,
although the activity of crude preparations may be readily destroyed at
70°C.   Moreover, while the purified enzyme shows no appreciable proteolytic activity at the higher temperatures, its activity fully recovers when
cooled to room temperature.   These changes in activity can be correlated
with the amount of protein nitrogen in solution.   Increase in alkalinity
catalyzes both the reversible and the irreversible inactivation of this
enzyme.   Anson and Mirsky (1933–34) have shown that, in 0.1 N hydrochloric acid solution, trypsin exists almost wholly in the active, native form
at 40°C but in an almost completely inactive, denatured form at 50°C,
and that the thermal diminution in activity is quickly restored on cooling.
The heat of reaction, ΔH, in the equilibrium between the active and
inactive forms was computed to be $+$ 67,000 cal per mole, independent
of the concentration of the enzyme, but the heat of reaction was evidently
decreased by protein denaturants such as small amounts of alcohol, as
well as at either acid or alkaline ends of a certain range in pH.

The reversibility of trypsin denaturation, and hence of observations of
the equilibrium changes, depends upon the conditions; in neutral solution,
for example, although the temperature of half-denaturation is relatively
high, the denatured form is digested so rapidly by the native form of the
enzyme that measurements of the equilibrium are scarcely possible.   The
equilibrium change and rate processes of essentially irreversible destruction are not necessarily affected quantitatively alike by various factors,
and in general it is important to take into account the conditions of the
experiment in judging the reversibility of denaturation of enzymes and
other proteins.

The reversibility of protein coagulation was probably observed on many
occasions before it was made the subject of quantitative investigations and
before its possible significance was appreciated.   The most familiar
example of coagulation, that of egg albumin, happens to be one that has
not yet been successfully reversed, in the sense that the native protein has
been regenerated, and this fact has perhaps supported the idea, still
somewhat prevalent, that the denaturation and coagulation of proteins is
a process that is irreversible in general.   There have been scattered reports,
however, indicating that a reversal of denaturation of other proteins was
observed at least as long ago as 1910 (Michaelis and Rona), or earlier

according to the somewhat less definite observations of rigor by Sachs (1864) and by Gotschlich (1893). Spiegel-Adolf (1926) studied the thermal denaturation of serum albumin in relation to pH and salts and concluded that the denaturation of this protein is easily reversible. Anson and Mirsky (1931a) succeeded in obtaining, from coagulated serum albumin, crystals of soluble protein which could be again coagulated, and which had other properties also of the original material. Reversal of denaturation of serum albumin yields a product which has almost the normal molecular size and shape (Neurath, Cooper, and Erickson, 1942a, b) and the original serological specificity (Erickson and Neurath, 1943). The denaturation of hemoglobin by various agents is apparently more difficult to reverse quantitatively than that of serum albumin, but the "reversed" product is qualitatively the same as the starting material with respect to the properties of absorption spectrum, loose combination with oxygen, relative affinities for carbon monoxide and oxygen, and poor digestibility by trypsin (Mirsky and Anson, 1929).

Although there now seems to be virtually no question that, under favorable conditions, the essential properties of certain proteins can be restored after denaturation, examples have been reported wherein the "reversed" product could be distinguished from the original native protein by solubility, electrophoretic mobilities, etc. (Roche and Combette, 1937; Roche and Chouaïech, 1940; Neurath, Greenstein, Putnam, and Erickson, 1944). As Anson (1945) has pointed out, however, these incomplete reversals to a substance identical with that before denaturation were not carried out under optimal conditions for reversal. Actually, in view of the complexity of protein molecules, it is scarcely surprising that the rather drastic changes accompanying denaturation require very discriminating treatment for reversal, and that full reversal is difficult to obtain. Perhaps the most convincing evidence of reversal is found in the recovery of catalytic activity of protein enzymes, since this property is one of the most sensitive indicators of native structure. A number of enzymes and their precursors are now known to undergo denaturation and reversal under appropriate conditions; they include trypsin, chymotrypsin, pepsin, trypsinogen, chymotrypsinogen, and pepsinogen (cf. Northrop, 1939; Anson, 1945; Northrop et al., 1948; Eisenberg and Schwert, 1951).

In connection with convincing evidence of the reversal of protein denaturation, Anson and Mirsky (1931b) explicitly noted the possibility that such a reaction might be important in ordinary cellular processes. In living cells it is impossible to apply all the criteria of denaturation that may be applied to proteins *in vitro*, and to a large extent kinetic data must provide the evidence. Such data may be very reliable, however, and conclusions reached therefrom can be supported, in some instances, by parallel results and other lines of evidence concerning the same or a similar system *in vitro*. This has been particularly true of the luminescent system of bacteria. We shall consider first the thermal inactivation of bacterial luciferase.

In Fig. 8.1 the numbered points under the temperature-activity curve for luminescence of *Photobacterium phosphoreum* represent the brightness of luminescence after a brief exposure to 35°C (1), followed by rapid cooling to 15°C (2), and then to 7°C (3). Previously it had been assumed, tacitly or otherwise (Morrison, 1924–25; Root, 1932), that the diminution in intensity at temperatures beyond the optimum was caused by the destruction of an enzyme essential to light emission, in accordance with the general theories discussed earlier in this chapter. The ready reversibility of this diminution, following short exposures to the high temperatures, makes the previous interpretation highly unlikely, for it is all but inconceivable that such a major fraction of the normal amount of enzyme could be destroyed and then resynthesized within the short space of several minutes. In Fig. 8.1 some destruction is evident, through the failure of luminescence to return completely to its former level upon cooling, but the difference is relatively small, and after only momentary exposures to the high temperatures the difference becomes negligible. Thus, in addition to a rate process of destruction, there is a very rapid reaction, in the nature of a mobile equilibrium, which contributes to the reduction in intensity at the higher temperatures. Furthermore, the influence of temperature on this reaction is of the same magnitude as the heat of reaction in the thermal denaturation of trypsin and other proteins.

The immediate recovery of luminescence by cooling, after quick exposures to relatively high temperatures, was independently rediscovered in 1942 (Johnson, Brown, and Marsland, a). It had been observed earlier by Eijkman (1892), Tollhausen (1889), Tarchanoff (1901), Harvey (1913), Beijerinck (1916), and possibly others, at a time when the precise interpretation of the equilibrium between native and denatured forms of the protein enzyme was hardly possible. Harvey (1917b) made similar observations with respect to the luminescence of *Cypridina* and attributed the reversible heat diminution "to a reversible change in the luciferase so that its active mass diminishes" (Harvey, 1920, p. 156); the luminescence [temperature] maximum of luminous organisms was viewed as "the point at which luciferase is reversibly changed so as to be no longer active" (Harvey, 1920, p. 157).

Quantitative studies with the partially purified *Cypridina* extracts have demonstrated (Chase, 1946) the reversibility of the thermal inactivation of luciferase *in vitro*. Earlier data had indicated that the heat of this inactivation is of the order of 50,000 cal (Chase and Lorenz, 1945). In bacteria, estimates of the heat of reaction for the corresponding equilibrium, among different species under similar external conditions, extend from 54,000 to 91,000 cal, with entropies of reaction of between 184 and 300 cal per deg (Brown, Johnson, and Marsland, 1942; Eyring and Magee, 1942; Johnson, Eyring, and Williams, 1942). With a given species, numerical values of the estimates are subject to considerable variation, partly because it is difficult to separate completely the relative effects of the above optimal temperatures on the reversible and on the irreversible denaturation; both reactions become increasingly important with rise in temperature, and the irreversible one becomes increasingly important with time of exposure. In all cases, however, it is clear that the heat of reaction is quite high, except in the presence of certain drugs which catalyze the denaturation reactions, as discussed in Chapter 10.

Formulation of reactions in the temperature-activity curve

If it be assumed, in accordance with the foregoing discussion, that the observed rate of an enzyme reaction at different temperatures is governed primarily by (1) the activation energy of the catalytic reaction and (2) an equilibrium between native and denatured forms of the catalyst, the theoretical expression is readily derived. For the present, a third important process, viz., the irreversible denaturation, will be omitted and we will examine in the following paragraphs the extent to which the above two reactions alone account for quantitative data with respect to the specific processes of bacterial luminescence, respiration, and growth.

Letting A_n represent the native, active form of luciferase in equilibrium (K_1) with A_d the reversible denatured, inactive form, and letting A_0 equal the total amount $A_n + A_d$ under conditions where essentially none of the enzyme undergoes irreversible destruction, we have

$$A_n \rightleftharpoons A_d$$

$$\frac{(A_d)}{(A_n)} = K_1 \qquad \text{or} \qquad (A_d) = K_1(A_n) \qquad (8.2)$$

Since $A_0 = A_n + A_d$, equation (8.2) in terms of total and active forms of luciferase may be written

$$(A_0) = (A_n) + K_1(A_n)$$

and

$$(A_n) = \frac{(A_0)}{1 + K_1} \qquad (8.3)$$

Substituting in equation (7.60), where (A) is identical with (A_n) of (8.3), and the other symbols have the same meaning as before,

$$I = \frac{bk'(L)(A_0)}{1 + K_1}$$

$$= \frac{b\kappa(kT/h)K^{\ddagger}(L)(A_0)}{1 + K_1}$$

$$= \frac{b\kappa(kT/h)e^{-\Delta H^{\ddagger}/RT}\, e^{\Delta S^{\ddagger}/R}(L)(A_0)}{1 + e^{-\Delta H_1/RT}\, e^{\Delta S_1/R}} \tag{8.4}$$

Equation (8.4) applies to a given enzyme reaction where the net rate is influenced only by the two reactions assumed. In living cells it is often difficult or impossible to ascertain the concentration of the reactants, i.e., enzyme and substrate, and $\Delta S^{\ddagger}$, therefore, cannot be readily separated from the concentration factor. It may be considered constant, however, and under steady state conditions the amount of substrate may likewise be considered constant. These unknown constants may then be lumped together with the proportionality constant b, the transmission coefficient κ, and the known constants k and h. Letting c stand for the resulting constant, we have

$$I = \frac{cTe^{-\Delta H^{\ddagger}/RT}}{1 + e^{-\Delta H_1/RT}\, e^{\Delta S_1/R}} \tag{8.5}$$

Equation (8.5) is in a form that may be applied to data with respect to the observed rates, on an arbitrary scale, of both single enzyme reactions and complex physiological processes. It is convenient to choose a scale wherein the maximum activity is taken as 100 at the observed optimal temperature, T_{max}. Numerical values for the constants may be estimated as follows.

The apparent activation energy, or μ, is very nearly the same as $\Delta H^{\ddagger}$, differing by only about 600 cal at room temperature ($T = 300°$ absolute). The reason for this slight difference is evident from the following equations. From Arrhenius,

$$k \propto v = Ae^{-\mu/RT} \tag{8.6}$$

and, from the theory of absolute reaction rates,

$$k' = \kappa(kT/h)e^{-\Delta H^{\ddagger}/RT}\, e^{\Delta S^{\ddagger}/R} \tag{8.7}$$

Taking the logarithm of k' and differentiating with respect to T at constant pressure,

$$RT^2 \frac{\partial \ln k}{\partial T} = RT^2 \frac{\partial}{\partial T}\left(-\frac{\mu}{RT}\right)$$

$$= -RT^2\mu\left(-\frac{1}{RT^2}\right) = \mu$$

$$\mu = RT^2 \frac{\partial \ln k'}{\partial T} = RT^2 \frac{1}{T} + RT^2 \frac{\partial}{\partial T}\left(-\frac{\Delta H^{\ddagger}}{RT}\right)$$

$$= RT + RT^2\left(\frac{\Delta H^{\ddagger}}{RT^2}\right)$$

$$= RT + \Delta H^{\ddagger}$$

(8.8)

This difference of around 600 cal between μ and $\Delta H^{\ddagger}$ is within the limits of experimental error in most biological rate determinations, and in practice the two constants are indistinguishable at normal pressure. The term RT does make an appreciable difference, however, in fitting the complete temperature-activity curve, as will be shown presently. In estimating $\Delta H^{\ddagger}$ it is sufficient to compute the slope of the line times R, through a temperature range well below the optimum on an Arrhenius plot of the data, in the same manner as in obtaining μ.

In estimating the constants for the denaturation equilibrium, ΔH_1 may be computed approximately from the descending slope of the curve at temperatures well beyond the optimum. When the rate has been reduced only slightly, at temperatures just beyond the optimum, the slope is not reliable because the influence of ΔH_1 is still small in comparison with $\Delta H^{\ddagger}$. When the rate has been very greatly reduced, the slope is generally too steep because of the contribution of the irreversible denaturation. A rough rule is to take the slope between about 20 and 40 per cent of the maximum rate on the above-optimum side of the curve and multiply by R, or, if $\log_{10}$ is used instead of natural logarithms, multiply by $2.303R$ ($\cong 4.6$). The resulting figure does not give a value for ΔH_1 directly, inasmuch as it actually represents a difference between ΔH_1 and $\Delta H^{\ddagger}$. The specific rate of the enzyme reaction, as well as the constant for the denaturation equilibrium, continues to increase with rise in temperature. Thus, to obtain the numerical estimate of ΔH_1 it is necessary to add the value obtained for $\Delta H^{\ddagger}$ in the low temperature range to the apparent value of ΔH_1 in the high temperature range. In so doing, the signs may be disregarded, for, although the slopes of the curve in these different ranges of temperature are opposite, the constants for the two reactions, i.e., rate process k' and equilibrium K_1, both increase with rise in temperature; the increase in k' is apparent in the increased reaction rate only up to the temperature (the optimum) where the increase in K_1 just balances the influence of k'. Further increase in K_1 is witnessed by the decrease in net rate. It is, of course, only because of the large differences in the constants for k' and for K_1 that the curve goes through its maximum, and it is possible to estimate the heats of the two reactions in regions of the curve where the one is small in comparison with the other.

Having obtained a value for $\Delta H^{\ddagger}$ and ΔH_1, a value for ΔS_1 may be computed from the relation

$$K_1 = e^{-\Delta H_1/RT}\, e^{\Delta S_1/R} \tag{8.9}$$

provided that K_1 is known for some temperature. At the optimum temperature, K_1 may be readily determined from the relation

$$K_{T\max} = \frac{\Delta H^{\ddagger} + RT}{\Delta H_1 - \Delta H^{\ddagger} - RT}$$

which is derived from equation (8.5) as follows. Taking the logarithm of (8.5),

$$\ln I = \ln c + \ln T - \frac{\Delta H^{\ddagger}}{RT} - \ln\left(1 + e^{-\Delta H_1/RT}\, e^{\Delta S_1/R}\right) \tag{8.10}$$

Differentiating with respect to T,

$$\frac{d\ln I}{dT} = \frac{1}{T} + \frac{\Delta H^{\ddagger}}{RT^2} - \left(\frac{e^{-\Delta H_1/RT}\, e^{\Delta S_1/R}}{1 + e^{-\Delta H_1/RT}\, e^{\Delta S_1/R}}\right)\left(\frac{\Delta H_1}{RT^2}\right) \tag{8.11}$$

Substituting from equation (8.9),

$$\frac{d\ln I}{dT} = \frac{1}{T} + \frac{\Delta H^{\ddagger}}{RT^2} - \frac{K_1\, \Delta H_1}{RT^2(1 + K_1)} \tag{8.12}$$

When K_1 is at the maximum (optimum) of the curve,

$$\frac{d\ln I}{dT} = 0 \tag{8.13}$$

Hence

$$0 = RT + \Delta H^{\ddagger} - \frac{K_{T\max}(\Delta H_1)}{1 + K_{T\max}} \tag{8.14}$$

and, solving for $K_{T\max}$,

$$K_{T\max} = \frac{\Delta H^{\ddagger} + RT}{\Delta H_1 - \Delta H^{\ddagger} - RT} \tag{8.15}$$

The remaining constant c may be arbitrarily chosen to make the maximum of the curve pass through any point of the ordinate. If the maximum is taken as 100, the value of c may be obtained by solving equation (8.5) when $I = 100$, and the appropriate values of $\Delta H^{\ddagger}$, ΔH_1, and ΔS_1, obtained from the data as described above, are employed. The relative rate or activity at any other temperature may then be calculated by means of equation (8.5).

The agreement between the calculated curve and the observed data will obviously depend not only upon the accuracy of the values of $\Delta H^{\ddagger}$, ΔH_1, and ΔS_1, but also upon the conformity of the process to the simple theoretical basis assumed. A closer agreement may usually be obtained by trying various numerical values for the heats and the entropy, differing somewhat from those first estimated. In physiological processes, however, it is generally found that the theory is oversimplified, and that reactions in addition to those assumed also influence the observed rate, with the result that the data cannot be fully accounted for on the basis of equation (8.5) alone. Because the enzymes are complex molecules, temperature and pressure (Chapter 9) may affect properties such as the heat content, entropy, and volume strongly, making the quantities ΔH, ΔS, and ΔV and the analogous quantities for activation strongly temperature and pressure dependent. This probably explains in part the inexact fitting. On the other hand, even among processes as complex as reproductive activity, this equation comes remarkably close to accounting quantitatively for the influence of temperature on the overall rate; and this agreement, together with the reversibility of the thermal inactivation, is evidence for the fundamental correctness of the theory.

A thermodynamic treatment of reaction rates

Before illustrating the application of equation (8.5) to data from experiments, it is of interest to consider in greater detail the general basis for temperature and other optima referred to briefly in the introduction (p. 26). Thus, if we write in the partition functions in equation (8.4), we have

$$I = b(\text{L})(\text{A}_0)\kappa \frac{kT}{h} \frac{Q^{\ddagger}}{Q_1 + Q_2} \qquad (8.16)$$

where $Q^{\ddagger}$, Q_1, and Q_2 are the partition functions for the activated complex, native protein plus free L, and inactive protein plus free L, respectively. All are referred to the same zero of energy, say the lowest energy state of the normal protein. Now there is no valid objection to writing $Q^{\ddagger}/(Q_1 + Q_2) = K^{\ddagger}$, where $K^{\ddagger}$ is the equilibrium constant between the activated complex and all other states of the enzyme. If we consider inhibited states (cf. Chapter 10),

$$I = b(\text{L})(\text{A}_0) \frac{k'}{1 + K + \sum_i K_i X_i^n}$$

$$= b(\text{L})(\text{A}_0)\kappa \frac{kT}{h} \frac{Q^{\ddagger}}{Q_1 + Q_2 + \sum_i Q_i(X_i\gamma_i)^{n_i}} \qquad (8.17)$$

Here X_i is the concentration of the ith inhibitor, n_i molecules of which form a compound with the enzyme A, making it inactive. $Q_i\gamma_i{}^{n_i}$ equals the partition function of the compound $(AX_i n_i)$ times the partition function for L divided by the partition function for n uncombined molecules of X_i in the solution. Although it is not possible to separate out the terms, γ_i can be thought of as the ratio of the partition function for the degrees of freedom coming from X_i in the compound $(AX_i n_i)$ divided by the partition function for free X_i. Thus γ_i is effectively an activity coefficient to multiply into the concentration X_i. Again, while keeping the concentration of inhibitors X_i constant, we may write

$$\frac{Q^{\ddagger}}{Q_1 + Q_2 + \sum\limits_i Q_i (X_i \gamma_i)^{n_i}} = K^{\ddagger} \tag{8.18}$$

and treat $K^{\ddagger}$ thermodynamically like any other equilibrium constant. True, it will behave in a very fancy way with temperature, showing first an increase and finally a decrease as the temperature is raised, but that does not matter.

The thermodynamics of an equilibrium constant involving the dissociation of simple fatty acids, which shows a maximum near room temperature, has been developed by Magee, Ri, and Eyring (1941). Following their development of the theory, we will omit writing the dagger on the various quantities, it being understood that the equations apply also to $K^{\ddagger}$ without change.

The dissociation constant K for any acid can be written

$$\ln K - \ln K_\theta = \frac{\Delta H}{RT} + \frac{\Delta S}{R} + \frac{(\Delta H)_\theta}{R_\theta} - \frac{(\Delta S)_\theta}{R} \tag{8.19}$$

where K_θ is the dissociation constant at some definite temperature θ. Making the following expansions and substituting them in equation (8.19) gives equation (8.20):

$$\Delta H = (\Delta H)_\theta + (\Delta C_p)_\theta (T - \theta) + \frac{1}{2}\left(\frac{\partial \Delta C_p}{\partial T}\right)_\theta (T - \theta)^2$$

$$\Delta S - (\Delta S)_\theta = \int_\theta^T \frac{\Delta C_p}{T}\, dT$$

$$= \int_\theta^T \frac{\left\{(\Delta C_p)_\theta + \left(\dfrac{\partial \Delta C_p}{\partial T}\right)_\theta (T - \theta)\right\}}{T}\, dT$$

$$\frac{1}{T} = \frac{1}{(T-\theta)+\theta} = \frac{1}{\theta}\left\{1 - \frac{T-\theta}{\theta} + \left(\frac{T-\theta}{\theta}\right)^2 - \left(\frac{T-\theta}{\theta}\right)^3 + \cdots\right\}$$

$$\ln K - \ln K_\theta = \frac{(\Delta H)_\theta}{R\theta^2}(T - \theta) + \left\{\frac{(\Delta H)_\theta}{R\theta^3} + \frac{(\Delta C_p)_\theta}{2R\theta^2}\right\}(T - \theta)^2$$

$$- \left\{\frac{(\Delta H)_\theta}{\theta} + \frac{2}{3}(\Delta C_p)_\theta - \frac{1}{6}\theta\left(\frac{\partial \Delta C_p}{\partial T}\right)\right\}\frac{(T - \theta)^3}{R\theta^3}$$

$$(8.20)$$

Although the expansion actually gives an infinite series in $(T - \theta)$, only the first three terms are retained above. This amounts to the justifiable assumption that $\partial^2 \Delta C_p / \partial T^2 = 0$. An equation analogous to (8.20), $d \ln$ activity at the melting point was derived earlier (equation 17, p. 283, Lewis and Randall, 1923). The development to this point is perfectly general. Considering now the case where there is a maximum value for K, at the maximum point we have

$$\frac{\partial \ln K}{\partial T} = -\left(\frac{\Delta H}{RT^2}\right)_m = 0 \qquad (\Delta H)_m = 0 \qquad (8.21)$$

If we take θ as T_{max}, equation (8.20) becomes

$$\ln K - \ln K_m = \frac{(\Delta C_p)_\theta}{2R\theta^2}(T - \theta)^2 - \left\{\frac{2}{3}(\Delta C_p)_\theta - \frac{1}{6}\theta\left(\frac{\partial \Delta C_p}{\partial T}\right)_\theta\right\}\frac{(T - \theta)^3}{R\theta^3}$$

$$(8.22)$$

The empirical equation

$$\ln K - \ln K_m = -p(T - \theta)^2 \qquad (8.23)$$

has been proposed by Harned and Embree (1934) to apply to the dissociation of the lower fatty acids: formic, acetic, propionic, and butyric acids. They give $p = 1.15 \times 10^{-4}$ as a general constant for all acids. An estimation of the constants in the equation (8.20) of Magee, Ri, and Eyring (1941) gave

$$\ln K - \ln K_m = -1.03 \times 10^{-4}(T - \theta)^2 + 3.72 \times 10^{-7}(T - \theta)^3$$

This curve with its cubic terms seems to fit the data better than the simpler equation (8.23). Figure 1.7 (p. 27) shows the curves calculated according to equation (8.20), together with the data from experiments.

The foregoing method could be readily applied to describe luminescence, and it would be correct but less instructive than the method of describing the behavior of reactants in terms of an equilibrium constant for the reversible denaturation of the enzyme. The latter method is followed from here on.

Calculation of temperature-activity curves in bacterial processes

To apply equation (8.5) to specific data, it is necessary to have evidence of the reversibility of the thermal denaturation of the system. General considerations make it seem likely that this equilibrium is concerned in the majority of biological reactions, though certainly not equally so.

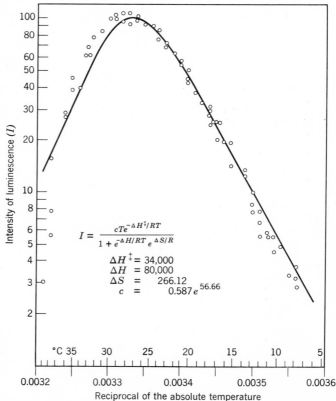

Fig. 8.24. Influence of temperature on the intensity of luminescence in *A. fischeri* (Johnson, Eyring, and Williams, 1942). The smooth curve was calculated in accordance with equation (8.5), with the constants as given in the figure.

Occasional reports of reversibility of the effects of above-optimal temperatures have not, as a rule, included sufficient data for analysis. For example, the oxidation of glucose by spores of aerobic bacilli has been shown to decrease in rate at 55°C, but to increase upon cooling to 50°C (Tarr, 1933). The magnitude of the change in rate over such a short temperature interval was sufficient to indicate a denaturation equilibrium, but data over a wide range in temperature are desirable.   Such data are as yet available with respect to relatively few processes.   It is appropriate to consider bacterial luminescence first, not only because the data are adequate, but also because it was the first process in living cells to which the quantitative theory formulated above was applied.

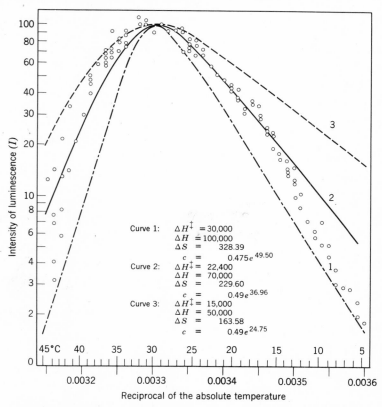

Fig. 8.25.   Influence of temperature on the intensity of luminescence in *V. phosphorescens* (Johnson, Eyring, and Williams, 1942).   The smooth curves were calculated in accordance with equation (8.5), with the constants as given in the figure.

Figures 8.24 and 8.25 show calculated curves and the experimentally observed points for intensity of luminescence in two species of luminous bacteria, *Achromobacter fischeri* and *Vibrio phosphorescens*, respectively (data of Johnson, Eyring, and Williams, 1942).   In these and in other species of luminous bacteria, reversibility of the temperature effects on luminescence both well above and well below the optimum has been demonstrated. In Fig. 8.24 the theoretical curve fits the data almost within the range of experimental error, except at the highest temperatures (above 37°C), where more reactions than the equation takes into account evidently contribute to the reduction in observed rate. At the lowest temperatures (5° to 15°C) the points tend to fall below the calculated curve, possibly because of the influence of other reactions in the total process of luminescence, or possibly because of a slight change in the value of $\Delta H^{\ddagger}$ for the same system at these low temperatures. Similarly, the points are somewhat too high at temperatures just above the optimum. In Fig. 8.25 three curves have been calculated with different values of the several constants in order to show how the curve varies with different values for the heats and entropy. The data in this figure were obtained by means of visual photometry (MacBeth Illuminometer) with a species of luminous bacteria which emits a relatively dim light that is not constant over long periods of time. Consequently the data are not so accurate as in the preceding. In spite of the scatter of the points, however, it appears that the simple theory is not adequate to provide a close fit between calculated and observed curves throughout the whole range of temperature. Each of the three curves seems to conform to the data over a limited range of temperature; curve 2 is the best general fit of the three, but discrepancies similar to those noted in Fig. 8.24 are again apparent.

The rate of oxygen consumption and of anaerobic reduction of methylene blue by *Rhizobium trifolii* in the presence of glucose as substrate is reversibly influenced by temperatures above as well as below the optimum (Koffler et al., 1947). The theoretical analyses for the two processes are illustrated in Fig. 8.26 by the solid and broken line, respectively, together with the points observed in the experiments. The fit of the theoretical curve to these data is close, and it is likely that here each process is limited very largely by the two reactions included in the formulation.

With regard to microbial reproduction in cultures, it has been known for a long time that, at temperatures only slightly above those permitting maximum rate, cell multiplication ceases and "disinfection" begins. In clinical application, the fever therapy used for paresis depends upon the fact that the spirochetes infecting the human brain are unable to withstand quite as high a temperature as the host tissues. The rate constants for the destruction of each evidently have such high heats and entropies of activation that a slight difference in temperature is sufficient to make the difference between viability and death of the cells, and the spirochete is the more sensitive. From a medical point of view, this is especially fortunate, inasmuch as it is difficult for the spirochetocidal drugs to penetrate through the choroid plexes from the blood stream to the brain and therefore cannot be readily carried to the desired site of action in the central nervous system. Local application of heat has been used in the treatment of bacterial infections also, its success depending upon the net difference in the effects of temperature upon various processes, including activity of the phagocytes, reproduction or disinfection of the pathogens, viability of the host cells, etc., although the advent of sulfanilamide,

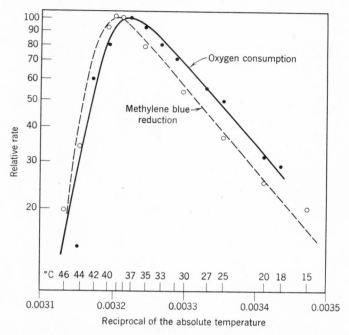

Fig. 8.26.   Relative rate of oxygen consumption (solid line, solid circles) and of methylene blue reduction (broken line, hollow circles) by *R. trifolii* (Koffler et al., 1947). The curves were calculated in accordance with equation (8.5) with constants for oxygen consumption of $c = 0.3775e^{21.61}$, $\Delta H^{\ddagger} = 13,400$, $\Delta H_1 = 96,000$, and $\Delta S_1 = 306.14$; for methylene blue reduction, $c = 0.3613e^{21.79}$, $\Delta H^{\ddagger} = 13,600$, $\Delta H_1 = 126,000$, and $\Delta S_1 = 399.72$.

penicillin, and other chemotherapeutic agents has made it possible to treat such infections without raising the temperature. In all these phenomena, it would be expected that at some temperature above the normal "optimum" a reduction in activity would take place by a reversible denaturation of essential enzymes; a decrease in consciousness, reversible on cooling, is very likely evidence of this type of reaction.

Quantitative kinetic evidence that reversible protein denaturation enters into the control of bacterial reproduction has been obtained in studies of

Escherichia coli (Johnson and Lewin, 1946c).   In liquid cultures of bacteria there is practically always a period, varying in length according to the species of organism and conditions of the experiment, when the rate of reproduction at any moment is proportional to the number of cells (the "logarithmic growth phase"), as if the rate were limited by the velocity of a single reaction.   During this period, therefore, a linear relation

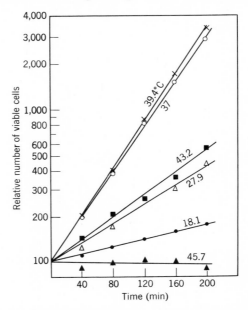

Fig. 8.27.   Rate of logarithmic growth of *E. coli* at different temperatures (Johnson and Lewin, 1946c). Each line is from a different experiment, in which the number of cells at the start varied between 5,400 and 18,000 per cubic centimeter. For comparison of the slopes, the number of cells is expressed in relative terms on the ordinate, 100 being taken as the initial number in each case.

exists between the logarithm of number of cells and time, and the slope of the line may be assumed to be proportional to the velocity of the limiting reaction.   If the counts of cell numbers by usual bacteriological methods are made over a relatively short period of 3 to 4 hr, on a culture in the early logarithmic growth phase when the population is relatively small (less than 100,000 cells per cubic centimeter), then the chemical changes in the environment (pH, O_2 tension, concentration of nutrients, etc.) resulting from growth in an adequate medium will be so small that they will not influence the rate of growth.   Under these conditions, with a simple culture medium, it has been found that the slope of the line

(Fig. 8.27) increases with rise in temperature up to a maximum at about 39°C, and then decreases, but remains straight at higher temperatures up to about 45°C, where multiplication ceases. The ready reversibility of thermal bacteriostasis is demonstrated by the data shown in Fig. 8.28. Evidence of a rate process of destruction, possibly of the same intracellular system whose reversible inactivation is responsible for cessation of

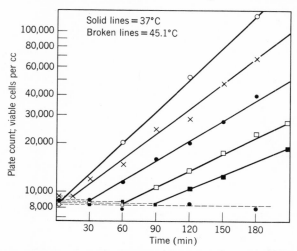

Fig. 8.28.   Reversibility of thermal bacteriostasis in *E. coli* (Johnson and Lewin, 1946c).   A series of aliquot portions of a culture in the logarithmic growth phase were placed at 45°C, with a portion left at 37°C as a control. After 14, 30, 60, and 90 min, respectively, one of the cultures at 45°C was replaced at 37°C.   Plate counts revealed that, although no increase in number of cells took place at 45°, reproduction was resumed essentially at once when the cultures were returned to 37°.   Some not readily reversible injury apparently occurred at 45°, increasing with time of exposure, as judged by the decrease in slope of the lines for subsequent reproduction at 37°C.

multiplication at 45°C, is also apparent in Fig. 8.28 in the progressively slower rate of reproduction at 37°C, following longer and longer exposures to 45°.

The rates of reproduction at different temperatures, under otherwise similar conditions, are plotted on the logarithmic scale of the ordinate against the reciprocal of the absolute temperature in Fig. 8.29.   The points are from a number of individual experiments such as those illustrated in Fig. 8.27, and the solid line is a theoretical curve calculated in accordance with equation (8.5), G representing the rate of reproduction. The heat and entropy of the denaturation equilibrium are again quite high, while the activation energy of the rate-limiting reaction is again typical of enzyme-catalyzed processes.   At temperatures above 45°C the observed rate of growth drops precipitously, much faster than the theoretical curve predicts, showing that, as in Figs. 8.24 and 8.25, the theoretical formulation is incomplete.   Elsewhere the agreement between the calculated curve and the observations is well within the range of experimental error. At temperatures below 18°C the reproductive rate is too slow to be measured accurately over the short periods of observation used.   Further

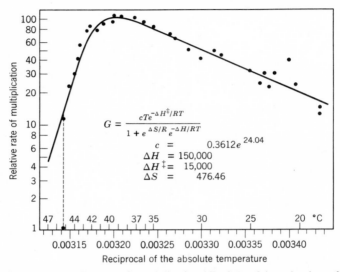

$$G = \frac{cTe^{-\Delta H^{\ddagger}/RT}}{1 + e^{\Delta S/R}\,e^{-\Delta H/RT}}$$

$$
\begin{aligned}
c &= \quad 0.3612e^{\,24.04}\\
\Delta H &= 150{,}000\\
\Delta H^{\ddagger} &= \quad 15{,}000\\
\Delta S &= \quad\quad 476.46
\end{aligned}
$$

Fig. 8.29.   Relative rate of multiplication (G) of E. coli in a simple medium as a function of temperature.   The maximum rate is arbitrarily taken as 100. The points are data from experiments, and the solid line is the curve calculated in accordance with the equation and constants given in the figure.

studies at the lower temperatures might reveal a more pronounced discrepancy between the data and the theoretical curve of this figure.

It is of particular interest that visible changes (Fig. 8.30) in the protoplasm of this same strain of bacteria take place at about the same temperatures at which heat reduces or stops growth, and that these changes are reversible after cooling (Heden and Wyckoff, 1949).   In electron micrographs of young cells the protoplasm is normally homogeneous in appearance but shows evidence of granulation if the cells are first heated a few minutes at 40°C in physiological salt solution.   In the absence of salt, granulation requires higher temperatures or probably longer periods of heating.   In salt solution the visible changes occurring as a result of heating for a few minutes at temperatures below 50°C are reversible after cooling and allowing the cells to stand in salt-free water.   At temperatures above 50° the changes are not reversible. Obviously the reactions responsible for these visible changes have the very high temperature coefficients characteristic of protein denaturation. Changes in the internal structure, especially the nuclei, would be interesting to investigate with reference to the effects of temperature by appropriate staining techniques

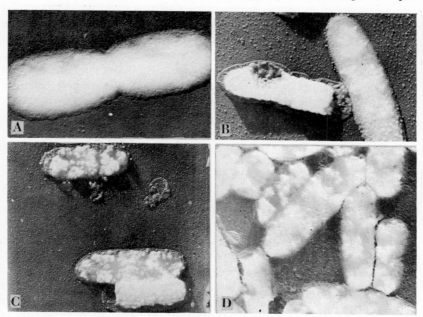

Fig. 8.30.   Electron micrographs of washed cells of *E. coli*, strain B, shadowed with gold and manganin (Hedén and Wyckoff, 1949).   All cells are from cultures at the start of the logarithmic growth phase at 37°C.   (A) A dividing cell from 1-hr broth culture, (17,000).   (B) Cells after being heated for 10 min at 40°C in physiological salt solutions showing fine granulation of the cytoplasm in one of them (10,000). (C) More pronounced and heavier granulation of cytoplasm in cells after being heated for 10 min in physiological salt solution at 45°C (10,000).   (D) Partial reversibility of granulation after being heated for 10 min in physiological salt solution at 45°C and then being kept in cold distilled water overnight (11,000).

(Robinow, 1945) and light microscopy which have been especially fruitful in revealing certain parts of bacterial cells.

Although the foregoing discussions provide evidence that the theory is fundamentally correct, the quantitative agreement between the curves and the data do not necessarily provide evidence that the same enzyme system is concerned in limiting the overall rate at the low and high temperatures. It should be pointed out, also, that the same calculated curves would not necessarily fit the data obtained in experiments with the same organisms under different conditions.   The position of the optimum temperature, as well as the slope of the curve on either side of the optimum, may be profoundly influenced by factors in the chemical environment of the cell, according to mechanisms such as those discussed in Chapters 9 and 10. The theory that has been discussed does not exclude the influence of additional reactions on the temperature-activity curve.   In the examples given, however, and probably in numerous others that remain to be analyzed, the chief effects evidently depend largely upon two reactions: the rate process of a limiting enzyme reaction and an equilibrium between active and inactive forms of the enzyme.   Though oversimplified, the theory is important, first, in providing a rational, quantitative basis for analysis of the data and, second, in satisfactorily accounting for some fundamental aspects of the temperature relationships which had previously been obscure, in particular the change in the temperature constants for the observed rate as the temperature is raised from low temperatures toward and beyond the optimum.

Relations between the reversible and irreversible denaturations

With all biological processes, in cells or in extracts, an irreversible destruction of the system becomes apparent at some point with rise in temperature.   The possibility of distinguishing between this rate process and the reversible thermal inactivation is sometimes clearly contingent upon the conditions of the experiment, e.g., in solutions of crystallized trypsin at different pH.   It is always contingent upon a difference in the numerical values of the heats and entropies of the two reactions, rate process and equilibrium.   It is also contingent upon the relative rates of the forward and backward reactions in the denaturation equilibrium, for if the backward reaction is too slow it might escape observation, or the system might be destroyed before there is a chance to observe it.   In general, the reversible reaction can be most easily recognized where (1) it is a mobile equilibrium, shifting almost immediately with change in temperature, and (2) it has a significantly lower heat and entropy of reaction than those of activation in the destructive process.   Luminescence fulfils these requirements and in addition has the unique advantage that its relative reaction rate may be measured virtually instantaneously, thereby permitting quantitative determinations of the apparent velocity during only momentary exposures to high temperatures.   Growth and many other processes require longer periods of time for rate measurements, and various complications may exist, such as more than a single, independent destructive reaction involving the same system.   To some extent, however, the complications can be satisfactorily resolved and appropriate formulations derived.   We will again consider luminescence first.

At 32.5°C, about 10°C above the normal optimum for luminescence of *Photobacterium phosphoreum*, the intensity of luminescence is reduced to about 25 per cent of its maximum but recovers if the cells are immediately cooled.   If the cell suspension is maintained at 32.5°, a rate process of destruction occurs with the kinetics of a first order reaction.   Over short periods of observation, cooling of a portion of the suspension at any time to the optimum temperature restores the brightness of luminescence by very close to the same extent that it did in the beginning (Fig. 8.31), i.e.,

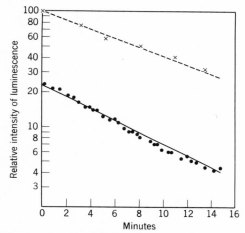

Fig. 8.31.   Destruction of the luminescent system in *P. phosphoreum* at 32.5°C.   Relative intensity of luminescence, on the logarithmic scale of the ordinate, is with respect to the intensity of 100 at the optimal temperature at 22.5°.   The crosses on the broken line show the intensity to which luminescence returned when cooled from 32.5° to 22.5° after successive intervals of time at 32.5°.

the percentage of increase on cooling is the same relative to the intensity at that moment.   The rate of decrease in brightness at the above-optimal temperatures, therefore, is a measure of the rate of irreversible destruction of the system, and the slope of the line at different temperatures (Fig. 8.32) provides a measure of the rate constants which may be plotted, as usual, as the logarithm against the reciprocal of absolute temperature (Fig. 8.33).

The data shown in Fig. 8.33 seem to indicate a linear relation between the logarithm of the rate of destruction and the reciprocal of the absolute temperature.   The slope of a line drawn by inspection through the points for each of the three repeated experiments would not be the same.   The line shown in the Fig. 8.33 was drawn by inspection as an average value with respect to all the points, and it has a slope indicating an activation energy of about 90,000 cal.　To the extent that it is in fact a straight line, it is evidence that a single reaction is involved, and the magnitude of the activation energy leaves no doubt that a protein is the type of molecule concerned.　This activation energy, however, could represent a reaction through which either the native or the reversibly denatured or both forms

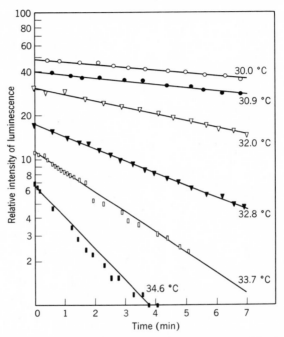

Fig. 8.32.　Rate of destruction of the luminescent system of *P. phosphoreum* at different temperatures above the normal optimum, where the intensity of luminescence is arbitrarily taken as 100.　The amount of decrease at 0 time provides an index to the equilibrium change between native and reversibly denatured forms of the enzyme, and the slope of the line at different temperatures provides a measure of the rate of irreversible denaturation.

of the enzyme are destroyed.　Taking these different possibilities into account, the general formulation for the intensity of luminescence, I, is

$$I = \frac{bk(\mathrm{L})(\mathrm{A}_{0_i})}{1 + K_1} e^{-\left(\frac{k_n + k_d K_1}{1 + K_1}\right)t} \qquad (8.24)$$

where (A_{0_i}) is the total initial amount of luciferase when time t is zero; k_n is the rate constant for the destruction of native luciferase; k_d is the rate constant for the destruction of reversibly denatured luciferase, and the other symbols have the same meaning as before.　When $t = 0$, equation (8.24) is the same as (8.4). In Fig. 8.33 the points with respect to the ordinates are proportional to the value of the exponent of e in equation (8.29).

Unfortunately, the data of Fig. 8.33 are not sufficient to justify the conclusion that k_n is the same as k_d. At temperatures close to the normal

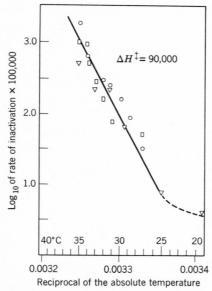

Fig. 8.33. Rate of destruction of the luminescent system of *P. phosphoreum* as a function of temperature, under the experimental conditions used. Circles, rectangles, and triangles represent data from repeated experiments, several months apart. The point at 20°C is too high to be in line with those at higher temperatures. At 20° the rate of destruction is so slow that, within the period of time necessary to obtain a measure of it, the destructive effects were probably mediated via several different mechanisms.

optimum the rate of destruction is relatively slow, and destruction may occur by more than one mechanism, leading to a general deterioration and loss of viability of some of the cells, or the destructive reactions may be partially compensated for by processes of repair. At these temperatures K_1 is relatively small, and the rate on the ordinate represents essentially $k_n + k_d K_1$, plus the other destructive mechanisms. On the other hand, at temperatures high enough to measure the rate over short periods of time, K_1 is large in comparison with 1, so the rate plotted on the ordinate is then equivalent to $k_n/K_1 + k_d$, and deviation from a linear relationship beyond the range of experimental error would require improbably large differences in the heats and entropies of activations for these rate constants.

Experiments with *Cypridina* luciferase extracts (Chase, 1950) have shown that the mechanism of thermal destruction includes more than one reaction. Standard amounts of the partially purified enzyme, in 0.01 *M* sodium chloride solution, buffered with 0.067 *M* phosphate buffer at *p*H 6.8, were subjected for various lengths of time to representative temperatures between 40° and 55°C. The remaining activity of the

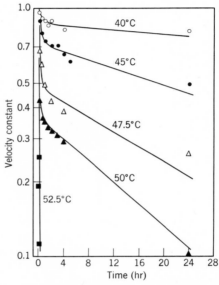

Fig. 8.34. Course of inactivation of partially purified *Cypridina* luciferase, at 40° to 52.5°C, *p*H 6.8 (Chase, 1950).

enzyme was then tested at 25°C by adding a standard amount of highly purified luciferin and measuring the velocity constant of the luminescent reaction. Under the conditions of the experiment the velocity constant could be taken as proportional to the amount of active enzyme. The course of the inactivation at different temperatures is illustrated in Fig. 8.34. The shape of the curves shows that the reaction is not first order when followed over a fairly long period of time, although the initial and later periods considered separately may each appear to be first order.

The curves in Fig. 8.34 are qualitatively similar to those for the denaturation of diphtheria and of staphylococcus antitoxin in the presence of 6 to 8 *M* urea (Wright, 1944, 1945; Wright and Schomaker, 1948a, b).

Figure 8.35 illustrates the relation between temperature and the rate of inactivation of diphtheria antitoxin in 7 M urea, pH 9.23 (Wright and Schomaker, 1948a). The influence of pH and of agents such as urea will be considered in more detail in Chapter 10. It may be remarked here, however, that the accelerating action of hydrogen or hydroxyl ions on the rate of denaturation may be looked upon as a process of catalysis; in effect, they lower the activation energy. Under their influence, however, the mechanism is different, and the products are not necessarily the same.

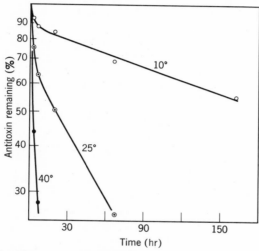

Fig. 8.35. The course of denaturation of partially purified equine anti-diphtheria toxin globulin in 7 M urea, pH 9.23, at 10°, 25°, and 40°C, respectively (Wright and Schomaker, 1948a).

In the absence of urea, at higher temperatures, antitoxin (tetanus) denaturation also shows evidence of more than one limiting reaction in that an initially rapid fall of titer at 65°C is followed by a slower fall (Gerlough and White, 1934).

The kinetics illustrated in Figs. 8.34 and 8.35 are susceptible of more than one interpretation. With antibody globulin it was shown that the specific rate is independent of the initial concentration of antibody at least for a considerable range in concentrations, and it was suggested at one time (Wright, 1944) that the non-first order rate might arise from a heterogeneity of the molecules. Reactions between antibody and simple haptens seem to indicate a normal distribution curve for the free energies of interaction and therefore, in this respect, a heterogeneity of the antibody molecules (Pauling, Pressman, and Grossberg, 1944). The curves in Fig. 8.35 and similar data could not be quantitatively accounted for on this hypothesis, but could be readily interpreted on the assumption that in urea the antibody simultaneously undergoes two reactions, one of which is reversible (Wright and Schomaker, 1948a). Letting N represent the native, active antibody; I, the irreversibly denatured antibody; and P a form into which it is reversibly converted, the reactions may be diagramed thus:

$$\text{I} \xleftarrow{k_1} \text{N} \underset{k_3}{\overset{k_2}{\rightleftharpoons}} \text{P} \tag{8.25}$$

In this, P is a product which either remains active (i.e., capable of neutralizing antitoxin) or, having lost its activity by reaction k_2 in the presence of urea, regains its activity after the urea is dialyzed out. Since P does not decompose by a reaction in effect like k_1, but rather reverts to N by reaction k_3, Wright and Schomaker referred to P as a "protected" form of the antibody. Whether the protected form is also an active form, however, is difficult to determine with certainty, inasmuch as the assay for the amount of activity in the specimen cannot be carried through in the presence of high concentrations of urea; i.e., on removal of urea, an inactive P might be rapidly converted to N by a reaction k_3' much faster than by k_3.

The formulation derived for applying the above reaction scheme to the data (Wright and Schomaker, 1948a) is given below. It is of interest also with respect to the kinetics of luciferase inactivation, which fits essentially the same theory, except that the form of luciferase corresponding to P, the "protected" form of antibody in urea, is definitely an inactive form of the enzyme (Chase, 1950), as discussed presently. In accordance with (8.25) the rate of change of N and of P with respect to time is given by

$$\frac{d\text{N}}{dt} = -(k_1 + k_2)\text{N} + k_3\text{P} \tag{8.26}$$

$$\frac{d\text{P}}{dt} = k_2\text{N} - k_3\text{P} \tag{8.27}$$

Letting N_i and P_i equal the initial concentration of N and of P, respectively, we may try as a solution of the above differential equations

$$\text{N} = N_i e^{-\lambda t} \tag{8.28}$$

$$\text{P} = P_i e^{-\lambda t} \tag{8.29}$$

Then

$$-\lambda N_i e^{-\lambda t} = -(k_1 + k_2)N_i e^{-\lambda t} + k_3 P_i e^{-\lambda t} \tag{8.30}$$

$$-\lambda P_i e^{-\lambda t} = k_2 N_i e^{-\lambda t} - k_3 P_i e^{-\lambda t} \tag{8.31}$$

Dividing both sides of (8.30) and (8.31) by $e^{-\lambda t}$ and rearranging,

$$0 = [\lambda - (k_1 + k_2)]N_i + k_3 P_i \qquad (8.32)$$

$$0 = k_2 N_i + (\lambda - k_3)P_i \qquad (8.33)$$

In the determinantal equation

$$N_i = \frac{\begin{vmatrix} 0 & k_3 \\ 0 & \lambda - k_3 \end{vmatrix}}{\begin{vmatrix} [\lambda - (k_1 + k_2)] & k_3 \\ k_2 & \lambda - k_3 \end{vmatrix}} \qquad (8.34)$$

since the numerator is zero, N_i can only be different from zero if the denominator vanishes, i.e., if

$$\lambda^2 - (k_1 + k_2 + k_3)\lambda + k_1 k_3 = 0 \qquad (8.35)$$

If we call the two roots of (8.35) λ_1 and λ_2, respectively, then

$$(\lambda - \lambda_1)(\lambda - \lambda_2) = \lambda^2 - (\lambda_1 + \lambda_2)\lambda + \lambda_1\lambda_2 = 0 \qquad (8.36)$$

Comparing (8.35) and (8.36), we see that

$$\lambda_1 + \lambda_2 = k_1 + k_2 + k_3 \qquad (8.37)$$

and

$$\lambda_1\lambda_2 = k_1 k_3 \qquad (8.38)$$

Since both λ_1 and λ_2 satisfy equations (8.28) and (8.29), these equations can be written in the more general form

$$N = N_1 e^{-\lambda_1 t} + N_2 e^{-\lambda_2 t} \qquad (8.39)$$

$$P = P_1 e^{-\lambda_1 t} + P_2 e^{-\lambda_2 t} \qquad (8.40)$$

Substituting (8.39) and (8.40) back into (8.26) and (8.27), and using the fact that the coefficients of $e^{-\lambda_1 t}$ and $e^{-\lambda_2 t}$ must vanish, gives

$$- \lambda_1 N_1 = - (k_1 + k_2)N_1 + k_3 P_1 \qquad (8.41)$$

$$- \lambda_2 N_2 = - (k_1 + k_2)N_2 + k_3 P_2 \qquad (8.42)$$

$$- \lambda_1 P_1 = k_2 N_1 - k_3 P_1 \qquad (8.43)$$

$$- \lambda_2 P_2 = k_2 N_2 - k_3 P_2 \qquad (8.44)$$

Introducing the definitions $N_{t=0} = N_0 = N_1 + N_2$ and $P_{t=0} = P_0 = P_1 + P_2$ and adding (8.41) and (8.42) gives

$$- \lambda_1 N_1 - \lambda_2 N_2 = - (k_1 + k_2)N_0 + k_3 P_0 \qquad (8.45)$$

Whence adding and subtracting $\lambda_2 N_1$ in (8.45) gives

$$(\lambda_2 - \lambda_1)N_1 - \lambda_2 N_0 = -(k_1 + k_2)N_0 + k_3 P_0$$

or $\qquad N_1 = \dfrac{(\lambda_2 - k_1 - k_2)N_0 + k_3 P_0}{\lambda_2 - \lambda_1} = \dfrac{(k_3 - \lambda_1)N_0 + k_3 P_0}{\lambda_2 - \lambda_1}$

Similarly, if $\lambda_1 N_1$ is added and subtracted in (8.45), the result obtained is

$$N_2 = \frac{(\lambda_2 - k_3)N_0 - k_3 P_0}{(\lambda_2 - \lambda_1)}$$

In the same way, equations (8.43) and (8.44) lead to the results

$$P_1 = \frac{k_2 N_0 + (\lambda_2 - k_3)P_0}{\lambda_2 - \lambda_1} \qquad \text{and} \qquad P_2 = \frac{k_2 N_0 + (\lambda_1 - k_3)P_0}{\lambda_1 - \lambda_2}$$

Writing

$$T = T_1 e^{-\lambda_1 t} + T_2 e^{-\lambda_2 t} \tag{8.46}$$

where $T_1 = N_1 + P_1$ and $T_2 = N_2 + P_2$, it follows that

$$T_1 = \frac{(k_1 - \lambda_2)N_0 - \lambda_2 P_0}{\lambda_1 - \lambda_2} \qquad \text{and} \qquad T_2 = \frac{(k_1 - \lambda_1)N_0 - \lambda_1 P_0}{\lambda_2 - \lambda_1}$$

Adding (8.26) to (8.27) gives

$$\frac{dT}{dt} = -k_1 N \tag{8.47}$$

Differentiating (8.46) yields

$$\frac{dT}{dt} = -\lambda_1 T_1 e^{-\lambda_1 t} - \lambda_2 T_2 e^{-\lambda_2 t} \tag{8.48}$$

Since $P = 0$ at $T = 0$, it follows that $N_0 = N_1 + N_2 = T_1 + T_2$. Hence equating the two equations (8.47) and (8.48) for dT/dt at $t = 0$ yields

$$k_1 = \frac{\lambda_1 N_1 + \lambda_2 N_2}{N_1 + N_2} = \frac{\lambda_1 T_1 + \lambda_2 T_2}{T_1 + T_2} \tag{8.49}$$

The latter relationship was used by Wright and Schomaker (1948a).

In fitting the equations to the data, equations (8.37), (8.38), and (8.49) provide expressions for the k's, once the values of the four constants, λ_1, λ_2, N_1, and N_2 are found. A value for N_2 may be obtained on the ordinate by extrapolating back to zero time the practically straight line portion of the curve that follows the initially rapid rate of denaturation. A value for N_1 is then readily obtained from the relation $N_1 = 1 - N_2$.

The slopes of the lines for the relatively rapid and slow rates of denaturation, respectively, may be used as means of obtaining numerical values of λ_1 and λ_2 under given conditions.

The curves calculated by Chase (1950) for luciferase denaturation on the basis of these formulations are in good agreement with the data. The reactions were diagramed as follows:

$$I \text{ (inactive)} \xleftarrow{k_1} N \text{ (active)} \underset{k_3}{\overset{k_2}{\rightleftharpoons}} \alpha \text{ (inactive)} \tag{8.50}$$

and the evidence for the inactivity of the product α of reaction k_2 consisted in the partial recovery of activity of the enzyme on standing at room

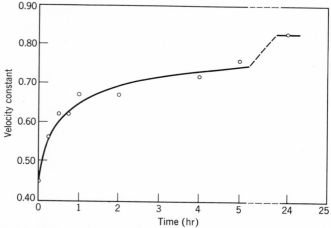

Fig. 8.36.   Recovery of luciferase activity on standing at room temperature, after a 55% reduction in original activity by heating at 48°C for 15 min (Chase, 1950).

temperature after heating to 40°C or above (Fig. 8.36).   This recovery was never complete, amounting at best to only about two-thirds of the original activity.   The reactions (8.50) do not include all the denaturation reactions that are significant within the range of temperatures (40° to 55°C) studied, inasmuch as k_1 was found to have an apparent activation energy that is roughly three times greater between 50° and 55° than between 40° and 50°C (Fig. 8.37), i.e., 200,000 as compared to 72,000, according to our estimation.   Thus k_1 could hardly represent a single reaction rate constant.   In addition to this complication, earlier studies (Chase and Lorenz, 1945) demonstrated that a virtually immediate reduction in activity of luciferase at 38°C is followed by complete recovery on cooling to 25°C.   These reactions, which would not be revealed by the methods used in the later experiments, are much too fast to be identical with k_2 and k_3 of (8.50). Thus a more nearly complete diagram of the denaturation reactions, though one which is very likely still oversimplified, would include the following:

$$
\begin{array}{ccc}
\text{I}' \text{ (inactive)} & & \\
& \searrow k_1' & \\
& & \text{N (active)} \underset{k_3}{\overset{k_2}{\rightleftharpoons}} \alpha \text{ (inactive)} \qquad (8.51)\\
& \nearrow k_1'' & \updownarrow K \\
\text{I}'' \text{ (inactive)} & & \text{N}_d
\end{array}
$$

in which the multiplicity of the irreversible reaction k_1 is represented by k_1' and k_1'', and K is the constant for the mobile equilibrium between the native enzyme N and the rapidly reversible reaction to the denatured form N_d. Presumably, N_d corresponds to A_d of equation (8.2), which pertains to bacterial luminescence.

The reaction scheme (8.51) resembles the one arrived at (8.52) through investigations of protein denaturation by ultracentrifugal analysis (Lundgren, 1939; Lundgren and Williams, 1939):

$$
\begin{array}{cc}
\text{Associated protein} & \\
\searrow & \\
& \text{Labile protein } (\alpha) \rightleftharpoons \text{Native protein} \qquad (8.52)\\
\nearrow & \\
\text{Denatured protein} & \updownarrow \\
& \text{Dissociated protein}
\end{array}
$$

Omitting for the moment the rapid equilibrium K in (8.51), the chief difference, aside from terminology, between (8.51) and (8.52) is that in (8.52) the irreversibly denatured protein arises from an equilibrium product α derived from the native protein, whereas in (8.51) the product α and irreversibly denatured protein are derived from the native protein by independent reactions. Chase (1950) noted that on the basis of kinetic evidence it is difficult to distinguish between these alternative schemes.

In the temperature analysis (Fig. 8.37) of the rate constants of reactions (8.50), it is evident that the gradual recovery of enzyme activity at room temperature, k_3, has a slightly negative activation energy. Ordinarily, this negative heat might be expected to cause the reaction to proceed both spontaneously and rapidly at this temperature. The fact that it actually takes place only slowly is readily understandable on the theory of absolute reaction rates. It is not clearly understandable on the approximate and incomplete theory of Arrhenius, which did not include the entropy of activation. The reaction evidently has a large negative entropy of activation. In terms of a potential energy surface, there is no energy barrier; the net motion of the molecules is always toward the lower energy levels, but the pathway may be thought of as leading from a very broad basin through a narrow passage (high negative entropy). Physic- ally, a broad basin means that the reactants can assume many different

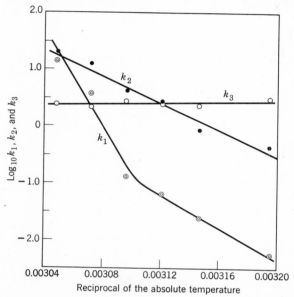

Fig. 8.37. Relation between the logarithm of the rate constants for the reactions diagramed in (8.50) and the reciprocal of the absolute temperature (Chase, 1950).

configurations. A narrow passage means that the allowable configura- tions for reaction have become greatly restricted, so there is little chance that a given molecule will reach the exact configuration required for completion of the reaction. Negative heats of activation are necessarily associated with negative entropies if the process is measurable. At room temperature a reaction goes at a measurable rate only if the free energy of activation is about 24,000 cal. Since $\Delta F^{\ddagger} = \Delta H^{\ddagger} - T \Delta S^{\ddagger}$, it follows that, if $\Delta H^{\ddagger}$ is approximately 24,000 cal, $\Delta S^{\ddagger}$ is approximately zero. If $\Delta H^{\ddagger}$ is appreciably less than 24,000 cal, then $\Delta S^{\ddagger}$ must be negative, whereas $\Delta S^{\ddagger}$ must be positive for rates falling in the range usually measured.

The preparation of antibody and of luciferase used in the experiments discussed above were not fully pure, and for this reason alone the most cautious investigators might find the interpretations not fully convincing. Results obtained by Kunitz (1948) with a pure, crystallized protein, viz., trypsin inhibitor from soybeans, demonstrate a remarkably similar phenomenon and should deprive skeptics of their comfort in the mysteries of possible complexity. Because of the purity of the system and the accuracy of the experiments, the studies by Kunitz call for special mention. Moreover, the kinetic data have been unusually thoroughly analyzed,

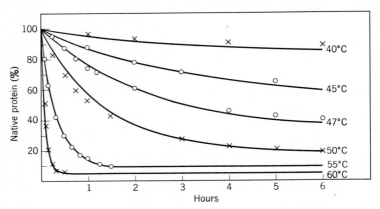

Fig. 8.38.   Influence of temperature on the rate of denaturation of soybean trypsin inhibitor in 0.5% solution, pH 3.0 (Kunitz, 1948).   The smooth curves are theoretical; the points represent observed data.

from the points of view of both classical thermodynamics and the modern reaction rate theory (Kunitz, 1948).

The trypsin inhibitor is a globulin, of molecular weight about 25,000, which inactivates trypsin by combining with it irreversibly to form a "trypsin soy-inhibitor compound" (Kunitz, 1945, 1946, 1947a).   This compound itself has been crystallized (Kunitz, 1947b) as well as the in- hibitor alone.   In solutions of a wide range in pH the inhibitor is stable at temperatures below 30°C, but at higher temperatures it undergoes both irreversible and reversible denaturation reactions, as judged by loss of trypsin inhibitory power, inability to crystallize, decreased solubility, and increased digestibility by proteolytic enzymes.   After cooling, the rever- sibly denatured protein regains its original properties of trypsin inhibition, crystallizability, solubility, and indigestibility by proteases.   The rate and amount of both denaturation and renaturation depend, as usual, on the conditions.   Exploratory experiments on the influence of pH, for example, showed that there is an optimal pH on both the acid and the alkaline sides of the isoelectric point of pH 4.5 for the reversal of denaturation, and that this renaturation is faster at the alkaline (*p*H 7 to 9) than at the acid (*p*H 2.6 to 3.4) optimum. Furthermore, although at 90°C the protein in acid solution (*p*H 2.5 to 3.5) is immediately and practically completely denatured, and gradually reverses if cooled within a minute or so, the amount that reverses becomes progressively less as the duration of exposure to 90° is lengthened.

Figures 8.38 and 8.39 illustrate the kinetics of denaturation and renaturation, respectively, of a 0.5% solution of the protein in 0.0025 *M*

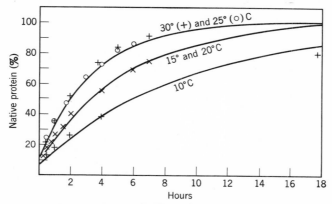

Fig. 8.39. Influence of temperature on the rate of renaturation of soybean trypsin inhibitor (Kunitz, 1948). The smooth curves are theoretical; the points represent observed data.

hydrochloric acid at different temperatures. The amount of native protein remaining in solution was determined at any point by adding acetate buffer, *p*H 4.5, which had been cooled to −3°C. A stable precipitate of denatured protein formed and was removed by filtration. The amount of native protein in the filtrate was determined by the optical density at 280 mμ. In these figures the smooth curves were calculated in accordance with the formulation for first order rates of the forward and backward reactions as follows.

Letting k_1 represent the rate constant for the reaction native → denatured, k_2 the rate constant for the reaction denatured → native, a the concentration of native protein at time t, a_0 the initial concentration of native protein at $t = 0$, A_0 the total amount of protein, $(A_0 - a)$ the concentration of denatured protein, a_e the concentration of native protein at equilibrium, and K the equilibrium constant $k_1/k_2 = (A_0 - a_e)/a_e$, we have

$$-\frac{da}{a\,dt} = k_1 \quad \text{and} \quad \frac{da}{(A_0 - a)\,dt} = k_2$$

The expression for the rate of reversible denaturation is given by the sum of these two equations, i.e.,

$$-\frac{da}{dt} = (k_1 + k_2)a - k_2 A_0 \qquad (8.53)$$

At equilibrium,

$$k_2 A_0 = (k_1 + k_2)a_e$$

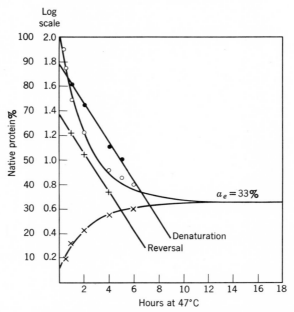

Fig. 8.40. Rate of denaturation and of renaturation of trypsin inhibitor at 47°C (Kunitz, 1948). The logarithmic plot is according to equation (8.55). The smooth curves are theoretical; the points represent data from experiments.

and, by substituting this expression for $k_2 A_0$ into (8.53), we have

$$-\frac{da}{(a - a_e)\,dt} = k_1 + k_2 \qquad (8.54)$$

which in the integrated form is

$$-\frac{d\ln(a - a_e)}{dt} = k_1 + k_2 \qquad (8.55)$$

When $\ln(a - a_e)$ is plotted against time, a straight line of slope $k_1 + k_2$ is obtained. Remembering that $K = k_1/k_2 = (A_0 - a_e)/a_e$, the separate values of k_1 and k_2 may be determined.

The equilibrium ratio between denatured and native protein at a given temperature is the same, whether the equilibrium is reached with specimens previously kept at lower or higher temperatures, as illustrated in Fig. 8.40 for 47°C. At 60°C or above, the rate of k_2 becomes negligible in comparison to k_1, and a_e, the amount of native protein at equilibrium, approaches zero, whereas at temperatures below 35°C the opposite is true,

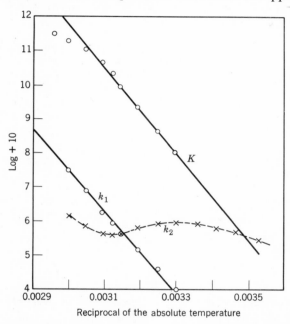

Fig. 8.41. Temperature dependence of the equilibrium and reaction rate constants in the reversible denaturation of trypsin soybean inhibitor (Kunitz, 1948). The smooth curves are theoretical; the points represent data from experiments.

and a_e approaches 100 per cent. Under these conditions the usual first order rate equation applies.

In Fig. 8.41 the influence of temperature on the rate constants k_1 and k_2, as well as on the equilibrium constant K, shows that the heats for the denaturation reaction and for the equilibrium are high and nearly the same as those for luciferase. Two other similarities to the luciferase data exist in the facts that (1) the heat of activation in the reversal of denaturation (k_2) is very low or negative, and (2) the irreversible denaturation, though not yet extensively studied for the trypsin inhibitor, appears to be higher than first order (Kunitz, 1948). With the latter protein the irreversible denaturation, according to preliminary measurements, is a second order reaction, in contrast to the reversible reactions which are first order.   Consequently the relative amount of irreversibly denatured protein, i.e., the percentage, increases at higher initial concentrations of the native protein.   Corresponding data with respect to luciferase are lacking, but the change in value of $\Delta H^{\ddagger}$ with rise in temperature is indicative of a process more complex than a single first order reaction.   The numerical values of the constants are summarized, for comparison, from the data of Kunitz (1948) and Chase (1950) in Table 8.2.

Table 8.2.   Thermodynamic and Rate Constants of Heat and Entropy for the Reversible Denaturation of Pure Trypsin Soybean Inhibitor, pH 3.0, and of Partially Purified *Cypridina* Luciferase, pH 6.8

Constant	Heat		Entropy	
	Trypsin Inhibitor	Luciferase	Trypsin Inhibitor	Luciferase
Rate of denaturation	$\Delta H^{\ddagger} = +55{,}350$	$\Delta H^{\ddagger} \approx +57{,}000$	$\Delta S^{\ddagger} = +95$	$\Delta S^{\ddagger} \approx +118$
Rate of renaturation	$\Delta H^{\ddagger} = -1{,}900$	$\Delta H^{\ddagger} \approx -3{,}000*$	$\Delta S^{\ddagger} = -84$	$\Delta S^{\ddagger} \approx -76*$
Equilibrium	$\Delta H = +57{,}380$	$\Delta H \approx +60{,}600*$	$\Delta S = +180$	$\Delta S = +196*$

* Estimated from rate constants calculated by Chase (1950).   The possible influence of impurities on the rate are disregarded, and the values given are only approximate because of some scatter of points of the plotted data.

In physiological processes the kinetics of recovery from thermal diminutions of activity have only rarely been studied in a manner adequate for analysis.   Gradual, or delayed, recovery in oxygen consumption in gill tissue of the clam, *Mytilus*, after heating to 40°C has been observed by Gray (1923), but the rate of recovery was not measured.   Some interesting data are available with respect to the rate of oxygen consumption of cerebral cortex slices of the rat (Field, Fuhrman, and Martin, 1944).   The change in rate at temperatures between 0.2° and 40°C are completely reversible on replacing the tissue slices at 37.5°C, provided that the exposure to temperatures as low as 0.2° was not continued for more than about 3 hr.   The μ value for the range between 10° and 37.5°, computed from the data given, amounted to 13,800 cal, with a progressive trend toward much higher values with decrease in temperature below 10°, and a progressive trend toward much lower values above 40°C (cf. also Himwich et al., 1940).   Furthermore, at 40.8° a rate process of irreversible destruction becomes apparent, increasing rapidly with rise in temperature (Fig. 8.42).   After exposure to temperatures between 40.8° and 45°, the rate at 37° remained constant for an hour, and no delay in the amount of recovery was observed. After exposure to 47.5°, however, the rate at 37.5° was constant for only 15 to 45 min, after which it continually diminished.

Except for the curve pertaining to 42.5°C, the data given in Fig. 8.42 are somewhat similar in kinetics to those in the denaturation of antibody,

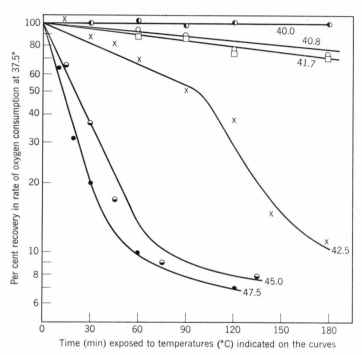

Fig. 8.42.   The rates of irreversible destruction of respiratory activity in cerebral cortex slices of rat brain, as judged by the amount of recovery at 37.5°C after exposure to higher temperatures for lengths of time indicated on the abscissa.   The subsequent steady state rate of oxygen consumption is expressed as per cent of the rate at 37.5°, at which no diminution in rate was observed for several hours.   These data are replotted, using a logarithmic scale on the ordinate from Fig. 4, p. 122, of Field, Fuhrman, and Martin (1944).

luciferase, and soybean trypsin discussed above. The process in brain slices appears to be more complicated, but it conceivably involves primarily a single species of protein molecules of an enzyme that limits the overall rate of oxygen consumption under the experimental conditions employed.   There is evidently a rapid equilibrium change to an inactive form at temperatures only slightly above 37.5°C, in addition to the irreversible destructions, taking place by more than one reaction, which become apparent at temperatures above 40°C. If we consider only the initial period of destruction, the rate is roughly first order (Fig. 8.42), and, when the rate constants computed from the slopes of the straight line portions of the curve are plotted as the logarithm against the reciprocal of absolute temperature, an approximately linear relation is obtained. From the latter relation we estimate an activation energy of the order of 116,000 cal, with an entropy of activation of 285 E.U.

Meaning of "protein denaturation"

The classical meaning of denaturation refers to solubility. The change, which for a long time was considered generally irreversible, was from a soluble to an insoluble form of the protein as a result of heat or other agents. No actual digestion of the molecule in the usual sense of the word was assumed. As protein chemistry has advanced, denaturation has been applied with reference to various changes from the "native" state under various influences, and a precise definition has become more, rather than less, difficult as the usage of the term has broadened. When a protein is denatured in the presence of urea, guanidine, or salicylate, for example, the product may remain in solution. In the process, other criteria of denaturation, such as an increase in the number of reactive sulfhydryl groups, are fulfilled. Thermal denaturation, wherein the protein is soluble until the temperature is raised, usually well above room temperature, is characterized as a rule by high heats and entropies of activation or of reaction, when reversible. Here, however, the heats and entropies may appear to be negative when urea catalyzes the process at room temperature. When catalyzed by acid, the energies and entropies of activation may be within the same range as those of ordinary reactions involving small molecules.

The word denaturation now has a general, often somewhat vague, meaning to the one who uses it with a sort of *chemische Gefühl*, stemming from long acquaintance with the vagaries of such enormous, unwieldy, and intricately organized molecules as those of a native protein. To biochemists denaturation has descended into the limbo of a popular rather than a scientific term; like the word life, it is convenient, useful, and full of meaning, but not susceptible of rigid definition.

The evidence of structural and chemical changes that accompany the denaturation of proteins under various conditions has been reviewed by Arnow (1936), Mirsky and Pauling (1936), Mirsky (1938), Eyring and Stearn (1939), Matthews et al. (1940), Barron and Singer (1943), Anson (1944, 1945), Neurath, Greenstein, Putnam, and Erickson (1944), Fankuchen (1945), Bull (1947), Rothen (1947), and others. We shall consider here only certain aspects which bear on the kinetic process and on the interpretation of the influence of such factors as concentration of ions and hydrostatic pressure. Temperature, of course, is always the primary factor. We shall adopt a rather plastic meaning of denaturation: any reaction through which one or more properties, such as catalytic activity

Table 8.3.* Examples of Protein Denaturation without Significant Changes in Molecular Weight, as Judged by Measurements of One or More of the Properties of Osmotic Pressure, Sedimentation, Diffusion, and Viscosity

| Protein | Denaturant | Molecular Weight | | Reference |
		Native	Denatured	
Albumin (egg)	6.66 M urea	35,000	36,000	Astbury and Lomax, 1935
			32,500	Huang and Wu, 1930
			32,000	Bull, 1940; Williams and Watson, 1937
		44,000	44,000	Rothen, 1942
Albumin (horse serum)	6.66 M urea	74,600	73,800	Burk, 1932
	8.0 M urea	71,900	77,800	Neurath, Cooper, Erickson, 1942a
	8.0 M guanidine hydrochloride		80,600	Neurath, Cooper, Erickson, 1942a
Globulin (horse serum)	6.66 M urea	175,000	173,000	Adair and Robinson, 1930; Burk, 1937b
	8.0 M urea	170,000	170,000	Neurath, Cooper, Erickson, 1942a
Gliadin	6.66 M urea	40,900	44,200	Burk, 1938
	1.7 M urethan		42,000	Burk, 1938
Hemoglobin and globin (sheep and dog)	6.66 M urea	65,300–66,600	63,000–64,900	Wu and Yang, 1932
Thyroglobulin	Heat, in aqueous and other solutions	650,000	650,000	Lundgren, 1939; Lundgren and Williams, 1939
Zein	8.33 M urea	40,000	40,000	Watson et al., 1936

* These and additional data are summarized by Neurath, Greenstein, Putnam, and Erickson, 1944, p. 211.

of enzymes, absorption spectrum, crystallizability, which are characteristic of the native protein, are reversibly or irreversibly lost, often with very large entropy changes, sometimes with large volume changes, but not necessarily with an appreciable change in molecular weight. The fact that a considerable number of proteins undergo little or no change in molecular weight when denatured in urea, guanidine, or other agents (Table 8.3) provides justification for considering the native and denatured forms as conformation isomers.   This type of isomer has identical primary bonds but has different possibilities of folding.   On the other hand, a considerable number of proteins dissociate into smaller fragments by reactions which accompany denaturation and which, therefore, might be considered an aspect of the denaturation process (Table 8.4); conversely, aggregation may accompany and be considered an aspect of denaturation, as witnessed by an increase in viscosity or by the formation of a coagulum.

Table 8.4.*   Examples of Protein Denaturation Accompanied by Dissociation, as Judged by Measurements of One or More of the Properties of Osmotic Pressure, Sedimentation, Diffusion, and Viscosity

Protein	Denaturant	Molecular Weight Native	Denatured	Reference
Albumin (egg)	0.05 N NaOH	36,000	16,000	Huang and Wu, 1930
Amandin	6.66 M urea	206,000	30,300	Burk, 1937a
Casein	6.66 M urea	75,000–100,000	33,000	Astbury and Lomax, 1935
Edestin	6.66 M urea	310,000	49,500	Astbury and Lomax, 1935
	HCl		17,000	Adair and Adair, 1934a
Excelsin	6.66 M urea	214,000	35,700	Burk, 1937a
Globulin (horse serum)	3 M guanidine hydrochloride	170,000	96,000	Neurath, Cooper, Erickson, 1942b
Hemocyanin	6.66 M urea	2,040,000	142,000	Burk, 1940
Hemoglobin (horse, beef)	HCl	69,000	39,000	Gralén, 1939
			39,000	Roche, Roche, Adair, Adair, 1932
	Urea		35,800	Huang and Wu, 1930
Tobacco mosaic virus	6 M urea	40,000,000	40,000–100,000	Stanley and Lauffer, 1939
Myosin	Urea	1,000,000	100,000	Wu, 1927

* These and additional data are summarized by Neurath, Greenstein, Putnam, and Erickson, 1944, p. 215.

Our usage of the term denaturation is, as usual, more convenient than precise and leaves as moot questions some of the familiar reactions which possibly belong in the same category, e.g., the oxygenation and reduction of hemoglobin, wherein the absorption spectrum is markedly altered, but wherein the volume change of reaction may be negligible (Johnson and Schlegel, 1948).   Changes in the absorption spectrum of visual purple on conversion to visual yellow under the influence of light probably involve changes similar to those accompanying the denaturation of visual purple by heat, alcohol, or acid (Wald, 1935; Mirsky, 1936).   In these and other instances, a complete understanding of the reaction depends upon adequate information concerning the structure of the native and of the altered protein, and the structure of neither is fully known.

Structure of native protein

"Native" implies that the molecule has the structure with which it has been formed and exists in the living organism. It is difficult, however, to determine the extent to which this native structure is altered by the procedures necessary for investigating it: in particular, those of extraction, crystallization, and measurement of different properties. The purified product is not necessarily homogeneous even after the most careful and gentle treatment. For example, although β-lactoglobulin was for a long time considered an especially well-defined protein, evidence of several major components has been found in recent studies (Li, 1946; McMeekin, Polis, della Monica, and Coster, 1948; Jacobsen, 1949). Bovine γ-globulin has been separated into as many as eight fractions, differing in mean electrophoretic mobilities and mean isoelectric points (Cann and Kirkwood, 1950). Moreover, in the living animal, the introduction of one or more antigens leads to the production of antibody globulin which combines, often very specifically, with a particular antigen, but which is otherwise indistinguishable from "normal" globulin. Thus, before combining with the antigen, the immune globulin and normal globulin might be considered isomeric forms of a native protein, differing slightly in configuration, perhaps only of terminal polypeptide chains as proposed by Pauling (1940b). Theoretically, immune globulins from a single animal could include at least as many isomers as there are specific antigens, and the latter are practically infinite. Native serum albumin, also, can evidently exist in solution in many molecular configurations of approximately equal energy, as judged by its affinity for anionic dyes at different concentrations and temperatures (Karush, 1950a). Even among enzymes, where catalytic activity is particularly sensitive to the structure of the molecule, there is reason to believe that crystalline preparations of erythrocyte catalase may include molecules of varying activities (Deutsch, 1951). On the basis of these and other considerations it seems that the structure of a given native protein is not unique but rather may encompass numerous isomers and closely related molecules.

As to the ultimate discrete units from which a protein is built, viz., the amino acids, there is virtually no question. The problem is how they are joined together and spatially arranged in the special configurations of the native molecule. The weight of accumulated evidence is that the primary structural basis is a polycondensation of the component amino acids through peptide linkages, by the splitting out of water between the carboxyl group of one and the α-amino group of the next (Hofmeister, 1902; Fischer, 1902, and subsequent papers; Schmidt, 1943). In addition to the chemical evidence, e.g., that acid hydrolysis of proteins yields amino acid end products, and that polypeptides may in turn be synthesized therefrom, it is well known that the same enzymes which split peptide linkages in small molecules also digest many proteins. Although it has been remarked that such action of enzymes does not provide unequivocal evidence of peptide linkages in native proteins (Linderstrøm-Lang, 1950), there are no substantial grounds for alternative hypotheses. With the approximately 30 l-amino acids accepted as naturally occurring at present, the number of different ways in which these thirty different molecules could be incorporated in a linear sequence is of the order of 30 factorial, or 2.65×10^{32}. If different numbers of the various acids are included, the number of possible combinations all but defy the imagination—many more than would seem necessary to account for the diversity of the naturally occurring substances. The data concerning the sequence of acids in a polypeptide chain, however, are generally incomplete at best, and there is abundant evidence that the precise manner in which the chains are "folded" is an equally, if not more, important aspect of protein structure and specificity. Certain limitations are imposed by bond angles and interatomic distances (cf. Neurath, 1940; Corey, 1948), but the possible configurations of even single polypeptide chains constituted of different numbers and kinds of amino acids is essentially infinite.

The search for a basic structure, beyond that of the polypeptide chain, has been difficult, and the extensive literature on the subject cannot be considered in detail here. It is now apparent (Schmidt, 1943), in general, that proteins are composed very largely of amino acid residues, in chains of from some 15 to 300 amino acids connected primarily by peptide linkages, leaving few amino or carboxyl groups freely exposed. Likewise, when sulphur-containing amino acids are included, relatively few reactive SH groups are exposed. The presence of a more or less common structural basis among proteins of different composition is suggested by various similarities of behavior.

The possibility that the native molecule is composed of a fabric of closed polypeptide chains (the "cyclol" theory) has been proposed and considered at length by Wrinch (1937a, b, c and later papers). In spite of its attractive features, however, this theory of a fabric has not been substantiated by subsequent studies.

The evidence favors essentially open chains folded into special configurations. X-ray diffraction studies of keratin and other proteins, for example, have indicated several types of folding, some of which are more or less readily reversible (Astbury and Sisson, 1935; Astbury and Bell,

1941). Thus, in normal, unstretched hair fibers the peptide chains are pictured as compressed, in an "α-keratin" form (Fig. 8.43A). On stretching of a moist hair fiber a reversible intramolecular rearrangement to an extended chain, the "β-keratin form" (Fig. 8.43B) is evidenced by the change in x-ray diffraction.

Although keratin is not a water-soluble protein, the intramolecular changes accompanying the α–β transformation are of much interest, for they are related to changes accompanying the denaturation of globular proteins in solution (Astbury and Lomax, 1935; Astbury, Dickinson, and Bailey, 1935), and to transformations accompanying the stretching of myosin (Astbury and Dickinson, 1940). With detergents, after first reducing the disulfide groups keratin goes into solution and can be made to precipitate out again; in this way artificial hair may be manufactured from chicken feathers (Lundgren, 1945).

According to the structural theory of protein denaturation proposed by Mirsky and Pauling (1936), the native molecule consists of one, or sometimes two or three, polypeptide chains folded into a unique configuration and held in this configuration by means of hydrogen bonds between peptide nitrogen and oxygen atoms, and between free amino and carboxyl groups of the diamino and dicarboxylic amino acid residues. In acid solution, hydrogen bonds may be formed also between two carboxyl groups. The energy of a strong hydrogen bond amounts to between 5,000 and 8,000 cal. The high activation energy of thermal denaturations may be accounted for in terms of the breaking of a fairly large number of such bonds, with subsequent formation of similar but weaker bonds. The high entropy of activation indicates that the number of accessible configurations is enormously increased on denaturation. The kinetic process and significance of the rate constants will be discussed presently.

Specific configurations for polypeptide chains in native proteins have been proposed by Pauling and Corey (1950, 1951a–g, 1952; Pauling, Corey, and Branson, 1951) after prolonged study of this difficult problem (cf. also Taylor, 1941; Huggins, 1943). They undertook to find all configurations for which the amino acid residues have the same interatomic distances and bond angles found in the substances simpler than proteins, and for which each CO and NH group is involved in the formation of a hydrogen bond. Polypeptide chains extended in a plane layer are characterized by this type of structure, the hydrogen bonds occurring between adjacent chains. In three dimensions, two spiral structures were arrived at (Fig. 8.43D–E). One consists of a three-residue spiral with about 3.7 residues per turn and each residue hydrogen bonded to the third next residue along the chain, and with a unit translation per residue of 1.47 Å. The second consists of a 5-residue spiral with about

5.1 residues per turn and each residue hydrogen bonded to the fifth next residue, and with a unit translation of 0.96 Å. The first of these configurations is possibly present in some of the fibrous proteins, including α-keratin and contracted myosin, as well as in some globular proteins, including hemoglobin. The second of these configurations is possibly present in "supercontracted" keratin, formed from α-keratin by a shrink-

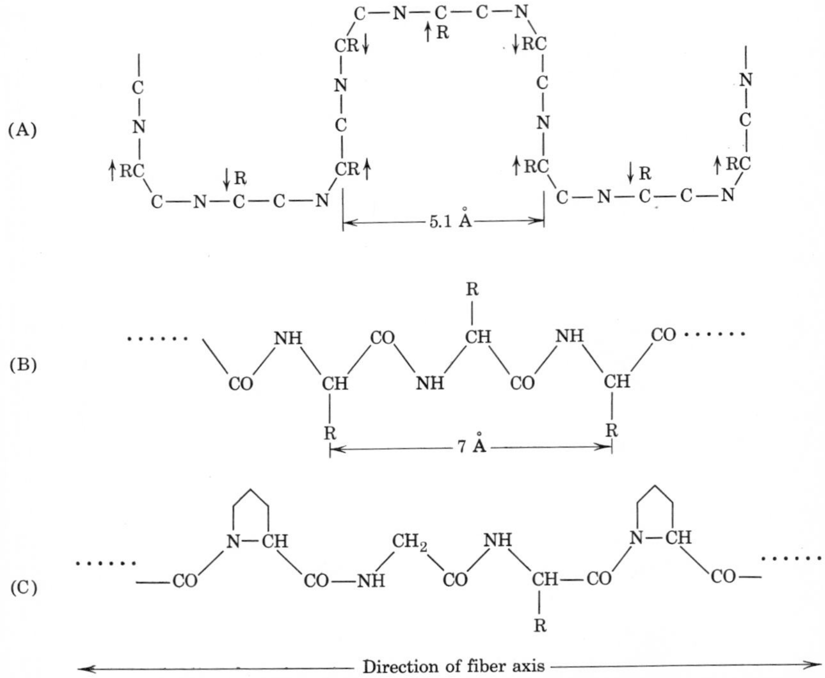

Fig. 8.43. (A) Type of folded polypeptide chain in α-keratin and α-myosin proposed on the basis of x-ray diffraction studies (Astbury and Bell, 1941; Astbury, 1941). (B) Completely extended chain. (C) Collagen fiber. Through the cross section of a fiber, a series of polypeptide chains presumably lie parallel or spirally arranged, held by side chain linkages such as the disulfide linkage between two cystine molecules, salt bonds between amino and carboxyl groups, ester linkages, and probably hydrogen bonds. During stretching, some of these linkages are altered, others are not.

age of about 35 per cent in the fiber direction. These structures are consistent with the x-ray diffraction data of Astbury and other studies. Detailed structures, based on the helical polypeptide chains, are proposed for synthetic polypeptides (poly-γ-methyl-L-glutamate, poly-γ-benzyl-L-glutamate) as well as for feather rachis keratin, hair, muscle, collagen, gelatin, hemoglobin, and other proteins (Pauling and Corey, 1951b–g).

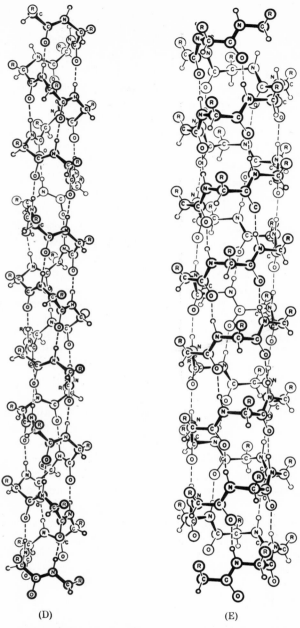

(D)   (E)

Fig. 8.43 (Continued).   (D) Diagram of a polypeptide helix with 3.7 amino acid residues per turn (Pauling, Corey, and Branson, 1951).   (E) Diagram of the polypeptide helix with 5.1 residues per turn (Pauling, Corey, and Branson 1951).

Pauling's structural theories emphasize the significance of hydrogen bonds in maintaining the integrity of the native molecule.   On this basis, the action of various denaturants is readily understandable, e.g., alcohol, urea, or salicylate affects hydrogen bonds, while acids supply protons to electronegative atoms which would otherwise share protons.   Similarly, bases remove protons which are needed in the hydrogen bonds.   It might be expected that, with the unfolding of a molecule held in a particular configuration by hydrogen bonds, the number of such bonds would decrease.   The data of Uzman and Blout (1950), however, indicate that as pepsin undergoes denaturation the intensity of the 3,260 cm^{-1} band of the infrared spectrum increases.   Since this band is associated with a hydrogen-bonded N—H frequency (Astbury, Dalgliesh, Darman, and Sutherland, 1948; Darmon and Sutherland, 1949), it would seem that the number of hydrogen bonds in the denatured molecules is greater than in the native molecules.   The significance of these data remains to be settled. Though in seeming contrast to the Pauling theory, they do not disprove it, inasmuch as different and more numerous hydrogen bonds could be established in the preparation of denatured pepsin.   The higher energy for the denatured state in water arises from the poor bonding of the hydrophobic groups to the water molecules.   The observed greater volume (Chapter 9) of the denatured state naturally arises from the understandable reluctance of water molecules to approach the oily hydrophobic group.

Unfolding of proteins at interfaces

Evidence that protein molecules have a capacity to unfold derives from data pertaining to x-ray diffraction, to viscosity, diffusion, and sedimentation, and to the remarkable spreading of protein films at the interface between air and water or other substrates.   Of these, the spreading and the properties of films is certainly the most spectacular, if not the most convincing line of evidence.   It was apparently first undertaken by Devaux (1903–1904), who found that films of egg albumin spread out to a thickness of between 30 and 80 Å on the surface of water.   The usefulness of this method of investigation, from the point of view of the theory of protein structure, had to await progress in other fields of physical chemistry, such as the understanding of bond angles and interatomic distances.   With refinements in quantitative techniques and accumulation of data from other sources the study of protein films mushroomed in the nineteen-thirties.   The methods and results have been reviewed by Neurath and Bull (1938), Langmuir (1938), Gorter (1941), Bateman (1945), Bull (1947), and Rothen (1947).

When a small amount of protein is added to a substrate of water or to aqueous solutions of salts, acids, bases, etc., the spreading power depends upon various factors. Some proteins spread readily on water buffered at their respective isoelectric points, e.g., egg albumin (Gorter, van Ormondt, and Dorn, 1932; Philippi, 1934; Gorter and Philippi, 1934; Schulman and Rideal, 1937; Bull, 1938b), serum albumin (Gorter and Grendel, 1928; Neurath, 1936), insulin (Gorter and van Ormondt, 1933), pepsin (Gorter, 1935; Philippi, 1936), and zein (Gorter and van Ormondt, 1933). On the other hand, fibrinogen (Gorter, Masskant, and van Lockeren Campagne, 1936), myosin (Gorter and van Ormondt, 1935) and tobacco mosaic virus (Seastone, 1938) undergo little or no spreading under the same conditions. Some proteins, such as gelatin and protamines, which are highly soluble in water, do not spread on water, apparently because they dissolve before they can unfold on the surface, although gelatin spreads on salt solutions.

The nature of the spreading process itself is not fully understood, inasmuch as the structure of the unspread molecule is not fully known. There is general agreement, however, that the spreading represents an unfolding or uncoiling of the polypeptide chains, and the quantitative data concerning the area and thickness of spread films, their surface pressure, and other properties have revealed some fundamentally significant relationships (cf. reviews cited). When fully spread, the film has a thickness of the order of 10 Å and is highly elastic and completely insoluble. For example, a spread film of egg albumin decreases to about one-half its former area after a pressure of 25 dynes per cm is applied against it, but returns to its former area after the pressure is released. From the Gibbs' equation,

$$\frac{dF}{d \ln c} = \sigma k T \qquad (8.56)$$

the relation between solubility and pressure can be computed. In this equation, F is the force in dynes per centimeter, c the concentration of substance in solution, σ the number of molecules in the adsorbed film per square centimeter, k the Boltzmann constant, and T the absolute temperature. At room temperature, with a monolayer of protein of molecular weight 35,000 giving a specific area of 1 sq m per mg, $\sigma = 1.157 \times 10^{12}$ molecules per cm^2, and $d \ln c = 14.5 \, dF$. With each increase in pressure of 1 dyne per cm, the solubility should increase 10^6 fold, and a pressure of 20 dynes per cm therefore should increase the solubility by a factor of 10^{120}. Experimentally, no increase in solubility could be detected (Langmuir, 1938); this leaves no doubt that profound changes in structure of the molecule occur in the formation of the film. The evidence from the accumulated data indicates that the polypeptide chains lie flat at the surface of the substrate, with a predominance of hydrophilic side chains projecting into the aqueous phase and a predominance of hydrophobic side chains into the air phase. The configuration is that of the β-keratin type, and the thickness corresponds to that of one polypeptide.

Figure 8.44 illustrates a force-area relationship for egg albumin spread on 35 per cent ammonium sulfate (Bull, 1945a). With this and other proteins the film area is a continuous inverse function of the pressure, as would be expected. Below about 1 dyne per cm the films behave with

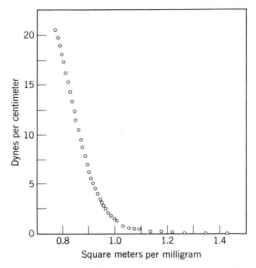

Fig. 8.44. Force-area relationship of egg albumin spread on 35% ammonium sulfate (Bull, 1945a).

properties of a gas, and the molecular weight can be calculated from the relation (Adam, 1926; Mitchell, 1935):

$$FA = nRT \qquad (8.57)$$

where $F =$ surface pressure in dynes, $A =$ the area of the film in square centimeters, $n =$ number of moles of gas, $R =$ the gas constant $=$ 8.31×10^7 ergs per degree per mole, and $T =$ the absolute temperature. Letting W represent the weight of the films in grams and M the molecular weight of the molecules in the film, $n = W/M$. If A is taken in square meters per milligram of protein, at 25°C $M = 24.6 \times 10^2/FA$. This expression, however, holds only for "infinite dilution," and departures from the ideal gas laws resulting from the attractive forces between molecules must be taken into account and corrected for by a modified van der Waals equation for a surface gas (Bull, 1947). Table 8.5 lists some data collected by Bull (1947) on molecular weights and film areas of gaseous films.   In this table it is apparent that the molecular weights for egg albumin are in satisfactory agreement with the generally accepted values (Cohn and Edsall, 1943), while the molecular weight of 12,000 for hemoglobin, in place of 65,000 for the unspread form, indicates considerable dissociation.   It appears that β-lactoglobulin also dissociates on surfaces, in the absence of cupric ions.

On application of pressures of between 1 and 20 dynes the protein films become compressed and reach a gel state.   In this region of pressures the effect of pressure has been expressed in terms of a coefficient of

Table 8.5.   Some Data on "Gaseous" Protein Films

Protein	Molecular Weight in Film	Area (sq m per mg)	Substrate Solution	Reference
Egg albumin	40,000		0.01 N HCl	Guastalla, 1939
	44,000	0.97	35% $(NH_4)_2SO_4$	Bull, 1945a
Gliadin	27,000		0.01 N HCl	Guastalla, 1939
Hemoglobin	12,000		0.01 N HCl	Guastalla, 1939
β-Lactoglobulin	17,100	1.25	20% $(NH_4)_2SO_4$	Bull, 1946
β-Lactoglobulin	34,300	1.40	20% $(NH_4)_2SO_4$ + (2.5×10^{-4}) M $CuSO_4$	Bull, 1946
Zein	20,100	0.83	2% $(NH_4)_4SO_4$	Bull, 1946

elasticity (Bateman and Chambers, 1939, 1941) or of a coefficient of compressibility (Bull, 1938; Neurath and Bull, 1938).   The latter coefficient is defined as $\delta = - \, dA/A \, dF$, which when plotted against A usually reveals a well-defined point of minimum compressibility, a point which probably indicates the smallest area to which the film can be compressed without some shearing or collapse.   Moreover, at this point, the calculated values for average cross-sectional area of amino acid residues in egg albumin correspond to that calculated from x-ray diffraction studies of fibers of the same protein (Bull, 1945a).   Bull (1938a) has compiled and evaluated the data for compressed fibers of nine proteins.   Despite the considerable variation in compressibility (σ) of films among different proteins and also of the same protein under different conditions, the area at the point of minimum compressibility is remarkably similar in all these instances.

In connection with the data of Table 8.6, Bull points out that the area Am in each instance is very close to 0.80 sq m per mg of protein, as is to be expected if the side chain residues of the compressed polypeptide chain are oriented vertically with respect to the surface on which they lie.

Moreover, since there is not enough room for consecutive side chains to be oriented in the same direction, and since the formation of a stable film depends upon the presence of both hydrophilic and hydrophobic groups, it seems evident that there is quite a strong tendency for the hydrophilic and hydrophobic side chains to alternate. Bull (1938b) has obtained experimental evidence that the air side of a protein film is predominantly hydrophobic.

Table 8.6. Some Data on Compressed Protein Films

Protein	Substrate	Area (*Am*) at Point of Minimum Compressibility (sq m per mg)	Pressure (*Fm*) at Minimum Compressibility (dynes per cm)	Coefficient of Compressibility	Reference
Muscle hemoglobin	HCl, *p*H 1	0.82	15	0.031	Jonxis, 1939
Horse hemoglobin	HCl, *p*H 1	0.80	15	0.029	Jonxis, 1939
	*p*H 6.8	0.75	18	0.015	Jonxis, 1939
Cow hemoglobin	*p*H 6.8	0.75	18	0.015	Jonxis, 1939
Oxidized cytochrome C	*p*H 10	0.78	10	0.043	Harkins and Anderson, 1938
Egg albumin	35% $(NH_4)SO_4$	0.82	14.6	0.010	Bull, 1945a
	0.01 *N* acetate, *p*H 416	0.71	15	0.028	Fourt and Schmitt, 1936
β-Lactoglobulin	35% $(NH_4)_2SO_4$	0.83	16.7	0.010	Bull, 1945b
Serum albumin	0.05 N acetate, *p*H 4.8	0.74	12	0.020	Neurath, 1936
Zein	2% $(NH_4)_2SO_4$		13	0.020	Bull, 1946

The changes in solubility and other properties as a result of the spreading of a protein are indicative of the same changes in structure that take place on denaturation by heat and in urea. The molecules in the film are denatured. Both native and heat- or urea-denatured egg albumin, when spread on a surface, give rise to the same pressure-area relationships, indicating identical structures (Bull, 1938b). The concepts of folded and unfolded states are of fundamental interest not only with respect to the structure of native and denatured forms of the protein molecule, but also with respect to the interpretation of the influence of hydrostatic pressure on the equilibria and rate processes of denaturation. The molecular volume changes that are revealed by the influence of hydrostatic pressure on certain denaturation reactions most probably arise from drastic changes in configuration. It is reasonable that such changes are again attributable to an unfolding of the native molecule from a globular to a more linear configuration. Unfortunately, it is not possible to make meaningful calculations of the change in volume of a globular protein when it is spread in a monolayer on a surface, with some of the side chains of amino acids sticking up into the air and others sticking down into the substrate. The effects of hydrostatic pressure on equilibria and rate processes in solution, however, provide a reliable and fairly accurate index to the net volume changes of the molecules in going from the initial to the final state or from the normal to activated state. The data from pressure experiments are discussed at more length in the next chapter. Evidence concerning the reactivity of molecules in films bears on the interpretation of the relationship of molecular structure, volume, and catalytic activity of enzymes.

Reactivity of proteins in films

Monolayers of proteins and other molecules can be tested for reactivity in the folded or unfolded state in films on the surface of a liquid, or after transference of the film onto a polished metal slide (Blodgett, 1934). Thickness of the film, which can be measured with some accuracy by optical methods (Blodgett and Langmuir, 1937), gives evidence of the amount of unfolding.

The fact that the configuration of molecules at air-liquid interface may strongly influence their reactivity has been demonstrated not only with protein enzymes, but also with their substrates. For example, the rate of destruction of lecithin by 0.001 per cent black tiger snake venom in the underlying solution is nearly 200 times slower when the surface area occupied by a single lecithin molecule is smaller by a factor of approximately 200, i.e., 0.47×10^{-16} as compared to 96×10^{-16} cm^2 (Rideal, 1939). Moreover, the orientation of long chain esters of organic acids influences their digestibility by pancreatin (Schulman, 1941).

The activity of proteins in films has been studied chiefly after deposition on slides. The results have not always been clear for two reasons: (1) uncertainty that the molecules in the film were completely unfolded, and (2) the possibility of a refolding to their former state during the test of activity. It seems clear from the experiments described by Rothen (1947) that monolayers of trypsin on a slide are inactive. There is evidence, however, that both trypsin and pepsin may regain their activity after spreading and then dissolving the film in solutions of substrates on which they normally act (Gorter, 1936; Langmuir and Schaefer, 1938, 1939). The residual activity of urease and catalase on slides (Langmuir and Schaefer, 1939) is probably due to incomplete unfolding, as is also the unimpaired activity of thick (45 Å) films of the very soluble enzyme saccharase (Sobotka, 1944). When catalase is adsorbed without unfolding, its catalytic activity is reduced to between 5 and 10 per cent, but there is no activity when it is deposited under the condition that the film thickness is of the order of an unfolded protein, i.e., 10 Å (Harkins, Fourt, and Fourt, 1940). There is no clear evidence that an enzyme remains catalytically active when its molecules are unfolded.

Tests of hormone activity have revealed that spreading causes a reduction of most of the activity of metakentrin, a gonadotropic principle of the anterior pituitary and also of the oxytocic principle of the posterior pituitary (Rothen, Chow, Greep, and Van Dyke, 1941). On the other hand, insulin undergoes no loss in activity as a result of unfolding. All three of these substances have to be assayed *in vivo*. Consequently there is the opportunity for the unfolded molecules to refold and go into solution with their normal configuration. Such a process seems to be possible with pepsin. The conclusions that can be drawn are (1) that unfolding of metakentrin or of the oxytocic hormone destroys most if not all of their activities, and (2) that insulin either refolds or remains active in the unfolded state. With insulin it is difficult to distinguish with certainty between the alternative interpretations. If it is the unfolded insulin molecule that is important at its site of action, then one wonders about the physiological significance, if any, of the folded form. The problem is not entirely academic, inasmuch as a possibility of physiological activity of a portion of the molecule is worth investigating for its practical implications.

Immune reactions offer a particularly interesting method of studying the relation between structure and activity. In one instance it has been demonstrated that the spread monolayers of an antibody retain their immunological specificity, namely that of antibody against specific pneumococcus polysaccharides I and III, respectively (Rothen and Landsteiner, 1942). Spread films of a number of protein antigens have likewise been found to retain immunological specificity to unspread antibodies (cf. also Chambers et al., 1940). It is evident, therefore, that the specific combination of antigen with antibody does not necessarily involve directly the native, folded antibody molecule of highly special configuration. Moreover, it is possible that the specific antigen-antibody reactions in solution normally occur between the antigen and the unfolded form of the antibody, inasmuch as an equilibrium between the folded and the unfolded forms of the antibody would be expected to exist. Support for this possibility is found in the effects of hydrostatic pressure on the specific precipitation of rabbit antiserum by a simple trihaptenic dye (Campbell and Johnson, 1946). Under pressures up to 10,000 psi the reaction was profoundly retarded, showing that a large volume increase is involved. When pressure was released, precipitation took place apparently normally. Since the volume change could scarcely have occurred in the relatively simple and small synthetic hapten molecule, it must have occurred in the antibody protein. Moreover, the volume change was evidently large (+ 50 cc or more). This is of the magnitude and direction found in certain protein denaturations (cf. Chapter 9), including the thermal denaturation of antitoxin (Johnson and Wright, 1946). Thus the antibody undergoes changes which in some measure correspond to those accompanying protein denaturation, either before or during the precipitin reaction. Unfortunately, other precipitation systems have not been studied from this approach, and the available data are by no means extensive. The problem calls for further study before general conclusions can be drawn.

Activation and stabilization by denaturants

Factors which influence the stability or activity of proteins are either definitely or potentially of immense biological significance. It is a remarkable fact that the same agents—high temperatures, urea, etc.— which promote the destruction of proteins may, in some instances, activate them. The formation of active tyrosinase from an inactive "protyrosinase" has been studied extensively by Bodine and his associates (Bodine, Allen, and Boell, 1937; Bodine and Allen, 1938; Bodine, Hall, and Carlson, 1940; Bodine and Tahmisian, 1943; Bodine, Tahmisian, and Hill, 1944; Bodine, 1945a, b; Bodine and Hill, 1945). Evidence was obtained of a natural activator in the centrifuged brei of grasshopper eggs containing protyrosinase. In addition, a large number of agents which generally promote the denaturation of proteins were found to activate the proenzyme. They include some natural and synthetic surface-active substances (sodium oleate, sodium dodecyl sulfate, aerosol OT, dupanol PC), denaturants (urea, urethan, acetone), heavy metal ions (Hg, Cu, etc.), and heat in neutral solutions. Depending upon the agent and the conditions of activation, effects injurious to, as well as favorable to, activation are apparent; likewise, certain differences in the properties of the activated enzyme occur, e.g., with respect to specificity or rate of reaction with the several phenolic substrates, stability to subsequent inactivation, and others. Figures 8.45 and 8.46 illustrate the influence of heat, sodium oleate, and urethan. It would seem likely that the general nature of the activation process is one of dissociation, either of an inhibitor combined in the protyrosinase, or of some portion of the protyrosinase molecule that, while intact, prevents catalytic activity and so acts as an inhibitor. The detailed mechanism of activation probably varies with the agent employed. It may be related to the mechanism of simultaneous or subsequent inactivation by the same agent (e.g., at higher temperatures or concentrations), but a different reaction must be concerned in the two processes of activation and destruction, respectively.

Examples of activation of physiological processes by brief exposures to high temperatures are not uncommon. Likewise, it is more the rule than the exception that "poisons" in very low concentrations stimulate reactions. For example, urea and related compounds in low concentrations cause a marked stimulation of oxygen consumption in grasshopper embryos (Bodine and Fitzgerald, 1949). Pharmacology is replete with examples of "stimulation" by relatively low concentrations of poisons or inhibitors. The action of inhibitors is discussed further in Chapter 10.

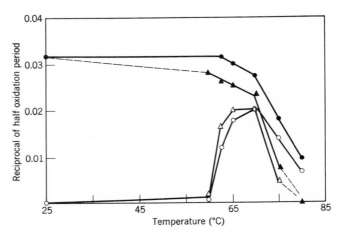

Fig. 8.45. Activation of tyrosinase by heating for 5 min (circles) and for 10 min (triangles) at different temperatures with (solid points) and without (open points) the addition of soldium oleate to the preparation (Bodine and Allen, 1938).

Germination of bacterial spores can sometimes be hastened by preheating to "sublethal" temperatures (Evans and Curran, 1943). Among some species the actual number of spores which germinate in a given population can be increased by more than thirty-fold if they are first heated for 10 min at 95°C (Curran and Evans, 1945). The significant reaction or reactions must have a very high temperature coefficient. Here, as with the activation of tyrosinase, the quantitative effects are modified by various factors; several reactions are accelerated by heat to different extents depending on the conditions, and only the net result is measured. The process of heat activation in bacterial spores studied by Curran and Evans is essentially irreversible, inasmuch as the spores remain in an activated state for some months. On the other hand, the induction of germination and increased respiration in ascospores of Neurospora appears to be a reversible reaction, since subsequent storage of the spores under conditions that prevent germination requires a second heat treatment (Shear and Dodge, 1927; Goddard, 1935).

The general problems of dormancy in seeds of higher plants, diapause in insect development, and related biological phenomena no doubt include various mechanisms of inhibition and activation. Some may be related to those involved in the conversion of protyrosinase to tyrosinase. Treatment with ether or chloroform was used to shorten dormancy as long ago as 1896 by Johannsen, and subsequent investigators have used acetone,

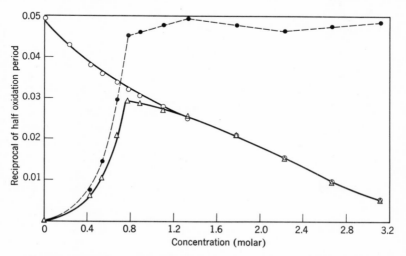

Fig. 8.46. Activation of tyrosinase by 15-min exposures to different concentrations of urethan (triangles) and of urethan plus a constant amount of sodium oleate (hollow circles). The solid circles and broken line indicate the amount of activation by urethan after allowing for simultaneous inactivation at each concentration of the drug (Bodine and Allen, 1938).

ethyl bromide, thiocyanate, and other substances, as well as exposure to cold or to moderate heat (Curtis and Clark, 1950). Diapause in insects seems to arise either from a temporary absence of factors, perhaps hormones, necessary for maintaining growth (Wigglesworth, 1933, 1934, 1936) or from an accumulation of substances which inhibit growth (Baumberger, 1917; Roubaud, 1919), or possibly from both of these causes. In any case—the production of hormones, the elimination of inhibitors, or other mechanisms—enzyme activity is doubtless involved.

Among purified proteins, stability may be increased or decreased by a large number of simple organic substances, depending upon the protein concerned. Serum albumin is stabilized against heat or urea denaturation by fatty acids, aromatic acids, alkyl sulfonates, acetyl tryptophan, and

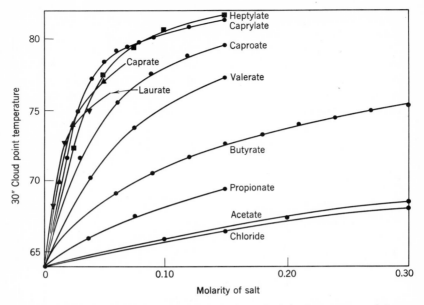

Fig. 8.47. Stabilization of serum albumin to heat in the presence of fatty
acid salts (Boyer, Lum, Ballou, Luck, and Rice, 1946).

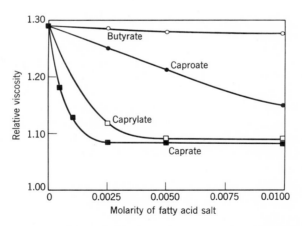

Fig. 8.48. Influence of fatty acid ions on the viscosity changes in bovine
serum albumin in 6 M urea solution (Boyer, Ballou, and Luck, 1947).

certain other substances (Boyer, Ballou, Luck, and collaborators, 1944–1947; Duggan and Luck, 1948; Scatchard et al., 1945). With increasing length of the fatty acid chain the temperature for perceptible precipitation (cloud point) within 30 sec is progressively increased; with heptylate or caprylate the increase may amount to about 15°C (Fig. 8.47). Similarly, the changes in relative viscosity in 6 M urea are opposed to a greater extent by the higher than by the lower members of the series (Fig. 8.48). The action of these substances evidently occurs by a combination with the native serum albumin. Caprylate apparently decreases rather than increases the stability of serum γ-globulin, diphtheria toxin, diphtheria antitoxin, and papain. Some substances which seem to stabilize serum albumin against precipitation by heat, heavy metal salts, or alcohol apparently do not stabilize the native protein, but rather render the denatured protein more soluble, inasmuch as their potency in raising the temperature for coagulation runs parallel with their potency in dissolving denatured protein. Examples are cyanate, thiocyanate, salicylate, and caffeine (Holtham and Schütz, 1949).

The kinetic process of protein denaturation

In aqueous solution of pH near that of maximum stability the denaturation of proteins is generally characterized by extraordinarily high activation energies. Arrhenius (1907), as well as other investigators shortly after the turn of the century, was aware of this fact (cf. Table 8.1, p. 199). In the classic studies by Chick and Martin (1910–1912) temperature coefficients (Q_{10}) higher than 600 were encountered, more than two orders of magnitude higher than the Q_{10}'s of 2 or 3 that are typical of ordinary chemical reactions. The excessively large effect of temperature is difficult to interpret even on the extended Arrhenius theory, since unreasonably high values of the steric factor, P in equation (1.12), must be assumed to account for the rate observed at, say, 50°C, when the value of E is 100,000 cal or more. Similarly, before the theory of absolute reaction rates it was difficult to account for the fact that the destruction of two different proteins, e.g., pancreatic proteinase and goat hemolysin (cf. Table 8.7), takes place with heats as different as 38,000 and 198,000 cal, respectively, but with rates that differ by a factor of less than 2 at 50°C. By the simple collision theory their rates would be expected to differ by a factor of 10^{107}. These apparent anomalies are readily understandable on the theory of absolute reaction rates through the influence of the entropy of activation. Where the rates are nearly the same but the activation energies very different, the entropy is sufficiently different to make the free energy of activation similar. Moreover, it is clearly because of the large entropies that protein denaturations with their high activation energies are able to proceed at measurable rates between temperatures of 50° and 100°C. The large entropies probably arise from a tremendous increase in randomness of the molecules; an entropy change of 100 cal per deg corresponds to an increase of about 10^{22} accessible configurations.

Table 8.7 lists the rate constants computed by Eyring and Stearn (1939) from data in the literature on the denaturation of a number of proteins

Table 8.7.   Kinetics of Denaturation and Enzyme Inactivation

(From Eyring and Stearn, 1939)

Substance	t (°C)	k' (sec^{-1})	$\Delta H^{\ddagger}$ (cal)	$\Delta S^{\ddagger}$ (cal)	$\Delta F^{\ddagger}$ (cal)	$T \Delta S^{\ddagger}$	pH	Reference
Insulin	80.0	1.0×10^{-4}	35,600	23.8	27,200	8,400	1.5	Gerlough and Bates 1932
Pepsin	25.0	5.47×10^{-4}	55,600	113.3	21,900	33,750	6.44	Steinhardt, 1938
Leucosin	55.0	1.2×10^{-3}	84,300	185.0	23,620	60,680	6.1	Lüers and Landauer 1922
Egg albumin	65.0	2.54×10^{-4}	132,100	315.7	25,400	106,700	5.0	Lewis, 1926b
Hemoglobin	60.5	4.3×10^{-4}	75,600	152.7	24,700	50,900	5.7	Lewis, 1926a
Trypsin	50.0	2.83×10^{-5}	40,160	44.7	25,700	14,440	6.5	Pace, 1930
Enterokinase	50.0	7.37×10^{-5}	42,160	52.8	25,100	17,050		Shinohara and Kilpatrick, 1934
Trypsin kinase	50.0	3.17×10^{-5}	44,260	57.6	25,700	18,600		Sookne and Harris 1937
Proteinase (pancreatic)	50.0	1.27×10^{-4}	37,860	40.6	24,750	13,100		Steinhardt, 1937
Lipase (pancreatic)	50.0	1.18×10^{-3}	45,360	68.2	23,330	22,030		McGillivray, 1930
Hemolysin (goat)	50.0	2.09×10^{-4}	198,000	537.0	24,550	173,500		Famulener and Madsen, 1908
Vibriolysin	50.0	3.0×10^{-3}	127,950	326.0	22,650	105,300		Famulener and Madsen, 1908
Tetanolysin	50.0	2.1×10^{-4}	172,650	459.0	24,350	148,000		Famulener and Madsen, 1908
Peroxidase (milk)	70.1	5.1×10^{-4}	185,300	466.4	25,300	160,000		Zilva, 1914
Rennen	50.0	6.7×10^{-5}	89,350	208.1	22,130	67,200		Arrhenius, 1907
Amylase (malt)	60.0	8.0×10^{-4}	41,630	52.3	24,230	17,400		Lüers and Wasmund 1922
Invertase (yeast)	50.0	7.7×10^{-5}	52,350	84.7	25,000	27,350	5.7	Euler and Lauren 1919
Invertase (yeast)	55.0	5.0×10^{-5}	86,350	185.0	25,700	60,680	5.2	Euler and Lauren 1919
Invertase (yeast)	50.2	3.5×10^{-5}	110,350	262.5	25,500	84,840	4.0	Euler and Lauren 1919
Invertase (yeast)	55.0	3.75×10^{-4}	74,350	152.4	24,400	50,000	3.0	Euler and Lauren 1919
Emulsin (wet)	60.0	4.0×10^{-3}	44,930	65.3	23,200	21,750		Tammann, 1895
Emulsin (dry)	100.0	1.48×10^{-4}	25,550	− 7.86	28,500	− 2,930		Tammann, 1895
Lipase (dry)	120.0	4.0×10^{-4}	(24,200)	(− 13.0)	(29,300)	(− 5,100)		Nicloux, 1904

and enzymes. It will be noted that in spite of large differences in the heats and entropies of activation among the different proteins in solution, ranging from some 35,000 to 198,000 cal per mole and from 23.8 to 537 E.U., respectively, the free energies of activation do not vary by more than 5,300 cal. The influence of pH is indicated in the data pertaining to invertase, wherein it is evident that the activation energy is highest at pH 4, and much lower at either pH 5.7 or 3.0. The difference in $\Delta F^{\ddagger}$, however, does not exceed 1,300 cal at any two pH values.

Further data with respect to acidity and alkalinity are given in Table 8.8 (Eyring and Stearn, 1939), along with other catalysts for the denaturation of egg albumin and hemoglobin. Certain relationships between the rate constants and the composition of the solvent are qualitatively apparent, as follows.

There is a slight but progressive decrease in the value of $\Delta F^{\ddagger}$ with rise in temperature (except with urea) at constant pH, and a decrease in the value of $\Delta F^{\ddagger}$ on either side of the pH of maximum stability. The value of $T\,\Delta S^{\ddagger}$ increases with temperature (except with urea), probably in large part because of the increase in T, but possibly also because of a slight increase in $\Delta S^{\ddagger}$. The value of $\Delta S^{\ddagger}$ decreases with decreasing pH, and probably also generally with large increases in pH, on either side of the point of maximum stability. The data concerning alkaline solutions are not very adequate and are somewhat uncertain of interpretation because of complicating reactions, such as partial digestion of the protein.

Among the different catalysts included in Table 8.8, it is apparent that urea and acid are the most effective in accelerating the rate with decreased values for $\Delta F^{\ddagger}$, $\Delta S^{\ddagger}$, and $T\,\Delta S^{\ddagger}$. Alcohol lowers the value for $\Delta F^{\ddagger}$, in comparison with water, by an amount that increases with concentration of alcohol, while ammonium sulfate has just the opposite effect (the data with respect to egg albumin are not sufficient to be conclusive). With these catalysts both $\Delta H^{\ddagger}$ and $\Delta S^{\ddagger}$ are increased, but because of the difference in signs and the amount of the respective changes the values of $\Delta F^{\ddagger}$, which determine the specific rate, are influenced differently. Dry heat (Table 8.7) is the most effective in raising the value of $\Delta F^{\ddagger}$ and therefore in slowing the rate of denaturation, but its effect on $\Delta H^{\ddagger}$ is intermediate between that of urea and that of ammonium sulfate. With both egg albumin and hemoglobin it is interesting to note that the decrease in $\Delta S^{\ddagger}$ with pH and temperature is roughly the same, changing, for the former protein, by about 250 units between pH 5 at 65°C and pH 1.5 at 37°C and, for the latter protein, by about 190 units between pH 5.7 at 60°C and pH 4.6 at 37°C.

The actual values of the constants in Tables 8.7 and 8.8 are provisional. To some extent they depend upon the particular conditions of the experiment, especially the purity of the protein preparations. They are probably subject to modification also by the initial concentration of protein employed, as shown by Casey and Laidler (1950, 1951) with pepsin. Thus the denaturation of pepsin in solution of pH 4.83 proceeds as a first order reaction, even though the initial concentrations differ by 1,000-fold. The initial rate, however, is a function of the initial concentration. Under given conditions, increasing the concentration of pepsin had the effect of speeding up the rate of its destruction. The energy of activation was lowered to about a third. Added protein may speed up a denaturation process, and yet the process can still follow unimolecular kinetics provided

Table 8.8. Kinetics of Denaturation of Egg Albumin and of Hemoglobin with Various Catalysts

(From Eyring and Stearn, 1939)

t (°C)	pH	Catalyst	k' (sec^{-1})	$\Delta H^{\ddagger}$ (cal)	$\Delta S^{\ddagger}$ (E.U. or cal/deg)	$\Delta F^{\ddagger}$ (cal)	$T\Delta S^{\ddagger}$	Reference
				Egg Albumin				
65.0	5.0	Water	2.54×10^{-4}	132,100	315.7	25,400	106,700	Lewis, 1926a
	6.76	Water	2.8×10^{-6}	128,200	295.2	28,400	99,800	Lewis, 1926a
	7.7	Water	1.8×10^{-5}	134,300	317.1	27,100	107,200	Lewis, 1926a
70.2	5.0	Water	5.1×10^{-3}	132,100	315.7	23,750	108,350	Lewis, 1926a
	6.76	Water	5.15×10^{-5}	128,200	295.2	26,900	101,300	Lewis, 1926a
	7.7	Water	3.8×10^{-4}	134,300	317.1	25,500	108,800	Lewis, 1926a
51.1	3.4	Water	2.76×10^{-4}	96,750	223.7	24,300	72,500	Chick and Martin, 1911
56.2	3.4	Water	2.88×10^{-3}	96,750	223.7	23,100	73,640	Chick and Martin, 1911
64.8	9.8	Water	1.15×10^{-5}			27,500		Chick and Martin, 1911
70.9		2 N (NH$_4$)$_2$SO$_4$	1.94×10^{-5}	87,500	174.2	27,600	59,900	Chick and Martin, 1911
75.4		2 N (NH$_4$)$_2$SO$_4$	1.03×10^{-4}	87,500	174.2	26,800	60,700	Chick and Martin, 1911
37.0	2.00	Acid	2.15×10^{-5}	48,400	76.3	24,750	23,650	Gerlough and Bates, 1932
	1.62	Acid	5.68×10^{-5}	36,900	41.2	24,100	12,770	Gerlough and Bates, 1932
	1.32	Acid	8.83×10^{-5}	36,700	41.4	23,900	12,830	Gerlough and Bates, 1932
25.0	1.72	Acid	4.8×10^{-6}	34,400	32.6	24,700	9,700	Gerlough and Bates, 1932
	1.52	Acid	6.4×10^{-6}	35,400	36.5	24,500	10,900	Gerlough and Bates, 1932
	1.35	Acid	8.2×10^{-6}	35,200	36.3	24,400	10,800	Gerlough and Bates, 1932
	1.02	Acid	1.59×10^{-5}	(35,400)	(38.5)	24,000	(11,400)	Gerlough and Bates, 1932
45.0	3.52	Acid	1.2×10^{-5}			25,780		Gerlough and Bates, 1932
	2.68	Acid	3.5×10^{-5}			25,100		Gerlough and Bates, 1932
	1.98	Acid	1.73×10^{-4}			24,100		Gerlough and Bates, 1932
	1.34	Acid	3.88×10^{-4}			23,590		Gerlough and Bates, 1932
25.0	1.35	Acid	8.2×10^{-6}	35,100	36.1	24,350	10,750	Cubin, 1929
37.0	1.35	Acid	8.5×10^{-5}	35,100	36.1	23,900	11,200	Cubin, 1929
45.0	1.35	Acid	3.83×10^{-4}	36,200	39.7	23,600	12,600	Cubin, 1929
0.0	5.9	Urea, 0.6 g per cc	1.7×10^{-3}	$-6,750$	-95.6	19,350	$-26,100$	Hopkins, 1930
23.0	5.9	Urea, 0.6 g per cc	7.0×10^{-4}	$-6,790$	-95.8	21,560	$-28,350$	Hopkins, 1930
				Hemoglobin				
60.5	5.7	Water	4.3×10^{-4}	75,600	152.7	24,700	50,900	Lewis, 1926a
	6.8	Water	1.05×10^{-4}	76,300	152.0	25,600	50,700	Lewis, 1926a
	8.0	Water	3.35×10^{-4}	77,300	157.3	24,840	52,460	Lewis, 1926a
68.0	5.7	Water	5.4×10^{-3}	75,600	152.7	23,530	52,070	Lewis, 1926a
	6.8	Water	1.35×10^{-3}	76,300	152.0	24,470	51,830	Lewis, 1926a
	8.0	Water	4.45×10^{-3}	77,300	157.3	23,660	53,640	Lewis, 1926a
64.0	6.76	0.15 N (NH$_4$)$_2$SO$_4$	3.41×10^{-4}	76,500	152.5	25,100	51,400	Lewis, 1926a

Table 8.8 (Continued)

t (°C)	pH	Catalyst	k' (sec^{-1})	$\Delta H^{\ddagger}$ (cal)	$\Delta S^{\ddagger}$ (E.U. or cal/deg)	$\Delta F^{\ddagger}$ (cal)	$T\Delta S^{\ddagger}$	Reference
					Hemoglobin (Continued)			
70.0	6.76	0.15 N (NH$_4$)$_2$SO$_4$	2.57×10^{-3}	76,500	152.5	24,200	52,300	Lewis, 1926b
64.0	6.76	1.14 N (NH$_4$)$_2$SO$_4$	5.45×10^{-4}	87,000	184.6	24,800	62,200	Lewis, 1926b
70.0	6.76	1.14 N (NH$_4$)$_2$SO$_4$	5.4×10^{-3}	87,000	184.6	23,700	63,300	Lewis, 1926b
64.0	6.76	2.27 N (NH$_4$)$_2$SO$_4$	9.1×10^{-5}	103,800	230.9	26,000	77,800	Lewis, 1926b
70.0	6.76	2.27 N (NH$_4$)$_2$SO$_4$	1.4×10^{-3}	103,800	230.9	24,600	79,200	Lewis, 1926b
64.0	6.76	3.03 N (NH$_4$)$_2$SO$_4$	2.44×10^{-5}	119,800	275.8	26,900	92,900	Lewis, 1926b
70.0	6.76	3.03 N (NH$_4$)$_2$SO$_4$	5.7×10^{-4}	119,800	275.8	25,200	94,600	Lewis, 1926b
45.0	4.85	Acid	1.7×10^{-4}	17,760	-19.9	24,100	$-6,330$	Gerlough and Bates, 1932
	4.23	Acid	2.53×10^{-3}	10,660	-36.9	22,400	$-11,730$	Gerlough and Bates, 1932
37.0	4.64	Acid	2.78×10^{-4}	11,300	-38.3	23,200	$-11,870$	Gerlough and Bates, 1932
	4.11	Acid	3.06×10^{-3}	10,700	-35.5	21,700	$-11,000$	Gerlough and Bates, 1932
25.0	4.52	Acid	2.29×10^{-4}	11,100	-37.8	22,400	$-11,260$	Gerlough and Bates, 1932
	4.08	Acid	1.76×10^{-3}	11,100	-33.7	21,150	$-10,040$	Gerlough and Bates, 1932
45.0	5.5	Acid	9.6×10^{-6}			25,920		Gerlough and Bates, 1932
	4.9	Acid	1.21×10^{-4}			24,320		Gerlough and Bates, 1932
	4.52	Acid	7.26×10^{-4}			23,190		Gerlough and Bates, 1932
	4.23	Acid	2.53×10^{-3}			22,400		Gerlough and Bates, 1932
60.5	6.0	Alcohol (none)	2.3×10^{-4}	76,250	153.4	25,100	51,150	Booth, 1930; Lewis, 1926a
45.0	6.0	Alcohol (20 volume %)	4.56×10^{-4}	107,400	263.9	23,500	83,900	Booth, 1930; Lewis, 1926a
33.0	6.0	Alcohol (30 volume %)	5.3×10^{-4}	117,000	308.9	22,500	94,500	Booth, 1930; Lewis, 1926a
60.5	6.5	Alcohol (none)	1.22×10^{-4}	75,050	148.5	25,550	49,500	Booth, 1930; Lewis, 1926a
45.0	6.5	Alcohol (20 volume %)	4.5×10^{-4}	102,600	248.8	23,500	79,100	Booth, 1930; Lewis, 1926a
33.0	6.5	Alcohol (30 volume %)	6.8×10^{-4}	120,100	319.5	22,300	97,800	Booth, 1930; Lewis, 1926a
60.5	7.0	Alcohol (none)	1.22×10^{-4}	76,050	151.5	25,550	50,500	Booth, 1930; Lewis, 1926a
45.0	7.0	Alcohol (20 volume %)	8.0×10^{-4}	98,200	236.1	23,100	75,100	Booth, 1930; Lewis, 1926a
33.0	7.0	Alcohol (30 volume %)	(1.1×10^{-3})	(128,500)	(348.0)	(22,000)	(106,500)	Booth, 1930; Lewis, 1926a
45.0	6.57	Alcohol (20 volume %)	4.52×10^{-4}	100,450	242.1	23,500	77,000	Booth, 1930
40.0	6.57	Alcohol (20 volume %)	3.5×10^{-5}	100,450	242.1	24,700	75,800	Booth, 1930
60.5	6.0	Alcohol (2 volume %)	5.06×10^{-4}	83,500	176.7	24,600	58,950	Booth, 1930
55.0	6.0	Alcohol (2 volume %)	6.0×10^{-5}	83,500	176.7	25,600	57,950	Booth, 1930

that the hydrophobic groups on the denatured protein can substitute in the activated complex for all the n protein molecules entering into it except the particular one which is in the act of being denatured.

With Casey and Laidler (1951) we assume that the activated complex is made from a cluster of n pepsin molecules which have ionized off m hydrogens. Let c represent the concentration of single-protein molecules, and c_n the concentration of clusters. Then we have the reaction

$$nc \rightleftharpoons c_n \tag{8.58}$$

with equilibrium constant K. Whence

$$c_n/c^n = K \tag{8.59}$$

If c_0 is the total concentration of protein that will be present if there is no clustering, we can write

$$c_0 = c + nc_n \tag{8.60}$$

Substituting (8.60) into (8.59) gives

$$K = c_n/(c_0 - nc_n)^n \tag{8.61}$$

When c_n is small, we have, using the binomial expansion and neglecting higher terms,

$$K = c_n/(c_0{}^n - n^2 c_n c_0{}^{n-1}) \tag{8.62}$$

Hence

$$c_n = \frac{K c_0{}^n}{1 + K n^2 c_0{}^{n-1}} \tag{8.63}$$

If now we assume that the cluster c_n ionizes to give m hydrogen ions and an activated complex, then

$$c_n \rightarrow c^{\ddagger} + m(\mathrm{H}^+) \tag{8.64}$$

with the equilibrium constant $K^{\ddagger}$. This gives

$$\frac{(c^{\ddagger})(\mathrm{H}^+)^m}{c_n} = K^{\ddagger} \qquad \text{or} \qquad c^{\ddagger} = \frac{K^{\ddagger} c_n}{(\mathrm{H}^+)^m} \tag{8.65}$$

The velocity of reaction v_0 is then

$$v_0 = \kappa \frac{kT}{h} c^{\ddagger} = \kappa \frac{kT}{h} K^{\ddagger} \frac{c_n}{(\mathrm{H}^+)^m} \equiv k' \frac{c_n}{(\mathrm{H}^+)^m} = \frac{k_0 K c_0{}^n}{(\mathrm{H}^+)^m (1 + K n^2 c_0{}^{n-1})} \tag{8.66}$$

Thus for low concentrations of the protein the rate is

$$v_0 = \frac{k_0 K c_0{}^n}{(\mathrm{H}^+)^m} \tag{8.67}$$

At high concentrations the rate is

$$v_0 = \frac{k_0 K}{(\mathrm{H}^+)^m K n^2 c_0{}^{n-1}} \tag{8.68}$$

Casey and Laidler show that m is 5 for pepsin (Fig. 8.49).   This is in accord with Steinhardt's results (1937), i.e., that the species of pepsin molecule which denatures is quintuply ionized, as discussed presently.

Although denaturation often is a first order reaction, it is by no means invariably so, and the order may change during the course of the reaction (cf. discussion in review by Neurath, Greenstein, Putnam, and Erickson, 1944).   Lauffer (1945) has found that the thermal destruction of Influenza

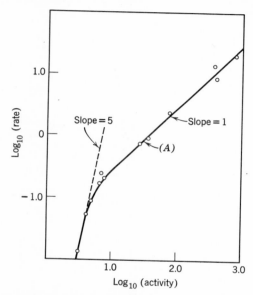

Fig. 8.49.   Relation between the logarithm of the initial rate of destruction (ordinate) and the initial concentration of active pepsin (abscissa) at pH 4.83 and 57.8°C (Casey and Laidler, 1951).

A virus hemagglutinin is of the three-halves order.   Moreover, in contrast to the situation with pepsin, the velocity of the reaction becomes less, rather than greater, with increasing initial concentrations of virus.   Some other viruses exhibit a similar inverse relation between initial concentration and velocity of denaturation by heat, or denaturation with urea at lower temperatures, e.g. tobacco mosaic virus (Price, 1940; Lauffer and Price, 1940; Lauffer, 1943) and the hemagglutinin of influenza virus studied by Miller (1944).

The meaning of the heat and entropy changes associated with protein denaturation (Tables 8.7 and 8.8) has been discussed at some length by Eyring and Stearn (1939).   Although, as pointed out earlier (p. 258), Mirsky and Pauling (1936) have emphasized the summation of the heats involved in the breaking of a large number of hydrogen bonds in accounting for the activation energy of thermal denaturation, it seems likely that other processes are also involved, their relative importance varying with the specific protein.

The studies of pepsin denaturation (Steinhardt, 1937; La Mer, 1937) are of particular interest. In essence, Steinhardt showed that the first order rate (for at least the first 80 per cent of the reaction) of loss in activity of crystallized pepsin at 25°C varies with the fifth power of the hydrogen ion concentration (Figs. 8.50 and 8.51). The theory was

Table 8.9.   The Kinetics of Pepsin Inactivation

pH	Process	$\log_{10} k'(\sec^{-1})$ 25°C 15°C	$\Delta H^{\ddagger}$ (cal)	$\Delta F^{\ddagger}$ (cal)	$\Delta S^{\ddagger}$ (cal/deg)
5.7	$P_0 \rightarrow P^{\ddagger}$	-6.996 -8.716	67,470	26,955	135.9
5.7	$P^{5+} \rightarrow P^{\ddagger}$	-1.696 -2.266	22,360	19,737	8.8
		$\log_{10} K'$	ΔH	ΔF	ΔS
5.7	$P_0 \rightarrow P^{5+}$	-5.3 -6.45	45,110	7,218	127.1
0	$P_0 + 5H_2O \rightarrow P^{5+} + 5H_3{}^+O$	-33.8 -34.95	45,110	46,030	-3.1
0	$5HOAc + 5H_2O$ $\rightarrow 5OAc^- + 5H_3{}^+O$	-23.75	-485	32,350	-110.2

advanced that the denaturation process consists first in the loss of five hydrogen ions, by ionization of the active form of the molecule, followed by an activation and decomposition of the unstable, ionized protein. Adding the heat of ionization of 9,040 cal for each of five hydrogens to an activation energy of 18,300 gives 63,500 for the overall reaction in accordance with the value obtained from the influence of temperature at 15° and 25°C. Thus most of the overall activation energy of 63,500 cal is accounted for in terms of heats of ionization. Further analyses, including the influence of temperature as well as pH, have been made by Levy and Benaglia (1950) with reference to the denaturation of ricin.

The heats, entropies, and free energies of activation for ionization and activation of pepsin at pH 5.7 have been calculated from Steinhardt's data by Eyring and Stearn (1939). The values are summarized in Table 8.9, together with the constants for acetic acid ionization at 25°C. In this table P_0 represents the protein before conversion to P^{5+} by the loss of 5 protons, and $P^{\ddagger}$ represents the activated complex which is formed from

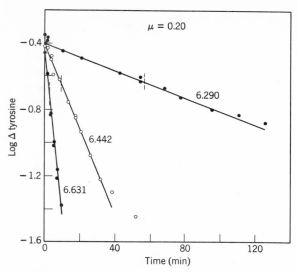

Fig. 8.50. Inactivation of pepsin at an ionic strength of 0.2 and 25°C, at *p*H 6.290, 6.442, and 6.631, respectively, buffered by *p*-nitrophenol (Steinhardt, 1937).

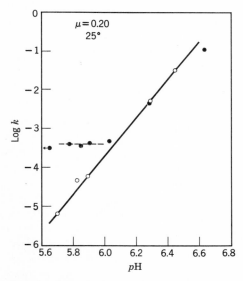

Fig. 8.51. Relation between log velocity of denaturation of pepsin and *p*H, at ionic strength 0.2 and 25°C, with *p*-nitrophenol buffer. The slope of the line is 5. Solid points are from reaction vessels that were shaken, thereby adding, below *p*H 6.1, denaturation for surface reactions (Steinhardt, 1937).

P^{5+} and which decomposes to products with the universal frequency, $\kappa kT/h$.

The data of Table 8.9 indicate that at pH 5.7 most of the entropy change (127.1 E.U.), as well as heat of activation (45,110), is associated with the preliminary ionization. The relatively small entropy increase of 8.8 E.U. in the formation of the activated complex from the ionized, presumably unfolded, molecule indicates very little change in the final step of activation. At pH = 0, the small negative entropy change of $-$ 3.1 E.U. for the ionization of the protein seems odd, at first glance, in comparison with the much larger decrease in entropy, $-$ 110.2 E.U., for the ionization of five moles of acetic acid. The difference indicates that the actual increase in entropy on opening up of the protein is now probably close to $+$ 100 E.U. The net change is the sum of the entropy increase resulting from unfolding and the entropy decrease from ionization in the acid solution.

The detailed picture of the nature of bonds broken during denaturation is not yet fully established. The view that salt bonds are significant (Eyring and Stearn, 1939) has been opposed by Jacobsen and Linder-strøm-Lang (1949). The salt or other bridges, however, whose breakage is of primary importance in the formation of the activated complex, are automatically broken on either side of a critical pH, and the position of this critical pH does not necessarily coincide with the isoelectric point of the protein. It apparently depends upon the relative number of acid and basic groups in the protein. In pepsin the pH of the isoelectric point is 2.85, while that of maximum stability is 5.28. The low isoelectric point indicates strongly ionizing acid groups. In egg albumin the pH of the isoelectric point is 4.55, while that of maximum stability is 6.76, again indicating the presence of strongly ionizing acid groups. In hemoglobin, on the other hand, the pH of the isoelectric point and of maximum stability practically coincide near neutrality, i.e., at about 6.8, indicating an approximate equivalence of acid and basic bridge-forming groups. From these relationships it would be expected that for proteins with very acid isoelectric points the maximum stability would be at a more alkaline pH, while for those with alkaline isoelectric points the maximum stability would be at a more acid pH than the isoelectric point.

The final step in activation involves the breakage of relatively strong covalent bonds which are not destroyed by ionization. Since the net change in entropy is small, it follows that this reaction either involves no unfolding reorganization, or, if there is considerable unfolding, then considerable refolding must undo the entropy increase.

The change in activation energy for denaturation in acid or bases arises from their influence on the salt or other bonds concerned. When broken thermally, the observed heat is the difference between the strength of the bond before breaking and the strength of the bond formed with the solvent after breaking. With urea the effect is probably largely on hydrogen bonds. Thus with urea the heat of activation may be negative. With alcohol or strong concentrations of salt it may increase to a higher value than with water. The binding of urea with the activated complex is probably very strong as judged by the large negative entropy of activation. The net heat of this binding is apparently much higher than that of water. In general, any factor which increases the solubility of the activated complex in comparison with the normal molecule will accelerate the rate of denaturation.

The action of urea, and also of urethan, sometimes gives rise to complex kinetics and temperature relationships of denaturation because each of these agents evidently enters into more than one reaction with the protein. For example, the rate of denaturation of tobacco mosaic virus in 6 M urea, buffered to about pH 7 with 0.1 M phosphate, is first order with respect to the concentration of protein, but the specific rate goes through a minimum at room temperature (Fig. 8.52; Lauffer, 1943). In sim-plest terms, the changing influence of temperature illustrated in Fig. 8.52 may be accounted for on the assumption that reversible combinations take place between the TMV protein and urea, characterized by different ratios of urea to TMV molecules in the complex so formed, and by different heats and entropies. The net effect of temperature then depends upon the difference between its effect on the dissociation of the TMV-urea complexes and on the specific rate of decomposition of these complexes. Thus, as the temperature is raised from 0° to about 20°C the effect of heat is greater in dissociating the more loosely bound urea molecules than it is in accele-rating the rate of decomposition of these and the more strongly bound urea-TMV complexes. The latter, however, will be more important at temperatures above 20° provided that the heats and entropies of activation

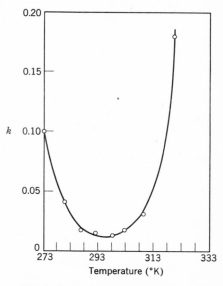

Fig. 8.52. Relation of the specific rate of denaturation of TMV, 4.5 mg per cc in 6 M urea, to the absolute temperature (Lauffer, 1943).

for their decomposition result in a higher free energy of activation.   The
quantitative relation between concentration of urea and the specific
reaction rate velocity at different temperatures (Fig. 8.53) shows that the
average ratio of urea to TMV molecules is, indeed, less at higher than at
lower temperatures.   The slopes of the lines in Fig. 8.53 indicate that the
rate is proportional to the 8.1 power of urea concentration at 0°C, and
to the 5.7 power at 45°C.   Details of the theory are available in the
original paper (Lauffer, 1943).

Evidence of similar "anomalies" in other viruses and proteins (Hopkins,
1930; Diebold and Juhling, 1938; Drabkin, 1939; Bawden and Pirie,
1940) suggests that it is a general
phenomenon of urea denaturations.
According to the particular protein
and range of temperature over
which the process is studied, it may
include either positive or negative
temperature coefficients or both.

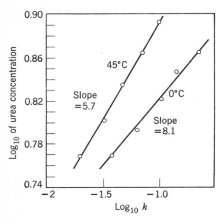

Fig. 8.53.   Rate of TMV denaturation
as a function of urea concentration at 0°
and at 45°C (Lauffer, 1943).

Parenthetically it may be remarked here that it would be of
interest to investigate the urea
denaturation of the blood and
other proteins of elasmobranch
fishes (sharks, dogfish, and other
cartilaginous fishes).   In physiological adaptation to osmotic
requirements, their blood, tissues,
and body fluids normally function
in an unusually high concentration
of urea, about 0.5 M (cf. Smith, 1936).   On general biological principles, it
would be reasonable to expect that their proteins would show a somewhat
unusual resistance to denaturation in urea.   The temperature relationship
of the urea denaturation would also be of especial interest if a minimum
rate occurred at a temperature near that of their accustomed environment.
The urea content of elasmobranch tissues may contribute to the survival
of these fishes in other ways than through an unusual solution of the
osmotic pressure problems of an organism living in a medium of hyper-
tonic salt solution.   They are thoroughly safe from the gourmet, though
palatability is improved by dialysis.   Predatory animals, however, are
probably much less discriminating in their delicacy of taste.

With β-lactoglobulin both a reversible and an irreversible or very slowly
reversible denaturation are favored by decrease in temperature between
37° and 0°C (Jacobsen and Christensen, 1948).   Figure 8.54 illustrates the

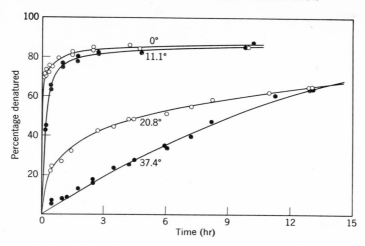

Fig. 8.54.   Denaturation of 2% β-lactoglobulin in 38% urea, pH 5.17, at temperatures between 0° and 37.4°C (Jacobsen and Christensen, 1948).

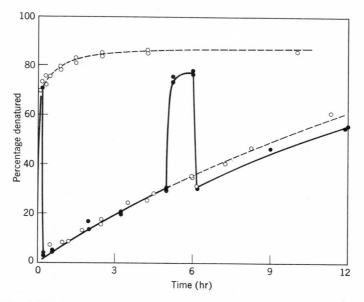

Fig. 8.55.   Reversibility of the effects of changing the temperature during the course of denaturation of β-lactoglobulin in 38% urea.   Broken lines indicate the reaction at constant temperature; the solid lines show the changes in amount of denatured protein after the reactants are mixed at 0°C for the first 6 min, warmed to 37.4°C for the next 5 hr, then cooled again to 0° for a period of 1 hr and rewarmed to 37.4°C (Jacobsen and Christensen, 1948).

rate process of denaturation at several temperatures within this range. Figure 8.55 shows the readily reversible effects on the amount of denatured protein by lowering and then raising the temperature during the course of denaturation at 37.4°C. Except for the fact that the influence of temperature under these conditions and with this protein is in the opposite direction, the data of Fig. 8.55 recall the experiments on the reversible and irreversible thermal inactivation of bacterial luminescence (Fig. 8.31). A thermal denaturation that is reversible on cooling also occurs in β-lactoglobulin (Linderstrøm-Lang, Hotchkiss, and Johansen, 1938).

The influence of urethan on proteins is of especial interest because of the extensive study it has received as a narcotic or inhibitor of biological processes (cf. Winterstein, 1926; Henderson, 1930). Meyerhof (1918) showed that the presence of salts is required for precipitation of proteins in solution by urethan. The rate of denaturation of egg albumin and of sheep serum proteins by urethan has been measured by Hopkins (1930). Bawden and Pirie (1940) studied the action of urethan and other simple organic agents on plant viruses; some were more resistant than others to urethan. More recently, the inactivation of bacteriophage by urethan has been investigated in relation to concentration, temperature, and hydrostatic pressure (Foster, Johnson, and Miller, 1949). At increased temperatures between 60° and 68°C the inactivation of free phage is accelerated by urethan. At the incubation temperature of 35°C multiplication of the phage in the host cell is reversibly inhibited by the same concentrations of urethan (Foster and Johnson, 1951).

The data on inactivation of free phage are illustrated in Fig. 8.56. The solid line, which conforms to the experimentally determined points within the limits of accuracy of the method, was calculated on the basis of equation (8.69), which assumes only one reaction catalyzed by urethan. In (8.69), P represents active bacteriophage, U represents urethan, k_0 the specific velocity of inactivation in absence of urethan, and k_u the specific velocity in the presence of a given concentration of urethan.

$$-\frac{d\mathrm{P}}{dt} = k_0(\mathrm{P}) + k_u(\mathrm{P})(\mathrm{U})^x = (k_0 + k_u(\mathrm{U})^x)(\mathrm{P}) \qquad (8.69)$$

The value of the exponent x was estimated from the slope of the curve (broken line in Fig. 8.56) which by inspection seemed to fit the points at the higher concentrations of urethan, and a value of k_u was estimated also in this region, where k_0 is small in comparison. The constants thus obtained and used in equation (8.69) are as follows: $k_0 = 2.9 \times 10^{-4}$ sec^{-1}, $k_u = 6 \times 10^{-2}$ sec^{-1}, and $x = 2.3$. Under the conditions of the experiment an average of 2.3 more molecules of urethan is combined with the activated than with the normal state of the molecule whose destruction results in inactivation of the phage. This fractional value, rather than an integer, probably means that the process of destruction is catalyzed by more than one distinct reaction with urethan. With tobacco mosaic virus there is evidence that the thermal denaturation is catalyzed at normal and increased pressure by three reactions with urethan (Fraser, Johnson, and

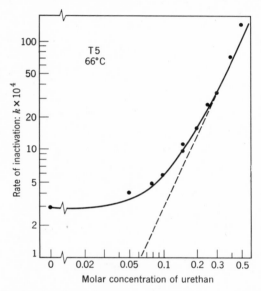

Fig. 8.56. Acceleration of the thermal inactivation of coliphage T5 by urethan at 66°C (Foster, Johnson, and Miller, 1949).

Baker, 1949). With either bacteriophage or tobacco mosaic virus the rate is first order with respect to the amount of native protein at various concentrations of the drug (as in equation 8.69). Additional data with respect to temperature and pressure, however, are required in order to clarify the mechanism of the reaction. All three parameters are significant, and the data from pressure experiments are sometimes especially useful, as discussed in the next chapter.

Hydrostatic Pressure and
Molecular Volume Changes

Le physiologiste n'a donc plus [qu'] à rechercher si, sous ces pressions énormes de plus de 600 atmosphères que supporte le fond de l'Océan, la vie existe; il doit maintenant essayer de déterminer dans quelles conditions elle peut se produire.

Regnard (1884)

Background of pressure studies in biology

On the dredging expedition of the *Talisman* in 1882–1883, organisms were found living in the depths of the sea at 6,000 meters below the surface, at depths where the hydrostatic pressure amounts to slightly more than 600 atmospheres (atm). The circumstance that living forms could tolerate such a pressure immediately stimulated inquiry into the effects of pressure on biological activity. The first extensive laboratory experiments on this problem were undertaken almost immediately by Regnard and Certes. Beginning in 1884, their papers were published in the *Comptes Rèndus* of the Académie des Sciences and of the Société de Biologie in Paris. A monograph on the subject by Regnard appeared in 1891.

Although there was no theory for the influence of hydrostatic pressure on chemical reaction rates at that time and no realization of the important influence of temperature on the biological response to pressure, and no really quantitative data were obtained, the results of these early experiments are of distinct interest. They provided a survey of the effects of pressures up to 1,000 atm on numerous biological processes and established some fundamental relationships which have been confirmed and extended by more precise studies in later years. On the other hand, a number of seeming discrepancies now exist. Moreover, some confusion seems to have arisen with regard to the general subject of the effects of high pressures on biological reactions. The discrepancies and confusion have arisen partly through failure to make such distinctions as those referred to in the following paragraphs. The original point of inquiry—the relation between pressure and activity of life in the deep sea—is still far from solution, but recent work has provided the basis for rational investigations and has paved the way toward an ultimate understanding of the problem.

To avoid misunderstandings concerning the nature of the phenomena under consideration, it is perhaps worth while to state explicitly that we will deal in this chapter solely with the action of hydrostatic pressure on rates and equilibria of reactions in solution, and with the molecular volume changes of reactions as determined by dilatometry. High pressures of air, oxygen, or other gases will not be considered; the mechanism of their effects is more complicated, since in addition to the influence of hydrostatic pressure as such the concentration of the reactants varies with the pressure, and mechanical effects on tissues may also be involved, e.g., through bubble formation on decompression. In aqueous solution the concentration of solutes (including gases, when there is no gas phase present) does not change under pressure by more than the compressibility of the fluid, which usually amounts to only a few per cent. It is important to remember also that hydrostatic pressure is uniformly exerted in all directions, in sharp distinction to pressures of deformation. Unequally applied pressures of a few dynes per square centimeter may be sufficient to deform and injure a cell, or to stimulate a sensitive tactile nerve receptor, whereas purely hydrostatic pressure applied to the same structures might be entirely without observable effect, unless the pressure exceeds some fifty or a hundred atmospheres. Among ordinary chemical reactions involving small molecules (apart from certain chain reactions, Stearn and Eyring, 1941), the influence of only 100 atm of hydrostatic pressure is generally imperceptible, and it is only because of the much larger molecules concerned in biological reactions that such pressures are able to exert pronounced effects.

An additional distinction concerning hydrostatic pressure alone may well be made at the start, namely, that the effects and mechanism of action on biological materials is likely to be quite different at pressures roughly between 1 and 1,000 atm, and between 1,000 and 5,000 or more atm, respectively. For convenience of discussion, we may refer to the former as moderate or high pressures, and to the latter as very high pressures. The physiological effects of moderate pressures are frequently reversible, sometimes quantitatively so, as soon as the pressure is released. Very high pressures, on the other hand, nearly always lead to drastic, permanent consequences. Furthermore, opposite effects on the same process sometimes occur at the two ranges of pressure, e.g., moderate pressures may retard or reverse protein denaturation, whereas the very high pressures are likely to accelerate protein denaturation.

Finally, it is important to distinguish between the changes that take place during the period of compression and those which may be observed after the release of pressure. The former type may, though not necessarily, include reversible changes, such as those of a mobile equilibrium which could not be detected except during the time that the material is under pressure.   The latter type necessarily comprise irreversible, or only slowly reversible, effects.

In the early experiments of Regnard and of Certes (1884–1891) the pressures employed did not exceed 1,000 atm, and most of the observations dealt with changes that could be noted after pressure had been applied and released at room temperature.   In 1885, however, Regnard constructed an apparatus with quartz windows which was capable of holding a pressure of 800 atm for several hours.   With it he observed the influence of various pressures on the activity of small aquatic organisms such as *Cyclops, Daphnia,* and *Gammarus pulex.*   With the first application of pressures not exceeding 100 atm the animals became agitated.   Above this pressure they became tetanized and fell slowly to the bottom of the vessel, apparently incapable of movement.   If the period of compression was short, the animals instantly recovered their activity on sudden release of pressure.   Longer periods of compression produced a coma, recovery from which required several hours at normal pressure.   Still longer periods of compression caused death.   These results are interesting because (1) they indicated the ready susceptibility of a living organism to the effects of moderate hydrostatic pressure, (2) some of the changes in activity were reversible, others not, indicating a multiplicity of reactions that were influenced, and (3) apparently stimulating, as well as inhibitory, effects occurred, the latter becoming more pronounced with higher pressures and longer times under pressure.   Regnard concluded, probably correctly, that the initial influence of pressure was on the nervous system.   Subsequent observations by Ebbecke (1935b) with a considerably larger variety of animals, including *Amphioxus* and fishes as well as invertebrates, confirmed the general results described by Regnard.   Many species showed increased activity at the lower pressures and a reversible cessation of movement on brief exposures to the higher pressures up to 600 atm. Prolonged paralysis occurred after longer exposures at moderate pressure or after short exposures to the highest pressures.

In experiments where the behavior of whole animals could not be observed while under pressure, Regnard found that any of a considerable number of species could be killed by subjecting them to pressures between 400 and 1,000 atm.   Some, including echinoderms and coelenterates, withstood 1,000 atm for an hour, then slowly recovered their normal activity.   Others, including molluscs, annelids, crustaceans, and ascidians, were more readily affected by 400 to 600 atm.   More complex organisms, fish and frogs, were compressed after first removing the air from the swim bladder or lungs.   Results similar to the preceding were obtained with a marine and with a fresh water species of fish: they were rendered immobile for several hours or killed by pressures as low as 300 atm. In both fish and frog, the heart stopped beating after 10 min at 600 atm. The tadpoles, however, appeared to be unaffected after exposure to 300 atm, and they recovered slowly after immobilization by 400 atm. Eggs of fish, after 6 hr of exposure to 200 atm, developed normally. After exposure to 300 atm the eggs hatched normally but developed more slowly, and after 400 to 600 atm they died in 6 to 2 days.

Regnard also studied the influence of pressure on microörganisms and enzyme reactions. Putrefaction of egg, milk, urine, blood, meat, etc., failed to occur in 2 to 7 weeks under a pressure of 700 atm. In similar studies by Certes there was evidence of retarded bacterial growth in various infusions of putrescible material kept under 350 to 500 atm pressure for 42 days. On the other hand, anthrax bacteria could be kept under 600 atm pressure for 24 hr without perceptible loss in virulence or capacity to reproduce subsequently at normal pressure. Fresh water algae were subjected to 600 atm for several hours. Afterwards they carried on photosynthesis as before, but died a few days later. Both Regnard and Certes found that fermentation by yeast is retarded under pressures of a few hundred atmospheres but is resumed after release of pressure; viable cells remained after several days at 300 to 400 atm (Certes and Cochin, 1884), and multiplication subsequently occurred in an appropriate medium. Recent studies (ZoBell and Johnson, 1949) seem to indicate a much greater sensitivity of viability in yeasts to similar pressures, but the discrepancy is probably more apparent than real; the stage of growth in a culture, type of medium, pH, the specific yeast, the temperature, and various factors which remain to be systematically investigated might be responsible for this and other seeming discrepancies which exist between the results of the older and more recent experiments. By the same token, undue significance should not be attached to differences between the actual pressures responsible for a given effect as observed by different investigators unless the experimental materials and conditions are known to be essentially identical.

Regnard subjected muscle, nerve, and red blood cells to high pressures and noted evidence of injury, but the extent to which such injury should be attributed to the influence of pressure is uncertain. It is not clear that the tissues were always placed in a physiologically favorable solution. In general, however, it is evident both from his studies and from those of his contemporary, Certes, that complex organisms and complex functions are more sensitive to injury or inhibition by hydrostatic pressure than are the relatively simple ones. The activity of digestive enzymes in saliva, gastric juice, or pancreatic juice, for example, was qualitatively unimpaired while under 1,000 atm. A few years later (E. Buchner, 1897; H. Buchner,

1897) fermentation was observed with juice pressed from yeast cells under 400 to 500 atm, and toxic extracts of bacteria prepared with the aid of the same pressures were found to be as active as the intact cells.

Trend of developments since Regnard and Certes

Since the time of Regnard and Certes the trend of research on the biological action of hydrostatic pressure has been influenced to a considerable extent by progress in solving the engineering problems of achieving high pressures in the laboratory and by the enthusiasm of investigators for testing the effects of higher and higher pressures on biological material. The development of the necessary apparatus had a practical as well as a theoretical objective, inasmuch as the rates of viscous flow, of polymerization reactions, and of other processes may be influenced by pressure in ways that are industrially important. In biology also the destructive effects of pressure that were demonstrated by Regnard and Certes on certain activities and forms of life suggested the possibility of practical applications for sterilization of solutions, for separation of or distinction between pressure-sensitive and pressure-resistant components, and for other purposes. The fact that some biological materials appeared to be resistant to the action of moderate pressures, such as the maximum of 1,000 atm studied by Regnard, constituted a challenge for research into the effects of higher and higher pressures on these materials.

It is more human nature than scientific acumen to undertake research with increasingly dramatic and powerful methods as they become available. Technical advances since 1900 have made it possible to apply hydrostatic pressures of not merely 1,000 atm, but of 10,000 and even 100,000 atm (Bridgman, 1931, 1946). As the methods were developed, higher pressures on biological materials were studied. Yet, there is probably no occurrence in nature of a biological process that is normally subjected to as great a pressure as 10,000 atm. From the viewpoint of the theory of biological reaction rates, the influence of pressures of between 100 and 1,000 atm is far more significant. In a sense, therefore, it is unfortunate that investigations of the type begun by Regnard and Certes did not receive continued emphasis and progressive refinement during the ensuing forty years. Apart from occasional studies during the intervening period, such as those of Krause (1902), Callery and Portier (1910), Ebbecke (1914), it was not until the late nineteen-twenties and early thirties that interest in the physiological action of moderate pressures reawakened; Cattell and Edwards, Fontaine, Brown, Marsland, and Ebbecke were the chief exponents. In the meantime the accumulated data with respect to the action of very high pressures has given rise to a widely prevalent view that the biological effect of high hydrostatic pressure in general is that of denaturing proteins or destroying life through protein denaturation or other poorly understood mechanisms.   Nothing is farther from the truth.

Acceleration of protein denaturation and other reactions under very high pressures

Before discussing the action of ordinary high pressures, up to about 1,000 atm, it is convenient to consider first the effects of very high pressures, roughly in the range between 1,000 and 10,000 atm and sometimes higher.   The theoretical basis of the effects of very high pressures has not been satisfactorily worked out with biological materials.   Although there is a fairly extensive literature, the observations are primarily empirical and as a rule the quantitative data are not adequate for theoretical analysis.   Most of the experiments have been done at room temperature, and possible significance of the temperature parameter has been largely ignored.   They are nevertheless of interest, especially because, in the intermediate range of pressure from somewhat below to somewhat above 1,000 atm, two different types of mechanisms may significantly influence the results.

Table 9.1 lists some of the results of pressures in excess of 1,000 atm that have been observed on a variety of biological materials.   It is intended only to give a general view, not an analytical nor a complete summary.   In each instance the material was subjected to the pressure designated and then observed for the effect after pressure was released.   The duration of compression is not listed in this table.   In some cases it was only transitory, and in others it was maintained for hours or days; usually it was maintained for a matter of minutes.   Not all the original publications give full information about the time relation.   In some instances it appears to be important, but in others not nearly so important as the actual amount of pressure, as discussed below.

Any discussion of the mechanism through which very high pressures affect biological processes or materials is limited by the availability of data suitable for analysis.   Compared to the extensive data that have accumulated with respect to the influence of temperature at normal pressure, the quantitative studies with respect to the influence of pressure at constant temperature are very few.   Both parameters, temperature and pressure, have but rarely been considered in relation to the same phenomenon, and even then never in considerable detail.   There are, however, some clues to the mechanisms involved, and some general relationships are apparent.

In the recent studies with simple systems, purified proteins in particular, more attention has been paid to the rate of change than formerly, when

Table 9.1. Examples of the Effects of Hydrostatic Pressures Generally in Excess of 1,000 Atmospheres on Biological Materials

Material	Approximate Pressure (atm)*	Results of Compression	Reference
		Proteins	
Egg albumin	5,000	Slight stiffening	Bridgman, 1914
	7,000	Completely coagulated	Bridgman, 1914
	7,500	Denatured, coagulated; —SH groups exposed	Grant et al., 1941
Carboxyhemoglobin	9,000	Coagulated	Bridgman and Conant, 1929
Equine serum globulin	3,000– 13,000	Gelated	Basset, Macheboeuf, and Sandor, 1933
Gelatin	2,000	Gelation accelerated	Leïpunskiĭ, 1940
Gelatin gel	3,000	Water squeezed out	Lloyd and Moran, 1934
Insulin	10,000	Coagulated but not physiologically inactivated	Dow, Matthews, and Thorp, 1940
Active trypsin plus its digest of gelatin or serum albumin	6,000	Resynthesis of product resembling initial, undigested material	Bresler, 1947
Active amylase plus its digest of starch	6,000	Resynthesis of product resembling initial, undigested material	Bresler, 1947
		Enzymes	
Yeast sucrase; pancreatic trypsin, trypsinogen, lipase, and amylase; laccase	8,000– 15,000	Some completely, others partially, inactivated	Macheboeuf, Basset, and Levy, 1933; Basset, Lisbonne, and Macheboeuf, 1933; Macheboeuf and Basset, 1934
Ribonucleodepolymerase	6,000	Reversible diminution in activity under pressure (pressure also affects polymerization of ribonucleic acid alone)	Vignais et al., 1951

* Different authors have used various units to designate the pressure: 1 atm = 1.033 kg/cm² = 14.696 psi = 1.0133 bars. In this table 1 atm is considered approximately equivalent to 1 bar, to 1 kg/cm², or to 15 psi.

292

Table 9.1 (Continued)

Material	Approximate Pressure (atm)*	Results of Compression	Reference
Enzymes (Continued)			
Pepsin, rennin	6,000	Inactivated	Matthews et al., 1940
Trypsin, chymotrypsin	7,600	pH 3, scarcely affected pH 7.6, partially inactivated	Curl and Jansen, 1950a
Pepsin	7,600	pH 2 to pH 5.2, largely inactivated	Curl and Jansen, 1950b
Chymotrypsinogen	7,600	pH 3.1 to pH 7.6, partially inactivated	Curl and Jansen, 1950b
Viruses			
Tobacco mosaic	8,700	Inactivated	Giddings et al., 1929
	8,000	Inactivated	Basset, Gratia, Macheboeuf, and Manil, 1938
	7,500	Inactivated, coagulated	Lauffer and Dow, 1941
Tobacco necrosis	3,000–5,000	Inactivated	Basset, Gratia, Macheboeuf, and Manil, 1938
Herpes (rabbit)	3,000	Inactivated	Basset, Nicolau, and Macheboeuf, 1935
Fièvre aphteuse (foot and mouth disease) (guinea pig)	3,000	Attenuated	Basset, Nicolau, and Macheboeuf, 1935
	4,000	Inactivated	Basset, Nicolau, and Macheboeuf, 1935
Rabies (rabbit)	4,000	Attenuated	Basset, Nicolau, and Macheboeuf, 1935
	5,000	Inactivated	Basset, Nicolau, and Macheboeuf, 1935
Yellow fever (*Macacus*)	3,000	Slightly attenuated	Basset, Nicolau, and Macheboeuf, 1935
Encephalomyelitis (rabbit)	7,000	Inactivated	Basset, Nicolau, and Macheboeuf, 1935
Avian pest	4,000	Inactivated, but retained antigenicity	Lepine et al., 1936
Bacteriophage vs. Staphylococci	2,000	Inactivated	Basset, Wollman, Macheboeuf, and Bardach, 1933; Basset, Wollman, Wollman, and Macheboeuf, 1935
B. typhosus, B. subtilis, and B. megatherium	7,000	Inactivated	

Table 9.1 (Continued)

Material	Approximate Pressure (atm)*	Results of Compression	Reference
Viruses (Continued)			
Vaccinia (rabbit)	4,500	Inactivated	Basset, Wollman, Macheboeuf, and Bardach, 1933; Basset, Wollman, Wollman, and Macheboeuf, 1935
Shope (rabbit), papilloma virus	4,000	Not inactivated	Wollman et al., 1936,
	6,000	Inactivated	Wollman et al., 1936
Roux (chicken), sarcoma filtrate	1,800	Tumors delayed	Basset, Wollman, Macheboeuf, and Bardach, 1935
	4,000	No tumors	Basset, Wollman, Macheboeuf, and Bardach, 1935
Antigens and Antibodies			
Tetanus toxin	13,500	Greatly attenuated or inactivated	Basset and Macheboeuf, 1932, 1933
Diphtheria toxin	13,500	Partially destroyed	Basset and Macheboeuf, 1932, 1933
	17,600	Mostly destroyed	Basset and Macheboeuf, 1932, 1933
Cobra venom	13,500	As lethal as before	Basset and Macheboeuf, 1932, 1933
Tuberculin	13,500	Not destroyed	Basset and Macheboeuf, 1932, 1933
Equine serum antigens	4,000	Anaphylactic specificity unchanged	Basset, Macheboeuf, and Perez, 1935
	4,000	New anaphylactic specificity	Basset, Macheboeuf, and Perez, 1935
Equine antitoxin (tetanus)	13,500	Gelated, partially inactivated	Basset and Macheboeuf, 1932, 1933
Typhoid bacterial filtrate	6,000	Superior to cells as immunizing antigen	Larson et al., 1918
Microörganisms			
Colon bacteria, staphylococci	3,000	Unaffected	Roger, 1895

Table 9.1 (Continued)

Material	Approx- imate Pressure (atm)*	Results of Compression	Reference
Microörganisms (Continued)			
Streptococci	3,000	Killed or retarded in growth	Roger, 1895
Anthrax	3,000	Partial loss of virulence; death of vegetative cells	Roger, 1895
Bacteria (various species)	6,000	Vegetative cells killed	Larson et al., 1918
Bacterial spores	12,000	Killed	Larson et al., 1918
Yeast cells	4,000– 6,000	Death preceded by cytoplasmic flocculation or coagulation	Luyet, 1937 a, b
Tumors and Tissues			
Brown-Pearce carcinoma	1,000	Resistant	Wollman et al., 1936
	1,800	Transplantability destroyed	Wollman et al., 1936
Rat sarcoma transplants	1,800	Inactivated	Basset, Wollman, Macheboeuf, and Bardach, 1935
Embryonic chick heart	1,000– 1,850	Reduction of subsequent growth in culture	Benthaus, 1937
	1,850	No subsequent growth; cells rounded, nuclei pyknotic	Benthaus, 1937
Erythrocytes	500– 2,000	Rounded	Ebbecke, 1936d, 1937; Haubrick, 1937
	5,000	Disintegrated	Dow and Matthews, 1939

only the end result was emphasized. Lauffer and Dow (1941) have shown that the coagulation of purified tobacco mosaic virus at 30°C under various pressures between 5,000 and 10,000 atm, proceeds as a first order reaction (Fig. 9.1). In this respect, the kinetics are similar to those of denaturation at around 70°C and at lower temperatures in the presence of urea. Furthermore, the products of denaturation under these different conditions are similar in that the protein becomes coagulated, the infective properties of the virus disappear, and the nucleic acid moiety is split off.

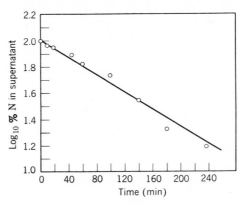

Fig. 9.1   The rate of coagulation of tobacco mosaic virus in 0.1 M phosphate buffer solution of pH 7 at 30°C under 7,500 atm of hydrostatic pressure (Lauffer and Dow, 1941). The pH of the buffer at normal pressure was 7; under high pressures the pH would be expected to shift to the acid (cf p. 302).

Infectivity disappears faster than solubility decreases, indicating that these properties measure different reactions. Additional evidence of a complexity of reactions occurring under pressures of 7,500 atm was found by ultracentrifugal analysis of partially denatured preparations. The soluble but non-infectious portion contained large amounts of a fairly homogeneous component, along with small amounts of a more rapidly sedimenting, inhomogeneous component. Under the higher pressure of 10,000 atm for the same length of time, only the former type of component remained in solution. In both cases the soluble material, though non-infectious, had no significant difference in nitrogen and phosphorus content from the normal virus. On the other hand, the insoluble material, which was always inactive, contained much less nitrogen and phosphorus than the normal virus.

Evidently, at least two types of products are formed in the denaturation of TMV under high pressure at 30°C: (1) a soluble, inactive product and (2) an insoluble, inactive product. Another complexity in the process as a whole consists in the fact that there appears to be an "optimum pressure" for denaturation. In a given period of time (45 min) at 7,510 atm, a maximum amount of coagulum was formed. It contained about 22 per cent of the initial nitrogen content of the specimen. No coagulum was formed within the same period of time at 5,050 atm, and only 6.8 per cent of the nitrogen was found in the coagulum at 8,500 atm; at 9,000 to 10,000 atm it was even less, amounting to less than 5 per cent. Similar results were not obtained with respect to infectivity, which was progressively reduced with increase in pressure. It would seem, therefore, that under pressures of more than 7,500 atm the virus is either denatured to a soluble, inactive product, or that the insoluble products are changed into different products that are soluble but inactive. Viewed in this way, the optimum pressure for denaturation, referred to earlier, is only an optimum pressure for insolubilization.

Both the denaturation at 30°C under 7,500 atm pressure, and at 67° to 73°C under 1 atm pressure (Lauffer and Price, 1940) are first order rate processes. At pH 7.05 and at the concentrations of virus employed, the thermal denaturation was found to have an activation energy of 153,000 cal between 67° and 73°C. By extrapolating the rate at the higher temperatures and normal pressure, down to 30°C, it turns out that at 30°C the rate under 7,500 atm is 10^{12} times the immeasurably slow rate at 1 atm. If these data are then used in equation (9.7), the value of $\Delta V^{\ddagger}$ would seem to be $-100,000$ cc per mole, or about 1/250 of the total volume of a mole of virus (Lauffer, 1949). Even though the molecular weight of the tobacco mosaic virus molecule is extraordinarily high, of the order of 40,000,000 (Stanley and Loring, 1938), it does not seem reasonable that a volume change of 100,000 cc per mole could take place in the formation of an activated complex from the normal molecule. If the same mechanism of reaction were involved at both 67° to 73°C and at all pressures at 30°C, it would follow that considerable denaturation should occur at 30° under pressures of 5,000 atm or less, whereas none was observed. The mechanisms must be different, and the value of $\Delta V^{\ddagger} = -100,000$ cc per mole is, therefore, of doubtful significance.

A multiplicity of reactions also in the denaturation of pepsin and rennin under pressure is apparent in the kinetics of the process (Matthews, Dow, and Anderson, 1940). Figure 9.2 illustrates the changing rates of inactivation of crystallized pepsin solutions subjected to 2,500 and 4,500 atm, respectively, at pH 4.8 and 35.5°C. With these proteins relatively little change in activity occurred after the first hour when the period of compression was continued for an additional 3 hr (Fig. 9.3).

The subsequent data of Curl and Jansen (1950b), however, show that the pH of 4.2 is not far from the pH of maximum resistance of pepsin to

denaturation under high pressure.   Moreover, at pH 4.0, the data of Curl
and Jansen indicate a progressive denaturation with increasing time of

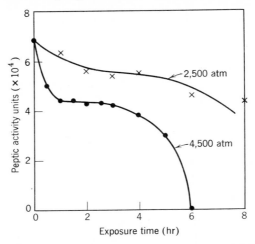

Fig. 9.2.   The rate of destruction of peptic activity at pH 4.8, under 2,500
and 4,500 atm, respectively, at 35.5°C (Matthews, Dow, and Anderson, 1940).

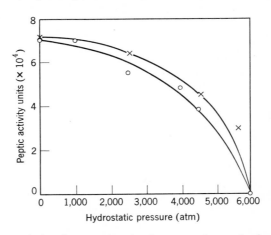

Fig. 9.3.   Relation between length of compression and of amount of
pressure on the activity of pepsin in solution of pH 4.8, at 35.5°C (Matthews,
Dow, and Anderson, 1940).   Upper curve (crosses), under pressure 1 hr;
lower curve (circles), under pressure 4 hr.

compression at 6,100 bars.   This fact would not be apparent from Fig.
9.3, since essentially all the activity was destroyed within the period of an
hour.   Furthermore, in Fig. 9.3, continuation of the 4-hr curve from the

point at 4,500 atm to zero activity at 6,000 atm is very probably misleading. From the relationships demonstrated by Curl and Jansen it would seem probable that essentially no activity of pepsin would remain after 4 hr under a somewhat lower pressure than 6,000 atm, so that the true curve would drop more sharply and, in fact, reveal an influence of time in the compressed state in this region of highest pressures studied by Matthews et al.

The study by Matthews, Dow, and Anderson (1940) included a few experiments with regard to the influence of temperature.   They indicated

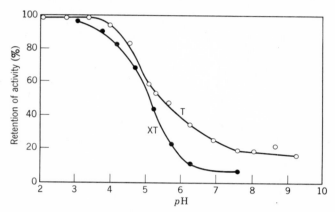

Fig. 9.4.   Relation between pH of the solution and amount of inactivation of trypsin (T) and chymotrypsin (XT) in 5 min. under 7,600 bars pressure (Curl and Jansen, 1950a).

that the effect of pressure has a small, positive temperature coefficient between 0° and 35.5°C.   Thus, at 0°, a 25 per cent decrease in peptic activity under 5,000 atm took place in 5 hr.   Under similar conditions but at 35.5°, the decrease amounted to 60 per cent.   The apparent activation energy over this range of temperatures amounts to about 5,600 cal.   For the loss in activity of rennin under pressure, at 0° and 23°C, an even lower value is indicated.

Curl and Jansen (1950a, b) have studied the rate of inactivation of trypsin, chymotrypsin, chymotrypsinogen, and pepsin with solutions of the crystallized proteins at 25°C under pressures between about 3,000 and 9,000 atm.   The sensitivity of these proteins to pressure differs, and depends markedly upon the pH of the solution as illustrated in Figs. 9.4 and 9.5.   Figure 9.4 shows that, although a large part of the activity of trypsin and chymotrypsin is lost in 5 min under 7,600 bars at alkaline pH, there is scarcely any loss at the quite acid pH of 3.   The curves in this figure resemble dissociation curves, and ionization may well be an important factor in the increase in susceptibility to pressure with increase in pH as observed for pepsin at normal pressure (see pp. 302–305). Apparently

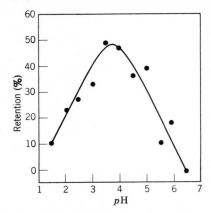

Fig. 9.5. Relation between pH of the solution and the inactivation of pepsin in 5 min under 6,100 bars pressure (Curl and Jansen, 1950b).

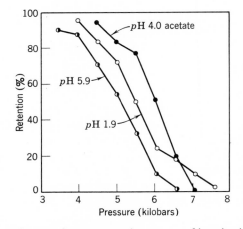

Fig. 9.6. Influence of pressure on the amount of inactivation of pepsin in 5 min at different pH (Curl and Jansen, 1950b).

the ionized, perhaps unfolded, form of the molecule is the species that becomes denatured under high as well as ordinary pressure. With pepsin (Fig. 9.5) there is a pH, between 3 and 4, of maximum stability against pressure which, as in thermal denaturation, occurs at a less acid pH than the isoelectric point.

The amount of inactivation increases with pressure either close to or on either side of the *pH* of maximum stability (Fig. 9.6).   With trypsin or chymotrypsin, on the other hand, a point is reached where further increase in either amount or duration of pressure leads to practically no further inactivation, as shown, for example, in Fig. 9.7.   Chymotrypsinogen differs from the three enzymes in that repeated applications of pressure on the same specimen seem to cause scarcely any more destruction than

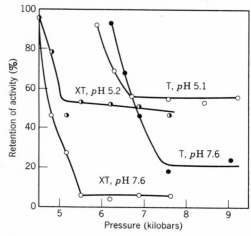

Fig. 9.7. Influence of the amount of pressure on the inactivation of trypsin (T) and chymotrypsin (XT) in 5 min at two different *pH* values (Curl and Jansen, 1950 a).

that brought about by the first application.   For convenience in comparing the influence of the various factors on the pressure inactivation of these proteins, the qualitative effects are summarized in Table 9.2.

The effects listed in Table 9.2 and discussed with reference to Figs. 9.2 to 9.6 seem to encompass a variety of complicated reactions as well as specific differences among the four proteins.   To some extent, however, these differences may be more apparent than real.   Additional data concerning each of the several parameters of pressure magnitude, duration, *pH*, etc., would probably reveal a greater similarity in general effects of pressure on all four substances.   For example, pepsin apparently has a *pH* of maximum resistance at *pH* 3.5 to 4, with rapidly decreasing resistance on either the more acid or the more alkaline side.   Trypsin and chymotrypsin also have a *pH* of maximum resistance in the form of a plateau at about *pH* 2 to 3.   The data show that the resistance is less at less acid *pH*, but data are lacking for the more acid *pH*.   In the latter range it is reasonable to believe that a corresponding decrease in resistance also exists.   In this event, the pH relationships to pressure inactivation would differ quantitatively, but not qualitatively, among the three substances.   Similarly, although duration of compression appears to be more important in some instances than in others, it is reasonable to expect that under appropriate conditions it will become relatively important or unimportant with each protein.

In general, there are at least two, and possibly four, mechanisms involving volume changes through which high pressures would be expected

Table 9.2.   General Influence of Several Factors on the Inactivation of Trypsin, Chymotrypsin, Chymotrypsinogen, and Pepsin by Hydrostatic Pressure at 25°C

(From data of Curl and Jansen, 1950a,b)

Factor	Effect on the Amount of Inactivation by Pressure of			
	Trypsin	Chymotrypsin	Chymotrypsinogen	Pepsin
Initial concentration	Increases with conc.	Increases with conc.	Decreases with conc.	Decreases with conc.
Duration of compression	pH 5.1, no effect pH 7.6, progressive increase	pH 5.2, no effect pH 7.6, progressive increase	No effect	pH 1.9 or pH 4 progressive increase
Amount of pressure	Reaches maximum; at pH 5.1 or 7.6	Reaches maximum; at pH 5.2 or 7.6	Reaches maximum	Increases with pressure, also with pH
Repeated application of pressure	Increased with each application	Increased with each application	No change after first application	Increased with each application
pH	Decreases with acidity, pH 9.2–2.0	Decreases with acidity, pH 9.2–2.0	Decreases with acidity, pH 7.6–3.1	Minimum at pH 3.5–4
Standing after pressure (test for reversibility)	No change, in $3\frac{1}{2}$ hr	No change, in 2 hr	No change, in 2 hr	

to influence the stability of proteins.   They are: by affecting (1) the amount of ordinary ionization or of zwitter ion formation, (2) the process of unfolding, following the weakening of hydrogen bonds, (3) the structure of the solvent, and (4) the degree of ionization of a buffer system.   Where phosphate buffer is employed, the last of these possible mechanisms is potentially of considerable significance because of the somewhat exceptionally large volume decrease of 24 cc per mole accompanying the dissociation of $H_2PO_4^-$ (Linderstrøm-Lang and Jacobsen, 1941). Kauzmann[1] has pointed out that, with the pH close to neutrality at atmospheric pressure, the pH of a phosphate buffer solution would be expected to become about 0.4 unit more acid under a pressure of 10,000 psi.

[1] Personal communication from Professor W. J. Kauzmann.

According to Steinhardt's data (p. 278) a five-fold ionization of pepsin is preliminary to its denaturation. Ionization is usually accompanied by a volume decrease, because of electrostriction; the water molecules are attracted closer to the charged ions and groups so as to make the total volume less than before ionization. The decrease in volume usually amounts to around 10 cc per mole of ionizing group, and an increase in pressure therefore favors the process of ionization. For example, carbonic acid dissociates with a volume decrease of 12 cc for the ionization of the first hydrogen (computed from data given by Sverdrup et al., 1942). In the sea, pressure increases approximately 1 atm for each 10 meters below the surface. The change in pH resulting from the influence of pressure on carbonic acid may be calculated for a given depth by means of equation (9.1):

$$\frac{(H^+)(HCO_3^-)}{(H_2CO_3)} = K_0 e^{-p\, V\Delta/RT} \tag{9.1}$$

where K_0 is the dissociation constant at zero pressure, p is the pressure in atmospheres, R is the gas constant ($= 82.07$ cc atm), and T is the absolute temperature. At 5,000 meters (roughly 3 miles) below the surface, $p = 500$ atm and the pH of a 1 M solution of carbonic acid would be about 0.1 unit more acid than under no pressure.[1] Other factors, of course, influence the change in pH of sea water in the depths as compared to that at the surface (cf. Sverdrup et al., 1942). In large molecules such as proteins the volume changes per ionizing group are additive, so that the total is much greater and the influence of pressure correspondingly more significant.

In contrast to the process of ionization, the process of unfolding is likely to involve a volume increase rather than a decrease. On unfolding, hydrophobic groups become exposed and, because they are less attracted to water than are the predominantly hydrophilic groups of the folded molecule, the volume of the system is greater. The actual increase, according to data that will be discussed presently, may amount to between 50 and 100 cc per mole. Here pressure will oppose the process of unfolding and consequently will oppose the process of denaturation.

Changes in pH will affect both the amount of ionization and the strength of hydrogen bonds. Since hydrogen bonds evidently play an important rôle in keeping the native protein folded in its specific configuration, it follows that changes in pH will influence the process of unfolding. The effect of pressure on ionization and on unfolding is in opposite directions. In general, the net effect will represent the influence of

---

[1] At 18°C and atmospheric pressure, the following relation is true:
$$(H^+)(HCO_3^-)/(CO_2 + H_2CO_3) = 3 \times 10.1.$$

pressure on the two processes, but the relative importance of the two will vary with the conditions and with the protein.

In addition to the above processes, very high pressures might be expected to affect the stability of proteins through changes in the structure of the solvent. Although the problem lends itself to investigation from this point of view, very few data are yet available with respect to biological materials. The structure of water is known to change under very high pressure. Of the five established forms of ice, viz., Ice I, II, III, V, and VI, only Ice I is less dense than water (Tammann, 1900; Bridgman, 1912; Bernal and Fowler, 1933). A rise in pressure, therefore, opposes the formation of Ice I while favoring the formation of Ice II, III, V, and VI. The stability of each form depends upon both the temperature and the pressure. At a little more than 2,000 atm Ice III, which is about 10 per cent denser than water, becomes stable as compared to Ice I, which is about 10 per cent less dense than water. Any radical change in structure or crushing of the solvent under very high pressures would be expected to change the stability of the highly ordered protein molecule.

With reference to a more precise, kinetic basis, let us assume now that an unstable form, P_u, is in equilibrium with a stable form P_s. The total amount of protein, P_0, is the sum of these two forms: $P_0 = P_u + P_s$. The process of destruction to products, P_d, may be represented in a manner analogous to the Michaelis-Menton theory (p. 174):

$$P_s \underset{k_2}{\overset{k_1}{\rightleftharpoons}} P_u \overset{k_3}{\to} P_d \tag{9.2}$$

$$\frac{(P_s)}{(P_u)} = K = \frac{k_2}{k_1} \tag{9.3}$$

where K is the equilibrium constant for the reaction between stable and unstable forms. The concentration of P_u, in terms of P_0 and K, is given, as in equation (8.3), p. 219, by

$$P_u = \frac{P_0}{1 + K} \tag{9.4}$$

The velocity of denaturation, v, is proportional to the concentration of the unstable form P_u times the rate constant for destruction, k_3, and hence

$$v = k_3(P_u) = \frac{k_3(P_0)}{1 + K} \tag{9.5}$$

As in the Michaelis-Menton formulations (p. 175, equation 7.54), the ratio of the velocity under given conditions to the maximum velocity is given by

$$\frac{v}{v_{max}} = \frac{1}{1 + K} \tag{9.6}$$

from which it is apparent that, when K is very small, v is approximately equal to v_{max}.   Conversely, when K is large, the velocity of denaturation is less than maximum and the influence of pressure may become negligible, depending upon the volume change of activation in k_3 of equation (9.5). The $\Delta V^{\ddagger}$ of k_3 is likely to be small if, as in pepsin, it involves only the breaking of one or two covalent bonds after ionization.   From (9.5) and (9.6) it follows that, when pressure has decreased K well below unity, further increases in pressure will not accelerate the process of denaturation. Likewise, changes in pH may accelerate or retard the process under pressure, according to whether they favor or oppose the stable form through their action on K.   In other words, if a particular change in pH fails to cause a necessary ionization, pressure is required, whereas, if acidity or alkalinity does the job, high pressures will then have little additional effect.

Influence of pressure on ordinary chemical reaction rates

Before considering the action of moderately high pressures, of less than 1,000 atm, on biological systems, it is profitable to discuss briefly the mechanism of pressure effects on the rates of ordinary chemical reactions. The theoretical basis first became available with the introduction of the theory of absolute reaction rates in 1935.   An extended account will be found in the review by Stearn and Eyring (1941).

The specific rate constant for any elementary process can always be written

$$k_p = k_0 e^{-p \Delta V^{\ddagger}/RT} \tag{9.7}$$

where k_0 is the rate at zero pressure, k_p is the rate under pressure p, and $\Delta V^{\ddagger}$ is the volume of the activated complex minus the volume of the reactants.[1]   In this equation, when p is taken in atmospheres, and the gas constant R in cubic centimeter atmospheres, 82.07 cc per mole, $\Delta V^{\ddagger}$ is expressed as cubic centimeters per mole at absolute temperature T. The prediction of the effect of pressure on rates requires only the estimation of $\Delta V^{\ddagger}$.

If the activated state is more ionized than the reactants, $\Delta V^{\ddagger}$ will be negative because of an increase in electrostriction, and pressure will speed the reaction.   If the activated state is less ionized than the reactants, the

---

[1] A convenient form of this relation for computing the value of $\Delta V^{\ddagger}$ from rates measured at different pressures is:

$$\Delta V^{\ddagger} = 2.303 \, RT \log_{10} (k_{p_2}/k_{p_1})/(p_2 - p_1) \tag{9.7a}$$

Similarly, for computing the volume change between the initial and final states of an equilibrium, the analagous equation is convenient:

$$\Delta V = 2.303 \, RT \log_{10} (K_{p_2}/K_{p_1})/(p_2 - p_1) \tag{9.7b}$$

converse will be true.   Other factors that modify the total volume occupied by molecules are rearrangements which bring to the molecular surface groups which bond better or worse with the solvent.   Moreover, any process which increases the number of primary bonds will cause a

Table 9.3.   Comparison of Experimental and Calculated Values of $\Delta V^{\ddagger}$

(From Stearn and Eyring, 1941)

Reaction	Pressure Range (atm)	$\Delta V^{\ddagger}$ Experimental (cc)	$\Delta V^{\ddagger}$ Calculated (cc)	Reference
Decomposition of methyl-allylbenzylammonium bromide	1–3,000	3.4	3.5 for breaking methyl bond 2.7 for breaking any other bond	Williams et al., 1936
Pyridine + ethyl iodide	1–3,000	− 16.3	− 15.8	Gibson et al., 1935
Pyridine + cetyl bromide	1–1,000	− 12.5	− 12.3	Fawcett and Gibson, 1934
Acetic anhydride + ethyl alcohol	1–1,000 (in alcohol)	− 14.0	− 13.3 for 1 C_2H_5OH per 1 anhydride	Williams et al., 1936
	1–3,000 (in toluene)	− 12.2		
Alkaline hydrolysis of CH_3COO^-	1–3,000	− 6.0	− 8.0	Williams et al., 1936
Ethoxide + ethyl iodide	1–3,000	− 4.0	− 11.0	Williams et al., 1936
Alkaline saponification of ethyl acetate	250–500	− 5.5	− 11.0	Cohen and Kaiser, 1914–15
Ethyl o-methylcinnamate	1–500	− 14.0 (in 31 % alcohol) − 12.4 (in 42 % alcohol)	− 12.3	Moesveld, 1923
Cinnamyl cinnamate	1–1,500	− 14.5	− 11.0	Moesveld and de Meester, 1928
Ethyl o-methoxycinnamate	1–1,500	− 15.5 (in 25 % alcohol) − 12.1 (in 38 % CH_3OH) − 16.8 (in 28 % acetone) − 16.2 (in 20 % C_3H_7OH)	− 12.7	Moesveld and de Meester, 1928
Ethyl benzoate	1–1,500	− 13.6	− 10.7	Moesveld and de Meester, 1928
Ethyl o-methoxybenzoate	1–1,500	− 11 3 (in 7 % alcohol) − 14.2 (in 2.5 % pyridine)	− 13.7	Moesveld and de Meester, 1928
Benzyl benzoate	1–1,500	− 17.9	− 10.7	Moesveld and de Meester, 1928
Ethyl anthranilate	1–1,500	− 10.4	− 11.6	Moesveld and de Meester, 1928
Linalyl acetate	1–1,500	− 16.2	− 17.4	Moesveld and de Meester, 1928
Bornyl acetate	1–1,500	− 24.5 (in 31 % alcohol) − 22.1 (in 41 % alcohol) − 24.5 (in 19 % C_3H_7OH) − 20.4 (in 3.5 % pyridine) − 25.0 (in water)	− 20.1	Moesveld and de Meester, 1928
$2H^+ + Br^- + BrO_3^-$	1–500	2.6		Moesveld, 1922–23
Acid inversion of sucrose	1–500	1 to 5 in HCl, H_2SO_4, or oxalic acid; −2 to −5 in phosphoric or acetic acid		Cohen and Valeton, 1916–18; Cohen and deBoer, 1913; Stern, 1896

contraction, since either homopolar or heteropolar distances between atoms are shorter than are the van der Waals distances.   Generally, $\Delta V^{\ddagger}$ is positive for unimolecular reactions, and Stearn and Eyring have obtained interesting results by using the relation

$$\Delta V^{\ddagger} = \frac{0.1 l^{\ddagger} V}{\sum_i l_i + r_1 + r_2 + 1} \qquad (9.8)$$

where $\sum\limits_{i} l_i$ is the sum of the bond lengths, l_i, taken along the direction of the decomposing bond; r_1 and r_2 are the covalent radii of the terminal atoms at either end, while the value unity corrects the two end covalent radii to van der Waals radii. The length, 0.1 $l^{\ddagger}$, corresponds to a 10 per cent expansion of the breaking bond. This amount of expansion for the breaking bond in the activated state is reasonable from quantum-mechanical calculations of approximate potential surfaces and also leads to agreement with measured pressure effects as illustrated in Table 9.3. This increase in length of the breaking bond over the original length of the molecule gives the percentage volume increase, and, when multiplied by the original volume V, the value of $\Delta V^{\ddagger}$ is obtained.

Similarly, for bimolecular reactions, the following expression is used:

$$- \Delta V^{\ddagger} = \frac{1}{\sum\limits_{i} l_i + \sum\limits_{j} r_j + 2} \Sigma V \qquad (9.9)$$

In equation (9.9) it is assumed that, from the sum of the molal volumes of the reactants, ΣV, 1 Å is squeezed out from between the collided molecules in the activated state. The other value unity in the denominator corrects the two outside radii of the collided activated complex from the homopolar (or ionic) radii to the van der Waals value. $\sum\limits_{i} l_i$ is the sum for the two molecules of the sum of the interatomic distances between the remote end atom and the reacting atom of each molecule; the r's are the covalent radii (or ionic radii if the reacting atom is charged, as, for example, oxygen in OH) of the end atoms and of the reacting atoms of the molecules. The calculated and observed values for a variety of bimolecular reactions are given in Table 9.3. The predicted values of $\Delta V^{\ddagger}$ in this table generally agree satisfactorily with the observed values. The occasional discrepancies indicate some added effect, such as electrostriction.

Physiological pressure-temperature relationships in luminescence, muscle, and other processes

In contrast to the influence of pressure on most of the ordinary chemical reactions, its influence on physiological processes and enzyme activity may be not only profoundly modified, but also even reversed in direction, by a change in temperature. Although the fact that temperature is indeed important in the biological response to increased pressure was noted by Cattell and Edwards in 1930 in a study of cardiac muscle, and by the same authors in 1932 in a study of striated muscle, an interrelationship of the pressure and temperature parameters was first recognized by Brown

(1934b, 1934–35). A large part of Brown's extensive data concerning this relationship with particular reference to muscle has not yet been published in the literature except in the form of abstracts. His experiments in 1934, however, showed clearly that the contraction of a muscle could be increased, decreased, or unaffected by pressure, according to the temperature of the experiment and the source of the muscle. The amount of contraction of a pectoral fin muscle of the red grouper (*Epinephelus morio*), for example, was decreased at temperatures below 14° to 16°C and increased at temperatures above 14° to 16°C. At 14° to 16°C the size of the contraction was not altered by pressures up to 204 atm (Brown, 1934–35). A similar situation was found with frog muscle in relation to temperatures above and below 5° to 6°C (Brown, 1934b) and the isometric twitch of auricular muscle of the turtle above and below 5° to 8°C. Since the average environmental temperature of the red grouper is about 10°C higher than that of the frog, it seemed apparent that the influence of temperature on the effect of pressure was related primarily to the normal environmental temperature of the specific animal, rather than to the actual temperature as such. This has proved to be an important concept.

In view of subsequent analyses of bacterial luminescence and other phenomena, the pressure-temperature relationships noted by Brown in 1934 seem altogether natural. At the time, however, the data were somewhat fragmentary, and no clear understanding of the mechanisms involved was actually possible prior to the theory for influence of pressure on chemical reaction rates, in 1935. A generality of the principles was suggested by previous observations of the influence of pressure at a given temperature (which was not always even recorded) on various processes; in some instances they were found to increase in rate or amount under pressure, but in others to decrease, and in still others to go through a maximum as the pressure was raised. The following are some examples of the last-mentioned phenomenon: the activity of small animals (Regnard, 1885c, Ebbecke, 1935a); tension in the frog sartorius muscle (Cattell and Edwards, 1932); the action potential in the natural rhythmicity of the auricular muscle of the terrapin (Edwards and Brown, 1934); the rate of beat of the isolated heart of the frog and of the cat shark *Scyllium* (Ebbecke, 1935a); central nervous activity in the spinal frog (Ebbecke, 1936b); and the excitability as well as conduction velocity in peripheral frog nerve (Grunfest, 1936). Other phenomena for which it would be desirable to have more data than are presently available with respect to the influence of temperature on the effects of pressure include the inhibition of blood coagulation (Ebbecke and Haubrich, 1939) and retraction (Haubrich, 1939), chemical processes in muscle (Deuticke and Ebbecke, 1937), muscle contracture (Regnard, 1884a; Ebbecke, 1935d–f;

Ebbecke and Hasenbring, 1935), and contraction of both smooth and striated muscle (Brown, 1936; Ebbecke, 1914; Ebbecke and collaborators, 1935–1936).

A rational interpretation, in quantitative terms, of the influence of pressure on biological systems was first published in 1942, with respect to bacterial luminescence (Johnson, Brown, and Marsland, 1942a,b; Brown, Johnson, and Marsland, 1942; Johnson, Eyring, and Williams, 1942; Eyring and Magee, 1942). The experiments included studies also of the relation between pressure and the effect of inhibitors, which will be discussed in the next chapter.

In bacterial luminescence, equations (8.4) and (8.5), p. 220, provide a basis for understanding the influence of pressure, as well as temperature, subject to some modification by a consideration of the Michaelis-Menton formulation (equation 7.53, p. 175), as discussed presently. Since

$$\Delta F^{\ddagger} = \Delta H_0^{\ddagger} - T\,\Delta S_0^{\ddagger} + p\,\Delta V^{\ddagger} \tag{9.10}$$

equations (8.4) and (8.5) may be written

$$I = \frac{bk'(\text{L})(\text{A}_0)}{1 + K_1} = \frac{c'Te^{-\frac{\Delta H_0^{\ddagger}}{RT}}\,e^{-\frac{p\,\Delta V^{\ddagger}}{RT}}\,e^{\frac{\Delta S_0^{\ddagger}}{RT}}}{1 + e^{-\frac{\Delta H_0}{RT}}\,e^{-\frac{p\,\Delta V}{RT}}\,e^{\frac{\Delta S_0}{R}}} \tag{9.11}$$

In equations (9.10) and (9.11) the subscript indicates the value of the property at zero pressure.

From equation (9.11) it follows that at constant temperature the net effect of pressure will be determined by the values of both $\Delta V^{\ddagger}$ and ΔV. The relative importance of these two terms, however, will vary with temperature, even if the values of $\Delta V^{\ddagger}$ and of ΔV themselves do not vary with temperature. Some slight variation of the volume changes with temperature and also with pressure are to be expected in accordance with the preceding discussion of volume changes in ordinary chemical reactions. With enzyme systems, however, a large variation in their effect on the overall rate at different temperatures will occur because the equilibrium constant K for the denaturation reaction of the catalyst is characterized by a high heat and entropy change. At temperatures well below the normal "optimum," therefore, K is negligibly small in comparison with 1, and so has virtually no influence on the rate. The effects of increased pressure then occur practically entirely through changes in the specific reaction rate constant k' of the numerator, other things being the same. Consequently, at a low temperature, measurements of the relation between the intensity of luminescence and the amount of pressure provide a means of determining the value of $\Delta V^{\ddagger}$ for the chosen conditions of pH, salt concentration, etc. In order to arrive at a value for ΔV, on the other hand, it is desirable to raise the temperature to some point well above the normal optimum, where K is large compared to 1. Here intensity of luminescence is modified by the influence of pressure on both $\Delta V^\ddagger$ and ΔV, and measurements of the relation between luminescence intensity and pressure yield the difference of these constants. As a rule, it might be expected that $\Delta V^\ddagger$ will be smaller than ΔV, just as the energy and entropy

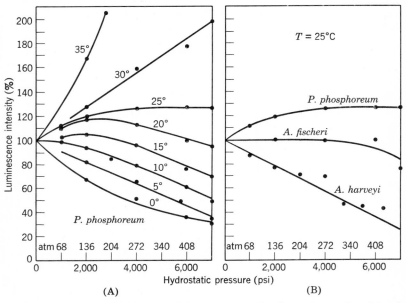

Fig. 9.8. (A) Intensity of luminescence of *P. phosphoreum* as a function of pressure at different temperatures. The intensity at normal pressure is arbitrarily taken equal to 100 at each temperature in order to show the per cent change in intensity with change in pressure. (B) Influence of increased pressure on the luminescence of three different species of bacteria at 25°C (Brown, Johnson, and Marsland, 1942).

of activation of the enzyme-catalyzed rate process are likely to be much smaller than the heat and entropy of reaction for the reversible denaturation of the protein. For this reason, the process as a whole may be expected to have an optimal pressure, as well as an optimal temperature.

Figure 9.8A shows the per cent change in luminescence intensity of the psychrophilic species of bacteria, *Photobacterium phosphoreum*, as a function of pressure at different temperatures. The actual intensity at normal pressure varied with temperature in the manner illustrated in Fig. 8.1, p. 190, but here the intensity is taken as 100 per cent at each temperature at atmospheric pressure in order to show more clearly the effect of pressure alone. Figure 9.8B illustrates the influence of pressure on the luminescence of three different bacterial species at a single temperature. The normal optimal temperatures of these species, under similar conditions of *p*H, salt content of the suspending medium, etc., are about 22°C for *P. phosphoreum*, 28°C for *Achromobacter fischeri*, and 30° to 32° for *A. harveyi*. Above these temperature optima, pressure in each case

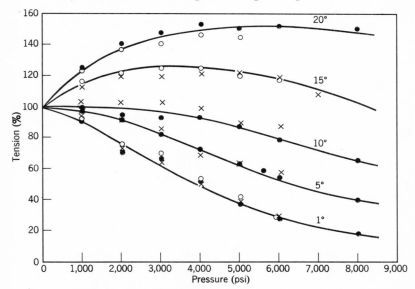

Fig. 9.9. Tension developed by turtle auricle in relation to hydrostatic pressure and temperature. Tension is expressed as a percentage of the control at atmospheric pressure. Data from three experiments are plotted. (Previously unpublished; by courtesy of Professor D. E. Brown.)

increases the intensity of luminescence, while at lower temperatures pressure decreases the intensity, and near the optima pressure has little effect. Thus the effect of pressure is clearly related to the temperature-activity curve characteristic of the species, rather than to the temperature of the experiment alone. The net effect of pressure may be reversed either by suitably changing the temperature with a single species, or by suitably changing the species at a single temperature.

From Fig. 9.8 it is obvious that the observed effect of pressure on luminescence is modified by temperature in much the same manner as described earlier (Brown, 1934b, 1934–35) for muscle (Fig. 9.9).

The data of Fig. 9.8 show, first, that the volume changes pertaining to both k' and K are large compared to ordinary reactions; otherwise pressures of the magnitude concerned would not exert so pronounced an effect. They show, second, that the volume changes pertaining to k' and to K, respectively, are unequal; otherwise the direction of the effect would not change with temperature, i.e., from decreasing the intensity of luminescence at low temperatures to increasing it at high temperatures. Near the normal temperature optimum the influence of pressure on k' and K balances out. At each pressure the effects on luminescence were readily reversible on release of pressure. The experiments were of short duration, however, seldom lasting more than a few minutes at any temperature. Some degree of irreversibility would be expected at the higher pressures, and especially at the higher temperatures where another rate process of thermal destruction occurs. Moreover, the kinetics of changes in luminescence, analogous to those which take place over a period of time following the sudden application or release of pressure on beating cilia or cardiac muscle (p. 320), have not been studied in detail.[1]

Qualitatively, the simplest interpretation of the data of Fig. 9.8 is that both the enzyme-catalyzed luciferin-luciferase reaction and the reversible thermal denaturation of the enzyme proceed with a large volume increase. By opposing the volume increase of activation in the former, luminescence is reduced, and this reduction is most pronounced at the low temperatures where essentially all the enzyme is in the native state. At high temperatures, on the other hand, as much as 90 per cent of the enzyme may be in the reversibly denatured state, and, since the volume increase of reaction is somewhat greater than the volume increase of activation of the catalytic process, the overall effect of pressure now is to increase the intensity of luminescence. Under pressure a larger percentage of the enzyme is in the native state; the denaturation is reversed. With the increase in amount of active enzyme, the luminescent reaction goes faster and the light intensity becomes brighter. These pressure-temperature relationships of luminescence intensity are somewhat clearer in Fig. 1.6 (p. 25), where the logarithm of the intensity is plotted as a function of temperature for three different pressures: 1, 262, and 476 atm, respectively. The points represent values observed in the experiments of Brown, Johnson, and Marsland (1942). The curves are theoretical, calculated by Eyring and Magee (1942) in accordance with equation (9.11), using parameters estimated from the data, as follows:

$$\Delta H_0^{\ddagger} = 17{,}220 \qquad \Delta V^{\ddagger} = 546.4 - 1.813T$$

$$\Delta H_0 = 55{,}260 \qquad \Delta V = -922.8 + 3.206T \qquad \Delta S_0 = 184 \text{ E.U.}$$

By taking into account the temperature dependence of the value of ΔV and of $\Delta V^{\ddagger}$, a much closer fit of the theoretical curves to the observed

---

[1] A study has been made with bacterial abstracts (Strehler and Johnson, 1954).

data is possible than otherwise. The variation of these volume changes with temperature could be real, or they could mean that the simple theory of equation (9.11) is inadequate. The alternative interpretations are not mutually exclusive; to some extent both factors are probably concerned. Since the luminescent system of bacteria has not yet been obtained in extracts,[1] it is not yet possible to investigate the pressure-temperature relations of this system apart from the intact, living cells, and it is not yet possible, therefore, to determine how much pressure influences the luminescent system itself. Among other things, pressures of the magnitude concerned in this instance have been shown to influence sol-gel equilibria in protoplasm in a manner that is affected by temperature, as discussed presently. A pronounced change in structure of the solvent would be expected to influence the velocity of an enzyme reaction. Bridgman has shown that, in aqueous solution, pressures of less than 1,000 atm have a negligible effect on the structure of the solvent. There is evidence that in aqueous solution the activities of lipase, pepsin, and pancreatic proteinase are reversibly retarded (Benthaus, 1941–42). Consequently the slowing of extracted enzyme action under pressure arises from causes other than the structural change of the solvent. In pressed muscle juice the rates of phosphorylation, dephosphorylation, and certain oxidation-reduction reactions proceed more slowly under 800 atm than at normal pressure, and glycolysis in blood is arrested at 2,000 atm, though it is apparently unaffected at 800 atm (Deuticke and Harren, 1938). Because of the relatively high protein concentration of these preparations, changes in viscosity under pressure, resulting from an influence on sol-gel equilibria, could be a factor in the effects of pressure on the reaction rates. The observed effect is in the opposite direction, however, to that which would be expected from the influence of pressure on sol-gel changes in myosin and other protoplasmic gels, inasmuch as the amount of gelation in these systems seems generally to decrease under pressure (Marsland and Brown, 1942).

The observed values of $\Delta V^{\ddagger}$ and of ΔV for a given enzyme system will be expected to vary, however, even with highly purified preparations, under the influence of several factors, including temperature. Laidler (1951) has considered in particular the influence of substrate concentration in relation to the Michaelis-Menton formulation under conditions where the amount of reversibly denatured enzyme is small, e.g., at temperatures well below the normal optimum. The velocity of the reaction is then given by equation (7.53):

$$V = \frac{k_3 k_1(S)(E_0)}{k_2 + k_3 + k_1(S)} \tag{7.53}$$

[1] See Addendum, Chapter 7, p. 185.

Neglecting k_3 in the denominator of (7.53) as likely in general to be small, and letting K_{ES} equal k_1/k_2, the equilibrium constant for the formation of the enzyme-substrate complex, equation (7.53) may be written

$$V = \frac{k_3 k_1 (S)(E_0)}{k_2 + k_1(S)} = \frac{k_3 K_{ES}(S)(E_0)}{1 + K_{ES}(S)} = \frac{k_{0_3} K_{0_{ES}}(S)(E_0) e^{-p(\Delta V_3^{\ddagger} + \Delta V_{ES})/RT}}{1 + K_{0_{ES}}(S) e^{-p\,\Delta V_{ES}/RT}}$$

$$(9.12)$$

where the subscripts zero indicate that the corresponding constants are for zero pressure. The overall effect of pressure will thus depend upon the volume change of activation pertaining to k_3 for the decomposition of the activated complex $(ES)^{\ddagger}$ formed from the enzyme-substrate complex ES, and on the volume change of reaction in the equilibrium combination between enzyme and substrate. It is clear from equation (9.12) that the net effect of pressure will be influenced by the concentration of substrate (S) as well as by the value of the equilibrium constant K_{ES}. When $K_{ES}(S)$ is much larger than unity, the effect will be determined chiefly by the value of $\Delta V_3^{\ddagger}$. When $K_{ES}(S)$ is much smaller than unity, the effect will be determined chiefly by the algebraic sum of $\Delta V_3^{\ddagger}$ and ΔV_{ES}.

Referring to Fig. 1.6, the temperature-dependent parameter used for $\Delta V^{\ddagger}$ in equation (9.11) by Eyring and Magee gives a value of 51.5 cc per mole at 0°C, and 11.6 cc per mole at 22°C. In part, this decrease from 51.5 to 11.6 cc probably represents a decrease in $K_{0_{ES}}$ with rise in temperature. The heat of reaction for the Michaelis-Menton constant for the luminescence of *Cypridina* extracts was estimated by Kauzman, Chase, and Brigham (1949) as 8,200 cal per mole (cf., discussion on p. 177). It is reasonable to believe that a similar relationship applies in bacteria. In this event, in order to explain by means of equation (9.12) the drop from 51.5 cc to 11.6 cc with rise in temperature we must assume that ΔV_{ES} is large and negative, since $(S)K_{0_{ES}}$ will decrease with rise in temperature unless of course (S) markedly increases with temperature. On the other hand, if $(S)K_{0_{ES}}$ increases with temperature, ΔV_{ES} must be positive to explain the observed results (cf. Laidler, 1951). The influence of pressure on the luminescence of *Cypridina* extracts varies with the purity of the luciferin and the manner of preparation of the luciferase (Bronk, Harvey, and Johnson, 1952). A systematic study of the influence of initial concentration of luciferin as well as of purification procedures for the enzyme on the observed effect of pressure is desirable in order to make a satisfactory analysis. In bacterial cells the concentration of substrate in the corresponding luminescent system cannot be so readily regulated, but it is reasonable to expect a difference in the influence of pressure on the luminescence of washed cells alone and of washed cells plus an excess of glucose (cf. discussion on pp. 180–181).

Unfortunately, the total of available data with respect to the relationship among K_{ES}, substrate concentration, and influence of pressure on the velocity of reaction is insufficient for an adequate analysis. Table 9.4 summarizes the volume changes that have been computed for crystallized enzyme preparations, as well as some data estimated by Laidler from the

Table 9.4. Net Volume Changes Computed According to Observed Influence of Pressure ($<$ 680 atm) on Specific Enzyme Reactions *in vitro*

Enzyme	Conc. used (enzyme)	Substrate	Conc. used (sub- strate)	pH	Temp. (°C)	Observed Vol. Change (cc/mole)	Reference
Salivary amylase	(Commer- cial prep.)	Starch	1%		Room (22°–23°)	− 22	Laidler, 1951; data of Benthaus, 1941–42
Pancreatic amyl- ase	(Commer- cial prep.)	Starch	2%		Room (22°–23°)	− 28	Laidler, 1951; data of Benthaus, 1941–42
Pancreatic lipase	(Commer- cial prep.)	Tributyrin	Very low		Room (22°–23°)	+ 13	Laidler, 1951; data of Benthaus, 1941–42
Pepsin	(Commer- cial prep.)	Gelatin	0.83%		Room (22°–23°)	+ 22	Laidler, 1951; data of Benthaus, 1941–42
Invertase	(Commer- cial prep.)	Sucrose	10%	7.04	30°	− 8	Eyring, Johnson, Gensler, 1946
	(Commer- cial prep.)	Sucrose	10%	4.5	30°	− 3	Eyring, Johnson, Gensler, 1946
Lysozyme	0.0015 mg/cc	*Micrococcus lysode- ikticus* (whole cells)	ca. 10^9 cells/cc	6.2– 8.7	35°	− 10 to − 24	Holyoke and Johnson, 1951
Formic dehydro- genase		Na formate		5.6– 9.5	30°	0	Borrowman, 1950
Chymotrypsin (crystalline)	0.00154 mg/cc	Casein	1%	·7.7	14.8°	− 13.8	Werbin and McLaren, 1951a
	0.0148 mg/cc	*l*-Tyrosine ethyl ester	0.02 M	7.8	25.1°	− 13.5	Werbin and McLaren, 1951a
Trypsin (crystal- line)	0.5 mg/cc	Casein	0.66%	7.3	25°–35°	− 5 to − 10	Fraser and Johnson, 1951
	0.076 mg/cc	β-Lactoglobulin	0.5%	8.1	25.1°	− 36	Werbin and McLaren, 1951b
	0.076 mg/cc	α-Benzoyl-1-arginin- amide isopropyl ester	0.04 M	7.76	25.1°	0	Werbin and McLaren, 1951b
	0.076 mg/cc	α-Benzoyl-1-arginin- amide isopropyl ester	0.011 M	8.1	25.2°	0	Werbin and McLaren, 1951b
	0.082 mg/cc	α-Benzoyl-1-arginin- amide	0.04 M	7.76	54.5°	...*	Werbin and McLaren, 1951b
	0.5 mg/cc	Casein	0.66%	7.3	55°	..*	Fraser and Johnson, 1951
Invertase	(Commer- cial prep.)	Sucrose	10%	7.03– 7.07	35°–45°	− 69*	Eyring, Johnson, Gensler, 1946

* Acceleration in observed rate under pressure at these temperatures evidently due to the retardation by pressure of a reversible and/or irreversible denaturation of the enzyme, proceeding with a large volume increase.

results obtained by Benthaus (1941–42) with commercial enzyme prepara- tions. Studies of trypsin and chymotrypsin action (Fraser and Johnson, 1951; Werbin and McLaren, 1951a,b) show that the net volume change depends upon the type of substrate as well as upon type of enzyme, and also upon the *p*H. It is difficult to make certain, on the basis of the data alone, the extent to which the net volume change represents $\Delta V^{\ddagger}$ or $\Delta V^{\ddagger} + \Delta V_{ES}$. In bacterial luminescence, also, the effect of pressure, at a temperature below the optimum (17.5°C, *P. phosphoreum*) is modified by changes in *p*H (Fig. 9.10).   With increasing acidity, pressure causes a reduction in the intensity of luminescence, and this reduction is not readily reversible on release of pressure.   At this temperature, luminescence is increased under pressure only at an extremely alkaline *p*H which promotes denaturation of the enzyme.

With reference to Fig. 9.10, in the acid region (e.g., *p*H 4.63), the activated state of the enzyme concerned clearly has a larger volume than

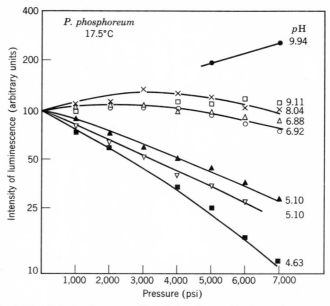

Fig. 9.10.   Relation between *p*H and the effects of hydrostatic pressure on the luminescence of *P. phosphoreum*.   The intensity at normal pressure is arbitrarily taken as equal to 100 at each *p*H (Johnson, Eyring, Steblay, Chaplin, Huber, and Gherardi, 1945).

the normal state since pressure cuts down the intensity of luminescence. The fact that the amount of the pressure effect decreases with increasing alkalinity suggests that activation involves the ionization off of hydrogen ions with an accompanying increase in volume, ΔV_1.   The hydrogen ion will probably be transferred to a buffer according to some such reaction as

$$\mathrm{H^+ + HPO_4^{2-} \rightleftharpoons H_2PO_4^-}$$

This reaction, involving phosphate buffer, has a volume increase, ΔV_2, of 24 cc per mole (cf. Table 9.7, p. 339).   The total volume change, $\Delta V^{\ddagger}$, in going to the activated state is thus

$$\Delta V^{\ddagger} = n(\Delta V_1 + \Delta V_2)$$

where n is the number of ions which must be split off to make the activated complex.   We can understand Fig. 9.10 readily if ΔV_1 is small compared to ΔV_2 and if n drops from a small positive number in acid solutions, changing over to negative values in alkaline solutions. ΔV_1 is made up of a volume decrease due to ionization of the protein, together with a probable increase in volume due to unfolding.

In muscle contraction there are a number of aspects to consider: the tension developed in a single twitch or in a prolonged tetanus, the rate and duration of contraction and relaxation, the action potential, the heat

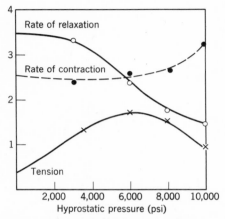

Fig. 9.11.   Relative changes in the rate of contraction, rate of relaxation, and amount of total tension in isometric responses of auricular muscle of the terrapin as a function of pressure at 23°C (Edwards and Brown, 1934).

production, the intrinsic rhythmicity of cardiac muscle, the tonus of smooth muscle, etc.   All these processes are subject to modification by pressure, and each one requires analysis in order to understand the whole. The physiology is more complicated than in luminescence, where only the intensity of the light is measured.   The fundamental similarity of the pressure-temperature relationships in tension of the turtle auricle and in luminescence of bacteria is evident in Figs. 9.8 and 9.9.   Other aspects of muscle activity in relation to pressure are illustrated in Fig. 9.11 for the terrapin auricle (Edwards and Brown, 1934).

The curve for tension in Fig. 9.11 is similar to that for bacterial luminescence at a temperature somewhat above the normal optimum (Fig. 9.8A).   To the extent that the quantitative response in muscle depends upon the influence of pressure on rate-limiting reactions controlled by enzymes, the mechanism of the effect in both luminescence and muscle is fundamentally the same.   From Fig. 9.11 it is evident that the rate of contraction, however, is not limited by the same mechanisms that control the amount of tension, inasmuch as it is scarcely affected by pressures up to 6,000 psi, but then gradually increases at higher pressures. On the other hand, the influence of pressure on the rate of relaxation is probably more closely related, inversely, to the influence of pressure on the amount of tension developed. Changes in magnitude of the muscle action potential show a general correspondence to the changes in muscle tension under pressure.

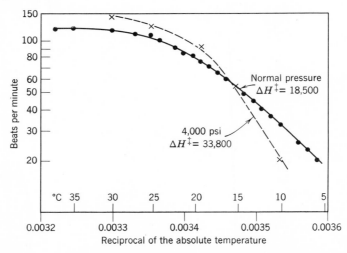

Fig. 9.12. Influence of pressure, in relation to temperature, on the frequency of intrinsic rhythmicity of cardiac muscle of *Rana pipiens* tadpoles from tissue culture (Landau and Marsland, 1952).

The rate of rhythmic contraction of cardiac muscle *in vitro* exhibits a general correspondence, in its pressure-temperature relationships, to luminescence and muscle tension, i.e., under pressure the rate increases at relatively high temperatures, is scarcely affected at an intermediate temperature, and decreases at low temperatures (Fig. 9.12). Depending upon the temperature concerned, however, the rates under pressure as represented by the broken line in Fig. 9.12 are steady state frequencies (at low temperatures) or only the initial rates just after application of pressure (at high temperatures), as illustrated in Figs. 9.13 and 9.14, respectively. Similar phenomena have been observed qualitatively in bacterial luminescence and quantitatively in the rate of ciliary beating at room temperature (Pease and Kitching, 1939). They are of particular interest with reference to the general problem of changes in biological reaction rates following changes in environmental conditions. Moreover, they are susceptible of quantitative interpretation on the basis of a general hypothesis involving consecutive reactions, as follows.

The rôle of consecutive reactions

The time course of the changes in luminescence intensity on application and release of pressure has not been studied in detail.   Visual photometry was used in the experiments of Brown, Johnson, and Marsland (1942); rapid changes in light intensity could not be satisfactorily recorded by this

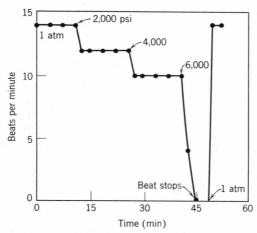

Fig. 9.13.   Influence of pressure at 10°C on the rate of beat of tadpole (*Rana pipiens*) cardiac muscle from tissue culture (Landau and Marsland, 1952).

method.   It was noticed, however, that, depending upon the temperature, certain rapid changes took place on release of pressure, e.g., at low temperatures luminescence merely returned to its initial value.   At high temperatures, on the other hand, a sudden release of pressure was followed by a momentary, excessive drop in intensity, which during the course of several seconds then returned to a level corresponding to that before compression.   This phenomenon was referred to as a "black-out."   In later experiments (Johnson, unpublished), wherein luminescence was measured by means of a photomultiplier and a short period galvanometer, the same effect was noticed.   In addition, it was observed that, immediately after a quick application of pressure at the higher temperatures, the intensity of luminescence rose to an excessively high value, from which it dropped in a few seconds to its new steady state characteristic of the pressure and temperature involved.   The steady state changed only slowly, decreasing slightly throughout the short period of 2 or 3 mins during which luminescence was measured at each pressure.

The data in Figs. 9.8 and 1.6 represent the essentially steady state intensity of luminescence at various pressures, rather than the maximum change immediately after application of pressure. In Fig. 9.12, however, the initial change in rate under pressure is plotted for the various temperatures. At low temperatures, in both luminescence and rate of cardiac beat, the initial change is essentially the same as the subsequent steady state, unless a certain amount of pressure is exceeded (Fig. 9.13). In

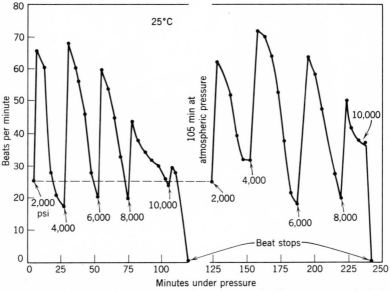

Fig. 9.14. Change in rate of beat of cardiac muscle (*Rana pipiens* tadpoles) from tissue culture, following rapid increases in hydrostatic pressure at 25°C (Landau and Marsland, 1952).

cardiac muscle of the tadpole at 10°C, pressures of 6,000 psi stop the beat, but the inhibition is completely reversible after short periods of compression. Luminescence does not show this sudden increase in sensitivity to pressure within the range up to about 10,000 psi.

In contrast to the simple change to a new steady state after application of moderate pressures at low temperatures, a changing rate after application of pressure occurs at the higher temperatures. In luminescence the change is fast, whereas in beating of cardiac tissue (Fig. 9.14) or cilia (Fig. 9.15) it is relatively slow. The subsequent levels, in comparison to those prior to compression, are also different among these three processes.

In interpreting the changing rates of the above processes after application or release of pressure, let us assume that the observed rate depends upon two consecutive reactions, with specific constants k_1 and k_2, whereby a substance or metabolite M_1 is converted to a metabolite M_2 under the influence of an enzyme E_1, and M_2 is converted to products under the influence of an enzyme E_2. The overall reaction may be written

$$M_1E_1 \xrightarrow{k_1} M_2E_2 \xrightarrow{k_2} \text{products} \tag{9.13}$$

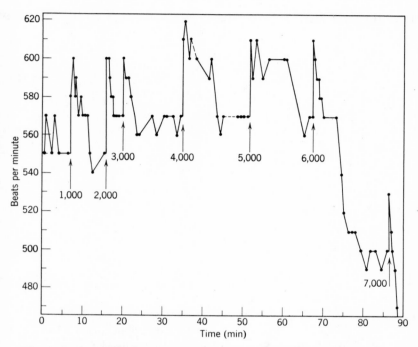

Fig. 9.15. Influence of successive increases in hydrostatic pressure on the frequency of beating of gill cilia of the mussel, *Mytilus edulis* L., at room temperature, measured stroboscopically (Pease and Kitching, 1939).

and represented schematically on a potential energy diagram (Fig. 9.16). At steady state,

$$\frac{dM_2}{dt} = M_1E_1k_1 - M_2E_2k_2 = 0 \tag{9.14}$$

In the non-steady state, if we assume that only M_2 is changing, we have

$$\frac{dM_2}{M_1E_1k_1 - M_2E_2k_2} = dt \tag{9.15}$$

Integrating,

$$\int \frac{-d\mathrm{M}_2\mathrm{E}_2k_2}{\mathrm{M}_1\mathrm{E}_1k_1 - \mathrm{M}_2\mathrm{E}_2k_2} = -\mathrm{E}_2k_2 \int dt$$

$$\ln(\mathrm{M}_1\mathrm{E}_1k_1 - \mathrm{M}_2\mathrm{E}_2k_2) = -\mathrm{E}_2k_2t + c$$

$$\ln(\mathrm{M}_1\mathrm{E}_1k_1 - \mathrm{M}_2\mathrm{E}_2k_2) = -\mathrm{E}_2k_2t + \ln(\mathrm{M}_1\mathrm{E}_1k_1 - \mathrm{M}_2\mathrm{E}_2k_2)_0$$

(9.16)

In (9.16) the subscript zero means at zero time, when during the steady

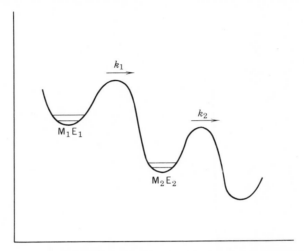

Fig. 9.16. Schematic potential energy diagram for two consecutive reactions limiting a physiological process.

state rate the conditions are changed, e.g., by application of hydrostatic pressure to the system. Solving (9.16) for the term $\mathrm{M}_2\mathrm{E}_2k_2$:

$$\mathrm{M}_2\mathrm{E}_2k_2 = \mathrm{M}_1\mathrm{E}_1k_1 + (\mathrm{M}_2\mathrm{E}_2k_2 - \mathrm{M}_1\mathrm{E}_1k_1)_0 e^{-E_2k_2t} \qquad (9.17)$$

In accordance with (9.17) the observed rate will vary not only with the specific reaction rate constants k_1 and k_2, but also with the concentration of metabolites M_1 and M_2, as well as the amounts of active enzymes E_1 and E_2. The amount of active enzyme may be expected to vary, in line with previous discussions, under the influence of various factors which cause reversible or irreversible inactivation of the catalytic property. In cells it is not always possible to distinguish the extent to which the effects of an environmental factor are to be attributed to changes in the M's, E's, and k's, respectively. There are examples, however, which quantitatively fit the simple hypothesis that M_1 is essentially constant and only the k's and M_2 are affected by an environmental factor such as pressure, other things remaining the same, e.g., the rate of ciliary beating (Fig. 9.17).

In analyzing the data of Fig. 9.17, we take $M_2E_2k_2$ equal to the number of beats per minute. This only amounts to absorbing a proportionality constant by an appropriate change of concentration units. The numerical values were estimated from the solid lines drawn in the graph. They are summarized in Table 9.5, together with the computed differences in rate, as a function of time, resulting from changes in pressure. The logarithms

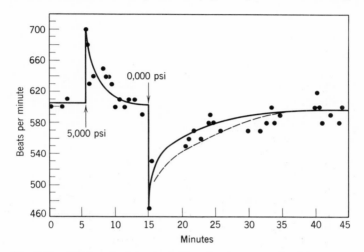

Fig. 9.17.   Changes in the rate of ciliary beating on application and release of 5,000 psi pressure at room temperature (Pease and Kitching, 1939). The solid line was drawn inspection by Pease and Kitching. The theoretical curves, calculated as described in the text, coincide with the solid line except where indicated by the broken line.

of these rates are plotted against the corresponding times in Fig. 9.18. The calculated curves satisfactorily describe the somewhat scattered experimental points.

From the rate constants, $k_2e^{-\Delta V_2^{\ddagger}/RT}$ and k_2 as indicated by the slopes of the lines in Fig. 9.18, the volume change of activation $\Delta V_2^{\ddagger}$ has the value 100 cc per mole. Similarly, the free energy of activation $\Delta F_2^{\ddagger}$ at zero pressure has the value 21.2 kcal. These are effective values, of course, for the whole process, and they do not necessarily represent a close approximation to the value appropriate to any particular one of the reactions involved. A complete analysis would require detailed information about the concentrations and identities of the reactants, and a complete formulation would require inclusion of the Michaelis-Menton

Table 9.5.   Changes in Rate of Ciliary Frequency under Hydrostatic Pressure

(Numerical values estimated from Fig. 9.17, from Pease and Kitching, 1939)

Time (min)	Increased Pressure (atm)	Observed Beats per Minute $(M_2E_2k_2)$	$(M_2E_2k_2) - (M_1E_1k_1)_0$	$\log_{10}$ $[(M_2E_2k_2) - (M_1E_1k_1)_0]$	Calculated Beats per Minute	
					Difference	Rate
0–5.4	0	604	..	...	..	..
		$(M_1E_1k_1)_0$				
5.5	340	700	96	1.982	96	700
		$(M_2E_2k_2)_0$				
6.0	340	670	66	1.819	66	670
7.5	340	635	31	1.401	31	635
10.0	340	613	9	0.95	9	613
15.0	340	604	0	.00	0	604
		$(M_1E_1k_1)_0$				
15.4	0	470	134	2.127	111	493
		$(M_2E_2k_2)_0$				
16.0	0	520	84	1.924	103	501
17.5	0	545	59	1.770	87	527
20.0	0	560	44	1.643	64	540
25.0	0	·577	37	1.568	40	564
30.0	0	587	17	1.230	20	584
35.0	0	593	11	1.041	11	593
40.0	0	596	8	0.903	6	598

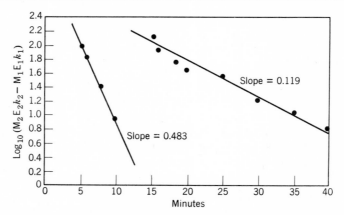

Fig. 9.18.   Analysis of data of Fig. 9.17 and Table 9.5 as described in the text. The slope of the line at the left gives the value of k_1 (under pressure) in reciprocal minutes, and the slope of the line at the right gives the value for k_2 at normal pressure.

treatment, the reversible and irreversible thermal inactivation, pH relationships, and other factors entering into the activity of each enzyme system capable of influencing the rate of the total process. The general picture as given by the simplified hypothesis discussed above, however, would remain fundamentally the same.

In addition to the processes of luminescence, rate of cardiac beat, and ciliary frequency, various other processes have been observed to vary during the course of compression or after release of pressure in manners

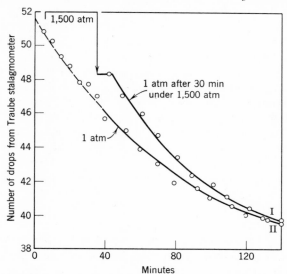

Fig. 9.19. Influence of temporary compression under 1,500 atm of pressure on the rate of hydrolysis of tributyrin by pancreatic lipase (Benthaus, 1941–42).

suggestive of a general mechanism similar to the one just discussed. The following are a few examples; others will become evident with further investigations of the sort suitable to reveal them.

The retardation by pressure of crude pancreatic lipase activity (Benthaus, 1941–42) is followed, on release of pressure, by an acceleration in rate above that of a control at normal pressure (Fig. 9.19). As a result, brief periods of compression during the initial course of the reaction do not appreciably slow the time required for nearly complete digestion. Evidently, under pressure, there is an accumulation of some intermediate product because of the retardation of some member of a sequence of reactions. Among complex physiological processes, the rate of oxygen consumption of various marine animals has been found to increase under pressure (at the temperature of the experiments), but to decrease below the initial level after pressure was released (Fontaine, 1928d, 1929b). Similarly, the rate of photosynthesis by the alga, *Ulva lactuca*, was found to increase after subjecting the specimens to pressures of 100 to 400 atm, and then to return slowly to the original rate after pressure was released (Fontaine, 1929f). Again, in cell division, temporary application of pressure (7,000 psi for 15 min, with *Arbacia* eggs) blocks the first cleavage, but after release of pressure cell division takes place more rapidly than in controls that have not been compressed. The controls and compressed eggs then go through the second and third cleavages at the same time (Marsland, 1938). There is evidence of a corresponding phenomenon in the rate of bacterial multiplication (*Escherichia coli*) at 25.3° and at 39.7°C (Johnson and Lewin, 1946d).

By the same fundamental mechanism, sudden changes in temperature, as well as in hydrostatic pressure, would be expected to give rise to longer or shorter periods of changing rates of a biological process, since it is unlikely that temperature will change $E_1 k_1$ and $E_2 k_2$ of (9.14) proportionately. The result would be either a lag in reaching a new steady state after the change in temperature (for luminescence, cf. Kreezer and Kreezer, 1947) or a momentary excessive rate. Furthermore, any factor which influences the concentration of the M's or the activities of the E's is potentially capable of causing analogous changes in rate. For example, the excessive rate of oxygen consumption in aerobic cells immediately following temporary anaerobiosis ("oxygen debt") can be interpreted on this basis; probably, also, the "flash" of bacterial luminescence (p. 184). The influence of temperature on the latter phenomenon is consistent with this view (Schoepfle, 1940). Also, rhythmic processes in biology, although often no doubt more complicated, may be expected in general to proceed in some measure through influences on the reaction mechanism diagramed in Fig. 9.16.

Retardation and reversal of protein denaturation under high pressures

Before the studies of luminescence there was no definite evidence that protein denaturation could be reversed or retarded by increased pressure. This circumstance can be attributed, in part, to the fact that the experiments with pressure were done under conditions that would not readily reveal such a phenomenon, and in part to the tendency to study the action of such high pressures that the chief result was to promote, rather than to oppose, denaturation. The first evidence that inactivation of enzymes could be not only reversed (Brown, Johnson, and Marsland, 1942) but also retarded (Johnson, Eyring, Steblay, Chaplin, Huber, and Gherardi, 1945) was based entirely on kinetic studies of luminescence in living cells. Evidence of similar effects on purified proteins *in vitro*, therefore, assumed a special interest.   Qualitative observations with human serum globulin (Johnson and Campbell, 1945) showed that the amount of precipitation at 65°C was decreased under a pressure of 750 atm.   The effect of pressure increased with alkalinity in the *p*H range between 5.15 and 6.8.   Also, when alcohol was added to accelerate the process at *p*H 6.0 and 65°C, the amount of precipitation under pressure was less than at normal pressure.   Quantitative studies of the same material (Johnson and

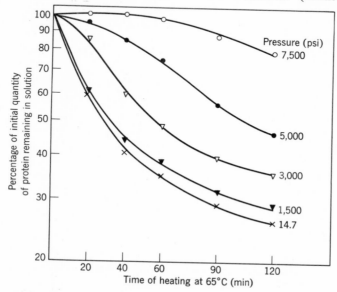

Fig. 9.20.   Influence of increased pressure on rate of precipitation of highly purified human serum globulin at 65°C, *p*H 6.0 (Johnson and Campbell, 1946).

Campbell, 1946) were carried out at various pressures.   The amount of protein remaining in solution after successive intervals of time was determined by centrifuging the specimens at 25,000 × gravity and making Kjeldahl nitrogen analyses of the supernatant.   Some typical results are illustrated in Fig. 9.20.

The data of Fig. 9.20 leave no doubt that the rate of serum globulin denaturation under the conditions involved is retarded with increase in pressure up to 7,500 psi.   The kinetics, however, does not lend itself to simple analysis.   Although the rate was found to be first order with respect to the initial concentration of protein, the specific rate varied during the course of denaturation, probably because of heterogeneity of the globulin molecules.   The changing rate makes it difficult to give a precise value for the volume change of activation, but the fact that a pressure of only some 500 atm causes such a profound retardation of denaturation (Fig. 9.20) shows that the volume change is quite large, of the order of 100 cc per mole.

The denaturation of tobacco mosaic virus at atmospheric pressure in neutral solution at 67° to 73°C proceeds as a first order reaction (Lauffer and Price, 1940) with an activation energy of 153,000 cal. The rate at 68.8°C was measured at atmospheric and 7,000 psi pressure by Johnson,

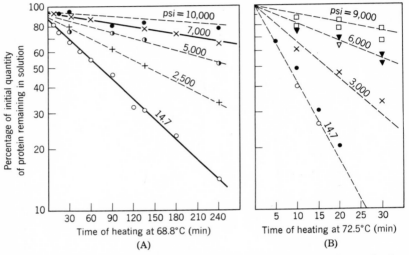

Fig. 9.21. Influence of increased pressure on the rate of tobacco mosaic virus denaturation at 68.8° (A) and at 72.5°C (B), in solution of *p*H 7.05 (Johnson, Baylor, and Fraser, 1948). The rates at normal pressure and 7,000 psi were measured [solid lines in (A)], and the remainder [broken lines in (A) and (B)] were computed as described in the text. The points represent the percentage of the initial amount of protein remaining in solution, according to Kjehldahl nitrogen determinations of the supernatant after high speed centrifugation of the specimens.

Baylor, and Fraser (1948), and found to be first order under increased as well as normal pressure. The difference in rate under pressure, calculated in accordance with equation (9.7), p. 305, indicated a volume increase of activation of approximately 100 cc per mole. The activation energy provided by the study of Lauffer and Price, together with this volume change, made it possible to predict the rate at other pressures, both at the same temperature of 68.8°C and at another temperature, 72.5°C. The results are shown in Figs. 9.21A and 9.21B, where the broken lines. represent the theoretically calculated rates and the points represent values observed in the experiments. Figure 9.22 shows the relation between the first order rates and hydrostatic pressure as calculated for the denaturation with an activation energy of 153,000 cal and volume change of + 100 cc per mole.

The above experiments with serum globulin and tobacco mosaic virus, respectively, were carried out with solutions containing phosphate buffer. Since, under 10,000 psi the pH would be expected to shift about 0.4 unit toward the acid (p. 302), the effect of pressure on the pH of the buffer would be expected to have some influence on the results. The thermal denaturation of tobacco mosaic virus, in particular, is especially sensitive to pH, inasmuch as the rate appears to be inversely proportional to the third power of hydrogen ion concentration (Lauffer and Price, 1940).

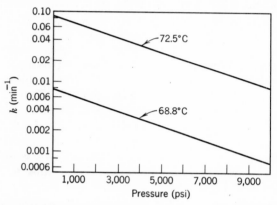

Fig. 9.22. Relation between first order rate constant and hydrostatic pressure in the denaturation of tobacco mosaic virus (Johnson, Baylor, and Fraser, 1948).

Figure 9.21 shows that, at 68.8°C, the rate is about one-tenth as fast under 10,000 psi as under normal pressure. This difference in rates is approximately the same as would be expected, at atmospheric pressure, by lowering the pH 0.4 unit, i.e., by a factor of $10^{(0.4 \times 3)} = 10.3$. Thus it might seem that the denaturation rate of tobacco mosaic virus affords a fancy way of measuring the influence of pressure on the pH of phosphate buffer. Actually, however, the situation is not that simple, for the net effect of pressure depends upon the influence of pressure on the ionization and unfolding of the protein as well as upon the ionization of the buffer. With serum globulin the influence of pressure in retarding thermal denaturation can scarcely be attributed to the change in pH of the buffer under pressure, since the effect of pressure is less at slightly acid pH's than near neutrality (Johnson and Campbell, 1945).

To anyone skeptical of conclusions arrived at purely on the basis of kinetic data on processes in intact, living cells, the results obtained with the highly purified proteins, serum globulin, and tobacco mosaic virus, respectively, will seem more convincing.   In living cells the evidence that the effects of pressure are on protein denaturation consists in the very high heats, entropies, and volume changes of reaction or of activation revealed by the kinetic analyses.   Similarly high values of the thermodynamic or rate constants are found in denaturation reactions involving only purified protein systems, when the rate is measured in terms of the classic criterion of denaturation, viz., solubility.

Although as yet only a few processes have been studied from this point of view, they are sufficiently varied to indicate that the retardation or reversal of protein denaturation under pressure is a fairly general phenomenon.   Because of considerations that have already been expressed concerning the action of pressure on denaturation (p. 302), it would be anticipated that the observed effect on a given system will vary with conditions of pH and other factors that affect the degree of ionization or strength of salt and hydrogen bonds.   Qualitative evidence of such variation with pH in the retardation of serum globulin denaturation under pressure has been referred to.   Quantitative data with respect to the activity of invertase show that both a reversible and an irreversible denaturation, as measured by change in catalytic activity of the extracted enzyme, are affected by pressure to an extent that depends upon the pH of the solution (Eyring, Johnson, and Gensler, 1946; Johnson, Kauzmann, and Gensler, 1948).   Figure 9.23 shows the observed rate at two pH values, under pressures of 1 and of 680 atm.   At low temperatures the effect of pressure is slight, indicating a small, negative net volume change of activation in the enzyme-catalyzed hydrolytic reaction.   The temperature at which denaturation of the catalyst becomes significantly limiting in the overall rate depends upon the pH of the solution.   At the alkaline pH of 7.03 to 7.07 this enzyme is denatured at a lower temperature than at the acid pH of 4.50.   Analysis of the volume change accompanying denaturation at the alkaline pH and 35° to 40°C can be made as follows.

First, we will assume that under the conditions involved the amount of irreversible denaturation of the enzyme is negligible.   This assumption is supported by the fact that no decrease in specific rate of hydrolysis during the course of the reaction was observed.   Secondly, we may assume that the diminution in observed rate at temperatures above 30°C results from an equilibrium change from active to inactive forms of the catalyst.   This assumption is supported by the demonstration of a thermal denaturation of invertase that is readily reversible on cooling (Chase, Reppert, and Ruch, 1944).   The pressure effects, at the temperatures and pH under consideration, may thus be attributed primarily to an influence of the equilibrium constant K of the denaturation.   Finally, we will assume that essentially all the enzyme is in the active state under a pressure of 680 atm, i.e., that K is then negligible. Letting I_0 represent the rate when K is very small, we have

$$I_0 = bk'(E_0)(S) \tag{9.18}$$

where b is a proportionality constant, (E_0) the total amount of enzyme, and (S) the concentration of the substrate, sucrose. Since (S) in these

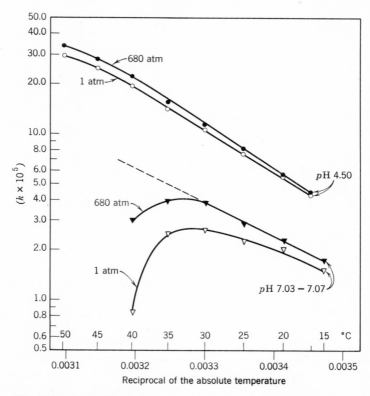

Fig. 9.23. Rate of hydrolysis of 10% cane sugar by 0.2% "Difco" yeast invertase in relation to pH, temperature, and increased pressure (Eyring, Johnson, and Gensler, 1946).

experiments was in great excess (10% sucrose solutions), it may be taken as constant. At temperatures where K becomes significantly large compared to 1, we have the rate, I_K,

$$I_K = \frac{bk'(E_0)(S)}{1 + K} \tag{9.19}$$

Dividing (9.18) by (9.19),

$$\frac{I_0}{I_K} = 1 + K \qquad \text{or} \qquad \left(\frac{I_0}{I_K} - 1\right) = K \qquad (9.20)$$

whence

$$\left(\frac{I_0}{I_K} - 1\right) = K_0 e^{-p\,\Delta V/RT} \qquad \text{and} \qquad \ln\left(\frac{I_0}{I_K} - 1\right) = \ln K_0 - \frac{p\,\Delta V}{RT}$$

$$(9.21)$$

Thus, in a plot of the logarithm of the expression $(I_0/I_K - 1)$ against pressure, a straight line of slope $-(\Delta V/RT)$ should result. Figure 9.24 shows such a plot of the data from experiments similar to those of Fig. 9.23. Values for I_K were obtained from the observed rate under the various pressures at these two temperatures. The straightness of the lines is evidence for the adequacy of the treatment. Their slopes indicate a value of 69 cc per mole for ΔV.

A formulation similar to equation (9.21) may be applied in obtaining the value of ΔH and ΔS for the same equilibrium:

$$\left(\frac{I_0}{I_K} - 1\right) = K_0 e^{-(\Delta H - T\,\Delta S)/RT}$$

or $\qquad$ $$\ln\left(\frac{I_0}{I_K} - 1\right) = \ln K_0 - \frac{(\Delta H - T\,\Delta S)}{RT} \qquad (9.22)$$

Here the value of the expression on the left is plotted against the reciprocal of the absolute temperature at constant pressure. In the low temperature region where K_0 becomes very small, this particular method of plotting becomes extraordinarily sensitive to the exact place of drawing the line for I_0. This is not a real difficulty, however, since one can show that a slight change in drawing I_0, well within the experimental accuracy, removes all seeming complications. When the method of (9.22) is applied to the data between 35° and 40°C, the heat of reaction in the same equilibrium is 71,600 cal, with an entropy of 232 E.U. The values for these constants are of the same magnitude as those for the irreversible denaturation at more acid pH (Table 8.7).

Other processes in which evidence has been found that protein denaturation is opposed by pressure include the proteolytic activity of trypsin between 35° and 55°C (Fraser and Johnson, 1951; Werbin and McLaren, 1951b), and the activity of formic dehydrogenase in *Escherichia coli* at 68°C, or in aged suspensions of the same organism at 30°C (Borrowman, 1950). Evidence for the retardation of irreversible protein denaturation by pressure has been found in the rate of destruction of luminescence of *Photobacterium phosphoreum* at 34°C (Johnson, Eyring, Steblay, Chaplin, Huber, and Gherardi, 1945), the rate of inactivation of bacteriophage T5 at 68°C (Foster, Johnson, and Miller, 1949), the disinfection of vegetative bacterial cells at 37° to 48°C (Johnson and Lewin, 1946b,d), and the killing of bacterial spores at 92° to 94°C (Johnson and ZoBell, 1949a).

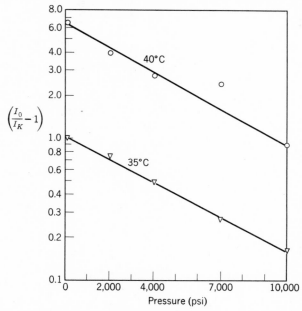

Fig. 9.24. Analysis of the data of Fig. 9.23, for volume change of reaction in the denaturation of invertase at pH 7.03 to 7.07, at 35° and 40°C. The slopes of the lines indicate a volume increase of 69 cc per mole in going from the active to the inactive form.

Among these different processes, denaturation occurs at measurable rates over short ranges of temperature as low as 34°C in luminescence and as high as 94°C in spore disinfection, a total range of 60°C. It is to be expected that the influence of pressure on the specific reaction rate constant will be measurable at temperatures where the rate constant itself is measurable. The fact that this occurs at relatively low temperatures with some systems and relatively high temperatures with others reflects the difference in heats and entropies of the specific constants concerned.

The kinetics of the bacteriophage inactivation (Fig. 9.25) is similar to that of tobacco mosaic virus denaturation in order of reaction and volume change of activation. In the absence of small amounts of added magnesium chloride the general effects of pressure are the same, but the kinetics is more complicated.

In contrast to the results with T5, the rate of destruction of bacteriophage T7 is accelerated by pressure.   Other exceptions to the retardation or reversal of denaturation by pressure have been found in (1) the

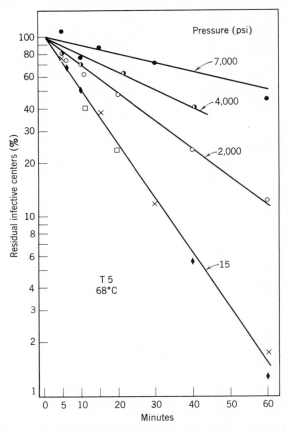

Fig. 9.25.   Inactivation of bacterial virus T5 in nutrient broth plus 0.005 M MgCl$_2$ at 68°C at pressures of 1 to 470 atm (Foster, Johnson, and Miller, 1949).

denaturation of methemoglobin by salicylate (Schlegel and Johnson, 1949), which is not appreciably influenced by either temperature or pressure, (2) the denaturation of staphylococcus antitoxin in 6 M urea at 25°C (Wright and Schomaker, 1948b), and (3) the inhibition of bacterial luminescence in the presence of certain carbamates (Johnson, Flagler, Simpson, and McGeer, 1951).

Dilatometric studies

The change in volume in going from the normal to the activated state can be reliably measured by the quantitative effects of pressure on the rate of the reaction. At any moment the number of molecules in the activated state in comparison to those in the normal state is so small that no other method is sufficiently sensitive to detect any change in the total volume of the system as a result of the activation process. It is often possible, however, to measure directly, by means of a dilatometer, the difference in volume between the initial and final states, and, unless the reaction is very fast, the total volume change can be measured during the course of the reaction, as, for example, in proteolysis. There is, of course, no necessary relation between the volume change of activation in the rate process and the volume change of reaction in the final as compared to the initial state.

Heymann (1936b) has studied the volume change accompanying the thermal denaturation of proteins and found that in all cases there was a volume increase of 0.20 to 0.23 cc per 100 grams of protein at the isoelectric point. On either side of the isoelectric point the volume increase was less by 25 to 65 per cent. From the data given, the net volume change of reaction can be readily computed. Thus, with serum albumin at pH 5, a volume increase of 0.2 cc per 100 grams of protein was found. The molecular weight is 68,000, so the volume increase amounts to 136 cc per mole. For egg albumin the volume increase amounted to 0.23 per 100 grams of protein at pH 4.9, 0.14 cc at pH 3.9, and 0.07 cc at pH 8.3. From these data, and a molecular weight of 35,000, the value of ΔV amounts to 80.3 cc per mole at pH 4.9, 49.2 cc per mole at pH 3.9, and 24.6 cc per mole at pH 8.3. Coagulation of the product occurred only at pH 4.9. It is interesting that there are examples of volume increases of reaction in denaturation, and that the order of magnitude is the same as the volume increase of activation according to the effects of pressure on the rate.

The cleavage of a peptide bond practically always results in a volume decrease because of electrostriction of the ion pair that is liberated. Rona and Fischgold (1933a,b) were the first to apply dilatometry in the investigation of proteolysis; they were followed by Sreenivasaya and Sreerangachar (1934, 1935; Sreenivasaya, Sastri, and Sreervangachar, 1934), who studied the contraction in volume accompanying the digestive action of trypsin and pepsin. Dilatometry has been used extensively in the Carlsberg laboratory as an approach to the understanding of proteolysis, with particular reference to protein structure and the nature of the initial changes in the process of digestion (Linderstrøm-Lang and Jacobsen, 1941; Jacobsen, 1942, 1947; Johansen and Thygesen, 1948; Korsgaard

Christensen, 1949; Jacobsen and Linderstrøm-Lang, 1949; Linderstrøm-Lang, 1950). At the outset, Linderstrøm-Lang and Jacobsen (1941) on the basis of available data (cf. Weber, 1930; Weber and Nachmannsohn, 1929; Cohn, McMeekin, Edsall, and Blanchard, 1934; McMeekin, Cohn, and Weare, 1935; Greenstein and Wyman, 1936) and on the basis of new measurements of their own, arrived at some general, rounded off values for the volume changes, as follows:

ΔV accompanying the formation of an amino acid dipole $= - 13.0$ cc per mole

ΔV accompanying the formation of a dipeptide dipole $\quad = - 15.5$ cc per mole

ΔV accompanying the formation of a tripeptide dipole $\quad = - 16.5$ cc per mole

ΔV accompanying the formation of a tetrapeptide or higher dipole $\qquad = - 17.0$ cc per mole

ΔV in ion pair formation $\qquad = - 17.0$ cc per mole

These values are influenced to a slight extent by the concentration of salt in the medium and by the temperature. In general, however, the simple cleavage of peptide bonds may be expected to result in a contraction, due to electrostriction, of 15 to 20 cc per mole, and never to exceed 25 cc per mole in solutions of pH 6 to 10 buffered with $NH_3-NH_4^+$, or unbuffered. Tables 9.6 and 9.7 list the ΔV's for specific reactions as given by Linderstrøm-Lang and Jacobsen.

For relatively simple substances such as benzoylargininamide (Jacobsen, 1942) or clupein (M.W. ca. 5,000), the volume decrease on digestion by trypsin or chymotrypsin is within the expected value, viz., close to 15 cc per mole, but with either native or denatured β-lactoglobulin the volume decrease amounted to as much as 50 cc per mole of peptide bond (Fig. 9.26).

Parenthetically, it may be remarked here that the large total volume decrease accompanying the enzymatic digestion of proteins makes the reported resynthesis of gelatin or serum albumin (Bresler, 1947) under very high pressures (6,000 atm; cf. Table 9.1, p. 292) interesting but somewhat surprising.

Linderstrøm-Lang has particularly emphasized the importance of initial changes in native protein molecules preceding their breakdown by endopeptidase action, i.e., the cleavage of "exposed" peptide linkages. The initial reaction catalyzed by the proteolytic enzyme may be akin to denaturation, or it may involve the splitting of a few peptide bonds that are especially concerned in making available the remaining peptide bonds to the action of the enzyme. It is natural to suppose that the excessively large contraction in the tryptic breakdown of β-lactoglobulin is associated with the initial reaction. The rate of this reaction relative to that of purely endopeptidase activity presumably varies during the course of

Table 9.6. Volume Changes of Reactions Involving Amino Acids and Simple Peptides

(From Linderstrøm-Lang and Jacobsen, 1941, including data of Weber, 1930)

Volume changes accompanying the formation of an ion pair, or of tetrapeptide or longer peptides, is indicated by ΔV_{ion}; of an amino acid dipole by ΔV_{dp}; of a dipeptide dipole by ΔV_{1dp}; and of a tripeptide dipole by ΔV_{11dp}. G = glycine; A = alanine; L = leucine; GG = glycylglycine, etc.

Reaction	ΔV Found	ΔV Calculated
$CH_3COOH + NH_3 \rightarrow CH_3COO^- + NH_4^+$	-17.4	$\Delta V_{ion}{}^1 = -18.0$
$CH_3COOH + NH_2CH_3 \rightarrow CH_3COO^- + NH_3{}^+CH_3$	-15.8	
$CH_3CONHCH_2COOH + NH_2CH_2COOC_2H_5 \rightarrow$		$\Delta V_{ion} = -17.0$
$CH_3CONHCH_2COO^- + NH_3{}^+CH_2COOC_2H_5$	-17.4	
$G^- + G^+ \rightarrow 2^+G^-$	-8.9	
$A^- + G^- \rightarrow {}^+A^- + {}^+G^-$	-9.9	$2\Delta V_{dp}$
$A^- + G^+ \rightarrow {}^+A^- + {}^+G^-$	-7.9	$-\Delta V_{ion} = -9.0$
$A^- + A^+ \rightarrow 2^+A^-$	-8.9	
$GG^- + G^+ \rightarrow {}^+GG^- + {}^+G^-$	-12.1	
$GG^- + A^+ \rightarrow {}^+GG^- + {}^+A^-$	-13.1	
$GG^+ + G^- \rightarrow {}^+GG^- + {}^+G^-$	-11.0	$\Delta V_{dp} + \Delta V_{1dp}$
$GG^+ + A^- \rightarrow {}^+GG^- + {}^+A^-$	-10.0	$-\Delta V_{ion} = -11.5$
$AG^- + G^+ \rightarrow {}^+AG^- + {}^+G^-$	-11.2	
$LG^- + G^+ \rightarrow {}^+LG^- + {}^+G^-$	-10.9	
$GG^- + GG^+ \rightarrow 2^+GG^-$	-14.2	
$AG^- + GG^+ \rightarrow {}^+AG^- + {}^+GG^-$	-13.3	
$AG^+ + GG^- \rightarrow {}^+AG^- + {}^+GG^-$	-15.2	
$AG^- + AG^+ \rightarrow 2^+AG^-$	-14.3	$2\,\Delta V_{1dp}$
$LG^- + AG^+ \rightarrow {}^+LG^- + {}^+AG^-$	-13.0	$-\Delta V_{ion} = -14.0$
$LG^+ + AG^- \rightarrow {}^+LG^- + {}^+AG^-$	-15.6	
$LG^- + LG^+ \rightarrow 2^+LG^-$	-14.4	
$AGG^- + G^+ \rightarrow {}^+AGG^- + {}^+G^-$	-12.2	
$AGG^- + A^+ \rightarrow {}^+AGG^- + {}^+A^-$	-13.2	$\Delta V_{dp} + \Delta V_{11dp}$
$AGG^+ + G^- \rightarrow {}^+AGG^- + {}^+G^-$	-11.9	$-\Delta V_{ion} = -12.5$
$AGG^+ + A^- \rightarrow {}^+AGG^- + {}^+A^-$	-10.9	
$AGG^- + GG^+ \rightarrow {}^+AGG^- + {}^+GG^-$	-14.3	
$AGG^- + AG^+ \rightarrow {}^+AGG^- + {}^+AG^-$	-15.3	
$AGG^- + LG^+ \rightarrow {}^+AGG^- + {}^+LG^-$	-15.7	$\Delta V_{1dp} + \Delta V_{11dp}$
$AGG^+ + GG^- \rightarrow {}^+AGG^- + {}^+GG^-$	-15.1	$-\Delta V_{ion} = -15.0$
$AGG^+ + AG^- \rightarrow {}^+AGG^- + {}^+AG^-$	-14.2	
$AGG^+ + LG^- \rightarrow {}^+AGG^- + {}^+LG^-$	-13.9	

Table 9.6 (Continued)

Reaction	ΔV Found	ΔV Calculated
$AGG^- + AGG^+ \rightarrow 2^+AGG^-$	$- 15.2$	$2\,\Delta V_{11dp}$ $- \Delta V_{1on}{}^1 = -16.0$
$A^- + {}^+G^- \rightarrow {}^+A^- + G^-$	$+ 1.0$	0
$GG^- + {}^+G^- \rightarrow {}^+GG^- + G^-$	$- 3.2$	
$AG^- + {}^+G^- \rightarrow {}^+AG^- + G^-$	$- 2.3$	
$LG^- + {}^+G^- \rightarrow {}^+LG^- + G^-$	$- 2.0$	$\Delta V_{1dp} - \Delta V_{dp} = -2.5$
$GG^- + {}^+A^- \rightarrow {}^+GG^- + A^-$	$- 4.2$	
$GG^- + {}^+A^- \rightarrow {}^+AG^- + A^-$	$- 3.3$	
$LG^- + {}^+A^- \rightarrow {}^+LG^- + A^-$	$- 3.0$	
$GG^- + {}^+AG^- \rightarrow {}^+GG^- + AG^-$	$- 0.9$	
$GG^- + {}^+LG^- \rightarrow {}^+GG^- + LG^-$	$- 1.2$	0
$AG^- + {}^+LG^- \rightarrow {}^+AG^- + LG^-$	$- 0.3$	
$AGG^- + {}^+G^- \rightarrow {}^+AGG^- + G^-$	$- 3.3$	$\Delta V_{11dp} - \Delta V_{dp} = -3.5$
$AGG^- + {}^+A^- \rightarrow {}^+AGG^- + A^-$	$- 4.3$	
$AGG^- + {}^+GG^- \rightarrow {}^+AGG^- + GG^-$	$- 0.1$	ΔV_{11dp}
$AGG^- + {}^+AG^- \rightarrow {}^+AGG^- + AG^-$	$- 1.0$	$- \Delta V_{1dp} = -1.0$
$AGG^- + {}^+LG^- \rightarrow {}^+AGG^- + LG^-$	$- 1.3$	
$G^- + NH_4^+ \rightarrow {}^+G^- + NH_3$	$+ 5.0$	ΔV_{dp}
$A^- + NH_4^+ \rightarrow {}^+A^- + NH_3$	$+ 6.0$	$- \Delta V^1{}_{1on} = +5.0$
$GG^- + NH_4^+ \rightarrow {}^+GG^- + NH_3$	$+ 1.8$	ΔV_{1dp}
$AG^- + NH_4^+ \rightarrow {}^+AG^- + NH_3$	$+ 2.7$	$- \Delta V^1{}_{1on} = +2.5$
$LG^- + NH_4^+ \rightarrow {}^+LG^- + NH_3$	$+ 3.0$	
$AGG^- + NH_4^+ \rightarrow {}^+AGG^- + NH_3$	$+ 1.8$	ΔV_{11dp} $- \Delta V^1{}_{1on} = +1.5$
$G^- + H_2PO_4^- \rightarrow {}^+G^- + HPO_4^{2-}$	$- 25.9$	$\Delta V_{dp} + \Delta V_{1on^2} = -26.0$
$A^- + H_2PO_4^- \rightarrow {}^+G^- + HPO_4^{2-}$	$- 24.9$	
$GG^- + H_2PO_4^- \rightarrow {}^+GG^- + HPO_4^{2-}$	$- 29.1$	ΔV_{1dp}
$AG^- + H_2PO_4^- \rightarrow {}^+AG^- + HPO_4^{2-}$	$- 28.2$	$+ \Delta V_{1on^2} = -28.5$
$LG^- + H_2PO_4^- \rightarrow {}^+LG^- + HPO_4^{2-}$	$- 27.9$	
$AGG^- + H_2PO_4^- \rightarrow {}^+AGG^- + HPO_4^{2-}$	$- 29.2$	ΔV_{11dp} $+ \Delta V_{1on^2} = -29.5$

Table 9.7. Some Measured Volume Changes of Reactions
(From Linderstrøm-Lang and Jacobsen, 1941)

Reaction	Solution 1	Solution 2	ΔV (μ)	ΔV (ml/mole)
$NH_3 + H_3{}^+O \rightarrow$ $NH_4{}^+ + H_2O$	10 ml 0.1 N HCl	10 ml 0.24 N NH$_3$ + 5 ml 0.1 N HCl	− 6.82	− 6.8
$NH_3 + HOOCCH_3 \rightarrow$ $NH_4{}^+ + {}^-OOCCH_3$	5 ml 0.102 N CH$_3$COOH 5 ml 0.100 N CH$_3$COONa	5.5 ml 0.24 N NH$_3$ + 5 ml 0.1 N HCl	− 8.85	− 17.4
$NH_2CH_2COOC_2H_5$ $+ H_3{}^+O \rightarrow$ $NH_3{}^+CH_2COOC_2H_5$ $+ H_2O$	10 ml 0.1 N HCl	5 ml 0.4 M glycinester hydrochloride + 12 ml 0.1 N NaOH	− 5.55	− 5.6
${}^+AGG^- + H_3{}^+O \rightarrow$ $AGG^+ + H_2O$	10 ml 0.1 N HCl	10 ml 0.2 M AGG	+ 10.08	+ 10.1
$AGG^- + H_3{}^+O \rightarrow$ ${}^+AGG^- + H_2O$	10 ml 0.1 N HCl	10 ml 0.2 M AGG + 0.6 ml 2 N NaOH	− 5.10	− 5.1
$HPO_4{}^{2-} + H_3{}^+O \rightarrow$ $H_2PO_4{}^- + H_2O$	(a) 10 ml 0.1 N HCl (b) 5 ml 0.1 N HCl	15 ml 0.0667 M Na$_2$HPO$_4$ 10 ml 0.0667 M Na$_2$HPO$_4$	+ 24.10 + 12.02	+ 24.1 + 24.0
$NH_3 + HOOCCH_3 \rightarrow$ $NH_4{}^+ + {}^-OOCCH_3$ NH_4 in 1 N KCl	2.5 ml 0.202 N CH$_3$COOH + 2.5 ml 0.200 N CH$_3$COONa + 5.0 ml 2 N KCl	2.5 ml 0.48 N NH$_3$ + 5.0 ml 0.1 N HCl + 7.5 ml 2 N KCl	− 7.22	− 15.4

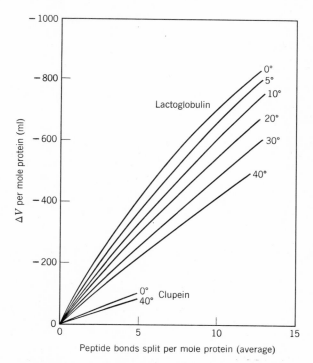

Fig. 9.26. Volume decrease in cubic centimeters per mole of clupein and of β-lactoglobulin at 0° to 40°C accompanying their breakdown with trypsin as catalyst (Linderstrøm-Lang, 1950).

339

hydrolysis and with temperature.   Thus, in Fig. 9.26, at 0°C the relation between the ΔV per mole of protein and the average number of peptide bonds split per mole of protein changes considerably between the start of the reaction, where the slope of the curve at the origin indicates as high as $-$ 80 cc per mole, and the latter part of the reaction, where the slope of the curve is equivalent to about $-$ 55 cc per mole.   At 40°C the relationship is nearly linear, and with a slope indicative of about 40 cc per mole.   These differences are possibly due to a much greater speed of the initial reaction at 0°C, resulting in greater accumulation of the product of the initial reaction.   The volume change in the formation of this product may be estimated on the following basis.   The total volume change due to electrostriction in the exhaustive tryptic breakdown of β-lactoglobulin may be estimated by extrapolating the 40° curve as a straight line to 35 peptide bonds (Miller, 1939).   This amounts to 1,400 cc per mole of protein.   Of this, about 700 cc can be accounted for through electrostriction accompanying the cleaving of peptide bonds, at 20 cc per bond. The difference is about 700 cc for the formation of the initial product.

The nature of an initial reaction responsible for such a large contraction in volume as the estimated 700 cc per mole has not been fully clarified. Justification for considering it a type of denaturation comes from the evidence that the slow alkaline denaturation of β-lactoglobulin at 30°C, pH 8.3, is accompanied by a volume decrease of 200 cc per mole (G. Johansen, referred to by Linderstrøm-Lang, 1950), which is of the same magnitude.   Furthermore, a contraction of about 250 cc per mole occurs in the denaturation of this protein in the presence of urea (Jacobsen and Linderstrøm-Lang, referred to by Linderstrøm-Lang, 1950).   Other lines of evidence support the view that some form of denaturation is preliminary to enzymatic proteolysis.   For example, Lundgren (1941) obtained by means of the ultacentrifuge and by electrophoresis data indicating that papain catalyzes the denaturation of thyroglobulin prior to catalyzing its hydrolysis.   Also, Korsgaard Christensen (1949) has found that active trypsin accelerates the denaturation of β-lactoglobulin in small concentrations of urea which of themselves have very little denaturing effect on the protein, as judged by changes in optical rotation of the β-lactoglobulin plus urea solutions together with various concentrations of trypsin.   On the other hand, the fact that the excessively large volume decreases during digestion of β-lactoglobulin are observed whether the substrate is in the native or already in a denatured state (Linderstrøm-Lang and Jacobsen, 1941) shows that these volume decreases are not necessarily, or certainly not wholly, associated with the initial reaction whereby the native structure is broken down prior to endopeptidase activity.   Moreover, the breakdown of a "superstructure" in macromolecules is sometimes accompanied by a volume increase, e.g., in the splitting or ribonucleic acid by ribonuclease (Chantrenne et al., 1947; Vandendriessche, 1951).

Figure 9.27 illustrates the volume change during the course of breakdown of sodium ribonucleate in the presence of two different concentrations of ribonuclease purified according to the method of Kunitz (1940).

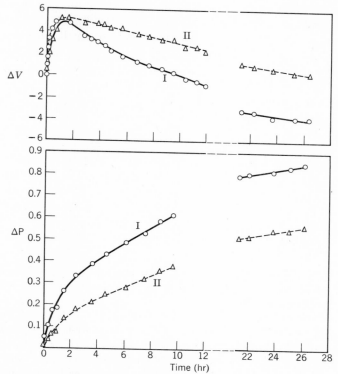

Fig. 9.27. Volume change (ΔV) in cc per mole, and phosphate bonds opened (ΔP) during the break-down of 1 % sodium ribonucleate, pH 4.6, at 30°C, in the presence of 0.0125 % (I) and 0.005 % ribonculease (II), respectively (Chantrenne, et al., 1947).

The volume change per number of phosphate bonds opened is shown in Fig. 9.28. The overall process obviously involves at least two different reactions characterized by volume changes of opposite signs. In accordance with other investigations of this enzyme, it may be considered to act in a dual capacity, first as a depolymerase and second as a phosphatase (Schmidt and Levene, 1938; Allen and Eiler, 1941; Fischer et al., 1942; Loring and Carpenter, 1943). The first reaction, that of depolymerization, is accompanied by a volume increase and occurs much faster than the subsequent phosphatase reaction, which is accompanied by a volume decrease. The difference in rates makes it possible to observe both types of volume changes in the dilatometer. From Fig. 9.28, the volume decrease of the phosphatase reaction may be estimated as -13 cc per equivalent, from the slope of the curve where this type of reaction predominates. By extrapolating this line back to the ordinate, a volume increase of between 8 and 9 cc per mole is estimated for the depolymerization. Although this volume increase appears to be small, the same type

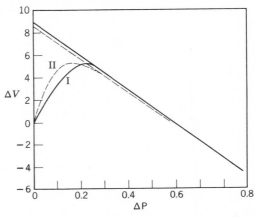

Fig. 9.28. Relation between volume change and number of phosphate bonds opened in the breakdown of sodium ribonucleate according to the data of Fig. 9.27 (Chantrenne et al., 1947).

of reaction would presumably involve a much larger increase in the much larger molecule of a protein. The data concerning the influence of pressure on the denaturation equilibria of enzymes demonstrate that large volume increases sometimes characterize the final over the initial state. The same thing is demonstrated by data of Heymann (1936b) for the thermal denaturation of egg and serum albumin. No general rule can be adduced at present for the amount or direction of volume changes accompanying the denaturation of different proteins or other large molecules under various conditions. Similarly, it is sometimes difficult to be certain of a dual catalytic activity of a proteinase, i.e., as a denaturase or depolymerase and as an endopeptidase, inasmuch as a normal equilibrium between native and denatured forms of the substrate would be shifted toward the latter form without direct catalysis as this form is removed by proteolysis.

The conversion of chymotrypsinogen to chymotrypsin is an interesting example of a process in which formation of the activated complex is accompanied by a volume increase, while the formation of the products is accompanied by a volume decrease.

The data of Curl and Jansen (1950b) show that in phosphate buffer, pH 7.6 at 25°C, the rate of chymotrypsinogen conversion is retarded under increased pressures of between somewhat less than 1,000 atm to 3,000 atm or more (Fig. 9.29). From Fig. 9.29 it is evident that the chymotrypsin-ogen to chymotrypsin reaction is reversibly retarded by pressures not in excess of about 3,000 atm. After 60 min under these pressures the

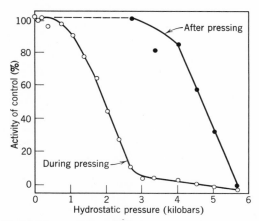

Fig. 9.29. Influence of increased pressure on the amount of conversion of chymotrypsinogen (0.225 mg protein nitrogen per cc) to chymotrypsin in the presence of trypsin (0.000134 mg protein nitrogen per cc) at 25°C, in phosphate buffered solution of pH 7.6 (Curl and Jansen, 1950b). The percentage of activity refers to the activity in a specimen subjected to pressure for 60 min, in comparison to a control at atmospheric pressure for the same length of time. The curve at the right shows the amount of activation of chymotrypsinogen in 60 min at atmospheric pressure, following a 60-min period under the respective pressures.

subsequent rate of the reaction was essentially the same as in the control at atmospheric pressure. After 60 min under higher pressures, however, the subsequent rate was diminished. The data are not sufficient to tell whether this diminution in rate should be attributed to a partial destruction of the chymotrypsinogen, of the trypsin, or of both. The reversible retardation for 60 min under pressures of less than 3,000 atm does not yield a straight line relation when the data of Fig. 9.29 are analyzed in accordance with equation (2.34) or (9.7b), showing that there is more than one reaction affected by pressure.

The rate of chymotrypsinogen conversion to chymotrypsin at atmospheric pressure and ordinary temperatures is a first order reaction, proportional to the amount of trypsin added. The influence of pH on the rate is similar to the pH relationship for the digestion of casein by trypsin. It has been suggested (Northrop et al., 1948) that the change from the catalytically inactive to the catalytically active form of the molecule involves the opening up of peptide bonds in closed ring, inasmuch as there was no evidence for an actual cleavage of the chymotrypsinogen molecule in the process. Dilatometric investigation of this problem has yielded significant results. An extensive analysis by Jacobsen (1947) has indicated that the process is complex in that several forms of active chymotrypsin may be produced as follows.

At $0°C$, the conversion of chymotrypsinogen, in the presence of trypsin, takes place in two steps. The first consists in the hydrolysis of a single peptide bond, giving a previously unrecognized product designated π-chymotrypsin with a specific activity 2 to 2.5 times that of the familiar form, designated α-chymotrypsin. The product of the first reaction, π-chymotrypsin, is converted by two competitive reactions into two additional, active forms. In this second step a product δ-chymotrypsin results from the tryptic hydrolysis of a single peptide bond of π-chymotrypsin, with a volume decrease of 31 cc per equivalent. The activity of δ-chymotrypsin is 1.5 times that of α-chymotrypsin. In competition with the formation of δ-chymotrypsin, the formation of α-chymotrypsin takes place spontaneously by the breaking of 3 peptide bonds of π-chymotrypsin, yielding in the product 6 to 9 times the number of titratable groups as are found in chymotrypsinogen. The previously unrecognized forms of active chymotrypsin, viz., π-chymotrypsin and δ-chymotrypsin, have not been isolated.

Changes in viscosity and volume

Viscosity changes, such as those involved in sol-gel equilibria, are important in many biological processes and may be accompanied by large volume changes. The amount of the volume change in isolated systems may be determined either through dilatometry or through the influence of pressure on viscosity. The latter method is more generally useful with intracellular systems.

Dilatometric studies of various systems *in vitro* have shown that the volume is affected by gelation in three ways (Heymann, 1935, 1936a; Freundlich, 1937): (1) no change, e.g., sodium oleate and other purely thixotropic gels; (2) a decrease, e.g., gelatin or agar; or (3) an increase, e.g., methyl cellulose. In general, the first of these types of gelation is isothermal, the second is exothermal, and the third is endothermal.

Consequently, the first type of gelation is essentially unaffected by changes in pressure or temperature, the second is furthered by pressure or cooling, and the third is opposed by pressure or cooling.   The sol-gel transformations in protoplasm and certain extractives generally behave according to the last mentioned of these types; i.e., gelation is increased by heat (at least, within certain ranges of temperature) and decreased by pressure (except at very high pressures which cause coagulation).   The temperature relations, however, are often complex; for example, the viscosity of the

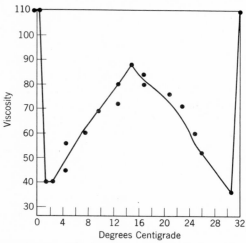

Fig. 9.30. Protoplasmic viscosity of *Cumingia* eggs as a function of temperature (Heilbrunn, 1924a).

cortical protoplasm of *Amoeba proteus* decreases on either side of a maximum at about 7°C (Thornton, 1935).   The protoplasmic viscosity of *Cumingia* eggs shows a maximum at 14° to 16°, and gelation occurs either at temperatures slightly above 0°C or around 30°C (Fig. 9.30; Heilbrunn, 1924a).   Gelation at the higher temperatures is apparently influenced by lipid constituents of the cell (Heilbrunn, 1924b; cf. also Bĕlehrádek, 1935).

It is profitable to consider briefly the meaning of the volume and temperature relationships in the three types of sol-gel equilibria mentioned above.   In thixotropic gels the sol state is characterized by a random distribution of long fibrous molecules.   These molecules, in order to form a gel, must have sites, such as positive and negative groups, where intermolecular combination may take place.

On standing in solution, through random agitation of the molecules by Brownian movement the combining sites are slowly and haphazardly brought together, so that a gel structure is gradually formed.   Mechanical agitation is sufficient to break the weak bonds and restore the sol state. Although heat increases the motion of the molecules and therefore increases the probability that they will happen to collide again at the proper sites, heat also dissociates the combination and in the isothermal gels the two effects balance out; hence the gelation has practically no temperature coefficient.   There is no change in the volume of the system, such as would occur by ionization or unfolding, and consequently there is no effect of pressure on the equilibrium.

In the second type, where gelation is exothermic and the system exhibits a volume decrease, hydrophilic groups are exposed and electrostriction occurs.   The bonds between the molecules forming the gel framework are stronger, and energy must be supplied to the system to break them apart.   Agar, for example, requires heating almost to $100°C$ for solation. It gels at a much lower temperature.   Water molecules "freeze" close around charges on the agar molecules, and a net decrease in volume occurs.

Gelation of the third type, which is endothermal and accompanied by a volume increase, evidently involves exposure of a predominance of oily, hydrophobic groups which attract the water molecules less and therefore increase the volume.   In the sol state the molecules are presumably in a globular configuration with the hydrophobic groups folded against similar molecules in the interior.   In going to the gel state the molecules unfold into a more linear or fibrous form.   They then combine to make the firm network characteristic of the gel.   Since heat favors the unfolding process, heat favors gelation and since pressure opposes the volume increase, pressure favors solation.   Here again, we have processes fundamentally the same as those involved in the denaturation of proteins, and susceptible in much the same way not only to temperature and pressure but to the presence of various chemical agents which further the folded or unfolded state.   Likewise, as in protein denaturation, both reversible and irreversible effects of pressure on gelation are to be expected. Actually, of course, the mechanisms of gelation among different systems do not fall so sharply into the three categories as might be supposed. Among proteins, for example, it is always the net effect that is observed, and it is likely that changes in electrostriction as well as unfolding are both generally concerned.

Pressure effects on viscosity and sol-gel equilibria

There is no clearer evidence of a significant change in the structure of a fluid than through a marked change in viscosity.   In biology, changes in the structure of a cell as a whole may accompany changes in the viscosity of its protoplasm. Typical plant cells, surrounded by a fairly rigid cellulose wall, are not so obviously deformed as a result of changes in state of the protoplasm within. In animal cells, which are usually surrounded only by an elastic membrane, profound alterations in morphology of the living unit take place, often reversibly, under the influence of factors such as increased pressure which alter the viscosity of the protoplasm or portions thereof. Factors other than pressure normally influence the viscosity of cellular components during the processes of cell division, amoeboid motion, fertilization, cyclosis, and other processes, probably including muscle contraction. The general biological action of pressure in relation to viscosity has been discussed by Marsland (1942, 1948).

Qualitatively, intracellular gels seem to conform in general to the type which Heymann (1935, 1936a) found are characterized by a volume increase in the process of going from the sol to the gel state. Quantitatively, the effects of pressure on viscosity in the biological processes studied thus far are remarkably similar. Measurements of relative viscosity have shown that the rigidity of the system is reduced by about 25 per cent with each increment of 1,000 psi pressure (although in some instances there is not much effect between atmospheric pressure and 1,000 psi). This quantitative relationship has been referred to as "Marsland's law" (Pease, 1946). The regularity of the per cent decrease per given increment in pressure indicates a simple exponential relation, as would be expected for a single reaction in accordance with equation (9.7b). The amount of decrease indicates a volume change of about + 102 cc per mole at a room temperature of 22°C. Some of the data pertaining to relative viscosities and rates of biological processes are plotted in Fig. 9.31, where the arbitrary value of 100 at atmospheric pressure and room temperature is used (Marsland, 1942). These data show the influence of pressure on the gel value of protoplasm of *Amoeba*, unfertilized *Arbacia* eggs, cleaving *Arbacia* eggs, cytoplasm of *Elodea* cells, extracted myosin of rabbit muscle (Marsland and Brown, 1942), the rate of cell division of *Arbacia* eggs, and the rate of cyclosis (protoplasmic streaming) of *Elodea* cells. The slope of the broken line, drawn on a logarithmic scale of the ordinate, indicates a volume change of 106 cc per mole.

From Fig. 9.31 it is evident that changes in the rate of a biological process are sometimes closely correlated with changes in viscosity of the protoplasm. Similar correlations either definitely or presumably exist between viscosity and macroscopic structures, such as chromatophores (Marsland, 1944), the plasmodium of a slime mold (Pease, 1940a), tentacles of a suctorian protozoan (Kitching and Pease, 1939), human erythrocytes (Ebbecke, 1936c, 1937), frog erythrocytes (Haubrich, 1937), cells of amoeba (Marsland and Brown, 1936) and paramecium (Ebbecke,

1935c, 1936c), and fine structures of cells at the time of cell division (Pease, 1941, 1946).

In general, the changes in macroscopic structure appear to result chiefly from, first, the solation of a gel state and, second, the action of surface energy forces. With cells that are normally spherical, e.g., *Arbacia* eggs, no macroscopic change in shape is apparent when they are subjected to

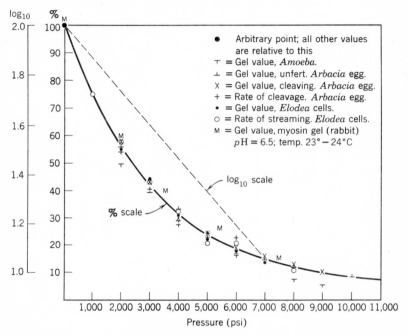

Fig. 9.31.   Changes in relative viscosity of protoplasm and in rates of some biological processes (Marsland, 1942).

pressures of some 680 atm. During the process of division, however, when the cells become elongated, pressure causes them to return to the spherical condition, as discussed presently. The normally ellipsoidal or biconcave discs of erhthrocytes become rounded under pressure, and likewise the normally irregularly shaped cells of *Amoeba*. The tentacles of the protozoan, *Ephelota coronata*, shorten and disintegrate into minute spherical droplets. The thin branches of naked protoplasm of the slime mold, *Physarum polycephalum* form rounded "reservoirs" under pressure (Fig. 9.32). When pressure is released, they gradually return to a branched structure with liquid channels through which the protoplasm ebbs and flows in communication with the main body of the plasmodium.

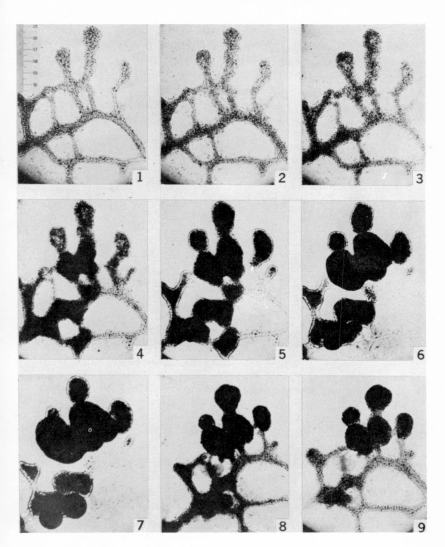

Fig. 9.32.   Influence of pressure on the plasmodium of *Physarum polycephalum* (Pease, 1940).   Photographs 2 to 7 were taken 5 min after each successive increase in pressure: 1, atmospheric pressure; 2, 1,000 psi; 3, 2,000 psi; 4, 3,000 psi; 5, 4,000 psi; 6, 5,000 psi; 7, 6,000 psi.   Photographs 8 and 9 were taken 5 and 35 min, respectively, after pressure was released.

Here, as in *Amoeba*, the movement of the protoplasm ceases reversibly when solation is essentially complete.

In *Amoeba* it has been possible to obtain quantitative measurements of relative viscosity by means of an ingenious device for centrifuging the specimens under pressure (Brown, 1934a; Marsland and Brown, 1936). The correlation between relative viscosity and shape of the cell is indicated in Fig. 9.33.   Sudden compression to about 250 atm is sufficient to stop protoplasmic streaming within the cell.   The effects are all rapidly

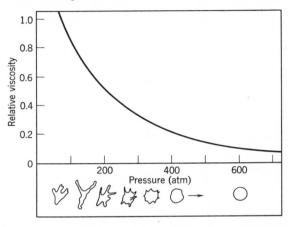

Fig. 9.33.   Change in form and relative viscosity of *Amoeba* in relation to hydrostatic pressure (Marsland and Brown, 1936). The diameter of the pseudopodia decreases progressively with rise in pressure, but the length increases under pressure up to 140 atm, then decreases with further rise in pressure.

reversible on release of pressure, provided that it has not been maintained for long periods of time.   Thus movement begins within 1 sec, if the pressure has not been maintained for more than 10 min.   After more than 30 min at pressures at 300 atm, however, 5 to 15 min are required for resumption of activity, and after an hour under such pressures the animals are sometimes dead.

Amoeboid-like cells, collectively referred to under the general head of chromatophores, are responsible for the rapid changes in color or degree of darkening that occur in many animals, invertebrates as well as vertebrates.   The chameleon is one of the most familiar examples of a vertebrate with this property of color change, but there are many others known in biology and there is an extensive literature concerning the mechanisms involved (e.g., reviews by Abramowitz, 1939; Parker, 1940; Waring, 1942).   The gross mechanism consists in an "expansion" or "contraction" of pigment granules toward the periphery or toward the center, respectively, of a specialized cell structure resembling in outline an amoeba with extended pseudopodia. The basic physical-chemical mechanism has not been fully solved. The chromatophores (melanophores) of fish scales, containing the black pigment melanin, undergo expansion in isotonic sodium chloride, while the chromatophores containing a yellow pigment undergo contraction in isotonic sodium chloride (Spaeth, 1916). Potassium chloride causes the opposite effect on melanophores of fishes, i.e., causes them to contract (Spaeth, 1916; Beauvallet, 1937), but potassium chloride causes frog chromatophores to expand (Thörner, 1929). The behavior of chromatophores in both invertebrates and vertebrates is influenced by endocrine secretions, especially of the (vertebrate) pituitary gland and by nerve activity. In the snake fish, *Ophiocephalus argus*, it has been shown that the chromatophores are controlled by adrenergic and cholinergic nerve fibers (Chang et al., 1939; Chin, 1939). The nervous control of chromatophores, through "neurohumors" has long been championed by Parker, and there is reason to believe that, at least in the catfish, the neurohumor causing expansion of the melanophores is acetyl choline, while the neurohumor causing contraction is adrenaline (Parker, 1940–1942).

The action of pressure on the behavior of chromatophores is of interest, particularly because of evidence that the process of expansion and contraction is accompanied by sol-gel changes resembling those that take place in the amoeba under pressure. Figure 9.34 illustrates the changes in state of dispersal of pigment in a single, isolated chromatophore from a fish scale under successive increments of hydrostatic pressure. Marsland's observations (1942, 1944) indicate that at each pressure the state of expansion seems to reach an equilibrium value within roughly a minute after the pressure is applied. Furthermore, in repeated experiments with the same specimen, the cell returns to apparently the same equilibrium at a given pressure. After periods of compression longer than 20 min, at pressures above 5,000 psi, however, the former states are not reached. By appropriate treatment with salt solutions (0.1 M sodium chloride, then 0.1 M barium chloride, then sodium chloride again; Spaeth, 1916), pulsation can be induced in certain melanophores. This process is also affected by pressure. The amplitude of the pulsation is reduced as the pressure is increased, apparently by opposing the inflow phase. After release of pressure a rapid contraction occurs and lasts longer than in the normal rhythm; this is reminiscent of the "black-out" in bacterial luminescence (p. 319), and reminiscent of changing rates of ciliary and cardiac frequency. Marsland's studies of melanophores included only a few observations of the influence of temperature on the effects of pressure.   It seemed that a low temperature (6°C) reinforced the pressure inhibition of contraction, while a high temperature (30°C) had the opposite effect.   If fish from the deep sea have chromatophores, it would be interesting to examine the pressure-temperature relations of contraction and expansion.   Since there is no light other than bioluminescence in the depths, any genetic adaptation which would permit the chromatophores to function under high pressures and low temperatures contrary to what

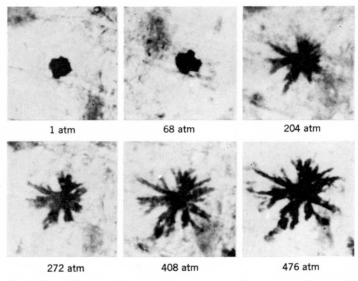

1 atm   68 atm   204 atm

272 atm   408 atm   476 atm

Fig. 9.34.   Influence of hydrostatic pressure on the amount of expansion of unicellular chromatophore of an isolated scale of *Fundulus heteroclitus* at room temperature (Marsland, 1942, 1944).

would be expected according to the above results would seem of little advantage to the organism.

Evidence for viscosity differences characteristic of the expanded and contracted state have been obtained with a centrifugal method (Marsland, 1944).   In either state, however, the viscosity proved to be so much greater than that of *Amoeba* (Brown and Marsland, 1936), or of sea urchin eggs (Brown, 1934a), that very high centrifugal forces were needed to displace the pigment granules and so obtain a measurement of relative viscosity.   Consequently, an air turbine giving a force of 70,000 × gravity was required (Marsland, 1944), and it was not possible to use the device for centrifugation at forces of only 7,000 × gravity while under hydrostatic pressure (Brown, 1934a).   Instead, the contracted melanophores were observed for displacement of granules and compared to expanded melanophores, each after centrifugation at 70,000 × gravity for 3 min. In the expanded state, brought about by any of several means (sodium chloride, physostigmine, acetyl choline solutions), displacement of the pigment granules always occurred under the high centrifugal force. In the contracted state brought about by potassium chloride or adrenaline, no displacement of pigment granules ever occurred under the same force or even a greater force of 125,000 × gravity. Evidently the expanded state is associated with a lower viscosity than that of the contracted state, which appears to be a firm gel. After centrifugation, the sedimented granules become redistributed by Brownian motion into the clear spaces, and the melanophore shows no sign of injury as a result of the treatment.

Evidence regarding the actual mechanism of contraction and expansion of the granules has been variously interpreted. Hooker (1914) expressed the view that movement of the pigment is accomplished by means of pseudopodia, i.e., that the melanophore is in fact an amoeboid cell. Spaeth, in 1916, concluded that the melanophore is a specialized type of smooth muscle cell. Shanes and Nigrelli (1941) have found birefringent material closely associated with and interconnecting the chromatophores in *Fundulus*. Appearance and disappearance of Brownian motion of the pigment granules are accompanied by changes in birefrigence of this material, and, when visible under polarized light, strands of the material seem to show a certain degree of rigidity and also contractility. We are inclined to the view that the mechanism is fundamentally the same as in the contraction and relaxation of muscle, however it differs in detail in cytological structure. "Synthetic muscle fibers," spun from purified actomyosin, readily contract on addition of adenosine triphosphate (Szent-Györgyi, 1947). From this fact structures accessory to special functions seem secondary in importance to the fundamental process.

Cell division[1]

The complete process through which one cell divides to form two cells involves a large number of reactions—both equilibria and rate processes —which pressure might be expected to affect. The same is true of growth, but growth may take place without cell division, and cell division may occur without growth in the sense that any considerable increase in the total amount of protoplasm takes place. Although growth and cell division are intimately related in the reproduction and development of organisms, there are circumstances where the two processes can be considered quite separate and distinct. For the moment we will confine our

[1] The general subject of "the mechanisms of cell division" has been considered in an interesting symposium of the New York Academy of Sciences, M. J. Kopac, Chairman (1951).

discussion very largely to cell division, reserving for the next section certain aspects of the problem of growth.

In cell division, work is performed and energy must be supplied. The ultimate source of this energy is oxidative reactions, aerobic or anaerobic, controlled by enzymes. From the fact that enzyme activity may be profoundly modified, reversibly, by increased pressure, it follows that one of the possible actions of pressure on cell division may be primarily on enzymes. In this event, a relation between temperature and the net effects of pressure, somewhat like the pressure-temperature relationship of luminescence, might be expected. On the other hand, from the fact that pressure may affect sol-gel reactions and the structure of cells as a whole, it follows that the action of this factor on cell division could be primarily through such mechanisms as these. Under different conditions, different types of reactions would be expected to limit the overall process.

With respect to the process of cleavage itself, apart from the problem of chromosome movement and other aspects of the nuclear machinery, pressure has been shown to retard, prevent, or even reverse the furrowing of various egg cells according to the amount of the pressure and stage of division (Marsland, 1938, 1939, 1950, 1951; Marsland and Jaffee, 1949; Pease, 1940b; Pease and Marsland, 1939; Rugh and Marsland, 1943). Table 9.8 summarizes some of the observations concerning the amount of pressure needed to block cell division or to cause rounding up of cells at room temperature. Except for the eggs of *Ascaris*, which cleave under a pressure of as much as 800 atm, the eggs of many animals fail to cleave under pressures as low as 200 to 400 atm. In *Ascaris* eggs, either gelation does not play a critical rôle in the same manner as in the eggs of the other organisms, or the type of gel is one that does not solate with a large volume decrease. Possibly a similar mechanism is concerned in cell division of deep sea organisms. Since deep sea organisms live under pressures seldom exceeding 800 atm, occurring at a depth of about 5 miles below the surface, the mechanisms found in *Ascaris* would suffice to meet their problem of high pressure posed by their natural habitat. Perhaps a solution to the problem pertaining to deep sea organisms can be achieved through further studies of *Ascaris*. There are indications that bacteria indigenous to the ocean floor at depths where the pressure approximates 500 atm are less susceptible to the inhibitory effects of pressure than bacteria isolated from or near the surface (ZoBell and Johnson, 1949). For example, *Bacillus submarinus* and *Bacillus thalassokoites* were found to grow abundantly under 600 atm of pressure at 30° or 40°C. At 20°C, however, no macroscopic evidence of growth under 500 atm was apparent after 6 days of incubation. Assuming that the effects of pressure and of cold are additive, as they are in other processes discussed in previous

Table 9.8. Amount of Pressure Required to Block Cell Division or to Cause Rounding of Certain Cells at Room Temperature

(From Pease and Marsland, 1939; plus some additional observations)

Cell	Pressure Required (atm)	Observer
Protozoa		
Amoeba dubia	400	Marsland and Brown
Amoeba proteus	400	Marsland and Brown
Paramecium		Ebbecke, 1936d
Echinodermata		
Arbacia (amoebocytes)	400	Marsland
Arbacia punctulata (egg)	330–400	Marsland, Pease
Arbacia punctulosa	< 330	Marsland
Echinorachnius parma	330	Pease
Paracentrotus lividus	330	Marsland
Psammechinus microtuberculatus	< 330	Marsland
Sphaerechinus granularis	400	Marsland
Nematoda		
Ascaris megalocephala var. univalens	> 800	Pease
Annelida		
Chaetopterus pergamentaceus	220–270	Pease
Mollusca		
Cumingia tellenoides	220–270	Pease
Planorbis sp.	270	Pease
Solen siliqua	230	Marsland
Insecta		
Drosophila melanogaster (block of pole cell formation)	330–400	Marsland
Tunicata		
Ciona intestinalis	200	Marsland
Amphibia		
Rana pipiens	ca. 600	Marsland and Jaffee, 1949
Microörganisms		
Various species of bacteria (except marine barophiles)	300–600	ZoBell and Johnson, 1949
Various species of yeast	300–600	ZoBell and Johnson, 1949
Myxomycetes (Mycetozoa)		
Physarum sp. (rounding of plasmodium)	300–400	Pease
Plants		
Elodea canadensis (stoppage of protoplasmic streaming)	300–400	Pease
Nitella flexilis (stoppage of protoplasmic streaming, 10° to 38°C)	680	Harvey, 1942

paragraphs, the question remains: how much or how fast do even these deep sea bacteria grow in their frigid, high pressure environment? Mixed microflora in mud freshly collected at depths up to 12,000 ft were found (ZoBell and Johnson, 1949) to develop in the laboratory sometimes more rapidly under 400 to 600 atm than under 1 atm, and perhaps they do so also at the cold temperature of their habitat. For such organisms the term "barophilic" was coined. The whole intriguing problem is still outstandingly lacking in experimental data, especially with respect to the pressure-temperature relationship of growth and metabolism.

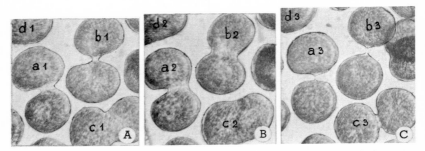

Fig. 9.35. Influence of applying a hydrostatic pressure of 6,500 psi on the cleaving eggs of *Arbacia punctulata* at room temperature (Marsland, 1938): (A) 10 sec after application of pressure; (B) 2 min later, still under pressure; (C) 2 min after release of pressure, immediately after (B). Although cell (b) had almost completely divided (b1), the cleavage furrow quickly receded under pressure (b2). When pressure was released, division was quickly resumed and completed (b3). Similar effects are apparent in the cells marked (a) and (c), respectively, which were at different stages of cleaving at the time pressure was applied.

Figure 9.35 illustrates the reversal of cell division in *Arbacia* eggs by application of pressure. The primary effect of pressure in this experiment seems to be upon the cortical gel of the egg. A few minutes before the formation of the furrow, the gel strength of the cortical region increases as much as ten-fold, and a stiffly gelated layer is pushed in with the furrow and grows through the less viscous interior of the egg as cleavage proceeds. Liquefaction of this gel under pressure causes the furrow to recede, and, if the pressure is maintained, the dividing cell assumes a nearly spherical condition again. After short periods of compression (ca. 2 min) cleavage is resumed at once. After the first cleavage is suppressed for periods of about 15 min, the first and second cleavages occur simultaneously, resulting in four cells, at about the same time as in a control kept at atmospheric pressure throughout. Observations of the eggs of *Paracentrotus lividus*, in which the unstained nuclei can be discerned with certainty, indicate that nuclear division can be successfully completed during a suppression of cleavage of the cytoplasm (Marsland, 1938). It is reasonable to assume that the presence of two daughter nuclei, in cells whose first cytoplasmic cleavage has been suppressed under pressure, is responsible in part for the direct division of such cells into a four-cell stage.

In the above experiments, subsequent development of compressed eggs into normal larvae took place. With frog eggs, the effects of pressure are somewhat more complicated, although in their main essentials they are the same as in *Arbacia* eggs (Rugh and Marsland, 1943; Marsland and Jaffee, 1949). The much greater amount of yolk and lipins in the

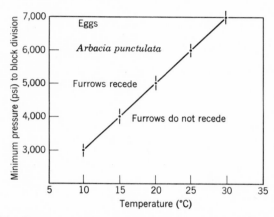

Fig. 9.36. Pressure-temperature relationship for blockage of cell division, and causing recession of furrows, in eggs of *Arbacia punctulata* (Marsland, 1950).

frog's egg than in the sea urchin's egg is apparently responsible for certain differences in its response to increased pressure. The subsequent development of the frog egg after compression sometimes leads to greatly deformed tadpoles (Rugh and Marsland, 1943).

In a critical study of the pressure-temperature relationship of cell division of *Arbacia* eggs, Marsland (1950) has provided quantitative data with particular reference to the strength of the cortical gel and its influence on division. The data, illustrated in Figs. 9.36 and 9.37, lend themselves to unusually simple analysis, as in the following discussion. Figure 9.36 summarizes the behavior of the cells as regards the amount of pressure required to block the cleavage process at different temperatures. Figure 9.37 shows the pressure-temperature relation of cortical gel strength, according to the time required for a standard displacement of pigment granules by centrifugation, under various hydrostatic pressures, at 7,250 × gravity.

Referring to Fig. 9.37, the fact that pressure reversibly decreases the gel strength suggests, in line with our previous discussion (p. 346), that the gel constituents exist in a folded-up, globular, and comparatively non-viscous state, in a concentration that we will designate by C_g, in equilibrium with an unfolded, fibrous state at concentration C_f. Thus

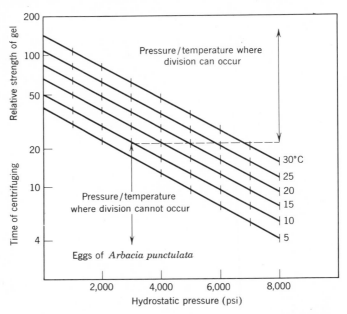

Fig. 9.37.   Pressure-temperature relationship of relative gel strength in the cortical protoplasm of *Arbacia* eggs (Marsland, 1950). Cell division is blocked whenever the gel strength is reduced to about 20% of the value at 25°C and atmospheric pressure.

the total concentration C_0 equals $C_g + C_f$, and $C_g/C_f = K$. For the viscosity η of the solution we may write $\eta = \eta_0 + ac_f + bc_g \approx ac_f$, where a and b are constants. Also, the maximum limiting viscosity η_m, when all the large molecules are in the fibrous form, is $\eta_m = ac_f$. Hence

$$K = \frac{C_g}{C_f} = \frac{\eta_m - \eta}{\eta} = \frac{\eta_m}{\eta} - 1 \qquad (9.23)$$

The fact that the relation between logarithm of viscosity and pressure in Fig. 9.37 is uniformly linear suggests that most of the molecules are in the globular state under the conditions involved, and consequently $\eta_m/\eta \gg 1$, so the number unity in the expression for K can be neglected.

Letting K_0 represent the value of K at no pressure, we have

$$K = K_0 \exp - (p \, \Delta V / RT),$$

and, rewriting (9.23), we have

$$K_0 = e^{-p \, \Delta V / RT} = \frac{\eta_m}{\eta} = e^{-(\Delta F_0 + p \, \Delta V / RT)} \tag{9.24}$$

From (9.24) we can write

$$\eta = \eta_m e^{(\Delta F_0 + p \, \Delta V) / RT} \tag{9.25}$$

Now, from the theory of rate processes (Glasstone, Laidler, and Eyring, 1941) we have

$$\eta_m = \frac{Nh}{V} e^{(\Delta F_0^\ddagger + p \, \Delta V^\ddagger)/RT} \tag{9.26}$$

Thus $\qquad \eta = \frac{Nh}{V} e^{\frac{\Delta F_0 + \Delta F^\ddagger + p(\Delta V + \Delta V^\ddagger)}{RT}} \equiv \frac{Nh}{V} e^{\frac{\Delta F_{01}^\ddagger + p \, \Delta V_1^\ddagger}{RT}} \tag{9.27}$

The quantities N, h, V, $\Delta F^\ddagger$, and $\Delta V^\ddagger$ in (9.26) are Avogadro's number, Planck's constant, the molal volume of flowing unit, the free energy of activation at zero pressure for viscous flow, and increase in volume of the activated over the normal state, respectively. It will be clear from (9.27) that $\Delta F_{01}^\ddagger$ and $\Delta V_1^\ddagger$ are the free energy increase and volume increase in going from the folded, globular form to the activated state for flow of the fibrous gel state. Writing (9.27) in logarithmic form gives

$$RT \ln (\eta V / nh) = \Delta F_{01}^\ddagger + p \, \Delta V_1^\ddagger \tag{9.28}$$

Fitting (9.28) to the data of Fig. 9.37 gives $\Delta V_1^\ddagger = 90$ cc.

It would be of interest to calculate the value of $\Delta F_{01}^\ddagger$. Figure 9 37 shows that, when the viscosity drops below a certain critical value η_c, cell division ceases. Substituting η_c for η in equation (9 28), the equation evidently is of the form

$$p = at + b \tag{9.29}$$

The experimental results give $a = 12.6$ cc $= [RT \ln (\eta_c V / nh)] / \Delta V^\ddagger$ Since $\Delta V^\ddagger = 90$ cc, and V is probably about 100 cc, a value for η_c would enable us to estimate a value for $\Delta F_{01}^\ddagger$. At present, however, η_c is available only in relative terms.

The parallel straight lines in Fig. 9.37 indicate conformity of the data to the simple theory discussed. Under the influence of pressure, viscosity evidently becomes the predominating factor limiting the process of cell division. The fact that nuclear division may occur during the suppression of cytoplasmic division, as mentioned earlier, shows that in some cells at least cytoplasmic cleavage is the more susceptible to pressure. Measurements of total respiration of the eggs, in relation to both pressure and temperature, are not yet available. Under some conditions the oxidative reactions may no doubt become the chief limiting factor as the ultimate source of energy, and it would be interesting to know if they are, like the process of nuclear division, less susceptible than the cortical gel to the action of pressure. Assuming that cytoplasmic cleavage is brought about primarily by a progressively developing layer of stiff gel in some regions more than in others, i.e., at the equator more than at the poles, it seems necessary to postulate an uneven metabolism. The process is understandable if the production of metabolic products in the region of the equator leads to gelation, while the production of metabolic products in the region of the poles leads to solation of the cortical layer. In this event, surface forces would be expected to cause the polar regions to bulge outward, causing a flow of plasmasol away from the cleavage plane. Since gelation presumably involves unfolding of fibrous molecules, the process of cell division again seems to involve molecular changes akin to those of protein denaturation. Various agents influence the change from folded to unfolded states of proteins, and it is natural to suppose that, in the present instance, normal metabolic products are the important agents.

The influence of pressure on the process of fertilization and on nuclear division has been investigated chiefly by Pease. Penetration of the eggs of *Strongylocentrotus purpuratus* by the sperm is prevented by 10,000 psi, although this pressure does not injure the fertilization capacity of the sperm (Pease, 1942). Mitosis and mitotic structures were studied in fertilized eggs of *Urechis caupo*, in which the stages of mitosis can be recognized in the living specimens (Pease, 1942); the spindle structure is particularly prominent in fixed specimens. Under 200 atm of pressure at room temperature the spindle appears to dissolve completely, and the chromosome movement is profoundly retarded. After the release of pressure, new cytasters appear in the cytoplasm, sometimes forming functional half spindles that take part in the movement of chromosomes or whole formative daughter nuclei. The reversible disappearance of the spindle fibers under the pressures involved is suggestive of sol-gel changes similar to those that occur in the cortical gel. At atmospheric pressure, chemical agents such as podophyllin or its derivatives, and colchicine, cause dissolution of the spindle and at certain stages block or reverse cell division (Cornman and Cornman, 1951).

With respect to the chromosomes themselves, the effect of pressure depends in part upon the state of the chromosome and in part upon the amount of pressure. In the early stages of mitosis (early prophase) the chromosomes are "uncondensed" and show a spiral structure. At this stage, pressures up to 1,000 atm seem to have no effect on the meiotic chromosomes of *Tradescantia* pollen mother cells (Pease, 1946). The similarly uncondensed giant chromosomes of *Drosophila* salivary glands show no visible effects as a result of such pressures (Pease and Regnery, 1941). In the late prophase and in the metaphase, however, under relatively low pressures of 200 to 400 atm, there is a tendency of the chromosomes to become sticky, fuse together, and round up. At higher pressures the tendency is accentuated, the chromosomes finally fusing in a single mass with no visible evidence of their individual identities. After pressures of as much as 1,000 atm, which caused virtually complete fusion, have been released, the chromosomes regain their visible identity and approximately normal shape but may remain fused. Because of the failure to unfuse, abnormal distribution of the chromosomal material may occur in the subsequent division stages. A genetic study of pressure-treated germ cells during the process of maturation might reveal some interesting mutations. Abnormalities in the development of tadpoles after the fertilized eggs have been subjected to high pressure during the early cleavage stages (Rugh and Marsland, 1943) probably result from chromosomal aberations.

The fusion and rounding up of chromosomes under moderate pressures seem to correspond to the phenomena of gel liquefaction observed in tentacles of suctorian protozoa, plasmodia of slime molds, and cortex of dividing eggs. In the chromosomes complete liquefaction evidently does not occur, however, since they are able to recover their normal appearance and individuality again at normal pressure. In line with our earlier discussions, portions of the chromosomal constituents, during the condensed phase, apparently exist in the unfolded, gel state and are transformed under pressure to the folded, globular state of less volume and less viscosity. The chromosomes of isolated plant and animal cell interphase (resting) nuclei have been shown to undergo reversible changes at normal pressure under the influence of electrolytes (Ris and Mirsky, 1949), and some probably related phenomena have been observed in the nuclear structures of luminous bacteria (Johnson and Gray, 1949). In isotonic sucrose or glycerol, isolated nuclei stain slightly and homogeneously by the Feulgen method or by methyl green, which are specific for desoxyribonucleic acid. In physiological salt solution the nuclear staining is more intense and confined to the visible, chromatin structure. These differences are accounted for through reversible extensions and condensations of the desoxyribonucleic acid component. In the uninjured, resting nucleus the chromosomes are extended, filling the available space. During the prophase of mitosis, a partial condensation of the chromosomes takes place, and during telophase extension occurs. According to Ris and Mirsky,

(1949), the volume of extended chromosomes in 30% sucrose may be 4 to 5 times greater than their volume in 0.8% salt solution. Reversible extensions and condensations are not observed in chromosomes from which the desoxyribonucleic acid and histone have been removed, nor in the lampbrush chromosomes, which contain very little desoxyribonucleic acid, of frog oöcytes. The extensions and condensations are associated with the desoxyribonucleic acid, and because of the volume change involved it would be interesting to have data concerning the influence of pressure on the isolated nuclei and isolated chromosomes in non-electrolyte and electrolyte solutions.

Since an initial volume increase characterizes the breakdown of ribonucleic acid in the presence of ribonuclease, according to the dilatometric investigations by Chantrenne et al. (1947; Vandendriessche, 1951) it might be anticipated that increased pressure would favor the condensed state of chromosomes. As mentioned above, however, pressure apparently does not affect the early prophase chromosomes or uncondensed giant chromosomes of Drosophila salivary glands. During late stages of mitosis in *Urechis* eggs, on the other hand, high pressures of 680 atm or more cause a reversible loss in staining properties (Pease, 1941), which is perhaps associated with the state of the desoxyribonucleic acid.

Growth

Growth involves diffusion of solutes across membranes, the activity of numerous enzymes, and usually cell division. From the data already discussed, it is obvious that a process so complicated as growth must entail many reactions which are accompanied by changes in volume and which, therefore, are subject to modification by increased pressure. In addition to the influence of pressure on catalytic reactions of enzymes, reversible and irreversible denaturation of proteins, and sol-gel equilibria, whereby both cellular activity and structure may be affected, there is another aspect to be considered with reference to growth, viz., the synthesis of biologically specific macromolecules. The specificity of such molecules depends in some measure upon the manner in which they are folded. It has been pointed out (Eyring, Johnson, and Gensler, 1946) that the asymmetric synthesis of one optical isomer in preponderance over the other, so characteristic of biological reactions, can scarcely proceed without a template mechanism, whereby one molecule furnishes a one- or two-dimensional pattern for the synthesis of a second one like it (cf. also Chapter 1, pp. 23, 30). A folded, globular molecule, however, cannot serve as a template. It must first unfold into a fibrous configuration, under the influence of some factor, presumably metabolic products, which favor the unfolded state of an equilibrium. Because of the volume changes likely to accompany unfolding of a large molecule, pressure would be expected to influence the process of synthesis by the template mechanism, and probably to retard it, since the volume change is likely to be in the direction of an increase. Any factor which would tend to maintain either the folded or unfolded state of the molecules important to synthesis would be expected to retard the process and thereby retard growth. Thus reproduction of enzymes, viruses, genes, or proteins in general would be expected to proceed more slowly under increased pressures. The amount of pressure required to affect the overall rate of growth will depend, of course, on the volume change of the reactions; likewise, the differential effect of pressure on synthesis, as a limiting factor, and on the mechanisms of, say, cell division.

As yet, there are only a few data concerning the influence of pressure on the rate of growth, beyond the early observations of Regnard and Certes, and occasional followers, that pressures of less than 1,000 atm retard microbial multiplication. There is evidence, however, of a pressure-temperature relationship qualitatively resembling that of luminescence, and consistent also with the data pertaining to division of egg cells. For example, the uniform rate of growth and reproduction of colon bacteria (*Escherichia coli*) during the early logarithmic growth phase is slightly retarded by 68 atm of pressure at temperatures below the normal optimum, and slightly accelerated by the same pressure at temperatures above the optimum (Johnson and Lewin, 1946d). The rate of growth (as judged by increase in number of viable cells), however, is particularly sensitive to somewhat higher pressures, of 300 atm or more, and, unlike luminescence, growth is not accelerated by such pressures at temperatures above the optimum; the total effect results in inhibition at all temperatures as shown in Fig. 9.38. The range of temperatures in Fig. 9.38 includes those which bring about disinfection, which becomes evident at about the same temperature that growth ceases. The curves have been drawn as though growth and disinfection were a continuous process, whereas two distinct, overall rate processes are concerned. Disinfection begins at about the temperature that growth ceases because the activation energy for disinfection happens to be higher by just the right amount. Different reactions limit the two processes. Figure 9.38 shows that the rate of disinfection is slower under pressures of both 68 and 340 atm, which also retard the thermal denaturation of proteins.

Observations of the amount of growth in pure cultures of a number of species of bacteria and some yeasts (ZoBell and Johnson, 1949) have shown that the effect of pressures up to 600 atm is modified by temperature in much the way that would be anticipated from the relationships apparent in the pressure-temperature data on enzyme activity and cell division and gelation.   As a rule, the growth-inhibitory effect of pressure is accentuated at low temperatures.   Recent evidence (ZoBell, 1952), however, has indicated that "barophilic" microörganisms from some of the greatest depths of the ocean, where the pressure exceeds 1,000 atm, develop more abundantly in the laboratory under 1,000 atm than under 1 atm at either 2.5° or 30°C.   Among common species of terrestrial bacterial, some grow under moderate pressures at temperatures sufficiently above the normal optimum to prevent growth at atmospheric pressure.   A similar phenomenon is probably involved in enabling the existence of a microbial flora at

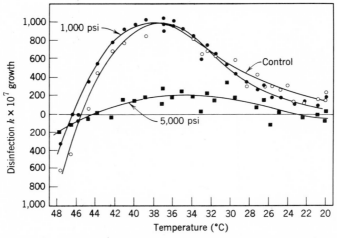

Fig. 9.38.   Pressure-temperature relationship of the rate of multiplication of *Escherichia coli* during the early logarithmic growth phase in a simple culture medium (Johnson and Lewin, 1946d).

excessively high temperatures in deep oil well brines.   Since only the end points have been observed after 1 to 4 days of incubation under different pressures and at different temperatures, the rates of growth during the intervening period largely remain to be investigated, although some data of this kind are now available (ZoBell and Oppenheimer, 1950).

Growth of some marine bacteria without cell division has been found to occur under increased pressure (ZoBell and Oppenheimer, 1950).   As a result, long thread-like cells develop under pressure (Fig. 9.39).   When placed at atmospheric pressure, these threads rapidly divide into the more familiar short rods of the species, recalling the rapid cleavage of *Arbacia* eggs after a period of suppressed cleavage under pressure (Marsland, 1938).   In ordinary cultures of typically small, rod-shaped species of bacteria, a few long thread forms are commonly encountered, and spontaneous variation sometimes leads to a marked increase in such forms (Reed, 1937). Average cell size in cultures newly inoculated is generally much greater than in older ("resting") cultures (Henrici, 1928). In some instances, e.g., the luminous bacterium, *Achromobacter fischeri*

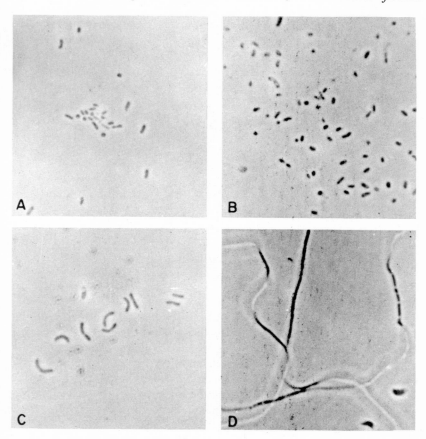

Fig. 9.39. Morphology of *Serratia marinorubra*, photographed in wet preparation by dark phase contrast, shortly after removal from culture tubes in which they had been incubated for 4 days at 23°C, under pressures of 1 atm (A), 200 atm (B), 400 atm (C), and 600 atm (D), respectively (ZoBell and Oppenheimer, 1950).

(Johnson and Gray, 1949), very young cultures under conditions favorable for rapid growth are comprised almost entirely of cells many times longer than those characterizing the stage of maximum growth. Small concentrations of penicillin, less than those causing an arrest of multiplication, lead to the growth of giant cells, long filaments, and other atypical forms of various species of bacteria, indicating a differential effect of penicillin on the processes of growth and cell division (Gardner, 1940; Gardner and Chain, 1942; Ross, 1946; Chain et al., 1949; Fleming et al., 1950). Among the interesting examples are those of the anaerobe, *Clostridium welchii*, as well as aerobic organisms, *Proteus vulgaris* and others, which, growing in the presence of small amounts of penicillin, produce long thread forms (Fig. 9.40) resembling those of *Serratia marinorubra* growing under 600 atm of pressure (Fig. 9.39). Possibly the same reaction (a sol-gel equilibrium?) is affected by penicillin at atmospheric pressure, and in absence of penicillin at high pressures.

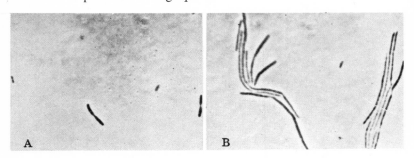

Fig. 9.40. *Proteus vulgaris*, photographed by phase contrast (A) 1½ hr and (B) 4 hr after seeding on agar containing 5 μg per cc of penicillin at room temperature (Fleming et al., 1950).

Addition of surface tension depressants, e.g., sodium oleate (Frobisher, 1928) to the medium also leads to the production of long and slender cells in species ordinarily composed of short rods (colon bacteria) and to an increase in size, at the expense of numbers, in species composed of spherical cells (staphylococci). Numerous species of both Gram positive and Gram negative bacteria are capable of growth without cell division at sufficiently low concentrations of magnesium ions in the medium (Webb, 1948, 1949a,b,c; 1951a,b; Nickerson, 1951).

The influence of pressure on the rate of growth of viruses has, as yet, been studied only with respect to bacteriophage (Foster and Johnson, 1951), using T2 and T7 phages against *E. coli* (Delbrück, 1946). The results are of interest particularly because the effects here must be primarily on enzyme reactions and synthetic processes. The bacterial host cells after infection do not reproduce at atmospheric pressure. Moreover, at 34° to 38°C, a pressure of 5,000 psi greatly reduces the rate of reproduction of normal cells of the same organism (Johnson and Lewin, 1946d). It can be safely assumed that under still higher pressures the reproduction and probably the growth of both infected and uninfected cells is essentially nil.

By an appropriate technique (Delbrück and Luria, 1942) the growing cells of the host can be infected with an average of 1 bacteriophage particle each. After a latent period whose length is characteristic of the virus and certain conditions of the experiment, the infected cells burst and liberate many new virus particles. During the latent period there is essentially no change in number of virus particles outside of the cells. The average number of particles liberated per cell at the end of the latent

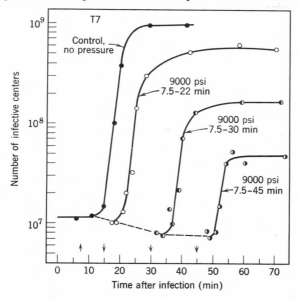

Fig. 9.41. Influence of pressure on the one-step growth of bacteriophage T7 against *E. coli* B (Foster and Johnson, 1951); 9,000 psi were applied to all specimens 7 min after infection and released, on different specimens, at the times indicated by the arrows pointing downward in the figure.

period, under given conditions, is characteristic of the virus. Thus, with bacteriophage T2 at 35°C, nutrient broth being used as the culture medium for the bacteria, the latent period is about 23 min, and during the following 5 min or so the infected cells burst, liberating an average of more than 100 new virus particles per cell. With T7, under corresponding conditions, the latent period is only 14 min, and a similarly large yield results when the cells burst.

With the method employed, pressure could not be applied immediately after infection. It could be applied, however, within 7 min after infection and subsequently released at any time desired. Figure 9.41 illustrates the results obtained with virus T7.

The data of Fig. 9.41 show that, when high pressure is applied at about the middle of the latent period and then released at the end of the normal latent period of a control at atmospheric pressure, the burst occurs after a slight delay and the yield is somewhat reduced.   When the pressure is maintained for successively longer intervals of time, a burst always occurs shortly after the pressure is released, and the yield becomes progressively less.   Also, under continued maintenance of pressure, the original titer decreases, indicating that the particles in some of the infected cells are destroyed.   The process of burst itself is not affected by pressure, according to the results of experiments on macroscopic clearing (lysis) of cells multiply infected with T7.   The most significant fact, from the present point of view, is that under pressure the development of the phage is reversibly blocked.   Although this effect might be attributed to the inhibition of enzyme reactions, it is reasonable to believe that it should be attributed in part to the inhibition of synthesis by a template mechanism (cf. Chapter 1, pp. 23, 30).   Thus, if the unfolding of globular molecules is accompanied by a volume increase, as would be expected, pressure would tend to keep them in the folded state and so prevent their serving as a template in the synthesis of a new molecule of the same biologically specific structure and configuration.   The pressure inhibition of growth of normal cells is no doubt due, in part, to the same effect.   Unfortunately, the minimum amount of pressure required to block the growth of bacteriophage has not been determined, nor its relation to temperature and other environmental factors.

Various factors, e.g., the presence of a drug such as urethan at atmospheric pressure, reversibly inhibit the growth of bacteriophage.   Drugs of this type evidently may influence the equilibrium between folded and unfolded states of proteins, including enzymes, and so influence both the catalytic activity of enzymes and more complex biological processes such as growth and reproduction of molecules and cells.   In synthetic reactions, inhibition would be expected to result in part from the action of urethan in keeping the globular molecules in an unfolded state.   The net result on the template mechanism would be the same as that of pressure in keeping the globular molecules in a folded state.   The action of urethan and other drugs, in relation to concentration, temperature, and hydrostatic pressure, is discussed in the next chapter.

Action of Inhibitors
in Relation to Concentration,
Temperature, and Hydrostatic Pressure

The human body is a chemical and physical problem, and these
sciences must advance before we can conquer disease.

Henry A. Rowland, "The Highest Aims of the
Physicist" (first presidential address of the American Physical Society, 1899)

Physically, a human being is a colony of bacteria, a mass of muscles,
a network of neurones, a collection of collagen—according to one's point
of view. The differences, other than functional, concern the details and
organization of fundamentally similar mechanisms. Consider, for
example, the basic aspects of two such seemingly unrelated phenomena as
luminescence and consciousness. Each has an optimum temperature.
Energy is supplied to each primarily through the oxidation of glucose.
Some enzymes with chemically identical prosthetic groups are involved in
both processes. Elimination of the supply of glucose to bacteria, e.g., by
washing the cells, dims luminescence. Elimination of the supply of
glucose to the brain, e.g., by an excess of insulin, dims consciousness.
Asphyxia blocks both processes. Small concentrations of ether, alcohol,
chloroform, urethan, urea, barbitals, or any of numerous other "narcotics"
reversibly or irreversibly inhibit the activity of either process. Luminescence, however, is far easier to measure than consciousness. The
addition of drugs to purified extracts of *Cypridina* or to living cells of
luminous bacteria immediately affects the intensity of luminescence in a
reversible manner, or leads to a rate process of irreversible destruction,
depending upon the agent and the conditions. In bacteria the steady
state level of light intensity is thus changed to a new steady state level of
light intensity (Fig. 10.1), or to a progressively decreasing level, which can
be quantitatively recorded with ease, accuracy, and convenience. Effects
on the extracted system can likewise be accurately recorded, and they
provide evidence of the site of action. It is again appropriate and

369

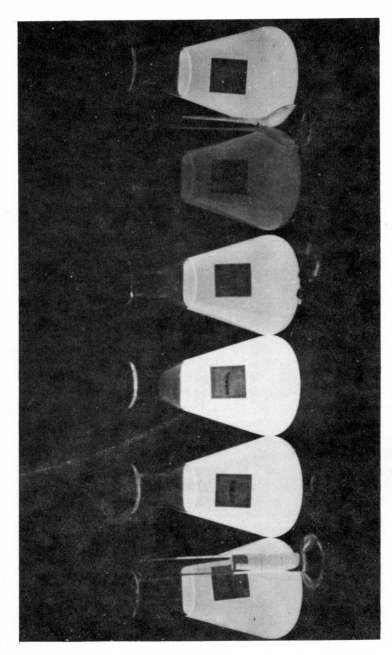

Fig. 10.1. Flasks of corresponding suspensions of luminous bacteria, *Photobacterium phosphoreum*, photographed by their own light. From left to right, small amounts of the following drugs were added to the respective flasks: 1, alcohol; 2, aspirin; control (no drug); 4, novocaine; 5, ether; and 6, sulfanilamide.

instructive to discuss the quantitative results obtained in studies of luminescence as an approach to the understanding of the action of inhibitors or drugs on diverse biological processes.

Site of action

In undertaking to analyze the effects of drugs or other agents on a physiological process, it is always desirable, though not always readily possible, to establish the site of action. Presumptive evidence that a given inhibitor acts upon some particular enzyme system is had when it can be shown that (1) the inhibitor acts upon an extracted system, known to be important in the physiological process, and that (2) it produces a quantitatively similar effect under corresponding conditions of concentration, temperature, pressure, etc., *in vitro* and *in vivo*. This evidence, however, is only presumptive unless, of course, it can also be shown that no other intracellular system is affected by similar concentrations of the inhibitor—a difficult problem indeed. In the living cell it is not unlikely that more than one system is susceptible to the effects of the inhibitor, and the one which is primarily responsible for the observed effects may be unknown.

Whenever a number of simultaneous, as well as consecutive, reactions are capable of influencing an overall rate, the inhibition of some of these reactions may result in an acceleration of the overall rate. For example, bacterial luminescence in a medium that is deficient in oxidizable substrates is increased by the addition of small amounts of cyanide (Van Schouwenberg, 1938). This effect probably depends upon a competition between the luciferin-luciferase system and the "dark" respiratory pathways for the limited amount of hydrogen donators; the latter pathway is more sensitive to cyanide, and, when it is inhibited by cyanide, a larger supply of hydrogen donators becomes available to the luminescent system, resulting in an increase in luminescence. Another interpretation, however, is reasonable here, viz., the stimulation of proteolysis by cyanide, a process which would also result in increasing the amount of available hydrogen donators. In this instance, cyanide would not be expected by a corresponding mechanism to cause any increase of luminescence in the extracted and purified system whose rate does not necessarily depend upon the availability of reducing substances (cf. discussion in Chapter 7).

There are examples, however, where cyanide increases the activity of more or less highly purified enzymes *in vitro*, either by combining with traces of heavy metal impurities, thereby abolishing their inhibitory effects, or under circumstances whereby S—S groups in a catalytically inactive form of the enzyme molecule are changed to SH groups characteristic of the catalytically active form (e.g., papain or cathepsin; Purr, 1935a,b). The complications which may arise from the "stimulating" effect of substances which are ordinarily thought of as inhibitors, and of some of the mechanisms concerned in this phenomenon, will be considered presently. For the moment, it is important only to note the fact—axiomatic among biologists—that the analysis of the action of an inhibitor on a physiological process is beset with many possible complications and requires a highly critical approach, with more than one line of evidence.

In luminescence as in other enzyme reactions, the inhibition may be either reversible or irreversible. The former type causes a retardation of light production, but does not of itself affect the total amount of light produced under given conditions, with a given amount of luciferin. The latter type reduces the total amount of light when the inhibitor combines only with the substrate and the specific rate constant of the reaction is not affected. Cyanide, for example, evidently combines irreversibly with purified *Cypridina* luciferin, reducing the total light emitted, as compared to a cyanide-free control, by rendering a portion of the luciferin unavailable to oxidation (Giese and Chase, 1940). Quenching agents (cf. p. 153) reduce the total amount of light by affecting the efficiency of luminescence. The data concerning the action of sodium azide (Chase, 1942) indicate that its effect is primarily one of quenching. Azide reversely reduces the total amount of light but does not affect the velocity constant of the reaction.

Among the group of substances which retard the rate of luminescence without reducing the total light of *Cypridina* extracts are sulfonamide compounds and narcotics such as urethan. Inhibitions of bacterial luminescence are caused by similar concentrations of the same drugs at temperatures near the optimum of the species concerned. Presumably, therefore, the physiological action involves the corresponding enzyme system. Furthermore, since the inhibition in either case is readily reversible, it follows that the combination between the drug and the enzyme system is an equilibrium reaction. Thus there is evidence regarding the general site and general nature of the inhibitory reaction. These facts, however, provide no evidence as to whether the drug combines with the luciferin or with the luciferase, nor the nature of the changes in either molecule through which light emission is retarded.

It is often assumed that, by varying the relative concentrations of enzyme and substrate in the presence of a given concentration of inhibitor, the site of action will be revealed by the kinetics of the reaction. This assumption holds for some conditions but not for others. In general, there are two cases: (A) the concentration of inhibitor that must be added in order to obtain a measurable effect is greatly in excess of the concentration of either the enzyme or the substrate; (B) the required concentration of inhibitor is of the same or of a lower order of magnitude than that of one or both of the components of the uninhibited system. Under the circumstances of case A there is no possibility of distinguishing by kinetic data which one of the two reactants, enzyme or substrate, combines with the inhibitor. The proof is as follows (Johnson, Eyring, and Williams, 1942).

Let us consider the two alternatives in case A, namely that the inhibitor combines only with the enzyme (case A1) and that the inhibitor combines only with the substrate (case A2). Let E_0 represent the total amount of enzyme, and S_0 the total amount of substrate. During the course of the reaction, A_0 remains constant under conditions in which no destructive reactions involving the enzyme take place. The concentration of substrate S changes as it is used up and as it is converted to a product S_1. In case A1 the inhibitor X enters into an equilibrium K_E with the enzyme E and (case 2), the inhibitor X enters into an equilibrium K_S with the substrate S. In either case, the result of the equilibrium is assumed to retard the reaction. Let n represent the number of molecules of X that combine per molecule of E or of S, respectively. The expressions for the rate V of the enzyme-catalyzed reaction in the two alternative situations are then derived as follows:

Case A1	Case A2
$E + nX \rightleftharpoons^{K_E} EX_n$	$S + nX \rightleftharpoons^{K_1} SX_n$
$\dfrac{(EX_n)}{(E)(X)^n} = K_E$	$\dfrac{(SX_n)}{(S)(X)^n} = K_S$
$(S_0) = (S) + (S_1)$	$(S_0) = (S) + (S_1) + (SX_n)$
$(E_0) = (E) + (EX_n)$	$(S_0) - (S_1) = (S) - (SX_n)$
$\quad = (E) + K_E(S)(X)^n$	$\quad = + K_S(S)(X)^n$
$\dfrac{(E_0)}{(E)} = 1 + K_E(X)^n$	$\dfrac{(S_0) - (S_1)}{(S)} = 1 + K_S(X)^n$
$(E) = \dfrac{(E_0)}{1 + K_E(X)^n}$	$(S) = \dfrac{(S_0) - (S_1)}{1 + K_S(X)^n}$
$V = bk'(S)(E)$	$V = bk'(S)(E)$
$V = \dfrac{bk'[(S_0) - (S_1)](E_0)}{1 + K_E(X)^n}$	$V = \dfrac{bk'[(S_0) - (S_1)](E_0)}{1 + K_S(X)^n}$

$$(10.1)$$

Equations (10.1) show that here there is no way to distinguish through the kinetics of the reaction between a reversible combination of the inhibitor with the enzyme and with the substrate. If the combination is only with the substrate, the inhibitor dissociates in accordance with the law of mass action as the substrate is used up, and the kinetics remains first order. The rate of the enzyme-catalyzed reaction in relation to time may be formulated from either case of equation (10.1). Thus, using the customary notation, we may let a represent the total amount of S, or S_0, and x the amount of S_1. Then

$$V = \frac{dx}{dt} = \frac{bk'[(S_0) - (S_1)](E_0)}{1 + K_{E \text{ or } S}(X)^n} \tag{10.2}$$

$$\ln(a - x) = \ln a - \left(\frac{bk'(E_0)}{1 - K_{E \text{ or } S}(X)^n}\right) t \tag{10.3}$$

or $\qquad \ln(a - x) = \ln a - kt \tag{10.4}$

Equation (10.4) is the integrated form of the usual first order equation, $dx/dt = k(a - x)$. A straight line of slope k is obtained when the logarithm of $(a - x)$ is plotted against time. The slope is less whether the inhibition takes place according to case A1 or according to case A2.

Under the circumstances of case B, there are three ways in which the relative concentrations of enzyme, substrate, and inhibitor may be involved with the inhibitor always in a concentration of the same or of a lower magnitude than one or both of the other reactants: (case B1) with the substrate concentration in great excess over that of the enzyme; (case B2) with the enzyme concentration in great excess over that of the substrate; and (case B3) with the enzyme and substrate concentrations of the same order of magnitude. The usual situation is case B1, wherein the substrate concentration is in great excess over that of the enzyme, at least at the start of an enzyme-catalyzed reaction. Case B2 probably occurs normally under certain conditions within cells, and it can be set up with extracted systems *in vitro*. For example, in the oxidation of elementary sulfur by the sulfur bacterium, *Thiobacillus thioxidans*, the water solubility of the substrate is so extremely low that, at any time, the concentration of the substrate in solution is reasonably much less than that of the enzyme. With extracted oxidative systems, e.g., those involving cytochrome, the relative concentrations of the different components may be readily varied in the study of inhibitor action (cf., for example, Keilin, 1930; Keilin and Hartree, 1938; Stotz et al., 1937–38; Haas, 1944). Case B3 probably also occurs normally within cells, where one enzyme system acts as the substrate for another system in a series of consecutive oxidations, as in the transfer of hydrogen or electrons from substrate to codehydrogenase to flavoprotein to cytochrome to cytochrome oxidase to oxygen (cf. Ball, 1944). With extracted systems it may occur among proteolytic enzymes, where the substrate has a molecular weight as high as or higher than that of the enzyme.

In all the case B situations, it is possible to distinguish, by means of the kinetics, the enzyme or substrate as the site of inhibitor action. Thus, if the substrate concentration is in excess over that of the enzyme, and the reaction rate is retarded by inhibitor concentrations much lower than that of the substrate, it must be the enzyme that is affected. For a measurable effect on the reaction rate by a combination between the inhibitor and the substrate, the inhibitor concentration must be of the same magnitude as that of the substrate. Whenever the inhibitor concentrations are of the same or of lower magnitude than the molecules with which it combines, the amount of inhibitor in solution is reduced by the reaction between the inhibitor and its combining site. The concentration of inhibitor that is added, therefore, is altered, and if it is effective in low concentrations it may be practically completely removed from solution, e.g., as in the inhibition of bacterial luminescence by naphthoquinones (Spruit and Schuiling, 1945) or by mercuric chloride (Houck, 1942). A similar situation with extracted systems, where the proportion of enzyme and substrate can be varied at will, permits titration of the inhibitor against its combining molecules, the kinetics of the reaction being used as an indicator. The kinetic formulations can be derived, but, whenever it is necessary to allow for the amount of inhibitor removed from solution, or to include the amount of enzyme combined with the substrate in the expression for the total amount of enzyme present in the free and combined states, the algebra becomes more complicated and the formulations sometimes extremely sensitive to experimental measurements of rates. It is only under these circumstances, however, that the site of action can be identified by means of the kinetics.

Although frequently more direct evidence than kinetic data, e.g., evidence from absorption spectra, is needed to distinguish between the enzyme and its substrate as the site of action of a reversible inhibitor, a probable distinction can sometimes be made on general considerations. The inhibitory effects of substances such as urethan, urea, etc., are so general, and sometimes so clearly related to their protein-denaturing action, that they probably affect the protein component of an enzyme system. It follows that, except with proteolytic enzymes, where both components of the system are proteins, this effect would be on the enzyme. With proteolytic enzymes the effect would still probably be on the enzyme, since it is usually the denatured form of the substrate that is digested, and agents which promote the denaturation of the substrate would be expected to aid, rather than to hinder, the digestion. The inhibitory effects of substances whose chemical structure is closely related to that of the normal substrate are very likely, *a priori*, to occur by a competitive mechanism

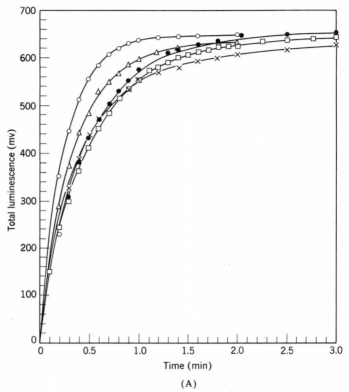

(A)

Fig. 10.2A. Total luminescence as a function of time, after adding 0.5 cc of *Cypridina* luciferase to 10 cc of 0.1 M phosphate buffer, pH 6.8, containing 0.05 cc of a butyl alcohol solution of luciferin (curve with hollow circles), or to a corresponding luciferin solution containing also 0.03 M sulfanilamide (solid circles), 0.001 M sulfapyridine (triangles), 0.0006 M sulfathiazole (crosses), or 0.25 M urethan (squares), respectively, at room temperature.

even when the relative concentrations of enzyme, inhibitor, and substrate are not known, as in intracellular systems. Here, by virtue of the structural similarity, the inhibitor combines with the enzyme in the same manner as the normal substrate, while by virtue of the slight structural dissimilarity the inhibitor is not acted upon by the enzyme. In effect, the amount of active enzyme is thereby reduced (cf. Welch, 1945; Wooley,

1947, 1951; Sexton, 1950; Martin, 1951). Examples of this type of inhibition are numerous. Sulfanilamide appears to act through such a mechanism in preventing the growth of bacteria and other microörganisms by competing with *p*-aminobenzoic acid, or a closely related substance

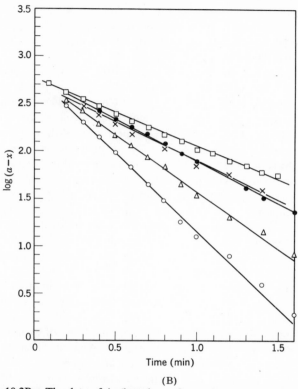

(B)

Fig. 10.2B. The data of A plotted as a first order reaction, assuming that the total amount of light (in millivolts) is proportional to the initial concentration of luciferin, *a*, and that the decreasing intensity with time is proportional to the rate at which *a* is converted to the product *x*. (From Johnson and Chase, 1942.)

that is presumably the normal substrate, prosthetic group, or key component of some as yet unidentified system (Woods, 1940). The evidence is based primarily upon the ability of small amounts of *p*-aminobenzoic acid to overcome the growth-inhibitory effects of large amounts of sulfanilamide. There are, however, a number of different "non-specific" antagonists of the sulfanilamide inhibition of growth (cf. Kohn, 1943), and *p*-aminobenzoic acid by itself is an inhibitor of growth in concentrations somewhat higher than those required for inhibitions by sulfanilamide alone; no simple theory accounts for all the facts now known (cf. Henry, 1944; Northey, 1948; Martin, 1951; Wooley, 1951). In luminescence both sulfanilamide and *p*-aminobenzoic acid are inhibitory, and no antagonistic effects (other than with respect to growing cultures of luminous bacteria; Johnson, Eyring, Steblay, et al., 1945) of the two drugs have been found. It is possible that both "compete" with the luciferin or inactivate a prosthetic group of the luciferase. The kinetic analyses are consistent with this view.

Identification of the luminescent system itself as the site of action of sulfonamides and of urethan on luminescence rests largely upon experiments with *Cypridina* extracts (Johnson and Chase, 1942). Figures 10.2A and 10.2B illustrate the reduction in velocity constant of the reaction by several sulfonamides and by urethan, respectively, with a given amount of highly purified luciferin and partially purified luciferase. The total amount of light is not appreciably affected, and the inhibition is reversible. The most convincing evidence of reversibility is that the addition of luciferase to luciferin in high concentrations of urethan results in no visible light emission. On addition of water to the inhibited system, however, luminescence appears at once, with reduction in concentration of urethan. Furthermore, corresponding dilutions of a control and of a urethan-containing reaction mixture cause the velocity constants of the reaction to approach the same value.

Much of the discussion in this chapter will be illustrated by data obtained with respect to bacterial luminescence. Investigations of the process in living cells carries with it some unavoidable uncertainty concerning the site of action, but from the point of view of experimentation it carries with it some distinct advantages. Among other things, the experimental material is virtually unlimited, in contrast to the limitations imposed by the precious supply of the *Cypridina* system and the tedious procedure for its purification. Moreover, in bacterial cells under favorable conditions the luminescent reaction is in a steady state (pp. 179, 183), so that each reading of luminescence intensity provides a measure of the rate, whereas in the first order decrease in intensity of the extracted system comparison of rates must always be made on the basis of slopes of the lines. The evidence for the site of action in bacteria depends largely upon comparison of the effect of the same inhibitory agent on the reaction in *Cypridina* extracts. The evidence that one system, rather than several, is affected in bacteria resides in the simplicity of the analysis, and the conformity of the data to a well-defined quantitative theory. The same agent, of course, often affects more than one system; for example, urethan reduces both the rate of oxygen consumption and the intensity of luminescence, and also retards or prevents reproduction of the cells.   Here again, however, luminescence is a favorable process to study, for it is much more sensitive to many inhibitors than is, for example, the rate of total oxygen consumption.   Figure 10.3 illustrates the differential effect of sulfanilamide on the intensity of luminescence and on rates of total oxygen consumption of three species of bacteria.   During an equivalent

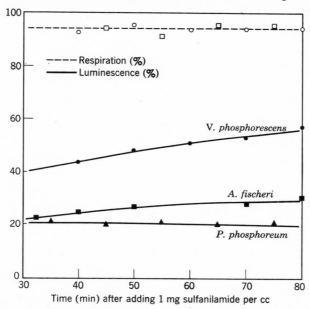

Fig. 10.3.   Influence of 100 mg of sulfanilamide per 100 cc of solution on the rate of respiration (broken line) and the intensity of luminescence (solid lines) in three species of luminous bacteria at their respective optimal temperatures in phosphate-buffered sodium chloride solution, pH 7.3; *Photobacterium phosphoreum*, 15.5°C (triangles); *Achromobacter fischeri*, 28°C (squares); and *Vibrio phosphorescence*, 32°C (circles).   Sulfanilamide was added at zero time (Johnson and Moore, 1941).

period of time, plate counts of the number of viable cells suspended in a solution containing 2.5 times the concentration used for Fig. 10.3 showed that viability was unaffected by sulfanilamide.

The actual amount of inhibition by sulfanilamide or other drugs depends, of course, upon the concentration of inhibitor added, in ways that will be discussed shortly.   It may also depend upon hydrostatic pressure and upon temperature, to extents determined by the mechanism of the reaction.   It is important to realize at the outset that, whenever there is a temperature dependence of the amount of inhibition caused by a given concentration of a drug, this dependence is related primarily to the temperature-activity curve of the specific process in the particular species, and under the particular experimental conditions concerned. This is analogous to the similar effects of impurities in lowering by comparable amounts the freezing point of liquids, which melt at quite different temperatures. By the same token, it is related also to the pressure-activity curves of the specific process of the organism and experimental

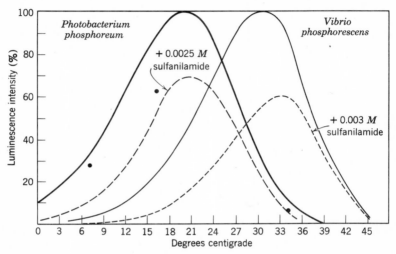

Fig. 10.4. Influence of temperature on the intensity of luminescence of suspensions of *Photobacterium phosphoreum* (heavy solid line) and of *Vibrio phosphorescens* (lighter line) and in corresponding suspensions of the same respective species in phosphate-buffered salt solutions containing small amounts of sulfanilamide (heavy and light broken lines). (From Johnson, Brown, and Marsland, 1942a.)

conditions. The temperature relationships in the effects of sulfanilamide on the luminescence of two species of bacteria, in which the optimum temperature for this process differs by about 10°C, are illustrated in Fig. 10.4.

The changes in intensity throughout the range of temperatures shown in Fig. 10.4 are reversible on either side of the respective optima, provided that the cells are maintained only momentarily at the relatively high temperatures. Since the amount of inhibition caused by sulfanilamide decreases with rise in temperature, it follows that the inhibition is partially reversible by heat, just as it is partially or completely reversible by centrifuging the cells and resuspending them in a drug-free salt solution. In both cases, the inhibitor dissociates from its site of action. The relative position of the normal temperature-activity curve and the corresponding curve for the inhibited systems in two different species is particularly clear in Fig. 10.4. The amount of sulfanilamide added to either species is nearly the same, i.e., 0.0025 and 0.003 M, respectively. It would obviously not be very meaningful to conclude that bacterial luminescence is inhibited by a certain per cent in the presence of these concentrations of the drug at some temperature without taking into account how the inhibition varies quantitatively in relation to the specific temperature-activity curve. For example, at 25°C, 0.0025 M sulfanilamide reduces the relative intensity of luminescence in *Photobacterium phosphoreum* from about 78 to 59, or by about 25 per cent. At the same temperature, 0.003 M sulfanilamide reduces the relative intensity of luminescence in *Vibrio phosphorescens* from about 78 to 30, or by about 62 per cent. At 30° the inhibitions amount to approximately 23 and 46 per cent, respectively, differing by a factor of 2. At the respective optimal temperatures for luminescence under the conditions concerned, however, the per cent inhibitions are much more nearly the same: approximately 30 per cent in *P. phosphoreum* at 20°C, or 40 per cent in *V. phosphorescens* at 31°C. A more precise basis than per cent inhibition at some specified temperature is needed for understanding the action of any inhibitor.

One is naturally led to the concept of a reduced temperature for these systems much as one thinks of a reduced temperature in equations of state for pure liquids. Thus for each system, instead of using as abscissa the actual temperatures, we may use the reduced temperature, i.e., the actual temperature divided by the temperature of the uninhibited maximum. In the same way we plot intensities not on an absolute scale but on a relative scale, taking the uninhibited maximum intensity as 100 per cent. If we plot various systems on scales reduced in this manner, the data are much more appropriately comparable, as has been found with the reduced equations of state for pure liquids. In biology the position of such things as temperature optima depends upon the ΔH and $\Delta H^{\ddagger}$ of the catalytic rate and denaturation equilibrium respectively (see p. 219), just as the boiling points of pure liquids depend upon their respective heats of vaporization. Systems involving more than one ΔH which are not in fixed proportions have no unique reduced temperature scale. Consequently in biological systems frequently involving many ΔH's the reduced temperature scale is much less precisely applicable than for pure liquids. From this point of view it is apparent that Bĕlehrádek's (1935) biological zero temperature—the low temperature at which the activity of a biological process ceases—is useful, but it is not the same as the reduced temperature scale discussed above.

The influence of concentration on the quantitative effect of a drug, at constant temperature and pressure, provides some useful information, but other parameters are important in reaching an understanding of its mode of action on any given system. For a long time it has been generally recognized that an enzyme, an antibody, or various types of conjugated proteins, such as hemoglobin, can be altered in at least two distinct ways: (1) by a specific poisoning of the active group, or (2) by a non-specific denaturation of the protein (Willstätter and Rohdewald, 1934; Clark, 1937). An example of the first type is the combination of carbon monoxide with the heme moiety of hemoglobin, or the combination of cyanide with the iron of cytochrome oxidase. With simple protein enzymes whose activity does not involve a prosthetic group, e.g., many hydrolases such as trypsin, pepsin, and invertase, specific poisoning may take place by combination of a substance at the site where the natural substrate or substrates normally combine. This is an aspect of "competitive inhibition," whether or not the inhibitory substance is structurally related to the normal substrate. Examples of the second of the above types are the inactivations resulting from narcotics such as urethan, urea, and other substances which promote reversible and irreversible denaturation of proteins, although these substances can act also in the manner of the first type. In some instances the distinction between these two types, which for convenience of discussion we will refer to as type I and type II, respectively, can be made with considerable assurance through kinetic studies. The theory and formulations that have been worked out with the aid of bioluminescence are given in the following paragraphs.

Analysis of reversible inhibitions of the first type (type I)

As indicated above, a type I inhibition involves the combination of a substance with an enzyme system in a manner that is independent of the denaturation of the protein. The substance may combine with or in place of the prosthetic group, or at the surface of the protein in place of the normal substrate, but as a result of the combination the structure of the protein itself is assumed to be essentially unaltered. Consequently, the reversible denaturation reaction with equilibrium constant K_1 is not influenced, and, since the inhibitor combines with groups that are not involved in this denaturation equilibrium, it combines with the native and reversibly denatured forms to the same extent. Let (X) represent the molar concentration of inhibitor, combining in a ratio r with the native form (A_n), as well as with the reversibly denatured form (A_d) of the enzyme in an equilibrium reaction with constant K_2. Let I_1 represent the rate of the reaction in absence of the inhibitor, and I_2 the rate in the presence of a given molar concentration of inhibitor. We then have (Johnson, Eyring, and Williams, 1942):

$$I_1 = bk'(L)(A_n) \qquad \text{(from equation 7.60)} \qquad (10.5)$$

$$A_n \rightleftharpoons A_d \qquad \frac{(A_d)}{(A_n)} = K_1 \qquad (A_d) = K_1(A_n) \qquad (8.2)$$

$$rX + A_n \overset{K_2}{\leftrightharpoons} A_nX_r \qquad\qquad rX + A_d \overset{K_2}{\leftrightharpoons} A_dX_r$$

$$\frac{(A_nX_r)}{(A_n)(X)^r} = K_2 \qquad\qquad \frac{(A_dX_r)}{(A_d)(X)^r} = K_2$$

$$(A_nX_r) = K_2(A_n)(X)^r \qquad (A_dX_r) = K_2(A_d)(X)^r = K_1K_2(A_n)(X)^r$$

$$(A_0) = (A_n) + (A_d) + (A_nX_r) + (A_dX_r)$$
$$= A_n + K_1(A_n) + K_2(A_n)(X)^r + K_1K_2(A_n)(X)^r$$

$$A_n = \frac{A_0}{1 + K_1 + K_2(X)^r + K_1K_2(X)^r}$$

$$I_1 = \frac{bk'(L)(A_0)}{1 + K_1} \qquad \text{(from equation 8.4)} \qquad (10.5a)$$

$$I_2 = \frac{bk'(L)(A_0)}{1 + K_1 + K_2(X)^r + K_1K_2(X)^r} \qquad (10.5b)$$

$$\frac{I_1}{I_2} = \frac{1 + K_1 + K_2(X)^r + K_1K_2(X)^r}{1 + K_1}$$

$$= 1 + K_2(X)^r \qquad (10.6)$$

$$\frac{I_1}{I_2} - 1 = K_2(X)^r = (X)^r e^{-\Delta F_2/RT} = (X)^r e^{-\Delta H_2/RT}\, e^{\Delta S_2/RT}$$

$$\ln\left(\frac{I_1}{I_2} - 1\right) = r\ln(X) - \frac{\Delta F_2}{RT} = r\ln(X) - \frac{\Delta H_2}{RT} + \frac{\Delta S_2}{R}$$

$$= r\ln(X) - \frac{\Delta F_{0_2}}{RT} - \frac{p\,\Delta V_2}{RT} \qquad (10.7)$$

Equation (10.7) follows from the mechanism assumed and provides a means of testing the conformance of data from experiments to this type of mechanism. If the data conform, a linear relation is obtained by plotting on the ordinate log $(I_1/I_2 - 1)$ against log X on the abscissa.

The slope of the line gives the value of r in equations (10.7), i.e., the ratio of inhibitor to enzyme molecules in the complex that is formed. For brevity and convenience of discussion, we will adopt the definition

$$\Gamma_1 \equiv \frac{I_1}{I_2} - 1 \equiv \frac{I_1 - I_2}{I_2} \equiv \frac{\text{fraction inhibited}}{\text{fraction uninhibited}} \equiv \frac{I}{U} \qquad (10.8)$$

The subscript 1 with Γ indicates that the inhibition is of the first type.

The ratio of the fraction inhibited over the fraction uninhibited is obviously the reciprocal of the expression "per cent uninhibited over per cent inhibited," or U/I, introduced by Fisher and Öhnell (1940) for analyzing the quantitative relation between concentration of cyanide and frequency of embryonic heart beat. This expression has since been applied by Fisher and others to various physiological processes and enzyme reactions (e.g., Armstrong and Fisher, 1940; Fisher and Stearn, 1942; Chase, 1942; Houck, 1942) as a means of determining the dissociation constant of the inhibitor according to the law of mass action at constant temperature and pressure. In their treatment,

$$\log (U/I) = \log K - a \log (N) \qquad (10.9)$$

is equivalent to

$$2.303 \log (I/U) \approx 2.303 \log K - 2.303r \log (X)$$

using the notation of equations (10.7) and (10.8). Fisher and others have shown that the numerical value of a varies widely among different processes, although K was not analyzed. Analysis of K requires temperature and pressure data, as discussed presently.

When a single equilibrium is involved, and the mechanism does not change with temperature, the variation in $\ln \Gamma_1$ with $\ln$ molar concentration of inhibitor is a series of parallel lines, with different intercepts on the ordinate. These lines coincide if there is no variation in Γ_1 at a given concentration of inhibitor, at different temperatures. In general, however, it would be expected that Γ_1 will increase with concentration and decrease with rise in temperature. By the mechanism assumed, heat will dissociate the complex formed between the inhibitor and the enzyme system. The heat of reaction in this equilibrium is obtained by plotting $\ln \Gamma_1$ against the reciprocal of the absolute temperature. The slope of the line is $\Delta H_2/R$. When plotted in this manner, a series of parallel lines results for different specified concentrations of the inhibitor.

The sulfanilamide inhibition of bacterial luminescence conforms fairly closely to this type of mechanism. The data are illustrated in Figs. 10.5, 10.6, and 10.7. The first of these figures shows the measured variation in luminescence intensity as a function of temperature, in suspensions of cells containing various concentrations of sulfanilamide. The per cent inhibition is obviously greater at low temperatures, and it decreases as the temperature approaches and exceeds the optimum. A practically complete elimination of the inhibition should result at a sufficiently high

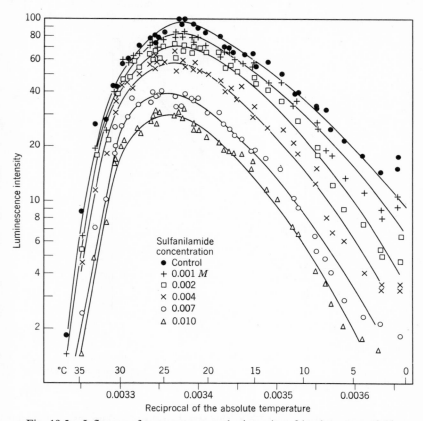

Fig. 10.5. Influence of temperature on the intensity of luminescence of *Photobacterium phosphoreum* suspended in phosphate-buffered sodium chloride solution containing various concentrations of sulfanilamide (Johnson, Eyring, Steblay, et al., 1945).

temperature, provided that no new mechanism becomes involved, but in the neighborhood of the normal optimum the reversible denaturation K_1 begins to reduce the net rate of the reaction. Because of the rapid increase in K_1 with the rise in temperature it is not possible to observe a practically complete elimination of the inhibitory effects of the drug; the overall rate is reduced so much by the increase in K_1 that the decrease in

K_2 becomes obscured.   As a result of these changing values of K_1 and K_2 with rise in temperature, there is a slight shift of the observed optimum, in the presence of the drug, toward higher temperatures.

Figure 10.6 shows the analysis of the data of Fig. 10.5 with respect to concentration of sulfanilamide.   The lines are satisfactorily straight, but there is a tendency for the slope to decrease with higher temperatures,

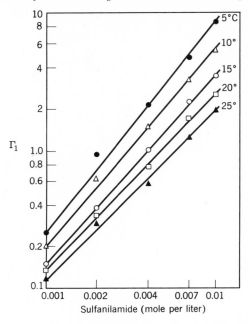

Fig. 10.6.   Analysis of the data of Fig. 10.5, in accordance with equations (10.7) and (10.8), for the relation between inhibition (Γ_1) and concentration of inhibitor at different temperatures (Johnson, Eyring, Steblay, et al., 1945).

changing from about 1.5 at 5°C to nearly 1 at 25°C.   The two facts, that the slope of 1.5 is not an integer and that the slope varies with temperature, show that more reactions are involved than equation (10.7) takes into account.   Presumably some additional reaction or reactions that contribute to the luminescent process are inhibited by sulfanilamide at low temperatures, but with rise in temperature these inhibitions practically disappear, and at 25°C a single system is predominantly affected, by a 1-to-1 combination with the drug.

Figure 10.7 shows the analysis of the data of Fig. 10.5 with respect to temperature.   The slopes of the essentially parallel straight lines indicate a heat of reaction of about 12,000 cal.

The formulation of equations (10.7) and (10.8) is useful in the analysis of competitive inhibitions, wherein the inhibitor evidently competes with the substrate for the active site of the enzyme. A particularly clear example is that of the competition between the structurally related succinate and malonate molecules for the succinic dehydrogenase of *B. coli* (*Escherichia coli*) (Quastel and Wooldridge, 1928). Here the amount of

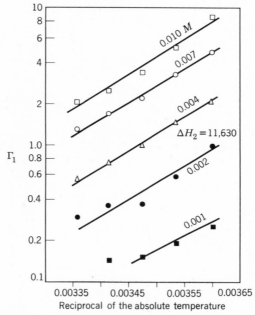

Fig. 10.7. Analysis of the data of Fig. 10.5, in accordance with equations (10.7) and (10.8), for the relation between inhibition and temperature, at various concentrations of sulfanilamide (Johnson, Eyring, Steblay, et al., 1945).

inhibition depends upon the ratio of concentrations of the two species of molecules, as illustrated in Figs. 10.8 and 10.9. In order to interpret Fig. 10.9 we refer to the Michaelis-Menton equation (7.54) whence, with a slight rearrangement, and in the case where k_3 is much smaller than k_2, we obtain

$$\Gamma_1 = \frac{V_{max}}{V} - 1 = \frac{K_m}{(S)} \qquad \ln \Gamma_1 = -\ln S - \frac{\Delta F_m}{RT} \qquad (10.8a)$$

Applying this equation to the data shown in Fig. 10.9, we get the line with negative slope in Fig. 10.10. The analysis shown in Fig. 10.10 indicates that the molecules compete on a 1-to-1 basis, i.e., one molecule

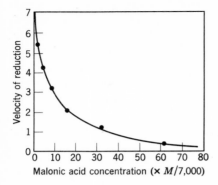

Fig. 10.8. Influence of various concentrations of malonate on the velocity of anaerobic methylene blue reduction by washed cells of *B. coli* in the presence of $M/140$ succinate (Quastel and Wooldridge, 1928).

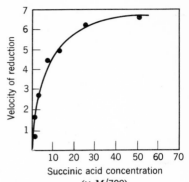

Fig. 10.9. Influence of $M/700$ malonate on the velocity of methylene blue reduction by washed cells of *B. coli* in the presence of various concentrations of succinate (Quastel and Wooldridge, 1928).

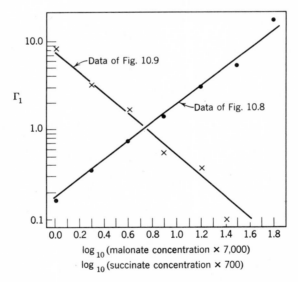

Fig. 10.10. Analysis of the data shown in Figs. 10.8 and 10.9, respectively, in accordance with equations (10.7), (10.8), and (7.54). For this purpose it was necessary to assume for Fig. 10.9 an uninhibited velocity of methylene blue reduction, at some concentration of succinate sufficient to eliminate, in effect, any influence of the malonate present. A value of 6.8, just slightly in excess of the highest velocity in the figure, was chosen as a reasonable approximation. The slope of each of the lines is unity.

of inhibitor X or of substrate S combines per enzyme molecule E.   Temperature data with respect to this inhibition would be interesting but are not available.   Since the concentrations of the two substances are of the same magnitude, however, the free energies of reaction are close.   Thus, if the inhibitor combines with a free energy ΔF_1 with the enzyme, while ΔF_2 is the corresponding free energy for the combination of substrate with enzyme, we have the two equations

$$\frac{(XE)}{(X)(E)} = e^{-\Delta F_1/RT} \quad \text{and} \quad \frac{(SE)}{(S)(E)} = e^{-\Delta F_2/RT}$$

At the concentrations at which inhibitor and substrate are competing on equal terms for the enzyme, $(XE) = (SE)$, and we must have $(X)/(S) = e^{(\Delta F_1 - \Delta F_2)/RT}$.   Now $(X)/(S)$ will be unity if $\Delta F_2 = \Delta F_1$.   In the general case, since at room temperature $RT = 600$ cal, it follows that, if $(X)/(S) = 10^X$, then $\Delta F_1 - \Delta F_2 = 1.38X$ kcal.   Thus a difference of 1.38 kcal in their free energies of combination will require that the more weakly combining substance be ten times as concentrated to achieve the same degree of combination with the enzyme.

The reversible effects of pH

The influence of pH is of especial interest, both because all enzyme systems exhibit a range of optimum pH for their activity under specified conditions (temperature, buffer composition, etc.) and because the velocity of the luminescent reaction in particular would be expected to vary with pH.   For example, in the luminescence of phthalic hydrazides, acidity appears to favor the un-ionized form of the molecule which emits light, whereas alkalinity favors the rate of the intermediate reactions. The net result is that the intensity of chemiluminescence is greater in alkaline than in acid solutions (p. 162).   Oxidative enzyme systems in general would be expected to be susceptible to the influence of pH whenever the rate of the reaction is limited by the degree of ionization of the oxidizable group or groups on the substrate or prosthetic group.   It would be expected also that the activity of the protein catalyst will, in general, change with ionization.   The problem of distinguishing, through kinetic data, which component of the system is responsible for an observed effect is the same problem as distinguishing between substrate and enzyme as the site of action of an inhibitor.   Moreover, since there are many possible reactions through which ions could influence the overall rate of an enzyme system, especially in living cells, complications are anticipated in any analysis based on a simple theory.   Furthermore, the rate-limiting reaction will be likely to change at the extremes of temperature, or of concentration of ions, or of hydrostatic pressure, or of other variables.

On the assumption that the influence of pH occurs through the same type of action as the influence of sulfanilamide, i.e., independently of the reversible thermal denaturation of the enzyme, the formulation for application to data is derived in the same manner. The data show that in considerable measure this assumption is justified, but there is also evidence of complicating reactions, in particular with respect to the influence of temperature in the alkaline range of pH. Using the same notation as previously, we will now let K_H represent the equilibrium constant for the dissociation of hydrogen ions, and K_{OH} the equilibrium constant for the dissociation of hydroxyl ions. Let m represent the number of hydrogen ions, and n the number of hydroxyl ions combining with an enzyme molecule. We then have for the sum of the various forms of the enzyme

$$A_0 = A_n + A_d + A_n(H^+)^m + A_n(OH^-)^n + A_d(H^+)^m + A_d(OH^-)^n$$

$$A_0 = A_n + K_1(A_n) + K_H(A_n)(H^+)^m + K_{OH}(A_n)(OH^-)^n$$
$$+ K_1 K_H(A_n)(H^+)^m + K_1 K_{OH}(A_n)(OH^-)^n$$

$$A_n = \frac{A_0}{1 + K_1 + K_H(H^+)^m + K_{OH}(OH^{-n}) + K_1 K_H(H^+)^m + K_1 K_{OH}(OH^-)^n}$$

$$I_1 = bk'(A_n)(L) = \frac{bk'(A_0)(L)}{1 + K_1}$$

$$I_2 = \frac{bk'(A_0)(L)}{1 + K_1 + K_H(H^+)^m + K_{OH}(OH^-)^n + K_1 K_H(H^+)^m + K_1 K_{OH}(OH^-)^n}$$

$$\left(\frac{I_1}{I_2} - 1\right) = K_H(H^+)^m + K_{OH}(OH^-)^n$$

or $$\ln \Gamma_1 = m \ln (H^+) + n \ln (OH^-) - \frac{\Delta F_H}{RT} - \frac{\Delta F_{OH}}{RT} \quad (10.10)$$

At the optimum temperature in phosphate-buffered sodium chloride of neutral pH, the addition of acid or alkali immediately reduces the intensity of bacterial luminescence. If appropriate amounts of alkali or acid are added soon to restore the pH to neutrality, the intensity quickly returns practically to its former level, unless the pH change was very great in either direction or was prolonged. At a very acid or very alkaline pH, a rate process of destruction is evident. It occurs at a rate that depends upon the pH and the temperature. The influence of pH on this rate will be discussed in connection with irreversible inhibitions. The influence of temperature has not been fully studied.

Figure 10.11 illustrates the largely reversible variation in intensity of luminescence of *Photobacterium phosphoreum* with pH at 22°C and atmospheric pressure. Equation (10.10) accounts satisfactorily for the data except in the most alkaline range where additional inhibitory reactions become important. Here I_1 to an excellent approximation is represented by the intensity or rate at the optimum pH, and I_2 the intensity at a

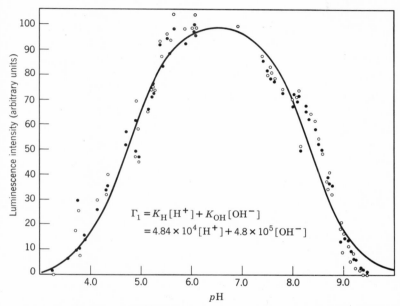

$$\Gamma_1 = K_H[H^+] + K_{OH}[OH^-]$$
$$= 4.84 \times 10^4[H^+] + 4.8 \times 10^5[OH^-]$$

Fig. 10.11. Luminescence intensity of *P. phosphoreum* as a function of pH in phosphate buffered sodium chloride solution at 22°C. The solid line is the theoretical curve calculated in accordance with equation (10.10) as given in the figure (Johnson, Eyring, Steblay, et al., 1945). Intensity recorded 1 min (solid circles) and 2 min (hollow circles) after adding acid or alkali.

different pH. Strictly, I_1 should be taken as the light intensity at zero concentration of (H$^+$) and (OH$^-$) but at the maximum of the curve the ions have usually changed the intensity negligibly. In either the more acid or more alkaline range, the relation between ln Γ_1 and log hydrogen or hydroxyl concentration, respectively, is a straight line of slope approximately equal to one. This relationship is illustrated in Fig. 10.12 for the acid range; a similar relationship holds for the alkaline range.

The data available with respect to the pH activity curve of *Cypridina* extracts do not extend through quite as wide a range of pH as illustrated in Fig. 10.11 for bacterial luminescence, but the curve is qualitatively

similar and the *p*H optimum occurs at nearly the same point, i.e., close
to neutrality (Fig. 10.13; Chase, 1948b). When the data of Fig. 10.13
are plotted in the manner of Fig. 10.12, the relationship is again linear,
on either side of the *p*H optimum, but the slopes of the lines have a
numerical value very close to 1.75. In view of chemical evidence that
purification of *Cypridina* luciferin is accompanied by certain changes in

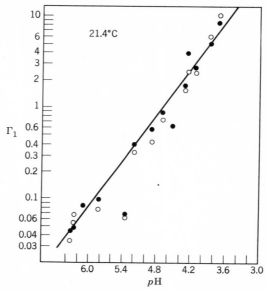

Fig. 10.12. Relation between ln Γ_1 and *p*H in the luminescence of *P.
phosphoreum* at 22°C. Small amounts of concentrated acid or alkali were
added to a rapidly stirred suspension of the cells in phosphate-buffered
sodium chloride solution of *p*H 7.0. The change in intensity of luminescence
was recorded 1 min (solid circles) and 2 min (hollow circles) after the acid
was added, and the *p*H of the solution was then determined by glass electrode
(Johnson, Eyring, Steblay, et al., 1945).

its properties of solubility (p. 128), it seems likely that the difference in the
slopes of the lines as compared to those for bacterial luminescence are to
be attributed to alterations in the *Cypridina* luciferin during the purification process. Thus, rather than a single hydrogen or hydroxyl ion, an
average of one and three-fourths hydrogen or hydroxyl ions becomes
accessible for dissociation.

The quantitative relationship shown in Fig. 10.13 is somewhat modified
by the proportion of sodium and potassium ions in the buffer. The
curves differ when only the sodium salts, only the potassium salts, or
mixtures of both salts of phosphoric acid are used in the buffer system.

Because of these differences Chase did not undertake to analyze the data according to equation (10.10), on the grounds that the cations "must distort the true pH-activity curve by an unknown amount." The meaning of "true," however, is a matter of definition. The measured pH activity curve is true, within the limits of experimental accuracy, for the particular conditions of the experiment. We have found that the observed points of Fig. 10.10 can be accurately described by equation (10.10). A close fit is obtained by this equation with the following constants:

$$\Gamma_1 = 10^{10.44}(H^+)^{1.76} + 10^{13.58}(OH^-)^{1.72} \qquad (10.11)$$

Other data show that these constants vary with different buffer salts.

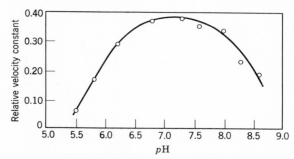

Fig. 10.13. Relation between pH and the relative velocity of the luminescent reaction of *Cypridina* extracts in KH_2PO_4–Na_2HPO_4 buffers at 24° and 26°C (Chase. 1948b). The smooth curve was drawn by inspection. A theoretical curve which fits the observed points with equal accuracy can be calculated by means of equation (10.10).

Significance of the buffer system and companion ions

To a greater or lesser extent, the pH activity curves of enzyme systems will be expected to vary with the buffer salts and other ions present in the solution. Even though only the cation, say, is to combine with the specific site on the protein, still the negative ion must be dragged into the new environment, or else an electrostatic bond between ion pairs must be broken. Thus, even though the anion is cast in the lowly rôle of "camp follower," how well it is accommodated will still considerably affect the degree of cation-protein combination. The studies of Steinhardt and his associates (Steinhardt, 1941, 1942; Steinhardt, Fugitt, and Harris, 1940, 1941; Steinhardt and Zaiser, 1950) on the relation between pH and the combination of various acids and bases with wool protein are especially significant, for they bear not only directly on the interpretation of pH activity curves of enzyme systems, but also on the relation between pH and the activity of various drugs.

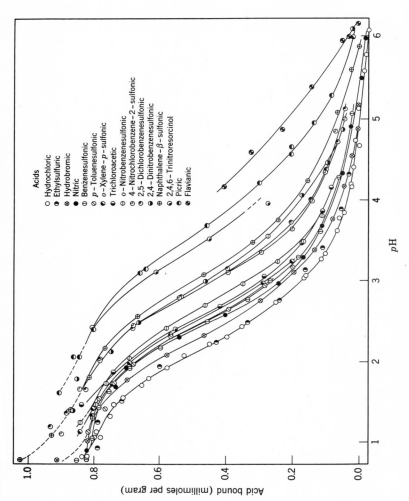

Fig. 10.14. Combination of sixteen different acids with wool protein as a function of pH at 0°C (Steinhardt, Fugitt and Harris, 1941; Steinhardt, 1941).

Figures 10.14 and 10.15 give impressive illustrations of the extent to which the amount of acid or of base that is bound to wool protein at constant temperature and pressure is influenced by the companion anions or cations respectively. The quantitative theory has been extensively

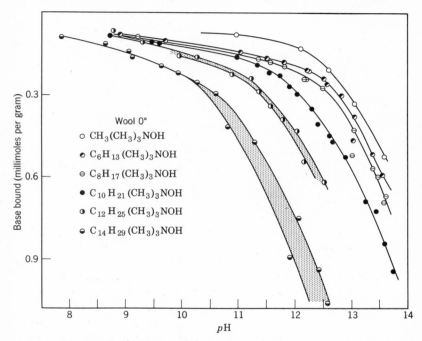

Fig. 10.15. Relation between pH and the combination of six homologous alkyltrimethylammonium hydroxides with wool protein at 0°C (Steinhardt and Zaiser, 1950). The shaded area in the curve at the left represents the range of uncertainty of the equilibrium positions resulting from the failure to attain complete equilibrium in the long periods of time (15 to 17 days) allowed for the two highest homologs. The affinity of the cations for the protein increases, as does the affinity of anions, with increasing molecular dimensions. The evidence indicates that the binding of large, organic cations as well as organic anions is brought about largely by van der Waals forces.

discussed by Steinhardt et al. and cannot be considered at length here; the details may be found in the original papers. It is worth while, however, to point out explicitly some general implications with reference to the effects of physiologically active, ionizable drugs. As an example, we will consider briefly the action of dinitrophenol and related compounds.

Certain nitro- and halophenols influence both the activity of various enzyme systems *in vitro* and *in vivo* and of complex physiological processes in cells, tissues, and whole organisms (Field, Martin, and Field, 1933; Ehrenfest and Ronzoni, 1933; Tainter and Cutting, 1933; Johnson, 1934; Shoup and Kimler, 1934; Krahl, Keltch, and Clowes, 1940; Haas, Harrer, and Hogness, 1942; Hotchkiss, 1944; Winzler et al., 1944; Clifton, 1946; Loomis and Lipmann, 1948; Peiss and Field, 1948; Pierce and Field, 1949; Clowes, 1951). In whole cells, tissues, or organisms, the net result in some instances is a very pronounced increase in activity, or in others a potent inhibition, depending upon the biological process and the conditions of the experiment. For example, the rate of total oxygen consumption may be accelerated several fold by relatively low concentrations of 2,4-dinitrophenol, of the order of 10^{-6} to 10^{-5} M. In higher animals, including man, small amounts of this substance may so increase the rate of oxidative metabolism and heat production that the body temperature rises to a fantastic extent; in extreme cases the animal is literally burned to death by the excessive heat of his own metabolism.

Such "stimulating" effects probably result, in general, from the retardation of competing reactions. On the other hand, it seems a bit curious that the excessively fast rate of oxidation and heat production should continue even after the body temperature of the organism has risen to a point well above that which would normally be considered the optimum. Ordinarily, a decline in activity of the enzyme systems would be expected at temperatures beyond the normal optimum, because of both a reversible and an irreversible denaturation of the catalysts. Evidently, the catalysts primarily responsible for heat production either have a higher temperature optimum than one would ordinarily suppose, or they are stabilized against thermal denaturation by the presence of dinitrophenol, possibly in the manner that serum albumen is stabilized by various fatty acids, acetyl tryptophan, or other substances (p. 269). If the latter possibility is correct, dinitrophenol also would have the remarkable property of opposing protein denaturation.

Fundamentally, the problem is still largely a matter of inhibition, and even the processes which are stimulated by relatively low concentrations of the drug are inhibited by somewhat higher concentrations. Stimulation of a complex process, by the inhibition of reactions which competitively limit the overall rate, depends upon the appropriate differential sensitivity of the catalysts. A differential sensitivity of various systems to the drug, under the same conditions, may also result in the simultaneous inhibition of one overall process and stimulation of another, e.g., cell division of *Arbacia* eggs may be blocked while oxygen consumption is increased several fold.

There are two more or less distinct ways in which dinitrophenol and related compounds modify the activity of biological processes. In the first way the un-ionized drug combines with the limiting system; in the second, the ionized form combines with the limiting system. Clowes (1951) and Krahl and Clowes (1938) have obtained evidence that the inhibitory effects on respiration and on cell division of sea urchins' eggs depend upon the concentration of the un-ionized form of the molecule inside the cell. The stimulation of respiration, however, is correlated with the concentration of the ionized form in the intracellular aqueous phase. Whether the combination involves primarily the ionized or the un-ionized molecule, it will be governed not only by the affinity of the particular system, but also by the pK of the particular drug and the particular pH of the chemical environment. In addition, where whole cells rather than extracted enzyme systems are concerned, the observed effect will be modified by the phenomena of permeability. The form that penetrates is the un-ionized molecule. Its penetration will therefore depend again upon the pH of the solution and the pK of the compound. In permeability and in combining properties of the un-ionized molecule, lipid solubility is also a factor.

There is yet another aspect of the pH activity curve in the *Cypridina* reaction that is of general interest, and that finds a parallel in the action of dinitrophenol on other systems. This aspect concerns the relation between pH and the total light produced. The mechanisms involved have been discussed (Chapter 7, p. 158). Fundamentally, the total light depends upon the rates of various competing reactions that result in 'ight emission on the one hand, or in the non-luminescent oxidation of luciferin or in the quenching of excited luciferin molecules on the other hand. The influence of pH and of anions such as chloride or iodide on the total light represents effects on the competing reactions. The influence of pH and of cations, such as sodium and potassium ions, on the velocity of light production without affecting the total luminescence represents effects on a common pathway antecedent to the competing reactions. The analogous situation, with reference to the action of dinitrophenol, is briefly as follows.

The washed cells of bacteria or other microörganisms ordinarily do not oxidize simple substrates to completion. For example, the oxidation of glucose, lactate, or acetate by the colon bacterium proceeds to not more than two-thirds or three-fourths of completion, as judged by the amount of oxygen consumed and carbon dioxide produced (Cook and Stephenson, 1928). The remaining one-third or one-fourth is apparently assimilated through reactions other than oxidative degradation, in a manner which, for the colorless alga, *Prototheca zopfii*, may be represented as follows (Barker, 1936):

$$CH_3COOH + O_2 \rightarrow CO_2 + H_2O + (HCHO) \qquad (10.12)$$

Now, in the presence of $M/600$ sodium azide or of $M/4,000$ 2,4-dinitrophenol, the normally incomplete oxidation of various substrates by various organisms goes to completion, but the rate of oxidation is only slightly affected (Clifton, 1937a,b). The evidence indicates that, at the temperatures used, these concentrations of azide or of dinitrophenol block the reactions leading to assimilation. The inhibition of assimilation, leading to complete oxidation of the substrate, does not necessarily involve the action of azide and of dinitrophenol on precisely the same reaction (Reiner and Spiegelman, 1947), just as the influence of various agents (including temperature) on the total luminescence produced by a given amount of *Cypridina* luciferin does not necessarily involve the same competing reaction. The independent variation of rate of reaction and of products of reaction where both common and competitive pathways are involved is undoubtedly of very widespread significance in biology. It is not only the basis for the observed effects of many drugs on physiological processes, but it also constitutes a fundamental part of the mechanisms controlling the normal physiology of organisms and the complicated phenomena of growth and differentiation of cells, tissues, and organs.

In *Cypridina* luminescence, Chase (1948b) is inclined to the view that the relation between pH and the velocity of the reaction represents an immediate effect of the ions on the enzyme. A final conclusion in both *Cypridina* and bacterial luminescence depends upon knowledge of the reaction kinetics for inhibitor concentrations known to be within the same or a lower magnitude than the substrate.

Relation of the pH activity curve to temperature

The pH activity curves of bacterial luminescence have been more fully investigated in relation to temperature and pressure than have those of *Cypridina* extracts. The results indicate that under some conditions the effects of pH directly concern the protein. In the acid range the influence of temperature on the inhibition of bacterial luminescence by hydrogen ions is remarkably similar to the influence of temperature on the inhibition by sulfanilamide. The per cent inhibition is greater at low temperatures and it decreases with increases in dissociation as the temperature is raised (Fig. 10.16). The data of Fig. 10.16 are analyzed in Fig. 10.17 on the assumptions that the luminescence intensity at pH 6.92 is essentially uninhibited by hydrogen ions (or by hydroxyl ions) at this pH, and that the inhibition is of the first type, in accordance with equation (10.10). The results of the analysis, through the range in pH concerned, justify these assumptions. The slopes of the lines in Fig. 10.17 indicate a heat of reaction of about 14,000 cal, which is very close to the 12,000 cal found for the sulfanilamide inhibition at pH 7.

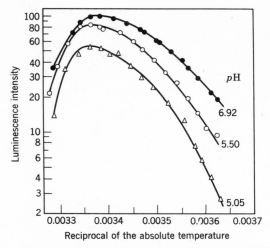

Fig. 10.16.   The temperature activity curve of luminescence of *Photobacterium phosphoreum* suspended in phosphate-buffered sodium chloride solutions of different pH in the acid range (Johnson, Eyring, Steblay, et al., 1945).

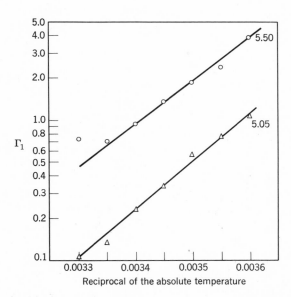

Fig. 10.17.   Analysis of the data of Fig. 10.16 in accordance with equation (10.10).   The slopes of the lines indicate a heat of reaction of about 14,000 cal (Johnson, Eyring, Steblay, et al., 1945).

In the alkaline range (Fig. 10.18) the temperature relations are more complicated than in the acid range, although it seems that only one hydroxyl ion is involved in the equilibrium at 22°C (p. 391). At relatively low temperatures the inhibition tends to be less, and to increase progressively with rise in temperature. At very high pH the optimum of the pH

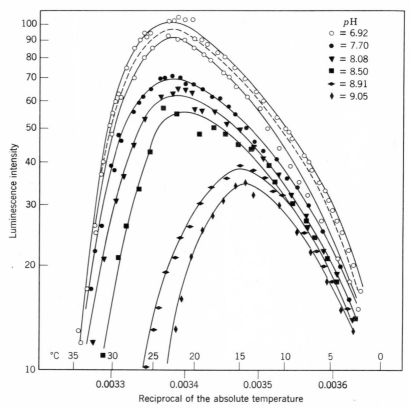

Fig. 10.18. The influence of temperature on luminescence of *P. phosphoreum*, suspended in phosphate-buffered sodium chloride solution of various pH in the alkaline range (Johnson, Eyring, Steblay, et al., 1945). The two curves at pH 6.92 were obtained with portions of the same cell suspension, about $1\frac{1}{2}$ hr apart; the dotted line is taken as a mean value.

activity curve is lowered by as much as 7° or 8°C, and the application of pressure causes the luminescence to increase (Fig. 9.10, p. 316). This pressure effect, however, occurs only in the most alkaline solutions, where the observed pH activity curve at 22°C drops more sharply with increase in pH than the theoretical curve of Fig. 10.11 predicts. Here additional reactions, irreversible as well as reversible, are evidently involved.   Equation (10.10) is therefore inadequate to account for the data over a wide range of temperature and pressure, although it does account satisfactorily for most of the *p*H activity curve at 22°C and atmospheric pressure.

In certain respects the effects of alkaline *p*H on bacterial luminescence are similar to those of various inhibitors of the second type, discussed in the next section.   Before discussing this second type of inhibitor, however, it is worth while to consider briefly some relationships found with respect to processes more complex than luminescence, e.g., growth.   Growth rates are of fundamental interest, but accurate and critical data suitable for analysis are unfortunately surprisingly scarce.   Although results of empirical interest have frequently been obtained, for example, by inoculating cultures of bacteria into media containing various concentrations of a given drug at one or a series of temperatures, and then judging the effect of the drug on the basis of the relative amount of growth in the cultures after some hours or days of incubation, such observations usually do not lend themselves to precise interpretations.   Experiments of this kind have indicated that the bactericidal effects of sulfanilamide are greatly increased at temperatures above the normal optimum (White and Parker, 1938; Lawrence, 1940), but the interpretation is obscure.   During the intervening period of incubation the reaction rates of many systems change with changes in the chemical environment with respect to *p*H, concentration of nutrients, concentration of metabolic products, etc., and also with changes in the physiological state of the cells.   To arrive at any simple interpretation it is necessary to vary only one factor at a time, keeping all others as constant as feasible, and then to measure the rate of the process. It is all but impossible to do this over a long period of time during the growth of a bacterial culture except by very complicated procedures.

The *p*H and temperature relationships of a drug's action on growth are governed by the same factors that govern the action of dinitrophenol on various processes, discussed above, and are again related, at the molecular level, to the phenomena discussed in connection with the combination of cations and anions with wool.   Thus, sulfonamide compounds enter into equilibrium combinations with various proteins, such as those of blood plasma, in a manner that depends upon *p*H and to a relatively small extent upon temperature (Davis and Wood, 1942; Davis, 1943), as would be expected from the foregoing discussions.   Certain correlations between the structure and the *p*K of various derivatives of sulfanilamide have been discussed with reference to the growth-inhibitory properties of the derivatives (Bell and Roblin, 1942).   Klotz (1944) has advanced a quantitative theory accounting for the effects of sulfonamides, in solutions of various *p*H, on bacterial growth, assuming that the action results from a reversible combination between the basic form of the drug and the neutral form of a protein in accordance with the law of mass action.

The available data concerning the influence of temperature on the sulfonamide inhibition of growth are not so extensive as would be desired for analysis. The data of Lee, Epstein, and Foley (1943b), however,

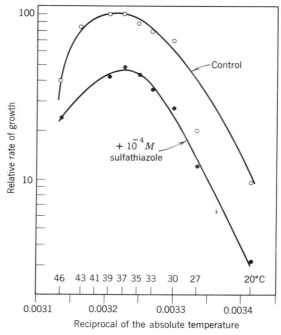

Fig. 10.19. Influence of temperature on the growth of *Streptococcus pyogenes* as measured by optical density of the cultures in a simple medium with and without $10^{-4}\,M$ sulfathiazole (data replotted from Fig. 1, p. 246, of Lee, Epstein, and Foley, 1943b).

indicate that the per cent inhibition in rate of growth of *Streptococcus pyogenes* by sulfathiazole in a simple medium is decreased with rise in temperature, especially in the region near the optimum (Fig. 10.19).

When the data of Fig. 10.19 are plotted in the manner of Fig. 10.17, the points are somewhat scattered, probably indicating that in the experiments concerned the quantitative effects of the drug on rate of growth were complicated by a number of reactions. A reasonable straight line, drawn by inspection through the available points, however, has a slope equivalent to 6,000 cal, as compared to 12,000 cal in luminescence.

The determination of cell numbers at frequent intervals over short periods of time, during the early logarithmic growth of a culture when the population of cells is much too small to measure by optical density, provides a simpler basis for analysis.   The action of sulfanilamide has not been studied in this manner, but there are data with respect to temperature and pressure (pp. 232, 364) and also quinine and pH.   A sudden change in pH at various temperatures immediately affects the rate of growth.   During the ensuing 60 to 90 min there is sometimes a period of readjustment in rate recalling phenomena such as the changing rate of ciliary beat following the application or release of pressure (p. 323).   The fundamental mechanism responsible for the changing rates is probably very similar, the determining factor in this case being pH rather than pressure.   Within 90 to 180 min after the pH is changed, the rate of growth has usually reached a new steady state.   Figure 10.20 shows the influence of temperature on the rate of bacterial reproduction during the 90- to 180-min period in media of different pH and in the presence of quinine.   In all cases the control was a culture in the corresponding medium at 37°C and pH 6.9; the changes in pH and temperature were made with portions of this culture.

The data illustrated in Fig. 10.20 probably represent the effects of pH and of quinine on more than a single reaction.   The action of quinine, in particular, evidently involves several reactions which may limit the rate of reproduction, depending upon the conditions (cf. Johnson and Lewin, 1946c).   Qualitatively, the influence of acid (pH 4.9) on reproduction is similar to the influence of acid and of sulfanilamide on luminescence, in that the inhibition is relatively great at low temperatures and decreases as the temperature is raised.   In acid solution (pH 4.9, 5.9) quinine has little effect, but in nearly neutral solution (pH 6.9) it causes an inhibition which is affected by temperature in much the same manner as the inhibition of luminescence by quite alkaline pH (Fig. 10.18).   The action of quinine here, as in various other biological processes, evidently depends upon the free alkaloid base (Crane, 1921; Rona and Block, 1921; Rona and Reinicke, 1921; Rona and Takata, 1922; Rona and Grassheim, 1923; Rona and Nicolai, 1927; Mayeda, 1928).   At the molecular level the same considerations apply as in the interpretation of the various actions of dinitrophenol or of sulfanilamide, and of the combination of organic acids or bases with wool protein.

The temperature relation illustrated in Fig. 10.20 for the action of a single concentration of quinine at pH 6.9 is of general interest, for there are many examples of increasing potency of a drug with rise in temperature, other factors remaining the same, as discussed later (pp. 408–422; 463–468).   The temperature relationships of penicillin effects are of particular interest because the mechanism of action of this important drug has not been clearly elucidated. There is evidence, however, that the inhibition of growth and the microbicidal effects of penicillin have a fairly high temperature coefficient (Hobby et al., 1942; Bigger, 1944; Lee, Foley, and Epstein, 1944; Lee and Foley, 1945; Eagle and Musselman, 1944). To

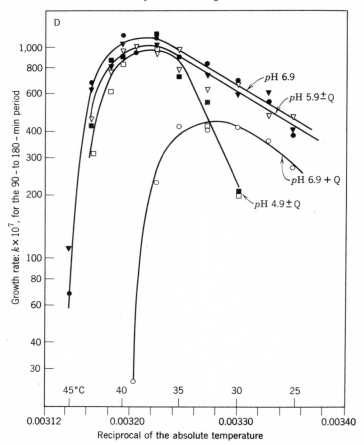

Fig. 10.20. The influence of temperature on the rate of reproduction of *Escherichia coli* in media of different *p*H and in the presence of 0.0007 M quinine (Q), according to the method described in the text (Johnson and Lewin, 1947).

some extent the influence of temperature on penicillin action is correlated with the influence of temperature on the rate of growth, i.e., rapidly growing microörganisms are much more susceptible to the action of the drug than are the same organisms in non-reproducing or "resting" stages. This is not a unique correlation, inasmuch as small concentrations of phenol act similarly. The meaning of this correlation is not clear; it does not hold at temperatures above the normal optimum, where the potency of both penicillin and phenol continue to increase with rise in temperature, although the rate of reproduction decreases. It seems probable, therefore, that at the molecular level penicillin acts through a mechanism similar to, though more specific than, numerous other substances which promote reversible and irreversible denaturation of enzymes and other proteins, as discussed in the following section.

Analysis of reversible inhibitions of the second type (type II)

The second type of inhibition referred to on p. 382 concerns primarily the protein component of the enzyme system and is related to the reversible thermal denaturation. The inhibitor U is assumed to combine in a manner that promotes the change from the active, native form of the enzyme A_n to the inactive, reversibly denatured form A_d. In effect, the inhibitor combines only with the denatured form. We will let K_3 represent the constant and s the number of molecules of U combining with one molecule of A_d. Actually there is no physical way to distinguish between the combination of U with A_d according to equilibrium constant K_3 and the combination of U with A_n according to K_1 times K_3; the final state is represented by the same compound, AU.

The typical inhibitor of this type is a lipid-soluble indifferent narcotic such as urethan, alcohol, ether, or chloroform. It does not follow, however, that all lipid-soluble narcotics act in the same manner on different enzyme systems, nor does it follow that different lipid-soluble narcotics, even in a homologous series, act in precisely the same manner on the same system. These points will be discussed in due course. When the inhibition by such substances is reversible by hydrostatic pressure, the substance very probably combines with hydrophobic groups normally folded within the native protein molecule. These groups are exposed by the process of unfolding accompanying the reversible denaturation. This reaction is likely to involve a large volume increase, in which event it can be significantly opposed by hydrostatic pressure. Thus, in the presence of the inhibitor, the equilibrium is shifted in the direction of the denatured form; some of the denatured molecules are combined with the inhibitor, others are not. Under increased pressure the equilibrium is shifted in the opposite direction, toward the native form, and this shift is accompanied by the dissociation of some of the inhibitor molecules. In general, temperature will similarly affect the equilibrium between the inhibitor and the enzyme, but the net effect of temperature is complicated by the fact that both K_1 and K_3 are involved. Thus, although a rise in temperature will be likely to dissociate the inhibitor from its combination with the denatured form, the rise in temperature may be even more effective in increasing the amount of the denatured form with which the inhibitor combines. The net results depend upon the numerical values of the thermodynamic constants of heat and entropy in the two equilibria. In spite of these complications, and of additional ones which arise from the fact that substances promoting the reversible denaturation are likely to promote also an irreversible denaturation of the protein, the formulations for the mechanism assumed are readily derived, and the data in some instances conform to them with remarkable simplicity.

Following the same method as in the derivation of equations (10.7) and (10.10), we have

$$A_0 = A_n + A_d + K_3(A_d)(U)^s$$

$$= A_n + K_1(A_n) + K_1 K_3(U)^s$$

$$A_n = \frac{A_0}{1 + K_1 + K_1 K_3(U)^s}$$

$$I_1 = \frac{bk'(L)(A_0)}{1 + K_1}$$

$$I_2 = \frac{bk'(L)(A_0)}{1 + K_1 + K_1 K_3(U)^s}$$

$$\frac{I_1}{I_2} = \frac{1 + K_1 + K_1 K_3(U)^s}{1 + K_1} = 1 + \frac{K_1 K_3(U)^s}{1 + K_1}$$

$$\frac{I_1}{I_2} - 1 = \frac{K_1 K_3(U)^s}{1 + K_1}$$

$$\Gamma_1 \left(1 + \frac{1}{K_1} \right) = K_3(U)^s$$

$$\ln \left[\Gamma_1 \left(1 + \frac{1}{K_1} \right) \right] = s \ln (U) - \frac{\Delta F_3}{RT} = s \ln (U) - \frac{\Delta H_3}{RT} + \frac{\Delta S_3}{R}$$

$$= s \ln (U) - \frac{\Delta F_{0_3}}{RT} - \frac{p \, \Delta V_3}{RT} \qquad (10.13)$$

For brevity and convenience of discussion, we will adopt the definition

$$(\Gamma_1) \left(1 + \frac{1}{K_1} \right) \equiv \Gamma_2 \qquad (10.14)$$

From equations (10.13) and (10.14) it follows that any inhibition conforming to this mechanism can be analyzed by plotting the logarithm of

Γ_2 successively against the logarithm of the molar concentration of U, against the reciprocal of the absolute temperature, and against hydrostatic pressure. Conformity to the mechanism is attested by linear relationships in each case, the slopes of the lines representing respectively the number s of molecules of U per molecule of A in the combination AU_s, the heat of reaction ΔH_3 divided by R, and the volume change of reaction ΔV_3 divided by RT.

Equations (10.7) and (10.13) show that Γ_1 and Γ_2 cannot be distinguished through the relation between the concentration of the inhibitor and its quantitative effect at constant temperature and pressure. Thus, for the first type,

$$\ln \left(\frac{I_1}{I_2} - 1 \right) = \ln \Gamma_1 = \ln K_2 + r \ln (X) = \ln (\text{constant}) + r \ln (X)$$

and, for the second type,

$$\ln \left[\left(\frac{I_1}{I_2} - 1 \right) \left(1 + \frac{1}{K_1} \right) \right] = \ln \Gamma_2 = \ln K_3 + s \ln (U) = \ln (\text{constant}) + s \ln (U)$$

At constant temperature and pressure the slope of the line relating the logarithm of (X) or of (U) to Γ_1 or Γ_2, respectively, is not affected by the value of the equilibrium constants. It is convenient, therefore, in analyzing data only for the value of r or of s, to plot only $\ln \Gamma_1$ against $\ln$ (concentration of inhibitor). A full analysis, however, always requires data concerning the influence of temperature and of hydrostatic pressure. Although other useful formulations have been derived for analyzing biological equilibrium reactions, they have generally been incomplete in failing to take into account the precise rôle of K_1 and the general significance of pressure (e.g., Lineweaver and Burk, 1934; Fisher and Öhnell, 1940; Goldstein, 1944). In some instances the effects of pressure alone are sufficient to indicate an inhibition of the second type among a group of different inhibitors (Fig. 10.21). The absence of a pressure effect, however, does not exclude the second type of inhibition, since denaturation of proteins, reversible as well as irreversible, is not necessarily accompanied by a net difference in volume of the final as compared to the initial state, or of the activated as compared to the normal state (cf. Chapter 9, particularly with reference to protein denaturation in the presence of urea).

It might be expected, *a priori*, that, among a considerable number of different inhibitors which affect luminescence or other processes, varying degrees of conformity to the simple mechanism of equation (10.13) would be encountered. It is generally found that the equation is more or less oversimplified in that it fits the data under some conditions but not under others, e.g., the theory and data agree over certain ranges of temperature or concentration of inhibitor, but deviations occur in other ranges of these variables. Such complications, however, are understandable and they are the inevitable consequences of the mechanism of action. As

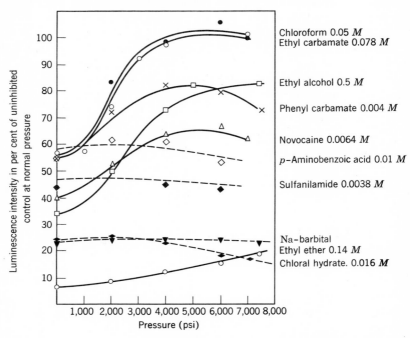

Fig. 10.21. Influence of hydrostatic pressure on the luminescence of *Photobacterium phosphoreum* suspended in phosphate-buffered sodium chloride solution, *p*H 7.3, at 17° to 18°C containing various inhibitors as indicated at the right of the figure. The luminescence of the control, without added inhibitor, is taken as 100 per cent at atmospheric pressure. Its intensity varied only slightly with pressure under these conditions (cf. Fig. 9.8A). The broken lines represent inhibitions that are not appreciably influenced by pressure; the solid lines represent inhibitions that are reduced by pressure. (From Johnson, Brown, and Marsland, 1942b.)

illustrations of the extent of both conformity to and discrepancies between the data and theory of equation (10.13), we will discuss the inhibitions of luminescence by ethyl carbamate (urethan) and ethyl alcohol, respectively.

The influence of temperature on the urethan and on the alcohol inhibition of luminescence is illustrated in Figs. 10.22 and 10.23. Qualitatively it is apparent that in both cases a given concentration of the agent is increasingly effective as the temperature is raised. This relationship, of course, is the opposite of that obtaining with sulfanilamide, or of acid pH (Fig. 10.16). On the other hand, it is generally similar to the effects of alkaline pH (Fig. 10.18). At temperatures well above the optimum, accurate determinations become difficult because of the rapidly changing

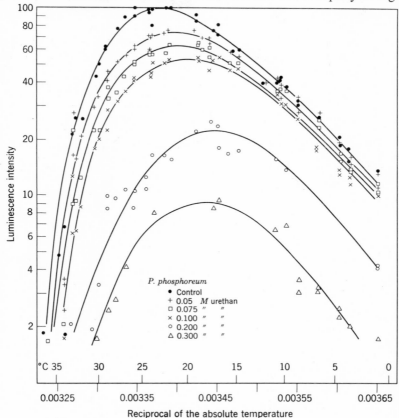

Fig. 10.22. The influence of temperature on the inhibition of luminescence in *P. phosphoreum* by different concentrations of urethan at neutral pH (Johnson, Eyring, Steblay, et al., 1945).

intensity of luminescence with slight differences in temperature and with time of exposure to these temperatures. There are indications, however, that at these high temperatures the inhibitory effects of small concentrations of such inhibitors as urethan or alcohol begin to decrease, because most of the drug becomes dissociated from its combination with the system. The temperature required for effective dissociation of most of the combined drug, however, is usually well above the point at which the catalytic activity of the system has already been greatly reduced by the high value of K_1.

The net effect of low concentrations of a drug is sometimes an increase in luminescence intensity above that of the drug-free control (Fig. 10.23).

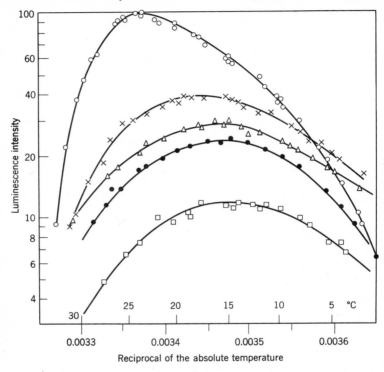

Fig. 10.23.   The influence of temperature on the inhibition of luminescence in *P. phosphoreum* by different concentrations of ethyl alcohol at neutral pH (Johnson, Eyring, Steblay, et al., 1945).

This apparent stimulation is a complication that cannot be accounted for by equation (10.13); it probably results from the inhibition of a competing reaction (p. 396, and discussion of antagonistic actions, p. 473).   Where such an effect occurs, the formulation of equation (10.13) cannot be used, although at a different temperature the reaction resulting in stimulation may become of negligible importance so that the formulation of equation (10.13) may then be employed.   The analysis of the data shown in Figs. 10.22 and 10.23 with respect to temperature is shown in Figs. 10.24 and 10.25, respectively, and the analysis with respect to concentration is shown in Figs. 10.26 and 10.27, respectively. The influence of pressure will be considered presently.

From Fig. 10.24 it is apparent that the urethan inhibition only partially conforms to the mechanism tested by this analysis. In the low temperature region, 5° to 20°C, the relationship is nearly linear, and the slopes

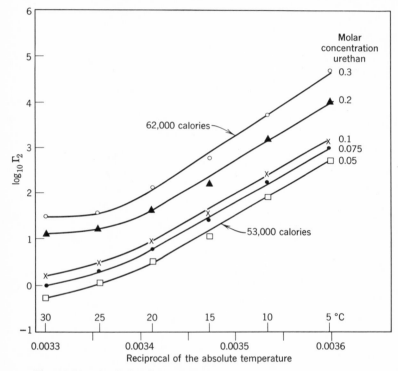

Fig. 10.24. Analysis of the urethan inhibition with respect to temperature in accordance with equation (10.13); data from Fig. (10.22).

of the lines indicate heats of reaction of 53,000 to 62,000 cal, the slopes increasing somewhat with concentration of urethan. Above about 20°C, the lines deviate in the direction of increased amount of inhibition, i.e., they curve upwards, and the amount of deviation in this direction increases with concentration of the drug. A corresponding analysis of the inhibition caused by alkaline pH's reveals the same general relationships, and the heat of reaction throughout the relatively low temperatures again amount to approximately 60,000 cal.

In the alcohol inhibition (Fig. 10.25) the points fall approximately along a straight line, from temperatures slightly above the point where a stimulation of luminescence is observed, up to well above the normal optimum. The slopes of the lines indicate a heat of reaction of approximately 37,000 cal. The broken lines show the type of curve which results

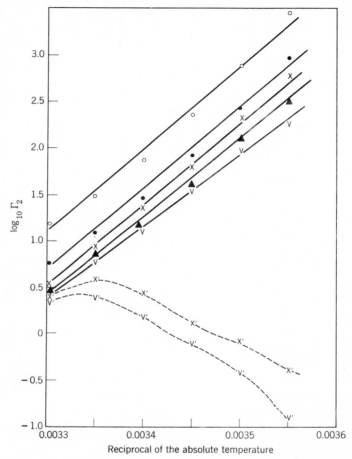

Fig. 10.25. Analysis of the alcohol inhibition with respect to temperature in accordance with equation 10.13; data from Fig. 10.23. The broken lines indicate the results of using equation (10.7) instead of equation (10.13) in the analysis.

when Γ_1, instead of Γ_2, is plotted against the reciprocal of the absolute temperature. Here it would seem that the analysis conforms fairly closely to the mechanism of Γ_2 and clearly not to the Γ_1 type of inhibition. There is again a tendency, however, for the slopes of the lines pertaining to the higher concentrations of alcohol to be somewhat steeper than those for lower concentrations.

The relation between drug concentration and amount of inhibition at different temperatures again shows that the action of either urethan or alcohol is somewhat more complex than equation (10.13) takes into account. With alcohol (Fig. 10.26) the points fall along straight lines, within the limits of experimental accuracy, but the slopes of the lines vary with temperature. At 10°C the slope is approximately 3.7, while at 25°

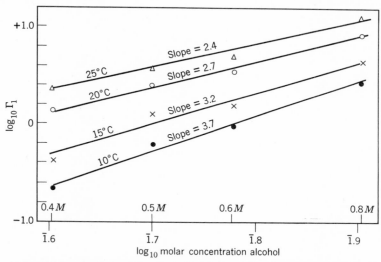

Fig. 10.26. Analysis of the alcohol inhibition of luminescence with respect to concentration at different temperatures, in accordance with equation (10.13); data from Fig. 10.23.

it is 2.4. The mere fact that the numerical values of the slopes are not integers indicates that they represent average values from more than one equilibrium reaction. With more than one reaction, involving different integral numbers of alcohol molecules per molecule of enzyme system, it is not surprising that the average number should vary with temperature. Each of the integral numbers is associated with a specific equilibrium constant, and it is unlikely that all these equilibrium constants will have identical heats of reaction. At any temperature the average number of alcohol molecules combined with the system depends upon the relative importance of the different equilibria, and the average number will change with change in temperature. Thus the slope of the lines in Fig. 10.26 decreases progressively, from 3.7 at 10°C to 2.4 at 25°C. The line at 30° (not plotted in the figure) is very close to the one at 25°.

With urethan (Fig. 10.27) there is a fairly abrupt change in slope, at a concentration of about 0.1 M urethan, at all temperatures. Below this concentration the slopes of the lines relating the logarithm of Γ_1 to the logarithm of urethan in solution vary from 1.3 at 5°C to 1.7 at 30°C. Above this concentration the slopes change from 3.1 at 5° to 2.4 at 20° to 2.6 at 30°. The same general interpretation, that of multiple equilibrium

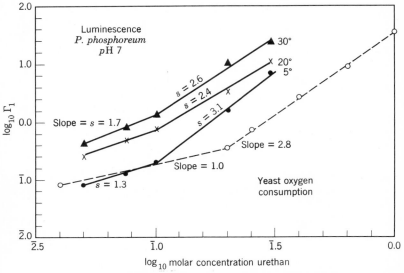

Fig. 10.27.   Analysis of the urethan inhibition of luminescence with respect to concentration at different temperatures, in accordance with equation (10.13); data from Fig. 10.22. The broken line represents data replotted from Fisher and Stearn (1942, Fig. 1, p. 113) for the urethan inhibition of oxygen consumption in yeast, at a temperature and pH not clearly stated.

reactions, applies to the non-integral values of these slopes and to the changes in slopes with both drug concentration and temperature. It applies also to the change in slope of the lines at the higher temperatures in Fig. 10.24. Although essentially complete reversibility of the urethan and of the alcohol inhibitions of luminescence has been demonstrated under various conditions, it is likely that irreversible effects contribute to the amount of inhibition at upper ranges of either temperature or concentration.

The irreversible reactions catalyzed by these and similar drugs are discussed in later paragraphs. For the moment, the important points with respect to the largely reversible effects is that they evidently involve more than one equilibrium reaction between the drug and its sites of action. Since the experiments referred to were carried out with intact, living cells, the question naturally arises, do the sites of action concern a single enzyme system or more than a single enzyme system? This question cannot be answered with certainty at the present time, but it can be definitely stated that the multiple equilibria *do not necessarily* concern more than a single enzyme system. By way of analogy, the denaturation of tobacco mosaic virus in the presence of urea (p. 282) obviously involves several distinct reactions between urea and the activated complex of the purified protein undergoing denaturation. Experiments with the influence of urethan in catalyzing the denaturation of purified tobacco mosaic virus also clearly indicate several reactions, as discussed presently. Furthermore, detailed analyses of the binding of small molecules, including organic and other ions, by proteins, especially serum albumin, have revealed that multiple equilibria with different thermodynamic constants of reaction are involved in a number of instances (Klotz and Curme, 1948; Karush and Sonnenberg, 1949; Karush, 1950a,b; Klotz, 1950; Scatchard, 1952).

In Fig. 10.27 the broken line is replotted from the data of Fischer and Stearn (1942) according to our formulation. This line refers to the urethan inhibition of respiration of yeast, at a temperature and pH which were not definitely stated. It shows again a fairly abrupt change in slope at a concentration close to that at which the change in slope occurs in the luminescent data. The steeper slope is 2.8, which is within the range of 2.6 and 3.1 found for luminescence. The data of Fischer and Stearn include many points from a series of experiments, and therefore provide a better basis for the average numerical values than the data for luminescence, which in Fig. 10.22 are taken from a single experiment. The lesser slope of the broken line in Fig. 10.27 is unity. It fits the data of Fischer and Stearn equally as well as the line which was drawn, with a slope of 0.75, in their figure. The slope of unity is readily understandable, but fractional slopes are of uncertain interpretation.

Although Fischer and Stearn interpret the change in slope of the broken line (Fig. 10.27) as representing the influence of urethan on two distinct, parallel enzyme systems involved in the total oxygen uptake, more evidence is required in order to substantiate this conclusion. If it is correct, the two systems obviously differ in their sensitivity to urethan. Since cell division is inhibited by the same concentrations of urethan which block the more sensitive of the supposed two systems, Fischer and Stearn suggest that it is by affecting the more sensitive system that cell division is blocked. Here again, however, additional evidence is required. Cell division may be blocked by other agents such as nitro- and halophenols at the same time that the rate of oxygen consumption is increased several fold (p. 396

and Fig. 10.28); this shows that the process of division can be blocked by combination of drugs with systems that do not limit respiration. Hydrostatic pressure readily blocks and even reverses cell division (p. 356), and, although its influence on respiration under similar conditions has not been investigated, it is reasonable to expect, by analogy with the effects

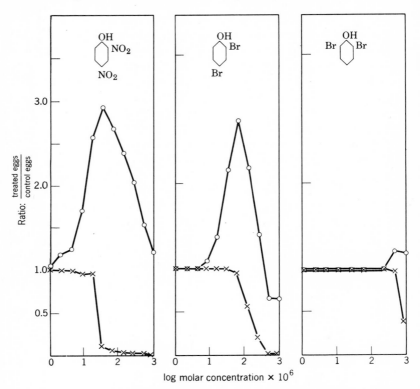

Fig. 10.28. Influence of three different substituted phenols on the rate of oxygen consumption (circles) and on cell division (crosses) of *Arbacia* eggs (from Clowes, 1951). The type as well as the position of the substituent are important factors in the effect of the drug.

of corresponding pressures on the intensity of bacterial luminescence, that the rate of respiration will be only slightly affected during the inhibition of division near the temperature optimum.

With reference to the relation between concentration of substituted phenols and the inhibition of cell division, it is interesting to note that the inhibitory equilibrium reaction evidently involves the combination of several inhibitor molecules with their site of action. When the data of

Clowes (1951) are plotted as $\log \Gamma_1$ against log concentration of drug added, the relation, for several derivatives that we have plotted in this manner, is linear within the accuracy of estimating numerical values

Table 10.1. Constants Estimated for Some of the Equilibrium Reactions of Some Inhibitors of Various Biological Processes, Usually at Room Temperature and Always at Atmospheric Pressure

(According to the Formulation of Fisher and Öhnell, 1940)

Process	Inhibitor	Per Cent of Process Stable Against Inhibitor*	Ratio of I Combining in Equilibrium = a	K	ΔF (kcal)	Reference for Original Data
Heart frequency	CN					
Fundulus embryo		28	1.6	5.6×10^{-7}	-8.6	Fisher and Öhnell, 1940
Salmon embryo		68	1.6	1.6×10^{-8}	-10.7	Armstrong and Fisher, 1940
Respiration (O_2)	CN					
Frog nerve		0	1.6	1.6×10^{-7}	-9.4	Schmitt, Skow, Bilinsky, 1936
Fertilized *Arbacia* eggs		14	1.2	1.1×10^{-5}	-6.8	Örström, 1932
Frog muscle, active		0	1.2	3.2×10^{-5}	-6.2	Stannard, 1939
Frog muscle, resting		0	0.84	1.4×10^{-3}	-3.9	Stannard, 1939
Frog kidney		0	0.73	2.2×10^{-3}	-3.7	Schmitt, Skow, Bilinsky, 1936
Wheat seeds		17.5	0.88	3.2×10^{-3}	-3.4	Commoner, 1939
Heart frequency	Azide					
Fundulus embryo		38	1.0	2.0×10^{-6}	-7.8	Armstrong and Fisher, 1940
Salmon embryo		50	0.96	1.2×10^{-7}	-9.5	Armstrong and Fisher, 1940
Total luminescence *Cypridina*						
pH 5.5		0	1.0	6.0×10^{-2}	-1.7	Chase, 1942
pH 6.5		0	1.0	9.5×10^{-2}	-1.4	Chase, 1942
Respiration (O_2)	Urethan					
"Cake" yeast		0	** $\begin{cases}1.0\\4.0\end{cases}$	0.74 120.0	-0.18 -2.8	Fisher and Stearn, 1942
Culture yeast		0	** $\begin{cases}1.0\\6.0\\4.0\end{cases}$	0.73 23.0 910.0	-0.18 $+1.9$ $+3.1$	Fisher and Stearn, 1942
Tetrahymena geleii		0	** $\begin{cases}0.9\\2.3\end{cases}$	0.84 2090.0	-0.1 $+4.6$	Ormsbee and Fisher, 1943
Fertilized *Arbacia* eggs		0	** $\begin{cases}0.5\\3.0\end{cases}$	0.84 0.01	-0.1 -2.7	Fisher and Henry, 1943

* When the overall process cannot be completely inhibited, the percentage of the process that is stable against the inhibitor is subtracted from the total before making the analysis.
** The different values for the constant a for the same process refer to slopes of the curve over different ranges of concentration of the inhibitor, e.g., as in Fig. 10.27.

from the published graphs, and the slopes of the lines are of the order of 2 to 4.

The results of some analyses of the action of cyanide, of azide, and of urethan on various processes, in accordance with the formulation of Fisher and Öhnell (equation 10.9) are summarized in Table 10.1. Most of these data were obtained or collected by Fisher and his collaborators, and we have computed the free energy change from the data given. Thus, as defined by Fisher and Öhnell (1940),

$$K = \frac{(E)(I)^a}{(EI_a)} = \frac{\% \text{ uninhibited}}{\% \text{ inhibited}}$$

where (E) represents the concentration of free enzyme, (I) the concentration of the inhibitor, and a the ratio of I combining per molecule of E in the formation of EI_a. Since

$$K = e^{-\Delta F/RT} = e^{-\Delta H/RT} e^{\Delta S/R} \qquad \text{(p. 52)}$$

the free energy change though not the heat and entropy can be readily computed for K at the temperature concerned. The actual temperature of the experiment is not given for all the data in Table 10.1. On the assumption that it was always close to room temperature, we have taken $RT = 600$ in computing the values of ΔF. The numerical values of ΔF for a given K will vary, of course, with the units in which the concentration of the inhibitor is expressed.

Where the influence of temperature on the inhibition has been studied, values for the heats and entropies can be computed. Table 10.2 lists the constants obtained in the analysis of the action of various drugs on bacterial luminescence. In this table the free energies of reaction are computed for the concentration of drug given in the table, and for 20°C, in accordance with equation (10.7) or (10.13). Because K is defined here as the reciprocal of the equilibrium constant used in Table 10.1, the ΔF's in Table 10.2 are of opposite sign. The numerical values of the constants in both Table 10.1 and Table 10.2 cannot be considered exact, because of the evidence already referred to that more than a single equilibrium is frequently involved in the measured effects of the inhibitor, i.e., the slopes of the lines in analytical plots of the data often vary somewhat with temperature, or with concentration. A precise analysis would require also that activity coefficients be taken into account in relation to the concentration of drug added.

Tables 10.1 and 10.2 show that the free energy changes are often not very different from zero. Since

$$K = e^{-\Delta F/RT} = \frac{(EI_a)}{(E)(I)^a}$$

according to our usual way of writing the equilibrium, it follows that

$$K(I)^a = \frac{(EI_a)}{(E)} = e^{-\Delta F/RT}$$

When the ratio of free to combined enzyme is unity, $K(I)^a$ will also equal unity and the free energy will be zero. The ratio "free to combined enzyme equals unity" occurs at 50 per cent inhibition, and whether or not the free energy for this inhibition will equal zero depends upon the concentration of the inhibitor. Obviously, when the inhibitor is present in unit concentration, the free energy will be zero, for then K equals 1. Moreover, under such circumstances, since $\Delta F = \Delta H - T \Delta S = 0$, then

Table 10.2. Constants Estimated for the Equilibrium between Various Inhibitors and the Luminescent Systems of Bacteria in Accordance with Equation 10.7 or 10.13, Respectively

Species of Bacteria	Inhibitor	r or s	Conc. (M)	ΔH (kcal)	ΔS (E.U.)	$T \Delta S$ (20°C)	ΔF (20°C) (kcal)	Reference
V. phosphorescens	Sulfanilamide	1.2	0.003	− 17.3	− 39.6	− 11.6	− 6.7	Johnson, Eyring, Williams, 1942
P. phosphoreum	Sulfanilamide	1.2	0.005	− 12.2	− 37.8	− 11.0	− 1.1	Johnson, Eyring, Williams, 1942
A. fischeri	Sulfanilamide	1.2	0.005	− 13.5	− 31.0	− 9.1	− 4.4	Johnson, Eyring, Williams, 1942
V. phosphorescens	Urethan		0.098	− 70.0	− 204.0	− 59.7	− 10.3	Johnson, Eyring, Williams, 1942
P. phosphoreum	Urethan		0.075	− 56.0	− 165.0	− 48.3	− 7.7	Johnson, Eyring, Williams, 1942
	Alcohol	2.7	0.4	− 37.0	− 128.0	− 37.5	+ 0.5	Johnson, Eyring, Steblay, et. al, 1945
A. fischeri	Phenobarbital	1.5	0.003	− 44.1	− 146.5	− 42.9	− 1.2	McElroy, 1943
	Barbital	1.0	0.015	− 46.0	− 152.8	− 44.7	− 1.3	McElroy, 1943
	Evipal	2.0	0.0047	− 46.0	− 152.9	− 44.8	− 1.2	McElroy, 1943
	Amytal		0.001	− 34.9	− 113.5	− 33.3	− 1.6	McElroy, 1943
	Chloral hydrate		0.01	− 36.8	− 122.0	− 35.7	− 1.1	McElroy, 1943
	Chlorotone	1.0	0.00014	− 49.2	− 166.5	− 48.8	− 0.4	McElroy, 1943
	Trianol	2.0	0.00098	− 48.8	− 171.3	− 50.2	+ 1.5	McElroy, 1943
	Benzamide	1.5	0.002	− 11.9	− 40.1	− 11.7	− 0.2	McElroy, 1943
	Salicylamide	1.0	0.0005	− 18.8	− 65.7	− 19.2	+ 0.4	McElroy, 1943

ΔH will equal $T \Delta S$. Such a relationship, however, is not the rule, inasmuch as ΔH will differ from $T \Delta S$ strictly in accordance with the concentration of inhibitor required for a 50 per cent inhibition, which may vary by several orders of magnitude among different inhibitors.

Although the quantitative theory is somewhat oversimplified, the constants such as those of Table 10.2 which represent average values are sufficient to account remarkably well for the quantitative effects of an inhibitor in relation to both concentration and temperature. The calculations have been carried out with reference to the urethan inhibition of the aerobic and anaerobic oxidation of glucose by the symbiotic nitrogen-fixing bacterium, *Rhizobium trifolii* (Koffler et al., 1947). In these experiments the reversible diminution in rate at temperatures above the normal optimum, and in various concentrations of urethan, were demonstrated. The constants for both the normal temperature activity curve and for those in the presence of added urethan were determined in the manner that has been indicated (pp. 219 and 405). The equation used for computing the rate at different temperatures and drug concentrations is

$$\text{Rate} = \frac{cTe^{-\Delta H^{\ddagger}/RT}}{1 + K_1 + K_1 K_3 (U)^s} \tag{10.15}$$

where K_1 refers to the equilibrium between native and thermally denatured forms of the rate-limiting enzyme, K_3 to the equilibrium constant between

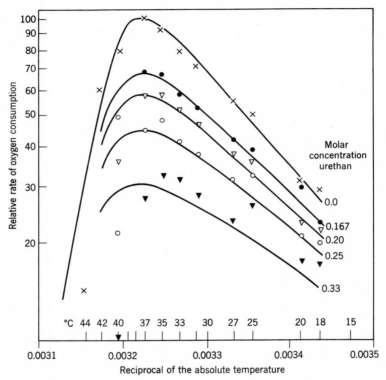

Fig. 10.29. Relation between temperature and the rate of oxygen consumption of *Rhizobium trifolii*, with glucose as substrate, in the presence of various concentrations of urethan, and without urethan. The smooth curves were calculated as described in the text; the points represent data observed in experiments (Koffler et al., 1947).

urethan in molar concentration (U) and the enzyme system, and s to the average ratio of urethan molecules combining per enzyme molecule. The results are shown in Figs. 10.29 and 10.30. The following constants were used in calculating the curves of Figs. 10.29 and 10.30:

Fig. 10.29

$c =$	$0.3775e^{21.61}$
$\Delta H^\ddagger =$	13,400.0
$\Delta H_1 =$	96,000.0
$\Delta S_1 =$	306.14
$\Delta H_3 = -$	85,000.0
$\Delta S_3 =$	$- 236.8$
$s =$	2.25

Fig. 10.30

$c =$	$0.3613e^{21.79}$
$\Delta H^\ddagger =$	13,600.0
$\Delta H_1 =$	126,000.0
$\Delta S_1 =$	399.72
$\Delta H_3 = -$	118,000.0
$\Delta S_3 =$	$- 366.2$
$s =$	2.5

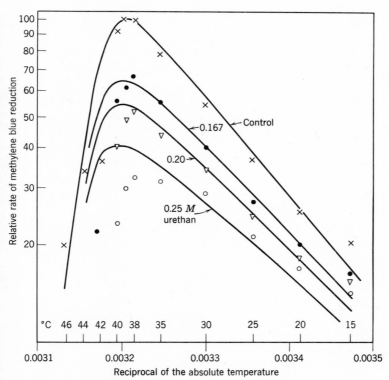

Fig. 10.30.   Influence of temperature on the rate of anaerobic methylene blue reduction by *R. trifolii*, with glucose as substrate, in the presence of various concentrations of urethan, and without urethan.   The smooth curves were calculated as described in the text; the points represent data from experiments (Koffler et al., 1947).

The normal temperature activity curves of Figs. 10.29 and 10.30 are satisfactorily described by the simple theory. Deviations between the predicted and observed values in the presence of urethan are to be expected because the equation used takes into account only a single equilibrium, whereas more than one equilibrium reaction involving urethan evidently takes part in the total inhibition. The deviations occur chiefly at the high temperatures, or with the highest concentrations of the drug, where the influence of multiple equilibria would be expected to be conspicuous. At temperatures below the normal optimum, or with moderate concentrations of the drug, the agreement between observed and predicted values is within the limits of experimental error.

With reference to the general influence of temperature on enzyme kinetics in the presence of inhibitors, the examples illustrated show that the observed apparent activation energy is subject both to pronounced increase (cf the steeper slopes in the presence of sulfanilamide or at acid pH in Figs. 10.5 and 10.16) and to pronounced decrease (cf. the less steep slopes at alkaline pH or in the presence of urethan or alcohol in Figs. 10.18, 10.22, 10.23, 10.29, and 10.30). The fully reversible difference caused by the inhibitor may amount to thousands of small calories above or below the value observed under corresponding conditions in the absence of the inhibitor. Since the foregoing theory, based on the assumption that a single enzyme is acted upon, accounts for the quantitative data with considerable accuracy, it is not necessary to assume that more than one enzyme is affected (cf. discussion, p. 415). The influence of hydrostatic pressure is understandable on the same theory.

The action of pressure on reversible inhibitions by drugs

The fact that the inhibition of a biological process by certain drugs can be eliminated or reduced by increasing the hydrostatic pressure was first discovered in bacterial luminescence (Johnson, Brown, and Marsland, 1942a,b), and most of the data yet available concern this process. The pressure relationships of urethan and of alcohol action, however, have now been studied with respect to intracellular processes in bacteria and in animals, and with respect to extracted systems, including purified proteins. It is convenient to consider first the relation between pressure and the alcohol inhibition of luminescence.

It will be recalled that at a temperature close to the normal optimum the net effect of increased pressure on the intensity of bacterial luminescence is quite small (Fig. 9.8, p. 310), apparently because the effect of pressure in retarding the rate of the limiting enzyme reaction is compensated for by the effect of pressure in reversing the denaturation of the enzyme. At such a temperature, however, the addition of a drug acting according to a type II inhibition causes the equilibrium between native and denatured forms of the enzyme to shift in the direction of the denatured form.   Because of the large volume increase accompanying this change, increased pressure causes the equilibrium to shift in the opposite direction, and, with the resulting increase in the amount of active

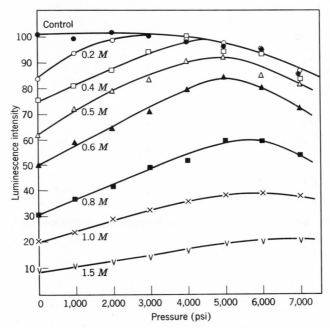

Fig. 10.31.   Luminescence intensity of *Photobacterium phosphoreum* as a function of hydrostatic pressure at 17.5°C, in the presence of various concentrations of alcohol in the phosphate-buffered sodium chloride solution, *p*H7, of the suspending medium (Johnson, Eyring, Steblay, et al., 1945).

enzyme, the net rate of the reaction increases.   A typical experiment is illustrated in Fig. 10.31.

Figure 10.31 shows that, under the conditions involved, the inhibition of luminescence by relatively small concentrations of alcohol (0.2, 0.4 *M*) is virtually abolished by raising the pressure to between 3,000 and 5,000 psi.   With higher concentrations of alcohol the inhibition is also reduced, but, as the pressure is progressively increased, a point is reached where the intensity of luminescence is reduced because of the effects of pressure on a different reaction; i.e., with relatively high concentrations of alcohol, the pressure cannot be raised sufficiently to eliminate the alcohol inhibition of luminescence without interfering, at the high pressures, with the

luminescent reaction through a different mechanism.   As a result of these
relationships the "optimal pressure" for luminescence is shifted to higher

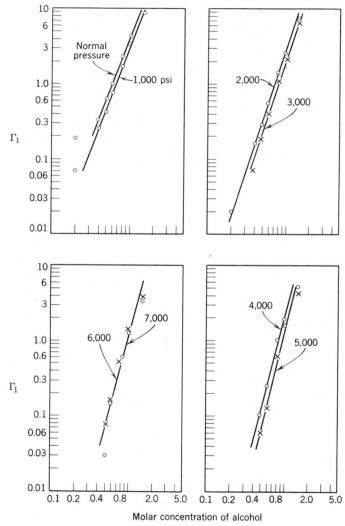

Fig. 10.32.   Analysis of the data of Fig. 10.31 with respect to the concentration of alcohol at different pressures (Johnson, Eyring, Steblay, et al., 1945).

pressures in the presence of increasing concentrations of alcohol, just as
the optimal temperature at atmospheric pressure is shifted to lower
temperatures (Fig. 10.23).

The data of Fig. 10.31 may be analyzed with respect to the two variables, concentration of alcohol and amount of pressure. Figure 10.32 shows the analysis with respect to the former, at eight different pressures, according to the formulation of equation (10.13) but omitting the variation of K_1 with pressure; i.e., Γ_1 rather than Γ_2 has been plotted on the ordinate. Actually, the variation in K_1 throughout the range of atmospheric to 7,000 psi of pressure at this temperature is small. The values of K_1, computed from the relation

$$\Delta F_{p_2}{}^0 = \Delta F_{p_1}{}^0 + \int_{p_1}^{p_2} \overline{\Delta V}\, dp \tag{10.16}$$

are found to vary from 0.03404 to 0.0295, or by only about 1.15 times, at this temperature. The slopes of the lines in Fig. 10.32, therefore, would be influenced by not more than 15 per cent by taking the variation of K_1 with pressure into account. The slopes as plotted, however, vary from 2.8 at normal pressure to 4.0 at 7,000 psi, or by about 1.5 times. The average number of alcohol molecules that combine with the enzyme is evidently greater at the higher pressures. Since the corresponding average number decreases with rise in temperature, it appears that, among the several equilibria established between the drug and enzyme system, the equilibria characterized by a low ratio of alcohol to enzyme molecules have a lower heat of reaction and a larger volume increase than those characterized by a high ratio of alcohol to enzyme molecules.

In analyzing the relation between pressure and the amount of inhibition by various concentrations of alcohol, the influence of pressure on K_1 has been taken into account (Fig. 10.33). As would be expected from the foregoing observations, the slopes of the lines vary with alcohol concentration, and the steepest slope is associated with the lowest concentration of alcohol. The net volume change, computed from the slope of this line according to the relation

$$\overline{\Delta V} = RT \ln \frac{(\Gamma_{2p_2} - \Gamma_{2p_1})}{p_2 - p_1} \tag{10.17}$$

amounts to about 154 cc per mole for the inhibition by 0.2 M alcohol, decreasing to about 60 cc per mole for the inhibition by 1.0 or 1.5 M alcohol. In equation (10.17), p is taken in atmospheres, and R in cc atmospheres per mole, i.e., 82.03, as usual.

The observed change in luminescence intensity under the influence of increased pressure in the presence of alcohol depends, of course, upon the temperature. For example, at a temperature well below the normal optimum, in the absence of an added drug, pressure reduces the intensity of luminescence. If an appropriate concentration of alcohol is added at such a temperature, the intensity of luminescence is reduced at normal pressure, and, as the pressure is raised, the intensity changes very little. The difference in intensity between the control and the suspension of cells to which alcohol has been added, however, becomes progressively less, and therefore the amount of inhibition becomes progressively less. At a temperature slightly above the normal optimum, the intensity of both the

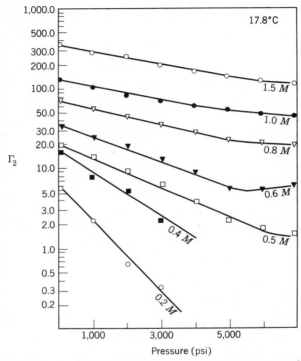

Fig. 10.33. Analysis of the data of Fig. 10.31 with respect to the influence of pressure at different concentrations of alcohol (Johnson, Eyring, Steblay, et al., 1945).

control and alcohol-inhibited luminescence increases under pressure, though to a greater extent in the presence of alcohol. At a temperature well above the optimum, the two increase by about the same amount under pressure, showing that in this case pressure has very little effect on the inhibition caused by alcohol. These relationships are illustrated in Fig. 10.34.

Figure 10.35 shows an approximate analysis of the data of Fig. 10.34. A more precise analysis would require calculating K_1 for each temperature as well as for each pressure, and plotting Γ_2 rather than Γ_1 on the logarithmic scale of the ordinate. The slopes of the essentially parallel lines for this concentration of alcohol at temperatures between 11° and 24.4° correspond to a volume increase of reaction of about 63 cc per mole. At 29°C the line is almost horizontal, and it becomes very close to horizontal when the appropriate values of K_1, which have been calculated for this temperature and these pressures, are taken into account in plotting the

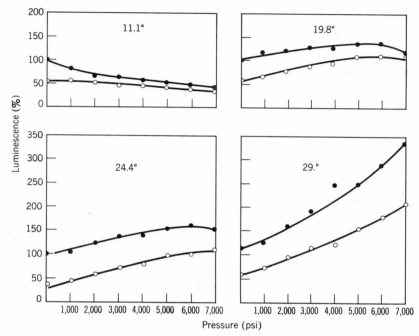

Fig. 10.34. The influence of pressure on luminescence of *Photobacterium phosphoreum* suspended in phosphate-buffered sodium chloride solution of neutral pH, with 0.5 M ethyl alcohol (hollow circles) and without alcohol (solid circles) at different temperatures (Johnson, Eyring, Steblay, et al., 1945). The intensity of the control at atmospheric pressure is arbitrarily taken as 100 per cent at each temperature. The relative intensity in the control at different temperatures varied in the manner illustrated in Fig. 1.6.

data. A probable interpretation of the disappearance of the effect of pressure on the alcohol inhibition at a relatively high temperature is as follows.

From equation (10.13),

$$\ln \Gamma_1 = \ln \left(\frac{K_1 K_3}{1 + K_1} \right) + s \ln (U) \qquad (10.18)$$

For a given concentration (U) of alcohol, the term $s \ln (U)$ remains constant, and the measured effects of pressure depend upon the relative importance of the volume changes of reaction associated with K_1 and with K_3. Thus, when K_1 is small, $\ln \Gamma_1$ is approximately equal to $\ln (K_1 K_3) + s \ln (U)$. When K_1 becomes large, as at temperatures well above the normal optimum, $K_1/(1 + K_1)$ is approximately equal to unity and $\ln \Gamma_1$ is approximately equal to $\ln (K_3) + s \ln (U)$. Referring to Fig. 10.35, it is evident that the slopes of the lines for the several temperatures are practically the same at the temperatures below 29°C. At 29°C,

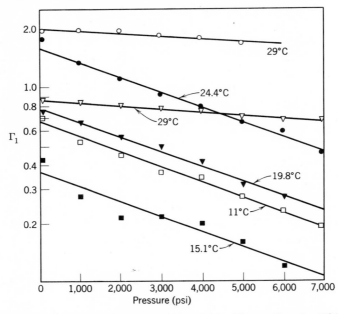

Fig. 10.35. Analysis of the data of Fig. 10.34. The two lines for 29°C are from repeated experiments in which the actual per cent inhibition by alcohol was not the same (Johnson, Eyring, Steblay, et al., 1945).

using 70,000 cal for ΔH_3 and 234 E.U. for ΔS, $K_1 = 3.04$, and $K_1/(1 + K_1) = 0.75$. Although this fraction of 0.75 is 25 per cent less than unity, it is sufficiently close to unity to cancel out to a major extent the importance of K_1 in the term $K_1 K_3/(1 + K_1)$. The effect of pressure, therefore, primarily concerns K_3 under these circumstances, and since the effects are small it follows that the volume change is small. Thus the large volume increase found at the lower temperatures is evidently associated with the change from the native to reversibly denatured forms of the protein, not with the actual combination of alcohol with the protein. This conclusion is consistent with our previous discussion of the mechanism of type II inhibitions.

Reversible inhibitions by a homologous series

For a long time it has been known that the potency of many narcotics is inversely related to their water solubility (Richet, 1893) and that the narcotic potency of members of a homologous series of alcohols, for example, increases with the length of the aliphatic chain in a manner that is correlated with the increase in capillary activity (Traube, 1891, 1904, 1910, 1913). In such a series the concentrations of isocapillary and iso-narcotic water solutions differ roughly, or sometimes very closely, by a factor of 3 for each methylene group in the chain; this relationship has become known as Traube's rule. It holds approximately for certain homologous series, such as the aliphatic alcohols, acting upon various physiological processes. The rule in this form does not hold for a homologous series of substances such as aliphatic hydrocarbons, which do not appreciably lower the surface tension of water-oil or water-air inter-faces, although the narcotic potencies of the hydrocarbons also increase roughly by a factor of 3 for each additional methylene group (cf. Hoeber, 1945).

In luminescence the effects of the homologous series of methyl to amyl alcohol are in approximate accord with Traube's rule when tested at temperatures below that of the normal optimum (Johnson, Eyring, and Kearns, 1943), as illustrated by the data of Table 10.3. Included in this table are data for the inhibition of respiration in goose erythrocytes, the inhibition of heart beat in frogs (Warburg, 1921), and the narcosis of polliwogs (Overton, 1901). The inhibitory concentrations of each alcohol are within the same order of magnitude for each process.

Of the four physiological processes included in Table 10.3 the narcosis of polliwogs appears to be the most sensitive, and luminescence the next most sensitive, as judged by the concentration of respective alcohols to bring about the observed effect. The narcosis of polliwogs, however, is the most difficult to express in quantitative terms, and the concentration of alcohol at its site of action in the nervous system is not necessarily the same as that of the solution in which the animals are placed. Some differences in the concentrations specified would be expected according to the temperature of the experiment in relation to the optimal temperature of the process, for reasons that have been discussed in preceding para-graphs. On the whole, the data pertaining to the different processes are remarkably similar. With *Photobacterium phosphoreum* at 15°C, the concentration of carbamates required for a 50 per cent inhibition of luminescence is found to decrease, as with the alcohols, by roughly one-third with each additional methylene group in the chain (Johnson, Flagler, Simpson, and McGeer, 1951). Furthermore, as pointed out by Brink and Posternak (1948), the inhibition of luminescence (data of

Taylor, 1934) is proportional to the thermodynamic activity of alcohols. The same is true for carbamates, if the assumption, probably correct, is made that their activity coefficients vary with different members of the homologous series in the same manner as those of the alcohols. The carbamate data summarized in Table 10.4 are based on a more recent study (Johnson, Flagler, Simpson, and McGeer, 1951).

Table 10.3. Molar Concentrations of Some Members of a Homologous Series of Aliphatic Alcohols Acting on Different Physiological Processes To Give the Specified Effects (Ratio of Concentrations Required for Successive Members of a Series To Give the Same Effect also Tabulated)

The data are from Johnson, Eyring, and Kearns (1943) on bacterial luminescence; Warburg (1921) on respiration and heart beat; and Overton (1901) on narcosis of polliwogs.

Alcohol	Luminescence, P. phosphoreum, 50% Inhibition at 11.5° to 15°C	Ratio of Conc.	Respiration of Goose Erythrocytes; 50% Inhibition	Ratio of Conc.	Frog Heart Beat	Ratio of Conc.	Narcosis of Polliwogs	Ratio of Conc.
Methyl	1.56		5.0		3.74		0.57	
		2.3		3.1		3.1		2.0
Ethyl	0.69		1.6		1.21		0.29	
		4.3		2.0		3.3		2.6
n-Propyl	0.16		0.8		0.37		0.11	
		3.6		5.3		3.4		2.9
n-Butyl	0.044		0.15		0.11		0.038	
		3.6		3.3		2.8		
n-Amyl	0.012		0.045		0.039			1.7
Iso-amyl	0.008						0.023	

The activity A of a substance is defined by the equation

$$A = e^{(F - F_0)/RT} = \frac{p}{p_0} = fN \qquad (10.19)$$

in which F is the partial molal free energy of the substance in a system of molecules; F_0 is the molal free energy of the substance in the standard reference state which for the narcotic is the pure substance; p and p_0 are the partial pressure of the solution and vapor pressure of the pure substance, respectively; f is the activity coefficient; and N is the mole fraction. *For homologous substances, roughly the same inhibition occurs at the same thermodynamic activity.*   This relationship has been implicit in various discussions of the problems of narcotics and inhibitions, but it was apparently first pointed out explicitly, and illustrated in a precise way with data concerning numerous drugs and physiological processes, by Ferguson (1939).   We will, therefore, refer to it as Ferguson's rule.

Table 10.4.   **Concentrations of Homologous Carbamates Required for a 50 Per Cent Inhibition of Luminescence in** *P. phosphoreum* **at 15°C; the Ratio of Concentrations between Successive Members of the Series; and the Relation of the Required Concentrations to the Thermodynamic Activity Coefficient**

(From Johnson, Flagler, Simpson, and McGeer, 1951)

Carbamate	Molar Conc.	Ratio of Conc.	Activity Coefficient* f_∞	Mole Fraction N	$f_\infty (N) \times 10^3$
Methyl	0.28		1.51	0.0050	7.55
		3.8			
Ethyl	0.073		3.69	0.0013	4.79
		3.0			
n-Propyl	0.024		14.4	0.00043	6.19
		4.7			
n-Butyl	0.0051		52.9	0.000092	5.86
		4.6			
Iso-amyl	0.0011		191.0	0.000020	3.82
		3.7			
n-Hexyl	0.00029		903.0	0.0000054	4.87
		3.9			
n-Heptyl					
n-Octyl	0.000074		12,300.0	0.0000013	15.9

* The numerical values of f_∞ in this column are aqueous activity coefficients at infinite dilution and 25°C for the corresponding aliphatic alcohols as given by Butler (1937).   It is assumed for the calculations in this table that the activity coefficients of the carbamates are in a constant proportion to those of the corresponding alcohol.

Although A varies with temperature, and also with concentration because of deviations from ideal solutions, such variations do not greatly influence the figures given in Table 10.4.   The comparison of potencies of the different members of a homologous series of narcotics on the basis of their activity is more rational than on the basis of Traube's rule.   Traube's rule actually reflects the difference in activity among the members of a homologous series (cf. Langmuir, 1917; Frumkin, 1925) as they might be measured by their surface activity.

In Table 10.4 the narcotic potencies of the different carbamates in terms of $f_\infty(N)$ vary by a factor of 4, whereas the concentrations vary by a factor of nearly 4,000. Ferguson (1939) and Brink and Posternak (1948) have shown that many organic compounds acting on diverse physiological processes have about the same potency at the same thermodynamic activity. The processes include the reversible suppression of reflex

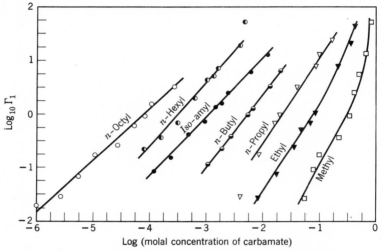

Fig. 10.36. Inhibition of luminescence of *P. phosphoreum* suspended in phosphate-buffered sodium chloride solution, of neutral pH at 15°C, by a series of homologous carbamates (Johnson, Flagler, Simpson, and McGeer, 1951).

response in tadpoles (Meyer and Hemmi, 1935), the reversible suppression of spontaneous movement of tadpoles (Vernon, 1913), the suppression of response of the frog gastrocnemius muscle to electrical stimuli (Kochmann, 1923), the narcosis of the tortoise heart (Vernon, 1912), the reversible suppression of spontaneous contraction in the isolated frog heart (Führner, 1921b), the reversible inhibition of respiration of goose erythrocytes (Warburg, 1921), the narcosis of mice (Führner, 1921a), the reversible suppression of transmission of nerve impulses (Posternak and Larrabee, 1948), surgical anesthesia in humans (Goodman and Gilman, 1941), the inhibition of development of sea urchins' eggs (Führner, 1904; cf. also Cornman, 1950b), the hemolysis of ox blood cells (Führner and Neubauer, 1907), the disinfection of *B. typhosus* (Tilley and Schaffer, 1926), and others.

The relation between the amount of inhibition of luminescence and the concentration of carbamate added to the bacterial suspension is illustrated in Fig. 10.36, plotted in accordance with equation (10.7). The relationship is linear, except that with methyl and ethyl carbamates the slopes increase at concentrations above those required for about 50 per cent inhibition. Furthermore, there is a tendency for the slope, at inhibitions of less than 50 per cent, to decrease as the length of the aliphatic chain of the different carbamates increases. Thus for methyl and ethyl carbamates these slopes are approximately 2, while for n-propyl carbamate the slope is 1.6, and for octyl carbamate it is 1.0. These changes in slopes complicate any simple correlation between the activity coefficient of the homologue and the concentration required for a given per cent inhibition, when more than a single per cent inhibition, such as 50 per cent, is considered. The changing slopes with increasing concentration of methyl or ethyl carbamate and the non-integral values of the slopes for some other members of the series are indicative of more than one equilibrium, as discussed in preceding paragraphs with respect to the effects of ethyl carbamate (urethan) and ethyl alcohol. Further evidence for a multiplicity of equilibria and the nature of these equilibria established by a particular carbamate is apparent in the effects of temperature and hydrostatic pressure. The temperature and pressure relationships are especially interesting because they indicate a change in the predominant type of inhibitory equilibrium in going from lower to higher molecular weight homologues, as we shall see.

Figure 10.37 shows the influence of temperature on the inhibition of luminescence by three different carbamates, each at a concentration causing a moderate effect at the normal optimal temperature. With methyl carbamate the temperature relationship resembles that of ethyl carbamate, as already discussed; the amount of inhibition increases with rise in temperature as the normal optimum is approached and exceeded. With propyl and higher carbamates, on the other hand, the reverse is true, the inhibition rapidly becoming less at temperatures above the optimum. This type of action is similar to the one found with sulfanilamide or hydrogen ions. In the present instance, however, the inhibition is replaced at relatively high temperatures by a stimulation that may amount to as much as a doubling of luminescence intensity as compared to the control. The mechanism of the stimulation is unclear.

The inhibition of a given reaction or process by a single carbamate sometimes exhibits the two types of temperature relationships just mentioned in regard to the action of ethyl and higher carbamates, respectively, on luminescence. For example, the inhibition of invertase activity by urethan decreases slightly with rise in temperature until near the normal optimal temperature of the enzyme, then increases with further rise in temperature (Johnson, Kauzmann, and Gensler, 1948). In *Arbacia* eggs, 0.028 to 0.078 *M* urethan is least effective at 20° to 21°C in slowing the rate of cleavage; at higher or lower temperatures a given concentration is more effective (Cornman, 1950a).

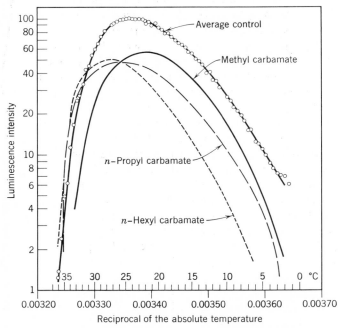

Fig. 10.37.   The influence of temperature on the inhibition of luminescence in *P. phosphoreum* caused by single respective concentrations of methyl, *n*-propyl, and *n*-hexyl carbamates.   Maximum intensity of the control is arbitrarily taken as 100.   The points on the control curve are single or averaged values from nineteen repeated experiments.   The points have been omitted from the other curves to avoid crowding the figure (Johnson, Flagler, Simpson, and McGeer, 1951).

The influence of pressure on the inhibition by moderate concentrations of methyl carbamate at a constant temperature is illustrated in Fig. 10.38. At each concentration, pressures up to about 3,000 psi progressively reduce the inhibition in a regular manner, as if a single equilibrium were primarily involved, with a volume change of between 60 and 70 cc per mole according to the slopes of the lines.   At pressures above about 3,000 psi, however, the slopes become much steeper, especially with the lower concentrations of the carbamate.   The change in slope is again evidence for more than a single equilibrium. The average volume change, computed according to the relation

$$\overline{\Delta V} = RT \frac{(\ln \Gamma_{1p_2} - \ln \Gamma_{1p_1})}{p_2 - p_1} \qquad (10.20)$$

corresponding to equation (10.17), amounts to 279 cc per mole for the pressure range 5,000 to 8,000 psi with 0.22 M methyl carbamate. At the same drug concentration the volume change similarly computed for the range 7,000 to 8,000 psi is 438 cc per mole. These volume changes of 279 and 438 cc per mole seem extraordinarily large. They may result in part from an unusually large experimental error associated with the measurement of very small inhibitions (between 2 and 8 per cent inhibition). Thus, if the value of I_1 in the expression $(I_1/I_2 - 1)$ were a few per cent too small, the measured value of I_2, even if fully accurate, would be relatively too large, and the value computed for Γ_1 would therefore be too small. The very large volume changes occur mostly under circumstances such as these (cf. also the effects of pressure on the inhibition by relatively low concentrations of alcohol, p. 426). The observed value of I_1 might

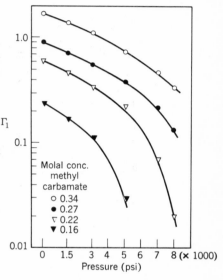

Fig. 10.38. Influence of pressure on the inhibition of luminescence in *P. phosphoreum* at 17°C by moderate concentrations of methyl carbamate (Johnson, Flagler, Simpson, and McGeer, 1951).

easily be too small because it is usually determined with a portion of the same suspension of cells a few minutes before that of I_2, and some decrease in the intensity of luminescence of a given suspension frequently occurs on standing. An error in the same direction would arise if the observed value of I_2 were too large by a few per cent. This error would arise if, in addition to the inhibitory effect of the drug, there were a simultaneous stimulating effect, through a different mechanism, corresponding to the increase in intensity over that of the control at temperatures above the optimum (Fig. 10.37) or below the optimum (Fig. 10.23) at appropriate concentrations of certain carbamates or of ethyl alcohol, respectively.

The observed effects of pressure vary with different members of the carbamate series, each at a concentration causing an inhibition of roughly 50 per cent at atmospheric pressure and 17°C (Fig. 10.39). Thus, while pressure reduces the inhibition by lower members of the series (methyl or ethyl carbamate), this effect becomes progressively less with increase in

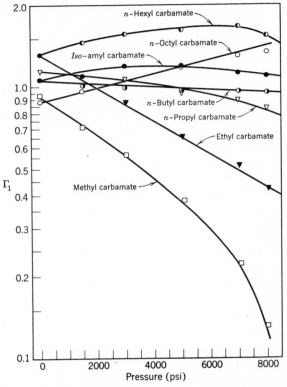

Fig. 10.39. The influence of pressure at 17°C on the inhibition of luminescence in *P. phosphoreum* by homologous carbamates in concentrations causing roughly a 50 per cent inhibition at atmospheric pressure (Johnson, Flagler, Simpson, and McGeer, 1951).

length of the aliphatic chain (propyl and butyl carbamates) until finally there is evidence of an increase in the amount of inhibition under pressure (*iso*-amyl, hexyl, and octyl carbamates).

Since all these experiments on the carbamate inhibition of luminescence deal with effects in intact, living cells, they possibly, though not necessarily, involve effects on more than one enzyme system. Whether they involve only one or more than one system, it is clear from the analyses of the data that more than a single equilibrium reaction can be established between a single carbamate and one or more enzymes limiting the process of luminescence.   The probability that a component of more than one enzyme system is affected is supported by the stimulating effects observed under some conditions.   On the other hand, the simplest interpretation for the inhibitory effects is that each homologue acts to a significant extent only upon the light-emitting system directly.   This interpretation is supported by two chief considerations: (1) the general sensitivity of the luminescent system, both in cells and in extracts, to the action of various narcotics, and (2) the known examples wherein the denaturation of a single, purified protein is catalyzed by urea or by ethyl carbamate through a multiplicity of reactions (pp. 282 and 442).

Of the several possible equilibrium reactions, with different characteristics of heat, entropy, volume change, and ratio of combining molecules, the particular equilibrium which predominates depends upon the conditions as well as upon the carbamate.   For example, with methyl carbamate the average ratio of drug to enzyme molecules increases, at atmospheric pressure and at temperatures below the normal optimum, when the concentration of the drug exceeds the amount required for about 50 per cent inhibition.   With octyl carbamate under the same conditions no such increase is apparent, but octyl carbamate is so insoluble in water that it is difficult to obtain a sufficiently concentrated solution to cause an inhibition of more than about 50 per cent; otherwise, a change in number of combining molecules at the higher concentrations would possibly be observed also with this higher member of the series.   The type of equilibrium most readily established by the higher members of the series seems to involve the combination of only one drug molecule per enzyme molecule or, in any event, a lower ratio of drug : enzyme molecules than in the type of equilibrium most readily established by lower members of the series.   Furthermore, the volume change is smaller, and the heat of reaction lower, as judged by the relative ineffectiveness of pressure and the relative effectiveness of a rise in temperature in counteracting the inhibition.   Possibly the higher carbamates inactivate the enzyme primarily by combining at the surface of the protein, whereas the lower carbamates combine more readily with hydrophobic groups which are normally folded up within the interior of the molecule but which are exposed through an unfolding, accompanied by a large volume increase, in the reversible denaturation reaction.

This analysis of the action of carbamates on bacterial luminescence is of some general interest because similarities in the effects of ethyl carbamate on luminescence and on other processes at constant temperature and pressure have been noted, and because the action of various narcotics on many different physiological processes is so generally related to the thermodynamic activity of the narcotic (p. 432). There is not yet sufficient quantitative data with respect to temperature and pressure relations of inhibition in other processes to discuss them at length. There is a remarkable correlation, however, between the action of pressure on the inhibition of luminescence by different carbamates and the action of pressure on the narcosis of amphibian larvae by the same carbamates, as described later (p. 512). Moreover, it has been shown that each of the series, ethyl to *n*-amyl carbamates, produces more than one effect on the resting potential of frog sciatic-peroneal nerves (Crescitelli, 1948). Low concentrations reversibly increase the resting potential slightly, at the same time causing an easily reversible conduction block. Higher concentrations cause a progressive depolarization and gradually lead to an irreversible conduction block. It is convenient to consider at this point the irreversible effects, in general, caused by various drugs and other agents.

Irreversible effects of drugs and other agents

By an irreversible effect we mean one from which no appreciable recovery occurs, without the intervention of such complex processes as growth and synthesis of a new supply of the substances affected. A reversible effect is one from which recovery occurs, whether slowly or rapidly, on removal of the agent responsible for the effect. As we define it, it involves primarily the same substances originally acted upon. Examples of rapid reversibility are the changes in light intensity of bacteria when quickly cooled from temperatures above the normal optimum, or the light emission that immediately takes place on the addition of water to a reaction mixture of luciferin and luciferase whose reaction has been inhibited by high concentrations of urethan. An example of slow reversal is the process of renaturation of thermally denatured trypsin inhibitor from soybeans (p. 247). Some inhibitions that are not appreciably reversed by removal of the inhibitory agent from the solution can be reversed by addition to the solution of another agent which itself has a sufficient affinity for the inhibitor. For example, the inactivation of enzymes and bacteriophage, or the "killing" of bacteria by mercuric chloride is irreversible in the usual sense, but the addition of cysteine, glutathione, mercaptans, hydrogen sulfide, thioglycolic acid, or even denatured proteins or adsorbents such as blood charcoal is sometimes sufficient to reverse the inhibition (Chick, 1908; Süpfle and Müller, 1920; Gegenbauer, 1921; Englehardt, 1922; Quastel and Wooldridge, 1927; Krueger and Baldwin, 1934; Gemmill and Hellerman, 1937; Hellerman, 1937, 1939; Fildes, 1940; McCalla, 1940). Bacteria "killed" by sodium hypochlorite, acriflavin, phenol or surface-active cations, respectively, can be revived by appropriate amounts of thiosulfate (Mudge and Smith, 1935), certain growth substances (McIlwain, 1941), activated charcoal or ferric chloride (Flett et al., 1945), and high molecular weight anions (Valko and DuBois, 1944), respectively.   In these instances death of the organism is judged primarily on the basis of its inability to reproduce.   The inhibitory agent does not dissociate sufficiently rapidly from its sites of combination in the cell, merely by diluting the medium, to

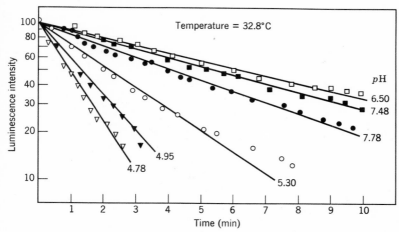

Fig. 10.40.   Influence of pH on the rate of destruction of the luminescent system of *Photobacterium phosphoreum* suspended in phosphate-buffered sodium chloride solution at 32.8°C (Johnson, Eyring, Steblay, et al., 1945).

permit recovery before the cell dies of old age or as a result of rate processes of destruction promoted, directly or indirectly, by the agent. The counteractant hastens the process of dissociation, and in effect neutralizes the action of the inhibitor, by combining with it usually at its site of action as well as in the medium.

In a strict sense, of course, there are no irreversible chemical reactions; the problem is always one of relative reaction rates involving a single system or several systems.   The reaction is considered irreversible when the rate in the forward direction is very great in comparison to the rate in the backward direction.   Temperature is always the factor of prime importance, whatever the catalyst—pure water, hydrogen or hydroxyl ions, various drugs—and wherever large molecules are concerned the influence of pressure is potentially significant.   As a typical biological process, let us again consider luminescence.

The luminescent system of bacteria suspended in a buffered salt solution of neutral pH undergoes both a reversible inactivation and a rate process of destruction at temperatures above the optimum, as already discussed (p. 235). The rate of destruction under these conditions has the high heat and entropy of activation characteristic of protein denaturation. It would be anticipated that factors influencing the rate of protein denaturation in general would act in a similar manner on this rate of destruction. For example, at a given temperature a pH dependence of the rate would be expected. Figure 10.40 illustrates such a relationship. Over short periods of observation the rate is first order at the various pH values between 4.78 and 7.78. Longer periods of observation at this and other

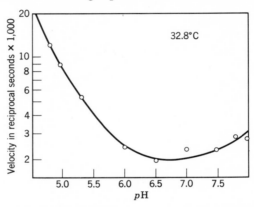

Fig. 10.41. Analysis of the first order rate constants as a function of pH from the data of Fig. 10.40.

temperatures have not been studied, and they would probably reveal complications such as those discussed in relation to the extracted enzyme of *Cypridina* (p. 238) and other proteins. The first order rate constants computed from the slopes of the lines in Fig. 10.40 are plotted as the logarithm against pH in Fig. 10.41. The minimum rate under the stated conditions occurs between pH 6.5 and pH 7.0, which is within the same range as the pH optimum for luminescence at lower temperatures. Here it is probably very close to the isoelectric point of the protein (cf. discussion on p. 280). In Fig. 10.41 the slope of a tangent to the curve in the most acid range is approximately 3.5, indicating that an average of 3.5 H ions combines with the protein undergoing denaturation.

At neutral pH the destruction proceeds with a large volume increase of activation as shown by the effects of increased hydrostatic pressure. The data are illustrated in Fig. 10.42. $\Delta V^{\ddagger}$ calculated from these data with the aid of equation (9.7) amounts to about 71 cc per mole and varies only slightly from this value at temperatures between 32° and 36°C. The quantitative effects of pressure illustrated in Fig. 10.42 resemble those shown in Fig. 9.21 concerning the denaturation of tobacco mosaic virus protein.

The denaturation of purified tobacco mosaic virus in neutral solution at high temperatures is catalyzed by low concentrations of urethan. As

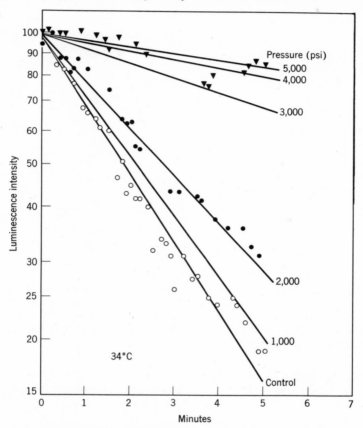

Fig. 10.42. The influence of hydrostatic pressure on the relative rate of destruction of the luminescent system of *P. phosphoreum* suspended in phosphate-buffered sodium chloride of neutral *p*H at 34°C (Johnson, Eyring, et al., 1945). The points are somewhat scattered because of errors in the visual photometry of a rapidly diminishing low intensity of luminescence.

with high concentrations of urea at low temperatures, several reactions are involved between the drug and the protein, and some of the reactions with urethan are evidently accompanied by large volume changes (Fraser, Johnson, and Baker, 1949). The data are illustrated in Fig. 10.43.

In Fig. 10.43 both curves are accounted for fairly closely on the assumption of not less than two reactions between urethan and the protein. The assumption of three such reactions gives a very close fit between calculated and observed data, as shown in the figure. Thus the overall rate is given by

$$\frac{d(\text{TMV})}{dt} = k(\text{TMV}) \tag{10.21}$$

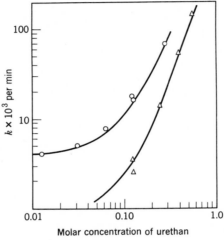

Fig. 10.43. Influence of urethan on the rate of denaturation of pure tobacco mosaic virus in phosphate buffer, pH 7.0, at 68.8°C, at normal pressure (circles) and under 7,000 psi of hydrostatic pressure (triangles), respectively. The solid lines are calculated according to the equation described in the text (Fraser, Johnson, and Baker, 1949).

where k represents the sum of all the individual specific reaction rate constants. Assuming that three reactions with urethan are involved,

$$k = k_0 + k_1(\text{U})^x + k_2(\text{U})^y + k_3(\text{U})^z \tag{10.22}$$

The concentration of urethan added is so large (0.025 to 0.15 M) in comparison to the concentration of protein (6.0 mg per cc, or about 0.00000015 M) that it may be assumed to remain constant. The numerical value of k_0 is obtained in experiments without added urethan. The numerical value of k_3 was chosen from the rate observed at relatively high urethan concentration, where k_0 is small relative to k_3, and a value of $z = 3$ was estimated from the slope of the line in the region of high urethan concentration. Values of the other constants, k_1, k_2, x, and y, were chosen to fit the data. Each of the k's is subject to modification by hydrostatic pressure, depending upon the volume change of activation, as given by equation (9.7).   The value of $\Delta V^{\ddagger}$ for k_0 was determined through the experiments referred to earlier (p. 328), and values for $\Delta V^{\ddagger}$ pertaining to k_1, k_2, and k_3, respectively, were estimated to fit the data.   The various constants used in calculating the curves of Fig. 10.43 are summarized in Table 10.5.   The activation energy for k_0 has been determined (p. 328), but, since the influence of different temperatures on the effects of urethan

Table 10.5.   Constants Used in Equation (10.22) in the Calculation of the Curves of Fig. 10.43 for the Rate of TMV Denaturation at Atmospheric and 7,000 psi of Hydrostatic Pressure in the Presence of Various Concentrations of Urethan

	k_0	k_1	k_2	k_3
x, y, or z		1	2	3
Atmospheric pressure	3.79×10^{-3}	2.2×10^{-2}	2.9×10^{-1}	1.9
7,000 psi	0.87×10^{-3}	0.38×10^{-2}	0.53×10^{-1}	0.68
$\Delta V^{\ddagger}$	100 cc	100 cc	100 cc	50 cc

has not been studied, no value can be given as yet for the $\Delta H^{\ddagger}$ pertaining to k_1, k_2, or k_3.

Equations (10.21) and (10.22) show that, in spite of the complexity of k, the rate still proceeds with first order-kinetics, as observed in the experiments.   Thus

$$-\frac{d(\text{TMV})}{dt} = k_0(\text{TMV}) + k_1(\text{U})^x(\text{TMV}) + k_2(\text{U})^y(\text{TMV}) + k_3(\text{U})^z(\text{TMV})$$

$$= [k_0 + k_1(\text{U})^x + k_2(\text{U})^y + k_3(\text{U})^z](\text{TMV}) \qquad (10.23)$$

The overall rate remains first order as long as the terms enclosed in the bracket of (10.23) remain constant and as long as the specific rate is proportional to the amount of undenatured TMV remaining at any moment.   The denaturation of purified serum globulin discussed earlier (p. 327) is more complicated, but the overall rate is retarded under increased pressure with, as well as without, low concentrations of alcohol which accelerate the process of denaturation (Fig. 10.44).

Although the concentrations of urethan and of alcohol required for the effects illustrated in Figs. 10.43 and 10.44, respectively, are the same as those which affect physiological processes in living cells, the temperature required for the denaturation and for observing an effect of low concentrations of these drugs on the purified proteins is much higher.   In general, however, the temperature required depends upon both the specific protein and the conditions, as discussed earlier (p. 381), in relation to reduced temperatures in equations of state. The thermal denaturation of some intracellular enzymes in a medium of neutral pH requires extraordinarily high temperatures, for example, the formic dehydrogenase of *Escherichia coli*, which shows little evidence of heat inactivation at temperatures below about 80°C (Johnson and Lewin, 1946a). This enzyme is

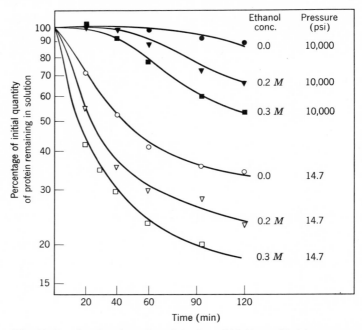

Fig. 10.44. Acceleration of precipitation of highly purified human serum globulin by alcohol, and retardation of precipitation by 10,000 psi of hydrostatic pressure, at 65°C (Johnson and Campbell, 1946).

in marked contrast to the luminescent system which, in the psychrophilic bacterium, *Photobacterium phosphoreum*, undergoes denaturation at a measurable rate at about 30°C or above. The temperature required for a measurable rate of denaturation of systems either *in vivo* or *in vitro* may be modified by many factors—pH, various ions, pressure, drugs, etc.—as shown in this and the two preceding chapters. Drugs such as alcohol or urethan, which promote both reversible and irreversible denaturations, in effect lower the temperature required for denaturation. Under conditions which require high temperatures, e.g., 65° to 70°C, to cause precipitation of a given protein in absence of the drug, the precipitation sometimes occurs at room temperature if a sufficiently high concentration of the drug is added.   Thus precipitation of purified human serum globulin occurs at 20°C in the presence of about 10 times the concentration of alcohol that accelerates precipitation, under otherwise similar conditions, at 65°C. Denaturation of many proteins without precipitation occurs at room

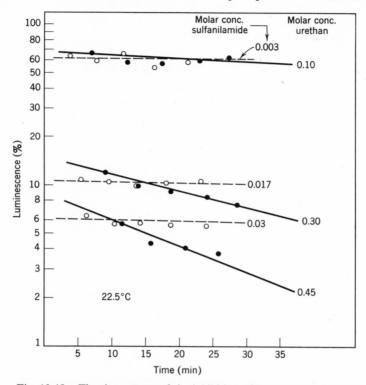

Fig. 10.45.   The time course of the inhibition of luminescence in *P. phosphoreum* at 22.50°C by sulfanilamide (broken lines) and urethan (solid lines), respectively, in concentrations that cause initially similar diminutions of intensity (Johnson, Eyring, Steblay, et al., 1945).

temperature in the presence of high concentrations of urea, as is well known.   The net effect of a drug is always governed by the thermodynamic and rate constants of the reactions that are involved, and these constants determine the temperature and concentrations necessary for a measurable effect.   Analyses of temperature relationships, such as those which follow, show that high concentrations of alcohol, urethan, or other drugs are often not required in order that they catalyze the denaturation of intracellular enzymes at physiological temperatures.

In luminescence at the normal optimum temperature, atmospheric pressure, and neutral pH, moderate inhibitions of 50 per cent or less by either sulfanilamide or urethan are immediate and are readily reversible. As the concentration of sulfanilamide is increased, the immediate inhibition becomes greater and then remains constant at any given concentration. As the concentration of urethan is increased, the immediate inhibition also becomes greater, but then progressively increases at a rate that depends upon the concentration added (Fig. 10.45).

Table 10.6. Influence of Temperature, Length of Exposure, and Concentration of Alcohol on the Amount of Inhibition of Oxygen Consumption, Expressed as Q_{O_2}, in Cerebral Cortex Slices of Rat Brain

(From Fuhrman and Field, 1948)

Temp. (°C)	Period of Time after Adding Alcohol (min)	Alcohol: Per Cent by Volume					
		0	1.9	3.8	5.7	7.6	9.5
20.0	30–180 (constant)	1.96	2.27	1.96	1.85	1.55	1.55
30.0	30–60	5.25	6.59	5.30	5.46	4.74	4.02
	60–120	5.25	6.08	5.30	5.46	4.17	2.68
	120–180	5.25	5.87	5.30	5.46	3.45	1.91
37.7	30–60	11.02	11.74	10.82	9.89	8.24	3.70
	60–120	11.02	11.74	9.68	7.82	3.61	1.39
	120–180	11.02	11.74	8.14	4.58	1.03	1.03

The results shown in Fig. 10.45 were expected on the basis of the difference in mechanism of inhibition by the two drugs, as already discussed. It is not possible, however, to predict *a priori* the relative extent to which a process will be reversibly inhibited through a purely equilibrium reaction and through a progressive destruction of the system. For example, moderate inhibitions by ethyl ether or ethyl alcohol of the activity in the central nervous system of mammals seem to be largely reversible. The same narcotics inhibit the respiration of slices of the rat brain *in vitro*, but here the inhibition is practically irreversible (Jowett and Quastel, 1937; Jowett, 1938). The inhibition by a given concentration of alcohol was found to be less at 34° than at 39°C (Jowett, 1938). Using the same material, i.e., rat cerebral cortex slices, Fuhrman and Field (1948) have obtained additional data with respect to the influence of temperature (Table 10.6).

Although more data would be desirable for a satisfactory analysis, the data of Table 10.6 are interesting in several respects. First, an increase in respiratory rate is observed with the lowest concentrations of alcohol, and, as in luminescence (Fig. 10.23, p. 410), the amount of increase is less as the temperature is raised. Secondly, at the lowest temperature (20°C) the reduction in rate by the various concentrations of alcohol remains constant. Reversibility of the inhibition under these conditions was apparently not tested, but it seems likely that it will be

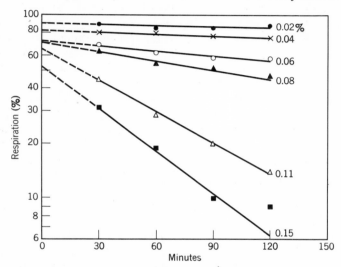

Fig. 10.46.   Data replotted from Jowett (1938) on the inhibition of oxygen consumption in rat brain slices by various concentrations of phenobarbital as a function of time.

found reversible, in contrast to the irreversible effects caused by similar concentrations of alcohol at the higher temperatures (Jowett, 1938). Thirdly, the rate of progressively increasing inhibition with time is greater both with increase in concentration of alcohol and with increase in temperature. Qualitatively, all these results would be expected on the basis of the preceding discussions of the mechanism of action of drugs of this type.

The action of phenobarbital ("luminal") on the respiration of rat brain slices seems to occur by fundamentally the same mechanism as the action of alcohol, and it bears significant points in common with the action of urethan and alcohol on luminescence, as well as with the action of heat alone on luminescence. In Fig. 10.46 we have replotted on a semi-logarithmic scale the data of Jowett (1938; Fig. 2, p. 326). Because the change in rate immediately following addition of the drug could not be measured by the method employed, data are lacking for this initial period, here extending through the first 30 min.   All curves in the original figure of Jowett (1938) were extrapolated as broken curves back to 100 per cent respiration at zero time.   In our Fig. 10.46 we have extrapolated the data for each drug concentration as a straight line (broken lines) back to zero time.   Although the rapidity of change in respiratory rate during the initial 30-min period represented by the broken lines has not been established, it is evidently fast compared to the rapidity of change during the subsequent period, represented by the solid lines.   For purposes of analysis, we will assume that the initial rapid reduction in rate arises from an equilibrium reaction, similar to that involved in the urethan or alcohol inhibition of luminescence, or the inhibition of luminescence at temperatures above the normal optimum in the absence of drugs (e.g., compare Fig. 10.46 with Fig. 8.32, p. 236).   Furthermore, we will assume that the progressive increase in amount of inhibition at a given drug concentration results from a rate process of destruction catalyzed by phenobarbital in fundamentally the same manner as the action of alcohol or urethan on the process of luminescence and on the denaturation of purified proteins. On these assumptions the data of Fig. 10.46 are plotted in Fig. 10.47, with interesting results.

Although the reversibility of inhibition was not critically examined in these experiments, we may assume with Jowett that the "moderate" inhibitions are probably reversible by removal of the drug.   Using a formulation derived from the law of mass action, and essentially the same as the one developed by Fisher and Öhnell (1940), Jowett (1938) showed that the moderate inhibitions after a 2-hr period can be quantitatively accounted for on the assumption that a reversible chemical combination occurs between the narcotic and some component of the respiratory system to which respiration is proportional.   Deviations from this relationship occurred with inhibitions which, at the end of 2 hr, amounted to more than about 40 per cent.   Since the lower concentrations of luminal required for the moderate inhibitions clearly do not catalyze a rapid rate of increasing inhibition, the agreement with the law of mass action is understandable.   In Fig. 10.47 this agreement is attested by the straightness of the lower line, with slope equal to unity.   This line for initial inhibition includes points for all the concentrations.   Deviations become progressively greater with increasing length of time because of the additional amount of inhibition resulting from the rate process of presumably irreversible destruction catalyzed by the same drug.   In Fig. 10.47 the upper curve deals separately with the latter process.   Except at the very low concentrations where the slope changes, most of the points fall along a straight line of slope equal to 2.25.   The change in slope and the non-integral value of 2.25 are understandable in terms of a multiplicity of reactions, possibly involving the same enzyme system, as in the examples discussed earlier.

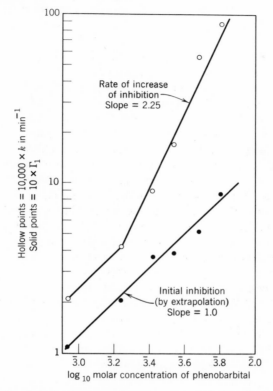

Fig. 10.47.   Relation between the concentration of phenobarbital and its initial effect on respiration of rat brain slices (solid points) according to the slopes of the broken lines extrapolated back to zero time on the ordinate of Fig. 10.46, and the relation between concentration of phenobarbital and rate of increasing inhibition after the initial effect (hollow circles) according to the slopes of the solid lines in Fig. 10.46.   The data are from Jowett (1938).

Unfortunately, variation with temperature of the effects of phenobarbital shown in Fig. 10.46 were not studied.   We would anticipate that the rate of increasing inhibition with time would also increase with rise in temperature.   The temperature dependence of the initial, probably easily reversible, inhibition by phenobarbital is more difficult to predict. It would increase or decrease with rise in temperature according to whether this action occurs chiefly in the manner of a lower or of a higher member of the homologous series of carbamates on luminescence (p. 434). At constant temperature the theory that has been discussed provides a satisfactory interpretation of the effects. Before the development of this theory in connection with the process of bacterial luminescence, the cause of the increasing inhibition with time of exposure was especially obscure (Quastel, 1943).

Cytological and other visible changes induced by narcotics

Because of the fairly general circumstance that drugs which promote a reversible denaturation of proteins are likely to catalyze also an irreversible denaturation, it would be anticipated that certain visible changes in cell structure caused by heat would appear at lower temperatures in the presence of the appropriate drug. A particularly interesting example of this phenomenon has been demonstrated in the effects of heat and of urethan on the nuclear structure of luminous bacteria (Johnson and Gray, 1949). In young, rapidly growing cultures of *Achromobacter fischeri* nuclear staining according to the methods developed by Robinow (1945) reveals discrete chromatin units in the typical shapes of spheroids, dumbbells, V's, Y's, etc., as usually found in rod-shaped bacteria under corresponding conditions (Fig. 10.48A). On incubation of a portion of the culture for a relatively short time at a temperature roughly 10 degrees higher than the normal optimum for growth of the organism, the nuclear bodies coalesce into a beaded or sometimes apparently continuous strand (Fig. 10.48B). Much the same results are obtained by incubating a portion of the original culture at a temperature roughly 10 degrees below the normal optimum with 0.5 M urethan in the medium (Fig. 10.48C). The concentrations of urethan required for a pronounced change in visible appearance of the nuclear structures are of the same magnitude but are somewhat higher than those which, at the same temperature, reversibly inhibit the production of luminescence and lead to a progressive destruction of the luminescent system. Also in concentrations of the same magnitude, urethan in the protozoan *Colpodo steinii* prevents mitosis, causes pycnosis of the nuclei, and reverts the actively dividing nuclei to the resting stage (Burt, 1945).

Phenomena related to the above have been observed with a variety of other biological materials, e.g., the reversible flocculation in the cytoplasm of yeast cells under the influence of amyl alcohol (Bancroft and Richter, 1931), the flocculation in nuclei of nerve cells in the presence of dilute alcohol, or the coagulation of protoplasm in various cells under the influence of disinfectants, metallic ions, and other agents (Marinesco, 1912). Correlations between the potency of a substance in causing narcosis of animals as well as inhibiting various biological processes, and

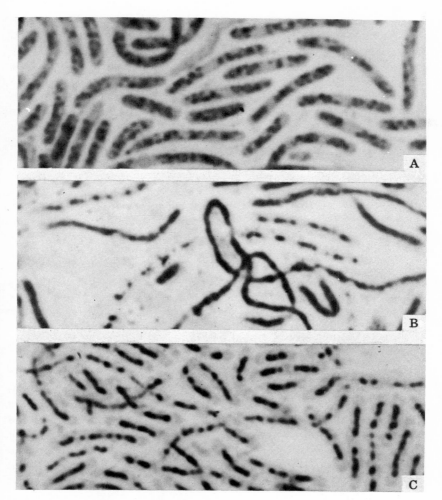

Fig. 10.48. Nuclear structures of the luminous bacterium, *A. fischeri*, stained by the osmic acid-HCl-Giemsa method of Robinow (1945). (A) Normal appearance in a young culture incubated 105 min at 28°C on brain-heart infusion agar containing isotonic (3%) sodium chloride. (B) Corresponding culture at 37°C for 80 min. (C) Corresponding culture after transfer to medium of the same composition except for the addition of 0.5 M urethan and incubating for 63 min at 20°C. (From Johnson and Gray, 1949.)

in bringing about a reversible opalescence of tissues or tissue extracts, have long been known and discussed (Ranke, 1867, 1877; Binz, 1877; Bernard, 1875; Salkowski, 1888, 1900; Formánek, 1900; Moore and Roaf, 1904; Winterstein, 1926; and others). They form the basis of the "precipitation theory" of narcosis (Bernard, 1875) according to which the action of narcotics on nerve cells is that of causing a semicoagulation that is reversible on elimination of the narcotic agent. Usually the concentration of the drug required for visible opalescence or precipitation is in

Table 10.7. Concentrations of Narcotics Required To Inhibit Succino-oxidase Activity of Liver and To Precipitate Nucleoproteins of Liver

(From Batelli and Stearn, 1913a)

Narcotic Agent	Molar Concentration for Inhibiting Oxidase Activity	Molar Concentration for Precipitating Nucleoprotein
Methyl alcohol	5.78	6.31
Ethyl alcohol	2.97	3.33
Propyl alcohol	1.09	1.44
Iso-butyl alcohol	0.41	0.46
Iso-amyl alcohol	0.18	0.24
Methylethyl ketone	0.82	0.94
Methylpropyl ketone	0.34	0.39
Ethyl carbamate	0.95	1.06
Propyl carbamate	0.39	0.48

excess of the concentration required to narcotize an animal or to inhibit a process such as respiration. In some instances, however, the concentrations effective in either phenomenon are nearly the same. Thus Warburg and Wiesel (1912) found that a precipitate in the juice expressed from yeast cells was brought about by various members of a homologous series of narcotics in concentrations only slightly higher than those required to inhibit oxidation in the yeast cells. Similarly Batelli and Stearn (1913a) found a close correlation between the concentrations of various narcotics that inhibit the oxidation of succinic acid by liver extracts, and that flocculate the nucleoproteins of the same organ (Table 10.7). On the basis of our preceding discussions, it would be expected that such correlations should exist in some instances, although their absence would not necessarily indicate any fundamental differences between the action of the drug on the physiological process and on solubility of the protein. Precipitation does not necessarily accompany denaturation, e.g., Meyerhof (1918) found that the presence of salts is required for the precipitation of proteins in solution by urethan although salts are not required for denaturation (Chapter 8).

Temperature relationships have usually been neglected in studies like those just discussed. From the present perspective, certain interpretations that were overlooked or were vague in earlier investigations now seem obvious. For example, some years prior to the biochemical demonstrations by Northrop, Anson, and others of the reversibility of protein denaturation and coagulation, Heilbrunn (1924b) noted that the protoplasm in eggs of the sea urchin and of the clam, *Cumingia*, undergoes a reversible coagulation at 32° to 33°C, and that the coagulation becomes irreversible if these temperatures are maintained for some time. In addition, Heilbrunn found that the effect of ether at ordinary temperatures resembles that of increased temperatures alone. At about the same time, Lepeschkin (1923, 1924) suggested that alcohol acts as a catalyst in the heat denaturation of proteins, on the basis of experiments with egg albumin, and discussed similar temperature relations of denaturation in the presence of ether, chloroform, benzol, and chloral hydrate, as well as the bearing of these relations on the theories of narcosis. Cooper and Mason (1927) discussed the analogy between the bactericidal effects of hot water and of alcohols and phenols. The elements of a general theory relating the seemingly diverse problems of protein denaturation, narcosis, reversible and irreversible effects of drugs, inhibitions of physiological processes, influences on the state of protoplasm, and thermal effects in general, including "disinfection," were at hand, but the data were not sufficiently extensive nor the evidence sufficiently clear and quantitative to form a precise and convincing general theory.

Disinfection

The term disinfection is usually applied to the "chemical" killing of bacteria and other microörganisms, whether they are parasitic or purely saprophytic, as distinguished from killing by "physical" means such as heat or radiation. The distinction is largely artificial and a matter of convenience, inasmuch as the killing process when hastened by the presence of "disinfectants" is fundamentally one of killing by heat, while, conversely, killing by raising the temperature is surely a chemical process. On still other grounds, the term is something of a misnomer, inasmuch as it is practically never applied to the process of killing pathogenic organisms in an infected host, but rather to the killing of either potential pathogens or saprophytes in or on contaminated, non-living materials.

According to its customary meaning, which we will follow, "disinfection" may be regarded as a special aspect of biological inhibitions, here referring to the inhibition of reactions essential to the continuation of life in the organism concerned. In this sense, the term is appropriate both to the killing of microörganisms in a culture and in an infected host.

Action of Inhibitors

Furthermore, on the basis of the foregoing discussions, it would be anticipated that the same relationships would be encountered with respect to the influence of temperature and drug concentration on the rate of disinfection as on individual enzymes or on physiological processes such as respiration; at the molecular level there is little difference.

The rate of disinfection on which theoretical interpretations must be based is a problem of special interest from the point of view of kinetics.

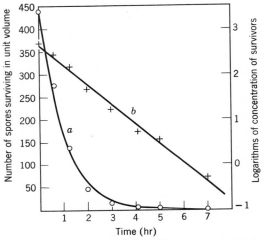

Fig. 10.49. The decrease in number of viable anthrax spores as a function of time in the presence of 5% phenol at 33.3°C (Chick, 1908). The points along the smooth (calculated) curve (a) represent the observed number of surviving spores in unit volume; corresponding points are plotted as the logarithm along the straight line (b).

It is usually measured in terms of the rate at which the number of individual cells in a population of microörganisms is reduced to a state of non-viability, i.e., to a state characterized by an inability to reproduce in a favorable medium. Frequently, though not always, this rate of decrease is exponential, whether under the influence of heat alone, or in the presence of alcohols, heavy metal ions, or other catalysts. Figure 10.49 shows a classic example of disinfection in the presence of phenol (Chick, 1908).

The exponential rate was first noted by Ikeda (1897) in undertaking to analyze data obtained by Kronig and Paul (1897). Since the kinetics is identical to that of a first order reaction, the interpretation of the "logarithmic order of death" has been the subject of much discussion (e.g., Ikeda, 1897; Madsen and Nyman, 1907; Chick, 1908, 1910, 1912,

1930; Eijkman, 1908, 1909, 1912; Watson, 1908; Reichel, 1909; Paul, Birstein, and Reuss, 1910; Reichenbach, 1911; Gregerson, 1916; Loeb and Northop, 1917; Brooks, 1918; Lee and Gilbert, 1918; Peters, 1920; Smith, 1921, 1923; Cohen, 1922; Falk, 1923; Fulmer and Buchanan, 1923; Falk and Winslow, 1926; Knaysi, 1930; Isaacs, 1932; Watkins and Winslow, 1932; Beamer and Tanner, 1939; Rahn, 1934, 1943, 1945a,b; Hinshelwood, 1946; Johnson and Lewin, 1946b; Lea, 1946). Thus in many instances the cells die at a rate proportional to the number remaining alive at any moment, as if each cell behaved in the manner of a single molecule, or as if the inactivation of a single critical molecule in each cell were sufficient to cause the death of that cell. It is difficult to conceive of the life of any cell as depending upon a single one of its constituent molecules, unless, as Rahn (1934) has suggested, the molecule is an essential gene. On the other hand, in the many instances where the logarithmic order of death has been found, it does not seem likely that the kinetics is purely fortuitous.

Exceptions to first order kinetics are likely to be encountered whenever the morphology of the organism or the conditions of the experiment are such that it is difficult to make accurate counts of the number of individual, viable cells at any time. For example, when the cells are normally aggregated into clumps of various sizes, as in staphylococci, or connected together in chains, as in streptococci, or when individual cells happen to occur in clumps for other reasons, the clump as a whole will give rise to only one colony in an agar culture. Thus it may be impossible to tell, by counting the number of colonies that develop, how many individual, viable cells are represented. It is clearly impossible to tell by this, the usual and most nearly reliable method, what proportion of cells is alive in any given clump. Moreover, it is often impossible by any known means to separate the aggregated cells without simultaneously killing or injuring some of the individuals.

Experimental error, however, is not the only reason for deviations from the logarithmic order of death. More complicated kinetics is to be expected whenever there is a significant variation among different individuals in susceptibility to death. Variations of this sort might arise from numerous possible causes. They would be expected to be more prevalent in older than in young cultures of bacteria. Finally, the rate of disinfection will be influenced not only by the number of molecules which must be destroyed to cause the death of a single cell, but also by the number of such molecules present in that cell, even when the destruction of only a single species of molecules is involved. Variations in the number of critical molecules among different cells is probably one of the causes for individual variations in susceptibility to the disinfectant agent.

The observed kinetics of disinfection under any given conditions thus depends upon a number of factors, including (1) the accuracy of determining the number of viable cells, (2) the number of molecules that must be destroyed in each cell to render that cell non-viable, (3) the total number of such molecules present in the cell, (4) the number of different species of molecules whose destruction leads to death, and (5) variations in individual susceptibility to the disinfectant, through possible variations in (2), (3), (4), or other causes. The whole problem, of course, is one which rests on the general theory of probability, as well as on the theory of chemical reactions, which itself involves probability theory. It has been considered by Rahn and others in relation to the probability theory. We will consider the theory briefly with some extensions appropriate to the present discussion.

Let us suppose that the death of any cell results from the destruction of some single species of molecule, of which there are m such molecules in a cell. Let n represent the number of the m molecules which must be destroyed to cause death. If we now assume that m is not a fixed number for all the cells, i.e., that m varies among the different cells of the population, the kinetics of disinfection will be influenced not only by the value of n but also by the value of m, and there are a great many possible variations. Thus we have the following series of cases, where the first numeral corresponds to m, and the second to n; the value of n, of course, is never greater than that of m.

$$(1, 1)$$
$$(2, 1), (2, 2)$$
$$(3, 1), (3, 2), (3, 3)$$
. . . .

In all cases with $n = 1$, i.e., whenever only one molecule per cell must be destroyed to cause death regardless of the number of similar molecules present, the kinetics will follow that of a first order reaction. The other cases, however, are very reasonable possibilities, and they influence either the slope or the shape of the curve, or both, as shown by the following examples.

Let p represent the probability that any molecule from a set n be destroyed at any time t, and let q represent the probability that it remain undestroyed. In general,

$$1 = (p + q)^m = p^m + mp^{(m-1)}q + \frac{m(m-1)}{2}p^{(m-2)}q^2 + \cdots$$

$$+ \frac{m!}{(n)(m-n)!}p^n q^{(m-n)} + \cdots + q^m \qquad (10.24)$$

The rate of disinfection depends upon the numerical values of m, n, and the rate constant k of the destructive reaction. The probability of a molecule's being decomposed is

$$p = 1 - q = (1 - e^{-kt}) \tag{10.25}$$

and the probability of a molecule's not being decomposed is

$$q = m_t/m = e^{-kt} \tag{10.26}$$

where m_t is the number of molecules undestroyed at time t. Postponing for the moment a discussion of the significance of k itself, we will consider the results of a few specific cases involving different values of m and n.

In the simplest case (1, 1), where m is 1 and n is 1, we have $(p + q)^1$, and $q = e^{-kt}$ gives the probability of survival. The number of surviving cells, C_t, at any time is then related to the number at the start in the same manner as the number of the essential molecules m_t at any time is related to the initial number, and therefore

$$\ln\left(\frac{C_t}{C}\right) = \ln\left(\frac{m_t}{m}\right) = -\int_{t=0}^{t} k\, dt \tag{10.27}$$

In this case, provided that k is a constant, a plot of the logarithm of the number of surviving cells from the start, $t = 0$, against time, yields a straight line of slope $= -k$ (Fig. 10.50). Now, if $m = 2$ and the destruction of either molecule in a cell results in death (case 2, 1), the relationship remains linear, but the slope is twice as steep for the same value of k. Here $(p + q)^2 = p^2 + 2pq + q^2$, and $q^2 = e^{-2kt}$ gives the probability of survival. Similarly in the general case containing m molecules in which n is 1, the number of cells surviving is given by $q^m = e^{-mkt}$. The slope of the logarithm of survivors against time is thus proportional to m.

The shape of this curve changes from linearity as the value of n increases. The simplest example is case (2, 2). Here we have $(p + q)^2 = p^2 + 2pq + q^2$, and the probability of cell survival

$$\Pi = 2pq + q^2 = 2e^{-kt} - e^{-2kt}$$

In the general case (m, n), the binomial contains $m + 1$ terms of which the last n terms give Π, the probability of survival. In Fig. 10.50 cases (5, 5) and (10, 10) are included as examples as well as (2, 2).

In the general case where k varies, we have $p = 1 - e^{-\int_0^t k\, dt}$ and $q = e^{-\int_0^t k\, dt}$, or more generally q is the fraction of molecules surviving at a particular time and p is the fraction destroyed. If we look back at Fig. 8.34, for example, and realize that inside a cell q for a molecule might be given by the ordinate, it should be clear that k can go through some very fancy variations with time. k might be a very complicated function of temperature, pressure, and disinfectant concentration (cf., for example,

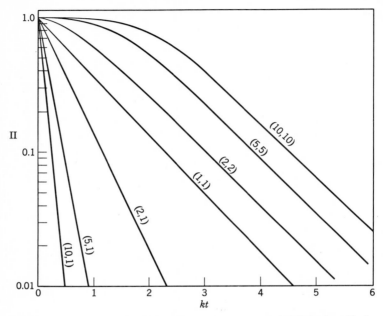

Fig. 10.50. Theoretical curves illustrating the rates of disinfection, Π, for some of the possible cases discussed in the text. For each curve the reaction rate constant has been arbitrarily taken equal to unity. The expressions used in calculating the curves for the different cases are:

Case	
(1,1)	$\Pi = q = e^{-kt}$
(2,1)	$\Pi = q = e^{-2kt}$
(5,1)	$\Pi = q = e^{-5kt}$
(10,1)	$\Pi = q = e^{-10kt}$
(2,2)	$\Pi = 1 - p^2 = 1 - (1 - e^{-kt})^2$
(5,5)	$\Pi = 1 - p^5 = 1 - (1 - e^{-kt})^5$
(10,10)	$\Pi = 1 - p^{10} = 1 - (1 - e^{-kt})^{10}$

Eijkman, 1912; Johnson and Lewin, 1946b). The surprising thing is that the kinetics of disinfection is so frequently simple.

It is interesting to note that implicit in the above theory is the fact that, if m and n vary with the age of a culture of bacteria, the rate of disinfection will vary correspondingly, even though k may remain constant. Thus, if

(5, 5) is the usual situation in young cells, and 4 of the 5 molecules have decomposed in old cells, the rate of disinfection will then resemble (1, 1) and the total process will be faster. On the other hand, if the usual situation in young cells is (1, 1) and a greater supply of the essential molecules m is accumulated in old cells, say $m = 10$, then the rate of disinfection will resemble (10, 10) and the total process will be considerably slower.

In a multicellular organism the theory of poisoning depends upon the death of n cells out of a total of m'. In this case the formal theory proceeds exactly as before except that now Π gives the probability of survival of a cell, and $(1 - \Pi)$ the probability of non-survival. Π and $(1 - \Pi)$ now take the place of p and q in the binomial expansion for survival of the whole organism. Obviously m' and n' have as many possible variations for the multicellular organism as there are variations of (m, n) for a single cell.

When survival of more than one type of molecule is critical for a cell, the theory is more complicated. If we use subscripts 1, 2, 3, etc., for the different types of molecules assumed to behave independently, we now consider the polynomial $(p_1 + q_1)^{m_1}(p_2 + q_2)^{m_2}(p_3 + q_3)^{m_3}$ and select out those terms which correspond to survival depending upon the values of m_1, m_2, m_3, etc. p and q will be determined by reaction rate theory as before. The extension of the theory to multicellular organisms with different kinds of critical cells follows precisely as before. Likewise, the theory may be extended to populations of multicellular organisms. Thus, beginning with populations of molecules in a single cell, and extending to populations of individual cells and to populations of multicellular organisms, there are hierarchies of higher and higher order in the chemical and probability theory.

Whatever the intimate mechanism responsible for the logarithmic order of death actually is, the kinetics is frequently consistent with the view that the death of a single cell is brought about by a single chemical event as in cases (1, 1), (2, 1), (3, 1), etc. Thus, when the slope of the straight line relating the logarithm of the number of survivors to the time of exposure to the killing agent is used as a measure of the rate of killing, the data are often analyzed with results similar to those of simple chemical reactions. Moreover, it is not uncommon to find that the temperature dependence of this rate is in accord with the Arrhenius relation, and, when water alone is the catalyst, the apparent activation energy is of the same order as in the thermal denaturation of proteins. Figure 10.51 is an example; the data indicate an apparent activation energy μ of some 85,000 cal. Wide differences in numerical values of μ are found, however, with different bacterial organisms and with different conditions, as one would expect (cf. Chick, 1930). When the process is catalyzed by acid, phenol, heavy metal ions, or other agents, the apparent activation energy may be lowered to values characteristic of ordinary chemical reactions. For example, the temperature coefficient for rate of disinfection in the presence of mercuric chloride at temperatures between 0° and 30°C is 2.5 for anthrax spores, and between 3 and 4 for the vegetative cells of *B. paratyphosus* (*Salmonella paratyphi*) as listed by Chick (1930). Within the same range of temperatures *B. typhosus* (*Salmonella typhosa*) undergoes

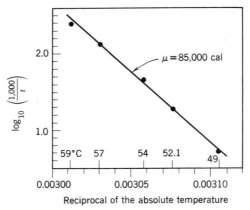

Fig. 10.51. Rate of disinfection of *B. typhosus* by hot water in relation to temperature. The data of Chick (1910) are here plotted as the log of the reciprocal of the time required for killing essentially all the individuals in equivalent populations of cells, against the reciprocal of the absolute temperature. The slope of the line in the figure indicates an apparent activation energy of 85,200 cal for this overall process.

disinfection in the presence of weak acid, with a temperature coefficient of 1.6. The disinfectant potency of a given concentration of phenol increases rapidly with temperature, as first noted by Robert Koch (1881). According to Chick (1908) the temperature coefficient (Q_{10}) is between 7 and 15, varying with the concentration of phenol. Disinfection with aliphatic alcohols, e.g., ethyl or normal butyl alcohol, at 20° to 40° has been found to have temperature coefficients of 9 to 54, varying with the range of temperature and with the test organism used (Tilley, 1942), as well as with the particular alcohol.

In analyzing the data of Krönig and Paul (1897), Ikeda (1897) found that, at constant temperature, the relation between concentration of mercuric chloride and time required for disinfection of anthrax spores is given by

$$C^n/V = \text{constant} \tag{10.28}$$

where n is a constant, C is the concentration of the disinfectant, and V is the velocity of the process. The same relationship has since been found to hold for various disinfectants acting upon various microörganisms; the values of n, according to the data from a number of investigations, are summarized by Chick (1930). In a theoretical discussion Watson (1908) suggested that the exponent n might signify the number of molecules of disinfectant which unite with one molecule of reacting constituent in the bacterium. Although, as Watson recognized, the significance of the

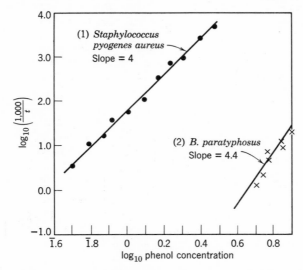

Fig. 10.52. Relation between concentration of phenol and rate of disinfection at 20°C, plotted according to equation (10.29) from the data of (1) Gregerson (1916) and of Chick (1908) and Watson (1908). The rate of disinfection is computed as 1,000 times the reciprocal of the time in minutes, required for killing essentially all the cells of the population.

exponent n in disinfection could scarcely be the same as in chemical reactions in general, equation (10.28) is essentially the same as

$$d(B)/dt = k(C)^n(B) \qquad (10.29)$$

in which the rate of change in concentration of living bacteria (B) with respect to time is equal to a constant k times the concentration of disinfectant to the nth power times (B). Equation (10.29) is obviously analogous to the rate equation (10.23) for the denaturation of tobacco mosaic virus with urethan. Using (10.29), a plot of log k against the reciprocal of the absolute temperature often results in a linear relationship, as it would if k represented the specific rate constant of an ordinary chemical reaction. Similarly, when the amount of disinfectant (C) is large, so that it remains in excess and may be considered constant, a plot of log n against log C often results in a linear relationship, as if n represented the ratio of drug molecules combining per protein molecule in the denaturation of proteins in solution. Figure 10.52 is an example, with reference to the disinfectant action of phenol at 20°C.

Disinfection is catalyzed by alcohols and other agents that inhibit luminescence, narcotize nerves, and influence most biological processes. At the respective sites of action in various processes, the action is fundamentally the same. It would be expected, therefore, that Ferguson's rule

Table 10.8. Ratios between the Thermodynamic Activity Coefficients of Some Homologous Alcohols and Ratios between the Potencies of These Alcohols in Killing Diverse Types of Organisms

(Values for ethyl alcohol are arbitrarily taken as unity in each case)

Alcohol	Activity Coefficient (from the data of Butler, 1937)	Germicidal Potency (Morgan and Cooper, 1912)	Disinfection (Tilley and Shaffer, 1926)		Toxicity to Paramecium (Kamm, 1921)	Killing of Cats (Macht, 1921)	Coagulation of Albumin at 50°C (Kamm, 1921)
			B. typhosus	S. aureus			
Methyl	0.4	0.95	0.65	0.77	0.8	0.8	0.9
Ethyl	1.0	1.0	1.0	1.0	1.0	1.0	1.0
n-Propyl	3.9	2.5	2.56	2.10	1.9	2.5	2.0
n-Butyl	14.3	9.0	6.8	5.65	4.5	16.6	5.0

(p. 431) would apply in disinfection as elsewhere. Table 10.8 lists the ratios between the killing potencies of aliphatic alcohols, from methyl to n-butyl, for representatives of the extremely simple to the extremely complex organisms, i.e., bacteria to cats. The ratios of the chemical potentials, computed from the data of Butler (1937) are listed for comparison. The value for ethyl alcohol is arbitrarily taken as unity in all cases. The numerical values for each of the other alcohols differ by a factor of about 3, at most, from the relative activity coefficient of that alcohol.

Studies of the influence of hydrostatic pressures, within the range of physiological interest, on the process of disinfection have as yet scarcely more than begun. The pressure-temperature relationships in the disinfection of *Escherichia coli*, both in growing cultures and in non-reproducing cells, with and without quinine, have been studied (Johnson and Lewin, 1946b,d). Although the relationships are somewhat complicated, and a number of different reactions are evidently involved, the rate of thermal disinfection is retarded by pressures up to 6,000 psi.   At relatively low temperatures the cells remain viable for long periods of time at atmospheric pressure, but here pressure accelerates their death.   The disinfection of bacterial spores at 92.5°C occurs at a rate that depends upon the medium (distilled water or phosphate-buffered sodium chloride solution) in which they are suspended, and the rate changes during the

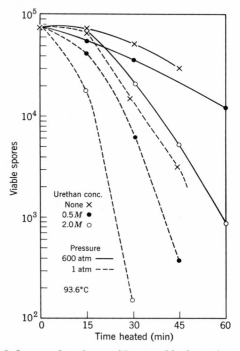

Fig. 10.53.   Influence of urethan and increased hydrostatic pressure on the rate of disinfection of *Bacillus subtilis* spores in phosphate-buffered sodium chloride solution, *p*H 7.0, at 93.6° (Johnson and ZoBell, 1949b).

course of the disinfecting process.   Urethan, in concentrations up to 2 *M*, does not influence the number of viable spores at room temperature, but accelerates the rate of killing at temperatures above 90°C.   Under a pressure of 9,000 psi the rate of disinfection is retarded either with or without urethan (Johnson and ZoBell, 1949a,b).   Representative data are illustrated in Fig. 10.53.

Temperature and drug action in warm-blooded animals

The range of variation in body temperature of warm-blooded animals is ordinarily so small that, at first thought, it would seem that temperature changes could scarcely have much effect on the action of drugs in these organisms. Variations in purely hydrostatic pressure are so slight that they are of purely theoretical interest; no warm-blooded animal is subjected in nature to any really significant variation in hydrostatic pressure. Of all mammals, whales experience perhaps the greatest changes in pressure, but they probably never dive to more than about 1,000 ft below the surface of the ocean, where the pressure amounts to some 30 atm, and the physiological effects of increased gas pressure in the lungs are more important than those of the relatively very slight increase in hydrostatic pressure itself. No experiments with significant increases in hydrostatic pressure can be conducted on lung-breathing animals. Thus, of the different parameters governing the action of a drug on warm-blooded animals, drug concentration is of the most obvious importance and has been most extensively studied.

Whenever a drug has a high temperature coefficient of action, however, slight variations in body temperature may be profoundly significant, and this is a matter of practical as well as theoretical importance. Perhaps the most familiar example, to some people at least, concerns alcohol. There is no reason to believe that the fundamental action of alcohol in man is any different from its action in frogs (Meyer, 1899) or on bacterial luminescence. At temperatures near the normal optimum, a slight rise in temperature markedly increases the potency of a given concentration of alcohol and, conversely, a slight fall in temperature decreases the potency. When excessive quantities have been imbibed, the equilibrium between the native and denatured forms of the enzymes affected by alcohol is shifted toward the denatured side, and a gradual process of destruction akin to that caused by heat alone is also catalyzed. The expression "boiled," like the premature report of Mark Twain's death, is an exaggeration, but full of meaning. Removal of the drug from the body normally occurs almost wholly by a fairly slow rate of oxidation, of about 10 cc per hr (cf. Goodman and Gilman, 1941). A significant removal from its site of action, however, can be immediately accomplished by lowering the temperature. Thus, a cold shower is sometimes of temporary advantage to the overindulgent, although at the same time it invites disaster from other causes. The same cold treatment reduces the rate of catalyzed destruction. The effect of alcohol alone in lowering of body temperature is to some extent a natural protection, like the slowing of metabolism, heart beat, etc., at temperatures above the optimum. In both instances, a physiological "compensation" is affected by reversible protein denaturation. The sobering effects of the cold shower no doubt involve several physiological mechanisms in addition to favoring the dissociation of alcohol from its sites of action, such as vasoconstriction in the peripheral circulation, possibly caused in part by a direct dissociation of alcohol from vasoconstrictor muscles and nerves, and in part by a release of adrenalin accompanying the shock of sudden cold.   These physiological changes help to raise the blood pressure, and they favor an increased blood flow and oxygen supply to the central nervous system; under some conditions, an increased oxygen supply aids recovery from alcoholic and other narcoses.   It is reasonable to believe, however, that the direct effect of a slight decrease in temperature, in lessening the amount of drug combined with its critical site of action in the central nervous system, is an important factor.   If it were not impossible to apply as much as 2,000 or 3,000 psi of hydrostatic pressure without irreparably damaging the air-filled organs and probably others as well, it should be possible to bring about sobriety of the individual at once by raising the pressure (cf. p. 512).

The action of numerous drugs has been studied with reference to variations in the body temperature of warm-blooded animals.   In some instances slight variations have profound effects, as shown by the following examples.

During fever the potency of dicumarol (Campbell and Link, 1941; Stahman et al., 1941) in reducing the amount of prothrombin in the blood and thereby retarding the rate of clotting is greatly enhanced (Richards, 1943).   Under conditions wherein the amount of prothrombin is the limiting factor, the time required for clotting of rat blood ("prothrombin time"; cf. Campbell, Smith, Roberts, and Link, 1941) after the injection of small amounts of dicumarol is five times longer, on the average, when the body temperature has been raised by less than 3°C as a result of pyrogenic agents.   In the absence of dicumarol the prothrombin time is essentially unaltered by this amount of fever, though presumably it would be altered (i.e., increased) by still higher temperatures.   Apparently this is another example in which a drug, in effect, lowers the temperature for the inactivation of enzyme systems, in this case the system concerned in producing prothrombin.   The data are given in Table 10.9.

Some even more striking examples of the influence of body temperature on the action of drugs have been reported by Chen et al. (1943a,b).   The average rectal temperatures of white mice, placed in air-conditioned environments at different temperatures between 20° and 40°C, varied from 34.65° to 38.48°C, or somewhat less than 4°C.   At the lowest temperature the amount of insulin required to produce convulsions after intravenous injection was nearly 90 times greater than the amount required for the same effect at the highest temperature.   The action of a number of other drugs studied by Chen et al. was likewise influenced by change in temperature.

The general subject of the relation between temperature and the observed effects of specific drugs on cold- and warm-blooded animals as well as on tissues and organs has been reviewed by Fuhrman (1946; cf. also Fuhrman and Weymouth, 1946; Hollinger et al., 1949). Quantitative data concerning the effects of a drug on whole organisms in particular are often difficult to obtain, and the observed effect often involves an action of the drug on several different systems. There are, of course, other ways in which the temperature relations are made more complicated than those of isolated enzyme systems. For example, the killing action

Table 10.9. Effect of 2.5 mg of Dicumarol on Prothrombin Time 24 hr after Being Injected into Rats of Different Body Temperatures

(Data from Richards, 1943)

	Group				
	A	B	C	D	E
Number of animals	9	7	10	7	11
Maximal rectal temperature (°C)	37.2–37.5	37.9–38.3	38.4–38.8	39.0–39.4	39.5–40.0
Prothrombin time (min)	1.78	4.1	5.92	6.16	8.92
Standard error	0.16	0.24	0.83	1.06	0.93
Relative rate of clotting, as reciprocal of prothrombin time; group A (controls) rate = 100%	100.0	43.0	30.1	28.9	20.0

of 2,2-bis(p-chlorophenyl)1,1,1-trichlorethane (DDT) used as a spray on adult house flies (*Musca domestica*) is faster at relatively low temperatures (Lindquist, Wilson, Schroeder, and Madden, 1945). Similarly, when applied externally, DDT preparations have been found more effective at low temperatures in the killing of adult mosquitoes, bedbugs, grain beetles, aquatic mosquito larvae, and shrimp (Lindquist, Madden, and Schroeder, 1946; Potter and Gillham, 1946; Richards and Cutkomp, 1946). Here it would seem that the drug has a negative temperature coefficient of action, as indeed it does with respect to the observed overall effect under the conditions concerned. It has been shown, however, that a negative temperature coefficient is found only when the DDT is externally applied, and only when the DDT is in dilute solution. When DDT is injected directly into the bodies of mosquito or of midge larvae, or when the concentration of DDT in the surrounding medium is raised from 1 part in a billion to 1 part in 10 million, the killing effect has a positive temperature coefficient (Fan et al., 1948). The negative temperature coefficient associated with externally applied, dilute solutions is evidently attributable to the fact that under these conditions the action is limited by the capacity of the outer cuticle of the insect body to absorb and concentrate the poison to a greater extent at low than at high temperatures.

In disease, complex changes occur in the delicately balanced relative rates of physiological reactions, each of which is modified by changes in temperature.   General experience has long indicated that temperature in warm-blooded animals is an important factor in susceptibility to disease, and, as we would expect, there is evidence that temperature is also important in the influence of various drugs on disease.   With respect to temperature alone, the classic experiment of Pasteur et al. (1878) showed that the natural immunity of chickens to anthrax depends upon their body temperature, which is normally between 41° and 42°C.   When their body temperature was lowered by immersing the chickens in cold water up to their thighs, they readily contracted the disease.   Pasteur and his associates attributed this phenomenon to the fact that the normal temperature of 41° to 42° is unfavorably high for the growth of the anthrax bacillus, i.e., it is above the growth optimum, where growth is slowed by mechanisms already discussed (Chapter 8).   On the other hand, Wagner (1890) found that the bacillus would grow in blood or serum outside of the body at a temperature of 43°C, and he attributed the phenomenon of susceptibility at lower temperatures to a decrease in phagocytic action.   To decide which of these factors is the more important, however, requires critical quantitative data; very probably, the decrease in phagocytosis and increase in rate of growth of the pathogen are both important; each factor acts in the direction of lowering resistance to infection.

In recent years analogous phenomena have been described with reference to other examples of natural resistance associated with body temperature, e.g., the resistance of rabbits to infection by *Cryptococcus neoformans* (Kuhn, 1949).   The temperature at which the cells of this organism cease to grow and begin to die apparently occurs between the average body temperature of mice and of rabbits.   Thus at 37.3°C the number of cells progressively increase, while at 39.4°C they progressively decrease.   Kuhn (1949) noted that mice with an average rectal temperature of 37.3°C readily and quickly succumbed to experimental infections, but rabbits with a mean temperature of 39.5°C were only rarely and slowly affected. He showed that environmentally induced elevated body temperatures prolonged life and increased the number of survivors among infected mice. With this particular disease, human infections are not accompanied by a rise in body temperature, but, as Kuhn points out, fever would perhaps aid recovery.   In diseases that are accompanied by fever, it is reasonable to believe that the rise in temperature is often a significant factor aiding recovery, and that in these cases fever is a natural, protective response of the organism to infection.

Among plants and cold-blooded animals the temperature of the organism is never very different from that of the environment, and the temperature of the environment sometimes confers a natural immunity to disease.   Kunkel (1936) has shown that certain virus diseases of peach trees can be cured by growth at temperatures above 35°C, and that the distribution of "peach yellows" in nature is governed by temperature; the disease does not occur in the southeastern United States, except in the mountainous regions where the temperature falls to less than 35°C for considerable intervals of time during the susceptible season.

With particular reference to the relation between temperature and the action of drugs on disease, we would anticipate that in some instances a similar result could be obtained either by raising the body temperature alone or without raising the temperature, by administering drugs which catalyze the thermal denaturation of proteins.   Ether is a drug whose action seems to depend primarily upon its protein-denaturating influence. It therefore is especially interesting that ether anesthesia has been found markedly effective in increasing the number of survivors of Swiss mice infected with Western equine encephalomyelitis virus (Sulkin et al., 1945, 1946).   Here we would expect that the combined effects of ether anesthesia and increased body temperature would be similar to an increased depth of anesthesia, with results that would be favorable or unfavorable depending upon the differential effect of ether in combating the virus on the one hand, and in doing harm to the body of the host on the other hand. With more specific drugs, such as penicillin, which have a fairly high temperature coefficient of action and which are relatively harmless to the body, the combination of chemotherapy and fever may be notably successful (Eagle, Magnuson, and Fleischman, 1947).   This combination has been employed in the treatment of paresis.

Even with single cells and extracted enzyme systems, complications in the analysis of the temperature and concentration relationships of drug action arise when two or more different drugs act simultaneously on the same system.   As a result, the total effect may be either a marked lessening or a marked augmentation of the effect of one or the other drug alone. The qualitative as well as the quantitative effect often depends upon both temperature and drug concentration, as shown by the discussion in the next section.

Synergism, potentiation, and antagonism between drugs

Synergism means cooperation, and antagonism means the reverse.   In medicine and pharmacology the two terms are used widely, but because of the lack of a generally applicable quantitative definition they are used chiefly in a qualitative sense.   The simultaneous action of two drugs may be qualitatively additive, in which event they are called synergistic, or the observed effect of the one drug may be lessened or practically abolished by the other, in which event they are called antagonistic.   In some instances the action of a given drug is "potentiated" by a different drug which of itself, in the concentration employed, has no measurable effect upon the process concerned.   There are numerous examples of all three phenomena, synergism, potentiation, and antagonism.   In a complex organism there are many mechanisms through which two drugs may facilitate or oppose each other's effects on a physiological process.   We will restrict our discussion chiefly to the cases where two or more drugs evidently act, or could act, at the same molecular site.

When the site of action is identical, synergism is not difficult to understand.   From the physical-chemical point of view, the problem is largely one of understanding the quantitative basis of the additive effects. Although the total inhibition by two drugs in given concentrations is sometimes judged on the basis of the arithmetic sum of the per cent inhibitions caused by each drug alone at its respective concentration, this basis may lead to erroneous interpretations.   The separate per cent inhibitions do not necessarily add to the same total as found for the per cent inhibition when the two are present at the same time.   The precise basis for interpreting additive effects depends upon the mechanism of action and requires definition of the conditions, as follows (Johnson, Eyring, and Kearns, 1943).

The simplest example is that of two drugs which do not combine with each other and which act interchangeably according to a Type I inhibition, one molecule of either being sufficient to inactivate one enzyme molecule. If the luminescent system is used as a model, with the usual notation, the formulation is derived by the same method as in problems considered earlier, i.e., a "conservation equation" is written to include the various forms of the free and combined enzyme.   Let X and Y represent the two inhibitors combining in equilibria with constants K_x and K_y, respectively. The total amount of enzyme A_0 is then

$$(A_0) = (A_n) + (A_d) + (A_nX) + (A_dX) + (A_nY) + (A_dY)$$

$$= (A_n) + K_1(A_n) + K_x(A_n)(X) + K_1K_x(A_n)(X) + K_y(A_n)(Y)$$

$$+ K_1K_y(A_n)(Y)$$

$$(A_n) = \frac{(A_0)}{(1 + K_1)(1 + K_x(X) + K_y(Y))} \tag{10.30}$$

Substituting in equation (10.5) the expression for (A_n) given by equation (10.30),

$$I_{x+y} = \frac{bk'(L)(A_0)}{(1 + K_1)(1 + K_x(X) + K_y(Y))}$$ (10.31)

Dividing equation (10.5a) by (10.31),

$$\frac{I_1}{I_{x+y}} = 1 + K_x(X) + K_y(Y)$$ (10.32)

Equation (10.32) applies to all concentrations of X and of Y including the situations where either one is zero.   Hence,

$$\left(\frac{I_1}{I_{x+y}} - 1\right) = \left(\frac{I_1}{I_x} - 1\right) + \left(\frac{I_1}{I_y} - 1\right)$$ (10.33)

Equations (10.32) and (10.33) provide formulations that can be applied in the analysis of data from experiments.   Equation (10.33) shows that at constant temperature and pressure the total inhibition by two drugs, acting in the manner defined above, is equal to the sum of the inhibitions in terms of the two expressions $(I_1/I_x - 1)$ and $(I_1/I_y - 1)$.   In accordance with the symbols we have adopted for this type of expression, we will refer to the expression of (10.33) as Γ_{x+y}, Γ_x, and Γ_y, respectively.   Thus equation (10.33) may be conveniently written

$$\Gamma_{x+y} = \Gamma_x + \Gamma_y$$ (10.34)

Since the values of the Γ's are not the same as per cent inhibition, it is clear that different totals will result when the per cent inhibitions and the Γ's, respectively, are added.

In the event that r molecules of either X or Y take part in the inactivation of one enzyme molecule, an *effective concentration*, $(X)_{eff}$, can be defined.   Thus

$$(X)_{eff} = \left(X + \left(\frac{K_y}{K_x}\right)^{1/r} Y\right)$$

$$\left(\frac{I_1}{I_{x+y}} - 1\right) = \Gamma_{x+y} = K_x \left(X + \left(\frac{K_y}{K_x}\right)^{1/r} Y\right)^r$$ (10.35)

$$(\Gamma_{x+y})^{1/r} = (\Gamma_x)^{1/r} + (\Gamma_y)^{1/r}$$

When two drugs, U and W, act according to a type II inhibition, the formulations are analogous, but expressions corresponding to Γ_2 rather than to Γ_1 apply.   Let s represent the average number of molecules required to denature one enzyme molecule. As before, we define an effective concentration $(U)_{eff}$, for (U):

$$(U)_{eff} = \left[(U) + \left(\frac{K_w}{K_u}\right)^{1/s}(W)\right]$$

$$\left(\frac{I_1}{I_{u+w}}\right)\left(1 + \frac{1}{K_1}\right) = K_u(U_{eff})^s + K_u\left[(U) + \left(\frac{K_w}{K_u}\right)^{1/s}(W)\right]^s$$

$$\left[\left(\frac{I_1}{I_{u+w}} - 1\right)\left(1 + \frac{1}{K_1}\right)\right]^{1/s} = (K_u)^{1/s}(U) + (K_w)^{1/s}(W) \qquad (10.36)$$

$$(\Gamma_{u+w})^{1/s} = (\Gamma_u)^{1/s} + (\Gamma_w)^{1/s}$$

At constant temperature and pressure, of course, equation (10.36) cannot be distinguished from equation (10.33). It should be noted also that, although the logarithm of the quantities Γ_x, Γ_y, Γ_u, or Γ_w plotted against log molar concentration of X, Y, U, or W, respectively, should yield a straight line, the logarithm of Γ_{x+y} or of Γ_{u+w} plotted against the log of the sum of the molar concentrations of X and Y or U and W, respectively, does not necessarily result in a straight line.

An example of synergism in the inhibition of bacterial luminescence by urethan and butyl alcohol is illustrated in Fig. 10.54. A linear relationship is obtained over a fairly wide range of concentrations with either drug separately, whereas the relationship is not linear with a constant concentration of butyl alcohol and increasing concentrations of urethan. The temperature and pressure relationships of this combined inhibition have not been investigated.

A linear relationship, such as that illustrated in Fig. 10.54 for the inhibition of bacterial luminescence by urethan alone, is substantial evidence that, under the conditions of the experiment, no other inhibitor is acting at the same site. When the relationship is definitely not linear, it is evidence that more than one reaction is involved in the observed inhibition. With highly purified extracts of *Cypridina* luciferin and partially purified luciferase, it might be expected that addition of a single inhibitor, such as urethan or sulfanilamide, would reveal a simple, linear relation with respect to the concentration added, when the data are plotted according to the formulations that have been discussed. Contrary to the first expectations, the data of Johnson and Chase (1942) for the separate effects of three different inhibitors on the velocity constant of the reaction clearly reveal non-linear relationships (Fig. 10.55). Since only the purified preparations had been used, these results were perplexing until it was recalled that butyl alcohol had been used as the solvent for the luciferin concentrate. The luminescent reaction mixture contained 0.05 cc of the butyl alcohol solution of luciferin in a final volume of 10 cc of dilute buffer. The final concentration of butyl alcohol, therefore, was only 1 part in 200 volumes of water, or about 0.054 M. It had been assumed that the seemingly small amount of butyl alcohol in the final

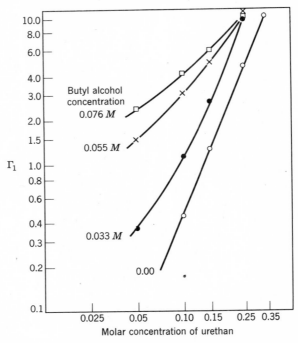

Fig. 10.54.   The inhibition of luminescence in *Photobacterium phosphoreum* by various concentrations of urethan alone (hollow circles) and corresponding concentrations of urethan plus the constant concentrations of butyl alcohol indicated at the left of the curves in the figure (Johnson, Eyring, and Kearns, 1943).

mixture would have no influence on the luminescent reaction.   The error of this assumption was apparent only after an attempt was made to analyze the inhibition caused by other agents, as shown in Fig. 10.55. Thus the velocity of the control reaction was evidently retarded by the amount of butyl alcohol present.   Table 10.3 (p. 430) shows that this concentration is of the same order as those which affect various biological processes, and in fact it was somewhat higher than that required to narcotize the polliwogs.   Exact comparisons, of course, would require taking into account the temperatures employed in the various experiments.

In the discussion thus far, it has been assumed that any two drugs of the types under consideration will not combine with each other in solution. This, again, is an assumption that calls for experimental evidence, and kinetic data are useful, though not fully conclusive. Thus, if two inhibitors formed a complex with each other in solution, to an extent that the biologically effective concentration of one or of both of them were reduced, the curve relating the amount of inhibition to the concentrations added would exhibit a more or less pronounced minimum, depending upon

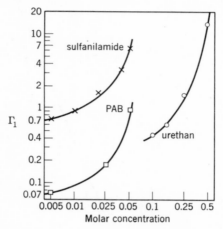

Fig. 10.55. Inhibition of luminescence in purified *Cypridina* extracts by *p*-aminobenzoic acid, urethan, and sulfanilamide respectively, at room temperature. The data of Johnson and Chase (1942) are plotted in accordance with equation (10.7). The curvature of the lines results from the presence of a small amount of butyl alcohol, used as a solvent for the luciferin concentrate, in the final reaction mixture. (From Johnson, Eyring, and Kearns, 1943.)

temperature and other factors. In bacterial luminescence the simultaneous effects of sulfanilamide plus alcohol (Fig. 10.56) or certain other inhibitors of the narcotic type (ether, urethan, etc.) illustrate such a phenomenon. The reactions involved are evidently equilibria, for they are readily reversible on removal of the drugs. Moreover, the order in which the drugs are added does not influence the results. For example, at 5°C, if 0.003 M sulfanilamide is added alone, the inhibition amounts to $\Gamma_1 =$ about 4. If 0.43 M alcohol is now added, the inhibition drops to $\Gamma_1 =$ about 2, or only half as much inhibition. In terms of per cent inhibition this change corresponds to a decrease from about 80 per cent inhibition to about 67 per cent. Thus, relatively low concentrations of alcohol partially antagonize the effects of sulfanilamide. Higher concentrations of alcohol, however, are additive in their effects to those of sulfanilamide.

Although the data of Fig. 10.56 are understandable on the basis that sulfanilamide and alcohol combine with each other in solution, it would

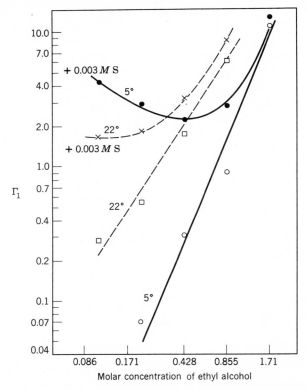

Fig. 10.56. Inhibition of luminescence in *P. phosphoreum* by increasing concentrations of ethyl alcohol alone at 5° and at 22°C, respectively, and by increasing concentrations of ethyl alcohol in the presence of a constant concentration of 0.003 M sulfanilamide at the same temperatures (Johnson, Eyring, and Kearns, 1943).

seem unlikely, *a priori*, that such combination would result in the formation of a stable compound. Physical evidence for complex formation might be obtained by infrared spectroscopy, but such data are not available. Interferometer measurements of the refractive index of 0.0329 M aqueous solutions of sulfanilamide in the presence of diethyl ether (Cagle, 1951)[1] have revealed no detectable compound formation. On the other

[1] Personal communication.

hand, solubility effects have provided physical evidence indicative of complex formation between sulfanilamide and drugs which, under appropriate conditions of temperature and concentration, antagonize the sulfanilamide inhibition of luminescence (Johnson, Eyring, and Kearns, 1943). Thus sulfanilamide is insoluble in ethyl ether, but a saturated aqueous solution of ether at 25°C will dissolve more than 30 per cent more sulfanilamide than an equal volume of water at the same temperature. Similarly, the addition of ether to an aqueous solution containing undissolved sulfanilamide will cause it to go into solution. Urethan, ethyl alcohol, and acetone also increase the solubility of sulfanilamide in water at concentrations somewhat higher than they have been observed to antagonize the sulfanilamide inhibition of luminescence.

The evidence is incomplete as to whether the drug antagonisms referred to above result from an actual combination between the two drugs in solution, or from a simultaneous combination of the two drugs with the enzyme to give an intermediate state of the catalyst that is more active than that of the enzyme combined with either drug alone (cf. pp. 29 and 223). The kinetic treatment in either case, however, is the same. As a matter of convenience, therefore, in the following discussion we will refer to the combination of the drugs with each other, without attempting to distinguish whether such combination takes place in free solution or only at the enzyme. On this basis, analytical formulations can be readily derived. Such formulations, however, become extremely sensitive to experimental error when applied to kinetic data. Moreover, when the two drugs are initially present in nearly the same concentration, it becomes necessary to take into account the amount of each removed from the freely dissolved state by the formation of a complex. In this case the formulation becomes complicated and unwieldy. We will consider first the simpler case.

The following derivation applies to the simultaneous action of two drugs, X and U, capable of complexing with each other, X acting according to a type I, and U according to a type II inhibition. The concentration of U is assumed to be always sufficiently in excess that it may be considered constant, i.e., not enough of U is removed from solution by combination with the enzyme and by combination with X to alter significantly the amount of free U originally in solution. Furthermore, in order to simplify the formulation, we will consider only the conditions wherein (1) X combines with U in a 1 : 1 ratio, with equilibrium constant K_4, and wherein (2) the free X and free U do not interfere with each other in combining with the enzyme. Following our usual procedure, we first obtain the conservation equation for the total amount of enzyme A_0 in terms of the amount of active enzyme A_n and the several equilibrium constants:

$$A_0 = (A_n) + (A_d) + (A_nX_r) + (A_dX_r) + (AU_s) + (AU_sX_r)$$
$$= (A_n)[1 + K_1 + K_2(X)^r + K_1K_2(X)^r + K_1K_3(U)^s$$
$$+ K_1K_2K_3(U)^s(X)^r]$$

$$A_n = \frac{A_0}{[1 + K_1 + K_1K_3(U)^s][1 + K_2(X)^r]} \tag{10.37}$$

$$\frac{I_1}{I_{x+u}} = \left[1 + \frac{K_1K_3(U)^s}{1 + K_1}\right][1 + K_2(X)^r]$$

Letting X_0 equal the initial concentration of X, we have, according to the assumed conditions,

$$(X_0) = (X) + (XU) \qquad \text{or} \qquad \frac{(XU)}{(X)(U)} = K_4$$

$$(X_0) = (X)[1 + K_4(U)] \qquad \text{or} \qquad (X) = \frac{(X_0)}{1 + K_4(U)} \tag{10.38}$$

Substituting for (X) in equation (10.37) the expression of (10.38),

$$\frac{I_1}{I_{x+u}} = \left[1 + \frac{K_1K_3(U)^s}{1 + K_1}\right]\left[1 + \frac{K_2(X_0)^r}{[1 + K_4(U)]^r}\right]$$

$$= \frac{I_1}{I_u}\left\{1 + \frac{I_1 - I_{x_0}}{I_{x_0}[1 + K_4(U)]^r}\right\}$$

$$\left(\frac{I_u}{I_{x+u}} - 1\right)\left(\frac{I_x}{I_1 - I_{x_0}}\right) = \frac{1}{[1 + K_4(U)]^r} \tag{10.39}$$

$$\left[\left(\frac{I_1 - I_{x_0}}{I_u - I_{x+u}}\right)\left(\frac{I_{x+u}}{I_{x_0}}\right)\right]^{1/r} - 1 = K_4(U)$$

Equation (10.39) is of a form suitable for application to experimental data. The extent to which it may be used for quantitative predictions is illustrated by the following example.

An average value for K_4 was computed from the effects of a single concentration of urethan and of sulfanilamide on the inhibition of luminescence in *Vibrio phosphorescens* at different temperatures. The intensities of luminescence of the control and inhibited suspensions of cells are plotted in Fig. 10.57. The relatively inaccurate method of visual photometry was used in this experiment, so the points are somewhat scattered.

Smooth curves were drawn by inspection in the manner that seemed best to fit the points, and numerical values for I_1, I_x, I_u, and I_{x+u} at different temperatures were taken from the smooth curves, as representing probably

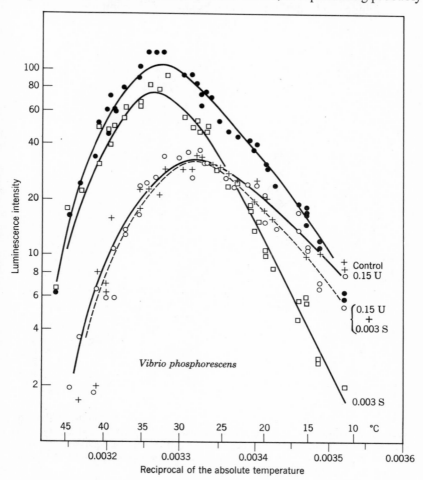

Fig. 10.57.   Influence of temperature on the luminescence intensity of *V. phosphorescens* in solutions of 0.003 M sulfanilamide, 0.15 M urethan, and 0.003 M sulfanilamide plus 0.15 M urethan, respectively, and with no added drug (Johnson, Eyring, and Kearns, 1943).

a better accuracy than the individual points.   These values are summarized in Table 10.10, together with values obtained in a similar experiment with *Photobacterium phosphoreum* over a different range of temperatures.   The average of the values for K_4 obtained in this manner was then made the basis for predicting the intensity of luminescence of *P. phosphoreum* observed at a single temperature in mixtures of various proportions of sulfanilamide and urethan. The observed and computed values are

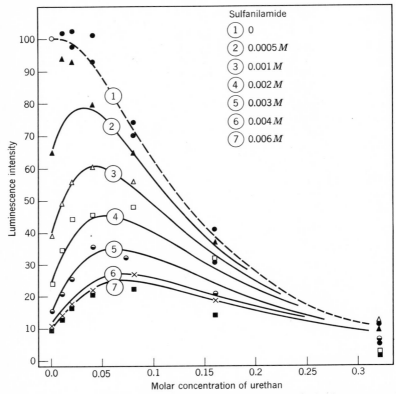

Fig. 10.58. Luminescence intensity of *P. phosphoreum* at 5°C in the presence of various concentrations of urethan and sulfanilamide, separately and mixed. The curves drawn as solid lines were calculated with the aid of equation (10.39) as described in the text, and the points represent the observed values (Johnson, Eyring, and Kearns, 1943).

shown in Fig. 10.58. The data of Table 10.10 and Fig. 10.57 call for brief discussion before Fig. 10.58 is discussed.

With reference to Table 10.10, it will be observed that the values computed for K_4 vary widely, all-told by as much as a factor of 7. The formulation used for computing K_4 from the data, however, is extremely sensitive to experimental error. For example, if all the measurements of luminescence intensity at 15°C were exactly correct except for the one pertaining to I_{x+u}, and the true value of I_{x+u} were actually 10 per cent higher than the value recorded in the table, K_4 would have been more than twice as large as the value that was computed, i.e., 148.6 instead of 73.7. In order to obtain a more nearly accurate value for K_4, when the accuracy

Table 10.10. Luminescence Intensity of *V. phosphorescens* without Added Drugs (I_1) and in the Presence of 0.003 *M* Sulfanilamide (I_x), 0.15 *M* Urethan (I_u) and 0.003 *M* Sulfanilamide plus 0.15 *M* Urethan (I_{x+u}) respectively, at Different Temperatures, Together with Similar Data for *P. phosphoreum* with 0.003 *M* Sulfanilamide and 0.075 *M* Urethan, Separately and Mixed

From Johnson, Eyring, and Kearns, 1943.   The numerical data are taken from smooth curves drawn by inspection through numerous observed values.   Values of K_4 are computed according to equation (10.39).

Temp. (°C)	I_1	I_x	I_u	I_{x+u}	$\left[\left(\dfrac{I_1 - I_x}{I_u - I_{x+u}}\right) \left(\dfrac{I_{x+u}}{I_x}\right) - 1 \right]$	K_4
			Vibrio phosphorescens			
15	15.8	4.15	12.2	9.9	11.05	73.7
20	34.0	13.3	21.0	18.0	8.30	55.3
25	62.0	34.5	30.5	29.0	14.40	96.0
30	100.0	65.5	30.7	29.5	12.05	80.4
35	91.0	68.0	19.5	17.0	2.82	18.8
			Photobacterium phosphoreum			
5	20.5	8.3	18.3	12.0	1.81	24.1
10	38.0	14.5	31.5	25.0	5.22	69.6
15	61.0	29.5	48.0	40.0	4.35	58.0
20	88.0	50.0	61.5	50.8	2.61	34.8
25	99.0	67.0	62.0	50.0	1.00	13.3

Average value for K_4 .   .   .   .   52.4

of measuring luminescence is limited, it is necessary to take the average of a number of determinations.   The results seem to yield a reasonably close approximation to the true value.

With reference to Fig. 10.57, the curve for the mixture of urethan plus sulfanilamide lies closely beneath the curve for urethan alone.   Because of the excess of urethan, as compared to the amount of sulfanilamide in this experiment, the amount of urethan that could be removed from physiological action by combining in a 1 : 1 ratio with all the sulfanilamide present could not exceed 2 per cent of the total urethan.   Actually, of course, not all the sulfanilamide combines with urethan, but apparently a large proportion of it does.   Thus sulfanilamide has very little effect on the urethan inhibition, but urethan has a great effect on the sulfanilamide inhibition.   The effect of the mixture, however, as compared to that of either drug alone, depends upon the temperature.   In effect, the addition of urethan to cells already inhibited by sulfanilamide changes the temperature relationship of inhibition from one that is characteristic of the latter drug's action to one that is characteristic of the former's.   Consequently the change in amount of inhibition resulting from the addition of urethan can be either in the direction of synergism, as at the higher temperatures, or in the direction of antagonism, as at the lower temperatures.   At some intermediate temperature, where the curves intersect, the total inhibition caused by each of the drugs, as well as by the mixture of both of them, is practically the same.   Over longer periods of observation, however, the inhibition might be expected to increase progressively with time whenever the inhibitory solution contains a significant amount of urethan, because of its catalysis of irreversible destruction at a rate depending upon both concentration and temperature.

The temperature at which the curves of the inhibited luminescence intersect depends upon the concentration of the drugs.   At the concentrations used for Fig. 10.57, the curves intersect at about 24°C, several degrees below that of the optimum in the control.   Here a slight variation of 2 or 3 degrees would cause urethan to seem either slightly synergistic or slightly antagonistic to the action of sulfanilamide alone, without changing the amount of the drugs initially present in solution.   This is probably an important factor in the interpretation of the influence of urethan on the sulfanilamide inhibition of processes such as bacterial growth.   Thus the precise temperature and its constancy would be expected to have a marked influence on the observed results.   Moreover, since measurements of growth rates require a much longer period of time than those of luminescence, the potentially antagonistic effects of urethan might be expected to become complicated by the rate process of destruction which it catalyzes at the same time.   Also, since experiments on rates of growth are usually conducted at the normally optimum temperature for growth in the organism concerned, it would be expected that the urethan antagonism of a sulfanilamide inhibition would be difficult to observe, inasmuch as the inhibitory action of urethan alone is much greater at a temperature near the normal optimum than at lower temperatures.   In spite of these several complications and of still another one which we will discuss presently in relation to potentiation, it has been shown that the sulfanilamide inhibition of bacterial growth can be overcome by the addition of the appropriate amount of urethan (McIlwain, 1942). As would be expected, this antagonism is evident only within a narrow range of sulfanilamide concentrations; at high concentrations so much urethan would have to be added, in order to tie up an inhibitory concentration of sulfanilamide that the urethan itself would prohibit growth.

A potentiating influence of urea as well as of urethan on the sulfonamide inhibition of bacterial growth is also readily understandable on the basis of the hypothesis discussed above. The essential facts are as follows. The inhibition of growth by various sulfonamide compounds is overcome by the addition of p-aminobenzoic acid (PAB) in concentrations as low as one-tenth to one-hundredth of the sulfonamide concentration. Because of the close similarity in structure of PAB and sulfanilamide, we would expect that PAB, like sulfanilamide, would form a loose complex with urethan or related drugs, and in the same manner have its physiologically active concentration reduced. Furthermore, since relatively low concentrations of PAB are involved, we would expect that relatively low concentrations of urethan or urea would be required to remove it, in effect, from physiological activity. Data from experiments show that such is indeed the case. The antagonism of the sulfonamide inhibition of growth in various species of bacteria is quite effectively eliminated by the addition of non-bacteriostatic concentrations of urea or of urethan (Tenenberg et al., 1942; Weinstein and McDonald, 1945). The inactivating effects of azochloramide (Neter, 1941, 1942; Schmelkes and Wyss, 1942) on the anti-sulfanilamide action of PAB apparently depends upon a similar mechanism. Under these conditions the significance of the combination between potentiating agent and the growth-promoting agent is much more important than that of the combination of the potentiating agent with the growth-inhibiting agent. With concentrations of urea, urethan, or azochloramide high enough of themselves to inhibit growth, the total effect is one of synergism. Their antagonism of the growth inhibitor is involved along with their direct action.

From the above relationships it follows that, in order to obtain an antagonism of the sulfonamide inhibition of growth by urea or urethan, there must be a very delicate balance not only between the concentrations of these two drugs, but also between these drugs and any other substance such as PAB, which in relatively small amounts is antagonistic to sulfonamide action. Thus the usual overall effect on growth would generally be expected to be one of apparent synergism. This is evidently the case, and it has been found to be of some clinical advantage (Tsuchiya et al.,

1942; Lee, Epstein, and Foley, 1943a; Holder and MacKay, 1942, 1943; Ilefeld, 1943).

In general, simple antagonisms of the urethan-sulfonamide type, as in luminescence, should be more readily apparent at relatively low temperatures, where the inhibitory effect of the antagonist itself is relatively unimportant. Contrary to the effect of PAB on growth, PAB does not antagonize the action of sulfanilamide on luminescence. Consequently, the possible presence of small amounts of naturally occurring PAB is not a factor that would complicate the effects of urethan and sulfanilamide mixtures on the luminescence of washed cell suspensions of luminous bacteria. Figure 10.58 shows the extent to which a numerical value of K_4, as estimated from the data of Table 10.10, is successful in predicting the quantitative effects of mixtures from the effects of each separately. The curves for the amount of inhibition by various proportions of urethan and sulfanilamide simultaneously present were all calculated by means of equation (10.39), using 50 as the numerical value of K_4. Except for the highest inhibitions, the agreement between the theoretical curves and observed points is remarkably close. The discrepancies could arise not only through an inaccuracy in the value of K_4 but also through other ways, e.g., the average number of molecules in the complex is not necessarily in exactly a 1 : 1 ratio, and the influence of additional inhibitory reactions at high concentrations of urethan probably becomes significant.

The influence of chloroform on luminescence and on the sulfanilamide inhibition of luminescence resembles the action of ethyl alcohol illustrated in Fig. 10.56. With chloroform, however, the required concentrations are much lower and are of the same order as those of sulfanilamide. If it is assumed as before that the two drugs combine, the formulation derived as follows is necessary in order to estimate the numerical value of the equilibrium constant from the observed amounts of inhibition. Letting X represent sulfanilamide and C represent chloroform, and assuming for simplicity that the combination occurs in a 1 : 1 ratio,

$$\frac{(XC)}{(X)(C)} = K_4$$

$$(X_0) = (X) + (XC) = (X) + K_4(X)[(X) - (X_0) + (C_0)]$$

$$= (X) + K_4(X)^2 + K_4(X)[(C_0) - (X_0)]$$

$$K_4(X)^2 + \{K_4[(C_0) - (X_0)] + 1\}(X) - (X_0) = 0$$

$$(X) = \frac{K_4[(X_0) - (C_0)] - 1 \pm \sqrt{\{K_4[(C_0) - (X_0)] + 1\}^2 + 4K_4(X_0)}}{2K_4}$$

Similarly,

$$(C_0) = (C) + (XC)$$

$$(C) = (C_0) - (X_0) + (X)$$

$$(C) = (C_0) - (X_0)$$

$$+ \frac{K_4[(X_0) - (C_0)] - 1 \pm \sqrt{\{K_4[(C_0) - (X_0)] + 1\}^2 + 4K_4(X_0)}}{2K_4}$$

Hence

$$\frac{I_1}{I_{x+c}} = \left(1 + \frac{K_1 K_3}{1 + K_1}\left\{(C_0) - (X_0) + K_4[(X_0) - (C_0)] - 1\right.\right.$$

$$\left.\left. \pm \sqrt{\{K_4[(C_0) - (X_0)] + 1\}^2 + 4K_4(X_0)}\right\}^s\right)$$

$$\left(1 + K_2\left\{\frac{K_4[(X_0) - (C_0)] - 1 \pm \sqrt{\{K_4[(C_0) - (X_0)] + 1\}^2 + 4K_4(X_0)}}{2K_4}\right\}^r\right)$$

$$(10.40)$$

We have not undertaken to apply equation (10.40) to the data.

The hypothesis that physiological antagonism between two such drugs as sulfanilamide and urethan results from the formation of a complex between the two is consistent with the kinetic evidence and the solubility data discussed above. The hypothesis is a reasonable one on the basis of other considerations. For example, urea has been shown to form complexes with straight chain aliphatic hydrocarbons and their derivatives in a manner depending upon the structure of the compound; the composition, crystal structure, oxidizability, and heats of formation of such compounds have been studied (Bengen, 1940; Bengen and Schlenk, 1949; Schlenk, 1949; Zimmerschied et al., 1949; Schlenk and Holman, 1950). The ability to form a complex with urea apparently depends upon having a linear chain of carbons, but not upon unsubstituted hydrogens. Thus, halogen, sulfur, and oxygen derivatives of the aliphatic compounds also form complexes with urea, provided that the linearity of the carbon skeleton is preserved. With long chain hydrocarbons, 11 or more moles of urea combine per mole of hydrocarbon. Possibly a similar but less stable complex is formed between urethan and sulfanilamide in solution, and between urea and p-aminobenzoic acid, giving rise to the physiological antagonisms referred to above.

In general, it might be anticipated that certain small molecules which combine with proteins would also combine with each other. They do not combine with the protein molecule as a whole, but with some small accessible group of the protein. The problem of the loose combination of physiologically active small molecules with other small molecules in solution is one which deserves further study. It is perhaps the basis of numerous instances of drug antagonisms which at present are not understood. For example, premedication with drugs such as barbiturates is often employed to induce a mild narcosis before operations. When ether is administered, the second ("excitement") stage appears despite the barbiturate depression (Barbour, 1936). In effect, ether antagonizes the action of the barbiturate. Several reasonable hypotheses could account for this phenomenon, among them a combination of the two drugs with each other. On the other hand, it is reasonable to expect that, if the barbiturate acts primarily by reducing respiration of the nerve cell, and low concentrations of ether by raising permeability of the membrane, then depression of nervous activity by either drug might be counteracted by appropriate concentrations of the two together (cf. discussion of nerve potentials in later paragraphs).

Other examples are known, of course, wherein two drugs with seemingly little or no affinity for each other are antagonistic in their inhibitory effects on a given process in living organisms. As long ago as 1875, Claude Bernard demonstrated an antagonism by ether of cyanide poisoning of rabbits. When the rabbits were first narcotized with ether, cyanide could be injected without poisoning them. When they recovered from the effects of ether, they became poisoned by the cyanide remaining in their bodies. An analogous antagonism between narcotics and cyanide occurs with respect to the respiration of goose erythrocytes (Warburg, 1911) and the reducing activity of frog muscle preparations (Lipschitz and Gottschalk, 1921), to the extent that the arithmetic sum of the per cent inhibitions caused by the narcotic and by cyanide separately may greatly exceed the inhibition caused by the two drugs when simultaneously present in the same respective concentrations; the inhibition caused by the two together may even be slightly less than that caused by either one alone (Warburg, 1911).

Although it is evident that narcotics can antagonize the effects of cyanide in various systems, it does not follow that the mechanism is the same in all cases. The only way it might be the same would be for the cyanide to combine with the narcotic. Though apparently unpublished and unauthenticated, there are some alleged cases of individuals having survived lethal doses of cyanide which were consumed while they were thoroughly drunk, conceivably because of a combination of cyanide with alcohol. Depending upon temperature and concentration, however, the alcohol might be expected to cause a reversible denaturation with unfolding of some cellular proteins. If cyanide combines more readily with groups made accessible by reversible unfolding of the protein, its toxicity is reduced as long as the protein remains in the unfolded state. This mechanism of antagonism would be somewhat analogous to the one by which cyanide poisoning of animals is treated with the aid of sodium nitrite or other substances with similar action (Chen, Rose, and Clowes, 1934). Nitrite oxidizes hemoglobin of the blood to methemoglobin, and methemoglobin combines with cyanide to form a stable un-ionized compound, cyanmethemoglobin. By this means animals can be protected from as much as 21 times the minimal lethal dose of cyanide. The net result of administering the antidote is the same as if cyanide combined with the antidote itself, whereas evidently the cyanide combines with a different substance which is formed in the animal as a result of the antidote. In other instances, death by cyanide can be prevented by a more direct combination of CN with another substance, such as one of the various carbohydrates and related compounds, including higher alcohols, to form cyanhydrin compounds (Violle, 1926; Szolnoki, 1926; Rosenberg, 1926; Puder, 1927; Forst, 1928, 1932). Usually these antagonists, to be effective, must be either mixed directly with the cyanide or administered before the cyanide, partly because their rate of combination with cyanide in the body is slow compared to the action of the poison on the body. It is said that one of the attempts to assassinate Rasputin consisted in giving him a dish of sweet pudding containing a dose of cyanide which, by itself, would kill a horse. Rasputin ate the pudding and suffered no ill effects, presumably because it contained a large amount of sugar with which the cyanide combined. His would-be assassins interpreted it differently. They concluded that, as they had feared, Rasputin was possessed of supernatural powers, and his position was only strengthened by this attempt on his life.

Drug antagonisms clearly have no uniformly general interpretation. The same is true for the frequently observed "stimulating" effects following the addition of a single drug in appropriate low concentrations. Relatively low concentrations of narcotics increase the intensity of bacterial luminescence; they likewise increase the velocity of the luminescent reaction in crude extracts of *Cypridina* (Taylor, 1934). Low concentrations of sulfanilamide and other agents which in relatively high concentrations are inimical to growth seem to stimulate growth in low concentrations (Johnson, 1942; Lamanna, 1942; Johnson, Carver, and Harryman, 1942). Stimulating effects of relatively low concentrations of various drugs which in higher concentrations cause inhibitions of a biological process have been observed in so many cases that this diphasic action of drugs at different concentrations has been referred to as the Arndt-Schultz law (cf. Clark, 1937). The same end result could obviously be brought about by way of different mechanisms, such as the inhibition of a competing reaction (cf. p. 396) or by combination of the drug with another substance which itself has been acting as an inhibitor. The stimulating effects of low concentrations of alcohol on brain slice respiration (Fuhrman and Field, 1948; Table 10.6) could result, as the authors point out, from the metabolism of alcohol as a naturally oxydizable substrate. A similar interpretation, however, would seem highly unlikely with reference to stimulation of the same process by diphenyloxazolidinedione (Fuhrman and Field, 1943).

Narcosis

The word narcosis is derived from the Greek, $ναρκοῦν$, meaning to benumb or stupefy. For centuries narcosis has been used to describe the effects of a narcotic, or "substance which when swallowed, inhaled or injected into the system induces drowsiness, sleep, stupefaction, or insensibility according to its strength and the amount taken" (*Oxford Dictionary of the English Language*). Narcotics in the form of alcohol or other substances have been known to man since time immemorial, and they appear as a device of intrigue in the earliest of modern English poetry (Chaucer, 1385):

> "He shal slepe as longe as euere the leste,
> The narcotykis & opijs ben so stronge . . ."

From the beginning, narcosis has referred primarily to a reversible state of relative inactivity of the nervous system under the influence of certain drugs. In more recent years, however, its meaning has broadened. Claude Bernard (1875) pointed out that many drugs which act as narcotics on the central nervous system have, in sufficient concentration, inhibitory effects on essentially all living cells. The same drugs, as we now know, may inhibit the catalytic activity of highly purified enzymes, and in some cases promote both a reversible and an irreversible denaturation of single proteins. Moreover, the same end result may often be achieved through the influence of cold, or of heat, or of ionic composition. In a broad sense, therefore, narcosis is an aspect of the general problem of factors which influence biological reaction rates, and any restriction of the term to the action of a particular group of drugs, or to drugs in general, is purely arbitrary. Ultimately, the interpretation is to be found at the molecular level, for it is only through the behavior of molecules that the highest functions are affected.

For the purposes of the present discussion we will define narcosis as any significant depression in physiological activity of cells or tissues, especially of the nervous system, that is significantly reversible. This definition suffers from the vagueness of the qualification "significant," but any precise demarcation between a negligible depression on the one hand and a profound depression, equivalent to deep anesthesia in animals, on the other hand, is obviously arbitrary and dependent upon quantitative units of measurement.   Slight depressions no doubt normally accompany slight changes in physiological states of the organism and extend through imperceptible gradations from the highest degree of conscious activity to sound sleep.   The same vagueness of "significant" applies with respect to the amount of reversibility as to the amount of depression.   We would anticipate that a certain amount of destruction would always accompany narcosis under the influence of ether, alcohol, chloroform, etc., for reasons that have been discussed in relation to their mechanism of action on proteins.   The above definition more or less excludes the use of the term narcosis with reference to single enzyme systems; it seems more appropriate to speak of the inhibition than of the narcosis of such simple systems, even though the narcosis of complex functions depends upon effects on simple systems.   Like other biological definitions, our definition of narcosis is more convenient than rigid.

Since the activity of a physiological process may be reversibly depressed or accelerated by diverse factors, it follows that narcosis may be induced or reversed through diverse factors, e.g., temperature, hydrostatic pressure, salts, drugs.   The mechanism by which these different factors achieve the same net result, however, is not necessarily the same, and according to our view of the problem it is a mistake to look for any single mechanism —change in permeability, in oxidative activity, in state of cell lipins, in potential differences across the membrane, etc.—as the general cause of narcosis.   To understand narcosis as a general phenomenon, it is necessary to examine the various specific requisites for the maintenance of normal activity and the manner in which they may come to limit normal activity under the influence of narcotizing agents.   In the following paragraphs we will consider briefly some of the important mechanisms, especially in nerve, through which physiological activity may be reversibly depressed, and the relation of these mechanisms to different theories of narcosis. References to the voluminous literature, including most of the older studies, are available in monographs and reviews, and in books on pharmacology or physiology, especially those of Winterstein (1926), Henderson (1930), Clark (1937), Quastel (1939), Heilbrunn (1943), and some others.

Essentially all living cells have a difference in electrical potential across the cell membrane, and factors which modify this potential may modify also the activity of the cell.   With nerve cells in particular, changes in the potential are always involved in excitation and propagation of the nerve impulse.   For a long time it has been known that, at rest under physiological conditions, the inner side of the membrane is negatively charged with respect to the outer side.   During excitation the positive charge on the outside momentarily disappears and a wave of electrical negativity, synonymous with the nerve impulse, spreads along the length of the cell from the region of stimulation. After the passage of the impulse, i.e., the "action potential," the membrane is quickly repolarized to its former state.

It now appears that at least the following conditions are essential to the normal activity of a nerve: (1) metabolism in the cell, giving rise to products which facilitate the diffusibility of ions, especially sodium, through the membrane; (2) a differentially permeable membrane through which some ions escape and enter faster than others, thus giving rise to a steady state "resting potential" or polarization of the membrane; (3) reversible changes in permeability of the membrane, permitting momentary depolarization in a relatively "leaky state," wherein the potential difference across the membrane is momentarily neutralized, and even polarized in the opposite direction, by the change in diffusibility of ions; (4) a recovery mechanism, following excitation and propagation of the impulse, whereby the resting potential is rapidly restored, accompanied by a reversal of the relatively leaky to the "non-leaky" state of the membrane; and (5) a favorable composition of the solution outside the cell, particularly with regard to sodium, potassium, and calcium ions. The operation of these aspects of nerve activity is considered further in Chapters 11, 12, and 14. For the moment, we will assume that all five conditions are *sine qua non* to normal activity.

In addition to the above, when biological processes, e.g., reflex and conscious activity, depend not only on the excitability of individual nerve cells but also upon transmission across one or more synapses, more complex factors of possible significance in narcosis become involved, and it is frequently difficult to determine which factor or factors are most critical.

Finally, although the precise rôle of cholinesterase in nerve remains to be established, it is difficult to believe that this extensively studied enzyme is without some basic significance. Moreover, many of the agents which are potent inhibitors of nerve activity are also potent inhibitors of cholinesterase activity. Some data concerning the potencies of various drugs acting on the cholinesterase of nerve and other sources are collected in Table 10.11 (cf. also Koelle and Gilman, 1949) and in Fig. 10.59.

The concentrations listed in Table 10.11 are provisional to the extent that they depend upon such factors as time of exposure to the drug, the specific ester hydrolyzed, the relative concentrations of enzyme and substrate, purity of reaction mixtures, temperature, and pH. The substrate in most cases was acetyl choline. Pronounced differences in sensitivity to the same drug are apparent with respect to the different sources of the enzyme. In general, a distinction can be made between "true" and "pseudo-cholinesterase" (Mendel and Rudney, 1943). True

Table 10.11. Inhibition of Cholinesterases from Various Sources by Various Drugs

Source of Cholinesterase	Inhibitor	Concentration (Molar)	Inhibition (%)	Temp. (°C)	pH	Reference
Human	Di-isopropylfluorophosphate					
Brain		1×10^{-6}	50	38	7.5–7.7	Mazur and Bodansky, 1946
		1.3×10^{-7}	50	38	7.4	Adams and Thompson, 1948
		3.0×10^{-7}	50	37	7.7	Grob, 1950
R.B.C.		3.9×10^{-6}	50	38	7.5–7.7	Mazur and Bodansky, 1946
		1.5×10^{-7}	50	38	7.4	Adams and Thompson, 1948
		4.0×10^{-7}	50	37	7.7	Grob, 1950
Serum		2.0×10^{-3}	50	38	7.5–7.7	Mazur and Bodansky, 1946
Plasma		0.029×10^{-7}	50	38	7.4	Adams and Thompson, 1948
		0.095×10^{-7}	50	37	7.7	Grob, 1950
Muscle		3.9×10^{-6}	50	38	7.5–7.7	Mazur and Bodansky, 1946
		2.5×10^{-7}	50	37	7.7	Grob, 1950
Monkey (Macacus rhesus)	Di-isopropylfluorophosphate					
Brain		3.2×10^{-6}	50	38	7.5–7.7	Mazur and Bodansky, 1946
R.B.C.		3.2×10^{-6}	50	38	7.5–7.7	Mazur and Bodansky, 1946
Serum		1.6×10^{-8}	50	38	7.5–7.7	Mazur and Bodansky, 1946
Horse	Di-isopropylfluorophosphate					
Serum		1.2×10^{-8}	50	38	7.5–7.7	Mazur and Bodansky, 1946
Serum (purified)		2.0×10^{-8}	50	38	7.5–7.7	Mazur and Bodansky, 1946
Serum		1.3×10^{-9}	50	20	7.4	Mackworth and Webb, 1948
Rabbit	Di-isopropylfluorophosphate					
Brain		3.2×10^{-6}	50	38	7.5–7.7	Mazur and Bodansky, 1946
R.B.C.		6.3×10^{-6}	50	38	7.5–7.7	Mazur and Bodansky, 1946
Serum		7.9×10^{-5}	50	38	7.5–7.7	Mazur and Bodansky, 1946
Pigeon	Di-isopropylfluorophosphate					
Brain		5.7×10^{-7}	50	38	7.4	Adams and Thompson, 1948
Lobster	Di-isopropylfluorophosphate					
Nerve		2.2×10^{-6}	31–44	23		Bullock, Grundfest, Nachmansohn, Rothenberg, and Sterling, 1946
Human	Eserine (physostigmine)					
Serum		2.0×10^{-7}	50	38	7.5–7.7	Mazur and Bodansky, 1946
Muscle		1.3×10^{-7}	50	38	7.5–7.7	Mazur and Bodansky, 1946
Rabbit	Eserine (physostigmine)					
Serum		1.3×10^{-6}	50	38	7.5–7.7	Mazur and Bodansky, 1946
Horse	Eserine (physostigmine)					
Serum		4×10^{-8}	50	20	7.4	Mackworth and Webb, 1948
		$2.5–5.0 \times 10^{-8}$	50	3.8		Ellis, Plachte, Straus, 1943
Electric eel						
Electric organ	Eserine (physostigmine)	3×10^{-8}	37	23		Bullock, Nachmansohn, and Rothenberg, 1946
Electric organ	Prostigmine	3×10^{-8}	38	23		Bullock, Nachmansohn, and Rothenberg, 1946
Human	Neostigmine					
Brain		4×10^{-7}	50	37	7.7	Grob, 1950
R.B.C.		3×10^{-7}	50	37	7.7	Grob, 1950
Plasma		4×10^{-8}	50	37	7.7	Grob, 1950
Muscle		3×10^{-7}	50	37	7.7	Grob, 1950
Human	Tetraethyl pyrophosphate					
Brain		3.2×10^{-8}	50	37	7.7	Grob, 1950
R.B.C.		3.5×10^{-8}	50	37	7.7	Grob, 1950
Plasma		5.0×10^{-9}	50	37	7.7	Grob, 1950
Muscle		3.5×10^{-8}	50	37	7.7	Grob, 1950
Human	"Parathion" (p-nitrophenyl-diethylthionophosphonate)					
Brain		1.3×10^{-5}	50	37	7.7	Grob, 1950
R.B.C.		1.2×10^{-5}	50	37	7.7	Grob, 1950
Plasma		1.5×10^{-6}	50	37	7.7	Grob, 1950
Muscle		1.5×10^{-5}	50	37	7.7	Grob, 1950
Human	N-mustard ($\beta\beta'$-dichlorodiethyl-N-methylamine HCl)					
Brain		8.7×10^{-5}	50	38	7.4	Adams and Thompson, 1948
R.B.C.		7.4×10^{-5}	50	38	7.4	Adams and Thompson, 1948
Plasma		69.0×10^{-5}	50	38	7.4	Adams and Thompson, 1948

Table 10.11 (Continued)

Source of Cholinesterase	Inhibitor	Concentration (Molar)	Inhibition (%)	Temp. (°C)	pH	Reference
Pigeon	N-mustard (ββ'-dichloro-diethyl-N-methylamine HCl)					
Brain		2.4×10^{-5}	50	38	7.4	Adams and Thompson, 1948
Horse Serum	Disec. butylfluorophosphonate	2.0×10^{-9}	50	20	7.4	Mackworth and Webb, 1948
	Di-isoamylfluorophosphonate	2.0×10^{-9}	50	20	7.4	Mackworth and Webb, 1948
	Di-n-propylfluorophosphonate	5.5×10^{-9}	50	20	7.4	Mackworth and Webb, 1948
	Diethylfluorophosphonate	8.0×10^{-9}	50	20	7.4	Mackworth and Webb, 1948
	Diphenylfluorophosphonate	6.3×10^{-8}	50	20	7.4	Mackworth and Webb, 1948
	Dimethylfluorophosphonate	1.0×10^{-7}	50	20	7.4	Mackworth and Webb, 1948
	Dithioethylfluorophosphonate	2.0×10^{-6}	50	20	7.4	Mackworth and Webb, 1948
	Dimethylaminophosphoryl fluoride	8.0×10^{-5}	50	20	7.4	Mackworth and Webb, 1948
	Diethylmethylaminophosphonate	3.0×10^{-4}	50	20	7.4	Mackworth and Webb, 1948
	Trimethyl phosphate	1.0×10^{-3}	50	20	7.4	Mackworth and Webb, 1948
	Vitamin B_1	1.7×10^{-3}	50	20	7.4	Mackworth and Webb, 1948
		1.8×10^{-8}	50	30		Glick and Antopol, 1939
	Ammonium fluorophosphate	1.0×10^{-2}	50	20	7.4	Mackworth and Webb, 1948
	Sodium fluoride	1.0×10^{-2}	50	20	7.4	Mackworth and Webb, 1948
	Methylene blue	2×10^{-6}	40			Massart and Dufait, 1940
		1.2×10^{-6}	50	37	7.3	Collier and Allen, 1942
	Cresyl violet	2×10^{-6}	20			Massart and Dufait, 1940
	Nile blue	2×10^{-6}	75			Massart and Dufait, 1940
	Janus green	2×10^{-6}	92			Massart and Dufait, 1940
	Thiazine methyl sulfonium perchlorate	1.6×10^{-6}	50	37	7.3	Collier and Allen, 1942
	Acriflavin	6.6×10^{-6}	50	37	7.3	Collier and Allen, 1942
	Phenothiazone	6.7×10^{-5}	50	37	7.3	Collier and Allen, 1942
	Cresyl blue	2×10^{-5}	35			Massart and Dufait, 1940
	Thionine	2×10^{-5}	20			Massart and Dufait, 1940
	Methyl violet	2×10^{-5}	85			Massart and Dufait, 1940
	Neutral red	2×10^{-5}	90			Massart and Dufait, 1940
	Methyl alcohol	2.6×10^{-1}	50			Mikhel'son, 1943
	Ethyl alcohol	6.9×10^{-2}	50			Mikhel'son, 1943
	Propyl alcohol	8.4×10^{-3}	50			Mikhel'son, 1943
	Isobutyl alcohol	7.5×10^{-3}	50			Mikhel'son, 1943
	Iso-amyl alcohol	3.7×10^{-3}	50			Mikhel'son, 1943
	Chloroform	6.2×10^{-3}	50			Mikhel'son, 1943
	Diethyl ether	13.5×10^{-3}	33			Mikhel'son, 1943
Human	"Nu-1250," the N-p-chlorophenyl-N-methylcarbamate of m-hydroxyphenyl-trimethylammonium bromide; cf. Aeschlimann and Stempel, 1946					
R.B.C.		1×10^{-9}	34	37	7.4	Hawkins and Mendel, 1949
		1×10^{-8}	66	37	7.4	Hawkins and Mendel, 1949
Plasma		1×10^{-4}	58	37	7.4	Hawkins and Mendel, 1949
Horse	"Nu-1250," the N-p-chlorophenyl-N-methylcarbamate of m-hydroxyphenyl-trimethylammonium bromide; cf. Aeschlimann and Stempel, 1946					
R.B.C.		1×10^{-8}	58	37	7.4	Hawkins and Mendel, 1949
Plasma		5×10^{-8}	66	37	7.4	Hawkins and Mendel, 1949
Dog	"Nu-1250," the N-p-chlorophenyl-N-methylcarbamate of m-hydroxyphenyl-trimethylammonium bromide; cf. Aeschlimann and Stempel, 1946					
Brain		5×10^{-8}	86	37	7.4	Hawkins and Mendel, 1949
Pancreas		1×10^{-7}	53	37	7.4	Hawkins and Mendel, 1949
Plasma		5×10^{-8}	87	37	7.4	Hawkins and Mendel, 1949

Table 10.11 (Continued)

Source of Cholinesterase	Inhibitor	Concentration (Molar)	Inhibition (%)	Temp. (°C)	pH	Reference
Rat	"Nu-1250," the N-p-chlorophenyl-N-methylcarbamate of m-hydroxyphenyltrimethylammonium bromide; cf. Aeschlimann and Stempel, 1946					
Plasma Fraction precipitated by half-saturated $(NH_4)_2SO_4$		5×10^{-9}	69	37	7.4	Hawkins and Mendel, 1949
Fraction not precipitated by same		1×10^{-6}	43	37	7.4	Hawkins and Mendel, 1949
Electric eel Electric organ	Quinine	100×10^{-5}	50			Nachmansohn and Schneemann, 1945
Ox Brain	Quinine	100×10^{-5}	33			Nachmansohn and Schneemann, 1945
Horse Serum	Quinine	2.5×10^{-5}	51			Nachmansohn and Schneemann, 1945
Guinea pig Pancreas	Quinine	5.0×10^{-5}	33			Nachmansohn and Schneemann, 1945
Electric eel Electric organ	Quinidine	50×10^{-5}	50			Nachmansohn and Schneemann, 1945
Ox Brain	Quinidine	100×10^{-5}	22			Nachmansohn and Schneemann, 1945
Horse Serum	Quinidine	1.25×10^{-5}	61			Nachmansohn and Schneemann, 1945
Guinea pig Pancreas	Quinidine	2.5×10^{-5}	35			Nachmansohn and Schneemann, 1945
Electric eel Electric organ	Cocaine	100×10^{-5}	25			Nachmansohn and Schneemann, 1945
Ox Brain	Cocaine	200×10^{-5}	27			Nachmansohn and Schneemann, 1945
Horse Serum	Cocaine	12.5×10^{-5}	51			Nachmansohn and Schneemann, 1945
Guinea pig Pancreas	Cocaine	12.5×10^{-5}	52			Nachmansohn and Schneemann, 1945
Electric eel Electric organ	Lobelin	12.5×10^{-5}	30			Nachmansohn and Schneemann, 1945
Ox Brain	Lobelin	50×10^{-5}	22			Nachmansohn and Schneemann, 1945
Horse Serum	Lobelin	1.56×10^{-5}	50			Nachmansohn and Schneemann, 1945
Guinea pig Pancreas	Lobelin	3.12×10^{-5}	44			Nachmansohn and Schneemann, 1945
Electric eel Electric organ	Caffeine	25.0×10^{-5}	50			Nachmansohn and Schneemann, 1945
Ox Brain	Caffeine	100×10^{-5}	30			Nachmansohn and Schneemann, 1945

Table 10.11 (Continued)

Source of Cholinesterase	Inhibitor	Concentration (Molar)	Inhibition (%)	Temp. (°C)	pH	Reference
Horse Serum	Caffeine	100×10^{-5}	0			Nachmansohn and Schneemann, 1945
Guinea pig Pancreas	Caffeine	200×10^{-5}	0			Nachmansohn and Schneemann, 1945
Human	(Curare alkaloids)	(Approx.)				(Winterstein and Dutcher 1943)
R.B.C.	d-Chondocurine	6×10^{-5}	47	37	7.35	Harris and Harris, 1944
Serum	d-Chondocurine	6×10^{-5}	36	37	7.35	Harris and Harris, 1944
R.B.C.	d-Tubocurarine chloride	12×10^{-5}	16	37	7.35	Harris and Harris, 1944
Serum	d-Tubocurarine chloride	12×10^{-5}	33	37	7.35	Harris and Harris, 1944
R.B.C.	d-Isochondodendrine, dimethyl ether	6×10^{-5}	13	37	7.35	Harris and Harris, 1944
Serum	d-Isochondodendrine	3×10^{-5}	17	37	7.35	Harris and Harris, 1944
Human Brain	Desomorphine	0.5×10^{-3}	50	37.5		Wright and Sabine, 1943
	Morphine	1.3×10^{-3}	50	37.5		Wright and Sabine, 1943
	Dilaudid	2.4×10^{-3}	50	37.5		Wright and Sabine, 1943
	Codeine	3.9×10^{-3}	50	37.5		Wright and Sabine, 1943
Serum	Desomorphine	0.2×10^{-3}	50	37.5		Wright and Sabine, 1943
	Morphine	1.3×10^{-3}	50	37.5		Wright and Sabine, 1943
	Dilaudid	2.6×10^{-3}	50	37.5		Wright and Sabine, 1943
	Codeine	0.8×10^{-3}	50	37.5		Wright and Sabine, 1943
Rabbit Brain	Desomorphine	0.3×10^{-3}	50	37.5		Wright and Sabine, 1943
	Morphine	1.1×10^{-3}	50	37.5		Wright and Sabine, 1943
	Dilaudid	1.9×10^{-3}	50	37.5		Wright and Sabine, 1943
	Codeine	4.0×10^{-3}	50	37.5		Wright and Sabine, 1943
Serum	Desomorphine	0.5×10^{-3}	50	37.5		Wright and Sabine, 1943
	Morphine	2.2×10^{-3}	50	37.5		Wright and Sabine, 1943
	Dilaudid	2.3×10^{-3}	50	37.5		Wright and Sabine, 1943
	Codene	4.0×10^{-3}	50	37.5		Wright and Sabine, 1943
Dog Serum	Desomorphine	0.6×10^{-3}	50	37.5		Wright and Sabine, 1943
	Morphine	1.9×10^{-3}	50	37.5		Wright and Sabine, 1943
	Dilaudid	1.4×10^{-3}	50	37.5		Wright and Sabine, 1943
	Codeine	3.8×10^{-3}	50	37.5		Wright and Sabine, 1943
Human Serum	Isopropylantipyrine	3×10^{-3}	80		7.8	Zeller, 1942b
	Antipyrine	3×10^{-3}	50		7.8	Zeller, 1942b
	Aminoantipyrine	3×10^{-3}	29		7.8	Zeller, 1942b
	Dimethylaminoantipyrine	3×10^{-3}	37		7.8	Zeller, 1942b
	Irgamid	2.5×10^{-3}	13		7.8	Zeller, 1942a
	Sulfathiazole	2.5×10^{-3}	18		7.8	Zeller, 1942a
	Benzoylsulfanilamide	2.5×10^{-3}	9		7.8	Zeller, 1942a
	Sulfanilamide	2.5×10^{-3}	-1		7.8	Zeller, 1942a
Frog blood	Ethyl alcohol	3.5×10^{-1}	30–70			Mikhel'son, 1946
	Urethan	3.4×10^{-2}	30–70			Mikhel'son, 1946
	Antipyrine	5.3×10^{-2}	30–70			Mikhel'son, 1946
	Chloral hydrate	6.0×10^{-3}	30–70			Mikhel'son, 1946
	Phenobarbital	8.7×10^{-3}	30–70			Mikhel'son, 1946
	Chlorotone	6.0×10^{-3}	30–70			Mikhel'son, 1946
	Acetanilide	7.4×10^{-3}	30–70			Mikhel'son, 1946
	Pyramidon	1.3×10^{-3}	30–70			Mikhel'son, 1946
	Phenacetin	2.8×10^{-3}	30–70			Mikhel'son, 1946
	Bromural	4.5×10^{-4}	30–70			Mikhel'son, 1946
	Thymol	6.5×10^{-4}	30–70			Mikhel'son, 1946

cholinesterase (or esterases) predominates in brain tissue and red blood cells (R.B.C.) and is active only on certain esters of choline. Pseudo-cholinesterase, from blood serum or plasma, is active toward both choline and non-choline esters. The two types of cholinesterase can be distinguished by both substrate and inhibitor specificities (Mendel, Mundell, and Rudney, 1943; Adams and Thompson, 1948; Hawkins and Mendel, 1949). The symptoms of cholinesterase poisoning *in vivo* are evidently

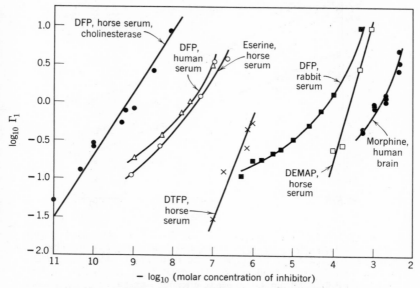

Fig. 10.59. The inhibition of cholinesterases of horse serum (Mackworth and Webb, 1948), human and rabbit serum (Mazur and Bodansky, 1946), and human brain (Wright and Sabine, 1943). The original data are replotted in accordance with equation (10.7). DFP, di-isopropylfluorophosphate; DTFP, dithioethyl-fluorophosphate; DEMAP, diethylmethylaminophosphate.

to be attributed, in some cases at least, to the effects of the drug on true cholinesterase rather than on pseudo-cholinesterase (Hawkins and Mendel, 1949).

Some of the quantitative relationships between drug concentration and inhibition of cholinesterase from different sources are illustrated in Fig. 10.59. In some instances, the relationship between $\log \Gamma_1$ and $\log$ concentration, under the conditions involved, is very nearly linear, in accordance with action on a single enzyme. In others, the relationship is a non-linear curve, indicating additional reactions, as, for example, when the added inhibitor combines with a constant amount of some other constituent (cf. Fig. 10.54, p. 472).

The slope of the line as drawn in Fig. 10.59 for di-*iso*propylfluoro-phosphate (DFP) acting on horse serum cholinesterase is 0.82, which is close to unity. With related inhibitors, such as dithioethylfluorophos-phonate and diethylmethylaminophosphate, larger concentrations are required for the same amount of inhibition of horse serum cholinesterase than are needed with DFP, and the slopes of the lines increase as they do

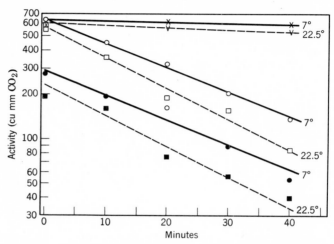

Fig. 10.60. The DFP inhibition of cholinesterase from the electric organ of *Electrophorus electricus* (data replotted on a semilogarithmic scale, from Figs. 1 and 2 of Nachmansohn, Rothenberg, and Feld, 1947). Solid lines, 7°C; broken lines, 22.5°C. Solid circles, 4.0 μg DFP per cc; hollow circles, 0.13 μg DFP diluted from 4.0 μg per cc after the successive lengths of time indicated by the value on the abscissa; crosses, corresponding dilution made at the start. The ordinate gives the activity of the preparations as a function of time on the abscissa. The checks, solid squares, and hollow squares, respectively, refer to the corresponding data obtained at 22.5°C, and with an undiluted concentration of 1.2 μg DFP per cc (solid squares), dilutions from 1.2 to 0.4 μg per cc after successive intervals of time (hollow squares), or dilution at the start (checks).

with lower members of the carbamates acting on luminescence (Fig. 10.36, p. 432).

DFP is not only a highly potent, but also an unusually specific, inhibitor of cholinesterase (Webb, 1948). Its action is of especial interest because very small amounts, of the order of milligrams, paralyze the central nervous system in man, and it is therefore of possible significance to human life in the hands of a ruthless enemy. Furthermore, it is of interest with reference to the general problem of drug antagonism, inasmuch as roughly equivalent amounts of atropine and certain other substances are a potent antidote. The mechanism of its action is of more than theoretical importance.

Like urethan, alcohol, phenobarbital, and numerous other drugs, DFP has a dual action in that it causes a reversible and an irreversible inhibition, the latter increasing progressively with time. The amount of reversibility thus depends upon how quickly the drug is removed after it has been added to the biological material concerned. It also depends, as we would expect, upon temperature. These relationships are clearly illustrated by

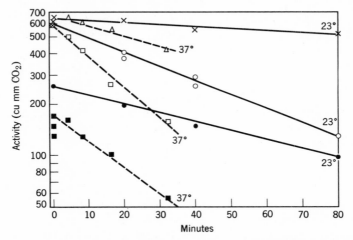

Fig. 10.61. The DFP inhibition of cholinesterase from the nucleus caudatus of ox brain, at 23°C (solid lines) and at 37°C (broken lines). The symbols have the same meaning as in Fig. 10.60 for the corresponding experiment with cholinesterase from electric organ. Undiluted concentration of DFP was 0.8 μg per cc, and the diluted concentration of 0.1 μg per cc at both temperatures. (Data replotted on a semi-logarithmic scale from Figs. 4 and 5 of Nachmansohn, Rothenberg, and Feld, 1947.)

the data of Nachmansohn, Rothenberg, and Feld (1947) with respect to the influence of DFP on cholinesterase from the electric organ of *Electrophorus electricus* (the electric eel) and from the nucleus caudatus of ox brain. In Figs. 10.60 and 10.61 we have replotted their data on a semi-logarithmic scale, which makes readily apparent the similarity between the dual action of DFP on these enzymes and the action of urethan, alcohol, or other drugs which catalyze both reversible and irreversible denaturations of systems already discussed. The initial inhibition is essentially completely reversible. The progressive increase in inhibition with time of exposure takes place with the kinetics of a first order reaction. With rise in temperature the reversible inhibition becomes greater in amount and the rate of destruction becomes faster. The general effects resemble those illustrated in Figs. 8.31 (p. 235), 8.32 (p. 236), 8.34 (p. 238), 8.35 (p. 239), 10.45 (p. 445), and 10.46 (p. 447), and the fundamental mechanism involved in these diverse connections is evidently much the same. Moreover, the dual action of DFP has been demonstrated with respect to other processes, including the conduction of nerve impulses in isolated nerve (Crescitelli et al., 1946; Toman et al., 1947), nerve action potentials (Bullock, Grunfest, Nachmansohn, Rothenberg, and Sterling, 1946), and the cholinesterases of blood serum (Mazur and Bodansky, 1946; Mackworth and Webb, 1948). The amount of initial reversibility varies, however, and in some instances appears to be small (Boyarsky, Tobias, and Gerard, 1947).

In nerve, small concentrations of DFP have a differential effect on the resting potential and the action potential. The resting potential has been frequently measured in terms of the "demarcation potential" or "current of injury" (DuBois-Reymond, 1843) by placing a suitable electrode on the surface of an uninjured segment of the nerve and a second electrode on a segment that has been so injured as to make the membrane freely permeable to ions. The injured portion is negative and the uninjured portion is positive. The potential difference is measured without permitting an appreciable flow of current. The potential thus observed is related to, but is usually much less than, the true potential across the uninjured membrane. In recent years a much finer technique has been developed whereby a microcapillary electrode is introduced into the cytoplasm and the potential across the membrane of a single living cell is measured with remarkable accuracy (Hodgkin and Huxley, 1939, 1945; Curtis and Cole, 1940; Graham and Gerard, 1946; Hodgkin, 1951). This potential, referred to as the "membrane potential," has been measured in striated muscle fibers (Graham and Gerard, 1946; Ling and Gerard, 1949a, b, c; Ling and Woodbury, 1949; Nastuk and Hodgkin, 1950), myelinated nerve fibers (Woodbury and Woodbury, 1950), isolated Purkinje fibers (Coraboeuf and Weidmann, 1949a, b), and intact, beating heart muscle (Woodbury, Woodbury, and Hecht, 1950; Hecht et al., 1950; Woodbury, Hecht, and Christopherson, 1951).

Figure 10.62 illustrates the effects of DFP on the action potential and demarcation potential as a function of the length of time the drug is allowed to act (Toman et al., 1947). The original data are replotted, from the published figure, on a semi-logarithmic scale. Although the data show that the demarcation potential is unaffected, or even slightly increased, by the concentration of DFP employed, the action potential undergoes a progressive decrease with time of exposure to the drug. The initial rate of this decrease conforms closely in its kinetics to that of a first order reaction. After about 50 per cent reduction, the points are somewhat scattered, probably because of changes in the concentration of DFP by hydrolysis. Below 10 per cent of the normal action potential the points are uncertain because of this same source of error, and also because of the difficulty of accurately estimating the numerical values of these points from the published figure (Toman et al., 1947, Fig. 1, p. 431). Higher concentrations of DFP (saturated solution) under the experimental conditions employed abolished the action potential within 30 sec, and within 5 min reduced also the demarcation potential.

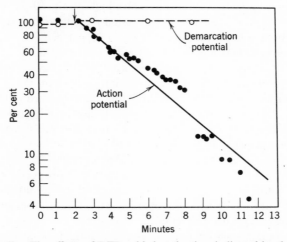

Fig. 10.62. The effects of DFP, added at the time indicated by the arrow, on the demarcation and action potential of the frog sciatic nerve (replotted on a semi-logarithmic scale from the data of Toman et al., 1947, Fig. 1, p. 431).

Since low concentrations of DFP reduce the action potential while scarcely influencing the resting potential, it appears that the primary effect of the drug is to "anchor" the permeability of the membrane in the relatively non-leaky state. At the molecular level, this effect apparently takes place through fundamentally the same mechanism that alcohol, urethan, etc., catalyze reversible and irreversible protein denaturation. The site of action probably involves enzymes, including cholinesterase, as well as other proteins. Since nerve cholinesterase is evidently located almost entirely with the membrane (Boell and Nachmansohn, 1940; Nachmansohn, 1945, 1946) and is especially sensitive to DFP, its activity is no doubt reduced. The activity of this and probably other enzymes changes as a result of excitation and is probably associated with the state of the membrane, being more active in the leaky than in the non-leaky state. It is reasonable to believe that structural changes in certain molecules of the membrane are simultaneously responsible for changes in permeability and in enzyme activity. Moreover, we may assume that these changes are similar to those involved in the reversible denaturation of proteins in general, and are subject to influence by the same factors.

Since higher concentrations of DFP reduce the demarcation potential, they evidently act on additional systems, probably including enzymes concerned with oxidative metabolism within the nerve cell.

The quantitative relation between the DFP inhibition of cholinesterase and blockage of the nerve impulse has not been clearly established. Nachmansohn and his collaborators (Bullock et al., 1947; Grundfest et al., 1947; Feld et al., 1948) have estimated that nerve block occurs when the cholinesterase inhibition exceeds 80 to 95 per cent. Crescitelli et al. (1946) have found that nerve conduction is unimpaired by an *in vivo* dose of DFP which reduces cholinesterase activity of the nerves to 2.3 per cent of normal, as judged by the effects of a similar dose on the activity of the enzyme in homogenates. Boyarsky, Tobias, and Gerard (1947) conclude that, with complete inhibition of cholinesterase activity, the frog sciatic nerve can still conduct impulses with entirely normal action potentials. Other data are summarized by Brooks et al. (1949). They seem to indicate that the amount of cholinesterase normally present is in great excess over that required for normal activity, and that a large proportion of it can be inactivated without appreciably interfering with the normal function. Whether it can be *completely* inactivated without abolishing normal function, however, is still uncertain. Although the experiments have been carefully and quantitatively carried out, it is difficult to correlate precisely the amount of inhibition of cholinesterase in an intact nerve and in a nerve homogenate.

Other examples, wherein a drug is a potent inhibitor of cholinesterase in extracts but has no effect on the action potential of the nerve, can probably be attributed in part to a failure of the drug to penetrate to the enzyme in the nerve. Thus both eserine and prostigmine are potent inhibitors of the extracted enzyme. Eserine but not prostigmine affects the action potential of nerves, evidently because eserine penetrates whereas prostigmine does not (Bullock, Nachmansohn, and Rothenberg, 1946). The same factor of permeability is evidently responsible for the failure of acetyl choline to have any influence on nerves when applied to myelinated axons, where the myelin sheath acts as a barrier to the penetration of non-lipid soluble substances; when applied at the nerve endings, free of the fatty sheath, acetyl choline can reach the effective site of its action.

The atropine antagonism of DFP (Grob, Lilienthal, Harvey, and Jones, 1947) is of particular interest but of uncertain interpretation. The alkaloid scopolamine, closely related to atropine in chemical structure, also antagonizes the physiological effects of DFP (Wescoe et al., 1948). Thus the effects of 1 to 3 mg of DFP on the central nervous system in man can be prevented or counteracted by 1 to 2 mg of atropine or by 1 to 3 mg of scopolamine. On the other hand, the drugs metrozole, strychinine, and gammexane, respectively, give rise to some of the same symptoms as DFP, but their effects are not antagonized by atropine or scopolamine. It has been shown (Hobbiger, 1951) that the cholinesterase activity of guinea pig blood, salivary glands, intestine, and brain recovers

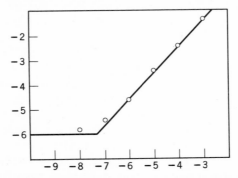

Fig. 10.63. Concentrations of atropine and acetyl choline which give a quantitatively similar response of isolated ventricular strip of the frog heart (Clark, 1926b). The slope of the line is unity. The logarithms of molar concentrations of atropine and acetyl choline are indicated on the abscissa and on the ordinate, respectively.

within 1 to 4 days when 2.0 mg atropine is first administered to the whole animal, and is then followed by 0.4 mg of tetraethylpyrophosphate, which poisons the enzyme cholinesterase in much the same manner as DFP. In an intact animal the atropine antagonism of these poisons could conceivably occur by a mechanism analogous to that of the amyl nitrite antagonism of cyanide (p. 485).

A quantitatively similar antagonism exists between atropine and acetyl choline in their effects on the isolated ventricular strip and the isolated rectus abdominis muscle of the frog (Clark, 1926a,b). In this case it was shown that acetyl choline is effective in minute amounts, acts quickly, and can be readily washed away from the tissue. Atropine antagonizes the effects of acetyl choline in approximately equivalent concentrations (Fig. 10.63). It also acts quickly, but unlike acetyl choline it is much more firmly fixed to the tissue and is very difficult to remove by washing.

These several antagonisms are understandable on the following general hypothesis. The action of atropine prevents acetyl choline from reaching its site of physiological action. Whether this occurs through an influence on permeability or through competitive adsorption on some key molecule concerned directly in the effects of acetyl choline is uncertain. DFP poisons cholinesterase, thereby preventing the normal destruction of acetyl choline which, when allowed to accumulate, causes spasms and other symptoms characteristic of such poisoning. Atropine counteracts the effects of DFP by preventing the accumulating acetyl choline from reaching its site of action, just as it does in the absence of DFP.

An inhibitory action of atropine on cholinesterase (Schaller, 1942) would not, on the above hypothesis, necessarily have any influence on its antagonism of acetyl choline or on its antagonism of poisoning by DFP. It is of interest that other inhibitors of cholinesterase, including physostigmine, neostigmine, and carbaminoylcholine, protect the enzyme from DFP (Koelle, 1946). An analogous phenomenon occurs in the effects of substrates, competitive inhibitors, and the prosthetic group on the activity of d-amino acid oxidase (Burton, 1951). Some of the same substances which inhibit the activity of this enzyme, e.g., l-leucine or sodium benzoate, also protect the enzyme from thermal inactivation, as does the prosthetic group, flavin adenine dinucleotide. Thus, if we assume that DFP poisons cholinesterase by catalyzing a thermal inactivation of the enzyme, it would not be a unique situation to find that atropine antagonizes this action of DFP by increasing the thermal stability of the enzyme.

With particular reference to the rôle of permeability in narcosis, there is abundant evidence that excitation, particularly of nerves, is normally accompanied by an increase in permeability, as we have assumed. The "permeability theory of narcosis" advocated by Hoeber (1907, 1926, 1945), Lillie (1909, 1912, 1913, 1916, 1932), Winterstein (1926), and others (cf. also Gellhorn, 1929) states that narcotics and anesthetics inhibit excitation by preventing an increase in permeability on stimulation, or by decreasing the permeability below normal. This theory is based on the evidence that in many instances the permeability does seem to change in the manner presumed, under the influence of narcotics, although the evidence has not always been really conclusive (cf. Heilbrunn, 1925). Actually, it has not proved to be a general rule that narcotics and anesthetics decrease cellular permeability in general; in some instances they seem to have no significant effect, in others they increase permeability, while in still others they have opposite effects on the same type of cell, e.g., erythrocytes, depending upon the specific animal from which the cells are obtained, or upon the specific substance whose rate of penetration is measured (Heilbrunn, 1925; Hoefler and Weber, 1926; Lucké, 1931; Holdheide, 1931; Weber, 1931; Jacobs and Parpart, 1932, 1937; Collander and Barlund, 1933; Schmidt, 1936; Saubert, 1937; Barlund, 1938). Without considering the evidence in detail, it is apparent that, from our point of view, narcosis will result whether the narcotizing agent directly affects the membrane itself or affects the metabolic reactions responsible for maintaining the normal potential difference across the membrane. When this potential difference is altered, the permeability is automatically altered; conversely, any significant change in the properties of the membrane will also alter the potential difference across it, other factors remaining the same. Thus, depending upon concentration and other conditions, narcotics might be expected to decrease permeability or to increase it, and narcosis to result in either case. Changes in permeability, whether in the direction of increase or of decrease, are capable of causing narcosis, but they may also be purely incidental to narcosis.

The action of salts, similarly, is not necessarily caused through a single mechanism. For example, various monovalent cations reduce the resting potential of nerve (Cowan, 1934; Shanes, 1944). The companion anions are much less important. Reversible reductions of the resting potential inevitably lead to some degree of narcosis. The mechanism involved in the influence of potassium chloride, etc., on the potential difference between the inside and the outside of the cell will be considered later (Chapters 11 and 12). Magnesium ions are one of the most general of narcotizing agents, whereas calcium ions may counteract the effect of the magnesium ions. The mechanism of these effects involves both the ability of the ions to diffuse through the membrane, and their ability to alter directly the properties of the membrane, as well as to affect the metabolism inside the cell.

In the remainder of this discussion of narcosis, we will consider briefly the mechanisms involved in the influence of cold, heat, hydrostatic pressure, oxidative metabolism, and metabolic inhibitors, including lipid-soluble and other narcotics.

Temperature, as always, is the most fundamental factor. Although the activity of enzymes in general, including those concerned in nerve function, decreases on either side of an optimal temperature, the reduction in activity obtained merely by cooling is apt to be much more readily reversible than the reduction in activity at high temperatures, because of the irreversible reactions that are characterized by high activation energies. For this reason, lowering the temperature is a more practical method of inducing narcosis in complex organisms than raising the temperature. Cold, in fact, has long been recognized as a narcotizing agent in warm-blooded animals. Thus, as long ago as 1646, Marcus Aurelius Severinus used cold as an anesthetic, and Larrey, the Surgeon-in-Chief of Napoleon's Grand Army, recognized the value of cold in reducing the pain of operations, especially amputations (Castiglione, 1947). After the Battle of

Borodino near Moscow, September 7, 1812, Larrey is said to have performed as many as 200 amputations in a single day. In recent years the use of cold as a localized anesthetic for amputations has been revived (Allen, 1938, 1939, 1941, 1942, 1943; Crossman et al., 1942; Mock and Mock, 1943; cf. also Field and Hall, 1944).

The influence of cold on nerves clearly depends upon several mechanisms, including general reductions in the rate of metabolism inside the cell, in the rate of diffusion of ions across the membrane, in the rate of conduction of the impulse, and in the rate of recovery after excitation. Moreover, to the extent that cholinesterase activity is essential to normal nerve function, it can become a limiting factor through the influence of temperature upon the rate of production of acetyl choline through complex metabolic reactions (Nachmansohn, Cox, Coates, and Machado, 1943), ultimately limited by the supply of glucose or pyruvate as well as by oxygen (Mann et al., 1938). In addition to the factors concerned in the influence of cold on the activity of a single nerve cell, in a complex organism there are also others, such as circulation of the blood, ventilation of the lungs, etc., that become important and limit the use of cold as a general anesthetic.

The net result has a complicated basis even in a single nerve. The effect of low temperatures on the resting potential, for example, is governed by the influence of temperature on the rate of metabolic production of ions or substances that influence the diffusibility of ions, which rate becomes less as the temperature is lowered, but the effect of temperature on the resting potential is governed likewise by the rate of differential diffusion of ions across the membrane, which is also reduced. Of these two processes, the rate of diffusion would be expected to have somewhat the lower temperature coefficient, but, since the net result depends upon the difference in their temperature coefficients, which is not likely to be large, the resting potential should not be greatly affected. Thus Blinks and Darsie (1936–37) have found that, although the rate of respiration of the alga, *Halicystis*, has a temperature coefficient (Q_{10}) of 2 or more between 5° and 25°C, the normal resting potential of 70 or 80 mv has a Q_{10} of only 1.1 to 1.2. Similarly, the resting membrane potentials (ca. 80 mv) of single muscle fibers, e.g., sartorius of the frog, have a Q_{10} of only about 1.1 between 4° and 30°C (Ling and Woodbury, 1949; Ling and Gerard, 1949a). Either above or below 30°, the potential becomes slightly less, indicating an optimal temperature, as would be expected. The action potential of muscle, however, has ordinary temperature coefficients for its various aspects, viz., rate of depolarization, rate of recovery, etc. (Ling and Gerard, 1949c; Nastuk and Hodgkin, 1950), and the same is true of nerve (Davis, 1926; Gasser, 1931; Hodgkin and Katz,

1949b). In nerve, as the temperature is lowered, the rate of conduction decreases (Helmholtz, 1850) and the height of the action potential decreases until a temperature is reached where the nerve becomes inexcitable (Gasser, 1931), even though the resting potential at this temperature is only slightly affected (Lorente de Nó, 1947).

The influence of heat in reversibly inhibiting various biological processes has already been discussed (Chapter 8). In nerve a "heat paralysis" occurs when the temperature is raised to a certain extent; excitability is lost, but recovery takes place on cooling, provided that the nerve is not heated to too high a temperature or maintained at the relatively high temperature for too long a period of time. Thus, with various species of frogs, heat paralysis of nerve trunks occurs at temperatures between 32° and 40°C (Thörner, 1920), and excitability is restored when they are cooled. Presumably the effect of heat here is fundamentally the same as in the reversible denaturation of proteins and enzymes in general, although some of the proteins and enzymes concerned in normal activity of a nerve are surely more susceptible to thermal inactivation, reversible as well as irreversible, than others. By the same token, some of these systems are more sensitive in nerve than in other tissues, and they are more sensitive to some drugs, particularly to those that act by the type II mechanism (p. 405) than to others.

Increased hydrostatic pressure of the appropriate magnitude has long been known to cause a reversible inhibition of many biological processes. The mechanisms are discussed in Chapter 9. Here again differences in susceptibility of different enzyme or other protein systems are to be expected, both within a given type of cell and in various tissues. In addition, the net results of pressure are likely to be modified by temperature and other factors for reasons already discussed. As yet, the temperature relations have not been studied with respect to the influence of pressure on nerve processes, nor is there sufficient evidence to indicate any one particular enzyme system of nerve as being quantitatively more significant than others in the observed effects of pressure.

Ebbecke (1936e) has pointed out certain general similarities between narcosis induced by hydrostatic pressure and narcosis induced by chemical agents. Thus, under either influence, reversible paralysis as well as irreversible damage occur in the most diverse of animal and plant processes; living forms and their organs arrange themselves, with respect to their relative sensitivities, in the same order; and subnarcotic amounts give rise to excitatory effects. In experiments with spinal frogs Ebbecke also noted that the central nervous system is especially sensitive to stimulation by relatively low pressures, and to paralysis by higher pressures. Pressures of some 300 atm, which have little effect (under the conditions involved) on muscle or peripheral nerve, paralyze the central nervous system, at first reversibly but, with continued compression, irreversibly also. Although he did not undertake to investigate the influence of pressure on the phenomenon of narcosis caused by drugs, Ebbecke (1914) did observe that isolated muscles shortened under pressure after they had been rendered unresponsive to ordinary stimuli by previous treatment with curare, 5% alcohol, or 6% sucrose.

Oxidative metabolism is the ultimate source of the electrical potential of nerve and other cells as well as the ultimate source of energy for all biological activities. The early evidence that cells narcotized with chloroform or certain other agents do not take up oxygen, or do so at a reduced rate (Winterstein, 1900, 1902; Fröhlich, 1904; Nagai, 1905) led to the "asphyxial theory of narcosis" (Verworn, 1909). The theory was inadequate in placing exclusive emphasis on aerobic metabolism, inasmuch as physiological processes which are not directly dependent upon oxygen, e.g., reproduction and fermentation in yeast, are susceptible to the action of narcotics (Warburg and Wiesel, 1912). Furthermore, it was soon demonstrated that certain processes could be readily inhibited by narcotics without an appreciable reduction in the rate of oxygen consumption, for example, cell division of sea urchin eggs (Warburg, 1910; Loeb and Wasteneys, 1913), and also that obligate anaerobes such as the intestinal worms, *Ascaris* (Winterstein, 1913), could be narcotized by chloroform or ether.

In spite of the inadequacies of the "asphyxial" theory, it was partially correct, and with the subsequent progress in biochemical research the discrepancies have become to a large extent understandable. In recent years interest was revived in the significance of oxidative metabolism, especially of the central nervous system, in the mechanism of narcosis (cf. Quastel, 1939, 1943). Thus conscious activity of the brain has long been known to be particularly sensitive to an adequate supply of oxygen (Wolff, 1936). Intellectual function is diminished in subjects breathing 10 per cent oxygen rather than the usual, approximately 20 per cent, oxygen (Kraines, 1937). Interruption of the cerebral circulation for only 6 to 8 sec is sufficient to cause loss of consciousness. A decreased oxygen supply to the cerebral cortex of the cat brain abolishes, in as little as 20 sec, the normal action potentials (Simpson and Derbyshire, 1934); irreversible damage follows within a very few minutes. Moreover there is evidence that the rate of oxygen consumption by the brain is reduced during anesthesia by barbiturates and other narcotics (McClure et al., 1939; Shaw et al., 1937).

In addition to a continuous, adequate supply of oxygen, normal brain function requires an adequate supply of glucose. The hypoglycemia resulting from an injection of insulin is accompanied by a change in electrical potentials of the cortex, and the potentials disappear if the hypoglycemia is prolonged (Hoagland et al., 1937; Maddock et al., 1939). With an adequate supply of both oxygen and glucose, phenobarbital slows the rate of cortical potential changes (Gibbs et al., 1937).

Evidence such as the above, as well as other evidence, makes it clear that a minimum overall rate of aerobic oxidation of glucose is normally required for conscious activity of the brain. Relatively slight reductions in this rate lead to cessation of this function, whether they result from

Table 10.12.   Influence of Various Narcotics on the Oxidation of Different Substrates by Minced Guinea Pig Brain

(From Jowett, 1938)

Substrate	Per Cent Inhibition by Narcotics, Concentration = 0.12%				
	Allyl*iso*-propylbarbiturate	Pheno-barbital	Chlorotone	Hyoscine	Chloral hydrate
Glucose	73	94	93	79	66
Na lactate	71	79	88	73	90
Na pyruvate	67	85	84	71	90
Na succinate	2	0	0	0	0
Na glutamate	28	50	59	60	62
p-Phenylenediamine	0	0	..	..	..

lack of oxygen, lack of substrate, or presence of enzyme inhibitors.   In fact, it has been estimated (Jowett, 1938) that an inhibition by various drugs of only about 15 per cent of normal brain respiration is sufficient to produce narcosis.   Experiments with brain slices and minced brain tissue *in vitro* indicate that, of various substrates which increase the rate of aerobic respiration (cf. Quastel, 1939), glucose, lactate and pyruvate are probably the most significant in maintaining normal activity.   Furthermore the oxidation of these substrates, and of glutamate, by brain is more sensitive to inhibition by various narcotics than is the oxidation of certain other substrates, such as succinate or *p*-phenylenediamine (Table 10.12).   The oxidation of the same substrates by tissues other than brain is also inhibited by various narcotics, though generally not to the same extent (Jowett and Quastel, 1937).

With a number of narcotics, the concentrations required to produce narcosis in animals are not very different from those which produce moderate inhibitions in the rate of glucose oxidation by brain cortex slices (Table 10.13).

In a study of isolated enzyme systems Michaelis and Quastel (1941) have shown that narcotics in low concentrations seem to affect primarily

Table 10.13. Concentrations of Various Narcotizing Agents Causing Narcosis in Animals and Inhibiting the Respiration of Brain Cortex Slices in the Presence of Glucose

(From Jowett, 1938)

Narcotic	Animal	Narcotizing Concentration (M)	Per Cent Inhibition of Respiration Caused by Narcotizing Concentration	Ratio between Concentration Required to Produce 15% Inhibition of Respiration and Narcotizing Concentration
Ethyl urethan	Rat	0.022	6	2.9
Magnesium ion	Rabbit	0.005 (excess above normal)	12	1.2
	Rat	0.005	13	1.2
Chloral hydrate	Rat	0.0013	10	1.6
Phenobarbital	Rat	0.00079	15	1.0
Chlorotone	Rat	0.0010	20	0.7
Evipan	Guinea pig	0.00062	17	0.9
Avertin	Rat	0.00106	31	0.4
Chlorotone	Guinea pig	0.0010	32	0.4

a particular tissue component, possibly a flavoprotein, as illustrated diagrammatically below (Quastel, 1943):

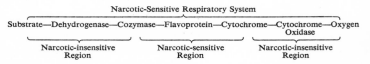

Thus, although many narcotics such as urethan and alcohol have been shown to affect various enzyme systems, the inhibition of respiration in some instances can be attributed primarily to an effect on some one enzyme system that is considerably more sensitive to these agents than are other systems.   It is undoubtedly for this reason that the analysis of their action on the whole complex process is frequently in accord with effects on a single enzyme (e.g., Figs. 10.46 and 10.47, pp. 447, 449).   Although the most sensitive system remains to be identified, the evidence suggestive of a flavoprotein is of particular interest in view of the possibility that luminescence, which is also especially sensitive to narcotics, is possibly inhibited also by effects on a flavoprotein enzyme.

From our point of view any considerable inhibition of respiratory metabolism will lead to narcosis, inasmuch as the continued production of metabolic products of the oxidation of glucose or certain other substrates is essential in order to maintain polarization of the nerve cells, other conditions remaining the same. Thus lack of oxygen leads to loss of excitability and depolarization. The same result may be obtained in the presence of oxygen, if small amounts of cyanide, of the order of 0.001 M are added (Gerard, 1930; Schmitt and Schmitt, 1931; Wright, 1947; Lorente de Nó, 1947).

There is another aspect of nerve activity, however, which makes aerobic respiration and the presence of certain substrates especially important, namely, the production of acetyl choline. Whatever the precise rôle of this substance, its synthesis in the brain apparently depends upon the presence of oxygen and either glucose, pyruvate, lactate, or, to a somewhat lesser extent, α-glycerophosphate or glutamate (Quastel, Tennenbaum, and Wheatley, 1936; Mann et al., 1938). On the other hand, anaerobic synthesis of acetyl choline takes place in the presence of adenosine triphosphate and the enzyme, choline acetylase, extracted from brain or peripheral nerves (Nachmansohn and Machado, 1943; Nachmansohn, John, and Waelsch, 1943; Nachmansohn and John, 1944, 1945). Evidently the need for aerobic metabolism in order to synthesize acetyl choline in the intact cell arises from processes of oxidative phosphorylation concerned with supplying the appropriate "high energy" phosphate esters (Lipmann, 1941) for the synthesis. The important point with respect to the action of narcotics is that nerve function may be abolished not merely by the reduction in respiration needed to keep the cells polarized, but also by the reduction in supply of acetyl choline.

In general, as we have remarked earlier, a significant, reversible interference with any of the five conditions essential to normal nerve activity will lead to narcosis. Even though certain narcotics evidently reduce the rate of total oxygen consumption by inhibiting a particularly sensitive enzyme system, as indicated by the work of Michaelis and Quastel (1941), the inhibition of other systems concerned with maintaining different conditions essential to activity may also be involved. Various metabolic inhibitors, such as flouride and iodoacetate, reduce the resting potential of nerve by interfering with different stages in the cycle of carbohydrate breakdown and phosphorylation (Shanes and Brown, 1942). The membrane potential of muscle fibers is likewise reduced by metabolic inhibitors in a somewhat complex manner (Ling and Gerard, 1949c). The inhibition of metabolism by iodoacetate as well as by anoxia or cyanide and other agents (Boyarsky, Rosenblad, Postel, and Gerard, 1949) leads to depolarization. Although certain drugs which are particularly active against choline esterase also affect brain and nerve respiration (Brooks et al., 1949), their effects on physiological activity cannot be assigned in general to a specific action against choline esterase, or to the inhibition of respiration, or to both.

Table 10.14. Distribution Coefficients between Olive Oil and Water, and Concentrations of Various Substances Required to Narcotize Polliwogs

(Henderson, 1930; from the data of Meyer, 1899, Baum, 1899, and later)

Narcotic	Ratio: Conc. in Oil/Conc. in Water	Narcotizing Concentration (M)
Trional	4.4	0.0013
Tetronal	4.0	0.0018
Butylchloral	1.6	0.002
Sulfonal	1.1	0.006
Bromalhydrate	0.7	0.002
Benzamide	0.6	0.002
Triacetin	0.3	0.01
Diacetin	0.23	0.015
Chloral hydrate	0.22	0.025
Ethylurethan	0.14	0.025
Monoacetin	0.06	0.02
Methylurethan	0.04	0.4
Alcohol	0.03	0.5

Among the various theories of narcosis, the theory of "lipoid solubility," proposed independently by H. H. Meyer and Overton, has probably been the most widely held.   It therefore calls for re-examination, in the light of what we have already discussed.

Although Meyer's publication (1899) preceded Overton's (1901), their theories had already been discussed and found identical in 1899.   In essence, the theory states (Meyer, 1899) that (1) all chemically indifferent substances, soluble in fats or lipins, act as narcotics on living protoplasm in so far as they can be distributed therein; (2) the action of such substances is most marked and most readily apparent on cells in which lipins are especially significant in cell function; and (3) the relative effectiveness of such substances depends upon their distribution coefficients between fat-like substances and water.   The roots of this theory actually extend back at least to the observations of Bibra and Harless (1847), i.e., that ether and other anesthetics are good fat solvents, and that during anesthesia fatty constituents of the brain seem to be dissolved out and redeposited in the liver. Later Hermann (1866) suggested that the site of action of anesthetics might be lecithin, cholesterol, and fat, in which the anesthetics readily dissolve.

The principal support for the Meyer-Overton theory rests upon the impressive correlation between lipid solubility and narcotic potencies of various substances. Both Meyer and Overton undertook to determine the distribution coefficients of various narcotics in olive oil and water,

Table 10.15. Correlation between the Influence of Temperature on Narcotic Potency and Distribution Coefficient between Olive Oil and Water

(From Meyer, 1901)

Narcotic	Dilution of Normal Solution Causing Narcosis of Frogs		Distribution Coefficient, Olive Oil/Water	
	3°C	30°C	3°C	30°C
Salicylamide	1 : 1300	1 : 600	2.23	1.40
Benzamide	1 : 500	1 : 200	0.67	0.43
Monacetin	1 : 90	1 : 70	0.093	0.066
Ethyl alcohol	1 : 3	1 : 7	0.024	0.046
Chloral hydrate	1 : 50	1 : 250	0.053	0.236
Acetone	1 : 3	1 : 7	0.140	0.195

and to determine the concentration of the same narcotics required for a similar degree of narcosis of polliwogs. Their data showed clearly that, in general, the more a substance dissolved in oil in preference to water, the less was the concentration in water required to cause narcosis (Table 10.14). Meyer (1901) showed also that with some narcotics the influence of temperature on the oil-water distribution was roughly paralleled by the influence of temperature on the amount of the narcotic required for narcosis (Table 10.15). These data seemed to provide strong support for the theory.

A large number of studies were carried out by various investigators who followed Meyer and Overton; some of their results provided further support for the theory, and others were equivocal, or they seemed at variance with it, according to the degree of quantitative agreement considered significant. Henderson (1930) has reviewed the experiments up to 1930. The work of K. H. Meyer and Gottlieb-Billroth (1920), Meyer and Hopff (1923), and Meyer (1937) developed the theory somewhat more precisely than originally. Some of their data are summarized in Tables 10.16 and 10.17 (cf. also Hoeber, 1945; Danielli, 1950).

Table 10.16.　Concentration in Air of Various Gaseous Narcotics
Required To Produce a Similar Narcosis in Mice, and Corresponding
Equilibrium Concentrations in Olive Oil

(From Meyer, 1937)

Narcotic	Concentration in Air : Volume Per Cent	Corresponding Equilibrium Concentration in Olive Oil: moles/liter $\times$ 10^2
Methane	370	8
Nitrous oxide	100	6
Acetylene	65	5
Ethyl chloride	5	7
Ether	3.4	9
Methylal	2.8	8
Carbon disulfide	1.1	7
Carbon tetrachloride	0.6	7
Chloroform	0.5	9
Range of variation	740 fold	1.8 fold

Table 10.17.　Concentration in Water of Various Substances Required
To Produce a Similar Narcosis in Tadpoles, and Corresponding
Equilibrium Concentrations in Oleic Alcohol

(From Meyer, 1937)

Narcotic	Concentration in Water: moles/liter	Corresponding Concentration in moles/liter $\times$ 10^2
Ethyl alcohol	0.33	3.3
Propyl alcohol	0.11	3.8
Butyl alcohol	0.03	2.0
Valeramide	0.07	2.1
Antipyrine	0.07	2.1
Pyramidon	0.03	3.9
Ether	0.024	5.0
Benzamide	0.013	3.3
Salicylamide	0.0033	2.1
Phenobarbital	0.008	4.8
o-Nitraniline	0.0025	3.5
Carbon disulfide	0.0005	3.0
Chloroform	0.00008	2.6
Thymol	0.000047	4.5
Range of variation	7,000 fold	2.5 fold

Tables 10.16 and 10.17 show that, in spite of the enormous differences in concentrations of various narcotics in air or in aqueous solution required to produce a given degree of narcosis, the corresponding equilibrium concentrations in oil are roughly the same. Meyer (1937) concludes from these data that "narcosis commences when any chemically indifferent substance has attained a certain molar concentration in the lipoids of the cell (or, to be more precise, in the lipoidic alcohols of the cell substance). This concentration depends on the nature of the animal or cell, but is independent of the narcotic." These same data, however, may also be regarded as the consequences of "Ferguson's rule" (p. 431), which is applicable as much to extracted enzymes, in the absence of cell structure and lipoidal constituents, as to functions of intact cells. Moreover the absence of any structural feature common to all the diverse substances represented emphasizes the general significance of this rule.

From our present perspective, the fundamental truth in the Meyer-Overton theory resides in its recognition of the affinity for hydrophobic media of substances usually classed as narcotics. The solubility of the narcotic in oil is an excellent index to its potency, but it is not itself the mechanism of physiological action.

The same type of bond is formed when a fat-soluble substance dissolves in olive oil and when it combines with a hydrophobic group of an enzyme or protein; the former provides the index, and the latter the physiological mechanism. It is not necessary to assume that the narcotic action in animals is caused by a solution of the substance in cell lipids; this hypothesis offers only a vague explanation, at best, of the mechanism of narcosis, except possibly at such high concentrations that the integrity of the cell structure is seriously, and probably irreparably, disrupted. Furthermore the Meyer-Overton theory as originally stated obviously cannot apply to the action of narcotics and anesthetics on extracted and even purified enzyme systems in aqueous solution functioning independently of the presence of lipids. The relationships between potency and oil solubility, however, apply also to these lipid-free systems. Here the interpretation of the relationship must be strictly at the molecular level, rather than in relation to complex cell structures and functions, and the meaning seems to be reasonably clear. Thus the potency is roughly proportional to the tendency of the narcotizing substance to seek out the hydrophobic groups of the protein enzyme. When the theory is interpreted this way, as Danielli has pointed out (1950), there is no real discrepancy between the Meyer-Overton theory and the theory of inhibitor action as we have developed it.

Apart from the few experiments of Meyer referred to above (Table 10.15), the Meyer-Overton theory has not stressed the significance of temperature. From our point of view, the increase in narcotic potency of ethyl alcohol, etc., with rise in temperature described by Meyer would be anticipated. The influence of temperature on the potencies of the other substances which Meyer studied depends, of course, upon their type of action, and it is more difficult to anticipate but not more difficult to interpret at the molecular level.

Because of the significance of hydrostatic pressure, as well as of temperature, in the action of narcotics on relatively simple systems such as extracted enzymes and bacterial luminescence, the effects of hydrostatic pressure on the action of narcotics in higher animals becomes especially interesting and important to test. A recent study of narcosis in tadpoles, the classic animal for this field of research, has provided evidence of a remarkable parallel between the influence of increased hydrostatic pressure on the inhibition of luminescence by certain narcotics and on the narcosis of tadpoles by the same substances (Johnson and Flagler, 1951). Although further studies are required before the generality of such a parallelism can be evaluated, the results bear directly on the general theory of the mechanism of enzyme inhibition as well as of narcosis.

The inhibition of bacterial luminescence caused by ethyl alcohol, ethyl carbamate, and amyl carbamate has already been discussed. Hydrostatic pressures of some 2,000 to 5,000 psi counteract, to a considerable extent, moderate inhibitions caused by alcohol and ethyl carbamate, but have little effect on the inhibition caused by amyl carbamate. At room temperature, tadpoles of the wood frog, *Rana silvatica*, as well as tadpoles of the salamander, *Amblystoma maculatum*, are readily narcotized when placed in tap water containing approximately the same concentration of these respective substances that moderately inhibit bacterial luminescence near the normally optimal temperature, viz., about 0.5 M alcohol, 0.1 M ethyl carbamate (urethan), or 0.001 M amyl carbamate.

With the aid of a large pressure chamber (cf. diagram in Botts, Johnson, and Morales, 1951) containing thick Herculite plate glass windows, it is possible to observe the larvae under increased hydrostatic pressure. Unnarcotized animals immediately respond by increased swimming activity when the pressure is raised to between 1,000 and 2,500 psi, in accordance with effects described by Ebbecke (1935b) on the activity of various marine animals. Higher pressures of 4,000 to 5,000 psi cause paralysis, from which the animals slowly recover after the release of pressure, or sometimes die. Salamander larvae appear more resistant to the injurious effects of the higher pressures than do frog larvae. When the animals narcotized in alcohol or urethan are placed in the pressure chamber, filled with the same solution in which they were narcotized, and the pressure is raised, there is an immediate recovery of apparently normal

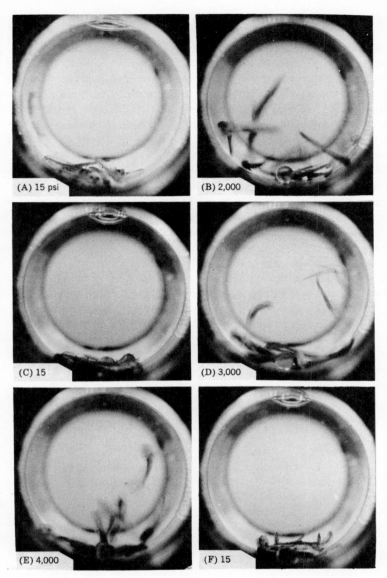

Fig. 10.64. Activity of *Amblystoma* larvae, in 2.5% alcohol, with successive changes in hydrostatic pressure over a total period of 4 min. Photographs were made through a window in the pressure chamber. The air bubble visible at the top of the compartment under atmospheric pressure disappears as the pressure is raised, and reappears as the pressure is released. The slight increase in amount of dissolved oxygen that occurred in this manner cannot account for the decreased narcosis, inasmuch as similarly narcotized animals showed no recovery when transferred to a corresponding narcotic solution which had been equilibrated with pure oxygen (Johnson and Flagler, 1951).

swimming activity at the appropriate pressure, usually around 2,000 psi. The results are most striking with the minimal narcotic dose required to abolish spontaneous activity and a response to gentle prodding at atmospheric pressure.   Repeated activity and inactivity of the animals in the narcotic solution take place as the pressure is successively increased and then released (Fig. 10.64).   When amyl carbamate, however, is used as the narcotizing drug, there is very little or no observable activity of the animals under pressure.

While the influence of increased hydrostatic pressure on whole complex animals involves effects on many systems, some of which are quickly injured at as little as 4,000 to 5,000 psi, the simplest and most likely interpretation of the influence of pressure on the degree of narcosis is in accordance with the same theory that applies in luminescence.   There is no reason to expect an appreciable change, for example, in the oil/water distribution of the narcotics under the pressures concerned.   The net effect will, in general, depend upon the relative effect on all the physiological reactions sensitive to increased hydrostatic pressure and their equilibrium states.   Thus, it is to be anticipated that temperature, as well as drug concentration and amount of pressure, will generally influence the observed results.   These particular results with amphibian larvae were uniquely anticipated through the theory developed from studies of bacterial luminescence.

Diffusion through Membranes and Transmembrane Potentials[1]

Es ist vielleicht nicht zu gewagt, schon hier die Vermutung aus-
zusprechen, dass nicht nur die Ströme in Muskeln und Nerven,
sondern auch namentlich die rätselhaften Wirkungen der elektri-
schen Fische durch die hier erörterten Eigenschaften der halbdurch-
lässigen Membranen ihre Erklärung finden werden.

Ostwald, 1890

Various lines of evidence indicate that essentially every living cell is bounded by a membrane whose presence and integrity are vital to the proper functioning of the cell. The thinness of the membrane—of the order of 100 Å—makes it difficult to produce a direct proof of its existence. Its presence is attested, however, by the reactions of the cell to its environment, by selectivity toward the penetration of substances, by a potential difference commonly of the order of 0.1 volt between the inside and the outside of the cell, and by numerous other observations.

The selectivity of the membrane is conditioned by the size, chemical nature, and organization of the particles of which it is composed. The presence of a transmembrane potential difference sharpens the selectivity of the membrane in that the membrane shows discrimination toward particles according to the magnitude and sign of their electrical charges and the direction in which they move.

The membrane thus exercises control over the relative amounts of substances entering the interior of the cell from the chemical pool surrounding it, thereby influencing functional activities of the cell. The task of regulating the molecular and ionic traffic into and out of the cell is only one of the duties of the membrane. Studies on nerve and muscle cells indicate that the potential difference E, which is conditioned, at least in part, by the selectivity of the membrane, in turn not only controls the selectivity of the membrane toward charged particles, but also affects

[1] The author of this chapter (M. J. P.) wishes to express his gratitude to the National Foundation for Infantile Paralysis for the aid which made possible the work on the problems discussed in this chapter.

profoundly the general state of "leakiness" of the membrane.   In nerve and muscle, if the value of E is decreased below a certain critical value, the general leakiness of the membrane increases, and the selectivity changes in such a way as to decrease the value of E still further.   Thus the mutual interaction of the selectivity and of E produces a rapid and large change in the transmembrane potential.   In nerve cells this drop in E at one spot initiates similar changes in the adjacent areas of the fiber. The propagation of such a disturbance along the fiber is the basis of transmission of impulses along the fiber.   In muscle fibers the local change in the membrane apparently initiates the contraction in the interior of the cell, while the propagation of the change along the length of the fiber insures that excitation will occur through the length of the fiber.

There is strong evidence that muscle and nerve fiber membranes are both structurally complex and labile; they are sensitive, more or less, to the magnitude of the transmembrane potential.   A clear understanding of the behavior of a simple stable membrane is obviously not a sufficient basis for interpreting the behavior of the complex and labile membranes of nerve and muscle cells, but it is a necessary prerequisite.   This chapter is devoted to an examination of the characteristics of simple, stable membranes.   Although other models have been advanced (e.g., Sollner, 1950), our discussion is restricted to two types, i.e., the neutral membrane and the acid or basic membrane, respectively, which lend themselves readily to theoretical analysis and have been widely employed.   An examination of the behavior of the more complex, labile membranes of living cells, particularly in nerve and muscle, is undertaken in Chapter 12. No attempt will be made to indicate the differences between the treatment of the problem of membrane permeability to be followed in this chapter and that given in some earlier publications (Reiner, 1937, 1941; Rosenberg, 1948).   The diffusion of neutral particles has been discussed extensively by Jacobs (1935).

The paradox of the permeability constant

The theoretical interpretation of experimental work on the penetration of ions through membranes is usually complicated by the fact that the membrane may change its properties when the experimental conditions are changed.   It is customary to meet this situation by treating the membrane in each experiment as a simple one, to calculate the permeability constant in each experiment, and to attempt to deduce some information about the nature of the membrane and the mechanism of the permeation, from the effect of the experimental conditions on the calculated value of the constant.

The familiar equation (11.1a) has been used for calculating the permeability constant P (Davson and Danielli, 1943):

$$f = P(C_i - C_o) \qquad (11.1a)$$

where f is the outward flow of the ion, and C_i and C_o are the inside and outside concentrations, respectively. If the ion is present on one side of the membrane only, equation (11.1a) takes the form of one of the following:

$$\overrightarrow{f} = PC_i \qquad \overleftarrow{f} = -PC_o \qquad (11.1b,c)$$

For example, let us assume that the following experimental results were obtained in an experiment in which the concentrations and the fluxes were measured:

	C_i	C_o	Moles per Sq Cm per Sec
M_1^+ :	0.300 M	0.025 M	$f_1 = 0.5 \times 10^{-10}$ (outward)
M_2^+ :	0.020 M	0.025 M	$f_2 = 2.3 \times 10^{-10}$ (inward)

Applying equation (11.1a), we calculate the values: $P_1 = 1.82 \times 10^{-10}$ moles per sq cm per sec per mole per liter. $P_2 = 460 \times 10^{-10}$. $P_2/P_1 = 253$. The two permeability constants thus appear to differ by a large ratio.

In the absence of any further experimental information it would be natural to speculate on the kind of peculiarities of the two ions or of the membrane that would account for the large ratio of the two permeability constants. Let us assume, however, that in further experiments with the aid of isotopes the outward and inward fluxes of M_1^+ were measured, with the following results:

$$\overrightarrow{f_1} = 3 \times 10^{-10} \qquad \overleftarrow{f_1} = 2.5 \times 10^{-10} \qquad f_1 = 0.5 \times 10^{-10}$$

Using these values to calculate the permeability constant, the calculated magnitude of the "constant" will depend upon which one of the three equations (11.1a,b,c) is employed:

$$\overrightarrow{P_1} = 10 \times 10^{-10} \qquad \overleftarrow{P_1} = 100 \times 10^{-10} \qquad P_1 = 1.82 \times 10^{-10}$$
$$\text{(11.1b)} \qquad\qquad \text{(11.1c)} \qquad\qquad \text{(11.1a)}$$

Thus questions arise about the reason for the three different values, the relative usefulness of each, and the significance of the high value of the ratio, P_2/P_1, calculated from the first set of data.

First, let us consider this paradox on purely theoretical grounds, using the following illustration. A diffusion system, containing ion M_3^+ is very close to, but not quite at, a Donnan equilibrium. In such a system the net flux f would be very small. The two fluxes in the opposite directions would be approximately equal. On the other hand, the inside and outside concentrations of the ion would be unequal. Let $C_i = KC_o$. Application of equations (11.1a,b,c) would give the following results:

$$\overleftarrow{P} : \text{very small} \qquad \overrightarrow{P} = K\overleftarrow{P}$$

This second illustration suggests the reason for the paradox and the method of resolving it. Equations (11.1a,b,c) do not take into account the transmembrane potential E usually present across the membrane. Consequently, the use of these equations may yield calculated values of P that are of uncertain theoretical meaning.

Equations (11.2a,b,c), given below, for the general case, as well as for those cases where the ion is present on one side only, are apt to give values of P which are more adequate for a theoretical analysis (cf. p. 539). In these equations Z is the exponential, $Z = e^{FE/RT}$.

$$f = P(C_i - C_oZ) \qquad \overrightarrow{f} = PC_i \qquad \overleftarrow{f} = -PC_oZ \qquad (11.2a,b,c)$$

Unfortunately, the available data on permeability are not adequate for making use of equations (11.2a,b,c) since the value of Z is unknown. As an illustration, however, let us assume that the transmembrane potential E was measured in the first example given above and found to be 58 mv (making $Z = 10$, at room temperature).

When only the net rates of penetration of M_1 and M_2 are available, we find that the given values, substituted in (11.2a), yield $P_1 = 10 \times 10^{-10}$ and $P_2 = 10 \times 10^{-10}$. Thus the ratio $P_2/P_1 = 253$, obtained with the use of equation (11.1a), gives us a measure of what we may call a mathematical artifact introduced by that equation.

When, in addition, the isotopic fluxes $\overrightarrow{f_1}$ and $\overleftarrow{f_1}$ are made available, we may use equations (11.2b,c) and we obtain the same values as that obtained with (11.2a), i.e., $\overrightarrow{P_1} = \overleftarrow{P_1} = P = 10 \times 10^{-10}$, and the situation no longer appears paradoxical.

The movement of cations across the membrane of the erythrocyte of the cat

Some of the problems presented by observed movements of cations through the membrane of the erythrocyte of the cat (Davson and Danielli, 1943) appear to be closely related to the paradox discussed in the preceding section. Davson (1940a) measured the rates of escape of sodium from the cell and the rates of penetration of potassium into the cell, as well as the effects of certain chemical agents on these rates. On calculating the permeability constants with the use of equations (11.1a,b,c), the striking and unexpected result was obtained that several agents produced opposite effects on the values of P_{Na} and of P_K. If one value increased, the other decreased, and vice versa. The relative magnitudes of some of the discrepancies in the two effects were astonishing.

In general, any significant change in the ionic composition of one of the solutions in a diffusion system, or any significant addition of active non-electrolytes to one of the solutions, is apt to change the value of the transmembrane potential (cf. p. 543). Let us assume, for example, that a given change in the outside solution makes the solution outside the cell more positive than in the control. This change would be accompanied by two effects. There would be a real increase in the rate of penetration of potassium *into* the cell and a real decrease in the rate of escape of sodium *from* the cell because of the change in the potential gradient. In addition, the new values of P_K and P_{Na}, calculated by means of equations (11.1a,b,c), would digress in opposite directions from the respective control values. Since these equations do not take into account the influence of the potential, the calculated change in the ratio P_K/P_{Na} may be astonishing in magnitude whenever the combination of experimental values is particularly unfavorable. If the change introduced in the outside solution decreases the value of E, the effects will be reversed, but again the changes in the calculated values of P_K and P_{Na} will be in opposite directions.

It would be unjustified to predict that, by using the more adequate equations (11.2a,b,c), it would be possible to eliminate all elements of surprise from the observed movements of sodium and potassium through the erythrocyte membrane, even though the qualitative explanation discussed in the preceding paragraph points in that direction. There can be no doubt, however, that the general use of equations (11.1a,b,c) can lead to erroneous theoretical conclusions. Teorell (1949a) has called attention to the inadequacy of the commonly used equations, which do not take account of the influence of the electrical field on the permeation of ions. The analysis of the problem given in this chapter is intended to include the theoretical equations and some of the experimental procedures needed for a fuller interpretation of the penetration of ions through membranes (cf. Davson, 1940b).

A few definitions

A system consisting of two solutions (with specified concentrations of solutes) separated by a permeable membrane will be referred to as a diffusion system. If any one of the concentrations is changed, this will be taken as a change to a different diffusion system.

Some of the symbols to be used are shown in Fig. 11.1. The concentrations of the jth ion in the inside and the outside solutions will be

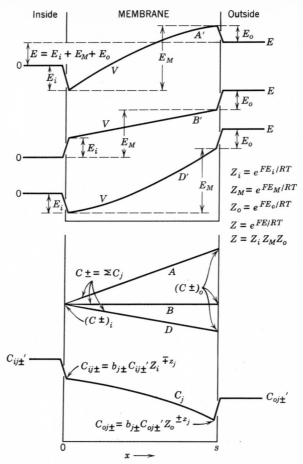

Fig. 11.1. Upper diagram: Examples of potential jumps, E_i and E_o, across the two interfaces and of the potential change E_M across the membrane proper. E_i and E_o may be positive or negative. Their values and signs are determined chiefly by the composition of the adjacent solution. The sign and magnitude of E_M are determined by the relative values of the total conductances of two competing teams of ions. The inside cations and the outside anions tend to impart a positive charge to the outside boundary; the outside cations and the inside anions tend to impart a positive charge to the inner boundary. The stronger of the two teams invariably controls the sign of E_M. The magnitude of E_M is a complicated function of the individual conductances. The total transmembrane potential E is the algebraic sum of E_i, E_M, and E_o. The signs of E_i and of E_o depend chiefly upon the compositions of the inside and outside solutions, respectively.

The potential gradient within the membrane is inversely proportioned to the local value of the ionic strength (compare A–A', B–B', and C–C').

Lower diagram: In a neutral membrane populated by univalent ions the total ionic concentration is a linear function of x. The concentration of the jth ion on the membrane side of either interface is proportional, at equilibrium, to the concentration of the ion in the adjacent solution, subject to an electrical correction factor. If the membrane is positive relative to the solution, cations are repelled and anions are attracted. The electrical correction factors are $Z_i^{\mp z}$ at the inner boundary and $Z_o^{\pm z}$ at the outer boundary, where $\pm z$ is the valence of the ion.

indicated by primed letters, C_{ij}' and C_{oj}', respectively. The concentration of the same ion within the membrane, at the inside boundary, will be called C_{ij}. The variable concentration within the membrane will be called C_j. The concentration on the membrane side, at the outside boundary, will be called C_{oj}.

The formal appearance of some of the equations is independent of whether they are applied to cations or to anions (cf. 11.9). In some cases it may be necessary to write separate equations for cations and anions, respectively; plus and minus subscripts will be used (cf. 11.12a,b). In some cases it may be convenient to combine the equations for cations and anions into a single equation (cf. 11.20); the upper set of signs applies to cations, the lower set, to anions. In equation (11.13) the summation is carried out over every ionic species, with the sign of each term depending upon whether the term originates from a cation or an anion. In equation (11.31) the summation is carried out separately, for cations and anions, respectively.

The total ionic concentration at a given point within the membrane will be called $C\pm$. The values of this quantity at the inside and at the outside boundaries will be represented by the symbols $(C\pm)_i$ and $(C\pm)_o$, respectively.

The local value of the potential will be represented by V; the potential changes at the inner and the outer surfaces by E_i and E_o, respectively. Each of these may be either positive or negative, with the convention that the potential change is positive if the potential increases outward from left to right. As will be seen later (p. 526), the sign of the potential change at each surface is determined chiefly by the composition of the adjacent solution and the distribution coefficients of its constituent ions.

The potential change across the membrane proper will be represented by E_M. Its sign is determined by the relative values of the total conductances at the two boundaries. If the conductance is greater at the inner boundary, E_M is positive. As shown later (equation 11.63), the potential gradient is inversely proportional to the total ionic concentration $C\pm$ if all the ions are univalent. Thus, when the total ionic concentration increases from left to right, as in case A, Fig. 11.1, and E_M is positive, the potential curve is concave downward (curve A'). When the total concentration decreases outward, as in case D, the potential gradient increases with x, as in D'. The potential gradient is linear (line B') only when the total ionic concentration is constant, as in case B.

The total transmembrane potential difference between the two solutions will be called E. It will be seen from the diagram that, if the four potential differences are given consistent signs, E is equal the algebraic sum of the other three: $E = E_o + E_M + E_i$.

If the jth ion in the inner solution happens to be in equilibrium with the same ion in the membrane, then $C_{ij} = b_j C_{ij}'$ (where b_j is the distribution coefficient of the ion), provided that the membrane boundary is at the same potential as the solution. If the potential of the membrane boundary differs from that of the solution by the quantity E_i, this equation is no longer valid. The value of C_{ij} is given by the equation

$$C_{ij\pm} = b_{j\pm} C_{ij\pm}' e^{\mp zFE_i/RT} \tag{11.3}$$

where F is Faraday's equivalent, z or $-z$ is the valence of the ion, R is the gas constant, and T is the absolute temperature. The equilibrium concentration of the jth ion at the outer boundary is given by an equation which is slightly different in form:

$$C_{oj\pm} = b_{j\pm} C_{oj\pm}' e^{\pm zFE/RT} \tag{11.4}$$

The dissymmetry between the two equations is due to the fact that a positive value of E_i indicates that the membrane is positive relative to the inside solution, whereas a positive value of E_o indicates that the membrane is negative relative to the outside solution (see Fig. 11.1).

For any potential difference E_k between two points the exponential factor $e^{FE_k/RT}$ plays a prominent rôle in the equations. For the sake of brevity this quantity will be referred to as the "exponential factor" of E_k and will be given the symbol Z_k. Thus the exponential factors of the four defined potentials will bear the symbols Z_i, Z_M, Z_o, and Z, respectively. In the lower diagram of Fig. 11.1 the boundary concentrations are given in terms of the exponential factors.

The value of Z_k for a given value E_k depends upon the temperature. In doing numerical calculations, it is convenient to remember that, at room temperature, $Z_k = 10$, if $E_k = 58$ mv. For any other value of E_k the value of Z_k may be calculated with the use of the formula

$$Z_k = 10^{E_k/58}$$

Thus, if $E_k = -116$ mv, $Z_k = 10^{-2}$; if $E_k = 30$ mv, $E_k = 10^{30/58} = 3.29$.

The steady state distribution of ions within the membrane

When the two solutions are introduced on the opposite sides of the membrane, or if a new electrolyte is added to a functioning diffusion system, there is an initial flurry of readjustment within the membrane. Eventually, a steady state distribution of ions is reached, and each ionic species moves across the membrane with a constant flux f_j. It will be instructive to examine some of the features of the steady state distribution within the membrane; this will give some indication of the complexity of the problem and will also have some bearing on diffusion system characteristics discussed later.

In Fig. 11.2 it is assumed that ions M_1^+ and X_2^- are present, among other substances, in the outside solution, but not in the inside solution. Ions M_3^+, M_4^{2+}, X_5^-, and neutral molecules N are present in the inside solution, but not in the outer solution. The first two substances must flow inward, whereas the last three must flow outward. Turning our attention to f_1, the flux of M_1^+, we can think of this flux as consisting of two components, one due to purely Brownian movement, which will be called the diffusion flux f_D, and the other due to the drift of the electrical particles in the field, which will be called the electrical flux f_E. The net flux is equal to the algebraic sum of the two components and is constant throughout the membrane. The relative values of the two component fluxes change from point to point. At A, where the concentration of M_1^+ is high, the electrical flux is larger than at B, where the concentration of the ions is smaller. It follows that the diffusion component must be lower at A than at B. Since the diffusion component is proportional to the concentration gradient, it follows that the concentration gradient of M_1^+ must increase toward the left, and that the concentration curve must be concave downward. Similar considerations will lead to the conclusion that the curves for X_2^-, M_3^+, M_4^{2+} must be concave upward, that for X_5^- must be concave downward, while the concentration of N is linear.

If the value of E_M is reduced to zero, through the imposition of an outside transmembrane emf, the curves become linear. If the sign of E_M is reversed, every curvature changes sign.

The slope of each curve at its lowest point is a direct measure of the total flux of the ion, since the concentration is zero at that point, and the electrical component is zero. If the value of E_M is raised to a very high positive value, the curvature of each curve increases, the slopes of curves 2, 3, 4 at the lowest point of each become negligibly small, while the slopes of 1 and 5 become very high. In other words, with very high values of E_M the electrical current is carried by the outside cations and the inside anions. If E_M is very high and negative, the current is carried by the inside cations and the outside anions. This has some bearing on the rectifying characteristics of a membrane.

The argument given above establishes the fact that concentration curves of cations and anions originating from the same side and absent on the other side possess curvatures of opposite signs. Furthermore, it can be readily shown that the curves of ions of the same valence type (e.g., K^+ and Na^+) originating on the same side differ in scale only; $C_m/C_n = C_{om}/C_{on}$. On the other hand, ions originating on the same side which carry charges of the same sign but of different magnitude (e.g., K^+ and Ca^{2+}) possess concentration curves whose curvatures have the same sign, but

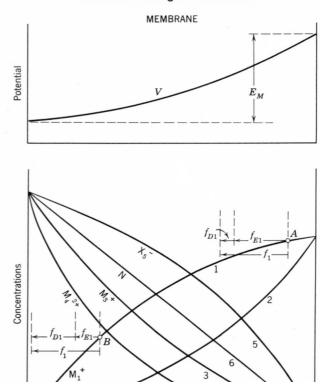

Fig. 11.2.   Upper diagram: E_M is assumed to be positive.

Lower diagram: In a uniform membrane the concentration of a neutral substance N at steady state is a linear function of x (line 6). The net flux of an ion, f, is constant throughout the membrane. f may be thought of as consisting of two components, the diffusion flux f_D and the flux f_E caused by the electrical drift. The relative importance of f_E is greatest where the concentration is highest. When the concentration of an ion is zero at one of the two boundaries, the concentration curve is concave downward if the net flux is in the direction of the electrical force; it is concave upward if the net flux is in the direction opposite the electrical force. The net flux at the lowest point of the curve consists of pure diffusion, and the concentration gradient at this point is proportional to the net flux. The curvature of the concentration curve increases as the magnitude of E_M increases. When the value of E_M is very large, the net flux of an ion is negligible if the flux is opposite the direction of the electrical force. The curvature is greater in the case of a bivalent ion than in the case of a univalent ion.

When the ion is present at both boundaries, its concentration is a complicated function of the potential gradient dV/dx. It is necessary to keep in mind that the net flux of an ion not only is a function of the inner and outer concentrations and of the transmembrane potential, but also depends upon the entire electrostatic pattern across the system, which in turn depends upon the ionic compositions of the two solutions, the distribution constants, and the mobilities of the ions.

the relative curvature is the larger, the larger the valence of the ion (compare curves 3 and 4, Fig. 11.2).

These observations have a direct bearing on the applicability of Henderson's equation (p. 559) to diffusion systems containing membranes. They also have a bearing on the "irritability" of the membrane to a change in E_M (p. 586).

As might be expected, the concentration curves of ions present at both boundaries are even more complex; a detailed discussion of these curves will not be useful for present purposes, and will be omitted.

Curiously enough, with all the complexity of the steady state distribution of individual ions, the total concentrations of ions follow rather simple laws. Thus, in neutral membranes, in the absence of coupled diffusion, the total concentration of ions is a linear function of x; see lines A, B, D of Fig. 11.1, and equation (11.33), p. 534.

Outline of the method of attack; generalized driving force and generalized resistance

Ionic flow from the inside to the outside solution is hampered by three resistances in series, viz., the transition region at the inside surface of the membrane, the membrane proper, and the transition region at the outer surface. As shown in equations (11.23), (11.24), (11.43), the flux of the jth ion, f_j, through each of these resistances may be represented, respectively, by (11.5a,b) through (11.7a,b):

$$f_j = \frac{a_{ij}^{*\prime} - a_{ij}^{*}}{R_{ij}} \qquad a_{ij}^{*\prime} - a_{oj}^{*} = f_j R_{ij} \qquad (11.5\text{a,b})$$

$$f_j = \frac{a_{ij}^{*} - a_{oj}^{*}}{R_{Mj}} \qquad a_{ij}^{*} - a_{oj}^{*} = f_j R_{Mj} \qquad (11.6\text{a,b})$$

$$f_j = \frac{a_{oj}^{*} - a_{oj}^{*\prime}}{R_{oj}} \qquad a_{oj} - a_{oj}^{*\prime} = f_j R_{oj} \qquad (11.7\text{a,b})$$

where a^* is the local electrochemical activity of the ion, defined in Table 11.1 (p. 530). These equations may be thought of as generalized Ohm's law equations, where the driving force between two points is equal to the difference between the electrochemical activities at the two points, and the generalized resistances, R_i, R_M, R_o, are functions given in equations (11.25), (11.42), (11.26).

When the flow is steady, the value of f_j is the same in all three equations. Adding the set of three equations on the right, we get

$$a_{ij}^{*\prime} - a_{oj}^{*\prime} = f_j(R_{ij} + R_{Mj} + R_{oj}) \qquad (11.8)$$

In the following, the total driving force for the jth ion is replaced by the single symbol ϕ_j, and the total resistance R_j is defined as the sum of all the resistances in series. These substitutions yield a formally simple equation for f_j:

$$\phi_j = a_{ij}{}^{*\prime} - a_{oj}{}^{*\prime} \tag{11.9}$$

$$R_j = R_{ij} + R_{Mj} + R_{oj} \tag{11.10}$$

$$\phi_j = f_j R_j \qquad f_j = \phi_j / R_j \tag{11.11a,b}$$

If the charges carried by the jth positive ion and the jth negative ion are z_{j+} and $-z_{j-}$, respectively, the electrical flux through the membrane due to each ion is given by (11.12a,b). The net flux, or current, I, is given by equation (11.13).

$$I_{j+} = z_{j+} f_{j+} F \qquad I_{j-} = -z_{j-} f_{j-} F \tag{11.12a,b}$$

$$I = F\Sigma \pm z_{j\pm} f_{j\pm} \tag{11.13}$$

The right side of equation (11.13) becomes an explicit function $I(E)$ of the transmembrane emf, after the equation is developed through the proper substitutions. The transmembrane potential may be adjusted to any desired value by the imposition of an outside emf. In that case there is a net electrical current through the membrane. Equation (11.13) may be used to determine whether the membrane exhibits any current-rectifying characteristics. If there is no imposed emf, the transmembrane potential E is developed by the diffusion system itself, and there is no net electrical current through the membrane, even though there may be a flow of matter through it. Thus the condition that the right side of the developed equation (11.13) is equal to zero will yield an equation from which E may be calculated.

In bold outline, then, the procedure will be as follows: The values of R_j will first be calculated. Substitution in (11.8) will yield equations for f_j. Substitution for f_j in (11.13) will yield an equation for the electrical current through the membrane. The condition that this current be zero will yield the equation for the transmembrane potential E.

THE NATURE OF THE POTENTIAL CHANGES AT THE TWO SURFACES AND THE VALUES OF R_{ij} AND R_{oi}

The nature of the potential change at a phase boundary

The following considerations show that, in general, there will be a potential change across the transition layer between the aqueous solution and the membrane, even when the system is in complete equilibrium. Let the distribution coefficients of the cations and anions be b_{j+} and b_{j-}, respectively. On the left membrane boundary the total equivalent concentration of the cations is $\Sigma z_{j+} b_{j+} C_{ij+}'$ in the absence of a potential difference. The total equivalent concentration of the anions is $\Sigma z_{j-} b_{j-} C_{ij-}'$. Since these two quantities are apt to be unequal, and since a difference of as little as 1 per cent between the two concentrations would give the membrane a net charge that would be responsible for an enormous potential across the transition layer, any *a priori* assumption that $E = 0$ is an unlikely one and it leads to a contradictory conclusion.

In the usual case the membrane contains an exceedingly small excess of charge of one kind, while the solution retains an equal amount of charge of the opposite kind. This produces a potential difference E_i. The equilibrium concentrations at the membrane boundary are then given by equations (11.14a,b), where Z_i is the exponential factor corresponding to E_i. The value of Z_i is given by equation (11.15), which states that cations and anions are present in equivalent amounts (disregarding the exceedingly small excess of charge of one sign):

$$C_{ij+} = b_{j+} C_{ij+}' Z_i^{-z_{j+}} \qquad C_{ij-} = b_{j-} C_{ij-}' Z_i^{z_{j-}} \qquad (Z_i = e^{FE_i/RT})$$
$$\text{(11.14a,b)}$$

$$\Sigma z_{j+} b_{j+} C_{ij+}' Z_i^{-z_{j+}} = \Sigma z_{j-} b_{j-} C_{ij-}' Z_i^{z_{j-}} \qquad \text{(11.15)}$$

The equilibrium values at the outside membrane boundary are given by

$$C_{oj\pm} = b_{j\pm} C_{oj\pm}' Z_o^{\pm z_{j\pm}} \qquad \text{(11.16)}$$

It may happen that the membrane boundary holds a layer of adsorbed, oriented polar molecules. In that case E_i is caused jointly by the layer of polar molecules and the layer of ions, together with the diffused layer of ions of opposite charge in the solution. However, this need not concern us, since the value of E_i is still controlled by condition (11.15), and equations (11.14a,b) and (11.16) are still valid.

Equations for the flux through the two transition regions

When the system is not in complete equilibrium and there is a net flow of ions, (11.14a,b) and (11.6) are no longer sufficient. Thus, if the net flux of the $j+$th ion is from left to right, C_{ij+} is smaller than the value given by (11.14a,b), and C_{oj+} is larger than the value given by (11.16).

The term "distribution coefficient," applied to a neutral substance, may be defined as the ratio of the concentration of the substance in the membrane to the concentration in the aqueous phase, when there is equilibrium between the two phases. What is the physical meaning of this term when applied to an ion? Let the specific rate constant of the jth ion for the transition from the solution to the membrane be K_{Wj}; let the constant for the opposite reaction be K_{Mj}. If the complexion of concentrations in the inside solutions is such that $E_i = 0$, the flux of the ion is given by equation (11.17). If, at the same time, the system is in equilibrium, f_j is zero, and equations (11.18a,b) are valid. Equation (11.19a) defines b_j as the ratio K_W/K_M. Equation (11.19b) shows that in a system in equilibrium, with no potential change across the transition region, b_j assumes the rôle of a distribution constant in its usual sense.

$$f_j = K_{Wj}C_{ij}' - K_{Mj}C_{ij} \tag{11.17}$$

At equilibrium, when $E_i = 0$:

$$f_j = 0 \qquad K_{Wj}C_{ij}' = K_{Mj}C_{ij} \tag{11.18a,b}$$

$$K_{Wj}/K_{Mj} = b_j \text{ (definition)} \qquad C_{ij} = b_jC_{ij}' \tag{11.19a,b}$$

Another way of looking at it is that b_j is the distribution coefficient which would operate if the particle did not carry a charge.

If E_i is not zero, (11.17) is not valid. Assuming that the top of the activated transition barrier is at the electrical potential αE_i relative to the solution, the two reaction rates are changed by the corresponding Arrhenius exponential factors, and equation (11.20) must hold.

$$f_{j\pm} = K_{Wj\pm}C_{ij\pm}'Z_i^{\mp\alpha_{j\pm}z_{i\pm}} - K_{Mj\pm}C_{ij\pm}Z_i^{\pm\beta_{j\pm}z_{i\pm}} \qquad (\beta_j = 1 - \alpha_j) \tag{11.20}$$

Equation (11.20) is to be used with the upper set of signs for cations and the lower set for anions. α and β are given the subscripts j to emphasize the fact that their values need not be the same for every ion. Henceforth these subscripts will be dropped, with the implicit understanding that different ions may have different values of these coefficients.

By a similar argument, the flux at the outside surface is given by equation (11.21):

$$f_{j\pm} = K_{Mj\pm}C_{oj\pm}Z_o^{\mp\beta z_{i\pm}} - K_{Wj\pm}C_{oj\pm}'Z_o^{\pm\alpha z_{i\pm}} \tag{11.21}$$

It is convenient, for subsequent handling, to rewrite (11.20) and (11.21) in the form

$$f_{(1\to2)j} = \frac{\text{"force"}}{\text{"resistance"}} = \frac{\phi_{12j}}{R_{12j}} = \frac{a_{1j}^* - a_{2j}^*}{R_{12j}} \tag{11.22}$$

Here $f_{(1\to2)j}$ is the flux from some plane 1 parallel to the membrane to plane 2; ϕ is the generalized "force" and is equal to the difference between the values of some intrinsic property of the ion at positions 1 and 2, respectively; R is the generalized resistance.

If the equations of the type of (11.22) are to be useful, the function a^* must be chosen in such a way that flow takes place from the plane where a^* is high to the plane where it is low. If there is no tendency to flow from 1 to 2, the two values of a^* should be equal.   Finally, for the sake of convenience in writing the equation, a^* should have a simple form. Once the function a^* is chosen, R is defined as the expression which will satisfy equation (11.22).

Clearly, the local concentration cannot be used as the function a^*. Thus the concentrations C_i' and C_i in the solution and in the membrane, respectively, are, generally, unequal, even when the system is in equilibrium.

The local thermodynamic activity of the ion is also unsuitable for identification with the function a^*.   To begin with, the activity coefficients are not easily determined in the common biological systems.   In this chapter the assumption will be made that the activity is proportional to the concentration.   Equality of concentrations in the interior and exterior solutions does not insure lack of flow, since the ion will flow from the side where its electrical potential energy is high to the opposite side.   If E is the transmembrane potential, the condition for complete equilibrium is $C_{ij\pm}' = C_{oj\pm}'Z^{\pm z_{j\pm}}$, a condition which must be met by every ion which can pass through the membrane.   If one point is taken in the membrane, the concentration is not a true measure of the local thermodynamic activity, which is equal to the ratio C/b.

We arrive at the following definition of the electrochemical activity a^*. Thermodynamic activities within each phase are taken to be proportional to the concentration, with the proportionality constant being different for the membrane than it is for the two aqueous solutions.   The thermodynamic activity in either aqueous phase is defined as equal to the concentration; this is the same as assuming that the solutions are ideal, an approximation frequently used in situations where the information regarding activity coefficients is inadequate.   The activity of the jth ion in the membrane, at a point where the concentration is C_j, is equal to C_j/b_j.   If the electrical potential at the same point is V_x, the corresponding exponential factor is $e^{\pm zFV_x/RT}$, the sign depending on the sign of the charge of the ion.   The function a^* is defined for each point as the product of the local value of the activity of the ion and the local value of the exponential factor appropriate to the valence type of the ion.

Table 11.1 gives the concentrations, activities, electrical potentials, and electrochemical activities at five points: (1) in the inner solution; (2) at the inner membrane boundary; (3) at some point within the membrane; (4) at the outer membrane boundary; (5) in the outer solution.

Figure 11.3 shows a numerical example illustrating the meaning and the significance of the various terms used.   As shown in the figure, it is assumed that the potentials, relative to the inner solution, are as follows: — 17.4, 23.1, and 58 mv.   The corresponding exponential factors, for a univalent cation, are, respectively, 0.5, 2.5, and 10. The value of b for the ion in question is taken as 0.04.

For purposes of discussion let us assume that the concentrations in the inside and outside solutions are 300 and 50 millimoles per liter, respectively, and that the membrane concentrations at the two boundaries are 24.4 and 7.84, as shown to scale in the lowest curve C. The electrochemical activities in the inside and outside solutions are 300 and $50 \times 10 = 500$, respectively. The ion flows inward.

The diagram illustrates the inadequacy of the equation $f = P(C_i - C_o)$, since according to this equation the ion flows "uphill." The activities,

Table 11.1

	(1) Inner Solution	(2) Inner Membrane Boundary	(3) Within the Membrane	(4) Outer Membrane Boundary	(5) Outer Solution
Concentrations	C_{ij}'	C_{ij}	C_j	C_{oj}	C_{oj}'
Chemical activities	$a_{ij}' = C_{ij}'$	$a_{ij} = C_{ij}/b_j$	$a_j = C_j/b_j$	$a_{oj} = C_{oj}/b_j$	$a_{oj}' = C_{oj}'$
Potentials	0	E_i	V_x	$E_i + E_M$	$E = E_i + E_M + E_o$
Electrochemical activities	$a_{ij}*' = C_{ij}'$	$a_{ij}* = (C_{ij\pm}/b_{j\pm})$ $\times Z_i^{\pm z_{j\pm}}$	$a_j* = (C_{j\pm}/b_{j\pm})$ $\times Z_x^{\pm z_{j\pm}}$	$a_{oj}* = (C_{oj\pm}/b_{j\pm})$ $\times (Z_i Z_M)^{\pm z_{j\pm}}$	$a_{oj}*' = C_{oj\pm}' Z^{\pm z_{j\pm}}$

reading from left to right, are 300, 610, 196, and 50, as shown by the broken curve. Evidently, the uncorrected chemical activities are also a poor measure of the tendency of the ion to flow. If we multiply each chemical activity by the local value of the exponential factor, we get the values 300, 305, 490, and 500, as shown in the diagram. The electrochemical activity is the more adequate measure of the escaping tendency of the ion; it can be seen that the ion flows "downhill" across the three resistances. The driving forces, at the inner surface, across the membrane, and at the outer surface, are, respectively, 5, 185, and 10 millimoles per liter. In this example the values of R_i, R_M, R_o, and R are in the ratio 5 : 185 : 10 : 200. The resistances at the two surfaces are relatively small, and the ion at each boundary is practically in equilibrium with the ion in the respective solution.

Table 11.1 gives directly the conversion factors from concentrations to electrochemical activities. The inverse factor may be written down by inspection; thus $C_{ij\pm} = b_{j\pm} a_{j\pm} * Z_i^{\mp z_j}$.

Returning to (11.20), we substitute the values of the concentrations in terms of the activities, isolate the quantity $a_{ij}* - a_{ij}*$ in the numerator, throw all the other quantities into the denominator, carry out all possible

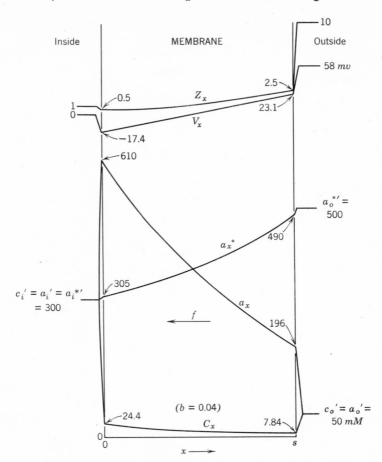

Fig. 11.3.   With an ion, neither the concentration C nor the activity a offers a suitable measure of the escaping tendency of the ion.   In the chosen illustration the net flux of the ion is inward, and the ion appears to be moving "uphill."

The electrochemical activity a^*, which is defined as the product of the local value of the activity and the local value of the exponential factor $Z_x^{\pm z}$, is a suitable measure of the escaping tendency of the ion.   An ion always moves in a "downhill" direction along the electrochemical activity curve.

The resistance between any two points is directly proportional to the difference between the two electrochemical activities.   In the diagram the three resistances in series are proportional to 5, 185, and 10, respectively. In this case the resistances at the two surfaces are relatively small, and it may be assumed, as a first approximation, that the ion on the membrane side of each interface is practically in equilibrium with the ion in the adjacent solution.

algebraic simplifications, and thus obtain equation (11.23) for the flux of
the ion through the inner surface.

$$f_{j\pm} = \frac{\phi_{ij}}{R_{ij}} = \frac{a_{ij}{}^{*\prime} - a_{ij}{}^{*}}{(Z_i{}^{\pm \alpha z_i})/K_{W_i}} \tag{11.23}$$

Similar treatment of (11.21) yields equation (11.24) for the flux of the ion
through the outer surface.

$$f_{j\pm} = \frac{\phi_{oj}}{R_{oj}} = \frac{a_{oj}{}^{*} - a_{oj}{}^{*\prime}}{[(Z_i Z_M Z_o{}^{\beta})^{\pm z_i}]/K_{W_i}} \tag{11.24}$$

These equations may be checked against (11.20) and (11.21) by substituting the various values of a^* with the use of Table 11.1. The
denominators on the right sides of (11.23) and (11.24) exhibit a certain
dissymmetry relative to the left and right surfaces. The dissymmetry
disappears if it is recognized that αE_i and $(E_i + E_M + \beta E_o)$ are, respectively, the potential values at the tops of the barriers for the transition
across the first interface and the second interface. If we call these
potential values $E_i{}^{\ddagger}$ and $E_o{}^{\ddagger}$, respectively, and the corresponding exponential factors $Z_i{}^{\ddagger}$ and $Z_o{}^{\ddagger}$, we can obtain, by inspection of (11.23) and
(11.24), the expressions for the resistances at the two interfaces:

$$R_{ij\pm} = \frac{(Z_i{}^{\alpha})^{\pm z}}{K_{W_i}} = \frac{(Z_i{}^{\ddagger})^{\pm z_i}}{K_{W_i}} \tag{11.25}$$

$$R_{oj\pm} = \frac{(Z_i Z_M Z_o{}^{\beta})^{\pm z_i}}{K_{W_i}} = \frac{(Z_o{}^{\ddagger})^{\pm z_i}}{K_{W_i}} \tag{11.26}$$

THE NATURE OF THE DIFFUSION POTENTIAL E_M; THE VALUE OF R_M

The nature of the diffusion potential

As soon as the two solutions are introduced on the two sides of the
membrane, the flow of ions and neutral molecules commences. When
the flow reaches a steady state, the concentrations of the non-electrolytes
within the membrane change linearly from one boundary to the other, and
the flux of each is proportional to the concentration gradient and the
diffusion constant of the substance. The situation is different in the case
of an ion. If, for instance, the inside solution contains a cation whose
concentration and diffusion constant are high, the initial rush of this ionic
species tends to establish a positive potential gradient along the membrane.
By the time steady state is reached, there is a steady state potential
gradient dV/dx along the membrane, which may be constant or may vary

from point to point. The concentration C_j and the potential V may be extremely complicated functions, depending upon the complexion of the system, but the following differential equation is satisfied at each point within the membrane:

$$f_j = f_{Dj} + f_{Ej} \qquad (11.27a)$$

where f_j is the net flux of the jth ion and is constant throughout the membrane, while f_{Dj} and f_{Ej} are the pure diffusion and the electrical drift components of the flux, whose relative values change from point to point. The same equation may be rewritten in the standard form:

$$f_{j\pm} = - D_j \frac{dC_{j\pm}}{dx} \mp u_j C_{j\pm} \frac{dV}{dx} \qquad (11.27b)$$

Here D_j is the diffusion constant of the ion, and u_j is its electrical mobility.

According to the modern theory of diffusion and electrical drift (Eyring, 1936; Polissar, 1938; Stearn and Eyring, 1940; Glasstone et al., 1941; Zwolinski et al., 1949), the Brownian movement of molecules and ions consists of a series of jumps from "cage" to "cage." If the frequency of jumps is n, and the mean length of the jump is L, the values of D and of u are given by the following equations:

$$D = \frac{nL^2}{6} \qquad u = \frac{zF}{RT} \frac{nL^2}{6} \qquad (11.28a,b)$$

From these equations the relation between D and u may be obtained:

$$D = \frac{RT}{zF} u \qquad (11.28c)$$

Substitution of (11.28c) in (11.27b) yields the differential equations for the flux, in terms of the mobility (11.29), (11.30).

$$f_{j+} = - \frac{RTu_{j+}}{z_{j+}F} \frac{dC_{j+}}{dx} - u_{j+}C_{j+} \frac{dV}{dx} \qquad (11.29)$$

$$f_{j-} = - \frac{RTu_{j-}}{z_{j-}F} \frac{dC_{j-}}{dx} + u_{j-}C_{j-} \frac{dV}{dx} \qquad (11.30)$$

In order to learn something of the nature of the potential gradient we multiply each equation represented in (11.29) by the factor $- z_{j+}^2/u_{j+}$, each equation represented in (11.30) by z_{j-}^2/u_{j-}, and add all the equations so obtained (11.31):

$$\Sigma(f_{j+}z_{j+}^2/u_{j+}) + \Sigma(f_{j-}z_{j-}^2/u_{j-})$$
$$= \frac{RT}{F} \frac{d(\Sigma z_{j+}C_{j+} - \Sigma z_{j-}C_{j-})}{dx} + \frac{dV}{dx} (\Sigma z_{j+}^2 C_{j+} + \Sigma z_{j-}^2 C_{j-}) \quad (11.31)$$

The expression on the left side of (11.31) is a constant, since it contains quantities which are independent of x. The first term on the right of the equation is zero, since the sum of the equivalent concentrations of the cations must be equal the sum of the equivalent concentrations of the anions. It follows that the last term on the right side must be a constant independent of x. Since the coefficient of dV/dx is the local value of the ionic strength, it follows *that at each point the slope of V must be inversely proportional to the local value of the ionic strength.*

If we multiply each equation (11.29) by z_{j+}/u_j, each equation (11.30) by z_{j-}/u_j, and add the resulting equations, we get (11.32).

$$\Sigma \frac{f_{j+} z_{j+}}{u_j} + \Sigma \frac{f_{j-} z_{j-}}{u_j}$$

$$= -\frac{RT}{F} \frac{d(\Sigma C_{j+} + \Sigma C_{j-})}{dx} - \frac{dV}{dx} (\Sigma z_{j+} C_{j+} - \Sigma z_{j-} C_{j-}) \quad (11.32)$$

The left side of (11.32) is a constant independent of x. The last term on the right side equals zero. The quantity $\Sigma C_{j+} + \Sigma C_{j-}$ represents the sum of the concentrations of all the ions present, and will be represented by the symbol $C_\pm$. It follows from (11.32) that the gradient of the total concentration of ions is constant and independent of x. Equations (11.33) and (11.34) represent the gradient of $C_\pm$ and its value, respectively; s is the thickness of the membrane.

$$\frac{dC_\pm}{dx} = \text{constant} = \frac{(C_\pm)_o - (C_\pm)_i}{s} \quad (11.33)$$

$$C_\pm = (C_\pm)_i + \frac{x}{s} [(C_\pm)_o - (C_\pm)_i] \quad (11.34)$$

It was shown in the preceding analysis that, in general, the potential gradient is not constant, and V is not a linear function of x. If, for example, E_M is positive, and the ionic strength at the left boundary is larger than the ionic strength at the right boundary, the slope of V has its smallest value at the left boundary, its largest value at the right boundary, and the curve representing V is concave upward.

Integration of the flux equations

Equations (11.29), (11.30) may be rewritten in the standard form of a linear differential equation (11.35). The formal solution of (11.35) is given in (11.36). Substitution of the limits $x_1 = 0$, and $x_2 = s$ yields equation (11.37).

$$\frac{dC_{j\pm}}{dx} + \left(\frac{z_{j\pm}F}{RT} \cdot \frac{dV}{dx}\right) C_{j\pm} = -\frac{z_{j\pm}Ff_{j\pm}}{RTu_j} \tag{11.35}$$

$$C_{j\pm}e^{\pm z_j FV/RT}\Big]_{x_1}^{x_2} = \int_{x_1}^{x_2} e^{\pm z_j FV/RT} \left(-\frac{z_j Ff_{j\pm}}{RTu_j}\right) dx \tag{11.36}$$

$$C_{ij\pm}Z_i^{\pm z_j} - C_{oj}(Z_i Z_M)^{\pm z_j} = f_{j\pm}\frac{z_j F}{RTu_j}\int_0^s e^{\pm z_j FV/RT}\, dx \tag{11.37}$$

In (11.37) the constant exponential factors were replaced by their corresponding Z-values.

Equation (11.37) has a form similar to the desired standard form

$$a_{ij}^* - a_{oj}^* = f_j \cdot R_{Mj} \tag{11.38}$$

A few transformations make the analogy more readily apparent. Comparison with Table 11.1 shows that the left side of (11.37) will be converted into the difference between the electrochemical activities if both sides of the equation are divided by b_j. Other changes are desirable in order to represent the right-hand side of (11.37) as a product, $f_j R_j$. $RTu_j/z_j F$ may be replaced with D_j. The definite integral can be seen to be a dimensional quantity representing a length. This is to be expected, since the resistance of the membrane proper should be proportional to the thickness s of the membrane. By multiplying the integral and dividing the integrand by s we serve the double purpose of bringing the quantity s into the open and converting the definite integral into a dimensionless quantity.

Finally, the definite integral is expressed in terms of V, the local potential relative to the inside solution. It is to be expected that the definite integral will acquire a simpler meaning if it is expressed in terms of $(V - E_i)$, the local potential relative to the left boundary. This can be accomplished by multiplying the integral and dividing the integrand by the constant $Z_i^{\pm z_j}$. Carrying out all the suggested changes, we obtain

$$a_{ij}^* - a_{oj}^* = f_{j\pm}\frac{sZ_i^{\pm z_j}S_{\pm z_j}}{b_{j\pm}D_j} \tag{11.39}$$

where

$$S_{\pm z_j} = \int_0^s \frac{1}{s} e^{\pm z_j F(V - E_i)/RT}\, dx \tag{11.40}$$

The definite integral $S_{\pm z_j}$, appearing in (11.39) and defined in (11.40) can be evaluated for certain relatively simple cases (see equation 11.75). In general, however, it either cannot be evaluated or its value is represented by an extremely complicated expression. Even in those cases where the integral may be evaluated, the solution contains parameters whose values are usually not available to the investigator. It so happens, however, that useful conclusions may be reached regarding the nature of the fluxes of different ions without a knowledge of the actual value of the definite integral. In order to emphasize this independence, we shall proceed to evaluate f_j, treating the definite integral as an undetermined constant whose value depends only on the valence type of the ion in question. We shall need to familiarize ourselves with certain characteristics of the definite integral, which may be deduced by inspection of equation (11.40).

Characteristics of the definite integral $S_{\pm z_j}$

The definite integral in (11.40) represents an area under a curve, whose ordinates equal the integrand. In Fig. 11.4 the lower diagram represents schematically the function $V - E_i$. The lower and upper values of this function are 0 and E_M, respectively. With the two boundary values given, the function may be concave upward as in A, linear as in B, or concave downward as in C. The corresponding exponential functions, divided by s, are shown schematically in the upper diagram, in curves A', B', C', respectively. The reciprocal of the exponential, divided by s, is shown in C'. To avoid confusion, only one curve of this type is shown.

The definite integral S_{+1} equals the area under curve A', B', or C', depending upon the shape of the potential function curve. It follows that the value of S_{+1} is not completely determined, even if the value of E_M is known. The value of S_{-1} equals the area under curve C'', B'', or A'' (the last two curves are not shown in the diagram). It follows that this definite integral is also not completely determined, even if the value of E_M is known.

Further consideration shows that S_{+2} is greater than S_{+1}, whereas S_{-2} is smaller than S_{-1}. If we define S_0 as the value of the definite integral when $z = 0$, we can see by inspection of (11.40) that $S_0 = 1$. This is the value of the definite integral for neutral molecules. From the geometrical interpretation of the definite integral we arrive at the following set of inequalities, when E_M is positive:

$$S_{+2} > S_{+1} > S_0 = 1 > S_{-1} > S_{-2} \qquad (11.41)$$

If E_M is negative, the order remains the same, but all the inequalities change sign.

To summarize, the value of the definite integral is the same for ions of the same valence type. It is different for ions of different valence types.

If the diffusion system is changed, by addition, subtraction, or replacement of one of the substances from either solution, the values of $S_{\pm z}$ changes, since either the shape of the potential function V is apt to

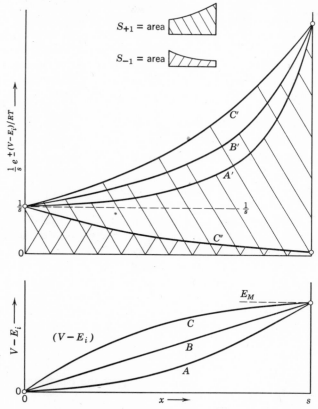

Fig. 11.4. Graphical interpretation of the definite integrals, S_{+1} and S_{-1}. The integral is equal to the area of the curve represented by the integrand. With the value of E_M given, the integral may have different values, depending on the potential pattern within the membrane. The value of the definite integral S_{+1} is smaller if the potential curve is concave upward than if the potential curve is concave downward (compare the pairs of curves A and A', B and B', C and C'). The relation is just the opposite in the case of S_{-1} (to avoid confusion, curves A'', B'' are omitted).

Since the definite integral contains no other property of the ion than its valence, the value of S is the same for all ions of the same valence type.

The dependence of the value of this integral on the potential pattern within the membrane is chiefly responsible for the fact that the net flux of an ion cannot be predicted if only the terminal concentrations, the transmembrane potential, the distribution coefficient, and the mobility of the ion are given. The net flux depends on the entire complexion of concentrations; any change in the complexion may change the net flux of a given ion, even if the terminal total concentrations and the transmembrane potential remain the same.

change, or E_M changes, or both. The relative change in the definite integral is the larger, the larger the charge carried by the ion. This leads to an important rule for experimental procedure. If it is desired to compare the permeabilities of two ions of the same valence type, it is important to measure both permeabilities in the same diffusion system. Permeabilities of two ions measured in two different diffusion systems are not comparable, even though the two values of the transmembrane potentials are known.

The value of R_M and the equations for the flux f_j

Comparison of (11.39) with equation (11.38), which represents the standard form, yields the expression for R_{Mj}:

$$R_{Mj\pm} = \frac{sZ_i^{\pm z_j} S_{\pm z_j}}{b_{j\pm} D_j} \tag{11.42}$$

We now have the values of R_{ij} (11.25), R_{Mj}^* (11.42), and R_{Mj} (11.26). The total resistance equals the sum of the three resistances, and the total driving force equals the difference of the terminal values of the activities. f_j equals the ratio of these quantities (11.43):

$$f_{j\pm} = \frac{\phi_j}{R_j} = \frac{\phi_j}{R_{ij} + R_{Mj} + R_{oj}} = \frac{C_{ij}' - C_{oj}'Z^{\pm z_j}}{\dfrac{(Z_{ij}^{\dagger})^{\pm z_j}}{K_{Wj}} + \dfrac{sZ_i^{\pm z_j} S_{\pm z_j}}{b_{j\pm} D_{j\pm}} + \dfrac{(Z_{oj}^{\dagger})^{\pm z_j}}{K_{Wj}}} \tag{11.43}$$

Recalling that $S_0 = 1$, substitution in (11.43) of the value $z = 0$ and replacement of the index number j with n give the equation for the flux of the nth neutral particle (11.44).

$$f_n = \frac{C_{in}' - C_{on}'}{2/K_{Wn} + s/b_n D_n} \tag{11.44}$$

A membrane is defined as "thick" if R_M is large enough to make the values of R_i and R_o comparatively negligible. Large values of s or values of bD/s which are small compared with K_W will produce a thick membrane. Thus the term "thick" is relative. A membrane may be thick toward one ion and thin toward another. Omitting the negligible terms from (11.43) and (11.44), we get equations (11.45) and (11.46) for the flux of ions and molecules, respectively, through thick membranes.

$$f_{j\pm} = \frac{b_{j\pm} D_{j\pm}(C_{ij\pm}' - C_{oj\pm}'Z^{\pm z_j})}{sZ_i^{\pm z_j} S_{\pm z_j}} \quad \text{(thick membrane)} \tag{11.45}$$

$$f_n = \frac{b_n D_n}{s}(C_{in}' - C_{on}') \quad \text{(thick membrane)} \tag{11.46}$$

Up to this point the flux equations were written in the form $f_j = (a_{ij}{}^* - a_{oj}{}^*)/R_j$. We define the reciprocal of R_j as the permeability of the ion, and get the following equations:

$$P_j = 1/R_j \tag{11.47}$$

$$f_{j\pm} = P_j(C_{ij\pm}{}' - C_{oj\pm}{}'Z^{\pm z_i}) \tag{11.48}$$

Equations for the two fluxes in experiments with isotopes

Assuming that different isotopes are used on the two sides of the membrane, their fluxes may be calculated on the assumption that they are different ions which happen to possess the same values of b_j, D_j, and u_j. Defining the outward and inward fluxes as $\overrightarrow{f_j}$ and $\overleftarrow{f_j}$, respectively, and substituting the boundary values in (11.48), once for each ion, we get equations (11.49) and (11.50). Since the value of P_j is identically the same in the two equations, we get, by division, the equation for the ratio of the two fluxes. As will be shown later (p. 546), equation (11.51) is of importance in the interpretation of experimental results.

$$\overrightarrow{f_j} = P_j C_{ij}{}' \tag{11.49}$$

$$\overleftarrow{f_{j\pm}} = - P_j C_{oj}{}'Z^{\pm z_i} \tag{11.50}$$

$$\overrightarrow{f_j}/\overleftarrow{f_j} = \frac{C_{ij\pm}{}'}{C_{oj\pm}{}'Z^{\pm z_i}} \quad \text{(ratio of absolute values)} \tag{11.51}$$

Equation (11.51) is essentially the same as the equations derived earlier for the ratio of the two fluxes by Teorell (1949b, 1951) and Ussing (1949a, 1951).

APPLICATIONS TO EXPERIMENTAL WORK ON THE PENETRATION OF SUBSTANCES THROUGH MEMBRANES

An experimentalist, confronted with a theoretical treatment of an idealized model of a biological phenomenon, naturally asks, "Can the theory be tested experimentally? If not, of what use is the theory?" Biological phenomena are characterized by an exquisite complexity. Many variables may be involved, with the influence of some often not even suspected. This situation is responsible for the fact that experimental work in the biological field is much more demanding than in the inorganic, while, at the same time, the latitude for the invention of theoretical models is greater. It is no wonder, then, that the biological experimentalist's attitude to a proposed theory is apt to be particularly stern.

Since the usefulness of a theory is to be judged by the assistance it offers in interpreting experimental results, let us consider the kind of information usually sought by means of experiments on the penetration of ions.

The following list of the types of information sought is intended to be illustrative, but not exhaustive: (1) the effect of the rate of penetration on the quantitative and even qualitative aspects of the reactions at the destination point; (2) the relation between the rates of penetration of different ions and the electrical potential across the membrane; (3) the relative permeabilities of different ions; (4) the effect of reagents on the structural properties of the membrane; (5) the effect of reagents on the permeabilities of different ions. It is to be expected that measurements of rates of penetration will supply direct information of types 2 to 5.

The experimental investigator is aware that the membrane he studies may change its properties if the experimental conditions are changed. Nevertheless, he assumes, and rightly so, that, if in each experiment on penetration the membrane is treated as a simple one, the calculated permeabilities of the various ions will give some indication of the relative ease with which different ions can penetrate the membrane; some indication of the mechanism of penetration; and, possibly, some indication of the nature of the membrane changes which take place when the experimental conditions are changed.

The model discussed in the preceding pages is the kind of model used for many years. The calculation, given in one of the early sections (p. 517), which leads to paradoxical values of the permeability "constants" is merely a quantitative illustration of the objection to the classical treatment of data raised by Teorell (1949a). However, the quantitative analysis of the classical model given in the preceding sections shows that equation (11.48), which takes account of the electrical forces is likely to give significant values of the permeability P.

The analysis shows that the calculated values of P, obtained for the same ion under different experimental conditions, may differ from each other, even if the distribution coefficient and the mobility do not change, since the value of P depends not only upon the transmembrane potential, for which equation (11.48) makes an allowance, but it depends also upon the total electrostatic pattern in the membrane, as can be seen from equation (11.43). The nature of the change is predictable, at least qualitatively, as will be shown in some illustrations.

Simple, complex, stable, labile membranes; definitions

If in a given diffusion system the quantities K_{Wj} are the same on both sides of the membrane, and if b_j, D_j (and, therefore, u_j) are the same throughout the membrane for a given diffusion system, the membrane is defined as simple.   If these conditions are not met, the membrane is defined as complex.   If these constants do not change when the diffusion system is changed, the membrane is defined as stable.   If the constants are changed when the complexion of one of the solutions is changed, the membrane is defined as labile.

Simple and coupled diffusion; obligatory and permitted coupling

Up to this point we considered a diffusion mechanism for ions and molecules of the simplest type, represented by the following illustrative equations:

$$\text{Na}^+ \text{ (inside)} \rightleftarrows \text{Na}^+ \text{ (outside)}$$

$$\text{N (inside)} \rightleftarrows \text{N (outside)}$$

The sodium ion may traverse the membrane either in its hydrated form or in a stripped form.   We must consider, however, the possibility of a more complicated mechanism, in which the two particles combine to form a complex and the complex diffuses through the membrane.   This type of diffusion will be called coupled diffusion.   If the particle cannot penetrate the membrane by itself, but can diffuse in the form of a complex, the coupling will be called obligatory.

The ratio of the two isotopic fluxes through a complex membrane

If the membrane is labile, a change in the diffusion system produces a change in P_j, both because of the change in the electrostatic picture and because of the change in the constants.   However, since the values of P_j in (11.49) and (11.50) are identical, equation (11.51) must hold for simple diffusion through a labile membrane.

If the membrane is complex, it may vary in properties continuously from one boundary to another.   It may consist of several layers.   It may even consist of a thin layer of solution sandwiched between two simple or complex layers.   Whatever the case, in principle we can section the membrane into n layers, each of which possesses simple characteristics. There will be n layers and $n + 1$ surfaces.   For each of these we may write the equation

$$a_{kj} - a_{(k+1)j} = f_j R_{kj} \tag{11.52}$$

If the diffusion is simple, none of the R terms will contain any concentration functions.   Adding the $2n + 1$ equations, and substituting for the terminal values of a, which are the only ones left, we shall get an equation of the same type as in the case of a simple membrane, namely,

$$f_{j\pm} = \frac{C_i' - C_o' Z^{\pm z_j}}{R_j} = P_{j\pm}(C_i' - C_o' Z^{\pm z_j}) \tag{11.53}$$

It follows that (11.49), (11.50) must still be valid, and the ratio (11.51) is valid for simple diffusion through any membrane whether the membrane is stable or labile, simple or complex.

The ratio of the two isotopic fluxes in coupled diffusion

It would be cumbersome to handle a general theory of coupled diffusion. The coupling reaction may take place in the solutions, at the surfaces of the membrane, or throughout the membrane. The rates of formation and of the dissociation of the complex may be large or small as compared with the rate of transport. The concentration of N may be so small that the competition for N by several ions will control the amount of the complex formed by the ion in question, or it may be so large that the concentration of the complex under investigation is independent of the concentrations of competing ions. Nevertheless, it would be desirable to discover a general test whereby coupling may be detected experimentally.

To show that penetration measurements with isotopes offer a ready test, let us assume, merely as an illustration, a simple case in which sodium ion forms a complex, NaN^+ in the aqueous solutions. We shall further make the simplifying assumptions that equilibrium is rapidly attained, that the rates of formation and of dissociation of the complex within the membrane are so small as to be negligible; that the complex owes its importance to a high mobility or a high distribution constant within the membrane, while the concentrations of the complex in the aqueous solutions are so small that the concentrations of free sodium in the solutions are practically the same as the total concentrations of the sodium ion. With these assumptions, we can derive a set of equations in which the diffusion through the membrane may be treated as that of two separate ions, (11.54 to 11.56).

$$f_{Na} = P_{Na}(C_{iNa}' - C_{oNa}'Z) \tag{11.54}$$

$$f_{NaN} = P_{NaN}(C_{iNaN}' - C_{oNaN}'Z) \tag{11.55}$$

$$C_{NaN}' = KC_N'C_{Na}' \approx KC_N'(C_{Na}')_{total} \tag{11.56}$$

where K is the equilibrium constant for the formation of the complex. The observed flux of sodium equals the sum of the two fluxes given by (11.54) and (11.55).

$$(f_{Na})_{obs} = C_{iNa}'[P_{Na} + KP_{NaN}C_{iN}'] - ZC_{oNa}'[P_{Na} + KP_{NaN}C_{oN}'] \tag{11.57}$$

If the system contains different isotopes of sodium on the two sides, the ratio of the observed outward flux of sodium to the observed inward flow is given by (11.58). It is clear that this experimentally observed ratio is not equal to the ratio of the electrochemical activities of sodium (as in 11.51), except in the special case when $C_{iN}' = C_{oN}'$.

$$\frac{\overrightarrow{f}_{obs}}{\overleftarrow{f}_{obs}} = \frac{C_{iNa}'[P_{Na} + KP_{NaN}C_{iN}']}{C_{oNa}'Z[P_{Na} + KP_{NaN}C_{oN}']} \tag{11.58}$$

In general, then, coupled diffusion may be detected with the use of isotopes and application of equation (11.51). If the ratio of the two fluxes is equal to the ratio of the electrochemical activities, the diffusion of the ion is simple. If the ratios are unequal, the diffusion is not simple. In the same system, one ion may flow by coupled diffusion while others flow by simple diffusion. Of course, if one ion is shown to flow by coupled diffusion, there must be at least one other substance which flows by coupled diffusion (p. 594).

General observations on the interpretation of penetration experiments

It appears from the preceding discussion that in a given experiment it is desirable to measure the transmembrane potential, and the two opposing isotopic fluxes, in addition to the usual data on the net flux and the concentrations in the two solutions. The treatment of data when the potential is unknown but the isotopic fluxes are known will be discussed later (p. 547).

Let us assume that the penetration of some ion M^+ is under investigation. If the concentration of M^+ is changed, say in the outside solution, the effect of the change in C_{oM} is taken care of by equation (11.48). There is bound to be, in general, one other effect, namely, that even though the membrane may be stable the change in C_{oM} causes a change in the ionic population within the membrane, with the accompanying changes in E and P_M.

If the surface resistance to M^+ is small compared with the bulk resistance, and if there are other ions of the same valence type characterized by a negligible surface resistance, the P values of all these ions change by the same factor, as can be seen by an examination of equation (11.45) for thick membranes. The P values of ions belonging to another valence type are affected differently, since the change in the definite integral $S_{\pm z}$ depends upon the valence type.

A careful investigation of the properties of the definite integral $S_{\pm z}$, which cannot be reproduced here for lack of space, shows that near the value $E_M = 0.1$ volt the relative change in S is of the order of the square root of the change in $Z^{\pm z}$. Thus, if, as a result of a change in experimental conditions, the transmembrane potential increases by 58 mv, the relative change in the Z values of sodium, calcium, and chloride ions are 10, 100, and 0.1 respectively. The expected relative changes in their P values would be of the order of 3, 10, and $1/3$, respectively. If the observed relative changes are numerically very much larger, or are in the opposite direction, the indications are either that the diffusion is not simple, or that the changes are produced not merely by the change in the electrostatic picture, but by the lability of the membrane itself.

Thus, in addition to the generally inevitable effect on the electrostatic picture, the change in C_M may have a specific effect. By forming or breaking vital linkages within the membrane, the ion may narrow or widen bottleneck passes, or, what is the same thing, affect the height of essential potential barriers. While the inevitable change in the electrostatic picture produces approximately the same change in the P values of ions of the same valence type, a specific change in the properties of the membrane may produce widely different changes, depending upon the size of the ion.

The same remarks apply to the situation where an ion other than that whose penetration is studied is added to or subtracted from one of the solutions. In fact, any change in the complexion of concentrations of ions in either one of the solutions is likely, in general, to change the electrostatic picture. This is accompanied by a change both in E and in the P values of all ions.

These observations lead to an important rule affecting the experimental comparison of the permeabilities of two ions. The measurements must be made with identical systems. Thus, if it is desired to compare the permeabilities of calcium and magnesium ions, it will not do to add calcium in one series of experiments and to add magnesium in another. The observed permeabilities will not necessarily be comparable, since the electrostatic pictures may be different in the two series. Both the calcium ion and the magnesium ion must be present in each series.

If the membrane is thick, and two ions of the same valence type flow by simple diffusion, their P values must be proportional to the respective fundamental products $b_j D_j$, as can be seen by an inspection of equation (11.45). If the membrane is not thick but also not too thin, the ratio of the P values gives an approximate value of the ratio of the bD values.

While the comparison of the $b_j D_j$ values of ions of the same valence type is relatively straightforward, inspection of equations (11.43), (11.45) shows that it would be difficult to draw any quantitative conclusions about the ratio of the two products $b_j D_j$, since the definite integral $S_{\pm z}$ has widely different values for ions of different valence type.

It has been shown earlier that, if the rate of penetration of a given ion is studied, and the concentration of the ion is varied, the permeability P_j

(equation 11.48) generally changes, because of the change of the electrostatic pattern caused by changing the system.   One special case merits particular attention.   If the ion under investigation is present in trace amounts, considerable relative changes in its concentration produce insignificant changes in the electrostatic pattern.   If the trace ion exhibits no specific effects on the structure of the membrane, and if its diffusion is simple and not coupled, the flux of this ion is given by the simple equation

$$f_{j\pm} = \text{constant } (C_{ij\pm}{}' - C_{oj\pm}{}'Z^{\pm z_j}) \qquad (11.59)$$

A non-electrolyte which does not affect the structure of the membrane and does not couple with one of the ions cannot affect the fluxes of the ions.   Therefore, if the addition of a particular non-electrolyte affects strongly the rates of penetration of the ions, it must be assumed either that the substance affects the membrane or that it couples with one of the ions.   Even if it participates in coupled diffusion with only one of the ions present, the change in the electrostatic pattern affects the rates of penetration of all the other ions.   It may be possible to discover the ion with which it couples by applying the isotopic test for coupling successively to the various ions.

Turning to experiments on the flow of non-electrolytes, several general statements may be made.   If the substance flows by simple diffusion, the ratio of the two isotopic fluxes must be equal to the ratio of the two terminal concentrations.   If the two ratios are unequal, it follows that the flow is not by simple diffusion.

Since an electrolyte or a non-electrolyte added to the system may affect the flow of the substance under investigation either by effecting a change in the structure of the membrane or by coupling with the molecule under investigation, it is desirable to distinguish between the two effects.   These two effects may be distinguished by applying the isotopic test for coupled diffusion to the added reagent.   This suggests a simple method of analyzing the effect of one electrolyte on the flow of other electrolytes. Thus, let us assume that the addition of magnesium chloride causes a strong change in the flow of the ions present in the original system.   The effect may be purely electrostatic, which is a general and unavoidable effect, but, in addition, the magnesium may also change the properties of the membrane.   Some light may be thrown on this question by a study of the flow of some non-electrolyte in the two systems.   If the effect of adding magnesium is purely electrostatic, the flow of the non-electrolyte remains unaffected.   If the addition of magnesium changes greatly the flow of the non-electrolyte, and the isotopic test shows that the diffusion of the non-electrolyte is simple in both systems, there is definite indication that magnesium changes the properties of the system.   If, however, the flow of the non-electrolyte remains unaffected on addition of magnesium, the results are inconclusive. It may so happen that ions flow through patches in the surface which are different from the route taken by the non-electrolyte. It is conceivable that magnesium influences the structure along the ionic route and still leaves the non-electrolytic route unaffected.

Quantitative interpretation of experimental results

It has been pointed out (p. 519) that the experimental values of the net flux and of the two terminal concentrations cannot be subjected to a quantitative analysis without information about the value of the trans-membrane potential or the values of the two opposing isotopic fluxes. Unfortunately, it is as yet difficult to find an adequate variety of experimental data which include all the needed information. For this reason the methods of treating complete experimental data will be illustrated here with the aid of hypothetical examples. In each case the assumed information will be given first. Concentrations will be expressed in moles per liter; fluxes in moles/sq cm/sec; permeabilities in moles/sq cm/sec per mole/liter. For convenience, all values of fluxes and permeabilities will be multiplied by the same factor, say 10^{10}.

CASE 1. The penetration of M_1^+ was studied. $C_i = 0.020$; $C_o = 0.025$. $f_1 = 3.45$, inward. $E = 58$ mv (i.e., $Z = 10$). The information is insufficient to decide whether the ion flows by simple or coupled diffusion. However, assuming simple diffusion, we can calculate the value of P_1 as follows:

$$- 3.45 = P_1(0.020 - 0.025 \times 10) \qquad P_1 = 15$$

CASE 2. The penetration of M_1^+ was studied. $C_i = 0.020$; $C_o = 0.025$. $\vec{f} = 0.30$; $\overset{\leftarrow}{f} = 3.75$. (The net flow, inward, may be obtained by difference and may be checked by chemical analysis.) The information is again insufficient to decide whether the ion flows by simple or coupled diffusion. However, assuming simple diffusion, it is possible to calculate tentatively the transmembrane potential and the value of P_1.

$$\frac{0.30}{3.75} = \frac{0.020}{0.025 \times Z} \qquad Z = 10 \qquad E = 58 \text{ mv}$$

$$P_1 \text{ (calculated as in case 1)} = 15$$

CASE 3. The same data were obtained as in case 2; in addition, the transmembrane potential was found experimentally; $E = 58$ mv (i.e., $Z = 10$). With these more complete data the isotopic test for simple flow may be applied:

$$\frac{0.3}{3.75} = \frac{0.020}{0.025 \times 10}$$

Since the test is positive, the flow of this ion is definitely by simple diffusion.   Moreover, the value of P_1 calculated either by the method of case 1 or by the method of case 2 is definite and not merely tentative.

CASE 4.   CALCULATION OF THE TRANSMEMBRANE POTENTIAL IN EXPERIMENTS WHERE IT CANNOT BE MEASURED DIRECTLY.   In case 2 the value of the transmembrane potential was calculated, but this value was only tentative, subject to the condition that M_1^+ flows by simple diffusion. Let us assume that the flow of another ion, M_2^+, was also measured, *in the same diffusion system*, and that the following experimental results were obtained for the second ion: $C_i = 0.350$; $C_o = 0.020$; $\overrightarrow{j} = 14.0$; $\overleftarrow{f} = 8.0$.

Assuming, tentatively, that this ion flows by simple diffusion, we may calculate, by the methods of case 2, the tentative values, $E = 58$ mv, $P_2 = 40$.   The fact that the tentative values of E, calculated separately from the fluxes of the two ions present in the same system are the same offers strong circumstantial evidence that the assumptions are correct and that the transmembrane potential is 58 mv.   The same evidence indicates, with equal strength, that the calculated values of the two permeabilities are probably correct.   The evidence may be strengthened by measuring the penetration of a third ion, preferably of a different valence type, but present in the same system.   The following case illustrates the treatment of data obtained with a bivalent ion.

CASE 5.   The investigation described in case 4 was extended by measuring the fluxes of a bivalent ion, M_3^{++}: $C_i = 0.020$; $C_o = 0.025$; $\overrightarrow{f} = 0.04$; $\overleftarrow{f} = 5.0$;   the net flow is 4.96, inward.

Assuming simple diffusion, we may calculate the values of Z and of P_3:

$$\frac{0.04}{5.00} = \frac{0.020}{0.025Z^2} \qquad Z = 10 \qquad E = 58 \text{ mv}$$

$$- 4.96 = P_3(0.020 - 0.025 \times 100) \qquad P_3 = 2.0$$

These calculated values of E and P_3 are only tentative, if considered by themselves.   When the evidence obtained from three ions is considered, the probability is very high that the value of the transmembrane potential is correct as calculated and that the values of the permeabilities are also correct.

It is well known that in a Donnan equilibrium the following relation holds for every ion:

$$\frac{C_{ij\pm}}{C_{oj\pm}} = Z^{\pm z_i} \qquad (11.60)$$

The same equation may be obtained from (11.48) by substituting the value zero for the flux of the ion. Equation (11.60) suggests that the transmembrane potential in a system inaccessible to electrodes may be calculated from the inside and outside concentrations of several ions present in the system, provided the system is in complete equilibrium. The method illustrated in cases 4 and 5 makes it possible to calculate the transmembrane potential when the system is not in equilibrium.

Now, let us compare the calculated values of P for the three ions.

Case	2	4	5
Ion	M_1^+	M_2^+	M_3^{++}
P	15	40	2

If the membrane is of the thick type, then, according to equation (11.45) for thick membranes, the ratio of the permeabilities gives directly the ratio of $b_1 u_1$ to $b_2 u_2$, provided the penetration measurements were obtained from the same diffusion system. The value of P obtained for the bivalent ion is not directly comparable with the other two, since the value of the definite integral S_{+2} is different from the value of S_{+1}. However, the value of S_{+z} is roughly proportional to the square root of Z. The value of this exponential factor in cases 2, 4, and 5 was 10 for univalent ions and 100 for bivalent ions. These two ratios differ by a factor of 10. It follows that the two values of S differ by a factor of approximately $10^{1/2} = 3.16$. Applying this factor to the calculated value of P_3, we form the rough estimate that the ratio $b_3 u_3 / b_1 u_1$ is 6.32/15, or 0.4. Similar estimates may be made when the calculated values of P for ions of opposite charge are compared.

CASE 6. This case illustrates the interpretation of data when a diffusion system is changed by the addition of an electrolyte. It also illustrates the magnitude of the error which may be introduced by the use of equation $f = P(C_i - C_o)$ (11.1a).

Let us assume that the system described in cases 2, 4, 5 was changed by the addition of an electrolyte, without changing the concentrations of M_1^+ and M_2^+. Let the observed isotopic fluxes in the changed diffusion system be as follows: $\overrightarrow{f_1} = 0.6$; $\overleftarrow{f_1} = 1.5$; $\overrightarrow{f_2} = 28.0$; $\overleftarrow{f_2} = 3.2$. With the methods illustrated in the preceding cases we can show that Z, calculated on the assumption of simple diffusion, is equal to 2.0, whether obtained from the fluxes of M_1^+ or from the fluxes of M_2^+. This indicates that the transmembrane potential in the new diffusion system is 17.4 mv. The new values of the permeabilities are $P_1 = 30$ and $P_2 = 80$. The values in the first system were 15 and 40, respectively. The doubling of the calculated values of P does not necessarily indicate that the addition of the electrolyte caused a change in the properties of the membrane. We must take into consideration the effect on the definite integral S_{+1} of the change in Z. Since Z has changed from 10 to 2, i.e., by a factor of 5, the definite integral is expected to decrease by a factor of approximately $5^{1/2}$, or 2.2. This change alone is sufficient to account for the increased values of P (equation 11.45). Thus, rather than indicating a change in the membrane, the data, interpreted in this manner, indicate that the membrane has not changed its properties.

Table 11.2.   Mathematical Artifact Caused by Use of Equation (11.1a)

Case	Ion	C_i	C_o	$\overrightarrow{f}$	$\overleftarrow{f}$	f	Calculated Values		
							E (mV)	P (Eq. 11.48)	P (Eq. 11.1a)
				(All values of f and P multiplied by 10^{10})					
				System I					
a 2	M_1^+	0.020	0.025	0.30	3.75	− 3.45	58	15	P_1 690
b 4	M_2^+	0.350	0.020	14.0	8.0	6.0	58	40	P_2 18.2
c 5	M_3^{++}	0.020	0.025	0.04	5.0	− 4.96	58	2	P_3 400
				System II (electrolyte added)					
d 6	M_1^+	Same as above		0.6	1.5	− 0.9	17.4	30	P_1 180
e 6	M_2^+			28.0	3.2	24.8	17.4	80	P_2 75.4

Table 11.2 contains the experimental values, the calculated values of E and the values of P calculated with the use of equations (11.48) and (11.1a). A comparison of the last two columns shows the magnitude of the mathematical error which may be introduced with the use of (11.1a). Thus, it would appear (lines a, b) that P_1 is 38 times as large as P_2. P_3 appears to be 22 times as large as P_2 (lines b, c). The addition of the electrolyte appears to decrease P_1 by a factor of 3.8 (lines a, d), while increasing P_2 by a factor of 4.1.

CASE 7.   THE MOVEMENT OF IONS ACROSS THE MEMBRANES OF *Sepia* AXONS.   Table 11.3 contains data on the movement of potassium and sodium across the membranes of *Sepia* axons, obtained by Keynes (1949)

This is an interesting case, in which the inside concentration of the ion whose rate of escape is measured is not known. To measure the outward flux of sodium, Keynes soaked the nerve in an artificial solution containing radioactive sodium. After a while, the nerve was transferred into an outer solution containing ordinary sodium, and the loss of radioactive count on the inside was followed. In this type of experiment the logarithm of the remaining count is plotted as a function of time, and the slope of the line obtained is a measure of the relative rate of escape of the radioactive ion. The absolute rate may be easily calculated if the inner concentration of the ion is known.

Keynes estimated that the inside concentration was at least 39 millimolar, but added that it could have been two or three times as large.

Table 11.3

Ion	C_i	C_o	$\overrightarrow{f}$	$\overleftarrow{f}$	f
	(moles per liter)			(moles per sq cm per sec $\times 10^{12}$)	
K^+	0.300	0.010*	83	27	56
Na^+	0.039k**	0.455*	19k**	76	$-(76-19k)**$

* The author does not give the specific outside concentrations, but states that sea water was used.
** See text.

For this reason the data on the outward flux of sodium are given in Table 11.3 in terms of an undefined multiplier k whose value must be 1 or larger.

Since the transmembrane potential across the *Sepia* axon was not directly measured in this experiment, it is not possible to apply the isotopic test for simple diffusion (equation 11.51) rigorously. However, an approximate indication may be obtained by substituting the known data into the equation and calculating the value of Z and, from this value, the value of E. Carrying out the substitution for potassium, we have

$$\frac{83}{27} = \frac{300}{10Z} \qquad Z = 9.75 \qquad E = 56.4 \text{ mv}$$

The value 56.4 mv is in fair agreement with the magnitude of the transmembrane potential expected in nerve, and the conclusion may be drawn that the major flux of potassium is due to simple diffusion. If there is any coupled diffusion of potassium, its extent must be relatively small.

Using the calculated value of Z and applying it to the data on sodium, we get the following results:

$$\frac{\overrightarrow{f}}{\overleftarrow{f}} = \frac{19k}{76} = 0.25k \qquad \frac{C_i'}{C_o'Z} = \frac{0.039k}{0.455 \times 9.75} = 0.00879k$$

It is evident that, independently of the value of k, there is a discrepancy between the two ratios by a factor of 29.7. No reasonable allowance for a possible error in Z will reduce this factor to the value 1 expected in the case of simple diffusion. It follows that, without knowing the value of the internal concentration of sodium, we can still conclude that a large part of the movement of sodium takes place by coupled diffusion.

It is difficult to estimate what part of the total inward flux is due to simple diffusion. However, it may be stated that the inward flux of sodium was 76, or less, while the inward flux of potassium was 27. Using equation (11.50), we may compare the permeabilities of potassium and sodium in resting *Sepia* axons.

$$P_K 0.010Z/P_{Na} 0.455Z \gtrless 27/76$$

$$P_K/P_{Na} \gtrless 16.1$$

Quantitative estimate of the strength of the ion pump

When the net movement of an ion is found to be "uphill," from a low to a high electrochemical activity, it is not necessary to perform the isotopic test to recognize the presence of active transport. The situation is different when the net flux is "downhill"; the movement may be taking place by simple diffusion, by simple diffusion aided by an ion pump, or by simple diffusion opposed by a relatively weak pump. For "downhill" flux, active transport can be detected only by means of the isotopic test.

In either case the isotopic test not only offers evidence of the existence of active transport but also yields information on the strength of the pump. A few numerical illustrations will indicate the type of information which may be obtained with the use of isotopes.

CASES 8a,b AND 9a,b,c,d. Let us assume six different diffusion systems (Table 11.4) in each of which the transmembrane potential, the inside concentration, and the outside concentration of some particular ion have been measured. With this information it is possible to calculate the electrochemical activities $a_i^{*\prime}$ and $a_o^{*\prime}$ of the ion in question. Let us assume that in each case these values are, respectively, 50 and 60 in arbitrary units. We assume also that in each case the net flux of the ion has been measured and that the values obtained are those given in the second column of Table 11.4. An inspection of these values will show that in cases 8a,b the ions move "uphill"; no further information is needed to recognize the existence of active transport. In cases 9a,b,c,d the ions move "downhill"; isotopic tests are needed to determine whether there is active transport.

Assuming that the values of the isotopic fluxes are those given in the third and fourth columns of Table 11.4, the ratio of the two fluxes in a given case offers evidence as to the existence and relative strength of active transport. The ratio a_i*'/a_o*' is 0.833 in all cases. In cases 8a,b the ratio $\vec{f}/\overset{\leftarrow}{f}$ is larger than 0.833, thus indicating, as expected, the existence of an outward ion pump. In case 8a this ratio is much larger than 0.833; this indicates that the pump is relatively strong. The pump operating in case 8b is much weaker.

Inspection of the values of the ratios of isotopic fluxes given in the fifth column will show that there is no active transport in case 9a. In

Table 11.4. Quantitative Estimate of the Strength of Ion Pumps

In all six cases $a_i*' = 50$, and $a_o*' = 60$, in arbitrary units; $a_i*'/a_o*' = 5/6 = 0.883$.
$\vec{f}$ is the net flux; $\vec{f}$ and $\overset{\leftarrow}{f}$ are the observed outward and inward fluxes, respectively.
$\overset{\rightarrow}{f_D}$, $\overset{\rightarrow}{f_P}$, $\overset{\leftarrow}{f_D}$, $\overset{\leftarrow}{f_P}$ are the calculated values of the components credited to simple diffusion (subscript D) and to the pump (subscript P). All fluxes are in arbitrary units.
$\overset{\rightarrow}{f_D}/\overset{\leftarrow}{f_D} = 5/6$. SP is the strength of the pump (see text).

Case	Observed Values			$\vec{f}/\overset{\leftarrow}{f}$	Components of $\vec{f}$		Components of $\overset{\leftarrow}{f}$		SP
	f	$\vec{f}$	$\overset{\leftarrow}{f}$		$\overset{\rightarrow}{f_D}$	$\overset{\rightarrow}{f_P}$	$\overset{\leftarrow}{f_D}$	$\overset{\leftarrow}{f_P}$	
8a	10 outward	10.6	0.6	17.7	0.5	10.1	0.6	...	− 101.0
8b	10 outward	100.0	90.0	1.11	75.0	25.0	90.0	...	− 1.67
9a	10 inward	50.0	60.0	0.833	50.0	...	60.0	...	0.0
9b	10 inward	0.5	10.5	0.0476	0.5	...	0.6	9.9	99.0
9c	10 inward	25.0	35.0	0.714	25.0	...	30.0	5.0	1.0
9d	10 inward	110.0	120.0	0.918	100.0	10.0	120.0	...	−0.5

case 9b the ratio is much smaller than 0.833, and this indicates the existence of a strong inward pump which operates in parallel with the movement of the ion inward by simple diffusion. The value of the ratio in case 9c is smaller than 0.833, but much closer to it; this indicates the presence of an inward pump which is weaker than that operating in case 9b. Finally, in case 9d the ratio is larger than 0.833, and this indicates that the simple diffusion of the ion inward is opposed, even though not completely compensated, by an outward pump.

The active transport of an ion M^+ is effected by diffusion of this ion in the form of some complex, say NM^+ (p. 594). As in any other kind of diffusion, the traffic of NM^+ takes place in both directions, and the net transport of M^+ takes place because one of the fluxes is larger than the other.   On the assumption that the weaker of these two fluxes is negligibly small, it is possible to obtain a measure of the strength of the pump. This will be illustrated by an examination of the data in cases 9c and 9b.

In case 9c the observed outward and inward fluxes are 25 and 35, respectively.   The net active transport of the ion, as shown by the isotopic ratio test, is inward.   On the assumption that the smaller of the two fluxes due to the pump is negligibly small, the outward flux by simple diffusion is 25.   It follows that the inward flux by simple diffusion is equal to $25 \times 6/5 = 30$ (equation 11.51).   The inward flux due to the pump is $35 - 30 = 5$.

In case 8b the outward flux is 100, and the inward flux is 90; the isotopic flux ratio indicates that there is active outward transport.   On the assumption that the smaller of the two fluxes due to the pump is negligibly small, the observed inward flux is due entirely to simple diffusion and is 90.   The outward flux by simple diffusion is equal to $90 \times 5/6 = 75$. The outward flux due to the pump is $100 - 75 = 25$.

The sixth through the ninth columns of Table 11.4 show the results of similar calculations for all six cases.   It is desirable to define some measure of the relative strength of the pump.   The choice of a definition is somewhat arbitrary.   Let us define this quantity as the ratio:

$$\text{Relative strength of pump} = \frac{\text{net flux by active transport}}{\text{net flux by simple diffusion}} = SP$$

As an illustration, in case 8a, $SP = 10.1/(0.5 - 0.6) = -101$.   The negative sign indicates that the two net movements are opposite in direction.   The numerical value of SP shows that the net flux by the pump mechanism is much greater than the net flux by simple diffusion. The values of SP for all six cases are shown in the last column of the table. It may be seen that in case 9b the observed net flux is due chiefly to the action of the pump.   In case 9c the pump and simple diffusion contribute equally to the observed net flux.

When a system is in a steady state, the flux of the pump is equal in magnitude but opposite in direction to the leakage by simple diffusion; the value of SP is -1.00.

THE TRANSMEMBRANE POTENTIAL IN DIFFUSION SYSTEMS CONTAINING A NEUTRAL MEMBRANE

Neutral and selective membranes

With the concentrations of the various ions in the inside and outside solutions specified, the value of the transmembrane potential E depends upon the values of the transmission constants (p. 528) K_{Wj}, the distribution constants b_j, and the mobilities u_j of the ions present. The transmembrane potential also depends upon the membrane model used. From among the various possible models let us select two for theoretical treatment: the neutral model and the selective model.

A membrane, particularly one containing proteins, may contain immobile charges, fixed to the framework of the membrane. Thus, at high pH the membrane may contain fixed carboxylate groups, $—COO^-$. At low pH it may contain fixed amino groups $—NH_2 \cdot H^+$. We will refer to these models as the acid and basic membranes, respectively. If the membrane does not contain a predominance of fixed charges of either sign, we will call it a neutral membrane.

In a basic membrane the population of mobile anions must be greater than that of mobile cations. Consequently the membrane is more permeable to anions than to cations. Similarly, an acid membrane is more permeable to cations than to anions. Finally, the permeability of a neutral membrane to ions of different signs is non-discriminatory, and depends only upon the relative values of the products $b_j u_j$ of the ions.

It may be worth while to emphasize at this point that equation (11.27) is valid both for neutral and selective membranes. Equations (11.35) to (11.51), developed from (11.27), are also valid, and it follows that flux characteristics, suggestions for experimental work on penetration of ions and for the interpretation of observed results, all based on these equations, are valid for both neutral and selective membranes. The mathematical analysis of the neutral membrane will be taken up first.

The functional relation in a neutral membrane between the potential gradient, the total ionic concentration $C\pm$, and the positional coordinate x; boundary values

Equations (11.31) and (11.32), in which z is the absolute value of the valence of the ion, are valid both for neutral and selective membranes. The integration of these equations for the general case, where polyvalent ions may be present, is exceedingly complicated. It is expedient to confine our analysis to the case in which the ionic population of the membrane contains univalent ions only. If the equations derived with this assumption are to be applied to, say, nerve membranes, it must be kept in mind that the simplifying assumption is equivalent to assuming that the distribution coefficients of the bivalent ions present in nerve are negligibly small, or that the concentrations of the bivalent ion in the two solutions are negligibly small.

With this assumption, equations (11.31) and (11.32) yield the simpler equations (11.61) and (11.62).

$$-\sum \frac{f_{j+}}{u_{j+}} + \sum \frac{f_{j-}}{u_{j-}} = \frac{RT}{F} \frac{d(\Sigma C_{j+} - \Sigma C_{j-})}{dx} + \frac{dV}{dx} C \pm \qquad (11.61)$$

$$\sum \frac{f_{j+}}{u_{j+}} + \sum \frac{f_{j-}}{u_{j-}} = -\frac{RT}{F} \frac{dC\pm}{dx} - \frac{dV}{dx} (\Sigma C_{j+} - \Sigma C_{j-}) \quad (11.62)$$

where $C\pm$, as defined earlier, is the local value of the sum of the concentrations of all the ions present. In a neutral membrane the first term on the right side of (11.61) is zero. Similarly, the last term in (11.62) is zero. The quantities on the left side of each of the two equations are constants independent of x. It follows from (11.61) that, in a neutral membrane, the local value of the potential gradient is inversely proportional to the local total ionic concentration (11.63):

$$dV/dx = K/C\pm \qquad (11.63)$$

where K is a constant, still to be determined.

From (11.62) it follows that in a neutral membrane the slope of the total ionic concentration $C\pm$ is constant and is given by equation (11.33). The value of this function is given in (11.34).

Substituting (11.34) in (11.63), we integrate the latter between the limits $x = 0$ and x, obtaining equation (11.64).

$$V - E_i = \frac{Ks \ln \dfrac{(C\pm)_x}{(C\pm)_i}}{(C\pm)_o - (C\pm)_i} \qquad (11.64)$$

The quantity $C\pm$, the total ionic concentration, begins to occur in the equations. Eventually, however, the ratio of the total populations will appear in the equations. It will be convenient to use for this ratio the symbol R_b^a, defined in (11.65).

$$\frac{\text{Total ionic concentration at point } a}{\text{Total ionic concentration at point } b} = \frac{(C\pm)_a}{(C\pm)_b} = R_b^a \qquad (11.65)$$

From this definition it follows that $R_i^o = 1/R_o^i$ and $\ln R_i^o = -\ln R_o^i$.

To solve for K, we substitute in equation (11.64) the boundary values for V and for the total ionic concentration at $x = s$, and obtain

$$E_M = Ks \frac{\ln R_i^o}{(C\pm)_o - (C\pm)_i} \qquad K = \frac{E_M}{s} \frac{(C\pm)_o - (C\pm)_i}{\ln R_i^o} \qquad (11.66a,b)$$

Substitution of the value of K in (11.64) gives the functional relation between V and x (11.67). Substitution of K in (11.63) gives the functional relation between the potential gradient and x (11.68). Substitution of boundary values of the ratio of ionic concentrations in (11.68) gives the boundary values of the potential gradient (11.69a,b).

$$V = E_i + E_M \frac{\ln R_i^x}{\ln R_i^o} \tag{11.67}$$

$$\frac{dV}{dx} = \frac{E_M}{s} \frac{R_x^o - R_x^i}{\ln R_i^o} \tag{11.68}$$

$$\left(\frac{dV}{dx}\right)_i = \frac{E_M}{s} \frac{R_i^o - 1}{\ln R_i^o} \qquad \left(\frac{dV}{dx}\right)_o = \frac{E_M}{s} \frac{1 - R_o^i}{\ln R_i^o} \tag{11.69a,b}$$

The conditions which determine the curvature of the potential curve are now apparent. If the total ionic concentrations at the two boundaries happen to be equal, the total concentration is constant throughout the membrane (11.34), and the potential gradient is constant (11.63) and equals E_M/s. This can also be shown with the use of (11.68), since, under the condition of constancy of population, the numerator of the fraction on the right side is zero, and the indeterminate ratio $0/0$ can be shown to be equal to 1.

From (11.63) it can also be seen that the potential gradient is highest at the boundary where the total ionic population has its lowest values.

It is instructive to estimate the magnitude of the potential gradients in living membranes. If E_M is of the order of 0.1 volt, and s is of the order of 10^{-6} cm, the potential gradient, if constant throughout the membrane, is of the order of 100,000 volts per cm. If the ionic population at the outside boundary is ten times the population at the inside boundary, then, from equations (11.69a,b) the potential gradient at the outside boundary is 39,000 volts per cm, and at the inside boundary it is 390,000 volts per cm. A realization of the magnitude of the potential gradients in natural membranes will be of importance when we consider, in a later section (p. 586), the probability of orientation of protein molecules and of enzymes within the membrane and at its boundaries.

Complete integration of the differential equation of flow, for neutral membranes

If the membrane is populated by univalent ions only, differential equations (11.29), (11.30) acquire the slightly simpler form (11.70).

$$f_{j\pm} = -\frac{RTu_j}{F} \frac{dC_{j\pm}}{dx} \mp u_j C_{j\pm} \frac{dV}{dx} \tag{11.70}$$

Rewritten in the standard form (11.71), and solved, the equation gives the solution (11.72).

$$\frac{dC_{j\pm}}{dx} \pm \left(\frac{F}{RT}\frac{dV}{dx}\right)C_{j\pm} = -\frac{Ff_{j\pm}}{RTu_{j\pm}} \tag{11.71}$$

$$C_{j\pm}e^{\pm FV/RT}\bigg]_{x_1}^{x_2} = -\frac{Fsf_{j\pm}}{RTu_j}\int_{x_1}^{x_2}\frac{1}{s}e^{\pm FV/RT}\,dx \tag{11.72}$$

Substitution of the limits $x_1 = 0$, $x_2 = s$ leads to equation (11.73). Division of both sides of (11.73) by $Z_i^{\pm 1}$ leads to (11.74), where $S_{\pm 1}$ is the definite integral.

$$C_{ij\pm}Z_i^{\pm 1} - C_{oj\pm}(Z_iZ_M)^{\pm 1} = f_{j\pm}\frac{Fs}{RTu_j}\int_0^s\frac{1}{s}e^{\pm FV/RT}\,dx \tag{11.73}$$

$$C_{ij\pm} - C_{oj\pm}Z_M^{\pm 1} = f_{j\pm}\frac{Fs}{RTu_j}\int_0^s\frac{1}{s}e^{[\pm F(V-E_i)]/RT}\,dx$$

$$= f_{j\pm}\frac{Fs}{RTu_j}S_{\pm 1} \tag{11.74}$$

Substitution of V, with the use of equation (11.67), and integration, yields the equation for $S_{\pm 1}$ (equation 11.75). Substitution of $S_{\pm 1}$ in (11.74) and rearrangement of terms yields equation (11.76) for f_j.

$$S_{\pm 1} = \int_0^s\frac{1}{s}e^{[\pm F(V-E_i)]/RT}\,dx = \frac{Z_M^{\pm 1}R_i^o - 1}{\pm FE_M/RT + \ln R_i^o}\frac{\ln R_i^o}{R_i^o - 1} \tag{11.75}$$

$$f_{j\pm} = \frac{RTu_j}{Fs}\cdot\frac{\pm FE_M/RT + \ln R_i^o}{Z_M^{\pm 1}R_i^o - 1}\cdot\frac{R_i^o - 1}{\ln R_i^o}(C_{ij\pm} - C_{oj\pm}Z_M^{\pm 1}) \tag{11.76}$$

The evaluation of E_M

The total electrical current caused by the diffusion of all the ions is given by (11.77).

$$I = F(\Sigma f_{j+} - \Sigma f_{j-}) \tag{11.77}$$

Recalling that $Z_M = e^{FE_M/RT}$; $FE_M/RT = \ln Z_M$, we substitute (11.76) in (11.77) and obtain equation (11.78) for I as a function of E_M.

$$I = RT\frac{R_i^o - 1}{s\ln R_i^o}\left[\frac{\ln Z_M + \ln R_i^o}{R_i^oZ_M - 1}(\Sigma C_{ij+}u_{j+} - Z_M\Sigma C_{oj+}u_{j+})\right.$$

$$\left. - \frac{-\ln Z_M + \ln R_i^o}{R_i^oZ_M^{-1} - 1}(\Sigma C_{ij-}u_{j-} - Z_M^{-1}\Sigma C_{oj-}u_{j-})\right] \tag{11.78}$$

Equation (11.78), giving the net current I as a function of E_M, is valid whether E_M is imposed by the application of an outside emf or whether it is due to the natural diffusion potential of the system. In the latter case the net electrical current is zero. We can, therefore, solve for the diffusion potential E_M by imposing the condition that the quantity within the square brackets of equation (11.78) equals zero.

In carrying out the calculation, it will be convenient to represent the sum $\Sigma C_{ij+}u_{j+}$ by the single term U_{i+}. This term represents the total conductance at the inner boundary due to the cations present there. U_{i-}, U_{o+}, and U_{o-} are similarly defined. The condition that the net electrical current is equal zero leads to equation (11.79).

$$\frac{Z_M U_{o+} - U_{i+}}{U_{o-} - Z_M U_{i-}} = \frac{\ln R_i^o - \ln Z_M}{\ln R_i^o + \ln Z_M} \cdot \frac{Z_M(C\pm)_o - (C\pm)_i}{(C\pm)_o - Z_M(C\pm)_i} \quad (11.79)$$

Equation (11.79) is the same, except for the symbols used, as Planck's equation for the liquid junction potential between two solutions (Planck, 1890; MacInnes, 1939, pp. 233, 461). The identity of the two equations is not fortuitous, since in both systems the physical problem is the same: given two planes with two sets of ions, the concentrations and mobilities of the ions; given that there is no mechanical mixing and that each ion migrates according to its mobility and charge, what is the potential difference between the two planes?

As with Planck's equation, (11.79) will not give an explicit solution for E_M. There are fundamental differences, however, between the applications of Planck's equation for liquid junction potentials and the application of (11.79) for the total transmembrane potential E. In the case of a liquid junction, Planck's equation yields the complete value of E. Equation (11.79) yields the value of E_M only. Furthermore, the concentrations appearing in Planck's equation are those found in the two solutions; the concentrations appearing in (11.79) are those at the two boundaries, on the membrane side.

In order to introduce E and the various concentrations C_j', we may make use of the following relations:

$$Z_M = ZZ_i^{-1}Z_o^{-1} \quad (11.80)$$

For "thick" membrane:

$$C_{o\pm} = 2Z_o\Sigma b_{j+}C_{oj+}' = 2Z_o P_o$$
$$= 2Z_o^{-1}\Sigma b_{j-}C_{oj-}' = 2Z_o^{-1}N_o \quad (11.81)$$

$$C_{i\pm} = 2Z_i^{-1}\Sigma b_{j+}C_{ij+}' = 2Z_i^{-1}P_i$$
$$= 2Z_i\Sigma b_{j-}C_{ij-}' = 2Z_i N_i \quad (11.82)$$

$$U_{o+} = \Sigma C_{j+}u_{j+} = Z_o\Sigma b_{j+}C_{j+}'u_{j+} = Z_o U_{o+}''$$
$$U_{o-} = \Sigma C_{j-}u_{j-} = Z_o^{-1}\Sigma b_{j-}C_{j-}'u_{j-} = Z_o^{-1}U_{o-}'' \quad (11.83)$$

These equations introduce new terms whose meanings are defined by the equations. Thus, P_o is the total positive ionic population that would be present at the outside boundary if there were no potential jump at the surface. N_i has a similar meaning for the negative ion population at the inner boundary. U_{o+}'' is the total conductance of the total positive ionic population at the outside boundary when E_o is zero. Equations similar to (11.83) may be written for the other two conductances appearing in (11.79). When the substitutions are made, and appropriate algebraic simplifications carried out, equation (11.84) is obtained.

$$\frac{ZU_{o+}'' - U_{i+}''}{U_{o-}'' - ZU_{i-}''} = \frac{\ln (N_o/N_i) - \ln Z}{\ln (P_o/P_i) + \ln Z} \cdot \frac{ZP_o - P_i}{N_o - ZN_i} \quad \text{(thick membrane)}$$

$$(11.84)$$

Equation (11.84) is not a simple one, even though summations have been replaced by single symbols. It contains mobilities and distribution constants as parameters, quantities which it would be difficult to estimate even approximately, let alone evaluate accurately. Clearly, this equation cannot be easily tested experimentally, even with simple artificial membranes. Nevertheless, the rigorous step-by-step derivation of the equation has served a useful purpose. As a side product of the derivation, certain conclusions have been reached as to the type of experimental information needed to yield a reliable interpretation of the penetration of membranes by ions. The derivation has also yielded a perspective on certain aspects of this difficult problem and a vantage point from which to examine the validity of less laborious but apparently more manageable solutions of the problem. As illustration, we may consider the suitability of the Henderson equation and of another, more recently developed, equation (cf. p. 562).

The Henderson equation

Henderson's solution of the liquid junction potential (Henderson, 1907, 1908; MacInnes, 1939) between two solutions of complexions C_{ij}, u_j and C_{oj}, u_j is given by equation (11.85), where the symbols have the same meaning as before.

$$E_M = \frac{RT}{F} \frac{(U_{i+} - U_{i-}) - (U_{o+} - U_{o-})}{(U_{i+} + U_{i-}) - (U_{o+} + U_{o-})} \ln \frac{U_{i+} + U_{i-}}{U_{o+} + U_{o-}} \quad (11.85)$$

Henderson's equation (11.85) has the seeming advantage over Planck's equation (11.79) that the former offers an explicit solution for E_M. If, however, (11.85) is to be used for calculating the total transmembrane potential E, substitutions of the type given in (11.80) and (11.83) have to be made.   The resulting equation would be complicated in form and, in addition, would contain the quantities Z_i, Z_o, and their reciprocals.

In addition, there is a question about the theoretical applicability of this equation to membranes.   Henderson's solution differs from Planck's, except in special cases.   Both were derived with mathematical rigor, and the difference is due to a difference in underlying assumptions.   In the Planck solution it is assumed that there is no mechanical mixing; the different ions distribute themselves within the membrane in accordance with their charges and the electrostatic pattern.   In the Henderson treatment a type of mechanical mixing is assumed, such that the ionic population at any point may be represented as a linear mixture of the populations at the boundaries.   Thus, if the composition at the inner boundary is given by the set C_{ij}, and the composition at the outer boundary is given by the set C_{ok}, then for any point in the interior of the membrane a number X can be found by means of which the composition at that point may be described by the set $XC_{ij} + (1 - X)C_{ok}$.

The mathematical analysis of the distribution of ions within a membrane cannot be given here, for lack of space.   Certain conclusions, however, bear on the question at issue, as follows.   (1) With the boundary concentrations of a given ion specified, the concentration in the interior of the membrane is a function of the electrostatic pattern as well as of the position.   (2) The function differs for ions belonging to different valence types.   (3) In general, Henderson's stipulation of a linear ionic composition is not satisfied in membranes.   (4) In certain special cases Henderson's stipulation is satisfied; in all these cases Henderson's solution is the same as Planck's.   In general, then, Henderson's equation is not strictly valid for diffusion through membranes.

Special cases with neutral membranes

It is well known that, when one solution contains a uni-univalent electrolyte, and is in contact with a K-fold concentrate of the same solution, Planck's equation gives (11.86) as the value of the liquid junction potential.

$$E = \frac{u_+ - u_-}{u_+ + u_-} \frac{RT}{F} \ln K \qquad (11.86)$$

where u_+ and u_- are the mobilities, in water, of the cation and anion, respectively.   For a neutral membrane we will consider the more general case where the outside solution is characterized by the set C_j, b_j, u_j, and the inside solution is a K-fold concentrate of the outside solution.   Substitution of the proper values in (11.84) gives equation (11.87) for the value of the transmembrane potential.

$$E = \frac{\dfrac{\Sigma C_{j+}'b_{j+}u_{j+}}{\Sigma C_{j+}'b_{j+}} - \dfrac{\Sigma C_{j-}'b_{j-}u_{j-}}{\Sigma C_{j-}'b_{j-}}}{\dfrac{\Sigma C_{j+}'b_{j+}u_{j+}}{\Sigma C_{j+}'b_{j+}} + \dfrac{\Sigma C_{j-}'b_{j-}u_{j-}}{\Sigma C_{j-}'b_{j-}}} \frac{RT \ln K}{F} \tag{11.87}$$

Equation (11.87), different from (11.86) in form, does not differ from it in substance. Equation (11.86) contains the difference and sum of the cationic and anionic mobilities. Equation (11.87) contains the difference and sum of two mean effective cationic and anionic mobilities. Equation (11.87), obtained by direct substitution of the given quantities in (11.84), shows that the two mean mobilities are each the result of weighting the membrane mobility of each ion by the product of its concentration in solution and its solubility in the membrane.

If we substitute unity for every b appearing in (11.87), we get the equation for the liquid junction potential in the general case, when one solution may contain any combination of univalent ions, and the second solution is a K-fold concentrate of the first.

If a neutral membrane separates a solution containing a uni-univalent salt and a K-fold concentrate of the same solution, equation (11.87) yields the simple equation (11.86) for the transmembrane potential, with the understanding, of course, that this time u_+ and u_- are the mobilities of the two ions in the membrane.

The simplicity of equation (11.86) and the relative simplicity of (11.87) are due to the following factors: when one solution is a K-fold concentrate of the other, the surface potentials E_i and E_o are equal in magnitude and opposite in sign; they cancel each other. The ionic population in the membrane at the inside boundary is a K-fold multiple, both in aggregate and in detail of the population at the outside boundary. It may be worth while to mention that this simplicity holds only in neutral membranes. In selective membranes this simplicity does not exist, and formulas (11.86) and (11.87) are not valid, except in the special case when the concentration of fixed ions is relatively insignificant, and the membrane behaves approximately like a neutral membrane.

There is a second type of diffusion system for which Planck's equation yields a simple formula. Thus, if one solution contains the electrolyte M_iX, and the second solution contains an equal concentration of an electrolyte possessing the same anion, say M_oX, and there is no membrane between the two solutions, the liquid junction potential is given by equation (11.88).

$$E = \frac{RT}{F} \ln \frac{u_{M_i} + u_X}{u_{M_o} + u_X} \tag{11.88}$$

If a membrane separates the two solutions, the equation for the trans-membrane potential obtained from (11.84) is not simple. The reason is that, since the two cations in general have different distribution constants, the values of E_i and of E_o are not simply related. Furthermore, the ionic populations in the membrane at the two boundaries are not equal. Thus, the condition which is responsible for the simplicity of equation (11.88) is absent.

The linear potential equation

As yet, it has not been feasible to apply a rigorous mathematical treatment to transmembrane potentials such as those of nerve during rest, excitation, and recovery. Even with simple membranes the equations are complicated and difficult to apply, as indicated in the foregoing discussions. Goldman (1943) made a useful simplification by assuming a constant potential gradient across the membrane. Though admittedly only an approximation, Goldman's approach yielded some interesting results. Hodgkin and Katz (1949a) used essentially the same equation to give an approximate mathematical expression to their theory concerning the rôle of sodium in the excitation of nerve. In essence, their model of the system may be represented by the following scheme:

Inside Solution			Outside Solution (Control)		
$(Na^+)_i'$	72		$(Na^+)_o'$	455	
$(K^+)_i'$	345	Neutral Membrane	$(K^+)_o'$	10	(11.89)
$(Cl^-)_i'$	61		$(Cl^-)_o'$	587	

The numbers give the concentrations in millimoles per liter in the inside and outside solutions in one of their control experiments. In other experiments the outside concentrations were changed.

Hodgkin and Katz started with differential equations which are essentially similar to (11.71). From the outset they simplified the integration of these equations by adopting Goldman's approximation that the potential gradient may be taken as constant throughout the membrane. The solution, expressed in the symbols used in the preceding pages, is given by equation (11.90).

$$E_M = \frac{RT}{F} \ln Z_M = \frac{RT}{F} \ln \frac{u_{Na}C_{iNa} + u_K C_{iK} + u_{Cl}C_{oCl}}{u_{Na}C_{oNa} + u_K C_{oK} + u_{Cl}C_{iCl}} \quad (11.90)$$

In order to give the solution in terms of the concentrations of the three ions in the two aqueous solutions, they used the relations: $C_{ij} = b_j C_{ij}'$ and $C_{oj} = b_j C_{oj}'$, thus obtaining equation (11.91).

$$E_M = \frac{RT}{F} \ln \frac{b_{Na}u_{Na}(Na)_i' + b_K u_K(K)_i' + b_{Cl}u_{Cl}(Cl)_o'}{b_{Na}u_{Na}(Na)_o' + b_K u_K(K)_o' + b_{Cl}u_{Cl}(Cl)_i'} \quad (11.91)$$

Equations (11.90) and (11.91) give the values of E_M, the potential difference between the inside and outside boundaries of the membrane proper. If the magnitudes of E_i and of E_o are negligibly small, the same equations give the value of the total transmembrane potential E. The values of the two surface potentials depend upon the concentrations and distribution constants of the ions in the adjacent solutions, and, since the values of the distribution constants are unknown, it is not possible to give a definite calculation. However, by assuming various values of the distribution constants we can obtain a picture of the expected pattern of values. This will enable us to form an estimate of the quantitative significance of the two surface potentials.

The results of such a calculation are given in Table 11.5. The values of E_i and of E_o were calculated with the use of equations (11.92) and (11.93).

$$E_i = 58 \text{ mv } \log_{10} \left(\frac{b_{\text{Na}}(\text{Na})_i' + b_{\text{K}}(\text{K})_i'}{b_{\text{Cl}}(\text{Cl})_i'} \right)^{1/2} \tag{11.92}$$

$$E_o = 58 \text{ mv } \log_{10} \left(\frac{b_{\text{Cl}}(\text{Cl})_o'}{b_{\text{Na}}(\text{Na})_o' + b_{\text{K}}(\text{K})_o'} \right)^{1/2} \tag{11.93}$$

Equation (11.92) may be derived in the following manner: Electroneutrality on the membrane side of the inside boundary imposes the following relation: $(\text{Na})_i + (\text{K})_i = (\text{Cl})_i$. Substitution for each of the three terms, with the use of equation (11.3), yields an equation containing E_i. Solution of this equation for E_i and substitution of numerical values appropriate for room temperature yields equation (11.92). Equation (11.93) may be obtained in a similar manner with the use of equation (11.4).

Since the experimentally observed total transmembrane potential was 48 mv, the value of E_M, given in the last column of Table 11.5, was obtained by difference. The surface potentials depend upon the ratios of the distribution coefficients, and for this reason the numbers tried are merely ratios.

Inspection of the table shows (case H) that the requirement $E_i = E_o = 0$ cannot strictly be met, since potassium would have to possess a negative distribution coefficient. Furthermore, the table shows that the surface potentials are, in general, of the same order as the observed transmembrane potential, and that the value of E_M is apt to differ from the observed value of E by a large amount.

From the preceding it is evident that in the control experiment the two surface potentials cannot both be zero. Dilution of the outside solution does not change this aspect of the situation, since with a neutral membrane dilution does not change the value of E_o. It follows that in a rigorous derivation the surface potentials may not be disregarded.

Returning to equation (11.90), we carry out the substitutions for the concentration terms, paying due attention to the effect of the surface potential on the relation between C_j and C_j'. As a result of this substitution we obtain equation (11.94) in place of (11.91).

$$E_M = \frac{RT}{F} \ln \frac{Z_i^{-1} b_{Na} u_{Na}(Na)_i' + Z_i^{-1} b_K u_K(K)_i' + Z_o^{-1} b_{Cl} u_{Cl}(Cl)_o'}{Z_o b_{Na} u_{Na}(Na)_o' + Z_o b_K u_K(K)_o' + Z_i b_{Cl} u_{Cl}(Cl)_i'} \quad (11.94)$$

Table 11.5.   Values of E_i, E_o, E_M Obtained with Various Assumed Relative Values of the Distribution Coefficients

(The observed value of the total transmembrane potential was 48 mv*)

$$E_M = 48 - (E_i + E_o)$$

Case	b_{Na}	b_K	b_{Cl}	E_i	E_o	E_M
A	1	1	1	24.1	3.02	20.9
B	2	2	1	32.8	− 5.7	20.9
C	10	10	1	53.1	− 26.0	20.9
D	1	1	2	15.4	11.7	20.9
E	1	1	10	− 4.9	32.0	20.9
F	1	10	1	51.2	0.7	− 3.9
G	10	1	1	36.0	− 25.9	37.9
H	1.289	− 0.0922	1	0	0	48.0

* Concentrations of Na, K, Cl from Hodgkin and Katz (1949a), Table 7: inside, 72, 345, 61 mM; outside, 455, 10, 587 mM.

To obtain the equation for the total transmembrane potential E, we make use of the relation: $E = E_M + E_i + E_o$ and of equation (11.95).

$$E_i + E_o = \frac{RT}{F} \ln (Z_i Z_o) \quad (11.95)$$

and thus obtain equation (11.96).

$$E = \frac{RT}{F} \ln \frac{b_{Na} u_{Na}(Na)_i' + b_K u_K(K)_i' + Z_i Z_o^{-1} b_{Cl} u_{Cl}(Cl)_o'}{b_{Na} u_{Na}(Na)_o' + b_K u_K(K)_o' + Z_i Z_o^{-1} b_{Cl} u_{Cl}(Cl)_i'} \quad (11.96)$$

(assuming constant potential gradient)

TRANSMEMBRANE POTENTIALS WITH SELECTIVE MEMBRANES; FLOW OF IONS THROUGH SELECTIVE MEMBRANES

The Teorell, Meyer-Sievers model of acid and basic membranes

The analysis of the properties of acid and basic membranes is of interest because of the light it may throw on the behavior of those natural membranes which are easily penetrated by ions of one sign, while forming a strong barrier to ions of the opposite sign. Teorell (1935, 1951), Meyer and Sievers (1936a), and Meyer and Bernfeld (1945b) carried out a useful analysis for membranes inserted between two solutions containing the same uni-univalent salt at different concentrations. It is advantageous to begin with their treatment, with some changes in symbols, and then to extend the analysis to the more general case where each solution may contain any number of univalent ions at any concentration.

Assuming that the framework of the membrane contains attached acid groups, —AH, and basic groups, —B, insertion of the membrane in an aqueous solution of ions is apt to be followed by exchange reactions:

$$\underset{\text{(in membrane)}}{-\text{AH}} + \underset{\text{(in solution)}}{M_j{}^+} = \underset{\text{(in membrane)}}{-\text{A}^- + M_j{}^+} + \underset{\text{(in solution)}}{\text{H}^+} \qquad (11.97)$$

$$\underset{\text{(in membrane)}}{-\text{B}} + \underset{\text{(in solution)}}{\text{H}^+ + X_j{}^-} = \underset{\text{(in membrane)}}{-\text{BH}^+ + X_j{}^-} \qquad (11.98)$$

The effect of reaction (11.97) is to produce a cationic concentration within the membrane which is higher than the concentration that would be present in the absence of the acid groups. This is accompanied by a decrease in the concentration of mobile anions in the membrane (cf. p. 569). The effect of reaction (11.98) is to increase the concentration of mobile anions and to decrease the concentration of mobile cations. Inspection of the equations shows that a high $p\text{H}$ in the aqueous solution favors reaction (11.97), and the membrane acts like an acid. A low $p\text{H}$ favors reaction (11.98), and the membrane acts like a base.

In undertaking to analyze the behavior of acid membranes, we may tentatively assume with Meyer and Sievers that the concentration of the immobile negative charge, —A$^-$, is constant throughout the membrane and is independent of the concentrations of the uni-univalent salt in the two solutions. This assumption has the advantage of simplifying the treatment, but at the same time calls for some discussion.

As a concrete example, we may use the simple case treated by these authors, in which the two solutions contain different concentrations of potassium chloride. Fixing our attention on the conditions prevailing at one of the surfaces, say the inside surface, we will use C_i for the concentration of potassium, the customary notation for the concentrations of H$^+$, with primed quantities indicating concentrations in the solution. Let the total concentration of the acid groups (ionized plus un-ionized) be A^*, and the concentration of the ionized groups be A. Finally, let the equilibrium constant of reaction (11.97) be K. The value of A must satisfy the following equilibrium equations:

$$\frac{C_i A(\text{H}^+)_i'}{(A^* - A)C_i'} = K \qquad A = \frac{K(A^* - A)C_i'}{C_i(\text{H}^+)_i'} \qquad (11.99\text{a,b})$$

Equation (11.99b) shows that, in general, the value of A varies both with the pH of the solution and with the concentration of the cation in the solution. However, if the pH of the solution is sufficiently high, reaction (11.97) is practically complete. Only in these circumstances is the value of A approximately constant, independent of small changes in the pH of the solution and of the concentration of the cation, and is approximately equal A^*.

From the preceding discussion it follows that the assumption $A =$ constant is valid only if the pH of the solution is much higher than the isoelectric pH of the membrane. Furthermore, it follows that any conclusions reached relative to the behavior of the diffusion system at low salt concentrations are applicable only if the concentrations of the salt are not so low as to begin to invalidate the assumption that reaction (11.97) is practically complete. These conditions were apparently satisfied in the studies of Meyer and Sievers (cf. p. 578).

Continuing with our analysis, the condition of electrical neutrality must be satisfied at each membrane surface, and, therefore, equations 11.100a,b must be satisfied.

$$\Sigma C_{oj-} = \Sigma C_{oj+} - A \qquad \Sigma C_{ij-} = \Sigma C_{ij+} - A \qquad (11.100a,b)$$

In the event that the membrane is "thick" enough to insure that the ions on the membrane side are practically at equilibrium with the ions of the respective solution, the membrane concentrations may be expressed in terms of the solution concentrations by means of equations (11.101a–d).

$$\Sigma C_{oj+} = Z_o \Sigma b_{j+} C_{oj+}' = Z_o P_o \qquad (11.101a)$$

Similarly,

$$\Sigma C_{oj-} = \Sigma Z_o^{-1} b_{j-} C_{oj-}' = Z_o^{-1} N_o \qquad (11.101b)$$

$$\Sigma C_{ij+} = Z_i^{-1} P_i \qquad C_{ij-} = Z_i N_i \qquad (11.101c,d)$$

As in equations (11.81–82), P and N, defined by the equations themselves, represent virtual quantities, namely, the cationic and anionic concentrations that would be present in the absence of electrical effects.

Substitutions of equations (11.101) in (11.100) yields quadratic equations from which the values of Z_o and Z_i^{-1} may be obtained:

$$Z_o = \frac{A}{2P_o}\left[1 + \left(1 + \frac{4N_o P_o}{A^2}\right)^{1/2}\right] \qquad (11.102a)$$

$$Z_i^{-1} = \frac{A}{2P_i}\left[1 + \left(1 + \frac{4N_i P_i}{A^2}\right)^{1/2}\right] \qquad (11.102b)$$

For later use it will be convenient to derive simpler formulas, to be applicable in those cases where $NP/A^2 \ll 1$, by expanding the square root into a series and discarding terms which become negligible (11.102c,d).

$$Z_o = \frac{A}{P_o}\left[1 + \frac{N_o P_o}{A^2}\right] \qquad \left(\text{when } \frac{N_o P_o}{A^2} \ll 1\right) \qquad (11.102c)$$

$$Z_i^{-1} = \frac{A}{P_o}\left[1 + \frac{N_i P_i}{A^2}\right] \qquad \left(\text{when } \frac{N_i P_i}{A^2} \ll 1\right) \qquad (11.102d)$$

Substitution of (11.102a) and (11.102c) in (11.101a) yields the value of ΣC_{oj+} (11.103a,b).

$$\Sigma C_{oj+} = \frac{A}{2}\left[\left(1 + \frac{4N_o P_o}{A^2}\right)^{1/2} + 1\right] \qquad (11.103a)$$

$$\Sigma C_{oj+} = A\left(1 + \frac{N_o P_o}{A^2}\right) \qquad \left(\text{when } \frac{N_o P_o}{A^2} \ll 1\right) \qquad (11.103b)$$

Substitution of (11.103a) and (11.103b) in (11.100a) yields the value of ΣC_{oj-}.

$$\Sigma C_{oj-} = \frac{A}{2}\left[\left(1 + \frac{4N_o P_o}{A^2}\right)^{1/2} - 1\right] \qquad (11.104a)$$

$$\Sigma C_{oj-} = \frac{N_o P_o}{A} \qquad \left(\text{when } \frac{N_o P_o}{A^2} \ll 1\right) \qquad (11.104b)$$

Finally, the sum of (11.103) and (11.104) gives the total ionic concentration, which will be represented, as before, by the symbol $C\pm$.

$$(C\pm)_o = A\left(1 + \frac{4N_o P_o}{A^2}\right)^{1/2} \qquad (11.105a)$$

$$(C\pm)_o = A\left(1 + \frac{2N_o P_o}{A^2}\right) \qquad \left(\text{when } \frac{N_o P_o}{A^2} \ll 1\right) \qquad (11.105b)$$

The ratio NP/A^2 appears frequently in these equations. It is important to keep in mind the physical meaning of this ratio. Equations (11.102a,b), (11.103a), (11.104a), and (11.105a) are exact, and hold for any value A. If we wish to obtain the equations for the corresponding quantities in a neutral membrane, all we need do is substitute the value $A = 0$ in (11.102a,b), (11.103a), (11.104a). After evaluating the indeterminate ratios 0/0, we get the following results:

$$Z_o = \left(\frac{N_o}{P_o}\right)^{1/2} \qquad Z_i^{-1} = \left(\frac{N_i}{P_i}\right)^{1/2} \left.\right\} \text{(neutral} \qquad (11.106a,b)$$

$$\Sigma C_{oj+} = \Sigma C_{oj-} = \tfrac{1}{2}C_{o\pm} = (N_o P_o)^{1/2} \left.\right\} \text{membrane)} \qquad (11.107)$$

Inspection of equation (11.107) shows that $(NP)^{\frac{1}{2}}$ is the concentration of cations or anions that would be present in the membrane surface if the fixed ions —A^- were absent, and the membrane were neutral, subject, however to the surface potentials ordinarily present in a neutral membrane.

The ratio NP/A^2 is a measure of the relative importance of the fixed ions. When the concentrations in the two solutions are high, this ratio is very high and the membrane behaves almost like a neutral membrane. When the concentrations in the two solutions are low, the relative importance of the presence of —A^- is increased, and the ratio NP/A^2 has a low value. In the discussion which follows it will be helpful to keep in mind that, if one of the solutions is diluted without changing the relative composition, the value of $(NP)^{\frac{1}{2}}$ varies proportionately to the concentration.

The transmembrane potential in an acid membrane

In the following discussion it is convenient to employ a line of approach similar to that used previously in the analysis of the properties of neutral membranes.

Equation (11.27b) is applicable, whether the membrane is neutral, acidic, or basic. Equations (11.61) and (11.62), derived for the case when $Z = 1$, are also applicable. The conclusions relative the nature of dV/dx, and of $dC\pm/dx$, however, depend on whether the membrane is neutral or not. In a neutral membrane $\Sigma C_{j+} - \Sigma C_{j-} = 0$. On the basis of this equation it has been concluded (see the discussion following equation 11.62) that in a neutral membrane the gradient of the total ionic concentration is constant, and the potential gradient is inversely proportional to the local total ionic concentration. In an acid membrane the following equation holds: $\Sigma C_{j+} - \Sigma C_{j-} = A$. Substitution of this equation in (11.61) and (11.62) yields (11.108) and (11.109), respectively.

$$\text{Constant} = \frac{RT}{F} \frac{dA}{dx} + \frac{dV}{dx} C\pm \qquad (11.108)$$

$$\text{Constant} = -\frac{RT}{F} \frac{dC\pm}{dx} - A \frac{dV}{dx} \qquad (11.109)$$

Since A is constant, dA/dx equals zero, and it follows from (11.108) that the potential gradient in an acid membrane is inversely proportional to the local total concentration of the mobile ions, as is the case in a neutral membrane. However, as will be seen from equation (11.109), the gradient of the total mobile ion concentration is, in general, not constant in an acid membrane. It follows that the problem of evaluating the transmembrane potential is more complex for an acid membrane than it is for a neutral one.

Fortunately, there are two special cases, for which the treatment is relatively simple.   In the first case the membrane separates two solutions containing relatively high concentrations of ions.   In these circumstances, the effect of the presence of the fixed ions, $—A^-$, is relatively unimportant, and the membrane acts as a slightly perturbed neutral membrane.   In the second case the concentrations of the ions in the two solutions are low, and the membrane exhibits certain properties, which are interesting by themselves and at the same time simplify the theoretical treatment.   These two cases are considered at some length in the discussion which follows.

Acid membranes in contact with concentrated and dilute solutions

First, let us consider the case when one surface of the membrane is in contact with a concentrated solution, and the latter is then gradually diluted.   From the definition of N and P (11.101), it follows that these quantities, as well as the quantity $(NP)^{1/2}$, vary proportionately to the concentration.   Moreover, the ratio $(NP)^{1/2}/A$ is also proportional to the concentration, since A is constant; at the same time this ratio is a measure of the relative importance of the presence of the fixed ions $—A^-$.

In Fig. 11.5 the abscissa represents the parameter $(NP)^{1/2}/A$.   The extreme right of the diagram represents concentrated solutions, while the extreme left represents dilute solutions.   The three curves show the values of $C\pm/A$, $\Sigma C_{j+}/A$, and $\Sigma C_{j-}/A$.   These values were calculated with the use of equations (11.103) to (11.105).

Figure 11.5 illustrates that in the presence of concentrated solutions the mobile cationic and anionic concentrations approach each other asymptotically.   This is to be expected, since, with increasing outside concentration, the relative importance of A decreases, and the behavior of the membrane approaches that of a neutral membrane.   Equations (11.103a,b) and (11.104a,b) show that the cationic and anionic concentrations approach asymptotically the function $(NP)^{1/2}$, from above and below, respectively, as the concentration increases.   The diagram shows that for values of $(NP)^{1/2}/A$ greater than 10 the membrane acts almost like a neutral one. It follows that a membrane separating two solutions, each of which satisfies this condition, may be treated as a neutral membrane.

The left side of Fig. 11.5 illustrates that in the presence of dilute solutions the mobile anionic population within the membrane becomes small and decreases with further dilution.   Expansion of the root binomial in equation (11.104a) shows that in dilute solutions the value of ΣC_{j-} approaches the function NP/A asymptotically.   It follows that the curve $\Sigma C_{j-}/A$ approaches the line NP/A^2 asymptotically.

In dilute solutions the cationic population approaches the value of A asymptotically and becomes practically independent of further dilution.

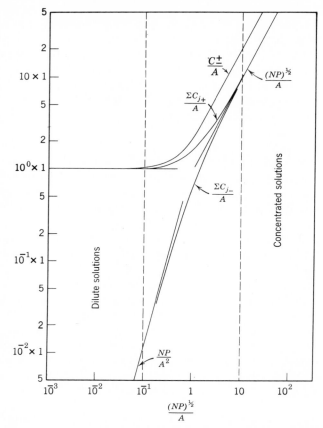

Fig. 11.5. Selective characteristics of an acid membrane as a function of the concentrations in the outside solution. A is the concentration of fixed anions within the membrane. $(NP)^{1/2}$ is the concentration of mobile cations and mobile anions that could be present at the membrane boundary in the absence of fixed anions. The outside solution is classified as "concentrated" or "dilute," depending on the ratio $(NP)^{1/2}/A$.

In the presence of a concentrated solution, the membrane shows very little selectivity. In the presence of dilute solutions the membrane becomes highly selective. In this case the cationic population becomes constant, equal to A, and independent of the outside concentration. The anionic concentration becomes small and proportional to the square of the outside concentration.

In the event that the fixed acid groups, $\neg AH$, are easily ionized, the transition region between dilute and concentrated solutions extends over an approximately hundred-fold range of concentrations. (If the fixed groups are very weak acids, the transition range is much longer.)

Since the mobile anionic population becomes negligibly small, the total mobile ionic population also approaches A and becomes constant and independent of further dilution.

Two practical conclusions follow from the results of this analysis: (1) the membrane does not show much discrimination between cations and anions when the concentrations in the solutions are high, and (2) the membrane shows discriminatory powers toward dilute solution. Thus the exclusion of anions becomes relatively more intense as the solutions are diluted.

The constancy of the total ionic population in the presence of dilute solutions carries an important implication. Since the local value of the potential gradient within the membrane is inversely proportional to the total concentration of mobile ions, (equation 11.108), it follows that, if both solutions may be classified as "dilute," the potential gradient within the membrane is constant, and the problem of evaluating the trans-membrane potential is greatly simplified. From Fig. 11.5 it is apparent that this condition is satisfied when the quantity $(NP)^{1/2}/A$ is smaller than 0.1 in both solutions.

To summarize the analysis of the diagram, diffusion systems containing an acid membrane may be classified in three groups, if the total concentrations of ions in the two solutions do not differ too much. There is a hundred-fold range of concentrations for which the behavior of the system is complex. Beyond this range, with more concentrated solutions, the membrane behaves like a non-discriminatory neutral membrane. With more dilute solutions the membrane is discriminatory, and the potential gradient within the membrane is constant.

Potentials, with acid membranes, in concentrate and dilute solutions

If solutions on the two sides of the membrane may be classified as concentrated (as compared with A), then the theoretical treatment is the same as for neutral membranes. The transmembrane potential is given by equation (11.84). If the inside solution is a K-fold concentrate of the outside solution, E is given by equation (11.87). Finally, if the outside solution is that of a uni-univalent electrolyte, and the inside solution is a K-fold concentrate of the same solution, E is given by equation (11.86).

An interesting set of properties appears when the solutions on the two sides of the membrane may be classified as dilute (compared to A). It was shown in the preceding section that in these circumstances the cationic concentration and the total mobile ionic concentration are approximately equal to A. The constancy of the mobile ionic concentration throughout the membrane brings about a constant potential gradient (11.108).

When the potential within the membrane is linear, the set of equations (11.70) turns into a set of linear differential equations with constant coefficients. The straightforward integration of these equations, coupled with the condition that the net electrical flux through the membrane is zero, yields equation (11.110) for E_M. The same equation may be obtained from (11.79) by imposing the condition that the total ionic concentrations are the same at the two boundaries.

$$E_M = \frac{RT}{F} \ln \frac{\Sigma u_{j+} C_{ij+} + \Sigma u_{j-} C_{oj-}}{\Sigma u_{j+} C_{oj+} + \Sigma u_{j-} C_{ij-}} \qquad (11.110)$$

Equation (11.110) is applicable in the general case where the potential within the membrane is linear. However, in the case of an acid membrane separating dilute solutions one more simplification is possible. In this type of diffusion system the anionic concentration within the membrane is negligibly small (Fig. 11.5). It follows that equation (11.110) may be replaced with the much simpler equation (11.111).

$$E_M = \frac{RT}{F} \ln \frac{\Sigma u_j C_{ij+}}{\Sigma u_j C_{oj+}} \qquad \text{(acid membrane, dilute solutions)} \quad (11.111)$$

By appropriate change in the argument, we may write the equation for the case of a basic membrane separating dilute solutions (11.112).

$$E_M = \frac{RT}{F} \ln \frac{\Sigma u_j C_{oj-}}{\Sigma u_j C_{ij-}} \qquad \text{(basic membrane, dilute solutions)} \quad (11.112)$$

The numerator and the denominator of (11.111) may be expressed in terms of the concentrations in the two solutions, since the ions at each membrane boundary have been assumed in equilibrium with the ions of the respective solutions; this substitution yields equation (11.113).

$$E_M = \frac{RT}{F} \ln \frac{Z_i^{-1} \Sigma u_j b_j C_{ij+}{}'}{Z_o \Sigma u_j b_j C_{oj+}} \qquad (11.113)$$

Substitution of the identity $(RT/F) \ln (Z_o Z_i) = E_o + E_i$ and transposition of these two terms lead to (11.114), which gives the value of E in terms of the concentrations in the two solutions.

$$E = \frac{RT}{F} \ln \frac{\Sigma u_j b_j C_{ij}{}'}{\Sigma u_j b_j C_{oj}{}'} \qquad \text{(acid membrane, dilute solutions)} \quad (11.114)$$

A similar treatment of (11.112) yields equation (11.115) for the transmembrane potential when a basic membrane separates two dilute solutions.

$$E = \frac{RT}{F} \ln \frac{\Sigma u_j b_j C_{oj-}{}'}{\Sigma u_j b_j C_{ij-}{}'} \qquad \text{(basic membrane, dilute solutions)} \quad (11.115)$$

Let us consider the change in the value of E if the outside solution is diluted K-fold. In this type of experiment another interesting property of selective membranes is important. It has been mentioned in several connections that in the dilute range of concentrations the cationic concentration at the outer boundary is approximately independent of the outside concentration and remains approximately equal to A. If the outside solution is changed by dilution, the relative concentrations of the various cations present remain constant, and the cationic population in the outside membrane remains approximately constant in total amount and in relative composition. It follows from equation (11.111) that dilution of the outside solution does not change the value of E_M. This property will be found to be of considerable importance when we consider the rates of penetration of ions through acid membranes (p. 574). A K-fold dilution of the outside solution will decrease the denominator on the right side of (11.114) by the factor $1/K$, and the value of E will increase by the amount shown in equation (11.116).

$$\Delta E = \frac{RT}{F} \ln K = 58 \text{ mv } \log_{10} K \qquad \text{(acid membrane, dilute solutions; effect of } K\text{-fold dilution of the outside solution)} \qquad (11.116)$$

In the analysis which led to equations (11.111) to (11.116) it was not necessary to make assumptions about the nature of the two solutions, other than the assumption that they both contain univalent ions and that they may both be classified as dilute. If the solutions are dilute, and, in addition, the inside solution is a K-fold concentrate of the outside solution, further simplification is possible. In these circumstances not only are the cationic concentrations at the two boundaries approximately independent of dilution and constant in magnitude and relative composition, but also the cationic populations at the two boundaries are approximately the same. It follows from (11.111) that E_M is not only independent of dilution, but is also approximately equal to zero. The transmembrane potential equals the sum of the two surface potentials. Since in these circumstances $C_{ij}' = KC_{oj}'$, we have the very simple equation, obtained from (11.114):

$$E = \frac{RT}{F} \ln K = 58 \text{ mv } \log_{10} K \qquad (K = C_i'/C_o') \qquad \text{(acid membrane)} \qquad (11.117a)$$

Equation (11.115) shows that, if the membrane is basic, the same equation will apply, with a change of sign:

$$E = -\frac{RT}{F} \ln K = -58 \text{ mv } \log_{10} K \qquad \text{(basic membrane)} \qquad (11.117b)$$

Rates of flow of ions through selective membranes

Experimental tests. According to the model discussed in the preceding pages, a membrane which discriminates between ions of opposite charge owes its selective characteristics to its ability to hold ions of the favored sign, while admitting only relatively small concentrations of ions of the opposite sign. Figure 11.5 shows that the membrane model discussed in the preceding sections possesses selective properties only in those cases where the adjacent solutions may be classified as dilute. Conversely, if a membrane is found to exercise selectivity, then according to this model the solutions are "dilute," and the discriminatory power of the model will increase if one or both solutions are diluted still further.

In an earlier part of this chapter (p. 543) certain general conclusions were reached relative to the characteristics of ion flow through membranes. These conclusions are applicable to diffusion systems containing selective membranes. On the other hand, from the preceding section it is evident that, with an acid or basic membrane separating dilute solutions, the value of E_M and the ionic population of the favored sign become insensitive to dilution of one or both solutions. These properties introduce certain additional ion flow characteristics which can be found in selective systems only.

In the discussion which follows, certain deductions will be made, each of which can be tested experimentally. Some of the tests would require the use of tracer isotopes, but, if these are not available, deductions bearing on the net flux may still be tested. For the sake of concreteness, it will be assumed that the membrane is acid and thus permits an easy flow of cations, while restricting the flow of anions. The conclusions reached may be readily extended by analogy to basic membranes.

CASE 1. (GENERAL CASE.) EFFECT OF DILUTION OF OUTSIDE SOLUTION. In a system containing an acid membrane and dilute solutions, since the flow of anions is negligible, and the net electrical current must be zero, the following equation holds approximately:

$$\Sigma \overrightarrow{f_{j+}} = - \Sigma \overleftarrow{f_{j+}} \qquad (11.118)$$

The presence of the negative sign on the right side of the equation is due to the convention that inward fluxes are considered negative.

If the small flux of the anions is neglected, the exchange of cations does not affect the tonicity of the two solutions. Any unbalance in tonicity cannot be taken care of quickly by the flow of ions; it must be adjusted by the flow of water or of non-electrolytes.

If the outside solution is diluted K-fold, the cationic population within the membrane and the value of E_M remain approximately stationary.

The rates of flow of the cations remain approximately constant:

$$\overrightarrow{f_{j+}}, \overleftarrow{f_{j+}}, f_{j+} \text{ are approximately constant and unaffected}$$
$$\text{by dilution} \tag{11.119}$$

The rule given in (11.119), however, requires some qualification. If the two opposite fluxes happen to be approximately equal for one of the ions, then the net flux, f_{j+}, is relatively small. In that case, relatively small changes in each of the two isotopic fluxes may cause a relatively large change in the value of f_{j+}; the latter will be sensitive to dilution of the outside solution.

The fluxes of the anions will exhibit an entirely different behavior. Equation (11.104b) shows that in the presence of dilute solutions the total anionic concentration in the membrane surface is proportional to the product NP. This product varies proportionately to the square of the concentration of the solution. If the outside solution is diluted K-fold, the anionic population in the outside membrane surface will decrease by the factor $1/K^2$. Since the relative composition of the solution is unchanged, concentration of each anion in the membrane surface will decrease by the same factor.

In a previous discussion (p. 573) it was concluded that, in this type of system (both solutions "dilute"), further dilution does not change the value of E_M appreciably and that the potential within the membrane remains almost linear. It follows that the inward flux of every anion present at the outside surface will decrease by the factor $1/K^2$. On the other hand, the outward flux of every anion present at the inside surface will remain approximately unchanged. Let the fluxes of the various anions in the control experiment be indicated by an asterisk. Then a K-fold dilution will produce the following results:

$$\overrightarrow{f_{j-}} = \overrightarrow{f_{j-}}^* \tag{11.120a}$$

$$\overleftarrow{f_{j-}} = \overleftarrow{f_{j-}}^* \, \frac{1}{K^2} \tag{11.120b}$$

$$f_j = \overrightarrow{f_{j-}} + \overleftarrow{f_{j-}} = \overrightarrow{f_{j-}}^* + \frac{1}{K^2}\overleftarrow{f_{j-}}^* \tag{11.120c}$$

(for the sake of consistency, the treatment of the inward flux as a negative quantity is continued). If tracer ions are available, the entire set of equations (11.120) may be tested experimentally. If tracer ions are not available, the following procedure will not only make it possible to test equation (11.120c), but will also make it possible to evaluate the two opposite fluxes in the control experiment: After the net flux f_j for several dilution factors K is measured, the measured values of f_j are plotted against the respective values of $1/K^2$. According to equation (11.120c) the points should fall on a straight line, whose slope is $\overleftarrow{f_{j-}}^*$ and whose intercept (at $1/K^2 = 0$) is $\overrightarrow{f_{j-}}^*$.

CASE 2. LEAKAGE OF AN ELECTROLYTE ACROSS AN ACID MEMBRANE. Let us assume that an acid membrane separates an outside solution containing C'-molar NaCl and an inside solution which is a K-fold concentrate of the outside solution. The conclusions reached in the preceding section relative to the effect of dilution on the different fluxes apply as well to this special case. This case, however, is relatively simple, and it is possible to carry out a calculation of the rate at which the salt will leak from the concentrated to the dilute side.

In the event that the system may be classified as dilute, equations (11.103b), (11.104b) give the concentrations of sodium and of chloride at the outer boundary, since there is present only one cationic and one anionic species. According to (11.81) and (11.82), $N_o P_o = b_{Na} b_{Cl} (C_o')^2$. The concentrations at the inner boundary may be obtained in a similar fashion. Since the inside solution is a K-fold concentrate of the outer solution, $N_i P_i = K^2 b_{Na} b_{Cl} (C_o')^2$. In addition, let us keep in mind that in a dilute system where the inner solution is a K-fold concentrate of the outer solution the value of E_M is practically zero, and the potential gradient is very small.

The conditions at the two boundaries may be represented by the following scheme:

	Inside Boundary	Thickness of Membrane $= s$	Outside Boundary
Conc. of Cl⁻ (small)	$\dfrac{K^2 b_{Na} b_{Cl}(C_o')^2}{A}$		$\dfrac{b_{Na} b_{Cl}(C_o')^2}{A}$
Conc. of Na⁺ (large)	$\left[A + \dfrac{K^2 b_{Na} b_{Cl}(C_o')^2}{A} \right]$		$\left[A + \dfrac{b_{Na} b_{Cl}(C_o')^2}{A} \right]$

(very small, approx. constant, potential gradient)

The leakage of the chloride ion is due partly to plain diffusion, since there is a difference of concentrations on the two sides, and partly to an electrical drift, since there is present a very small potential gradient. The diffusion flux is a small quantity, since the difference between the two concentrations is small. The electrical drift is a small quantity of a higher order, since it is proportional to the product of a very small potential gradient and a small concentration. It follows that the electrical drift of the chloride ion may be neglected, as compared with the diffusion flux.

Employing the usual notation, D_{Cl} representing the diffusion constant of the ion, the net flux of the ion outward is given by (11.121)

$$f_{Cl} = (K^2 - 1)(C_o')^2 \frac{D_{Cl} b_{Na} b_{Cl}}{sA}$$

$$= \text{constant } (K^2 - 1)(C_o')^2 \qquad (11.121)$$

The flux of the sodium ion must be the same as that of the chloride ion, since the net electrical flux must be zero. In calculating the flux of the sodium ion it is necessary to allow for the electrical drift, since the latter is of the same order of magnitude as the diffusion flux. A calculation, in which small magnitudes of higher order are neglected, gives the same result as equation (11.121). Thus, the leakage of sodium chloride across the acid membrane is given by equation (11.121). This equation may be tested experimentally. As an illustration, let us consider the following two systems:

System 1:   0.002 M NaCl;   acid membrane;   0.001 M NaCl ($K = 2$)

System 2:   0.006 M NaCl;   acid membrane;   0.002 M NaCl ($K = 3$)

With these data, the theory predicts that the ratio of the two fluxes equals

$$\frac{(9 - 1)0.002^2}{(4 - 1)0.001^2} = 10.7$$

if the assumption is correct that the system is "dilute." Thus a quantitative test of the assumption is possible.

Electrical tests for acid and basic membranes

A diffusion system containing m ions on one side and n ions on the other offers, at least in principle, the possibility of $m + n$ ion flow tests under varying conditions. These tests give the most direct evidence of the selectivity of the membrane. Measurements of the transmembrane potential give less direct and less variegated evidence. Nevertheless, it is often convenient to use electrical tests.

In working with biological systems it is usually difficult to vary both the inside and the outside solutions at will. However, changes in the outside solution may be readily accomplished. According to equation (11.116), if in a diffusion system containing an acid membrane and dilute solutions the outside solution is diluted K-fold, the transmembrane potential at room temperature will increase by 58 mv $\times \log_{10} K$, provided all ions flow by simple diffusion. This relation, of course, is subject to experimental test.

If the membrane is basic, and the solutions are dilute, a K-fold dilution of the outside solution will decrease the value of E by 58 mv $\times$ $\log_{10} K$. This can be seen from the following argument. Let B represent the concentration of the fixed cations, $-BH^+$. If the outside concentration is small, the concentration of anions in the membrane is B, and is much greater than it would be in the absence of the fixed cations. This is made possible by a negative value of E_o, which causes anions to leave the solution and to accumulate in the membrane. If the outside solution is diluted K-fold, the value of E_o must become even more negative, by the amount $- RT/F \ln K$. Since E_i and E_M are unchanged in a basic membrane separating dilute solutions, this quantity represents the total change in E.

Experiments with acid and basic membranes

Among the interesting experiments that have been carried out, Meyer and Sievers (1936b) and Meyer and Bernfeld (1945b) employed the following procedure in their experiments: The outside solution was always a solution of a uni-univalent electrolyte. The inside solution was always a two-fold concentrate of the outside solution. The concentrations were varied over as wide a range as feasible, the inside solution always being kept twice as concentrated as the outside solution. In each case the transmembrane potential E was measured.

We may list the following expectations, in accordance with the previous analysis of this problem. When the solutions are concentrated, the selectivity of the membrane is negligible and it acts almost like a neutral membrane. The value of E is fairly independent of the concentrations provided the ratio of concentrations is not changed. It is given by equation (11.122), which is the same as (11.86), with $K = 2$:

$$E = \frac{u_+ - u_-}{u_+ + u_-} \times 58 \text{ mv } \log_{10} 2 \qquad (11.122)$$

E may be positive or negative, depending upon whether the cation is faster or slower than the anion. This equation is valid for both acid and basic membranes in concentrated solutions.

In the dilute range the value of E again becomes stationary and independent of the concentrations under the chosen condition that the ratio of concentrations is kept constant. Substitution of $K = 2$ in (11.117a,b) yields the following values:

$$E = 17.4 \text{ mv} \quad \text{(acid membrane)}$$
$$E = - 17.4 \text{ mv} \quad \text{(basic membrane)}$$

$$(11.123a,b)$$

Finally, a reference to Fig. 11.5 shows that the transition from the constant value with dilute solutions to the constant value with concentrated solutions should take place within the relatively short range of 2 logarithmic units of concentration.

These theoretical expectations are in agreement with the observed experimental results. The stationary value of E in dilute solutions was approximately 17.4 mv when the range of stationary potential was reached. In those cases where the dilution was not pursued far enough to reach a stationary value E, the results are consistent with the predicted trend. In the experiment with KCl and a basic membrane the value of E approaches -17.4 mv at high dilutions. Every curve shows a transition range of approximately 2 logarithmic units, after which a new stationary value is reached [in accordance with (11.112)].

Meyer and Sievers pointed out that their complete equation for E changes into the simple form of (11.122) when A is negligibly small, i.e., in concentrated solutions. It may be worth while to call attention to the fact that their equation, on substitution of $A = \infty$ and after evaluation of the indeterminate expression obtained through this substitution, yields equation (11.123a).

Remaining for consideration is the implicit assumption that at each surface the ions in the solution are in equilibrium with the ions in the membrane; also, the explicit assumption that the value of A is constant and independent of the concentrations (cf. p. 565). The first assumption is reasonable since the membranes used were very thick when expressed in terms of the number of jumps an ion would have to make to traverse the membrane; the surface resistance must have been negligible by comparison.

The second assumption can be shown to be justified when the exchange equilibrium constant, equation (11.99a), is large. It is instructive to examine what the consequences would be if the constant K were small. With a small constant and dilute solutions, the exchange reaction (11.97) proceeds to a small extent only. $(A^* - A)$ is approximately equal to A^*. A is variable and equals the concentration of the cation $C\pm$. In these circumstances, with a small equilibrium constant and small outside concentration, equation (11.99a) leads to equation (11.124):

$$C\pm = K_1(C_+')^{1/2} \qquad (11.124)$$

where K_1 is a proportionality constant. The concentration of the anion at each boundary must be small by comparison. Thus the concentrations of the cation at the inner membrane boundary and at the outer boundary are proportional to the square roots of the respective concentrations in the aqueous solution. Since the concentrations of the anions are relatively small, even in comparison with these small cation concentrations, equation (11.111) for E_M is valid, and the value of E_M is given by equation (11.125).

$$E = \frac{RT}{F} \ln \left(\frac{C_{i+}'}{C_{o+}'} \right)^{1/2} \tag{11.125}$$

The values of E_o and of E_i are given by (11.126a,b):

$$E_o = \frac{RT}{F} \ln \frac{K_1(C_{o+}')^{1/2}}{b_+ C_{o+}'} \tag{11.126a}$$

$$E_i = \frac{RT}{F} \ln \frac{b_+ C_{i+}'}{K_1(C_{i+}')^{1/2}} \tag{11.126b}$$

Adding the three equations, we get an equation for E (11.127):

$$E = \frac{RT}{F} \ln \frac{C_{i+}'}{C_{o+}'} \tag{11.127}$$

Comparing with (11.117a), we find that the stationary value of E, in very dilute solutions, is independent of whether the fixed groups in the membrane are strong or weak acids. Obviously, the limiting value of E at high concentrations, when the membrane acts as a neutral one, must be independent of the strength of the acid groups. It follows that the limiting values at high and low concentrations observed experimentally by Meyer and Sievers are not sufficient in themselves to justify the assumption that the membrane groups are completely ionized and that the value of A is constant. However, the magnitude of the concentration range over which the value of E changes from one stationary value to the other offers strong evidence that the assumption is correct.

The diagram in Fig. 11.5 was calculated on the assumption that ionization of the groups is complete, since the value of A was assumed constant. Under these conditions the transition range is of the order of 2 logarithmic units. Analysis shows that, if the fixed groups acted as a very weak acid, the transition range would be very much longer, roughly for the same reason that the titration curve of a weak acid is much longer than that of a strong acid. Since the transition ranges in the values of E observed by Meyer and Sievers were very close to 2 logarithmic units, the evidence is fairly strong that the assumption of a constant value of A is valid.

THE RECTIFICATION OF ELECTRIC CURRENTS BY MEMBRANES; ELECTRICAL TESTS FOR STABILITY OF MEMBRANE

Definitions and assumptions

Given a diffusion system with fixed concentrations in the two solutions, the imposition of an emf E across the membrane will produce an electrical current I (amperes per sq cm) across the membrane. If the transmembrane potential is increased by a small amount dE, the current is changed by the small amount dI. If the value of E happens to equal the natural transmembrane potential of the system, the electrical current is zero.

The ratio current/emf is a measure of the conductance of the system. However, the ratio will differ, depending upon whether the denominator contains the total transmembrane potential E, or the potential change within the membrane proper, E_M. It will be useful to define several conductances as follows:

Differential conductances:

$$Q_D = - dI/dE_M \qquad Q_D' = - dI/dE \qquad (11.128a,b)$$

Integral conductances:

$$Q = I/E_M \qquad Q' = - I/E \qquad (11.129a,b)$$

Limiting values, when E is, respectively, very large and positive or very large and negative:

$$Q_+ = \lim Q = \lim Q' \quad (\text{as } E \to \infty) \qquad (11.130a)$$

$$Q_- = \lim Q = \lim Q' \quad (\text{as } E \to - \infty) \qquad (11.130b)$$

In line with our previous analyses, we assume that the membrane is stable, i.e., that the values of the various distribution coefficients and mobilities are independent of E. The general problem is rather complex; for this reason the simplifying condition will be considered wherein the resistances at the two surfaces are small, as compared with the total resistance.

Under this condition, the values of E_i and of E_o are determined by the compositions of the solutions; they are constant and are independent of E. Since $E = E_M + E_i + E_o$, it follows that

$$Q_D = Q_D' \qquad (\text{``thick'' membrane}) \qquad (11.131)$$

The differential conductance, and a test for unstable membranes

The electrical current is proportional to the sum of the individual fluxes, with each flux assigned the proper sign (11.132):

$$I = F\Sigma \pm f_{j\pm} \qquad (11.132)$$

The differential conductance may be obtained by differentiation of (11.132)

$$Q_D = - dI/dE = - F\Sigma \pm df_{j\pm}/dE \qquad (11.133)$$

When the value of E is changed by the infinitesimal value dE, a new steady state is established after a short period of readjustment. In the new steady state each individual flux f_j has changed by a small amount df_j. Each flux f_j is a smooth function of E; its derivative is finite at every point. It follows that Q_D has a definite value for every value of E; this value is a function of E and is independent of whether E is increased by a small amount or decreased by the same amount. The current is not rectified when the changes in E are small.

In particular, if the imposed emf is changed from the natural trans-membrane potential E by the small, but finite, amount $\pm\, \Delta E$, the current changes from zero to a value given approximately by (11.134)

$$I = -\, Q_D(\pm\, \Delta E) \quad \text{(approx.)} \tag{11.134}$$

Equation (11.134) suggests an experimental test for the detection of instability of the membrane, which may be illustrated by the observations of Cole (Cole, 1941; Curtis and Cole, 1950) on the conductance of the membrane of the squid giant axon. It was found that, when ΔE is $-\,5$ mv, the conductance of the membrane is more than twice as high as when ΔE is $+\,5$ mv. According to equation (11.134) the conductance should be approximately independent of the sign of ΔE if the latter is small. The question therefore arises as to whether 5 mv is a "small" or a "large" value for ΔE.

If we combine the constants appearing in equation (11.74) into a single constant k_j and solve for f_j, we obtain equation (11.135).

$$f_{j\pm} = k_{j\pm} \frac{C_{ij\pm} - C_{oj\pm} Z_M^{\pm 1}}{S_{\pm 1}} \tag{11.135}$$

We substitute (11.135) in (11.132) and regroup the terms into two classes, those which contribute toward the outward current and those which contribute to the inward current. In the absence of an imposed emf, the two sums must be equal, since the net current is zero.

$$I = \Sigma\overrightarrow{I} - \Sigma\overleftarrow{I} = 0 \quad \text{(when } \Delta E = 0) \tag{11.136a}$$

$$I = \left(\frac{F\Sigma k_{ij+}C_{ij+}}{S_{+1}} + \frac{FZ_M^{-1}\Sigma k_{oj-}C_{oj-}}{S_{-1}} \right)$$
$$- \left(\frac{F\Sigma k_{ij-}C_{ij-}}{S_{-1}} + \frac{FZ_M\Sigma k_{oj+}C_{oj+}}{S_{+1}} \right) \tag{11.136b}$$

If the membrane is stable, a change in E_M causes a change in I through the changes in the following factors: Z_M, Z_M^{-1}, S_{+1}, S_{-1}. A change of

5 mv changes the value of Z_M by the factor $10^{5/58} = 1.22$. The value of Z_M^{-1} changes by the reciprocal of this factor, or 0.82. An examination of the properties of S_{+1} and of S_{-1} shows that, for small values of ΔE, the relative changes in these quantities are approximately equal the square root of the relative changes in Z_M and Z_M^{-1}, respectively, or 1.11 and 0.91, respectively. Examination of equation (11.136b) shows that, for $\Delta E = 5$ mv, equation (11.137a) holds approximately.

$$I = 0.91\Sigma\overrightarrow{I} - 1.11\Sigma\overleftarrow{I} = -0.20\Sigma\overrightarrow{I} \quad (\Delta E = 5 \text{ mv}) \quad (11.137a)$$

Similarly, when $E = -5$ mv, equation (11.137b) holds approximately.

$$I = 0.20\Sigma\overrightarrow{I} \tag{11.137b}$$

Thus the approximate rule that the value of $S_{\pm}$ varies as the square root of $Z_M^{\pm 1}$ leads to the conclusion that the conductances should be approximately the same for positive and negative increments in E_M. The discrepancy between the two conductances arises from the fact that the rule is not exact. Analysis shows that the errors in S_+ and in S_- tend to compensate in equations (11.137a,b), and the two conductances should not differ by more than 25 per cent when $E = \pm 5$ mv. For values of ΔE greater than 58 mv, the conductances for different signs of ΔE may differ by a large factor.

Since, in the experiments under consideration, the two conductances differed by a factor greater than 2, the difference is most likely due to one of the following effects or to a combination of the two effects. (1) The membrane of the squid giant axon is unstable; it becomes "tighter" when the transmembrane potential is increased, and it becomes more "leaky" to ions when the potential is decreased. (2) The metabolic reactions which are responsible, in part, for the transmembrane potential are affected in such a way as to oppose and partly compensate changes in the transmembrane potential.

The complexity of results obtained with somewhat higher potentials (Cole, 1941; Curtis and Cole, 1950) leave no doubt that the membrane of the giant axon is far from simple.

Stable membrane conductances for large values of E

Equation (11.78) gives the value of I in a neutral membrane. The right side of this equation contains six binomials, in each of which one term becomes negligibly small compared with its partner, as E_M acquires very large positive values. When E_M acquires large negative values, a similar situation arises, the other term in each pair becoming negligibly small.

Thus $\ln Z_M = FE_M/RT$; when E_M acquires very large positive or negative values, this term becomes large compared with $\ln R_i^o$, and the latter may be neglected. Carrying out these simplifications for very large numerical values of E_M, we obtain equations (11.138a,b).

$$I = -RT \frac{R_i^o - 1}{s \ln R_i^o} \frac{FE_M}{RT} \left[\frac{\Sigma C_{oj+} u_{j+}}{R_i^o} + \Sigma C_{ij-} u_{j-} \right] \qquad (E_M \to +\infty)$$

(11.138a)

$$I = -RT \frac{R_i^o - 1}{s \ln R_i^o} \frac{FE_M}{RT} \left[\Sigma C_{ij+} u_{j+} + \frac{\Sigma C_{oj-} u_{j-}}{R_i^o} \right] \qquad (E_M \to -\infty)$$

(11.138b)

Recalling that R_i^o is the ratio of the total ionic population at the outside boundary to the total ionic population at the inside boundary of the membrane (equation (11.65), it follows that in a neutral membrane this ratio also equals the ratio of the two cationic populations or the ratio of the two anionic populations. Solving for Q_+, the integral conductance at very high positive values of the potential (11.130), and for Q_-, the integral conductance at very high negative values, and comparing these two quotients, we obtain (11.139).

$$\frac{Q_+}{Q_-} = \frac{\dfrac{\Sigma C_{oj+} u_{j+}}{\Sigma C_{oj+}} + \dfrac{\Sigma C_{ij-} u_{j-}}{\Sigma C_{ij-}}}{\dfrac{\Sigma C_{ij+} u_{j+}}{\Sigma C_{ij+}} + \dfrac{\Sigma C_{oj-} u_{j-}}{\Sigma C_{oj-}}}$$

(11.139)

The two fractions in the numerator on the right side of the equation represent the mean mobilities of the outside cations and the inside anions, respectively. These are the ions which carry the inward electrical current when E_M is large and positive. The two fractions in the denominator represent the mean mobilities of the inside cations and the outside anions, respectively. These are the ions which carry the outward electrical current when the potential is large and negative.

The existence of a natural transmembrane potential is due to the fact that one team of ions (e.g., inside cations and outside anions) tends to move electricity faster than the opposing team. One is naturally tempted to assume that this behavior will be reflected in the conductances at very high positive and negative values of E_M. Thus it seems reasonable to assume that, if the natural transmembrane potential is positive, $Q_- > Q_+$, since with a high negative transmembrane potential the current is carried by the ionic team which wins in a free competition. It turns out that this is not always the case, as is apparent from the following three examples.

Let us consider the behavior of three diffusion systems. In each case the inside and outside ionic concentrations are given. The mobilities of the ions are given in parentheses; all quantities are given in arbitrary units.

System 1		System 2		System 3	
Inside	Outside	Inside	Outside	Inside	Outside
100 M_1^+	10 M_1^+	100 M_1^+	10 M_2^+	100 M_1^+	100 M_2^+
(3)	(3)	(3)	(5)	(3)	(5)
100 X_1^-	10 X_1^-	100 X_1^-	10 X_2^-	100 X_1^-	100 X_2^-
(2)	(2)	(2)	(1)	(2)	(1)
$E_M > 0$		$E_M > 0$		$E_M < 0$	
$Q_+/Q_- = 1$		$Q_+/Q_- = 7/4$		$Q_+/Q_- = 7/4$	

While the equation for the actual value of E_M may be complex, it is relatively easy to decide whether E_M is positive or negative. If the value of E_M is temporarily kept at 0 by the imposition of the proper emf, the ions move each according to their diffusion constants, which are proportional to the electrical mobilities. If the imposed emf is removed, the movement will continue in the first instant, but will start to build up a charge across the membrane, the sign of which will depend upon the relative values of the total conductance of the team which tends to make the outside positive and of the total conductance of the opposing team. Thus in system 3 the two conductances are in the ratio 400/700, and E_M will be negative.

Turning to system 1 and applying equation (11.139), we find that $Q_+/Q_- = 1$, since the sum of the average mobilities of the inside cations and of the outside anions equals the sum of the average mobilities of the outside cations and of the inside anions. This appears puzzling at first sight. When E_M is very large and negative, the current is carried chiefly by a high concentration of fast cations and a low concentration of slow anions. When E_M is large and positive, the current is carried chiefly by a low concentration of fast cations and a high concentration of slow anions. One would expect that the conductances would be different in the two cases. The difficulty is cleared up when we recall that in system 1 the potential gradients at the two boundaries are not the same. Since the potential gradient is inversely proportional to the total local ionic concentration, the gradient is 10 times as large at the outside boundary as it is at the inside boundary. Thus, when E_M is large and negative, the high concentration of inside cations is subject to an electrical force which is 10 times smaller than the force affecting the low concentration of outside anions. When allowance is made for this phenomenon, the difficulty disappears.

It is interesting to note that the ratio of the two limiting quotients is 1 for any diffusion system, containing any number of ions, provided the inside solution is a K-fold concentrate of the outside solution. This may be seen by substitution of the equation: $C_{ij} = KC_{oj}$ in equation (11.139).

Inspection of the three systems shows that there is no simple correlation between the sign of the natural value of E_M and the ratio of the two limiting quotients. The former is determined by the relative values of the total conductances of the two opposing teams. The latter is determined by the sum of the average mobility of the cations and the average mobility of the anions in each team.

Rectification by an acid membrane in a dilute solution system

In a dilute solution system containing an acid membrane, the mobile ionic population consists chiefly of cations, and the contribution of the anions to the total conductivity is negligible. In this system the total cationic concentrations approximately equal the concentration A of the fixed anions at the two boundaries, and the potential gradient is approximately linear. The ratio Q_+/Q_- equals the ratio of the mean mobilities of the outside cations and the inside cations, respectively:

$$\frac{Q_+}{Q_-} = \frac{\Sigma C_{oj+} u_{j+}}{A} \bigg/ \frac{\Sigma C_{ij+} u_{j+}}{A}$$

In the simple case where the inside solution contains a single electrolyte M_1X, and the outside solution contains another electrolyte M_2X, this ratio gives directly the ratio of the mobilities of the two cations:

$$Q_+/Q_- = u_{M_2}/u_{M_1}$$

It follows that the ratio is independent of the concentrations of the binary electrolyte in the two solutions.

THE ORIENTATION AND DRIFT OF POLAR MACROMOLECULES IN MEMBRANES; IRRITABILITY

The discussions thus far have dealt with stable membranes only. In seeking to understand the phenomena of irritability we must consider unstable membranes and inquire into the possible mechanisms involved in their instability.

Significance of molecular orientation

Biological membranes may be expected to contain polar molecules, and these molecules tend to orient in the presence of a potential gradient.

For ordinary polar molecules the effect of the potential gradient is exceedingly small. In the case of polar macromolecules, the high potential gradient prevailing in living membranes (of the order of 10^5 v/cm) and the high dipole value of the molecule combine to bring about a considerable orientation in the preferred direction. This orientation may constitute an important aspect of the structure of the membrane.

The orientation would be expected to have also a considerable influence on the "irritability" of the membrane to changes in the transmembrane potential. We may distinguish three cases. (1) If the orientation is relatively small, a change in E_M may produce a large relative increase in orientation, while still leaving the absolute extent of orientation small. In this case the change in E_M will have no serious effect on the structure of the membrane. (2) If the orientation is very nearly 100 per cent complete, a decrease in E_M may cause a large relative increase in the extent of disorder, while still leaving the molecules nearly 100 per cent oriented. In this case also the change in E_M will have only a small effect on the structure of the membrane. (3) If the extent of orientation is intermediate, a change in E_M will produce a considerable change in the absolute number of oriented molecules, and the effect on the structure of the membrane may be considerable. For this reason it will be of interest to examine the probable extent of orientation of polar molecules in living membranes.

Polar molecules do not tend to drift in an electrical field when the potential gradient is constant. If the potential gradient is variable from point to point, the polar molecules tend to drift toward the points where the potential gradient is high. As already indicated, the potential gradient within a membrane is, generally, not constant. It will be of interest to examine the effect of a variable gradient on the accumulation of polar molecules near one of the surfaces.

Finally, some macromolecules may alternate between two or more tautomeric forms. If one of the forms has a particularly high dipole moment, this form will be favored by a high potential gradient. A change in E_M may change the equilibrium between the several forms and thus affect the structure of the membrane.

There are some experimental indications that in certain cases enzymes are aggregated at one or both membrane surfaces. Since enzymes are protein molecules and are apt to be polar, it is possible that the aggregation at a membrane surface may be due, at least in part, to the large potential change at each surface. There is considerable evidence that the activity of a given enzyme is associated with the attachment of the substrate to some particular spot on the enzyme surface. It is not unlikely that the activity of an enzyme attached to a surface is dependent on its orientation relative to the surface; thus the active spot may be buried in the membrane and inaccessible to the substrate. A change in E_M may affect both the concentration of the enzyme near the surface and its orientation, thus producing a strong effect on the metabolic reactions, some of which may be responsible for the normal functioning of the membrane itself.

A quantitative estimate of the probable extent of orientation of polar molecules in membranes

In the analysis of sedimentation and centrifugation data it is customary to ascribe an ellipsoidal shape to long molecules to simplify the mathematical treatment. In some gas law calculations it is convenient to think of the molecules as consisting of six groups, with two groups moving parallel or antiparallel to one of the coordinate axes. Since the object of the present calculation is to estimate only the order of magnitude of the orientation effect, the following mathematical liberties appear justified. The polar molecule will be represented by a rectangular parallelipiped (see Fig. 11.6). Let the six faces be labeled $-$, $+$, A, B, C, D. We will take the dipole axis as perpendicular to the first two faces of the molecule, with its direction from face $-$ to face $+$. We will assume that the molecule can occupy only the six orientations in which one of the principal axes is parallel to the x axis. These six orientations will be labeled according to which of the six faces looks outward along the x axis. Thus, if E_M is positive, and, therefore, the potential gradient is positive, orientation ($-$) is the favored one. In the absence of a potential gradient each orientation has a certain probability, determined by the local molecular environment. Let these probabilities be P_+, P_-, P_A, etc.

If the dipole moment of the molecule is μ, and there is a potential gradient dV/dx, the energy of full orientation equals the product $\mu\ dV/dx$. The dimensionless ratio X may be defined by equation (11.140).

$$X = \frac{\mu\ dV/dx}{kT} \qquad (11.140)$$

where k is the Boltzmann constant (cf. Young and Reiner, 1937).

In the presence of a potential gradient the probabilities of the six orientations become proportional, respectively, to the following quantities:

$$P_+ e^{-X}; \quad P_- e^{X}; \quad P_A; \quad P_B; \quad P_C; \quad P_D$$

It is not possible to proceed with the analysis without some information concerning the relative values of the various P's. For illustrative purposes we will assume that they are all equal. Let the probabilities of the

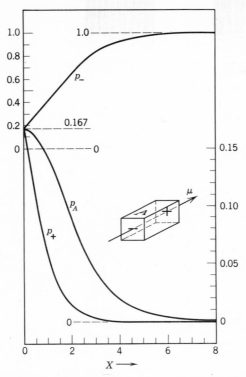

Fig. 11.6. Effect of potential gradient on the orientation of polar molecules. Insert: simplified model of polar molecule used for illustrative calculation. The direction of the dipole moment is from the face marked minus to the face marked plus.

p_- is the probability that the dipole moment will be parallel to the potential gradient. p_+ is the probability that the dipole moment will be in the opposite direction. p_A is the probability that some particular one of the other four faces will be looking outward. X is the ratio $(\mu\,dV/dx)/RT$. When the potential gradient is zero, each of these probabilities equals $1/6$.

If the structure and properties of the membrane depend upon the average orientation of the macromolecules, these properties will be rather insensitive to a 50 per cent decrease in the potential gradient for values of X which are either much smaller than 1 or greater than 6.   The properties of the membrane will be most sensitive to the relative value of the potential gradient when X has a value between 2 and 3.   The potential gradients in living membranes and the dipole moments of proteins are of such magnitudes that the value $X = 2$ is probable.

six orientations in the electric field be p_+, p_-, p_A, etc.   These probabilities are given by equations (11.141a,b,c).

$$p_+ = e^{-X}/(e^{-X} + e^X + 4) \qquad \text{(11.141a)}$$

$$p_- = e^X/(e^{-X} + e^X + 4) \qquad \text{(11.141b)}$$

$$p_A = 1/(e^{-X} + e^X + 4) \qquad \text{(11.141c)}$$

The numerical values of the three probabilities are shown graphically in Fig. 11.6, as a function of X.   The diagram shows that beyond $X = 6$ the orientation is practically 100 per cent ($-$).

The value of X is proportional to the local gradient, which, in turn, is proportional to E_M.   If the latter is of such a magnitude that $X = 8$, then a 50 per cent decrease in E_M will change the value of X to 4, at which value the probability of orientation ($-$) is still 93.2 per cent (Fig. 11.6); the 7 per cent change is not apt to cause a serious change in the structure of the membrane.

If the value of X is 0.2, a 50 per cent decrease in E_M will change the value of X to 0.1, and p_- will change from 20.2 per cent to 18.4 per cent; again, the effect on the properties of the membrane is not apt to be large.

Let us suppose that $X = 2$.   A 50 per cent decrease in the value of E_M will change the value of X to 1, and the value of p_- will change from 64.1 to 38.4 per cent, a total of 25.7 per cent; this large change is apt to produce a strong effect on the properties of the membrane.

Thus the conclusion is reached that the membrane structure will be particularly sensitive to the values of E_M if X has a value somewhere around 2.   Similar considerations show that, if the enzymatic activity of a protein is dependent on its orientation, the activity will be sensitive to the value of E_M if the value of X is in the vicinity of 2.

Now let us estimate the magnitude of the dipole moment to give this value of X. X is defined in equation (11.140). $k = 1.38 \times 10^{-16}$ ergs per degree Centigrade.   The value of T is 291 at 18°C.   1 volt = 1/300 esu. Substituting these values, we get the numerical formula for X (11.142).

$$X = 8.31\mu \times 10^{10}\, dV/dx \qquad (V \text{ in volts}) \qquad \text{(11.142)}$$

The potential gradient in the living membrane is probably of the order of 10^5 volts/cm (cf. p. 556).   Substituting this value of dV/dx, and the value 2 for X, and solving for μ, we find $\mu = 240 \times 10^{-18}$ esu or 240 Debye units.   This is a reasonable magnitude for the dipole moment of a protein, since values ranging from 170 to 1400 Debye units have been reported in the literature (Cohn and Edsall, 1943).

In these calculations it was assumed that every one of the six orientations is equally probable in the absence of a potential gradient.   It is not difficult to see how the argument needs to be modified if a preferred orientation exists even in the absence of a potential gradient. Thus, if 95 per cent of the molecules are in orientation $(-)$, the introduction of a positive potential gradient cannot change the degree of orientation very much. However, a negative potential will shift the steady state closer to a distribution of 50 per cent in state $(-)$ and will change the membrane into the irritable state.

It may be more appropriate to treat the macromolecules as multipoles, rather than dipoles. However, the purpose of the preceding calculation is to indicate that the magnitudes of the "dipole moments" reported in the literature are sufficiently large to bring about a strong dependence between the magnitude of the potential gradient and the orientation of the macromolecules.

The drift of polar macromolecules when the potential gradient is not constant

According to a previous discussion (p. 555), the potential gradient is inversely proportional to the local mobile ionic concentration. Let us assume that the ionic concentration is twice as great at the inner boundary as it is in the outer boundary. In that case the potential gradient is twice as great at the outer boundary as it is at the inner boundary. Let the dipole moment of the molecule and the outer potential gradient be of such magnitudes that the value of X_o is 6; then the value of X_i is 3. If the chances of finding the molecule at each boundary are equal in the absence of the potential gradient, the probability of finding the molecule at the inner boundary is proportional to $e^3 + 4 + e^{-3} = 24.15$. The probability of finding it at the outer boundary is proportional to $e^6 + 4 + e^{-6} = 407.4$. It follows that, after a lapse of sufficient time, the concentration at the outer boundary will be 16.7 times the concentration at the inner boundary. If E_M is decreased by 50 per cent, and is kept at the new value for a long enough time, the calculated probabilities will be in the ratio $24.15/8.70 = 2.77$. In theory, at least, there should be a drift of the molecules inward after the change in E_M. The adjustment to the new steady state resulting from drift must be much slower than the adjustment to a new steady state involving only changes in orientation, since the former involves a drift across the membrane, whereas the latter requires only a local rotation.

The effect of the potential gradient on tautomeric equilibria

Let us consider the case in which a molecule can exist in two tautomeric states, I and II. As a concrete illustration let us assume that the equilibrium constant $(I)/(II) = K = 10$. In the absence of a potential gradient, 90.9 per cent of the molecules are in state I and 9.1 per cent in state II. If the dipole moment in state II is twice as great as in state I, and if the values of X for the normal value of E are 3 and 6, respectively, for states I and II, then, in the presence of the normal potential gradient, the probabilities of the two states are proportional to (10×24.15) and 407.4, respectively (for calculations, see preceding section). In the presence of the normal potential gradient, the distribution will be 37.3 per cent in state I, and 62.7 per cent in state II.

If the value of E_M is reduced by 50 per cent, the probabilities of the two states will be proportional to (10×8.70) and 24.15, respectively. The distribution will change to 78.4 per cent in state I, and 21.6 per cent in state II. This type of shift may be responsible, in part, for the irritability of the membrane.

Other electrical factors contributing to the irritability of the membrane

Macromolecules usually participate in a rapid equilibrium between the neutral molecule and ionized molecules, carrying in some cases relatively large charges. Assuming, for the sake of concreteness, that the chief constituents in a given equilibrium carry a negative charge, the presence of a positive E_M will increase the probability that the macromolecule will be found at the outer boundary. A 50 per cent drop in E_M will decrease this probability and will cause a drift of the macromolecules toward the inner boundary; this readjustment may cause a serious change in the properties of the membrane. This change is apt to be slow, since it requires a drift of large molecules across the membrane.

There is another response to a change in the electrostatic pattern which is apt to be faster. It is well known that certain colloidal systems are sensitive to the ratio of the concentrations of such ions as Ca and K. At one of the boundaries, say the outer one, the following ratios must hold:

$$\frac{C_{Ca}}{C_K} = \frac{C_{Ca}' b_{Ca} Z_o^2}{C_K' b_K Z_o} \qquad \frac{C_{Ca}}{C_K^2} = \frac{C_{Ca}' b_{Ca} Z_o^2}{(C_K')^2 b_K^2 Z_o^2} \qquad (11.143a,b)$$

If a change is made in the composition of the outer solution, the value of Z_o is apt to change to some new value, Z_o'. Even if the solution concentrations of potassium and calcium are left unchanged, the ratio of concentrations at the membrane boundary will change by the factor Z_o'/Z_o. The effect on the structure of the membrane at the boundary will depend upon the nature of the competition between the two ions. Assuming that the two ions compete in the formation of complexes, the equilibrium involved may be one shown in (11.144a) or in (11.144b).

$$R'CaR^{++} + K^+ = R'K^+ + R + Ca^{++} \qquad (11.144a)$$

$$R'CaR^{++} + 2K^+ = R'K^+ + RK^+ + Ca^{++} \qquad (11.144b)$$

In the first case a change in the value of Z_o will affect the equilibrium and may affect seriously the structure of the membrane. In the second case, a change in Z_o will change the ratio C_{Ca}/C_K but will leave the ratio C_{Ca}/C_K^2 unaffected and will thus leave the equilibrium undisturbed.

ION PUMPS

It has been recognized for some time that the distribution of certain ions between the inside and outside of various cells requires some mechanism of active transport, or "ion pump," in addition to the process of simple diffusion. The purpose of the following discussion is to examine the theoretical aspects of two of the possible mechanisms. The first involves the coupling of an ion with a product of the cell's metabolism. The second involves coupling between the ion and a constituent of the membrane in a process activated by an exergonic reaction at the inner boundary of the membrane.

Accumulation, excretion, and ion pumps

Let us consider a diffusion system consisting of a cell and an exterior solution, with concentrations and transmembrane potential as given below.

Inside	Membrane	Outside
400 mM M_1^+	Membrane	40 mM M_1^+
50 mM M_2^+	$E = 58$ mV	600 mM M_2^+
45 mM X^-	($Z = 10$)	450 mM X^-
plus other ions and molecules		plus other ions and molecules

Now, suppose that it has been established experimentally that the membrane is permeable to all three ions and that the system is in a steady state, i.e., that the concentrations do not change with time. Under these conditions the electrochemical activities of M_1^+ are the same on both sides of the membrane (400 and 40 $\times$ 10, respectively). Similarly, the electrochemical activities of X^- are the same on both sides (45 and 450 $\times$ 0.1, respectively). On the other hand, the electrochemical activity of M_2^+ is 120 times as large on the outside as it is on the inside. The net flux of M_1^+ and of X^- must be zero, while there must be a net flux inward of M_2^+. Since the system is at steady state, it follows that there must be present some mechanism which excretes the same ion from the cell into the exterior solution. This mechanism is referred to as an ion pump.

The terms "accumulation" and "excretion" appearing in the literature carry the meaning given explicitly, and more often implicitly, by the author of each paper. In the present discussion the term "excretion" will be applied to M_2^+ only. It is not customary to say that in a Donnan equilibrium the cell accumulates ions of one sign and excludes ions of the opposite sign. By analogy, we shall refrain from saying that the cell described in this discussion excretes X^- or accumulates M_1^+.

It may well be that some ion pumps operate on a principle which is as yet unfamiliar. Since only well-defined mechanisms are susceptible of analysis, however, we will proceed tentatively on the plausible assumption that ion pumps are associated with coupled diffusion. Various kinds of coupling may still be operative in different diffusion systems. The illustrations given in the following sections are offered merely as examples of the analysis of an ion pump once the mechanism has been specified.

Ion pump operated by coupled diffusion

As a first illustration, let us consider a diffusion system with the following specifications: The outside solution is circulated, and every concentration in this solution is kept constant. Among the substances present in the outside solution there is an ion M^+ whose concentration is kept at the constant value C_{oM}'. On the inside there is a metabolic process which produces neutral molecules N at a constant rate; each of the concentrations of all the ions is allowed to seek its own level. Finally M^+ and N can form a complex, NM^+ in a rapid, reversible reaction whose constant is $K = (NM^+)/(N)(M^+)$. If this system is left for a sufficiently long time, a steady state will be reached. At the steady state the inner concentration of M^+ will be smaller than the outer concentration of the same ion by some factor $1/m$, while the outer concentration of N will be smaller than the inner concentration by some factor $1/n$. The concentrations at the steady state may be represented as follows:

	Inner Solution		Outer Solution
M^+	$C_{iM}' = \dfrac{1}{m} C_{oM}'$		C_{oM}'
		Membrane	
N	C_{iN}'	$(E;\ Z)$	$C_{oN}' = \dfrac{1}{n} C_{iN}'$
NM^+	$C_{iMN}' = \dfrac{K}{m} C_{oM}' C_{iN}'$		$C_{oMN}' = \dfrac{K}{n} C_M' C_{iN}'$
Other cations	$C_{ij+}' = Z C_{oj+}'$		C_{oj+}'
Anions	$C_{ij-}' = Z^{-1} C_{oj-}'$		C_{oj-}'

The net flux of the jth cation is zero; it follows that $C_{ij+}' = Z C_{oj+}'$. Similarly, $C_{ij-}' = Z^{-1} C_{oj-}'$. The net flux of M^+ outward in the form of the complex is exactly balanced by the net flux of M^+ inward by simple diffusion. Since there is a continuous diffusion of the ion inward by simple diffusion, the electrochemical activity of the ion outside must be greater than the electrochemical activity of the same ion inside:

$$\frac{1}{m} C_{oM}' < Z C_{oM}' \qquad mZ > 1 \qquad (11.145\text{a,b})$$

On the other hand, the electrochemical activity of the complex NM+ must be greater on the inside:

$$\frac{K}{m} C_{oM}' C_{iN}' > \frac{ZK}{n} C_{oM}' C_{iN}' \qquad n > mZ \qquad (11.146\text{a,b})$$

For every mole of M+ leaking inward there is a mole of NM+ moving outward. The net result is a transfer of N from a state of high activity to a state of low activity. Free energy is lost in this process. From the thermodynamic point of view, no work is accomplished, and the efficiency of the system as a whole is zero.

When a water pump just manages to maintain the water level constant in a leaky mine, the efficiency of the system is zero. Nevertheless, we may examine the efficiency of the pump itself by comparing the power needed to lift the water leaking in with the power expended by the pump. Similarly, we may calculate the efficiency of the ion pump by comparing the free energy needed to move a mole of M+ outward with the free energy lost in the process of lifting, namely, the change of free energy accompanying the transfer of one mole of N outward.

Comparing the electrochemical activities of M+ in the two solutions, we find that the free energy needed to lift a mole of the ion to the higher level of activity is given by equation (11.147).

$$\Delta F_{M} = RT \ln (mZ) \qquad (11.147)$$

Similarly, the free energy lost in the transfer of a mole of N outward is given by equation (11.148). The efficiency of the pump is given by equation (11.149). From equation (11.146b) it is clear that the efficiency of the process is less than 1, indicating that no thermodynamic principles are violated.

$$\Delta F_{N} = - RT \ln n \qquad (11.148)$$

$$\text{Efficiency} = \frac{\ln (mZ)}{\ln n} \qquad (11.149)$$

We may now examine the characteristics of the system which determine the efficiency of the ion pump.

Efficiency of the ion pump

At steady state the net flux of M+ inward is equal to the net flux of NM+ outward. When the assumption that the resistances at the two surfaces are relatively small is justified, we may use equation (11.45) for the net flux of each ion. The diffusion coefficients of the two ions are proportional to their mobilities. The electrical terms appearing in the denominator of (11.45) are the same for both ions, since they belong to the same valence type; similarly, the value of the definite integral S is identical for both ions. The equality of the two net fluxes leads to the condition that equation (11.150) must be satisfied at steady state.

$$b_{\mathrm{M}}u_{\mathrm{M}} \left[ZC_{o\mathrm{M}}' - \frac{1}{m} C_{o\mathrm{M}}' \right] = b_{\mathrm{NM}}u_{\mathrm{NM}} \left[\frac{K}{m} C_{o\mathrm{M}}'C_{i\mathrm{N}}' - Z\frac{K}{n} C_{o\mathrm{M}}'C_{i\mathrm{N}}' \right]$$

(11.150)

Since this is an equation in Z, it may appear at first glance that the transmembrane potential is completely determined by the pump system and that the other ions distribute themselves in accordance with the potential created by the pump, in a purely passive manner, without exerting any influence on the value of Z. A closer inspection of the equation shows that it contains four variables whose values at the steady state become stationary; these are Z, m, n, and $C_{i\mathrm{N}}'$. It follows that four conditions must be met at steady state, for each of which an equation may be written. The first condition is given by equation (11.150). Two other conditions require that the inner and the outer solutions, respectively, must be electrically neutral. Finally, the fourth condition specifies that the rate of formation of N must equal the rate at which it leaks through the membrane. The concentrations of other ions enter the equations and affect the value of Z.

The pump tends to make the outside solution electrically positive. Nevertheless, E may be negative or positive, depending upon the rate of formation of N and on the complexion of concentrations in the two solutions. For any complexion, if the rate of formation of N is high enough, E is bound to be positive.

In order to calculate the efficiency of the pump we need to compare the value of mZ with that of n (equation 11.149). Solving (11.150) for mZ, we get (11.151).

$$mZ = n\, \frac{b_{\mathrm{M}}u_{\mathrm{M}} + Kb_{\mathrm{NM}}u_{\mathrm{NM}}C_{i\mathrm{N}}'}{nb_{\mathrm{M}}u_{\mathrm{M}} + Kb_{\mathrm{NM}}u_{\mathrm{NM}}C_{i\mathrm{N}}'}$$

(11.151)

Dividing the numerator and denominator on the right side by $b_{\mathrm{M}}u_{\mathrm{M}}$, we get (11.152), where B is defined by (11.153).

$$mZ = n\, \frac{1 + B}{n + B}$$

(11.152)

$$B = \frac{Kb_{\mathrm{NM}}u_{\mathrm{NM}}C_{i\mathrm{N}}'}{b_{\mathrm{M}}u_{\mathrm{M}}}$$

(11.153)

Substitution of mZ in (11.149) would yield the value of the efficiency of the pump. However, the equation would be unwieldy. For this reason a graphical method is preferred. We may substitute various values of n and B in (11.152) and calculate mZ for each pair of values. The values of n and mZ may then be used in (11.149) to calculate the efficiency of the pump for the chosen values.

In selecting values of B we must be guided by the physical meaning of this ratio. If we multiply both the numerator and the denominator of (11.153) by the inside concentration of M^+, we obtain (11.154).

$$B = \frac{b_{NM}u_{NM}(KC_{iM}'C_{iN}')}{b_M u_M C_{iM}'} \qquad (11.154)$$

It can be seen by inspection that B represents the ratio of the outward flux of the complex to the outward flux of M^+ moving by simple diffusion. Thus B is a measure of the intensity of the pump. From (11.152) it may be seen that, if $n \gg B$, the value of mZ approaches $B + 1$. In other words, $B + 1$ is the maximum value of mZ which may be built up by the pump. In muscle and nerve the value of m, which is the ratio of the outside to inside concentrations, is of the order of 10 for sodium. Z is of the order of 10. Thus mZ is of the order of 100. For use in pumps where the exclusion is less drastic, we will extend the value down to 30 as the lower limit of B to be used in the calculations.

The upper limit of B is dictated by the known ratios of permeabilities of organic molecules to the permeabilities of ions. Inspection of (11.154) shows that, if B is large, its large value must be due chiefly to the ratio of permeabilities of the complex and of the ion. The permeability of organic molecules is larger than those of ions by a factor of the order 10^3 to 10^5. If N is an organic carrier for the ion, it may be expected that replacement of the water of hydration by an organic molecule increases the permeability of the ion by not more than a factor of 10^4. For this reason the value $B = 3000$ will be taken as the upper limit.

The calculated values of mZ as a function of n and B and of the efficiency of the pump as a function of mZ and B are shown in Fig. 11.7. Thus, when $mZ = 100$ and $B = 300$ (point D), the value of n is 151, and the efficiency of the pump is 92 per cent (point D'). When $B = 3000$, the efficiency is nearly 100 per cent (point A'), and the value of n is just a trifle over 100. The two diagrams show that, if $B = 100$, the value $mZ = 100$ can just barely be reached at a very high value of n and at a very low efficiency.

The insert shows that the pump works at a high efficiency, so long as mZ is well below $0.5B$. However, some of the substance N must be

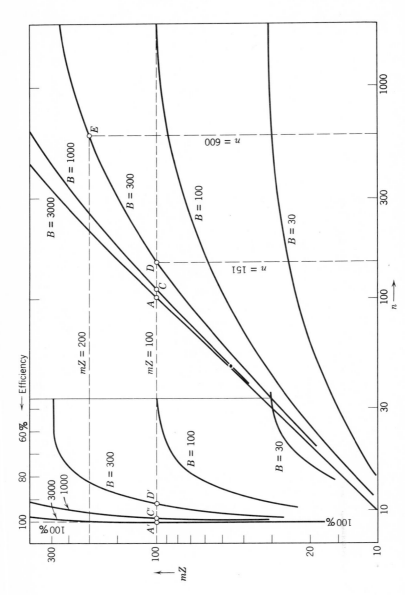

Fig. 11.7. Ion pump efficiency. Lower diagram: values of mZ as a function of n, for five different values of B (see text). B is the ratio of the conductance of the complex NM^+ to the conductance of the simple ion M^+. For a given value of B the highest possible value of mZ is $B + 1$. The efficiency is not far from 100 per cent for values of mZ which are much smaller than B.

Upper diagram: The efficiency of the pump, $\ln (mZ)/\ln n$, as a function of mZ, for the same five values of B.

leaking through the membrane by simple diffusion. If this leakage is charged against the pump, the efficiency may be much smaller.

From the foregoing, it appears that the intensity of the pump is limited by the value of B. There is another limitation on the intensity of the pump which we may illustrate by means of a quantitative example. Thus let us assume that a value $mZ = 200$ is needed for the proper functioning of the cell and that $B = 300$. According to Fig. 11.7, this can be accomplished if $n = 600$ (point E). It will be recalled that n is the ratio of the inside concentration of the metabolic product N to the outside concentration. Considering that the precursor of N must pass through the outside solution before entering the cell, a value $n = 600$ is a rather stringent requirement. It means that the precursor must not produce N on the outside, or that the rate of production must be much lower than on the inside. It also means that the molecules of N which leak out through the membrane by simple and coupled diffusion must be carried away efficiently by diffusion and convection, and, finally, that the concentration of N in the outside solution must be even smaller. The ion pump model described in the next section is not subject to these limitations.

Ion pump coupled with an exergonic chemical reaction

Let us assume that there is present in the membrane a neutral molecule N capable of combining with the ion M^+ in the presence of an enzyme, which will be called enzyme I. At the outer boundary, enzyme I is present and the following rapid equilibrium is established (Fig. 11.8):

$$N + M^+ \overset{\text{Enzyme I}}{\rightleftharpoons} NM^+ \qquad \Delta F = 0 \qquad (11.155)$$

At the inner boundary enzyme I is absent. There is present an energy-rich substance G capable of changing into the energy-poor substance J, by way of the exergonic reaction (11.156).

$$G = J \qquad \Delta F = -Q \qquad (11.156)$$

The concentrations of substances G and J are kept constant by relatively rapid metabolic reactions within the cell. Reaction (11.156) cannot take place by itself because of the absence of the appropriate enzyme. The value of ΔF, given in (11.156), is to be taken not as the standard free energy of the reaction but as the free energy of the reaction corresponding to the concentrations of G and J present at the inner membrane boundary.

Finally, we assume that at the inner boundary an enzyme is present (enzyme II) which is capable of coupling reactions (11.155) and (11.156) in a rapid, reversible equilibrium (11.157).

$$G + N + M^+ \overset{\text{Enzyme II}}{\rightleftharpoons} J + NM^+ \qquad \Delta F = 0 \qquad (11.157)$$

The free energies are zero, in both (11.155) and (11.157), since the substances are in equilibrium in both cases. While the net free energy in equilibrium (11.157) is zero, this overall reaction effects a transfer of energy. The energy Q of reaction (11.156) is used to increase the concentration of NM^+ and to decrease the concentrations of N and of M^+.

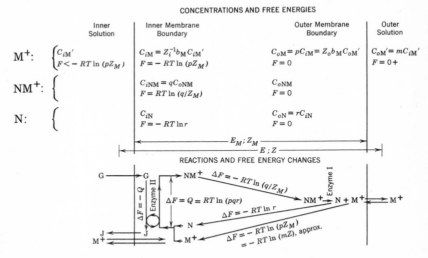

Fig. 11.8. Upper part: concentrations and free energies of M^+, NM^+, and M. The free energies of the three particles are zero at the outer membrane boundary, by definition. The electrochemical free energy of these substances at any other point is calculated from the ratio of its electrochemical activity and the electrochemical activity of the same particle at the outer boundary.

Lower diagram: At the outer boundary the complex ion is kept by enzyme I in equilibrium with its two constituents. M^+ and N leak inward. At the inner boundary, in the presence of enzyme II, an exergonic reaction is coupled with the endergonic formation of the complex ion. The free energy of the exergonic reaction is used to lift NM^+ to a state of high activity. The complex ion diffuses outward, and the cycle is completed. The net result of the cycle is the waste of the free energy, Q. The efficiency of the system as a whole is zero, but the efficiency of the pump is equal to the ratio of the energy wasted through the leakage of M^+ to the free energy lost by the exergonic reaction.

The concentrations of the various substances at steady state, the chemical reactions, and diffusion processes are shown schematically in Fig. 11.8. The vertical scale in the lower diagram gives, schematically, the electrochemical free energy of the respective substance. At the inside boundary, enzyme II facilitates the transfer of energy from reaction (11.156) to reaction (11.155). At the outside boundary enzyme I facilitates the decomposition of the complex. The various concentrations are given in the upper part of Fig. 11.8; m, p, q, and r are numbers bigger than one. The electrochemical free energy of each substance is shown in brackets, just below the concentration. Since the change in free energy is independent of the level at which the standard free energy is defined, the free energies of M^+ and of N are defined as zero at the outer membrane boundary. Since NM^+ is in equilibrium with these substances, its free energy is also zero. The electrochemical free energy of M^+ at the inner boundary is $-RT\ln(pZ_M)$, since the concentration at this point is smaller than at the outer boundary by the factor $1/p$, and the electrical potential is smaller by E_M. The free energies of the other substances are obtained in a similar fashion. The free energy of M^+ in the outer solution is larger than at the outer boundary; however, if the resistance at the surface is relatively small, the difference in free energies is also small. Similarly, the free energy of M^+ in the inner solution is a little smaller than the free energy at the inner boundary.

The lower diagram shows the free energy losses in each of the three spontaneous diffusion processes. Since there is no net change in the concentrations of M^+, NM^+, and N, the net result of the movement of M^+ through the cycle is the conversion of one mole of G into J. The free energy Q of this reaction pays for the losses. The free energy of formation of the complex at the inner boundary may be obtained from the difference between the free energy of the product and the free energy of the reactants. Since reaction (11.157) is at an equilibrium, the free energy of formation of the complex at the concentration present at the inner boundary must equal Q. This gives an equation for Q in terms of p, q, r (11.158).

$$Q = RT\ln(pqr) \tag{11.158}$$

The energy of reaction (11.156) is completely wasted, and the efficiency of the system as a whole is zero, as in the first illustration. The efficiency of the pump, considered as a device needed to provide the energy required to pump M^+ outward, is given by equation (11.159).

$$\text{Efficiency} = \frac{RT\ln(pZ_M)}{Q} = \frac{\ln(pZ_M)}{\ln(pqr)} \tag{11.159}$$

The evaluation of the right side of (11.159) is, in general, laborious. The calculation is much simpler in those cases where the resistance at the two surfaces may be neglected. In these cases the free energy loss in the diffusion of M^+ from the outer solution to the inner solution is practically the same as free energy lost in the diffusion from the outer boundary to the inner boundary. In these circumstances, $RT\ln(pZ_M)$ may be replaced by $RT\ln(mZ)$.

Another simplification is achieved when we consider the probable value of r, which is the ratio C_{oN}/C_{iN}. The following considerations indicate that this ratio is apt to be rather close to 1.

It is to be expected that the carrier N will be found in the membrane at much higher concentrations than the complex NM^+. Furthermore, its mobility is apt to be larger, since it is a smaller molecule. For these reasons the relative value of the difference between C_{oN} and C_{iN} is apt to be small, and the ratio r is apt to be close to 1. Hence the product pqr may be replaced with pq, to a fair degree of approximation. Carrying out the two suggested simplifications, we obtain (11.160)

$$\text{Efficiency} = \frac{\ln (mZ)}{\ln (pq)}, \quad \text{approx.} \tag{11.160}$$

It remains to eliminate the product pq from (11.160). The condition that, at steady state, the inward flux of M^+ equals the outward flux of NM^+ yields equation (11.161). Solving for Z_M, we obtain (11.162). Multiplying both sides of (11.162) by C_{oM}/C_{iM}, we obtain (11.163).

$$Z_M u_M C_{oM} - u_M C_{iM} = u_{NM} C_{iNM} - Z_M u_{NM} C_{oNM} \tag{11.161}$$

$$Z_M = \frac{u_M C_{iM} + u_{NM} C_{iNM}}{u_M C_{oM} + u_{NM} C_{oNM}} \tag{11.162}$$

$$Z_M \frac{C_{oM}}{C_{iM}} = \frac{1 + \dfrac{u_{NM} C_{iNM}}{u_M C_{iM}}}{1 + \dfrac{u_{NM} C_{oNM}}{u_M C_{oM}}} \tag{11.163}$$

Carrying out the substitutions (11.164 to 11.166),

$$\frac{u_{NM} C_{iNM}}{u_M C_{iM}} = B \quad \text{(definition of } B\text{)} \tag{11.164}$$

$$Z_M \frac{C_{oM}}{C_{iM}} = Z_M \frac{b_M C_{oM}' Z_o}{b_M C_{iM}' Z_i^{-1}} = mZ \tag{11.165}$$

$$\frac{C_{oNM}}{C_{oM}} = \frac{1}{pq} \frac{C_{iNM}}{C_{iM}} = \frac{1}{n} \frac{C_{iNM}}{C_{iM}} \quad (n = pq; \text{ definition of } n) \tag{11.166}$$

we obtain equation (11.167).

$$mZ = n \frac{1 + B}{n + B} \tag{11.167}$$

The efficiency of the pump, given in (11.160), may be rewritten as in (11.168).

$$\text{Efficiency} = \frac{\ln (mZ)}{\ln n} \tag{11.168}$$

Equations (11.168) and (11.167) are formally the same as (11.149) and (11.152), respectively. The physical meaning of B and of n are different in the two models. In the second illustration the value of B gives the ratio of the total conductance of the complex to the total conductance of the uncoupled ion at the membrane boundary (11.164).

The value of B is determined by the magnitude of Q, the free energy loss in the exergonic reaction. Since Q may be as high as 10,000 cal, high values of B are possible. The value of the efficiency as a function of mZ may be obtained from the insert of Fig. 11.7, for $B = 30$, 100, 1000, or 3000. As in the first illustration, the efficiency is high if B is much greater than mZ.

Efficiencies approaching 100 per cent may appear surprising at first glance. The calculations were made on the assumption that the resistances at the two surfaces are negligible. If allowance is made for the losses at the two surfaces, the efficiency is less than 100 per cent. In principle, however, it is possible to have diffusion systems in which this correction is rather small. The real reason for the high efficiency may be seen by analogy with a chemical plant in which the raw materials are pumped to the top floor, and the reaction products and waste products are allowed to flow down. If the materials flowing down operate a turbine connected to the lifting pump, and if the friction is small, the efficiency of the pump may be close to 100 per cent.

In calculating the efficiency, the existence of the substance G at the inner boundary was taken for granted. If the pump is charged with the free energy needed to produce G, the calculated efficiency becomes much smaller. The energy needed to excrete a mole of M^+ is $RT \ln (mZ)$. At 18°C RT equals 583 cal per mole. If $mZ = 150$, the minimum free energy needed to excrete a mole of M^+ is 2,920 cal. If the free energy of formation of a mole of G in the inner solution is 10,000 cal, the efficiency of the pump is only 29.2 per cent.

Note added in proof: The following recent publications deal with some of the topics discussed in this chapter: Butler (1952), Danielli (1952), Linderholm (1952), Teorell (1953), Ussing (1952), and Ussing (1953).

Physical Chemistry of Cell Irritability and of the Nerve Impulse[1]

The most serious deficiency, no doubt, is the lack of any pertinent
evidence as to the intimate mechanism of the "nerve membrane"
and its functional changes.

Katz, *Electric Excitation of Nerve*

This chapter is devoted to an examination of certain aspects of the problem of irritability of living cells. The most conspicuous and the most thoroughly studied manifestation of irritability is to be found in the local changes taking place when a nerve is subjected to an electrical stimulus. The electrical properties of nerve fibers apparently do not differ significantly from those of other living cells (Curtis and Cole, 1950). Conclusions reached relative to the nature of irritability of nerve fibers may thus be tentatively applied to other irritable cells, and particularly to muscle fibers.

The major part of this chapter deals with a physiochemical theory of irritability and accommodation (cf. abstract Polissar, 1952e). The rest of the chapter is concerned with other properties of the nerve membrane, in the light of physiochemical properties of systems consisting of two electrolytic solutions separated by a membrane, as discussed in the preceding chapter. A systematic account of the problem of nerve is not included. General as well as various special aspects of the problem are discussed in a number of excellent monographs and reviews of the subject (Brazier, 1951; Curtis and Cole, 1950; Erlanger and Gasser, 1937; Höber, 1945; Hodgkin, 1951; Lloyd, 1950; Katz, 1939a; Lorente de Nó, 1947; Schaefer, 1944; Ussing, 1949b; von Muralt, 1946; *Annual Reviews of Physiology*, articles on Nerve, Muscle, Bioelectric Potentials, and on Permeability).

The experimental facts essential for consideration of the theory as developed herein will be presented first. Other experimental facts will be presented as the need arises.

[1] The author of this chapter (M. J. P.) wishes to express his gratitude to the National Foundation for Infantile Paralysis for the aid which made possible the work on the problems discussed in this chapter.

EXPERIMENTAL OBSERVATIONS ON THE IRRITABILITY AND ACCOMMODATION OF NERVE

Propagated impulse; adequate and inadequate stimuli

Figure 12.1A represents an excised nerve-muscle preparation. The short, numbered vertical line segments represent appropriate electrodes, which may be used either to stimulate the nerve or to measure the difference of potential between two points on the surface of the nerve. *I* represents a point on the nerve injured either mechanically or chemically.

If electrodes 2 and 3 are connected to a source of electrical stimulus, and if a strong enough stimulus is used, the muscle contracts. *The stimulus* produces a *propagated impulse.* If a very weak stimulus is used, the muscle does not contract. If, in a series of experiments, progressively stronger stimuli are used, there is a definite strength of the stimulus above which the muscle responds and below which the muscle does not respond. Thus stimuli may be classified as *subthreshold*, *threshold*, and *superthreshold.* (This description is oversimplified, for didactic purposes, and represents the behavior of an idealized nerve consisting of nerve fibers all having the same threshold.)

Injury potential

If electrode 1 is placed at the point of injury, and a movable electrode, 2, is placed on the uninjured part of the nerve, a potential difference is observed. The uninjured nerve is positive relative to the injured point. The magnitude of the *injury potential* depends upon the distance x from the point of injury. The relation between the injury potential and x is shown schematically in Fig. 12.1B. The "half value" of x is of the order of 1 mm. It follows that the potential difference between electrodes 3 and 4, located two or three centimeters away from the point of injury, is practically zero; the injury potential measured between electrode 1 and a far electrode, such as 3, is independent of x. If the temperature of the nerve is changed at point *I*, or if the chemical environment is changed at that point, the effect on the injury potential at a far point 3 is negligibly small. On the other hand, if the temperature or the chemical environment is changed at the far electrode, the change in the observed injury potential is apt to be appreciable. These observations suggest that the source of the electromotive force responsible for the injury potential is located at the uninjured point of the nerve.

Monophasic and diphasic action potentials

We may arrange electrodes 5 and 6 (Fig. 12.1A) for conveying a stimulus to the nerve, with three separate testing circuits to keep track of the

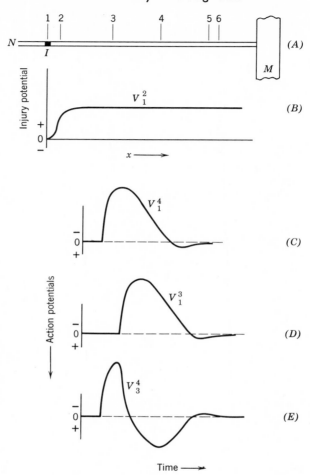

Fig. 12.1. (A) Schematic representation of a nerve-muscle preparation. The nerve is injured at point I. The numbered line segments represent stimulating or exploratory electrodes.

(B) Schematic diagram for injury potential. V_1^2 represents the potential of point 2 relative to point 1. Abscissa: distance from injured spot along nerve. The injury potential becomes constant within a distance of a few millimeters.

(C), (D), (E) Schematic representation of monophasic and diphasic action potentials, of the relation between the two kinds of potentials and the distance of the explored spot from the source of the propagated impulse. The propagated impulse, originating at 5 or 6, to the right of point 4, arrives at point 4 first. The diphasic potential is the difference between the two monophasic potentials. In accordance with usual practice, negative values of the potential are drawn upward.

potential differences between the pairs of points 1–3, 1–4, and 3–4. After a subthreshold stimulus the observed potential changes are minute. If the stimulus is above threshold, the observed temporal courses of the three potentials are shown schematically in Figs. 12.1C,D,E. Following the well-established custom of the physiologists, changes of the potential in the negative direction are indicated by an upward displacement of the potential curve. Turning our attention to the potential record for the pair 1–4, we find that, after a small delay following stimulation, the potential at 4 begins to fall, passes through a minimum, after which it rises again, increases to a value slightly greater than the original value, and finally returns asymptotically to its original value.

The potential record for the pair 1–3 is similar to that for 1–4, except for a small time delay. This indicates that the potential disturbance moves away from the stimulated electrodes without losing its intensity. The lag of the record 1–3 behind that of 1–4 is due to the fact that point 3 is farther from the origin of the stimulus. The ratio of the distance between 3 and 4 to the difference between corresponding points on the two curves equals the speed of propagation of the impulse along the nerve.

If the potential of a point b, relative to a point a, is indicated by the symbol V_a^b, the relation between the instantaneous values observed in the three circuits may be represented by the following identity:

$$V_3^4 = V_3^1 + V_1^4 = V_1^4 - V_1^3$$

It follows that the instantaneous value of the change of potential observed in the circuit 3–4 must equal the algebraic difference of the instantaneous values observed in 1–4 and in 1–3. This accounts for the more complex appearance of the record obtained from electrodes 3–4. The first two records show *monophasic action potentials*. The third record shows a *diphasic action potential*.

The strength-duration curve

Let us assume that a pair of electrodes, c and a (Fig. 12.2A), is used to stimulate the nerve; that a direct current of constant strength, I, is used for stimulation, with c serving as cathode, and a serving as anode. The two pairs of electrodes, 1–c and 1–a, are used to keep a record of the course of the potential value at the surface of the nerve at the points c and a, respectively. With this arrangement it is possible to determine the time needed for a constant current of strength I to insure excitation of the nerve. In addition, it is possible to tell whether excitation originates at the cathode or at the anode.

In a typical experiment, represented by line AB (Fig. 12.2B), the constant current is applied at zero time, and the critical point is reached

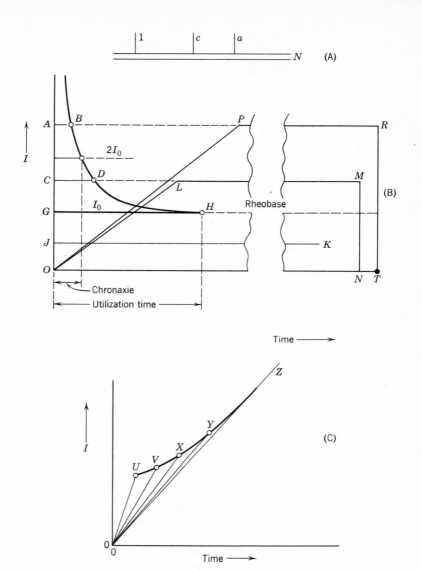

Fig. 12.2. (A) Arrangement of conditioning and recording electrodes. *a*, anode; *c*, cathode, 1-*c* or 1-*a* may be used as recording electrodes.

(B) The strength-duration curve *BDH*. There is a minimum strength of the stimulating current, the rheobase, below which no excitation takes place. At higher strengths the time needed for stimulation is a function of the strength of the current. Utilization time: time of excitation with rheobasic current. Chronaxie: time of excitation with twice-rheobasic current. Excitation at the cathode is indicated with open circles; at the anode, with solid circles. After the first impulse the nerve accommodates to the current, as in *ABPR*. If level of accommodation is high enough, excitation at anode takes place on opening circuit, as at *T*. At high values of *I* curve may be represented by equation: It = constant.

(C) The gradient-duration curve *UVXY*. The time of excitation depends upon the rate of rise of stimulating current. With some exceptions, there is a minimum gradient below which excitation does not take place. Even with higher gradients, there may be no excitation if the current is not allowed to rise indefinitely, as in *OPR*, diagram (B).

at the time indicated by point *B*. Excitation originates at the cathode. If the circuit is opened before the time t_B, no excitation takes place. If the experiment is repeated, with a weaker current, as in *CD*, the current must be applied for a longer time.

A complete series of experiments with the same nerve yields the *strength-duration* curve *BDH*. This experimental curve exhibits the following characteristics. At high values of *I* the curve may be represented quite well by equation (12.1):

$$I \cdot t = \text{constant} = Q_0 \qquad \text{(definition of } Q_0\text{)} \qquad (12.1)$$

At lower values of *I* equation (12.1) does not fit the curve. There is a limiting value I_0, below which the current does not excite the nerve no matter how long it is applied. This limiting value of the current is called the *rheobase* of the nerve. The time needed to excite the nerve with a current of rheobasic strength is called the *utilization time*. The time needed to excite the nerve with a current of strength $2I_0$ is called the *chronaxie* of the nerve.

If a similar series of experiments is performed with another nerve, the strength-duration curve of the second nerve is, in general, different, but the two curves are similar in appearance. In fact, while one nerve may be many times slower than a nerve of another type, both strength-duration curves may be represented fairly accurately by the dimensionless equation (12.2), where *k* is a parameter whose dimension is that of time. The values of I_0 and of *k* change from one nerve to another.

$$I/I_0 = 1/(1 - e^{-t/k}) \qquad (12.2)$$

Examination of equation (12.2) shows that for very small values of t/k it may be replaced by the simpler equation:

$$I \cdot t = I_0 k = \text{constant} \qquad (12.3)$$

This equation is similar to equation (12.1). The chronaxie of the nerve may be obtained by substituting in (12.2) the condition $I = 2I_0$. Solving the equation, we obtain

$$\text{Chronaxie} = 0.693k \qquad (12.4)$$

The adequacy of equation (12.2) is acceptable only with reservations. Although it offers a good fit at high and intermediate values of *I*, the equation is inadequate for values of *I* which are only a few per cent greater than I_0. Thus, according to this equation, *t* should approach infinity as *I* approaches I_0. Indirectly, the experimental evidence indicates that, as *I* approaches I_0, *t* approaches a finite value, the utilization time.

Excitation with currents of increasing strength

Let us assume that a nerve is stimulated with a current having the following characteristics: At zero time the current is zero, but the strength of the applied current increases at a constant rate. The results of this type of experiment are summarized in Fig. 12.2C. There is a minimum rate of rise of current below which no excitation takes place. If the time gradient of the current is above this minimal value, excitation takes place at a time which is a function of the rate of rise of the current. The excitation originates at the cathode (cf. Katz, 1939a; Schaefer, 1944). Curve $UVXY$ may be called the *gradient-duration curve*.

Accommodation; opening excitation at the anode

Returning to Fig. 12.2B, the sequence $OLMN$ represents an experiment in which the strength of the stimulating current, starting from zero, increases at a constant rate up to point L. From this point the strength of the current is maintained constant for a long time. There is no excitation, despite the fact that in experiment CD, in which the same strength of current is applied from the outset, excitation follows stimulation during the shorter period t_D. The adaptation of the nerve to a constant current level reached in slow stages is called *accommodation*. Accommodation may be achieved in a different manner. Thus, in experiment CD excitation takes place only once. If the stimulus is continued (DLM), there is no further excitation.

In the experiment represented by the sequence OPR the nerve is allowed to accommodate to a higher level of the current strength. While there is accommodation in this experiment, just as in experiment OLM, a qualitative difference may appear when the circuit is opened. If accommodation has been accomplished at a high enough level of current strength, then, shortly after the circuit is opened, excitation takes place. Whereas closing excitation originates at the *cathode*, opening excitation originates at the *anode*. The minimum strength of the current needed to produce opening anodic excitation is greater than the minimum strength needed to cause closing cathodic excitation (i.e., rheobasic strength). Anode-break excitations do not normally occur in some preparations (Hodgkin, 1951).

An acceptable theory of the irritability of nerve should answer the following questions: Why does closing excitation originate at the cathode? What is the significance of the strength-duration curve? What is the nature of the singularity at the lowest point, H, of the strength-duration curve? What is the nature of the processes which produce accommodation? Why does opening excitation originate at the anode? Why is the threshold for opening anodic excitation greater than the threshold for closing cathodic excitation?

Before attempting to answer these questions, it is desirable to examine some of the changes which take place in a nerve subjected to an electrical stimulus. It will be convenient to consider separately the effects of a brief shock with a strong current and the effects of a prolonged stimulus with a moderate or weak current. We should keep in mind, however, that there is no definite boundary between these two types of stimuli.

Quantitative measurement of the "irritability" of a resting and of an electrically conditioned nerve; a few definitions

The problem of defining quantitatively the irritability of a nerve is somewhat similar to the problem of defining quantitatively the effort needed to bring a leaky vessel to overflowing. Neither definition can be given in one sentence without seeming arbitrary.

For the benefit of any reader who is not familiar with the language of neurophysiology, a few definitions will be given. Some of these definitions were expressly coined to facilitate the present discussion.

The *excitation* of a nerve is accompanied by and is recognized by the appearance of a *propagated action potential*. An *adequate stimulus* produces excitation. An *inadequate stimulus* fails to produce excitation; nevertheless it *conditions* the nerve, in the sense that the response of the nerve to a second stimulus, applied soon after the first one, is different from the response which would have been elicited in the absence of the first stimulus.

With an adequate stimulus there comes a point in time from which the nerve will proceed to excitation, even if left on its own. This point will be called the *critical point*. This is not to imply, however, that the state of the nerve at the critical point of a given stimulus is the same as the state of the nerve at the critical point of a stimulus of a different type. The *pattern of a stimulus* is defined as the complete description of the time variation of the applied current. The state of a nerve at the critical point is, in general, a function of the pattern of the stimulus.

The effects produced on the parts of the nerve in contact with the stimulating anode and cathode, respectively, are different. For this reason the stimulus is defined as *anodic* or *cathodic*, depending upon whether the part of the nerve under investigation is in contact with the anode or with the cathode.

The fundamental processes taking place in the development of many biological end results are not fully known. Nevertheless, we may speak, in a vague sort of way, of the "time constants" of these processes, and we may assert, on purely experimental grounds, that the interval of one minute is small compared with the shortest time constant in the overall mechanism of the development of, say, cancer. In the same sense we may define as a *rapid* stimulus or a *shock* a stimulus whose duration is much smaller than the smallest *time constant* of the still inadequately known fundamental machinery of the nerve.

It is convenient to sharpen the definition of a shock by considering the stimulus a shock only if the *strength of the stimulus*, as measured by the physiological effect it produces, may be characterized quantitatively by a single number whose value is independent of the pattern of the stimulus. In the discussion of the strength-duration curve for constant currents (Fig. 12.2B) it was stated that, with high values of I, the quantity, $It = Q_0$, needed to produce excitation, is independent of I. This is only a special case of a more general observation, that, if the time t of the stimulus is made short enough, the physiological effect is a definite function of the integral, $\int I\,dt = Q$, and is independent of the detailed pattern of the stimulus (Katz, 1939a; Schaefer, 1944). It follows that the strength of a shock may be given unambiguously by the quantity Q, whose dimension is that of electric charge. The threshold shock of the normal nerve has the value Q_0. Unfortunately, the value of Q_0 is a function of the experimental arrangement. It may change with the size of the electrode, with the distance between the electrodes, with the distance of each electrode from the surface of the nerve, and with the orientation of the line joining the two electrodes relative to the axis of the nerve.

For these reasons the strength of a shock is specified as the dimensionless ratio: Q/Q_0, where Q_0 is the strength of the threshold shock of the resting nerve under the same experimental conditions. With this scale of strengths, the strength of the shock which is just adequate to excite the normal nerve is arbitrarily assigned the value 1; other shocks may be described as 0.95 threshold, 1.10 threshold, etc. If both electrodes touch the normal nerve, there is a minimum value Q_0 which produces excitation at the cathode. If the cathode is on a normal part of the nerve, and the anode is at an injured point of the nerve or at some distant point, the value of Q_0 may be different, and, therefore, the scale of strengths may be different. If, with the second arrangement of electrodes, the polarity of the electrodes is reversed, excitation does not take place, even with shocks many times larger than threshold. Thus we must distinguish between *cathodic* and *anodic shocks*.

If a given spot on the surface of a normal nerve is subjected to an inadequate slow stimulus or to an inadequate shock, there is no excitation, but the properties of the nerve at the spot and in its vicinity change. We choose from among the many properties which may be investigated the one most significant to the present discussion, namely, the sensitivity of the spot to an additional cathodic shock. We assign a numerical scale to this property as follows: After the spot is subjected to the desired pattern of conditioning, the minimum strength of the cathodic shock needed to produce excitation is determined. The new threshold of the spot under investigation is assigned the value of this just-adequate shock. For example, if a slow anodic stimulus is applied, and if at the end of the stimulus it takes a cathodic shock of strength 1.2 to produce excitation, the new threshold has the value 1.2. We will have occasion to speak of the *threshold increments*, and, in order to avoid negative values, of *threshold decrements*. Thus in the preceding example the threshold increment is 0.2; if the new threshold has the value 0.75, the threshold decrement is 0.25.

It will be worth while to summarize some of the experimental observations described so far, and to add a few more, using the defined terms. If the two conditioning electrodes are in contact with two normal spots on the nerve, the stimulus may be described as anodic or cathodic, depending upon which of the two spots is under examination. A cathodic shock of strength smaller than 1 does not excite, but lowers the threshold. A cathodic shock of strength 1 or greater produces excitation. An anodic shock does not produce excitation, no matter what its strength may be; however, it raises the threshold. A slow anodic stimulus raises the threshold. A slow cathodic stimulus lowers the threshold. When the value of the threshold reaches zero, the critical point is reached, and excitation is initiated.

The threshold decrement (or increment, as the case may be) resulting from a conditioning stimulus decreases spontaneously with time, and eventually the threshold returns to the normal value 1. If the spot is conditioned by an anodic shock, the resulting threshold increment decreases approximately exponentially with time. If the spot is conditioned with a weak cathodic shock, the decrement decreases approximately exponentially with time. A more detailed description is given in connection with Fig. 12.3.

The parts of the nerve adjacent to the electrically conditioned spot also suffer a change in threshold. In general, the change is in the same direction as that of the conditioned spot. However, the magnitude of the increment, or of the decrement, decreases approximately exponentially with the distance from the electrode.

The complex of changes in the properties of the nerve during and following an electrical conditioning is called *electrotonus*. The part of the nerve immediately under the cathode and in the vicinity is said to be in a *catelectrotonic state*. The section of the nerve at the anode is said to be in an *anelectrotonic state*. In general, the catelectrotonic state is characterized by a threshold decrement, whereas the anelectrotonic state is accompanied by a threshold increment. The irritability is said to be

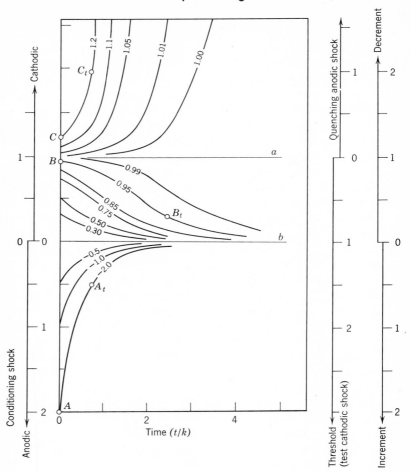

Fig. 12.3. The temporal course of the threshold following a cathodic or an anodic shock. For explanation, see text. Abscissas: time, represented as a multiple of the time constant k of the exponential decay following anodic stimulation. Ordinates: Values of the conditioning shock, the threshold, the testing shock or the quenching shock, depending upon the scale used. These values are represented as multiples of the critical threshold of resting nerve.

The regularity of the curves below horizontal line b suggests that the properties of the membrane are not seriously affected by an anodic shock. The change in the shape of the curves between a and b, as the critical value of the shock is approached, indicates a gradual change in the properties of the membrane. The appearance of the curves above a suggests that passage through the critical region is accompanied by a reversible change. (Redrawn from Katz, 1937.)

supernormal in *catelectrotonus* and *subnormal* in *anelectrotonus*. The decrease in the potential of the outside surface caused by cathodic conditioning is called *catelectrotonic potential*. The increase caused by anodic stimulation is called *anelectrotonic potential*. Both changes are called *electrotonic potentials*.

The temporal course of the electrotonus after a conditioning shock

The curves given in Fig. 12.3 show the results obtained by Katz (1937) in an investigation of the threshold changes following a conditioning shock. The number accompanying each curve gives the strength of the conditioning shock: positive numbers indicate a cathodic shock; negative numbers, an anodic shock. Henceforth each curve will be referred to by the number accompanying it.

The horizontal lines *a* and *b* separate the curves into three groups. The group of three curves lying below *b* was obtained with a conditioning anodic shock. The six curves lying between *a* and *b* were obtained with conditioning cathodic shocks of strength smaller than 1. The five curves above *a* were obtained with conditioning cathodic shocks of strength 1 or greater.

It may be worth while to mention that each curve does not represent the results of a single continuous experiment. Each curve represents the results of a series of experiments in each of which the same conditioning shock was used; the allowed lapse of time subsequent to the conditioning was varied. A description of the experimental techniques used in each of the three types of conditioning will facilitate the discussion of the significance of the results presented in this series of curves.

To obtain a point (e.g., point A_t) on the -2.0 curve, an anodic shock of strength 2.0 is applied. This gives the first point on the curve (point A). Since a test cathodic shock of strength 3.0 at zero time would be needed to bring about excitation, the threshold at zero time is 3.0, as may be read from the threshold scale shown to the right of the diagram. The zero value of the increment is 2.0. After a lapse of time t, the strength of the cathodic shock needed to bring about excitation is determined. As an illustration, if the required strength of the cathodic shock is 1.5, the threshold value at this time is 1.5, and the value of the threshold increment is 0.5 (point A_t, curve -2.0). A series of points so obtained, with various values of t, defines the curve. The other two curves below *b* were obtained in a similar fashion.

Curve 0.95 was obtained in a series of experiments in each of which a cathodic conditioning shock of strength 0.95 was used. It follows that, at zero time, the threshold decrement was 0.95, and the threshold value was 0.05. Point B_t represents the following experimental result: At the time t, corresponding to this point, it took a cathodic test shock of strength 0.7 to bring about excitation. It follows that the threshold value at this time was 0.7, and the decrement value was 0.3. The other curves lying between lines a and b were obtained in a similar manner.

The points of curve 1.2 were obtained using a cathodic conditioning shock of strength 1.2. In this series the value of the decrement at zero time was 1.2, and the zero time value of the "threshold" might be called -0.2. In the absence of interference, the process of excitation would follow its usual course. However, it was found possible to quench the excitation process by the application of an anodic shock; the minimum strength of the quenching shock was a function of the time elapsed after the conditioning. Thus, at the instant corresponding to point C_t, it took an anodic shock of strength 1.0. At this point the value of the "threshold" was -1.0, and the value of the decrement was 2.0.

Turning to an overall survey of the curves shown in Fig. 12.3, we make the following observations: A conditioning anodic shock produces an increase in threshold. The threshold subsequently decreases with time, approaching the value 1.0. Although a diagram of the type given in Fig. 12.3 does not show it clearly, a quantitative analysis of the temporal course of the three curves appearing below line a shows that the increment in each case decreases approximately exponentially with time.

An inspection of the six curves in the middle group shows that the temporal course of the decrement obtained with an inadequate cathodic shock cannot be described as simply as the temporal course of the increment produced by an anodic shock. In the curves obtained by a weak cathodic conditioning (0.30 and 0.50), the decrease in the value of the decrement follows the exponential law of decay fairly well. However, as the strength of the conditioning shock is increased, the shape of the curve changes gradually from the simple exponential curve 0.30 to the S-shaped curve 0.99.

The most striking evidence on the behavior of nerve near its critical point is offered by the curves appearing near the top of Fig. 12.3 (1.00 to 1.2). These curves show that the passage through the critical point is not an irrevocable event. With an anodic shock of the proper strength it is possible not only to slow down the course of excitation but also to eliminate it completely. Furthermore, the curves show that the changes taking place after the critical point is passed are not of an abrupt nature, but are progressive in character. To use a crude analogy, forcing a nerve past the critical point is like pushing a ball up an incline, and over the brow of a hill, but not like pushing the ball up an incline and over the edge of a cliff. The effort needed to retrieve the ball, just after the critical point is passed, is small and increases progressively with time. Dittler

(1925) showed that in muscle an action potential already initiated can be annihilated by an anodic current applied within the period 0.1 to 1.0 msec.

Figures 12.4A and 12.4B are offered as a bridge between the discussions of the changes accompanying a shock and the changes accompanying a slow stimulus with a constant current. These figures show again the effects of a cathodic and of an anodic shock, respectively, on the threshold of the nerve. In these figures positive values of the threshold are indicated in the upward direction. The curves are only schematic, but we recognize the following features: A cathodic shock decreases the threshold and increases the irritability (point A). An anodic shock produces the opposite effect (point C). In both cases the effect fades away with time. However, still another effect is brought to light through the device of exaggerating it in the schematic diagram: Before reaching its resting state, the nerve passes through a state of *post-cathodal subnormal irritability* (at B), i.e., the threshold increases beyond the value 1.0 before the final state is reached. Similarly, after an anodic shock, the nerve passes through a state of *post-anodal supernormal irritability* (at D) (Curtis and Cole, 1950).

Figures 12.4C and 12.4D show the temporal course of the threshold in stimulation with cathodic and anodic constant currents, respectively. The two curves will be discussed in the sections which follow. Obviously, the four curves appearing in Fig. 12.4 differ from each other, both qualitatively and quantitatively. An adequate theory of irritability will enable us to tell whether these differences are caused by the operation of different mechanisms or whether they are due to the effects of different experimental conditions on the same mechanism. Meantime, it may be worth while to call attention to a degree of unity exhibited by all four curves, which may be described as follows.

A stimulus, whether slow or fast, causes a change in the threshold. A cathodic stimulus decreases the threshold, whereas an anodic stimulus increases it. At the termination of the stimulus the value of the threshold drifts back to normal. While doing so, it crosses the boundary between subnormal and supernormal thresholds and only later does it approach the permanent normal value. The post-stimulus excursion across the boundary is smaller than the first excursion caused by the stimulus. This post-stimulus "overshoot" is much smaller in stimulations with a shock than in stimulations with a constant current of long duration.

Threshold changes accompanying a cathodic stimulus with a constant current

The temporal course of the threshold accompanying stimulation with a constant current may be determined as follows: In a series of experiments, in each of which the same strength of stimulating current is used,

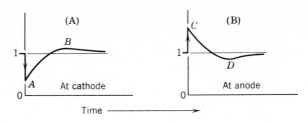

Effect of Shock

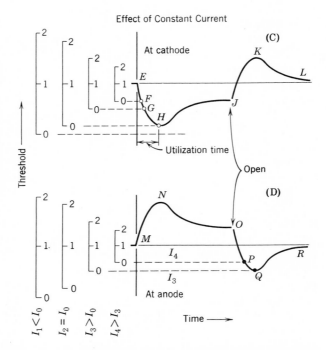

Effect of Constant Current

Fig. 12.4. (A), (B) The temporal course of the threshold after a cathodic and an anodic shock, respectively. With a weak shock, the change in the threshold produced by the shock decays with time, passes through a maximum or minimum, respectively, and eventually approaches zero. The magnitude of the excursion beyond normal values, at *B* and at *C*, is exaggerated in these schematic diagrams.

(C), (D) The temporal course of the threshold accompanying cathodic or anodic stimulation, with constant currents.

The same curve may be used schematically for a sequence of currents of increasing strength, through the device of employing different scales for the ordinates. The magnitude of the scale is inversely proportional to the strength of the current.

Opening excitation is indicated by solid circles; closing excitation, by open circles. Current I_2 is rheobasic for closing cathodic excitation but is inadequate for opening anodic excitation. The rheobase for the latter process, I_3, is larger than I_2. The passage of the threshold curve through a minimum value, at *H*, accounts for the existence of a finite utilization time. The four curves in this figure may be described as follows: Cathodic stimulation lowers the threshold; anodic stimulation raises the threshold. In both cases discontinuance of the stimulus is eventually followed by an "overshoot" in the opposite direction.

618

the magnitude of the minimum cathodic shock needed to excite the nerve is determined as a function of time.   The results obtained with a cathodic constant current are shown schematically in Fig. 12.4C (Erlanger and Blair, 1931; Lloyd, 1950; Curtis and Cole, 1950).

Several threshold scales are shown to the left of the diagram.   Disregarding, for the moment, all but the largest scale on the extreme left, we may describe the observations as follows: The threshold begins to decrease the instant the stimulus is applied, but with a constantly decreasing rate.   Eventually the value of the threshold reaches a minimum (point H), and then it begins to increase, but with a progressively decreasing rate.   When the circuit is opened (at J), the threshold begins to increase rapidly, passes the normal value 1.0, climbs to a maximum, and, finally, approaches slowly the normal value.   The excursion into supernormal values is smaller than the maximum excursion into subnormal values.

Curve $EFKL$ of Fig. 12.4C represents schematically the results obtained with a cathodal current of a certain strength.   A stronger current would give a similar curve, but with larger ordinates.   In order to represent the results obtained with a sequence of currents of increasing strength, it would be necessary to show on the same diagram a corresponding family of curves.   In so far as the representation is schematic, the diagram may be simplified by the use of a single curve accompanied by a series of decreasing ordinate scales.   Such a series of scales is given on the left of the diagram.   The sequence of four scales, from left to right, corresponds to a sequence of four currents, I_1, I_2, I_3, I_4, whose strength increases in the indicated order.

To determine the physiological effect of the weakest current, I_1, we examine the curve with the aid of the largest scale.   We find that at no time does the threshold value reach zero, and we conclude that I_1 is a current of subrheobasic strength.   The effect of the largest current, I_4, may be predicted with the aid of the smallest scale on the extreme right. We observe that the threshold reaches zero value at F, and we conclude that the critical state is reached at the time t_F.   With the smaller current, I_3, the critical state is reached at the end of a longer period, t_G.

Evidently, in a sequence of experiments with increasing currents, ranging from the value I_1 to the value I_4, there must be some value (labeled I_2 in the diagram) for which the threshold passes through its minimum at zero value, at the time t_H.   This would be the rheobasic current, I_0.

Assuming that a theoretical, or empirical, equation is available, giving the threshold-time relation, with I as a variable parameter, the strength-duration curve may be obtained by solving the following problem: For any given value of I, what is the value of t at which the threshold reaches the value zero? The solution will give t as a function of I. The rheobase is that particular value of I for which the minimum value of the threshold is zero. The utilization time is the time at which the threshold reaches zero value when the current is rheobasic.

The theoretical significance of the utilization time

Turning our attention to the strength-duration curve in Fig. 12.2B we recognize that point H carries the distinction of being the lowest point on the curve. It represents the weakest exciting (i.e., rheobasic) current and the maximum time allowance which the accommodation process will provide for excitation (i.e., the utilization time). Examination of the minimum-threshold point H, Fig. 12.4C, in conjunction with the threshold scale for the rheobasic current, I_0, shows that, since the threshold value zero is maintained only for a single instant, point H carries another distinction. It represents a combination of circumstances in which the opportunity to excite the nerve exists only for a fleeting moment. Should there be a momentary decrease in the exciting current, because of some statistical fluctuation, the opportunity to excite is missed, and the accommodative process takes over; the threshold begins to rise.

Finally, it seems plausible that the utilization time carries a theoretical significance which far outweighs its other claims to distinction. From what has been said previously it follows that with any subthreshold current the threshold-time curve passes through a minimum. Let us call the time of passage through the minimum the *threshold-minimum time*. Should it be shown experimentally that for any given nerve the threshold-minimum time is independent of the strength of the current, then the utilization time gives the value of this constant directly. In that case the utilization time represents a fundamental time constant in the accommodative process of the nerve. A hypothetical model discussed later (p. 649) has this particular property.

Threshold changes accompanying an anodic stimulus; opening excitation at the anode

The changes taking place at the anode are shown schematically in Fig. 12.4D. The threshold changes are in a direction opposite to the threshold changes at the cathode. As long as the current is maintained, the threshold is above normal and the irritability is subnormal. When the circuit is opened, the threshold decreases rapidly, reaches subnormal values, passes through a minimum, then approaches gradually its normal value. This accounts for the subnormal irritability during the stimulation and the post-anodal supernormal irritability.

The physiological effect on opening depends upon the strength of the current. On examination of curve $MNOPQR$ in conjunction with the various threshold scales on the left, we find that, if the stimulating current is of rheobasic strength I_0, the threshold excursion into subnormal values is not large enough to reach the value zero, and, therefore, there is no excitation. It takes a current I_3, stronger than I_0, to produce opening anodic excitation. Stimulation with a current stronger than I_3 also produces opening anodic excitation.

It has been indicated above that the experimental evidence on the changes taking place in the threshold may be used to interpret the strength-duration curve, the rheobase, the utilization time, accommodation, post-cathodal subnormal irritability, post-anodal supernormal irritability, and opening excitation at the anode. However, the following fundamental questions still remain to be answered: Why does cathodic stimulation lower the threshold? What is the nature of the mechanism which conditions the peculiar changes in the threshold and thus accounts for accommodation? What is the nature of the critical state, which is reached when the threshold value is zero? These questions will be considered in the following sections.

PRESENT THEORIES OF IRRITABILITY AND OF ACCOMMODATION

Bernstein's polarized membrane model

Bernstein (1902) proposed the following qualitative model of the nerve fiber membrane: The membrane is normally permeable to potassium ion only. Since the inside concentration of potassium is greater than the outside concentration, the membrane is polarized by a diffusion potential, with the outside surface carrying the positive charge. This type of model is shown graphically in Fig. 12.5A, with the slight modification that the permeabilities of the membrane to sodium and chloride ions are shown schematically to be small but not completely negligible. A weak shock causes a slight depolarization, as is shown in Fig. 12.5B, but the original potential is restored soon after the termination of the shock. However, if the shock is strong enough, it affects critically the properties of the membrane. The membrane becomes more permeable, and it becomes depolarized. Figure 12.5C shows schematically the condition of the membrane in the depolarized state. Local currents from adjacent areas depolarize these areas and lead to depolarization of the next adjacent areas; the spread of this disturbance accounts for the propagation of the impulse.

Recently it has been found experimentally that the membrane potential of certain types of nerve and muscle not only drops to zero on stimulation,

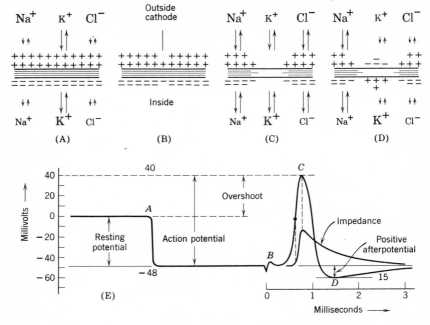

Fig. 12.5. (A) Bernstein's interpretation of the transmembrane potential. The membrane is permeable to potassium. The presence of a higher concentration of potassium inside insures a positive resting potential.

(B), (C) A weak cathodic stimulus depolarizes the membrane slightly. The initial state is recovered when the stimulus is removed. A strong cathodic stimulus changes the properties of the membrane; other ions can penetrate the membrane, and the latter is depolarized. Current leakage from adjacent areas depolarizes the latter, and the impulse is propagated along the nerve.

(D) Recent observations show that the polarization of the membrane is reversed at the height of the action potential. Hodgkin and Katz assume that the permeability to sodium becomes much greater than permeability to other ions.

(E) Direct evidence of the reality of the resting transmembrane potential and of the reversal of polarization in excitation. When an electrode penetrates the membrane, its potential drops (point A). Excitation raises the inside potential above that of the outside potential (point C). In the recovery process the transmembrane potential first reaches a higher-than-normal value (point D) and eventually reverts to normal value.

The impedance curve shows the change in conductance of membrane during action potential. The upward swing indicates an increased conductance. The upward swing of the curve becomes appreciable and fast near the point of inflection of curve BC.

(Curve AB, schematic; curve BCD, redrawn to scale from Hodgkin and Katz, 1949a; impedance curve redrawn schematically from Cole and Curtis, 1939).

but actually reverses sign, so that the outside surface becomes negative relative to the inside surface (Curtis and Cole, 1942; Hodgkin and Huxley, 1939, 1945). Hodgkin and Katz (1949a) have offered the following interpretation of this observation: On excitation, the membrane changes its properties in such a way that the permeability to sodium becomes much greater than the permeability to potassium and chloride ions. Since the concentration of sodium is greater outside the fiber, the reversal of polarity is accounted for. Figure 12.5D shows schematically the state of the membrane at the height of the negative phase.

The most direct evidence for the reality of the transmembrane potentials in resting nerve and muscle fibers and for the reversal of polarity in some types of fibers may be obtained with the use of one inside electrode. When electrodes 1 and 2 are applied to the surface of a fiber, the potential of 2 relative to 1 is zero, as is shown in the early part of the curve in Fig. 12.5E. If electrode 2 is made to penetrate the membrane (point A), its potential drops to a negative value, showing that the inside is negative relative to the outside of the membrane. If, after a while, the fiber is stimulated at some distant point, the inside electrode may register the stimulating shock (as at point B); after a short delay, equal to the time of arrival of the propagated physiological impulse at the point explored by the inside electrode 2, the potential of this electrode begins to rise, passes a maximum at some positive value, decreases to a minimum, and finally approaches the resting value. The total excursion beyond the value zero is called the *overshoot*; the excursion beyond the resting value is called the *positive afterpotential*. Thus, in the record drawn to scale in Fig. 12.5E, the resting potential is 48 mv, with the outside positive; the overshoot is 40 mv, with the outside negative; the positive afterpotential is 15 mv, and at this time the transmembrane potential is 63 mv.

The mathematical models of Rashevsky and of Hill

Considerable progress has been made in applying mathematical methods to the problems of excitation and accommodation (Blair, 1932; Hill, 1935; Monnier, 1934; Rashevsky, 1933).

Rashevsky assumes that the stimulating current affects the magnitudes of two antagonistic factors, ϵ and j. The factor ϵ is excitatory; the factor j is inhibitory. When $\epsilon \geq j$, the nerve is excited. At first Rashevsky was inclined to identify the two factors with excitatory (monovalent) and inhibitory (bivalent) ions. Later, however, he left the two factors undefined (Rashevsky, 1950).

Hill makes similar assumptions, but from the beginning does not specify the physical nature of the two factors.

Rashevsky starts with the following two differential equations:

$$d\epsilon/dt = KI - k(\epsilon - \epsilon_0) \tag{12.5}$$

$$dj/dt = MI - m(j - j_0) \tag{12.6}$$

where I is the intensity of the current, K, k, M, and m are constants, and the subscript zero refers to values at zero time.

Hill starts with a somewhat different set of differential equations:

$$d\epsilon/dt = KI - k(\epsilon - \epsilon_0) \tag{12.7}$$

$$dj/dt = M(\epsilon - \epsilon_0) - m(j - j_0) \tag{12.8}$$

Since each term in a differential equation implies a quantitative statement regarding the properties of the dependent variable, the differences between the two pairs of equations imply different assumptions regarding the behavior of the two factors. The usefulness of each of the two approaches must be judged by its success in matching the experimental facts.

The mathematical relations derived from Hill's differential equations have been subjected to extensive experimental tests, the details of which may be found in Katz's informative monograph (1939a). There are some discrepancies between experience and Hill's theoretical expectations (Katz, p. 33). Thus, with Hill's assumptions the rheobase should be the same for closing excitation at the cathode and opening excitation at the anode; actually, the threshold for opening excitation is well above that for closing excitation. Some data do not fit well the derived equation (Katz, p. 22). On the other hand, according to Katz (p. 26), "Of greater significance, however, is the fact that the voltage-capacity curves obtained on a large number of nerves, and made under a variety of experimental conditions, follow the equation very well, in many cases with an almost embarrassing accuracy."

In this connection, another quotation from the same monograph (p. 13) is relevant: "The theories proposed independently by Rashevsky, Monnier, and Hill aim at a simple description of the events which lead to excitation. They have been worked out on a few, very general assumptions, which, intentionally, do not imply the physical nature of the processes described, but are derived from elementary physiological experience."

Notwithstanding the usefulness of this approach in correlating empirically a number of experimental observations, it remains desirable to look for the physical basis underlying differential equations of this type. The discussion which follows deals with a physical model which is consistent with the observations described in the preceding pages, and which, for the present, forms an adequate basis for their interpretation.

A QUANTITATIVE PHYSICOCHEMICAL APPROACH TO THE PROBLEM OF IRRITABILITY AND ACCOMMODATION

Membrane changes accompanying excitation

There is convincing experimental evidence that, in agreement with Bernstein's assumption (1902), the membrane is subject to profound changes in the process of excitation (Curtis and Cole, 1950). According to Curtis and Cole, it is becoming increasingly apparent that the phenomenon of excitation is primarily related to the cell membrane. It seems plausible that, by means of an "interpolation" from the membrane changes observed when the critical point is passed, we can gain some clues as to the nature of the processes which bring the membrane to the critical point.

The problem is concerned with the mechanism whereby an adequate electrical stimulus, applied locally, originates excitation of the nerve. Very likely, the mechanism is the same as that operating when an impulse originating at a distant point arrives at the point under investigation. Cole and Curtis (1939) took simultaneous records of both the action potential and of the impedance of the membrane of a giant squid axon during the passage of an impulse. At, or very near, the maximum of the action potential the membrane resistance is smaller than at rest by a factor of at least 50. The relation between the temporal courses of the action potential and of the impedance is highly significant. This relation is shown schematically in Fig. 12.5E. In the early stages the potential curve leads the impedance curve. The potential curve begins to rise, with a progressively increasing rate, while the impedance curve remains horizontal. There is little doubt that the change in the potential at this early stage is caused by current leakage from the spot under investigation into the rapidly approaching front of the propagated impulse. The conductance curve begins to rise rapidly at, or very near, the time at which the potential curve passes through its point of inflection. The conductance curve reaches its maximum at approximately the same time that the potential curve reaches its maximum.

For our purposes the experimental observations of Cole and Curtis (1939) may be summarized as follows:

The first sign of an approaching propagated impulse is manifested by a change in the polarization of the membrane. If this change is accompanied by a change in the conductance, the latter change is, at first, below the observation threshold. However, the change in the conductance begins to be appreciable near the point of inflection in the potential curve. From that point on, the change in conductance rises rapidly and reaches its maximum value approximately simultaneously with the maximum of the depolarization.

Additional evidence that the resistance of the membrane decreases on excitation is available from studies with radioactive isotopes. Thus Keynes (1949) found that the fluxes of both sodium and potassium increase during excitation. The change in the resistance is not merely quantitative, but is qualitative as well. Thus, in order to interpret the reversal in the sign of the polarization of the membrane at the height of activity, Hodgkin and Katz (1949a) found it necessary to assume that the ratio: (permeability to sodium)/(permeability to potassium) changes from a value much smaller than 1 to a value much larger than 1.

The experimental evidence makes it clear that profound changes in the properties of the membrane take place at or near the point of reversal of the membrane-penetrating current. In the subsequent discussions of this phenomenon the following tentative assumption will be made: There is no discontinuity, in the mathematical sense, in the rate of changes of the properties of the membrane. The properties of the membrane change continuously from the onset of stimulation. However, the changes are at first entirely too small to be observed. While the initial rate of change is very small, its time derivative is high. The small value of the rate in the early stages, the high value of the derivative, and the practical limitations of the observational technique combine to give the observable change the appearance of a sudden start and of a very rapid progress thereafter. Comparison with other physicochemical processes possessing a critical region lends plausibility to the assumption of mathematical continuity.

There is available experimental evidence that the membrane is subject to changes even with subthreshold stimuli. Thus the peculiar rectifying characteristics of the squid giant axon membrane, observed by Cole and Curtis (Cole and Curtis, 1941; Curtis and Cole, 1950), with subthreshold currents, cannot be interpreted in terms of a stable membrane whose properties are independent of the applied polarizing current. The nerve membrane does not show the simple rectification expected in simple membranes. The observations of Katz on the rate of decay of the threshold decrement in a nerve conditioned by subthreshold cathodic shocks show clearly that the mechanism of decay changes gradually as the strength of the conditioning shock approaches threshold values (see Fig. 12.3, curves 0.30 to 0.99).

Tentative hypothesis as to the physicochemical nature of the threshold

The mathematical theories of Rashevsky and of Hill, as noted above, assume the existence of two factors, one excitatory, the other inhibitory, whose nature is left undefined. In the following hypothesis it is assumed that the change in the transmembrane potential E is the chief factor determining the change in the structure of the membrane. A detailed examination of this assumption is postponed to a later section (p. 688). For the moment, it is sufficient to remark that the strong influence of E on the state of the membrane is assumed to result from a combination of the high magnitude of the potential gradient and the large values of the dipole moments of some of the molecules forming the membrane (Chapter 11, p. 590).

A given transmembrane potential demands a particular state of the membrane. In turn, each instantaneous state of the membrane demands a particular value for the transmembrane potential. In the wake of a subthreshold stimulus, conditions are such that the two demands cannot be simultaneously satisfied. The system is unstable and changes spontaneously back to the stable resting state. However, if the stimulus is strong enough, a critical region is passed; once beyond this region, the unstable system changes spontaneously to a new state, tentatively identified with the state of the system at the height of the action potential.

A cathodic stimulus is excitatory because it brings the system closer to the critical region. An anodic stimulus is inhibitory because it carries the system away from the critical region. The change in the threshold is proportional to the change in the transmembrane potential.

In the usual method of stimulating a nerve with two outside electrodes on the surface of the axon, the potential V of the outside surface of the membrane, relative to some distant point of constant potential, is changed by the application of a current; the potential U of the inside surface, relative to the same point is then not directly under control. U changes spontaneously in response to the changing transmembrane current. Since the change in the threshold is proportional to the difference, $\Delta V - \Delta U$, even a stimulus of the simplest pattern produces complicated changes in the threshold. In order to investigate the temporal course of the threshold, it is necessary to examine the temporal course of V and of U while the stimulus is in progress. An examination of these quantities shows that the fundamental assumption regarding the nature of the threshold changes leads to conclusions which are in agreement with experimental observations. Before undertaking a mathematical analysis of this problem we need to inquire into the nature of the critical region.

A physicochemical analog

The literature on nerve abounds with electrical, chemical, mechanical, and mathematical analogs. Analogs are useful in bringing an economy of thought. The physicochemical analog employed in the following discussion has quantitative characteristics which simulate in several ways the phenomena of irritability, excitation, and conduction.

The analog consists of a long tube containing a fluid mixture whose components are capable of participating in a strongly exothermic reaction. The rate of the reaction at room temperature is exceedingly small, but its temperature coefficient is very high. This system may be stimulated by supplying heat to a small section of the tube. The strength of the stimulus, I, is defined as the rate at which the heat is supplied. A stimulus is defined as a shock if the rate of supply of heat is high and the duration is short enough to make it possible to neglect the leakage of heat by convection and conduction. The effect of a given stimulus is examined by observing the surface temperature at some distant point. Excitation is said to take place if the stimulus causes the propagation of a reaction along the tube. It is assumed, of course, that the heat of reaction produced at the stimulated point and the fraction of this heat conveyed to adjacent sections of the tube are both large enough to excite the adjacent sections. The terms, subthreshold, threshold, and above threshold stimulus, to be used in speaking about this system, are self-explanatory.

Nature of the critical region; excitatory and inhibitory factors

In the analog, with an above-threshold stimulus of constant strength, the nature of the critical point can be easily described. The critical point in a given experiment is passed at that temperature at which the chemical reaction becomes self-sustaining, i.e., at the temperature at which the rate of evolution of heat by the exothermic reaction becomes equal to the rate of loss of heat to the surroundings.

We may list as excitatory factors those which tend to bring the system closer to the critical point: the stimulating heat current, the chemical reaction, and a high temperature in the adjacent sections of the tube. The following are inhibitory factors: leakage of heat to the surroundings, low temperatures in adjacent regions, and approach of the chemical reaction to equilibrium.

The term critical point has a definite meaning when applied to a given experiment. Thus in a certain experiment the critical point may have been reached at the end of 1 minute, when the local temperature was 100°C. In this experiment the critical point was at 100°C. We cannot assert, however, that 100°C is the critical point of the system. Let us assume that in a second experiment a weaker, but still above-threshold, stimulus is used; that the temperature 95°C is reached at the end of 5 minutes, and that the stimulation is continued. The rate of heat loss in the second experiment at a given temperature is smaller than the corresponding rate in the first experiment, since the adjacent regions are warmer. It follows that in the second experiment the critical point will be reached at a lower temperature.

If the temperature coefficient of the reaction is high enough, the critical points in a series of different experiments may still be confined to a rather narrow range of temperatures. Thus in Fig. 12.6 the rate of evolution of heat in the exothermic reaction is shown schematically by a single curve as a function of the temperature. The rates of heat loss are also shown for five different experiments, each as a function of temperature. In each experiment the critical point is reached when the two rates are equal.

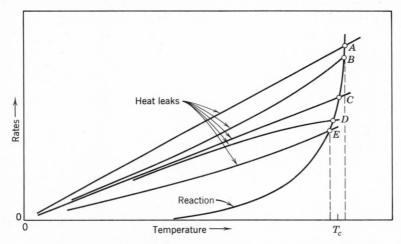

Fig. 12.6. The critical point in the "stimulation" of an exothermic reaction is reached when the reaction produces heat at a rate equal to the rate of leakage of heat. If the rate of the reaction may be represented by the approximate formula, rate $= R = R_o e^{cT}$, and if R_o is exceedingly small, straight lines and shallow curves passing through the origin intersect the rate curve within a small range of values of T; this small range is the critical region of the system.

The diagram shows that, if this point is reached at a high enough value of T, large variations in the rates of loss of heat cause relatively small changes in the critical temperature. If this is the case, we may speak of the approximate value of the critical temperature T_c of the chemical system.

Turning our attention to the problem of nerve, we may classify as excitatory factors those which tend to decrease the transmembrane potential. Among these are the cathodic stimulus, inward cationic fluxes, and outward anionic fluxes. Among the inhibitory factors we may list anodic stimuli, leakage of the charge along the outside surface of the membrane, outward cationic fluxes, and inward anionic fluxes.

At any given instant during stimulation the magnitude of each ionic flux is determined by the potential pattern and the ionic concentration pattern across the membrane, and by the changing properties of the membrane itself.

We have already made the assumption that the reaction whereby the membrane changes its properties progresses continuously even at the early stage of a threshold stimulus. We add the further assumption, which will be discussed later (p. 688), that both the tendency of this reaction and its rate are favored by a decrease in the transmembrane potential. In the idealized analog both the rate of the reaction and the rate of evolution of heat are single-valued functions of the temperature. In the system represented by nerve the situation is much more complex. Before we can describe the critical conditions in this system we need to consider the characteristics of a labile membrane in the presence of a changing transmembrane potential.

The potential demand of a stable membrane

When a membrane is placed between two non-identical solutions, there is, in general, a potential difference E_1 across the membrane. The value of the transmembrane potential between a specified pair of solutions depends upon the nature of the membrane, except in special cases. Thus, with a specified pair of solutions, the value of E, the transmembrane potential, is a physical property of the membrane. Let us refer to this quantity as the potential demand of the membrane relative to the given pair of solutions and represent it by P.D.M.

If an external source of emf is applied across the membrane, the transmembrane potential may be maintained at a value which is different from that demanded by the membrane, as long as the external emf is applied. In these circumstances the P.D.M. manifests itself in the nature of the electrical current passing through the membrane. In a stable membrane the current is always restorative, i.e., in a direction which tends to satisfy the potential demand of the membrane. Thus, if the imposed emf E is greater than E_1, the P.D.M. of the membrane, there is an inward electrical current. When the outside source of emf is removed, the transmembrane potential reverts after a finite time to E_1. The situation is different when the membrane is labile and tends to change its properties in response to the instantaneous value of the transmembrane potential.

The P.D.M. curve of a labile membrane

As an example of a labile membrane responsive to the value of the transmembrane potential, let us consider the nerve (or muscle) fiber membrane. If the value of E is increased from the resting value by an applied emf, the membrane becomes less permeable to ions. Conversely, if E is decreased, the membrane becomes more "leaky." When the depolarization is carried far enough, the membrane changes its properties in such a way as to demand a reversal of polarity. At high values of E the permeability to potassium ions is much greater than that to sodium ions; since the concentration of potassium ion is greater inside the fiber, the membrane demands a positive value of E. The evidence seems to indicate that, when the membrane is depolarized strongly enough, it changes to a state which favors the passage of sodium ions; since the concentration of sodium is greater on the outside, the membrane in this state demands a negative value of E. Thus it is plausible to assume that, when very high positive values of E are imposed upon the membrane, the latter changes into a state whose P.D.M. approaches the potassium concentration potential, whereas at high negative values of E the P.D.M. approaches the sodium concentration potential.

The P.D.M. characteristics of a membrane of this type are shown schematically in Fig. 12.7A. In this diagram the abscissas give the value of the transmembrane potential E. The ordinate of a point on the curve gives the P.D.M. of the membrane. The curve may be interpreted as follows. At high positive values of E the membrane approaches asymptotically a state whose P.D.M. equals the potassium concentration potential; at high negative values of E the P.D.M. approaches a value which is negative and equal to the sodium concentration potential. The curve $ABPQRC$ shows the gradual transition between these two states. The instantaneous mutual interaction between the transmembrane potential and the P.D.M. may be illustrated by the following examples. When $E = E_4$, the membrane tends to reach the state represented by point Q; in this state the membrane demands that $E = E_8$. When $E = E_5$, the membrane tends to reach state R; in this state the P.D.M. is E_7. In both cases there is a disparity between the value of E and the value of the P.D.M. of the corresponding point on the curve.

The three points A, B, C on the curve are of particular interest. These are the points of intersection of the curve with the unit slope line CBA passing through the origin. They represent the only three states of the membrane in each of which the potential demand of the membrane is in agreement with the value of E calling for the respective state.

Let us assume that the transmembrane potential is E_1 and that the membrane is in the state A. The values of E and of the P.D.M. are the same, and the system is in a stable state. Let this situation represent the nerve in the resting state. We will further assume that at some given instant the value of the transmembrane potential is changed, more or less rapidly, to $E = E_4$ by means of an external emf transmitted by way of an outside electrode and an inside electrode inserted axially into the fiber.

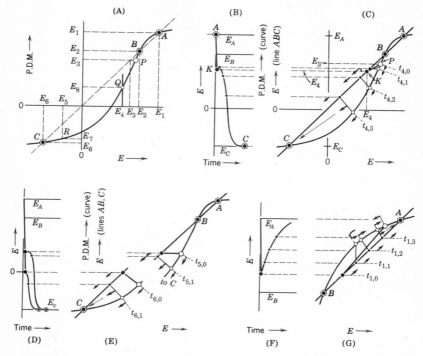

Fig. 12.7.   (A)   The potential demand of a nerve fiber membrane.   Abscissa: value of transmembrane potential.   Points on the curve represent the state of the membrane demanded by the corresponding transmembrane potential.   The ordinate of each point represents the transmembrane potential demanded by the respective state of the membrane.   In this diagram it is assumed that at the end of a certain stimulus the value of E was left at E_4, whereas the membrane was passing through state P at the instant the stimulation was terminated.

(C), (E), (G)   Analysis of the spontaneous courses of four combinations left in the wakes of four different stimuli.   The two points of a given combination are called conjugate points.   Both the abscissa and the ordinate of the point on the unit slope line give the instantaneous value of the transmembrane potential E.   The tie line in each combination connects the solid circle with its conjugate on the curve.   The latter represents the instantaneous state of the membrane.   The ordinate of the point on the curve represents the instantaneous potential demand of the membrane.   In general, the two demands are in conflict, and the system is unstable; as a result, the combination drifts spontaneously in a manner governed by rules I and II stated in the text. A, B, C are double points representing the only three combinations in which there is no conflict between the demands of the two points.

(B), (D), (F)   The temporal course of E obtained by projection of the successive positions of the solid circle in the associated diagrams (C), (E), and (G).   The same curves are given, with different scales, in Fig. 12.8M.

If the changes in the state of the membrane could take place instantaneously, the state of the membrane at every instant during stimulation would be represented by a point on the curve corresponding to the instantaneous value of E.   In particular, when E reaches the value E_4, the membrane would be in the state indicated by point Q.   However, since the changes are of a physical or a chemical nature, the changes proceed at some finite rate;   as a result there is a lag between the instantaneous state of the membrane and the state called for by the instantaneous value of E.   Let us assume for the sake of concreteness that at the instant when E reaches the value E_4 the membrane passes through state P.   Let us also assume that stimulation is stopped at this instant.   The system is left in an unstable state, since the membrane is not in the state called for by the instantaneous value of E, and, on the other hand, the value of E is not equal to E_3, the value demanded by the instantaneous state of the membrane.   The events following immediately after the termination of the stimulus may be described as follows.   The transmembrane potential will begin to increase from the value E_4, trying to reach the value E_3, in accordance with the demands of the membrane.   At the same time the membrane will proceed to change from state P, in the direction PQ, attempting to reach the state Q called for by the instantaneous value of E_4. Briefly stated, the line E_4Q, representing the instantaneous value of E, will start moving to the right; the point P, representing the instantaneous state of the membrane, will start moving along the curve in the direction PQ.   While these two elements keep changing with time, their goals also keep changing.   The ultimate outcome of this mutual interaction, with shifting goals, may be represented more conveniently by the type of diagram shown in Fig. 12.7C.

The spontaneous behavior of the system subsequent to a stimulus

In Fig. 12.7C the abscissas represent the instantaneous value of E. Since the two coordinates of a point on the unit slope line ABC are always equal, the instantaneous value of E may also be represented by a point (solid circle) on this line.   Thus point K indicates that the instantaneous value of E is E_4.   The instantaneous state of the membrane may be represented by a point (open circle) on the curve; a tie line may be used to indicate the simultaneous values of E and of the P.D.M.   Thus the pair *combination K-P* indicates that the instantaneous value of E is E_4, whereas the instantaneous state of the membrane is P, whose demand is that $E = E_3$.   The two points connected by a tie line will be referred to as *conjugate points.*

For the sake of conciseness it will be convenient to speak of the movement of each of the two points of a combination, rather than to speak of the changes taking place in the value of E and in the state of the membrane. Thus, referring again to Fig. 12.7C, we may say that point K tends to move upward along the unit slope line, and its instantaneous goal is to reach the value E_3 demanded by the membrane. At the same time point P tends to move downward along the curve toward the point on the curve situated directly below K so that it may reach the state demanded by the instantaneous transmembrane potential.

If the system is left in a state represented by some other combination of two conjugate points, the movements of the points are apt to be different. For economy of thought it will be helpful to apply the following general rule.

Rule I. When the system is left in an unstable state represented by a pair of conjugate points, the point on the unit slope line tends to move along the line in the direction which will bring it to the horizontal line passing through its conjugate; the point on the curve tends to move along the curve in the direction which will bring it to the vertical line passing through its conjugate point.

With the use of this rule we can predict the ultimate fate of a given combination. In Fig. 12.7C let the combination K-P represent the state of the system as a whole at the time $t_{4,0}$. According to rule I the combination will undergo both a translation and a clockwise rotation. Eventually there must come an instant $t_{4,1}$ at which the orientation of the combination is horizontal. At this instant the solid circle is momentarily stationary, whereas the open circle continues in its downward motion. As a result of this motion the orientation of the combination changes again, and the point on the unit slope line commences to move downward. The diagram shows two subsequent positions of the combination, at $t_{4,2}$ and at $t_{4,3}$, respectively. It should be clear that the ultimate destination of this combination is point C. This point, as well as points B and A, will be referred to as *double points*, since they lie both on the curve and on the unit slope line; they represent combinations in which there is no conflict between the demands of the two points.

An examination of the arrows located just above the unit slope line will show that the temporal course of E may be described as follows. At the termination of the stimulus, $E = E_4$; thereupon the value of E rises spontaneously, reaches a maximum, begins to decrease, and finally reaches the value E_C. Figure 12.7B shows the temporal course of E more clearly. The line AK shows the course of E during the forced depolarization by the imposed emf. The curve KC shows the spontaneous changes taking place after the stimulation is terminated. The same curve is represented in Fig. 12.8M, with different scales, by the solid branch of curve 4. This branch represents the first phase of an action potential. The **dashed** branch represents the recovery phase of the action potential and is not the subject of the present discussion.

The upper part of Fig. 12.7E illustrates the case when, at the end of the stimulation, there is left a combination (at $t_{5,0}$) whose orientation is horizontal. The point on the unit slope curve (solid circle) is momentarily stationary, i.e., the value of E is momentarily stationary; on the other hand, the conjugate point on the curve starts moving downward. At a later instant $t_{5,1}$, the orientation is not horizontal any more, and both points move as indicated by the arrows. The ultimate destination of this combination is also the double point C. The potential-time course is shown in Fig. 12.7D (upper curve) and also in Fig. 12.7M (solid branch of curve 5). Note that the initial slope of the curve is zero.

The lower part of Fig. 12.7E shows the behavior of a combination whose orientation is "northwest to southeast" to start with. As indicated by the arrows and, as shown more clearly in the lower curve of Fig. 12.7D, the value of E starts falling at a finite rate from the very beginning and eventually reaches the potential of the double point C.

The three combinations examined so far were all located within the lower loop BC of the "figure 8" made by the curve and the unit slope line. In all three cases the ultimate destination of the combination was at the double point C. Let us consider the fate of a combination located entirely in the upper loop of the figure. An illustration is given in Fig. 12.7G, in which the loop AB is drawn on a larger scale. Let us assume that at the time $t_{1,0}$ stimulation of the fiber is stopped and the system is left in the state represented by the combination $t_{1,0}$. Application of rule I will show that the combination will pass successively through the orientations shown in the diagram and marked $t_{1,1}$, $t_{1,2}$, and $t_{1,3}$. It should be clear that the ultimate destination of this combination is at the double point A. The spontaneous behavior of each of the four combinations examined so far is in agreement with a second rule governing the movement of the combinations.

Rule II. If a combination is situated in a region where the curve lies below the unit slope line, the ultimate destination of the combination is at the double point at the lower end of the region. If a combination is situated in a region where the curve lies above the unit slope line, its ultimate destination is at the double point at the upper end of the region.

Stimulation with internal electrode; temporal course of transmembrane potential

With the use of an internal electrode and an external electrode facing it across the membrane, it is possible to impress upon the membrane the desired time course of forced depolarization (Cole, 1949; Marmont,

1949; Hodgkin, Huxley, and Katz, 1952). Turning to Fig. 12.8H, let us assume again that point *A* represents the resting state of the membrane.

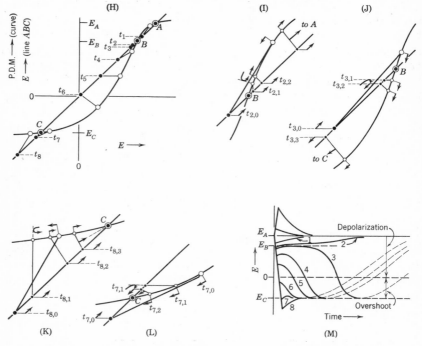

Fig. 12.8.   (H) A nerve fiber is forcibly depolarized by means of internal and external electrodes.   The diagram shows schematically the successive positions of the combinations which represent the instantaneous states of the system as a whole at the successive instants t_1, t_2, $\cdots$, t_8.   Only the solid circles of the combinations at t_2 and t_3 are shown.

(I), (J), (K), (L)   Analysis of the spontaneous behavior of the system when stimulation is stopped at the instants t_2, t_3, t_8, and t_7, respectively.   The analysis of the spontaneous behavior of the system when stimulation is stopped at t_1, t_4, t_5, and t_6 is given in Fig. 12.7.

(M)   Slanting solid line: Temporal course of *E* during the forced stimulation.   Solid curves 1, 2, $\cdots$, 8: The spontaneous temporal course of *E* subsequent to the stimulus when the latter is discontinued at t_1, t_2, $\cdots$, t_8, respectively.   Upper two curves: Spontaneous temporal course of *E* subsequent to a forced increase in *E*.   Dashed curves: Recovery phase following the "rising" phase of the action potential and brought about by the slow development of restorative influences.

Let us assume also that, with the use of two electrodes facing each other across the membrane, the membrane is depolarized, more or less rapidly, until at the time t_8 the value *E* is that shown by the solid circle near the bottom of the unit slope line. Because of the lag in the readjustment of the state of the membrane, when stimulation is stopped at t_8, the system is left in a state represented by the combination marked t_8 whose orientation is "southwest to northeast." Since in this region the P.D.M. curve is above the unit slope line, the ultimate destination of this combination is at the double point C, according to rule II, stated earlier. In Fig. 12.8K this combination is shown on a larger scale. In this diagram t_8 is called the new zero time, $t_{8,0}$. Rule I, stated earlier, enables us to predict in detail the movement of the combination while it is on its way to point C. It may be seen that in this case the movement of the solid circle is monotonically upward. The temporal course of E is shown more clearly by the schematic curve 8 in Fig. 12.8M. This curve is similar to the curve obtained experimentally by Hodgkin, Huxley, and Katz (1952, Fig. 8, curve 153).

Let us assume that in another experiment stimulation is stopped at a time t_7 (Fig. 12.8H) when the pair combination stradles point C. In this case the two conjugate points begin to move toward each other (rule I). There are two alternative possibilities. Either the combination eventually finds itself entirely above C or it finds itself entirely below C. In either case the ultimate destination of the combination is at the double point C (rule II). An illustration of the second alternative is shown on a large scale in Fig. 12.8L. It may be seen from the movement of the solid circle that E increases at first, passes through a maximum at $t_{7,1}$, and eventually reaches the value E_C. This behavior is shown schematically in curve 7 of Fig. 12.8M (cf. Hodgkin, Huxley, and Katz, 1952, Fig. 8, curve 115).

If stimulation is stopped at time t_1 (Fig. 12.8H), the combination left in the wake of the stimulus has the orientation shown in the figure. The same orientation is shown on a larger scale in Fig. 12.7G. In this figure t_1 is called the new zero time, $t_{1,0}$. The temporal course of E was discussed earlier and is shown in both Fig. 12.7F and Fig. 12.8M (curve 1).

If stimulation is stopped at time t_4 (Fig. 12.8H), the combination left in the wake of the stimulus behaves as shown in Fig. 12.7C. The temporal course of E is shown in Fig. 12.7B and in Fig. 12.8M (solid branch of curve 4; cf. Hodgkin, Huxley, and Katz, 1952, Fig. 8, curves 38, 57, 77).

Inspection of Fig. 12.8H will show that the combinations at t_4, t_5, and t_6 are all situated between points B and C. It follows that, if stimulation is stopped at any one of these instances, the respective combination will reach point C (rule II), i.e., excitation will take place. The orientation of the combination depends upon the rate at which the forced depolarization takes place. If the rate is very high, the lag of the open circle behind the solid circle is large, and the resultant orientation is "northeast to southwest." If the forced depolarization is carried out slowly, the combination is almost vertical.　The combinations at t_5 and at t_6 show intermediate orientations.　The spontaneous behavior of these combinations was examined in Fig. 12.7E.　The membrane potential-time curves are shown in Fig. 12.7D and in Fig. 12.8M (solid branches of curves 5 and 6).　Since Hodgkin, Huxley, and Katz used rapid shocks, none of the experimental curves obtained by them shows the appearance of curves 5 and 6 of Fig. 12.8M.

The temporal course of the transmembrane potential in the critical region

Of particular interest is the spontaneous behavior of the system when, at the end of the stimulus, it is left in a state represented by a combination which straddles point B.　Two such combinations are indicated in Fig. 12.8H, at times t_2 and t_3.　In this figure only the solid circle of each of the two combinations is shown.　In Fig. 12.8I and Fig. 12.8J the same combinations are shown at the instants $t_{2,0}$ and $t_{3,0}$, respectively.　In Fig. 12.8I the two points of the combination at $t_{2,0}$ begin to move toward each other (rule I).　At some instant $t_{2,1}$ the combination reaches a vertical orientation above point B.　At this instant the open circle is momentarily stationary, whereas the solid circle continues moving upward. The latter movement forces the open circle to start moving upward, and eventually the combination reaches the double point at A (rule II).

Let us consider the rates of movement of the points when the combination is in the close vicinity of point B.　The instantaneous rate of change of each point depends on the distance between its instantaneous position and its instantaneous goal.　At the instant $t_{2,1}$ the instantaneous goal of the solid circle is the point on the curve situated on the horizontal line passing through the open circle.　It is important to keep in mind that Fig. 12.8I is drawn on a large scale and that the distance between the instantaneous position and the instantaneous goal of the solid circle at time $t_{2,1}$ is very small.　It follows that the rate of movement is very small.　It may be stated as a general rule that the movement of either point of the combination is slow when the combination as a whole is situated in the close vicinity of point B (or of one of the other double points).　The temporal course of the transmembrane potential in Fig. 12.8I is represented by curve 2, Fig. 12.8M.　E changes fairly rapidly while the two points approach both each other and the vicinity of point B. There follows a very slow change while the two points hover in the vicinity of point B.　Eventually, as the combination leaves the vicinity of B, on its way to point A, the rate of change increases.　Later on, when the combination approaches A and the distance between the instantaneous position and the instantaneous goal begins to decrease again, the rate of movement also begins to decrease.　These factors account for the peculiar shape of curve 2 and the marked differences between this curve and the "exponential" curve 1. Curve 2 is similar to the experimental curves obtained by Hodgkin, Huxley, and Katz (1952, Fig. 9, lowest two of the family of curves labeled "11.8 to 12").

Let us assume that stimulation is stopped at a time t_3 (Fig. 12.8H). Let this instant be called the new zero time $t_{3,0}$, as in Fig. 12.8J. We will assume that the absolute value of $t_3 - t_2$ is small but is large enough to produce large relative changes in the distances between each of the two conjugate points and point B (cf. Figs. 12.8I and 12.8J). In that case the combination left at t_3 will eventually acquire a horizontal orientation just below point B, as is illustrated by the combination $t_{3,1}$. It should be clear that, according to rule II, the ultimate destination of this combination will be at the double point C. Furthermore, the rates of change of this combination will be small until after it leaves the vicinity of point B. The expected temporal course of E is shown schematically in the solid branch of curve 3, Fig. 12.8M. The curve starts with a finite slope, passes through an exceedingly shallow maximum, and proceeds toward the potential of state C. This curve is similar to five experimental curves obtained by Hodgkin, Huxley, and Katz (1952, Fig. 9).

When the transmembrane potential is *increased* by an emf applied through electrodes facing each other across the membrane, the end of the stimulus leaves the system in a state which may be represented by a combination (not shown in Fig. 12.8) situated above the double point A, with the point on the unit slope line farther away from A than the point on the curve. The reader may satisfy himself that this combination will drift back to A and that the value of E will decrease monotonically. Two such curves, representing two different strengths of polarization, are shown at the top of Fig. 12.8M. They are similar to the five experimental curves obtained by Hodgkin, Huxley, and Katz (1952, Fig. 8, curves −9.6 to −115).

The interpretation of the experimental curves shown schematically in Fig. 12.8M, with the aid of Fig. 12.8H, may be summarized as follows. Electrical stimulation of the membrane produces a demand for a change in the state of the membrane. The membrane changes its properties at a finite rate. At the termination of the stimulus the system as a whole is left in an unstable state, since, in general, the instantaneous state of the membrane is not that demanded by the instantaneous transmembrane potential and, at the same time, the instantaneous value of the transmembrane potential is not that demanded by the instantaneous state of the membrane. If the combination left in the wake of the stimulus is situated above B, the system reverts to the resting state A without excitation; if the combination is left below B, the system changes spontaneously to state C, i.e., excitation takes place.   Attention to the manner in which the two points of a given combination move yields detailed information about the nature of the spontaneous temporal course of the potential subsequent to stimulation.   In particular, this approach offers a simple explanation of curves such as 2 and 3, Fig. 12.8M, obtained when the stimulus leaves the system near the critical region.   Let us now consider what light this method of approach sheds on the nature of the critical state of the system in a given experiment.

Nature of the critical state

For any specified rate of forced depolarization there is a critical instant t_{crit}.   This is the time at which the combination is so situated that it straddles point B, with the two points at such distances from B that, if the stimulation were stopped at that instant, the two points would spontaneously meet at point B.   The value of E_{crit} at t_{crit} is slightly below E_B.   If the experiment is repeated, with a lower rate of forced depolarization, the value of t_{crit} is, naturally, larger; the value of E_{crit} in the second experiment is slightly higher than the critical value in the first experiment, since the lag is smaller, and both points are closer to point B at the critical time.   In the extreme case when the forced depolarization is carried out slowly, the two points arrive at B almost simultaneously, and the critical potential is E_B.   At the other extreme, when the forced depolarization is exceedingly fast, the lagging point of the pair combination is still practically at A at the critical instant, whereas the leading point on the unit slope line is somewhere below B.   Judging from the experimental results of Hodgkin, Huxley, and Katz, who used rapid shocks, the difference between E_{crit} (rapid depolarization) and the value $E_{crit} = E_B$ (very slow depolarization) is very small.   Thus in a series of experiments in each of which the respective critical point is reached at different rates, the values of E_{crit} fall within a small range extending from E_B downward.

The description "low rate of depolarization" is relative.   It is assumed that the rate of depolarization is low compared with the rate of depolarization in a shock; yet, not so low as to allow time for the development of those secondary slow changes which, when fully developed, lead to the restoration of the fiber to the resting state subsequent to the development of the actual potential.   The present discussion does not deal with the changes exemplified by the dashed branches of the curves shown in Fig. 12.8M.

Stimulation with constant currents and external electrodes

In the preceding discussion it was assumed that an internal electrode and an external electrode facing each other across the membrane were employed.   With this experimental arrangement the transmembrane potential may be given the desired temporal course during stimulation. The situation is different when the two electrodes are applied externally at two points along the fiber, and the stimulus consists of a constant current of strength I. The potential at the outside surface of the membrane under one of the electrodes changes in a complicated fashion. The potential at the internal surface under the same electrodes changes in a different fashion. The change in the transmembrane potential ΔE follows yet a different course. It may be safely assumed that in a given experiment the critical point is reached when ΔE reaches some critical value $(\Delta E)_{crit}$, and that this value is approximately the same for different strengths of the stimulating current.

If the functional relation between E, t, and I can be formulated, this relation will give the time of arrival at the critical point as a function of t, i.e., the strength-duration curve. The mathematical description of the temporal course of E with a subadequate stimulus should promote the understanding of the nature of the process responsible for accommodation, opening excitation at the anode, and other post-stimulus changes. The derivation of the functional relation between I, t, and E will be undertaken in the next section.

In setting up the desired differential equations it will be necessary to employ parameters whose values obviously must depend on the instantaneous properties of the membrane. Referring again to Fig. 12.8H, the ordinate of a point on the P.D.M. curve offers a measure of the difference between the state of the membrane at that point and the resting state of the membrane at A. These ordinates begin to change rapidly only after the steep part of the curve is reached. Since there is a lag between the point moving on the curve and the point moving on the unit slope line, we may assume, as a first approximation, that, up to the time the solid circle reaches the critical region, the open circle is still on the nearly horizontal part of the curve; in consequence the properties of the membrane remain nearly constant up to the critical point, and the use of constant parameters is justifiable, as a first approximation.

When the stimulus consists of a current which, starting from zero intensity, increases at a constant rate ($I = ct$), Fig. 12.8H may still be used to interpret the experimental results, provided that c is not too small. If c is small, the lag between the two points of the combination is also small, and the use of constant parameters is not justifiable. Furthermore, if c is sufficiently small, the calculated time of arrival at the critical point is large enough to allow the development of the secondary restorative changes which in the usual experiment with a constant current come into play only after the action potential is fully developed (cf. Hodgkin, Huxley, and Katz, 1952; Hodgkin and Huxley, 1952a,b,c,d).

The temporal course, in stimulation, of the outside potential, of the inside potential, and of the transmembrane potential

Letting the potential at the outside surface of the membrane relative to some point whose potential remains constant be V, and the potential at the inside surface relative to the same point be U, the transmembrane potential is given by the equation $E = V - U$.

When an anodic stimulus is applied at the outside, the value of V begins to rise at once. Eventually, the local inward transmembrane current affects the value of U, and the inside potential also rises. If the stimulus is applied for a long enough time, a steady state is established, and the value of E reaches some steady value, which is greater than E_0. For every value of V there is a steady state value of U which is in equilibrium with it.

If a variable anodic stimulus is used, of such a nature that V increases at an exceedingly slow rate, the membrane has the opportunity to keep up the appropriate value of E. The values of V and of U in such an experiment are shown in Fig. 12.10B, where the ordinates represent potentials, and the abscissas represent time. The value of E increases continuously. The course of ΔE is shown in diagram (D).

The temporal courses of V, U, and of ΔE with an exceedingly slow cathodic stimulus are shown in diagrams A and C of Fig. 12.10. In this case the transmembrane potential decreases continuously.

The readjustment of the ionic concentrations within the membrane, in response to a changing transmembrane potential, is not an instantaneous process. Figure 12.9 shows schematically the concentration "profiles" of sodium and of potassium, respectively, for the cases when the transmembrane potential is zero (as in case A), and when E has two different positive values (as in B and C). The reason for and the nature of the curvatures of the concentration curves were discussed in connection with Fig. 11.2. If the system is changed suddenly from the pattern represented by B to that represented by C, the steady state is not reached until the total amount of sodium within the membrane is increased, and the total amount of potassium is decreased by the amounts indicated, respectively, by the shaded areas. It is desirable to carry out a rough calculation to determine whether the half time of this process is negligible in comparison with the half time of the other processes taking place in a stimulated nerve.

The concentration of sodium, the major ion on the outside of the nerve fiber, is normally of the order of 0.5 M, or 5×10^{-4} moles per cc. Let the distribution coefficient of this ion be b. The total amount of sodium per square centimeter of membrane, whose thickness is of the order of 10^{-6} cm, is of the order of $5 \times 10^{-10}b$ moles. The change in the sodium content from one steady state to another is of the order of $5 \times 10^{-11}b$ moles.

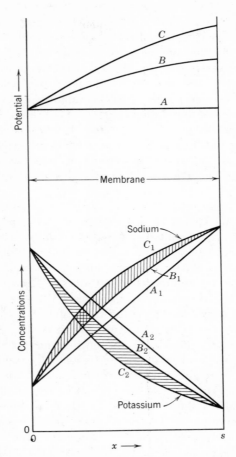

Fig. 12.9. Upper diagram: Three schematic examples of the potential pattern across the membrane. A: The transmembrane potential E is zero. B, C: Potential patterns for two different steady state values of E. The corresponding distributions of concentrations of sodium and of potassium are shown schematically in the lower diagram.

Lower diagram: If the transmembrane potential is changed from E_C to E_B, the total amount of sodium within the membrane must decrease, and the total amount of potassium must increase, by amounts proportional to the respective shaded areas, before the new steady state is fully established. This process takes time, of the order of a millisecond. It follows that the inside potential U does not keep pace with the imposed variation of the outside potential V, but lags behind unless variations in V are exceedingly slow.

The flux of radioactive sodium in resting nerve is of the order of 10^{-10} moles per sq cm per sec (Keynes, 1949). When electrostatic equilibrium is disturbed, the flux changes. Part of the change in flux is accounted for by a change in the number of ions crossing the membrane; the remainder is accounted for by a change in the sodium content of the membrane. A generous allowance for the latter part would be as much as 10^{-10} moles per sq cm per sec. At this rate it would take $0.5b$ sec to complete the change of the sodium content. Half times in the excitation process of nerve are of the order of 1 msec. It follows that b would have to possess a value much smaller than 0.002 to render negligible the time of readjustment of ions within the membrane, and this seems unlikely. Thus we conclude that the readjustment in the value of U lags by an appreciable time.

The temporal courses of U and of V, when a constant current stimulus is applied at the outside of the membrane, are shown in Figs. 12.10E,F for cathodic and anodic stimuli, respectively. At zero time, when the circuit is closed, the value of V responds at once to the charges introduced by the electrode, with a finite rate of change. At zero time there is no transmembrane current, and the value of U does not change momentarily; the slope of the U curve is zero at zero time. Eventually, the value of U changes in the same direction as the value of V.

The corresponding courses of ΔE are shown in diagrams G and H, respectively. At the cathode the transmembrane potential decreases rapidly, passes through a minimum, and eventually reaches the steady state value. At the anode the transmembrane potential increases rapidly, passes through a maximum, and eventually also reaches the steady state value. The six curves shown in Figs. 12.10E,G were plotted to scale from equations developed in a later section. They show that the transmembrane potential passes through a minimum at the cathode and through a maximum at the anode, before reaching the steady state value. This need not always be the case; in the process of developing the mathematical equations, the nature of the physical conditions which bring about these critical points in the transmembrane potential curve will be examined.

Some fundamental differential equations and the nature of the curves of U, V, and E

Let the instantaneous value of the change in the outside potential be v, the change in the value of the inside potential be u, and the change in the transmembrane potential be w.

$$V - V_0 = v \qquad U - U_0 = u \qquad \Delta E = v - u = w \qquad (12.9)$$

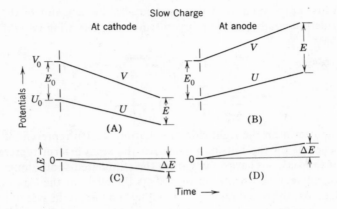

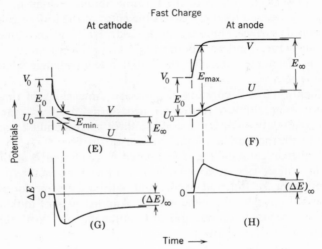

Fig. 12.10. (A), (B), (C), (D) If the outside potential V is changed very slowly, the membrane manages to maintain, at each instant, the steady state appropriate to the instantaneous value of V. The inside potential U keeps pace with the outside potential, and the transmembrane potential E decreases monotonically at the cathode and increases monotonically at the anode.

(E), (F), (G), (H) If the outside potential is changed rapidly, the changes in U lag behind. The initial value of dU/dt is zero. With a constant stimulating current, the value of the transmembrane potential passes through a minimum at the cathode, and through a maximum at the anode. Eventually, the transmembrane potential approaches a constant value, smaller than E_0 at the cathode and larger than E_0 at the anode. Since the change in the threshold is proportional to the change in the transmembrane potential, the temporal course of the threshold (Fig. 12.4) during stimulation with constant currents is accounted for.

As a first approximation let us assume that the behavior of the outside and inside potentials may be represented by the following two differential equations:

$$\frac{dv}{dt} = AI - \frac{1}{B}v - \frac{m}{B}(v - u) \qquad (12.10)$$

$$\frac{du}{dt} = \frac{n}{B}(v - u) - \frac{q}{B}u \qquad (12.11)$$

The first term on the right side of equation (12.10) represents the effect of the current on the outside potential; the second term represents the effect of the leak of charge away from the stimulated spot, along the outside electrolyte; the third term represents the effect of the leak of charge inward, across the membrane. The first term on the right side of equation (12.11) represents the effect of the transmembrane current on the inside potential; the second term represents the effect of the leak of charge away from the inside surface, along the inside electrolyte. At zero time, starting with resting nerve, v and u are both zero; at zero time the outside potential changes at the finite rate AI; the initial rate of change of the inside potential is zero.

The quantity B is a constant, having the dimensions of time. m, n, and q are dimensionless ratios, all necessarily positive; their values represent the relative importance of the three corresponding processes as compared with the leak along the exterior of the fiber.

The mathematical handling is facilitated if we choose B as the unit of time; this unit equals approximately Hill's first time factor (p. 660); it will be different for different nerves, but will be the same for all experiments carried out with the same nerve. Another way of looking at it is that time is measured as a multiple of the time unit B. With this change the equations read as follows:

$$dv/dt = ABI - v - m(v - u) \qquad du/dt = n(v - u) - qu \quad (12.12a,b)$$

We may rearrange the terms in the two equations and write the result in operator form:

$$(D + 1 + m)v \qquad\qquad - mu = ABI \qquad (12.13)$$

$$- nv + (D + n + q)u = 0 \qquad (12.14)$$

where D is the operator d/dt; in the equation which follows D^2 is the operator d^2/dt^2.

To eliminate v from this pair of simultaneous differential equations, we multiply the first equation by n, and the second equation by the operator $(D + 1 + m)$, then add the resulting equations:

$$[D^2 + (1 + m + n + q)D + (n + q + mq)]u = nABI \quad (12.15)$$

The general solution of this differential equation is as follows:

$$u = C_1 e^{r_1 t} + C_2 e^{r_2 t} + K \qquad \left(K = \frac{nABI}{n + q + mq} \right) \qquad (12.16)$$

C_1 and C_2 are constants whose values depend upon the initial values of v and u. r_1 and r_2 are the two roots of the following quadratic equation:

$$r^2 + (1 + m + n + q)r + (n + q + mq) = 0 \qquad (12.17)$$

The solution of a second order linear differential equation may be an oscillatory function if the roots of the quadratic equation are imaginary, or non-oscillatory if the roots are real. Analysis of the quadratic equation (12.17) shows that r_1 and r_2 are both real and negative for all positive values of m, n, and q. It follows that u is a non-oscillatory function; the functions v and w are also non-oscillatory, since they contain the same exponentials. Since v represents what is usually known as the electrotonic potential, and w represents the change in the transmembrane potential, this conclusion is of considerable practical interest. It shows that the type of model under consideration is not adequate for interpreting the phenomena of oscillation, which are known to occur when the concentration of calcium is reduced or under some other conditions. The chief inadequacy of this type of model resides in the fact that equations (12.5 to 12.8, 12.10, 12.11) do not allow for the gradual changes in the membrane, but assume that the whole change takes place suddenly when the critical point is reached. Thus, although the theory is sufficient to account for the nature of the strength-duration curve, accommodation, opening excitation at the anode, and the post-stimulus changes in threshold, a more elaborate model is needed in order to account for oscillation. Since the aspects for which the model is adequate are of fundamental interest, the theory is developed further on this basis in the following paragraphs.

Substitution of (12.16) in (12.12b) gives the value of v as a function of t:

$$v = \frac{n + q + r_1}{n} C_1 e^{r_1 t} + \frac{n + q + r_2}{n} C_2 e^{r_2 t} + \frac{n + q}{n} K \qquad (12.18)$$

Since both r_1 and r_2 are negative, both v and u approach limiting values at infinite time. These are the steady state values for v and u with a given constant current I; these steady state values are independent of the initial conditions, which control the values of C_1 and C_2 only. The steady state values with current I may be obtained from (12.16), (12.18), and (12.9):

$$v = \frac{n + q}{n + q + mq} ABI \qquad u = \frac{n}{n + q + mq} ABI \qquad w = \frac{q}{n + q + mq} ABI$$

$$\text{(steady state values)} \qquad (12.19a,b,c)$$

To solve for C_1 and C_2 we substitute the initial conditions, $t = 0$, $v = 0$, $u = 0$, in equations (12.16) and (12.18). Substitution of the values of C_1 and C_2 yields the values of v, u, and w for the case of stimulation with constant current I.

$$v = [-(n + q + r_1)r_2 e^{r_1 t} + (n + q + r_2)r_1 e^{r_2 t}$$
$$-(n + q)(r_2 - r_1)]\frac{ABI}{(r_2 - r_1)(n + q + mq)} \quad (12.20)$$

$$u = [-nr_2 e^{r_1 t} + nr_1 e^{r_2 t} + n(r_2 - r_1)]\frac{ABI}{(r_2 - r_1)(n + q + mq)} \quad (12.21)$$

$$w = [-(q + r_1)r_2 e^{r_1 t} + (q + r_2)r_1 e^{r_2 t}$$
$$+ q(r_2 - r_1)]\frac{ABI}{(r_2 - r_1)(n + q + mq)} \quad (12.22)$$

Thus all three functions are directly proportional to the stimulating current I. It follows that, once the curve of one of the functions is drawn, the same function for a current which is k times as strong may be drawn by increasing the ordinates of the first curve k-fold. A simpler method is to use the same curve and to indicate a scale of ordinates which is smaller by the factor $1/k$. Another property which follows from the proportionality to I is that, if one of the functions has a critical point (i.e., a maximum or a minimum), the critical point occurs at the same value of t for all values of I. Finally, if we use the same values of the parameters both for cathodic and anodic stimulation, the curves for cathodic stimulation are the mirror images across the time axis of the corresponding curves for anodic stimulation.

For the interpretation of accommodation, it is important to know whether the function w possesses any critical points (maxima or minima), and, if so, under what conditions. A critical point appears when the first derivative of the function is zero. Since r_1 and r_2 are both negative, the slope of each curve obviously approaches zero at infinite time. From our point of view the significant question is whether the three functions possess critical points at finite times.

The function v can have a critical point only if the following equation is satisfied:

$$(n + q + r_1)e^{r_1 t} = (n + q + r_2)e^{r_2 t} \quad (12.23)$$

This equation possesses a solution only if the coefficients of the exponentials appearing on the two sides of the equation are of the same sign. To determine whether this condition is met, we examine the sign of the product $(n + q + r_1)(n + q + r_2)$. The values of the two roots, r_1 and r_2, may be obtained from equation (12.17). Omitting the details of the analysis, the indicated product equals $- 4mn$. Since the product is always negative, the function v does not possess any critical points; v is monotonic.

The function u possesses critical points when $e^{r_1 t} = e^{r_2 t}$. Since the two roots r_1 and r_2 are different, this condition is satisfied only at infinite time, as mentioned earlier, and at $t = 0$. Thus the function u is also monotonic.

From equation (12.22) it may be seen that the function w possesses a critical point when the quantities $(q + r_1)$ and $(q + r_2)$ have the same sign. Comparing their signs by the method of products, one finds that the product equals $n(1 - q)$. It follows that the function w possesses a critical point only under the condition that q is less than 1.0. Inspection of equation (12.11) yields a physical interpretation of this condition. The function $\Delta E = w$ possesses a critical point only in those cases in which the dissipation of the inside charge by conduction through the inside solution is slower than the dissipation of the outside charge by conduction through the outside solution.

When the condition $q < 1$ is met, w possesses a minimum in cathodic stimulation and a maximum in anodic stimulation. Anticipating an interpretation which is given later on, we may identify the time at which the minimum occurs in w as the utilization time of the nerve. This quantity, as may be readily verified, is given by the following equation:

$$\text{Utilization time} = t_{\min} = t_{\max} = \frac{1}{r_2 - r_1} \ln \frac{q + r_1}{q + r_2} \qquad (12.24)$$

The value of w at the critical point may be obtained by substitution of the value of $t_{\max}$ in equation (12.22). However, the formula obtained for this quantity is rather complicated; for convenience we may refer to it by the symbol $w_{\max}$, $w_{\min}$, or w_M, as the case may require.

Temporal course of V, U, and ΔE during stimulation and after the circuit is opened

In discussing the relation of these curves to the problems of stimulation, it will be convenient to refer to the graphs of the curves for some concrete case, with specific values for m, n, and q, such as the following:

$$m = 0.1 \qquad n = 0.1 \qquad q = 0.05 \qquad (12.25)$$

With these values of the parameters, the roots, r_1 and r_2, of the quadratic equation (12.17) are -0.1397 and -1.110, respectively. For stimulation with constant current I from rest, the changes v, u, and w are given by the equations:

$$v = (-0.0758e^{-0.1397t} - 0.892e^{-1.110t} + 0.968)ABI \qquad (12.26)$$

$$u = (-0.737e^{-0.1397t} + 0.0929e^{-1.110t} + 0.644)ABI \qquad (12.27)$$

$$w = (0.661e^{-0.1397t} - 0.985e^{-1.110t} + 0.324)ABI \qquad (12.28)$$

$$w_{max} = 0.729ABI, \text{ at } t_{max} = 2.545 \qquad (12.29)$$

$$w_\infty = 0.324ABI \qquad (12.30)$$

I is positive for anodic stimulation, and negative for cathodic stimulation. The three curves are shown to scale in Figs. 12.10E,F,G,H for cathodic and anodic stimulation.

Figure 12.11A shows schematically the patterns of the currents operating at three selected instants in the course of an experiment with cathodic stimulation. At zero time, current I is initiated; the resulting temporal course of ΔE, which has been discussed earlier, is shown again in curve OA. The various currents in operation after the steady state is reached are shown in the middle scheme. The transmembrane current i_M, and the longitudinal currents in the outside solution, i_1 and i_2, just compensate for the loss of charge I, into the cathode, and the potential at the outside surface remains stationary. The inside longitudinal currents, i_3 and i_4, just balance i_M. The magnitude of each of these currents is determined by the instantaneous pattern of potentials in this region. At the instant the circuit is opened, to be referred to as the new zero time, the current scheme is as shown on the extreme right. At zero time the potential pattern is momentarily the same as before the circuit was opened. Momentarily, the values of i_1, i_2, i_3, i_4, i_M are the same as they were before zero time; current I is absent, and there is an unbalance at the outside surface; consequently the outside potential V rises rapidly. On the other hand, the three currents operating at the inside surface are still in balance, and U remains constant. It follows that E begins to increase at a rapid rate. With time, as the outside potential rises, i_M decreases, creating an unbalance at the inside surface, and U begins the rise. The curve in diagram A shows that the value of ΔE increases, passes through a maximum, and finally fades away, leaving the transmembrane potential at the resting value. The second branch of the curve, starting with point B, is identical in shape with the first branch, starting with O, except for a 180-degree rotation about the time axis and a vertical shift of the entire curve.

During the post-stimulus period differential equations (12.12a,b) still hold, with the value zero substituted for I. The initial values of v and

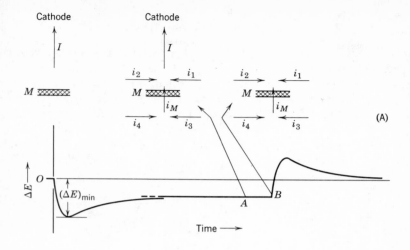

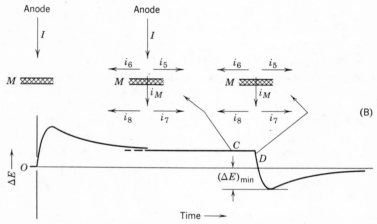

Fig. 12.11. (A) Upper part of diagram: Current patterns at various times. Lower diagram: Temporal course of transmembrane potential during and after stimulation with a constant current. During stimulation, currents i_1, i_2, i_3, i_4, i_M, I all affect the values of the outside potential V and of the inside potential U. At A, when steady state is established, $I = i_1 + i_2 + i_M$, and $i_M = i_3 + i_4$, the values of V, U, E remain stationary. At B, when the circuit is opened, at the new zero time, balance of currents outside the membrane is disturbed, and value of V begins to increase at a finite rate. Momentarily, currents i_3, i_4, i_M are still in balance, and zero value of dU/dt is zero. Transmembrane potential increases rapidly, passes through a maximum, and only later approaches its resting value.

(B) The effects of the stimulus at the anode are similar to those at the cathode, but in the opposite direction. If the stimulus is strong enough, the excursion of E into values below normal is large enough to become critical. This accounts for opening anode excitation. Since, for a given current strength, $(\Delta E)_{min}$ at the anode, on opening the circuit, is smaller than $(\Delta E)_{min}$ at the cathode, on closing, it takes a larger current to produce opening anodic excitation than that necessary to produce closing cathodic excitation.

651

of u are those attained in the steady state of the first period, namely $0.968ABI$ and $0.644ABI$, respectively; see equations (12.26), (12.27). Solving the new pair of differential equations, substituting the new boundary conditions, and using the same values for the parameters m, n, and q, we obtain the equations for v, u, and, by subtraction, for w, during the second period (equations 12.31, 12.32, 12.33). The same set of equations applies to both cathodic and anodic stimulation, with the only difference that I is a negative quantity in cathodic stimulation and a positive one in anodic stimulation.

$$v = (0.0758e^{-0.1397t} + 0.892e^{-1.110t})ABI \qquad (12.31)$$

$$u = (0.737e^{-0.1397t} - 0.0929e^{-1.110t})ABI \qquad (12.32)$$

$$w = (-0.661e^{-0.1397t} + 0.985e^{-1.110t})ABI \qquad (12.33)$$

$$t_{\text{crit}} = 2.545 \qquad w_{\text{crit}} = -0.405ABI \qquad (12.34)$$

The entire course of the function $\Delta E = w$ is shown, to scale, in Fig. 12.11, both for cathodic and for anodic stimulation. Since a decrease in the transmembrane potential brings the system closer to the critical point, while an increase carries it away from the critical point, these curves simulate the experimental observations on the temporal course of the threshold: With a cathodic constant-current stimulus, the threshold decreases, passes through a minimum, then reaches a steady value. On opening, the threshold becomes supernormal and finally returns to its resting value. The opposite effects take place at the anode. With a strong enough current, the critical point is reached at the cathode on closing. On opening, the critical point may be reached at the anode, but it takes a stronger current to produce opening excitation at the anode.

An equation for the strength-duration curve

Figure 12.11 shows that, with a constant-current cathodic stimulus, the transmembrane potential passes through a minimum at a time t_M. If the current is weak, the decrement in E at the minimum is smaller than the critical change, $(\Delta E)_C$, and there is no excitation. Since the effect is proportional to the strength of the current I, there is some particular value of the current I_0 for which the value of ΔE at the minimum is just critical. This is the current of minimum strength for excitation, or the rheobasic current. The time at which the function is at its minimum, t_M, is the utilization time.

Seeking an expression for the strength-duration curve is equivalent to seeking an answer to the following question: What must be the strength of the current I if the change in the transmembrane potential is to reach the critical value in a specified time t, where t is smaller than the utilization time, t_M? If a current of rheobasic strength is used, the value of $\Delta E = w$, at the time t, expressed as a fraction of the critical value, is given by the ratio w/w_M, where w is given by equation (12.22) for the general case and by equation (12.28) for the particular set of values of the parameters chosen in the illustrative calculation; w_M is the maximum numerical value of the same function. This ratio is smaller than 1. As pointed out earlier, with a fixed set of parameter values, the values of w at a given time are proportional to the strength of the stimulating current. It follows that the fraction w/w_M is a function of t which is independent of the strength of the current, and that the critical time t_M is also independent of the strength of the current. Furthermore, it follows that, in order to get excitation in a time t, which is shorter than the utilization time, the strength of the current to be employed must be larger than the rheobasic strength, in the ratio w_M/w. This gives us the mathematical expression for the strength-duration curve:

$$I/I_0 = w_M/w \tag{12.35}$$

$$I_0/I = w/w_M \tag{12.36}$$

It is the usual practice to give the strength-duration curve by plotting the values of I/I_0 against the time of excitation, as in Fig. 12.2. It may also be given in the form of a plot of I_0/I against time. In fact, the latter method has its advantages since, in the former, the curve approaches the vertical axis asymptotically and extends to infinity, whereas in the latter the entire curve may be shown in a finite region.

Equation (12.36) shows that the strength-duration curve may be obtained by plotting the ratio w/w_M against time. This has been done, for the illustrative case, in Fig. 12.12. It may be worth while to mention that the entire curve $AB \cdots JK$ is the same as that appearing in Fig. 12.11A, except for a change in scales. In the light of the preceding discussion it can be recognized that the branch $ABCDE$ is the strength-duration curve for the chosen illustrative example and that t_E, at point E, is the utilization time.

The coordinates of point K on the second branch of the complete curve show that in an anodic stimulus the minimum value is reached at the time $t = 2.545$ after break, and that the value of w/w_M at this point is 0.555. Thus it would take a minimum current strength at least 1.8 times rheobasic strength to insure opening excitation at the anode. With a different set of parameters, the value would be different. With the same set of parameters, a current of strength $4I_0$ will produce opening excitation at the anode at the time t_H.

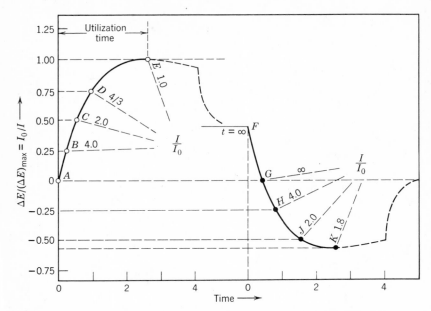

Fig. 12.12.　Curve $AB \cdots JK$ is similar to the curve shown in Fig. 12.11B; the scales are different. Abscissas: Time, expressed as a multiple of the time constant B of equation (12.10). This time constant equals approximately the quantity usually referred to as Hill's first time factor. Ordinates: The dimensionless ratio $(\Delta E)/(\Delta E)_{max}$.

A current of rheobasic strength will bring the system to the critical point at the utilization time t_E (point E). The same current will produce one-half the critical change in the time t_C (point C). However a twice-rheobasic current will produce the critical change in the same time t_C, since the effect is proportional to the strength of the current. It follows that curve $ABCDE$ is a form of the strength-duration curve, in which values of I_0/I are plotted against time. The customary form, in which I/I_0 is plotted against time, is shown to scale in Fig. 12.2B, with the value of I_0 equal to 1.0. Another method of giving I/I_0 as a function of time is shown in Fig. 12.13.

Open circles indicate cathodic closing excitation; solid circles, anodic opening excitation. With a rheobasic current, the drop in the transmembrane potential is only $0.555 \times$ critical value (point K) for the values of the parameters chosen in the illustrative calculation. For this reason it would take at least $1.8 \times$ rheobasic current to produce opening anodic excitation. The critical time is finite, even for the strongest currents. Thus a current, $I = 4I_0$, will bring the system to the critical point at the time t_H after opening. A current of infinite strength will bring about critical conditions at the time t_G after opening.

Experimentally obtained strength-duration curves are often tested for agreement with equation (12.2) (Katz, 1939a; Schaefer, 1944).

$$I/I_0 = 1/(1 - e^{-t/k}) \qquad (12.2)$$

Since in this equation the value of I/I_0 is a single-valued function of the variable t/k, curves which are in agreement with this equation but which

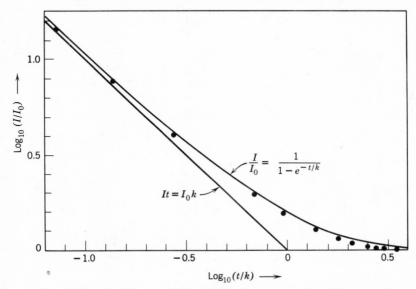

Fig. 12.13. Another standard method of representation of the strength-duration curve. Curve: Graph of the "standard equation" given in the figure. Unit slope straight line: The asymptote of the curve. In testing an experimental curve or a theoretical equation against the standard curve, the values of $\log_{10} t$ are changed by a constant quantity, to produce coincidence of the asymptotes of the two curves. .

Circles: Values of $\log_{10} (I/I_0)$ calculated with the use of the proposed physicochemical theory. Each point was shifted 0.145 logarithmic unit to the right. Since the standard equation calls for an infinite utilization time, experimental and theoretical curves digress from the standard curve at the lower end. Different theories may give excellent agreement with the standard curve through the major part of the curve; they digress from the standard curve and from each other near the lower hand. However, this method of testing is not sensitive enough to discriminate between different theories.

possess different values of k all have the same shape and can be brought into coincidence by a change in the time scale. The procedure consists in plotting $\log_{10} (I/I_0)$ against $\log_{10} t$ and shifting the curve horizontally. This test, applied to the theoretical strength-duration curve of Fig. 12.12, is shown in Fig. 12.13. In this figure the solid curve is a plot of equation

(12.2), to be referred to henceforth as the standard equation. The unit slope line represents the asymptote to the standard curve. The circles represent the values of I/I_0 given by equation (12.35), with each value of $\log_{10} t$ increased by the constant number 0.145. The fit is evidently quite satisfactory except at the lower end of the curve.

Complete agreement between the standard curve and the experimental curve for a nerve possessing a finite utilization time or for a theoretical equation calling for a finite utilization time is not to be expected, since the standard curve approaches the horizontal axis asymptotically, while the experimental or theoretical curve reaches the horizontal axis at the utilization time. Furthermore, agreement between experimental curves, the standard curve, and other theoretical curves near the lower end of the curve is apt to be illusory, since this method of comparing curves becomes rather insensitive to differences between the ordinates when the ordinates become small enough.

Significance of the test against the standard curve

The fact that experimental curves match the standard curve (12.2) quite well calls for an examination of the nature of the conclusions which may be drawn from this fit.

Let us assume that the magnitude P of an undefined property of the system must reach a critical value P_C, before excitation can take place. The form of the strength-duration curve will obviously depend upon the nature of the assumptions made relative the changes in P during stimulation. Let us assume, as a first approximation, that the temporal course of P is defined by the following equation:

$$\frac{dP}{dt} = AI - \frac{1}{k}(P - P_0) \qquad (12.37)$$

Integration of this equation yields (12.38):

$$kAI(1 - e^{-t/k}) = P - P_0 \qquad (12.38)$$

The condition that P must reach some undefined value P_C at the time t gives one form of the equation of the strength-duration curve:

$$kAI(1 - e^{-t/k}) = P_C - P_0 \qquad (12.39)$$

According to equation (12.39), there is a minimum value of I, to be called the rheobasic strength, I_0, for which the condition is met at infinite time. From (12.39) the value of I_0 is given by the equation

$$kAI_0 = P_C - P_0 \qquad (12.40)$$

Combining the last two equations, we obtain the standard strength-duration curve:

$$I/I_0 = 1/(1 - e^{-t/k}) \qquad (12.2)$$

Thus the conditions which lead to the standard equation are very broad in scope. For example, the nature of the property P need not be specified, nor is it necessary to make any assumptions as to the value of P_C. As an illustration of the versatility of the standard equation, we may calculate the strength-duration curve of the analog described earlier (p. 627).

We will assume that in this case the controlling property of the system is the temperature and that the critical point is reached at a temperature T_C at which the leak of heat just equals the rate of heat production by the exothermic reaction. Assuming, as a first approximation, that the heat leak is proportional to the change of temperature, and disregarding the heat provided by the reaction during the period of stimulation, we obtain the following differential equation:

$$\frac{dT}{dt} = AI - \frac{1}{k}(T - T_0) \qquad (12.41)$$

The form of this equation is identical with that of (12.37), and it follows that the strength-duration curve of the analog is of the standard form.

The versatility of the standard equation entails some disadvantage. If the strength-duration curve of a process possessing a critical point is exactly of the standard form, nothing can be said about the nature of the controlling property or about its critical value. The only conclusion that is justified is that equation (12.37) is satisfied, i.e., that the unknown property tends to increase proportionately to the strength of the stimulus and, at the same time, follows the law of exponential decay.

The standard equation calls for an infinite utilization time. It follows that an experimental curve showing a finite utilization time, or a theoretical curve calling for a finite utilization time, cannot fit the standard equation perfectly.

Let us consider the conclusions which may be drawn from a partial fit. Since an infinite number of curves may give a partial fit to a given curve, we need some quantitative measure of the partial fit. Referring to Fig. 12.13, the curve to be tested is moved parallel to itself until its asymptote coincides with the asymptote to the standard curve. The ratio of the ordinate of the curve to the ordinate of the standard curve at $\log_{10}(t/k) = 0$ may be defined as a quantitative measure of the degree of fit. Figure 12.13 shows that the curve defined by the circles gives a good fit by this standard of comparison.

The significance of a good fit becomes apparent when we consider the next step in our effort to obtain a more precise equation. Let us assume that, as a second approximation, the differential equation for the value of the undefined property P is written as follows:

$$\frac{dP}{dt} = AI - \frac{1}{k}(P - P_0) \pm \frac{m}{k}(Z - Z_0) \qquad (12.42)$$

where Z is some other property of the system having the same physical dimensions as P. In that case m is a dimensionless ratio. Different values of m will give different strength-duration curves. If m is given values ranging from zero and up, the resulting curves will change from one showing a perfect fit to curves showing a progressively poorer fit. The smaller the absolute value of m, the better is the fit.

Another factor which may contribute to a good fit is the nature of the quantity Z. If Z happens to be a function whose derivative at zero time is zero, the importance of the third term on the right of equation (12.42), for small values of t, is small, and the fit is improved. Finally, if m is small, and the derivative of Z at zero time is zero, an excellent fit may be expected.

It follows from this analysis that, when an experimental strength-duration curve shows a good fit to the standard equation, the only conclusion that may be strictly drawn is that the simple differential equation (12.37) is reasonably satisfactory. Similarly, when a theoretical equation shows a good fit, the only conclusion that may be drawn is that the third term in the improved differential equation for P is relatively unimportant, for one or the other of the two reasons given above.

In the present theory of excitation and accommodation, the controlling property P is the quantity $w = v - u$. Combining equations (12.12a,b), we have the following equation:

$$dP/dt = ABI - (1 + m + n)(P - P_0) - (1 - q)u$$
$$P_0 = 0 \qquad u_0 = 0 \qquad (12.43)$$

This differential equation is of the same form as (12.42), and u is a function whose value and whose derivative at zero time is zero. Thus a good fit to the standard equation is insured, but the good fit does not necessarily offer strong evidence in support of the validity of the third term on the right side of the equation. In Hill's theory the controlling factor is the value of $(\epsilon - j)$, which quantity we will call P. Combining equations (12.7) and (12.8) we get

$$dP/dt = KI - (k + M)(P - P_0) + (m - k - M)(j - j_0) \quad (12.44)$$

This differential equation is also similar to (12.42), and the derivative of the function j is zero at zero time.   This again insures a good fit to the standard curve, but again the good fit does not necessarily support the underlying fundamental assumptions on which equations (12.7) and (12.8) are based.

Thus, since a number of differential equations give a good fit to the standard curve, the significant part of the test is not to be found in the good fit in the early part of the curve.   To discriminate between two theories, or to compare a theoretical equation with the experimental curve, it is necessary to compare the lower ends of the curves.   Unfortunately, this test becomes rather insensitive at the lower end, as may be seen by inspection of Fig. 12.13.   It would seem that plotting the quantity $(I/I_0 - 1)$, or some function of it, either against time or against some function of t, would give a considerably more discriminating test.

Similarities and differences between the proposed physical model and Hill's mathematical model

Hill's theory has been subjected to extensive tests, and for this reason it will be desirable to compare the two models in some detail.   Let the change in the excitatory factor ϵ be called v, the change in the inhibitory factor j be called u; the difference, $v - u$, is again defined as w.   To bring to light the similarities and differences between the fundamental equations, we substitute different symbols for the constants of Hill's equations (12.7, 12.8):

$$\frac{dv}{dt} = AI - \frac{1}{B}v \tag{12.45}$$

$$\frac{du}{dt} = \frac{n}{B}v - \frac{s}{B}u \tag{12.46}$$

Rearranging the terms in Hill's equations, we compare the equations for the mathematical model with those for the physical model:

Hill's Mathematical Model   Physical Model

$$\frac{dv}{dt} = AI - \frac{1}{B}v \tag{12.47a}$$ $$\frac{dv}{dt} = AI - \frac{1}{B}v - \frac{m}{B}(v - u) \tag{12.48a}$$

$$\frac{du}{dt} = \frac{n}{B}(v - u) - \frac{s - n}{B}u \tag{12.47b}$$ $$\frac{du}{dt} = \frac{n}{B}(v - u) - \frac{q}{B}u \tag{12.48b}$$

$$\frac{dw}{dt} = AI - \frac{1 + n}{B}w$$ $$\frac{dw}{dt} = AI - \frac{1 + m + n}{B}w$$

$$- \frac{1 + n - s}{B}u \tag{12.47c}$$ $$- \frac{1 - q}{B}u \tag{12.48c}$$

Comparing equations (a) in the two sets, we observe that the only difference between them is in the term $(m/B)(v - u)$. Equations (b) in the two sets are equivalent, since $(s - n)$ and q are both constants. It follows that both sets of fundamental equations will give approximately the same results if the constants, $(s - n)$ and q, are small; they will also give equivalent results in those tests in which the value of $(v - u)$ is small. Thus, under certain conditions, the two sets of equations will give approximately equivalent results. The two systems, however, will not give the same results with more stringent tests.

If we restrict our attention to very strong and moderate currents, where the time of excitation is relatively small, and the value of u remains relatively small, then, neglecting the third term in each equation (c) in the two sets, we get the following approximate equations:

Hill's Mathematical Model							Physical Model

$$\frac{dw}{dt} = AI - \frac{1 + n}{B} w \quad (12.47d) \qquad \frac{dw}{dt} = AI - \frac{1 + m + n}{B} w \quad (12.48d)$$

(approximate equations, when u is negligibly small)

Both equations are identical in form with (12.37); it follows that both equations will give the standard strength-duration curve, equation (12.2); in other words, both exact equations will give curves whose asymptotes are identical with the asymptote of the standard equation, and will show a good fit with the standard equation.

Let us recall that, in matching an experimental equation with the standard curve, $\log_{10} (I/I_0)$ is plotted against $\log_{10} t$, and the curve is shifted horizontally until the two asymptotes coincide. The value of the shift in the abscissa gives the value of $\log_{10} k$ of the nerve. Comparing the last two equations with equation (12.37), we get the following two equations, which relate the experimental value of k to the coefficient B in the fundamental differential equations.

$$B = (1 + n)k \qquad \text{(Hill's equation)} \qquad (12.49)$$

$$B = (1 + m + n)k \qquad \text{(physical model)} \qquad (12.50)$$

We conclude that the value of k obtained by the graphical method is not identical with the "first time constant" B, defined by the differential equation, but is smaller by the factor $1/(1 + n)$ and $1/(1 + m + n)$, respectively, in the two systems. However, since m and n are small ratios, the error is not large. These equations also show that the unit of time, B, adopted in the analysis of the physical system (p. 646) is approximately equal to the value of the "first time constant" obtained by the graphical method.

Since in both systems the change in threshold equals w, both systems will give good agreement in experimental tests in which the duration of the stimulus is not too long, and in which the value of u remains relatively small. For a more stringent comparison of the two systems of differential equations we must turn our attention to experiments of longer duration.

The system of differential equations discussed above predicts that, in a stimulation of long duration, the threshold, when steady state is reached, is less than 1 at the cathode and greater than 1 at the anode (see Fig. 12.11). The analysis also showed that the rheobasic strength for opening anodic excitation is greater than the rheobasic strength for closing cathodic excitation. Both predictions are in agreement with observations. On the other hand, as Katz (1939a) has pointed out, Hill's "two time factor theory" predicts that at steady state the threshold is zero and that the rheobasic strengths for opening and closing excitation are equal, in contrast to observations.

This property of the two-factor theory is not inherent in the fundamental system of equations proposed by Hill (12.45, 12.46). These equations contain three time factors. However, in order to reduce the number of factors, Hill assumed the equality of two of the factors ($n = s$, in equation 12.46). Without this assumption the equations contain the parameters $1/B$, n, and s. With this assumption the number of parameters is reduced to two. Inspection of equation (12.46) will show that, with $n = s$, and at steady state, when $du/dt = 0$, we must have $v - u = w = 0$; the change in the threshold is zero. When the circuit is opened, the value of w at the anode becomes negative and reaches the same absolute value at the minimum as the absolute value reached at the maximum during stimulation. This accounts for the equality of the two rheobasic strengths in the two-factor theory. We will return to the examination of this assumption after considering the predicted behavior of the threshold with currents of rising strength.

The minimal current gradient

If the stimulating current is not constant, but, starting from zero strength, increases at a constant rate, the value of I in the fundamental differential equations should be replaced with the function: $I = ct$, where c is positive for anodic stimulation and negative for cathodic stimulation. Experimental observations show that, with this type of stimulation, there is a minimal gradient c below which there is no excitation, even with prolonged stimulation (see Fig. 12.2c). There are, however, exceptions to this rule.

It can be shown that the fundamental differential equations of Rashevsky, of Hill, and of the model presented here all predict that, after a long enough time, the derivative of each of the variables represented in the respective system of differential equations approaches a constant value. The long range values of the variable determining the magnitude of the threshold can be shown to be represented by the following equations: Rashevsky's mathematical model:

$$\epsilon - j = \text{constant} + (K/k - M/m)ct \tag{12.51}$$

Hill's mathematical model:

$$\epsilon - j = \text{constant} + [(m - M)Kct]/mk \tag{12.52}$$

Physical model:

$$V - U = \text{constant} + qABct/(n + q + mq) \tag{12.53}$$

In each case the constant is a function of c and of the parameters of the differential equations. Inspection of the three equations shows that, in each case, the threshold reaches any specified value, if a long enough time is allowed, either at the cathode or at the anode, depending upon the sign of c and on the values of the parameters. All three equations predict excitation if t is large enough.

Rashevsky (1948) meets this difficulty by assuming that M/m is larger than K/k. This, however, introduces another difficulty, since, with this condition, excitation should take place at the anode. This difficulty is met by adding another assumption, namely, that when the current is strong enough to give negative values to ϵ it becomes injurious to the nerve. Finally, to explain the exceptions to the minimal gradient rule, Rashevsky assumes that in nerves which do not obey this rule the value of M/m is smaller than K/k.

Hill's assumption that the two constants of his second differential equation are equal accomplishes two purposes. It reduces the number of time factors by one and it meets the difficulty of interpreting the existence of a minimal gradient current, as may be seen by inspection of equation (12.52). While satisfying the observations with rising currents, the assumption is made at the cost of failing to satisfy the observations with respect to the values of the threshold at steady state, when constant currents are used, and also with respect to the experimental observations on the relative values of rheobasic strengths for opening and closing excitation.

Furthermore the assumption $m = M$ is rather stringent. Inspection of equation (12.52) will show that, if there is a small difference between these two parameters, excitation should take place at a high enough value of t. It seems improbable that these two constants, describing two different processes, will be exactly equal.

Equation (12.53) shows that the existence of a minimum current gradient may be explained on the assumption that $q = 0$.   This assumption would leave unaffected the conclusions relative to the change of the threshold at steady state and the magnitude of the rheobase for opening excitation.   However, since q is a measure of the leakage of the inside charge longitudinally, along the inside electrolyte, it would be inconsistent to assume that $q = 0$.

It would seem that the difficulty is only an apparent one and that it may be resolved by a more careful examination of the fundamental assumptions.   Equations (12.12a,b) are admittedly only approximately correct.   As is the case with all approximate solutions, the error increases progressively with increases in the range of values of the independent variable t.   This may be illustrated by the following argument, showing the parallellism between the range of t and the degree of accuracy required in the fundamental equations.

Stimulation with very strong currents of short duration may be represented quite accurately by the equation

$$dw/dt = dV/dt = ABI \qquad \text{(first approximation)} \qquad (12.54)$$

This equation leads to the strength duration curve $It = \text{constant}$.

If moderate currents are used, and a greater time is required, the following equation will give fairly accurate results:

$$dw/dt = dV/dt = ABI - (1 + m + n)V \qquad \text{(second approximation)}$$
$$(12.55)$$

This equation yields the standard strength-duration curve.   It begins to fail when the value of I approaches I_0 and the value of t increases.   The next approximation is represented by the pair of equations (12.12a,b) (third approximation).   The preceding analysis has shown that this pair of equations interprets a number of physiological observations.

It is to be expected that, if a slowly rising current is used, the range of t, with a minimal gradient of current, will be still larger, and the third approximation will not be accurate enough to account for all the observations.

Finally, with progressively smaller values of c in the equation $I = ct$, the use of constant parameters in the differential equations becomes less and less justifiable.   With very small values of c the secondary restorative changes in the system acquire progressively greater importance.

The temporal course of the threshold subsequent to a shock

A shock, by definition, is a stimulus whose duration is so short that the accommodation mechanism of the nerve produces very little effect by the time the shock is completed. If the shock changes the outside potential by the amount S, the zero time values of V and U are

$$V = S \qquad U = 0 \qquad (\text{at } t = 0) \tag{12.56}$$

The differential equations (12.12a,b) are still applicable to the events immediately following the shock, if we use the value $I = 0$. Integrating the equations and substituting the initial values, we get the equation for w as a function of time:

$$w = (- 0.0924e^{-0.1397t} + 1.0924e^{-1.110t})S \tag{12.57}$$

This function may be represented as follows:

$$w = 1.0924e^{-1.110t}S(1 - 0.0846e^{0.97t}) \tag{12.58}$$

The last equation is illustrative of the fact that decay of the threshold increment or decrement follows approximately the law of exponential decay, for a reasonably long fraction of the time. However, eventually the change in the threshold passes the zero value, reverses its sign, passes a minimum value, and finally approaches the rest-value zero (see Figs. 12.4A,B).

With the particular values of the parameters used in the illustrative calculation, w changes sign at $t = 2.55$. The overshoot passes through its minimum at $t = 4.68$, at which time $w = - 0.0422S$. If the threshold value of a cathodic shock is S^*, the minimum value of the anodic shock which will produce opening excitation is $S^* \cdot (1/0.0422) = 23.7S^*$. It was indicated earlier (Fig. 12.12) that, with the same constants, the rheobasic strength for opening anodic stimulation with constant currents is only 1.8 times the rheobase for closing stimulation. Since the ratio of the two rheobasic strengths is a measure of the accommodation, we conclude that accommodation is greater when steady state is reached with a constant current stimulus.

The similarities and differences between the temporal courses of the threshold, the catelectrotonic potential, and the transmembrane potential

Figure 12.14D, redrawn from Hodgkin's (1937) data, shows a striking parallelism between the temporal course of the threshold T and the catelectrotonic potential V in a type of experiment which is referred to later in more detail. Since in the present model the magnitude of the threshold varies with the transmembrane potential, it is of interest to examine whether any parallelism exists between ΔE and ΔV, i.e., between the changes in the transmembrane potential and in the electrotonic potential.

Figure 12.14B shows, to scale, the curves of ΔU, ΔV, and ΔE. The curves are the same as those appearing in Figs. 12.10E,G, except for a difference in scales and for the range of t shown. They are given by equations (12.27, 12.26, 12.28). The ordinates are plotted as multiples of the quantity ABI. The vertical distance $D'D$ represents the (unspecified) transmembrane potential at rest, E_0. Stimulation with a constant current is started at zero time (point D). As remarked earlier, the transmembrane potential passes through a minimum value (point F''). It may be seen that the curves of the transmembrane potential and of the electrotonic potential are practically identical to start with and follow similar courses down to the time t_F.

The behavior of the three potentials following a shock is shown in Fig. 12.14A. The curve of ΔE was plotted with the use of equation (12.57). At zero time the shock decreases both V and E by the quantity S (line AB). In this case the value of S was taken as 0.729, in arbitrary units, to provide a direct comparison with curve $DF''G''$, whose minimum occurs at -0.729. Curves for ΔV and ΔU were calculated by using equations (12.59, 12.60), which are the equations satisfying condition (12.56).

$$v = (0.0106e^{-0.1397t} + 0.989e^{-1.110t})S \qquad (12.59)$$

$$u = (0.103e^{-0.1397t} - 0.103e^{-1.110t})S \qquad (12.60)$$

Figure 12.14A shows that the curves of ΔV and of ΔE appear to be closer than the corresponding pair in Fig. 12.14B. This is due partly to the fact that the absolute values of these quantities approach zero in Fig. 12.14A. There is a large difference in the relative values of ΔV and of ΔE. While the former remains negative and approaches zero value asymptotically, the latter becomes positive, passes through a maximum, and only later approaches zero value asymptotically. In this connection it is of interest to note that the threshold curve in Fig. 12.14D changes sign before acquiring the value zero.

While Fig. 12.14B represents the behavior of the three curves in a subthreshold stimulation with a constant current, Fig. 12.14C shows the same curves as they would appear in a stimulation with a just-adequate current. The curves are identical with the corresponding curves in the upper diagram up to the critical point J. The curves beyond t_J were drawn schematically. These curves show, schematically, that, at the peak of excitation, the sign of the transmembrane potential is reversed; the outside potential V, relative to an electrode at some distant point, is smaller than the inside potential U. This reversal may account for an interesting observation made by Hodgkin (1937), namely, that a propagated impulse which fails to pass a region blocked by cold or pressure produces on the other side of the block a transient decrease in the threshold, accompanied by a catelectrotonic change. He showed that both threshold and potential changes have identical spatial and temporal configurations. Figure 12.14D, in which the temporal course of the threshold and potential are shown for an experiment with a cold block, illustrates the similarity between these two quantities. Both curves are plotted on the same time scale, scales of arbitrary units being used for the ordinates.

Hodgkin found that, if the propagated impulse arriving at the blocked region was replaced by an electric stimulus of appropriate form applied directly to the blocked region, extrapolar changes of identical spatial distribution were obtained. However, in this case the threshold change was smaller by a factor of 2, approximately. Thus a blocked impulse produces a threshold lowering of about 25 per cent. An equally strong catelectrotonic potential, applied directly, lowered the threshold by 14 per cent.

A comparison of Figs. 12.14B and 12.14C suggests a possible explanation for the greater effectiveness of a blocked impulse in producing threshold changes beyond the block. Let us assume that the imposed electrotonic change is represented by curve DFG. At the point F the outside potential has been artificially decreased. In the region beyond the block, the leakage of current lowers the outside potential and causes a drop in the threshold. At the same time the inside potential at the stimulated region is less than normal (point F'). Leakage through the

---

Fig. 12.14.   The parallelism between the transmembrane potential E, the electrotonic potential ΔV, and the threshold T.

(A)   The temporal course of ΔE, ΔV, and ΔU, after a shock. E_0 is the (unspecified) resting value of the transmembrane potential.

(B)   The temporal course of the same three quantities during stimulation with a constant current.   These curves are similar, except for the units of scale, to the curves shown in Figs. 12.10 E,G.   The stronger parallelism in case of a shock is somewhat deceptive, since it is due to the fact that both quantities approach zero.   There is a strong qualitative difference in (A), in that ΔE overshoots the normal value zero and becomes positive for a while.

According to the theory discussed, there should be a strong parallelism between the course of the threshold and the course of the transmembrane potential.   Figure (D) (redrawn from Hodgkin, 1937) shows the experimentally observed parallelism between the courses of the threshold and the catelectrotonic potential.   Note that ΔT overshoots beyond the value zero, while ΔV approaches zero value asymptotically.

(C)   Schematic representation of changes taking place beyond the critical point.   The three curves are identical with those in (C) up to the critical point J.   Beyond the critical point, U becomes larger than V by an amount equal to the overshoot of Fig. 12.5E.   This may explain Hogkin's experimental observation that the threshold changes beyond a block, produced by the blocked impulse, are approximately twice as large as changes produced by an imposed electrotonic change of the same strength (see text).

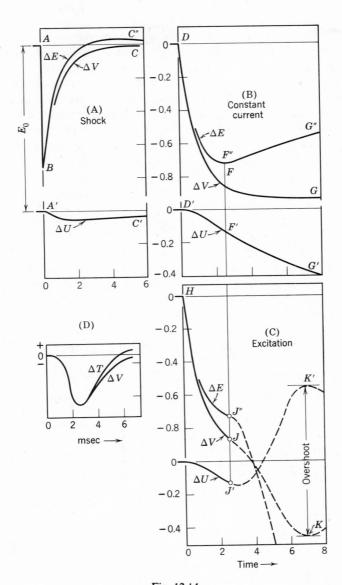

Fig. 12.14

inside solution lowers the inside potential beyond the block, partly compensating the effect of the outside potential, since the threshold is affected by the difference between the two potentials.

If a propagated impulse is stopped by the block, the temporal course of the outside potential at that point is given by curve *HJK*. This time, however, the inside potential is larger than normal (point *K'*). The leakage of current through the inside electrolyte from the block to the region beyond serves to increase the inside potential beyond the block, thus cooperating with the outside leak in decreasing the transmembrane potential, instead of hindering the effect of the outside lateral leak. It is to be expected, therefore, that a blocked impulse will be more effective than an imposed electrotonus of equal pattern and strength.

IONIC PROPERTIES AND THE TRANSMEMBRANE POTENTIAL IN THE RESTING STATE

The theory developed in the preceding pages has required no reference to the differences in behavior of different ionic and molecular species. Some of the most important problems of nerve and muscle electrophysiology, however, make it necessary to take account of such differences.

Various types of nerve and muscle may differ greatly in the concentrations of ions within the fiber and in the outside ionic concentrations which are suitable for studying the electrical properties of the fibers. The various details may be found in Hodgkin's review (1951).

Broadly speaking, an examination of the electrical behavior of a given fiber should take into account the ratio of the inside to the outside concentration of each of the major ions which can penetrate the membrane, and the values of the transmembrane potential at rest and at the height of activity of the fiber. Table 12.1, compiled from more detailed tables given by Hodgkin, shows ranges of observed values. Brief as it is, Table 12.1 contains data which pose some of the major questions of nerve and muscle electrophysiology: What is the nature of the transmembrane potential? What are the mechanisms of accumulation of potassium, of exclusion of chloride ion, and of the very striking exclusion of sodium against both a concentration and electrical gradient? What is the nature of the processes which account for the depolarization and overshoot during activity? What is the nature of the recovery process?

Evidence for the presence of a sodium pump

It is possible to set up diffusion systems consisting of a semipermeable membrane separating two solutions containing arbitrary concentrations of ions. Left by itself, without a supply of energy, each system will spontaneously reach a Donnan type of equilibrium.   In the equilibrium state there is a potential difference across the membrane; the ratio of the two concentrations of a penetrating ion satisfies the Nernst equation:

$$C_i'/C_o' = e^{\pm zFE/RT} \qquad (12.61)$$

where z is the absolute value of the valence of the ion, F is Faraday's constant, E is the potential of the outside solution relative to the inside

Table 12.1.   Ranges of Concentrations, Concentration Ratios, and Potentials in Nerve and Muscle Fibers

Compiled from data given by Hodgkin (1951).   Concentrations are given in milliequivalents per kilogram of water; potentials, in millivolts.

	Inside (C_i')	Outside (C_o')	Ratio (C_i'/C_o')
Potassium ion	110.0 to 410	2.5 to 10	23.0 to 68
Sodium	12.0 to 110	120.0 to 460	0.08 to 0.31
Chloride	1.2 to 83	120.0 to 540	0.01 to 0.15
Deficiency of inorganic anions	120.0 to 300		

Resting transmembrane potentials:	61 to 95 (outside positive)
Potentials at height of activity:	-31 to -60 (outside negative)
Action potentials:	96 to 134

solution; the plus sign applies to cations, the minus sign to anions.   It takes laborious efforts to determine whether the concentrations of potassium ion or of chloride ion in muscle and nerve satisfy the Nernst equation. On the other hand, it may be seen by inspection of Table 12.1 that nerve and muscle fibers are capable of maintaining a low inside concentration of sodium, contrary to the tendency of the potential gradient to concentrate this ion on the inside.

The earliest explanation of this observation was that the membrane is impermeable to sodium ion.   This explanation left unanswered, among other things, the question, How was the deficiency of inside sodium established to start with, when the fiber was formed?   It demanded almost absolute impermeability to sodium ion, else the maintenance of the deficiency for a span of many years could not be accounted for.

The experiments of Heppel (1939, 1940) showed that muscles of rats raised on a diet deficient in potassium exchanged nearly half of the inside potassium for sodium.   After restoration of the normal diet, the abnormally high inside concentration of sodium was reduced, and the normal concentration of potassium was established.

Heppel's observations and the observations of Fenn and Cobb (1936) and of Steinbach (1940) left no doubt that muscle membranes are permeable to sodium.   Dean (1941) introduced the idea that the apparently abnormally low inside concentration of sodium and the movement of sodium against both a concentration and a potential gradient indicate the existence of a mechanism for the active extrusion of this ion.   This view has gained wide acceptance (cf. reviews, Ussing, 1949b; Hodgkin, 1951).   For a detailed discussion of the problem of active transport of ions, the reader is referred to Ussing's review.

In some of the more recent investigations the ratio of the outward to inward fluxes of sodium has been compared with the expected relation for simple diffusion.   For simple diffusion the following relation must hold (Chapter 11, p. 539):

$$f_{Na,\,out}/f_{Na,\,in} = (C_{iNa}'/C_{oNa}') \cdot e^{-FE/RT} \qquad (12.62)$$

The experimentally observed ratios have been found to be much larger than those predicted by equation (12.62), by a factor of 25 to 50 (Hodgkin, 1951).   This indicates that the assumption of simple diffusion will not account for the observed movement of sodium ion; it must be assumed that the movement of sodium by simple diffusion is augmented by some other process.

Nature of the sodium pump

There is ample evidence that active transfer of substances is found not only in nerve and muscle fibers but in other types of cells as well (Höber, 1945;   Ussing, 1949b;   Hodgkin, 1951).   The mechanism of active transfer, which may be responsible for the accumulation or exclusion of substances by cells, is one of the fundamental problems of physiology. Unfortunately, there is no experimental evidence, at the time this is written, that clearly indicates the nature of the mechanism of active transfer of sodium in nerve and muscle fibers.   In the absence of further experimental information, one can only speculate on the possible nature of the pump.   Such speculation is apt to be of value, since it may suggest the type of experiments that will produce the desired information.   It may also lead to some conclusions regarding the effect of the sodium pump on the transmembrane potential.

Sodium may be pumped by some unusual mechanism, or it may be pumped by coupling with a molecule or an ion.   As an example of the first type of pump, let us consider the mechanism suggested by O. H. Schmitt (1951, p. 86).   Here it is assumed that an enzyme anchored to the membrane catalyzes an exothermic reaction in which sodium ion is one of the participants.   The energy produced in the exothermic reaction may be transformed into the kinetic energy of the particles leaving the enzyme.   It is conceivable that part of the energy-rich sodium leaving the enzyme is shot outward, across the membrane. This would constitute a sodium pump. The efficiency of such a pump would increase if the enzyme anchored at the surface is oriented in a favorable direction.

We can estimate the minimum value of the kinetic energy needed for this chemomechanical pump. To overcome the influence of the unfavorable potential rise of about 60 mv, the kinetic energy of the particle would have to be greater than 0.06 ev, or 1400 cal per mole. This requirement, taken by itself, is rather mild. However, if the thickness of the membrane is of the order of 100 Å, the energy needed to enable the particle to batter its way through the membrane would seem to be prohibitively large.

Turning to more conventional models, we consider pumps in which the sodium ion combines with another particle X, and the complex so formed moves outward by ordinary diffusion. The particle X will be called the carrier. Several possibilities come to mind. The carrier may be a product of metabolism inside the cell; on the other hand, it may be a particle which can exist in the membrane only, and operates the pump by shuttling back and forth across the membrane, loaded with a sodium ion on the outward trip, and returning single on the inward trip. We will use the symbols P and S for the two alternatives, respectively. The carrier may be a neutral molecule or an anion. We shall use the symbols 0 and — for these two alternatives. The coupling of the two particles may take place within the inside solution or at the membrane. We will use the symbols I and M for these two alternatives. Finally, the driving force of the pump may be due to the concentration gradient of the carrier, i.e., due to the fact that the concentration of the carrier is exceedingly small in the outside solution; on the other hand, it may be due to coupling with a highly exergonic reaction. These two possibilities have been discussed in Chapter 11 (pp. 594 and 599). We will indicate the two alternatives with the symbols c and e, respectively. Thus the nature of the pump may be indicated by a combination of four symbols. For example, the combination $P-Ic$ indicates that the carrier is an anionic metabolic product, that the coupling with sodium takes place in the inside solution, and that the pump operates in virtue of the fact that the concentration of the carrier in the outside solution is exceedingly small.

With four symbols, and two alternative values for each, sixteen combinations are mathematically possible. However, combinations containing both S and I are theoretically impossible, and combinations containing S and c are meaningless. Eliminating these combinations, we are left with ten possible combinations. These are shown in Table 12.2. Eyring, Lumry, and Woodbury (1949) suggested that sodium may be pumped out by combining with one of the anionic metabolic products.

This pump would be classified as *P–Ic* or *P–Mc*, depending upon whether the coupling takes place in the inside solution or at the membrane. The redox pump proposed by Conway (1951) could be classified as *S–Me*.

A great deal of experimental work may be required to determine the nature of the sodium pump. It would seem that extension of the work on the isotopic fluxes of sodium, both inward and outward, would offer a very promising method of attack on this problem. With a concentration ratio $C_i'/C_o' = 0.1$ and a transmembrane potential of the order of 58 mv, the outward flux of sodium by simple diffusion is of the order of one-hundredth of the inward flux. It follows that, if the outward flux is of the same order as the inward flux, as is found experimentally, the outward flux is due chiefly to the pump and offers a fairly accurate measure of the rate of pumping. It would therefore be of particular interest to determine the effect of changing the experimental conditions on this outward rate. In addition, it may be possible to discover the nature of the carrier X by adding, on the outside, substances which are possible candidates for the carrier X, and studying the effect of these substances on the inward flux of sodium. Finally, by adding substances containing tagged atoms, and studying the inward and the outward fluxes of these substances, it may be possible to find a correlation between the flux of some one substance and the operation of the pump.

As an illustration of some of the possible experimental approaches we may consider the expected characteristics of the sodium pumps listed in Table 12.2. The driving force of any pump whose symbolic representation contains the symbol *c* is based on the very small concentration of the carrier X in the outside solution. With such a pump the addition of a relatively small concentration of X to the outside solution would decrease the rate of the pump markedly. This effect is listed in line *A* of the table. On the other hand, a pump in which the formation of NaX is coupled with an exergonic reaction, either in the inside solution or at the inside surface of the membrane, would not be affected strongly by the addition of X. This characteristic offers an experimental method of searching for the nature of X.

Assuming that some particular substance X′ is suspected to be identical with the carrier X, tagged atoms may be used to apply the isotopic flux test for simple diffusion, as represented by equation (12.62). If the carrier is of the shuttle type *Se*, with the carrier confined to the membrane, the added substance X′ and the carrier X cannot be identical. The isotopic test can only succeed if the carrier originates in the inside solution (type *P*). This is indicated in line B of Table 12.2. In pumps of type *c* the concentration of X in the outside solution must be very small to start with. Addition of this substance to the outside solution would result in a strong flux of the substance inward, by coupled diffusion, which may be detected by application of equation (12.62) to the two observed fluxes of this substance. In pumps of type c the observed value of the ratio given on the left side of the equation would be too small, whereas in pumps of type e the ratio would be too large.

Table 12.2. Classification of Sodium Pumps

Nature of carrier: P, product of metabolism inside cell; S, shuttling constituent of membrane.

Valence of carrier: 0, neutral molecule; —, anion.

Coupling takes place: I, within inside solution; M, at membrane.

Driving force: c, concentration gradient of carrier; e, energy of coupled exergonic reaction.

	Nature of Carrier		Valence of Carrier		Coupling at		Driving Force	
	P	S	0	—	I	M	c	e
1	P		0		I		c	
2	P		0		I			e
3	P		0			M	c	
4	P		0			M		e
5	P			—	I		c	
6	P			—	I			e
7	P			—		M	c	
8	P			—		M		e
9		S	0			M		e
10		S		—		M		e

		P	S	0	—	I	M	c	e
A	Effect on pumping rate of adding carrier to outside solution							Decr.	Small
B	Can isotope test be applied to carrier?	Yes	No						
C	Effect of decrease in E on rate of coupling					None	?		
D	Is the transport of an additional cation mandatory?			No	Type P Yes				
E	Effect of pump on trans-membrane potential			Increase					

A decrease in the transmembrane potential, effected, say, by the addition of potassium to the outside solution, would have a general effect on the flux of every ion, including those participating in the pump mechanism. In addition, if this rate depends upon the local potential gradient, there may be a specific effect on the rate at which sodium is coupled with the carrier. Since experimental evidence indicates that a change in the transmembrane potential affects the properties of the membrane, the rate of coupling may be affected, if the coupling takes place at the membrane, i.e., in pumps of type M.   On the other hand, if the coupling takes place in the inside solution, the rate of coupling will be unaffected by the magnitude of the transmembrane potential.   This is indicated in line C of Table 12.2.

Effect of the sodium pump on the transmembrane potential

In order to add some concreteness to the discussion of the effect of the pump on the transmembrane potential, let us consider the concentrations prevailing in one of the experiments of Hodgkin and Katz (1949a).

	Inside Solution	Outside Solution	
Na:	72 mM	455 mM	Transmembrane potential:
K:	345	10	48 mv
Cl:	61	587	

First, we may ask a purely academic question: If the outside concentrations were kept constant, and there were no sodium pump, what will be the Donnan-type concentrations and the transmembrane potential after final equilibrium has been reached?

In the inside solution there is an anionic deficiency of 356 millimoles per liter.   When this is balanced by 356 millimoles per liter of some non-diffusible ions, P^-, calculation shows that the final concentrations would be as follows:

	Inside Solution	Outside Solution	Ratio
Na:	734	455	1.61
K:	16.1	10	1.61
Cl:	394	587	1/1.61
P^-:	356		

$$E = 58 \log_{10} 1.61 = 12 \text{ mv}$$

The usefulness of this rough computation lies in showing that, with non-diffusible anions present on the inside, a positive transmembrane potential is to be expected, as well as some unequal distribution of each ion between the two sides.

Turning to a more practical question, we may ask: Given the concentrations of the diffusible ions in the two solutions, how does the presence of the pump affect the theoretical calculation of the transmembrane potential E?   In Chapter 11 the problem of deriving theoretical equations for the transmembrane potentials with selective and non-selective membranes in the presence of simple diffusion was shown to be rather involved. However, certain qualitative conclusions may be easily reached which bear on the influence of the pump on the transmembrane potential.

The diffusible ions may be grouped into two separate teams.   Members of one team tend to make the transmembrane potential positive.   Members of the second team tend to make the transmembrane potential negative.   The two teams will be referred to as the positive and the negative teams, respectively.   Members of the two teams are listed below. The subscripts i and o refer to the location of the member, whether in the inside solution or in the outside solution.   Hydrogen ion is also listed, for the sake of assessing the relative importance of this ion in each of the two teams (see p. 681).

Positive Team	Negative Team
K_i	K_o
Na_i	Na_o
H_i	H_o
Cl_o	Cl_i

If the pump is not allowed to operate, then, in principle, the values of the concentrations, of the distribution coefficients, and of the mobilities of the various ions determine the magnitude of the transmembrane potential.   If the pump is allowed to operate, its effect on the transmembrane potential depends upon whether it adds to the strength of one team or the other, or whether it affects the strength of neither.

If the carrier X is a neutral substance, then, clearly, the effect of the pump is to add another ion, NaX^+, to the positive team; in this case it is readily apparent that the pump increases the transmembrane potential. If the carrier X^- is negative, then, at first thought, it might appear that the transmembrane potential is not affected, since the product of the coupling, NaX, is a neutral molecule.   The following analysis, however, shows that the transmembrane potential should increase.

It is convenient to consider separately pumps of the shuttle type and pumps where the carrier originates in the inside solution (types S and P of Table 12.2).

In the pump of the shuttle type there is a flux of the neutral substance, NaX, outward through the membrane.   There is an inward flux, of equal magnitude, of the carrier X^- moving back on its return trip.   This ion belongs to the positive team.   It follows that this type of pump increases the transmembrane potential.

The argument given in the preceding section does not apply to the sodium pump in which X^- is a metabolic product of the inside solution. In this case, as in the preceding case, there is also a flux of NaX outward. However, in pumps of type c (Table 12.2) the flux of X^- inward is negligible.   In pumps of type e there may be a considerable flux of X^- inward, in which case the positive team is strengthened, and the transmembrane potential is increased. There is yet another factor, however, which is even more important. The effect of this factor becomes apparent when we consider the resting state of a nerve or a muscle fiber *in vivo*. Here we may assume that the concentration of every substance is stationary. The net movement of sodium by simple diffusion is inward. However, for every mole of net inward transport of sodium by simple diffusion there is a mole of NaX moving outward. The net effect is the transport of X^- outward. It follows that this process must be accompanied by a net transport of some cation Y^+ outward, otherwise the two solutions would not be maintained electrically neutral.

Another argument may be used to show that, in this type of pump, there must be a net transport of some cation Y^+. The carrier X^- is a metabolic product, by hypothesis. For every anion formed continuously inside the cell a cation must also form somewhere in the chain of reactions, since the raw material entering the cell is electrically neutral. It follows that the cations so formed, or others produced by exchange reactions, must continuously be transported outward. They may be transported outward as molecules, YX. Nevertheless, for every ion X^- moving outward as NaX there must be a companion ion Y^+ moving outward, either as a free ion or coupled with a neutral molecule. Thus in pumps of the type *P* (Table 12.2) the outward movement of a cation Y^+ is mandatory. This ion, added to the positive team of ions, increases the magnitude of the transmembrane potential.

A temporary change in the ionic concentrations in the intercellular fluid may change the system from steady to non-steady state. This, however, may only affect the rate of formation of Y^+, and the conclusion that the pump increases the transmembrane potential still holds. Finally, we should consider the possibility that the sodium pump operates by a different mechanism in excised nerve and muscle. Such a possibility is rather improbable. If true, it would profoundly affect many of the interpretations of the operation of nerve *in vivo* which are based on information obtained with excised nerve. The fact that phenomena *in vivo* can often be so nicely explained in terms of experiments with excised nerves speaks against this possibility.

We still need to consider the further possibility that the same carrier operates the pump in excised nerve as *in vivo*, but the formation of X^- is stopped and the nerve "lives off its capital." A sample calculation shows that this assumption is also unlikely. Thus Keynes (1949) measured the outward flux of sodium from *Sepia* axons. The outward flux was $19 \cdot 10^{-12}$ moles per sq cm per sec. The inside concentration of sodium was $39 \cdot 10^{-5}$ moles per cc. The diameter of the axon was 0.0212 cm. Using these figures, the calculated initial rate of outflow was 33 per cent of the inside sodium contents per hour. Consequently, if the concentration of the carrier X^- is of the same order as that of sodium, or 0.019 M, and is not replenished, the nerve will markedly change its characteristics in a relatively short time. In other nerves, whose diameter is very much smaller, the surface/volume ratio is larger, and the depletion will proceed at an even faster rate.

It seems safe to conclude, therefore, that every pump represented in Table 12.2 increases the transmembrane potential, as is indicated in line E of the table. It follows that any theoretical derivation of the formula for the transmembrane potential should take cognizance of the presence of the sodium pump. Neglect of this factor is apt to introduce a serious error in the derived formula. The magnitude of the error is apparent from a comparison of the outward total flux of sodium and the inward flux of potassium. In Keynes' experiment, the two fluxes were not very different. Since the outward flux of sodium is chiefly due to the pump, neglecting this flux is as serious as neglecting the flux of potassium.

The lists of ionic members of the positive and negative team, given earlier, contain hydrogen ion among the others. The relative influence of a given ion on a team is proportional to the product $C'bu$, of the concentration, the distribution coefficient, and the mobility of the ion. Since the concentrations of the hydrogen ion are of the order of 10^{-6} M, or less, while the concentrations of the other ions are of the order of 0.1 M, it may be expected that hydrogen ion will exert a relatively small direct influence on the magnitude of the transmembrane potential and may be disregarded in the derivation of the formula for E (cf. further discussion, p. 681).

Exchange reactions

The direct evidence for the permeability of membranes to sodium comes from experiments in which it is shown that there is a net transport of sodium across the membrane. Ussing (1949b) points out that the results of experiments with radioactive tracers should be interpreted with caution. Ussing assumes that the membrane may contain a substance X which forms a stable complex with sodium. The complex, NaX^+, may shuttle back and forth across the membrane, exchanging one isotope of sodium for another at each of the two surfaces, without first dissociating into the two constituents. By such a mechanism, radioactivity could be exchanged between the two solutions, without any net transport of sodium taking place.

An exchange reaction could be equally well suspected in the exchange of isotopes of any other ion across a membrane. If this is done, the quantitative conclusions reached from observations on the exchange of isotopes of any other ion across a membrane are left in a state of suspense. Moreover, conditions for an exchange reaction are more stringent than those for coupled diffusion in general, and to this extent it is less probable. For example, the carrier X must not let go of the ion at either surface, but must insist on trading one isotope for the other.

In view of the demonstrated net transport of sodium against both a concentration gradient and a potential gradient, it is difficult to dismiss the existence of some sort of sodium pump. The presence of an exchange reaction would affect the calculation of the rate of operation of the pump, but the qualitative conclusions pertaining to the pump would not be greatly modified. For these reasons, and in order to proceed on the simplest hypothesis justified by available data, the possible existence of exchange reactions will be omitted in the discussions which follow.

Energy demands of large and small fibers; possible location of the sodium pump power plant

Diameters of nerve fibers cover a large range of sizes, from about 1 μ (cf. Grundfest, 1940) to 500 μ in the giant axon, a ratio of 500 : 1. The ratio surface area/volume extends through the same range. If we assume that the magnitude of the transmembrane potential is approximately the same in all nerve fibers (cf. Curtis and Cole, 1950), and that the membrane is approximately the same in all, these assumptions lead to some intriguing questions.

A given nerve trunk may contain large and small nerve fibers. These fibers share the same intercellular fluid. What can be said of the composition of the inside solutions of fibers of widely varying size?

If the composition of the inside solution is the same in all fibers of a given nerve trunk, the leakage of sodium per unit area is the same for all fibers within the trunk, provided the transmembrane potentials and the membranes are approximately the same. On the other hand, the leakage per unit volume of inside solution is inversely proportional to the diameter of the fiber. If the reaction which provides the energy for the sodium pump takes place at the membrane surface, there is no logical inconsistency in the assumptions of equal potentials, similar membranes, and similar internal compositions. On the other hand, if the energy-producing reaction takes place in the internal solution, the rate of this reaction per unit volume of the solution must be larger in the smaller fibers; this conclusion, however, would be inconsistent with the assumption of equality of composition.

The problem, as stated, is oversimplified, since some fibers are myelinated, others are not. This added complication, while answering some of the questions, raises others. Leakage of sodium in myelinated fibers probably takes place at the nodes of Ranvier. What effect does this have on the relative rates of operation of the sodium pump in myelinated and unmyelinated nerve fibers? Again, the speed of propagation of the nerve impulse along the fiber is different for myelinated and unmyelinated fibers of the same size. It differs for fibers of the same type but of different diameters. What bearing, if any, does the difference in the rates of leakage of sodium have on this problem? Further experimental research is needed before these questions can be answered.

The mechanism of transport of potassium and of chloride ions across nerve and muscle membranes

In principle, the active transfer of an ion may be detected by the application of the isotopic flux ratio test (Chapter 11, p. 551). For a cation of valence 1 the theoretical ratio of the two isotopic fluxes for simple diffusion is given by an equation similar to (12.62). This test is valid for both steady state and non-steady states of the system. If the system is in a steady state, the two concentrations are stationary and, for simple diffusion, the two fluxes are equal; therefore equation (12.61) is also satisfied. If the observed ratio of outward to inward flux is too high, an active outward transport is indicated. If this ratio is too low, either there is an active inward transport of the ion, or part of the ion in the inside solution is not free but is present in bound form.

In practice, the ease of detection of active transport depends upon the accuracy of the measurements and upon the vigor of the pump. Thus for sodium the experimental value of the ratio appearing on the left side of equation (12.61), or (12.62) as the case may be, differs from the theoretical value for simple diffusion by a factor of 25 to 50. Even rough measurements of the quantities appearing in these equations are sufficient to demonstrate the fact that the movement of sodium in nerve and muscle is not by simple diffusion alone.

The situation is different when the pumping of some other ion is weak. The weaker the pump, the greater is the experimental accuracy required to detect it. In experiments, excised fibers are often not in a steady state. Equation (12.62), applying in this case, calls for measuring five quantities: the two concentrations, the two fluxes, and the transmembrane potential. This is a difficult task requiring the use of several fibers. The accuracy of the data becomes subject to the variability from one fiber to another, to the gradual changes taking place while the experiment is in progress, and to other complications involved in work with biological material. Thus the available evidence justifies hardly more than the provisional conclusion that, if there is any active transfer of potassium or chloride ion in muscle or in nerve, its extent is very small compared to the transfer of sodium (cf. Ussing, 1949b; Hodgkin, 1951; Spiegelman and Reiner, 1942).

Nature of the transmembrane potential

In attempting to interpret the transmembrane potential of nerve and muscle, let us start with the following experimental results: The membrane is permeable, to various extents, to potassium, sodium, and chloride ions. The inside solution contains a greater concentration of very slowly penetrating anions than does the outside solution. A fairly vigorous sodium pump is probably in operation. To within the limits of experimental error, the active transfer of potassium and of chloride ions is small.

From the discussions in Chapter 11 it appears that, in general, there is a potential difference at each surface of separation of a membrane and of a solution (cf. p. 526). It also appears that, in general, there is a potential difference E_M across the membrane proper (cf. p. 532). We conclude that, as a rule, there is a transmembrane potential E which equals the algebraic sum of the three potentials:

$$E = E_i + E_M + E_o \qquad (12.63)$$

Given the condition that the composition of the outside solution is maintained approximately constant, the composition of the inside solution should eventually become constant. Since the concentration of essentially non-penetrating anions is larger on the inside, we expect that, when steady state is reached, the outside solution will be positive relative to the inside solution, even in the absence of a sodium pump. In the illustrative example given earlier (p. 674) the expected potential is 12 mv.

The effect of the sodium pump is to increase the transmembrane potential. The more vigorous the pumping action, the larger is the increase. However, the transmembrane potential approaches an upper limit asymptotically, even with an infinitely strong pump. To continue with the illustrative example, let us assume that the pump is ideal and is exceedingly fast. In that case, the inside concentration of sodium is practically zero at steady state. Electrical neutrality is maintained on both sides and, in addition, the potassium and chloride ions must satisfy equation (12.61). Applying these conditions, we may calculate the composition of the inside solution and the value of the transmembrane potential:

	Inside Solution	Outside Solution	Ratio
Na:	0	455 mM	
K:	371.8 mM	10	37.2
Cl:	15.8	587	1/37.2
P⁻:	356		

$$E = 58 \cdot \log_{10} 37.2 = 91 \text{ mv}$$

It would appear, then, that such semiquantitative considerations give a reasonable account of the experimental facts. They explain the existence of a potential, its sign, and its order of magnitude. The exclusion of sodium is effected by the pump. The accumulation of potassium and the exclusion of chloride ion is in accordance with expectations for ions moving by simple diffusion and influenced by the transmembrane potential. There appears to be no need for the assumption of any special devices other than the sodium pump. This is not to say that the expressed interpretation militates against the assumption of other factors affecting the transmembrane potential and the distribution of ions. It merely eliminates for the time being the need for such assumptions.

The rôle of metabolic products

Under physiological conditions, every living cell produces a constant stream of metabolic products, which in some form eventually leave the cell. The products which leave in neutral form are of no particular interest to the present discussion, with the exception of the product which may act as the carrier in an active transfer mechanism. If any of the products leave as ions, the cations add to the strength of the positive team (p. 675) and the anions add to the strength of the negative team. To this extent they affect the magnitude of the transmembrane potential. Since they must leave in equal numbers, the effect on the potential will depend upon the product, $C'bu$, of each species, where b is the distribution coefficient, and u is the mobility of the ion within the membrane. With the possible exception of bicarbonate ion, which tends to lower the transmembrane potential, the ions are apt to be present in small concentration. Therefore, there is no a priori reason to assign any considerable influence to ionic metabolic products. However, since it has been suggested occasionally that the outward movement of hydrogen ion influences the potential strongly and effects the accumulation of potassium ion, the rôle of hydrogen ion merits special attention in this discussion.

The rôle of hydrogen ion

Teorell (1935) showed that, if an ion is continuously produced on one side of a membrane, the steady outflow of this ion across the membrane may affect strongly the transmembrane potential and produce accumulation or exclusion of other "passive" ions, in response to the electrical field. Space does not permit a detailed discussion of the theoretical treatment of this effect given by Teorell. In a second paper Teorell (1937) described experimental tests of the theory. In one experiment a solution containing 0.1 M perchloric acid and 0.1 M ammonium chloride was separated by a membrane from another solution containing 0.1M

ammonium chloride. The concentration of the perchloric acid was kept constant to correspond to the condition wherein a diffusing metabolite is maintained constant. In accordance with the theory, it was found that the movement of hydrogen ion across the membrane caused an accumulation of ammonium ion on the side containing the perchloric acid. Let us consider the applicability of this mechanism to a living cell.

The living cell produces carbon dioxide and carbonic acid continuously. Some of the carbonic acid may leave in dissociated form. Since hydrogen ion is expected to be faster than bicarbonate ion, the question arises whether the outward flux of hydrogen ion has a strong effect on the transmembrane potential and on the accumulation of ions.

We have had several occasions to use the concept of two competing teams of ions, the positive team tending to create a positive transmembrane potential, the negative team having the opposite effect. In order to assess the relative influence of an ion in a given team, it is misleading to compare the effect of the ion with that of its companion alone. The significant comparison is that of the ion in question with the strongest ion in the team to which it belongs. Thus the influence of the internal hydrogen ion should be compared with that of the internal potassium ion. While it is probably true that hydrogen ion has a higher mobility in the membrane than does potassium, the relative influence of an ion on a team is determined not by its mobility alone, but by the product $C'bu$. The concentration of potassium ion in the inside solution is of the order of 0.3 M. The concentration of hydrogen ion is of the order of 10^{-6} M, or less. Since it is hardly likely that the product bu is 300,000 times as great for hydrogen as it is for potassium, we arrive at the conclusion that the influence of hydrogen ion solely as a member of either one of the two diffusing teams is rather insignificant, and that changes of the pH of the outside solution, by one or two units, will have little direct effect on the resting potential. In fact, the experimental evidence (Lorente de Nó, 1947) indicates that changes in external pH in the range 5.5 to 8.0 have little effect on the nerve. The success of Teorell's experiment was apparently due to the fact that a high concentration of a strong acid was used.

While hydrogen ion may play an insignificant rôle as a member of either of the two teams, this ion, however, is potentially a significant chemical agent. As such, it may play a strong but unpredictable rôle. As an illustration of these two different aspects of the influence of hydrogen ion, let us examine the experimental observations of Ussing (1949a) on the rôle of pH in the active transport of sodium through frog skin.

When an isolated frog's skin separates a Ringer's solution containing 0.115 M sodium ion from an outside solution containing 0.003 M sodium, with the anatomical inside surface of the skin facing the Ringer solution, sodium ion moves inward against the concentration gradient, and the inside solution shows a positive potential relative to the outside solution. This indicates the existence of a sodium pump. Before we examine the experimental observations, it is interesting to attempt a prediction as to the effects of changing, in separate experiments, the pH of the outside solution and the pH of the inside solution, respectively. It will be convenient, in this case, to define as the positive team the team of ions which tends to impart a positive potential to the inside solution. The concentrations of the significant ions are:

	Inside Solution (negative team)	Outside Solution (positive team)
Na^+:	115 mM	3 mM
H^+:	C_i'	C_o'

The outside hydrogen ion and the outside sodium ion belong to the same (positive) team. It may be expected that, as long as the pH of the outside solution is much higher than 3, the influence of the hydrogen ion on this team will be small; changes in the outside pH will have little effect on the behavior of the system. However, as the pH begins to approach the value 3, the influence of the hydrogen ion will begin to be appreciable. Near this value a decrease in pH is expected to have the following effects: the transmembrane potential will increase, because of the increase in the concentration of an influential member of the team. The flux of sodium inward will decrease, because of the increase in the unfavorable potential. The inward flux of chloride ion will increase, because of the favorable change in the transmembrane potential. These predictions are in agreement with Ussing's observations. The observed pH effect is small in the pH range 6 to 5. At around 3 to 4, a decrease in the outside pH decreases the inward flux of sodium and increases the inward flux of chloride ion. In this series of experiments the effect on the transmembrane potential was not studied.

If hydrogen ion near pH 6 lacks influence on the positive team, it is to be expected that its influence on the negative team would be even smaller, since the concentration of sodium on the negative team is much larger than the concentration of sodium on the positive team. Yet, it was found that the transmembrane potential is sensitive to the inside pH even in the range 6 to 8. A decrease in the inside pH caused a decrease in the transmembrane potential. Despite the favorable change in the potential, the inward flux of sodium decreased. While the change in potential is in the direction expected from the strengthening of the negative team, the effect on the inward flux of sodium shows that a different explanation need be sought.   If the effect of increasing the inside concentration is due merely to changing the strength of the negative team, without any changes in the properties of the skin, one would expect that the inward flux of sodium would increase with decreasing inside pH, because of the favorable change in the transmembrane potential.   It seems clear, therefore, that the influence of the inside pH is not due to the activity of hydrogen on the negative team, but to some more profound chemical influence, either on the structure of the inside surface of the skin or on the mechanism of the sodium pump.   Similarly, it would seem that the sensitive part of the skin, or of the pump, is located near the inside surface.

To summarize this discussion, hydrogen ion is expected to lack influence as a member of one of the diffusion teams, at usual biological values of the pH.   On the other hand, in situations where the properties of the system are in a state of flux, because of chemical reactions, hydrogen ion may have a strong but unpredictable influence as a chemical agent.   This accounts for the lack of influence of the pH on the resting potential, when the membrane is stable.   It possibly accounts also for the peculiar effects of pH on the afterpotentials (cf. Brazier, 1951), since the membrane is in a state of flux in the post-excitation period.

THE NATURE OF THE OVERSHOOT

Experimental evidence and theories

If the action potential is due solely to the depolarization of the membrane, its magnitude cannot be greater than that of the resting potential. The experiments of Hodgkin and Huxley (1939) and the independent experiments during the period 1939–1942 of Curtis and Cole (1942) have demonstrated the existence of action potentials which were greater than the resting potential.   In addition, Nastuk and Hodgkin (1950), Woodbury, Woodbury, and Hecht (1950) have demonstrated the presence of an overshoot in muscle fibers.   For a description of the experimental methods and for other references the reader is referred to Hodgkin's review (1951).   There is no doubt that, in some nerve or muscle fibers, the polarization of the membrane may be reversed at the height of the action potential.

Several tentative explanations for the reversal of polarization have been offered.   One explanation was based on the assumption that, in the active state, the permeability of inside organic anions becomes very large (Hodgkin and Huxley, 1945; Höber, 1946; Eyring, Lumry, and Woodbury, 1949).   Another explanation was based on the assumption of a change in the orientation of dipoles in the surface of the membrane

(Hodgkin and Huxley, 1945).   At the present time, the most attractive and widely accepted interpretation of the overshoot is that of Hodgkin and Katz (1949a).

The Hodgkin-Katz theory

Hodgkin and Katz start with the tentative assumption that in the active state the permeability of the membrane to sodium becomes much greater than the permeability to other ions.   Since the concentration of outside sodium is much greater than the inside concentration, this simple assumption accounts for the reversal of the polarity of the membrane during activity.

The most convincing experimental evidence demonstrating the importance of sodium in the reversal of polarity comes from observations on the effect of changing the concentration of the outside sodium (Hodgkin and Katz, 1949a; Nastuk and Hodgkin, 1950; Huxley and Stämpfli, 1951; Hodgkin, 1951).   Thus, when the concentration of outside sodium is decreased progressively, in separate experiments, the magnitude of the action potential decreases progressively, approximately 58 mv for every ten-fold decrease in the concentration of sodium.   This observation is in accordance with the assumption that in the active state the sodium ion is the most influential ion in each of the two competing teams of ions. On the other hand, the effect on the resting potential of changing the outside concentration of sodium is rather small.   This observation supports the assumption that in the resting state the permeability to sodium is small.

Application of the linear potential equation to nerve membrane

In the derivation of equation (11.96) it was assumed that the only influential fluxes across the membrane are those of sodium, potassium, and chloride ions.   In the discussion given earlier in this chapter (p. 672) it was indicated that the outward flux of the complex responsible for the pumping of sodium outward is only a little smaller than the inward flux of sodium by simple diffusion.   It follows that the presence of this flux may not be disregarded in the derivation of the equation, no more than the inward flux of sodium may be disregarded.   However, if the mechanism of the pump is specified, it is a simple matter to make an allowance for this additional flux.   As an illustration, let us consider the mechanism in which a complex ion NaX^+ is formed in the inside solution and flows outward by simple diffusion.   If the outside concentration of the complexing substance X is negligibly small compared with its inside concentration, the inward flux of the same complex ion may be disregarded.   In that case equation (11.96) need only be replaced by (12.64), which differs from the former by a single term in the numerator of the fraction appearing on the right side.

$$E = \frac{RT}{F} \ln$$

$$\times \frac{b_{\text{NaX}}u_{\text{NaX}}(\text{NaX})_i{}' + b_{\text{Na}}u_{\text{Na}}(\text{Na})_i{}' + b_{\text{K}}u_{\text{K}}(\text{K})_i{}' + Z_iZ_o{}^{-1}b_{\text{Cl}}u_{\text{Cl}}(\text{Cl})_o{}'}{b_{\text{Na}}u_{\text{Na}}(\text{Na})_o{}' + b_{\text{K}}u_{\text{K}}(\text{K})_o{}' + Z_iZ_o{}^{-1}b_{\text{Cl}}u_{\text{Cl}}(\text{Cl})_i{}'}$$

$$(12.64)$$

Obviously, equation (12.64) is subject to the same limitation as (11.96), namely, that the assumption of a constant potential gradient is justifiable. Since the constancy of the gradient is produced by equality between the ionic populations at the two edges of the membrane (p. 556), there is no *a priori* objection to the use of this assumption in some particular system. However, if the outside solution is diluted extensively, the assumption cannot be applicable with equal accuracy to the system containing the dilute solution.

From the derivation of equations (11.90), (11.96), and (12.64) it may be seen that it is implicitly assumed that the membrane is in a condition of steady state. When the experimental conditions are changed, the fluxes and concentrations within the membrane pass through transient values and eventually reach the new steady state values. The establishment of the new steady state within the membrane may be recognized by the fact that the transmembrane potential has reached a new but steady value. This has some bearing on the applicability of the equations under consideration to the evaluation of the overshoot.

The maximum value of the overshoot in excitation occurs at the peak of the spike. Since the measured potential reaches the peak of the spike very rapidly and immediately begins to decrease, it is doubtful that the membrane is really at a steady state at the peak of the spike. For this reason it is questionable whether the linear potential equation is applicable to the evaluation of the overshoot. However, since the afterpotential changes much more slowly, it is possible that the equation may be applicable to the evaluation of the afterpotential. Finally, the membrane is likely to be in a steady state when the nerve is at rest, and there cannot be any objection on that score to the application of the approximate equation (12.64).

Possible mechanisms in the sodium permeability changes

Employing the terms used in our earlier discussions, we may express the Hodgkin-Katz interpretation as follows. The outside sodium is a member of the negative team, i.e., the team of ions whose movement across the membrane tends to produce a negative transmembrane potential (p. 675).   In resting nerve, the permeability to sodium is relatively small. Consequently this ion lacks influence in the team, and a change in its concentration affects the transmembrane potential to a small extent only. On the other hand, on excitation the permeability to sodium increases greatly and this ion becomes the most influential member of the negative team.   As a result, when the outside concentration of sodium is large enough, the negative team prevails over the positive team and the polarity of the membrane is reversed.   Furthermore, the magnitude of the reversed polarity, i.e., the overshoot, becomes sensitive to the concentration of the now influential outside sodium ion.

Let us inquire whether this enhancement in influence of the sodium ion may be brought about solely by the critical change in the transmembrane potential during stimulation, and without any changes in the properties of the membrane itself, i.e., without any change in the values of the parameters b_j and u_j of the various ions.   Suppose that we represent the unspecified complexing particles by A, B, C, $\cdot$ $\cdot$ $\cdot$, respectively.   Sodium may exist within the membrane as a cation, Na^+ or NaA^+, as a neutral molecule, NaB, or as an anion, such as NaC^- or NaD^{--}.   An imposed drop in the transmembrane potential increases both the outward flux of the cations and the inward flux of the anions.   Both of these effects act in a restorative manner in that they tend to increase the transmembrane potential and, therefore, they alone cannot be responsible for the reversal in polarity.   Moreover, since the same argument applies to all ions present in the membrane, we arrive at the general conclusion that none of the pre-existing ions can be responsible for the reversal in polarity if the membrane itself remains unchanged by the stimulus.   In particular, the overshoot cannot be caused by the change in the flux of a pre-existing ion such as NaD^{--}.   In this detail the present interpretation differs from that of Hodgkin, Huxley, and Katz in 1949 (cf. Hodgkin, 1951).

Accepting the necessity of a change in the membrane, on the basis of the available evidence, the mechanism of the change in permeability to sodium is still to be interpreted.   One possible mechanism would involve the production, within the membrane, of an abundant supply of a neutral molecule X, capable of forming a very mobile complex NaX^+.   When the outside concentration of sodium is high, the net movement of this complex is inward, thus accounting both for the increased leakage of sodium inward and for the reversal in polarity of the membrane.   The fact that the unhydrated sodium ion has a smaller diameter than that of potassium, and that it has, therefore, a greater tendency to form complexes, supports the hypothesis that here again, as in the sodium pump, sodium is the important complex-forming ion.

NATURE OF THE CRITICAL STATE

Experimental evidence on the nature of the critical conditions

An adequate blow imparted to the steel ball of a pinball machine sends the ball up an incline, past the top barrier, and into the obstacle course. With an inadequate blow, the ball returns to its place of origin. The ultimate destination of the ball is settled at the end of the quick blow. Yet, if only the obstacle course is available for inspection, it may take some time after the blow before the observer may know what the outcome of the effort will be. An analogous situation occurs when nerve is stimulated with a shock or with a constant current of high intensity but short duration. The ultimate outcome is settled at the termination of the stimulus, at the end of a time interval of the order of 0.01 msec. If the outcome of the stimulus is judged by the appearance of a rapid change in the transmembrane potential or of a rapid rise of the potential at the outside surface (electrotonic potential), it may take 0.20 to 0.50 msec before the nature of the outcome is known.

In the pinball machine the decisive critical quantity is the kinetic energy of the ball at the end of the blow. An expert player may be able to tell at the end of the blow whether his effort is successful. To a less expert player the critical event associated with the blow is the passage of the ball beyond the barrier. Similarly, in the simplest type of stimulation, namely, with a shock, the decisive quantity appears to be a definite critical change in some potential caused by the delivery of a critical quantity of electricity. However, in the absence of clear information on the nature of events initiated by the shock, the event most readily identifiable as critical is the change in the direction of the transmembrane current from outward to inward. Even with our limited knowledge of the processes taking place, it is evident that, beyond this event, the transmembrane current begins to favor depolarization instead of opposing it.

The observations of Cole and Curtis (1939) on the course of the impedance of the membrane in a full-blown action potential indicate a large increase in the conductance of the membrane. This increase becomes both appreciable and conspicuous near the time at which the transmembrane current changes direction from outward to inward (see Fig. 12.5E). It was concluded in Chapter 11 that some rectification by a membrane is to be expected, even if the properties of the membrane do not change. The conductance increases when the fastest ions carry the current and decreases when the slowest ions carry the current. At first thought it may appear that these changes may be associated with simple rectification and that, qualitatively, they do not necessarily indicate a change in the properties of the membrane. However, the increase in conductance apparently takes place at a time which is incompatible with this simple assumption. As was mentioned before, the dramatic increase in conductance takes place when the current is in the inward direction. Since in the resting state potassium ions have a higher mobility than sodium, one would expect a higher conductance for outward and not for inward currents. Thus the experimental observations show that, in active nerve, more than simple rectification is involved, and there is either a general increase in the mobilities of the ions, or there is at least an increase in the mobility of sodium ion. In either case a change in the properties of the membrane is indicated.

Changes in material systems are usually caused by changes in free energies of reactions. Let us now consider the following question: Are the changes in the properties of the membrane associated with some particular value of one of the free energies or with some gradual change? The following illustrations help to clarify the meaning of the question. In the operation of an automatic sprinkler system the critical event is the melting of the restraining bar. The critical point may be described as the temperature at which the free energies of the solid and of the liquid metal are equal. On the other hand, when an explosive mixture is heated, the critical point cannot be described simply in terms of the free energy of some particular reaction. The critical event is reached when two rates are equal—the rate of heat generation by the reaction and the rate of dissipation of heat by the system. The nature of the factors which affect the free energy of reactions in the nerve membrane will be considered later. For the moment, we consider only the question whether the changes taking place in the nerve membrane at and near the critical event are more like the changes at and near the melting of a pure solid, when the free energy reaches a definite value, or whether the critical event is reached by way of gradual changes affecting the relative rates of a number of cooperative and competing processes.

The observations of Cole and Curtis (1941) (see also Curtis and Cole, 1950; Cole, 1941; and Hodgkin, Huxley, and Katz, 1949) on the rectification of currents by the squid axon membrane yield a partial answer to this question. With subthreshold currents the transverse impedance is smaller at the cathode than it is at the anode. Hodgkin, Huxley, and Katz (1949) concluded that their observations are consistent with the assumption that the permeability to sodium varies with the transmembrane potential, that the change appears to be a continuous one, and that there is no sudden alteration of permeability at some critical voltage.

In the discussion of the temporal course of the threshold subsequent to a shock it was pointed out that the observations illustrated in Fig. 12.3

indicate that changes in the membrane take place even with subthreshold shocks. The change in the nature of the curves becomes easily perceptible beyond 50 per cent–threshold shocks. It becomes gradually more pronounced as the critical region is approached. Furthermore, there is no abrupt change when the critical region is passed (Fig. 12.3, curves 1.00 to 1.2).

Additional evidence that the membrane changes are gradual is available from the measurement of the temporal course of the transmembrane potential subsequent to a shock (Fig. 3 of Hodgkin, Huxley, and Katz, 1949). As in the observations by Katz (Fig. 12.3), there is a gradual transition in the shape of the transmembrane potential-time curve when the magnitude of the applied shock approaches the threshold value. The whole family of Hodgkin's curves for transmembrane potentials with subthreshold shocks shows a striking similarity to the family of Katz's curves for the course of the threshold subsequent to a subthreshold shock. The results obtained by Hodgkin et al. with superthreshold shocks of varying intensity also show that there is no abrupt change in the course of the transmembrane potential even when the critical conditions are passed.

Thus the evidence is strong that the potential changes introduced by the stimulus bring about gradual changes in the properties of the membrane and that these changes, in turn, affect the subsequent temporal course of the potential. Although it has been established that the effect of the changes within the membrane is to increase the leakiness of the membrane and, apparently, to favor the transport of sodium against that of potassium, entirely too little is known as yet about the chemical or physical nature of these changes to allow profitable speculation about them.

Still, it is interesting to speculate on a less remote problem, namely, on the manner in which the change in potential brings about the changes in the membrane. Broadly speaking, two types of explanations have been offered. In the first type, the immediate effect of the change in the potential is to produce an accumulation or depletion of substances at one or both surfaces and that this change in concentration starts the chain of chemical or physical events which account for excitation. In the second type of explanation it is assumed that the immediate effect of the change in potential is to affect directly the structure and properties of the membrane and that the chain of physical and chemical events is only secondary.

An adequate discussion of the first type, which we may call the "accumulation hypothesis," would require numerous assumptions regarding the many theoretical possibilities. For example, changes in concentration may take place at the inner surface or at the outer surface of the membrane. At each place, accumulation may be caused by flow into or out from the membrane, resulting in an increase in concentration on one side of the surface and a depletion on the other side. Finally, at each place the effect of the potential on the concentration of each of the theoretically significant ions should be considered. In preference to a detailed discussion of this approach, let us examine in somewhat further detail the *a priori* hypothesis that a changing potential field affects the structure of a membrane containing macromolecular dipoles, as already suggested by the discussions in the preceding and the present chapters.

Orientation of dipoles; excitation

Apart from the accumulation hypothesis, when we look for the first link in the chain of events initiated by electrical stimulation, the choice is rather limited. We are left principally with the facts that the added electrical field changes the energy stored in the double layer of charges, modifies the rates of movement of the ions, and affects the degree of orientation of dipole molecules. Of these three, the last mentioned appears to be the most important, but the other two call for brief comment.

The two layers of ions on the opposite faces of the membrane exert a pressure on the membrane by virtue of their mutual attraction. A change in the density of the two surface layers changes the pressure. However, an estimate of the pressure shows that it is entirely too small to exercise any control on the structure of the membrane. The change in the rate of drift of the ions produced by the change in the field cannot of itself cause any serious changes in the properties of the membrane.

Thus we turn to the influence of the electrical field on the orientation of dipoles. The large potential gradient prevailing in the membrane and the usually high dipole moments of macromolecules have led other writers to the suggestion that membrane changes are initiated by the reorientation of dipoles in response to the change in the potential gradient (Danielli, 1941; Schaefer, 1944; Eyring, Lumry, and Woodbury, 1949). The calculations given in Chapter 11 indicate that, with the usual potential gradients prevailing in the membrane, major changes in the orientation of dipoles can take place with a change of 25 mv in the transmembrane potential, provided the dipole moment of the particles is of the order of 200 to 300 Debye units. Values as high as 1400 Debye units for the dipole moment of proteins have been observed (Cohn and Edsall, 1943). It seems plausible to assume that the first effect following the change in the potential gradient imposed by the stimulus is on the orientation of the macromolecular constituents of the membrane.

There is no general orientation of protein molecules in a very dilute aqueous solution. The situation is undoubtedly different in the membrane.

Even in the absence of a potential gradient, the mutual interaction of the constituents imposes some orientation of the dipoles. A transmembrane potential changes the orientation of some of the polar particles, and the larger the potential gradient; the greater is the fraction of the particles whose orientation is affected by the field. Thus it is to be expected that a gradual decrease in the transmembrane potential will be followed by a gradual change in the structure of the membrane.

Different parts of the macromolecules may exhibit different affinities for the ions and molecules present in the membrane. For this reason the orientation of the macromolecules may affect their availability for combination with the migrant population of the membrane. Conversely, added substances, such as drugs, may affect the structure of the membrane by favoring that structure which allows a reaction with the added substances. Some drugs may favor the more leaky structure; others, the tighter structure. The former will increase the irritability of the nerve; the latter will decrease it. Drugs may also affect the metabolic reactions of the nerve and, specifically, the reactions involving the operation of the sodium pump.

The rôles of E_i, E_M, and E_o in the initial stages of excitation; an experimental approach

If the first effect of the electrical stimulus is to change the structure of the membrane, the responsible component of the potential is the drop E_M across the membrane proper. If the first effect of the stimulus is to produce accumulation at one of the surfaces, E_i or E_o is the influential component. A shock applied at the outside surface changes rapidly the values of E_o, E_M, E, and the outside potential V. The immediate effect on the inside potential U and on E_i is small. The effect of a constant current stimulus applied at the outside surface is somewhat more complex. Some of the differences between the effects of a shock and of a constant current are shown in Fig. 12.14A,B.

When the shock is delivered by an inside electrode, the following quantities change at once: E_i, E_M, E, U. The following quantities suffer only a small change: E_o, V. If the cathode is applied at some spot on the nerve, and the anode is applied at some distant point, then, with a constant current stimulus, the value of E passes through a minimum and later approaches a steady state value. Let us assume that the two stimulating electrodes face each other across the membrane. In that case the value of E changes monotonically, and this affects radically the accommodative properties of the nerve fiber. Specifically, if the stimulating current increases at a constant rate, starting with zero, the transmembrane potential rises continuously. If excitation is initiated by a particular value of E_M, then there can be no accommodation, no matter how slow the rate of change of current.

It seems plausible that a judicious use of both inside and outside stimulating electrodes, in separate experiments, with concurrent measurements of U, V, E, and of the threshold would give valuable information on the relative importance of each of the three components of the transmembrane potential and should throw light on the question whether the initial effect of the stimulus is due to accumulation of ions at one of the surfaces or to a more direct influence on the structure of the membrane.

In the theory of irritability discussed in the earlier part of this chapter the tentative assumption was made that the instantaneous value of the transmembrane potential E is the factor determining the structure of the membrane. According to this view, a change in E introduces immediately a demand for a change in the structure. However, the response of the membrane to this demand is not instantaneous, but proceeds at a finite rate. If E changes continuously, the change in the membrane lags behind E. A very crude formula for the rate of change of the structure of the membrane can be given.

Let X be the difference between the instantaneous value of E and the value of E which would maintain the simultaneous structure of the membrane. When X is small, the rate of change of the membrane structure is proportional to X. However, as X increases, the rate increases much faster. For an admittedly oversimplified discussion of the nature· of the lag between the instantaneous structure of the membrane and the changing transmembrane potential we may make use of the formula: rate $= Ke^{aX}$, where K and a are constants. This is the formula which was used in the qualitative interpretation of Fig. 12.8D.

Possible effects of the potential field on the rates of enzymatic reactions

Recent experimental evidence seems to indicate that the efficiency of some enzyme systems is due in part to a concentration and organization of these systems at surfaces. In this connection, the observations of Libet (1948) are of particular interest. Libet found that in the giant axons of the squid *Loligo pealii* the ATP-ase activity is concentrated at the surface.

Enzymes are large molecules and are apt to have high dipole moments. Thus, change in the potential field may affect the orientation of an enzyme located at the surface or in the interior of the membrane. The change in orientation may either mask or make more readily available a part of the enzyme surface which is essential for catalytic activity. In addition, changes in configuration of the enzyme molecule, analogous to those accompanying reversible protein denaturation under the influence of various factors as discussed at some length in Chapters 8 to 11, possibly occur also under the influence of changes in the potential field. It is further conceivable that one of the immediate effects of the electrical stimulus is to slow down the pumping of sodium through an action on the enzymes. This effect, by itself, will not change the relative permeabilities in the simple diffusion of sodium and of potassium, but it may cooperate with the stimulus in decreasing the polarization of the membrane. Therefore, in a detailed examination of the action of the pump in a stimulation, the possible effect of the electrical field on the action of the pump may have to be taken into consideration.

Recovery from excitation

When we compare the properties of the irritable nerve membrane with those of an inert membrane, we find that the nerve membrane possesses two attributes which enable it to serve its peculiar function. The sodium pump maintains indefinitely, at least in the living organism, the concentration differences across the membrane which serve as the immediate source of energy needed for the generation of an impulse. The second important attribute is the ability of the membrane to change its properties rapidly in response to an adequate depolarization. It is tempting to assume that one or both of these attributes are also responsible for the processes which lead to the ultimate restoration of the resting state, after the fully developed action potential has served its purpose.

As an example, we may assume that the sodium pump serves an important rôle in the restoration of the resting state. Thus an outward sodium pump whose intensity increases greatly when the membrane is depolarized could serve such a rôle. Pursuing this thought a little further, it is clear that a sodium pump whose intensity rises rapidly in response to a depolarization would be effective in maintaining the transmembrane potential near its rest value, but it would also be effective in preventing the development of an action potential.

Let us assume, however, that the sodium pump possesses the following characteristics. The pump is capable of reaching high intensities in response to a demand, but it is sluggish in changing from one rate to another. In that case the sequence of events accompanying stimulation would consist of the following steps.

(1) An adequate stimulus changes the properties of the membrane, with the accompanying phenomena, discussed earlier, which lead to the development of the action potential. In this phase, commonly referred to as the rising phase of the action potential, the pump does not respond fast enough to prevent the depolarization of the membrane.

(2) Time and the reversal of polarity enable the pump to increase its

intensity to a level at which it is capable of starting the repolarization of the membrane.   During the early stages of this phase the labile membrane, whose time constant is by hypothesis greater than that of the pump, responds to the rising transmembrane potential and retraces backward the series of changes of state suffered during the first phase; in consequence, the ratio (permeability to sodium)/(permeability to potassium) decreases; this speeds up the recovery process and accounts for the autocatalytic nature of the first part of the recovery phase.

(3) When the permeability to sodium is sufficiently suppressed, further changes in the permeability to sodium are of relatively little significance, and the temporal course of the potential reflects the changing rate of the pump; this accounts for the stage commonly referred to as the negative afterpotential.

(4) Finally, because of the sluggishness of the sodium pump in adjusting to instantaneous conditions, when the resting potential is reached the pump is still overactive, and this accounts for the appearance of a positive afterpotential (cf. Fig. 12.5E, p. 622).

In seeking the reason for the sluggishness in the readjustment of the rate of the sodium pump let us examine, merely by way of illustration, the pump depicted in Fig. 11.8 (p. 600).   In the resting state the energy-yielding substance G is present at a steady concentration.   A sudden depolarization of the membrane increases the flux of NNa^+ outward, and this acts in a restorative manner.   If, in addition, the permeability of this complex ion increases, as do the permeabilities of sodium and potassium ions, the pump is capable of preventing the development of the action potential.   However, the supply of the energy-yielding substance G depends upon a more or less long chain of precursor reactions.   Whereas the free potassium and sodium fluxes can respond rapidly and continuously to the changing potential and to the changing properties of the membrane, the maintenance of the concentration of G depends on a more or less cumbersome supply train of reactions and diffusion processes.   The initial surge of the pump is apt to deplete the local supply of the substance G, and the pump does not immediately live up to its full potentialities. However, with the passage of time the readjustments in the steady states of the reactions and diffusion processes in the "supply train" enable the pump to increase its capacity and intensity and to bring about the sequence of events leading to recovery of the resting state.

Any theory of the recovery process will have to conform with the informative and valuable experimental observations published recently by Hodgkin and his associates (Hodgkin, Huxley, and Katz, 1952; Hodgkin and Huxley, 1952a,b,c).   These observations deal with the temporal course of the net ionic current through the nerve membrane when a depolarizing potential is "clamped" across the membrane by means of internal and external electrodes. Whereas the experimental observations deal with the net ionic currents through the membrane, the authors' interpretations involve admittedly tentative assumptions regarding the sodium and potassium components of these currents (Hodgkin and Huxley, 1952d).

Their assumptions and interpretation of the full course of an action potential may be briefly stated as follows. An adequate depolarization changes the properties of the membrane in such a way as to favor the passage of sodium; this accounts for the action potential and the over-shoot. Meanwhile the membrane slowly undergoes still another change in which the permeability to sodium decreases, whereas the permeability to potassium increases. This accounts for the recovery phase. Thus it is assumed that the membrane returns to its original rest state not by retracing backwards the sequence of changes which lead to the action potential but by some different path. The flux due to the sodium pump is completely disregarded.

It has been calculated earlier (p. 674) that in the absence of the sodium pump the transmembrane potential would tend to acquire a value of the order of 12 mv, whereas in the presence of an infinitely strong pump the value would be of the order of 91 mv (p. 680). The actual value, 48 mv, attests to the importance of the rôle played by the sodium pump in the resting state. There is no obvious reason to assume that the pump suspends its activity during an action potential. On the contrary, physical considerations suggest that the activity of the pump will increase when the transmembrane potential is lowered. This may explain the discrepancy observed by the authors in their theoretical paper (Hodgkin and Huxley, 1952d). They found that their predicted value for the exchange of sodium was too low, whereas the predicted exchange of potassium was too high. In an earlier paragraph of this section it was suggested that restoration of the membrane to the resting state may be brought about by a strong but delayed surge in the activity of the sodium pump. If this is indeed the case, the restoring outward current consists largely of the sodium complex and not of potassium ions. This would account for the fact that the observed exchange of sodium is larger, whereas the observed exchange of potassium is smaller than those predicted by the hypothesis which disregards the rôle of the sodium pump.

It is possible that the unpublished experiments by a tracer technique, mentioned by Hodgkin and Huxley (1952a, p. 456), will prove decisively the postulated sequence of permeability changes and will thus show that the membrane does return to the resting state by a new path. Nevertheless it is difficult to see that a complete explanation of the action potential can be given without allowance for the flux of the sodium pump and for the changes in the flux caused by depolarization.

Afterpotentials and rates of transformation within the membrane

From our previous discussions, the transmembrane potential, even with the simplest type of membrane considered, must contain, in general, three components, E_i, E_M, and E_o. E_i depends chiefly upon the state of the inner surface of the membrane, E_o depends chiefly upon the state of the outer surface, while E_M depends on the state of the membrane as a whole. It is not likely that nerve and muscle membranes are homogeneous throughout their thickness, and it is conceivable that during the post-excitation period the two surfaces and the bulk of the membrane may be changing at different rates.

If this is true, it follows that during recovery the value of the trans-membrane potential depends upon at least four factors, the state of the membrane at each of the two surfaces, the state of the membrane in the interior, and the strength of the sodium pump.   Each of these factors, no doubt, is in a state of flux during the post-stimulus period.   If all four factors change at rates whose half-times are approximately the same, it would be expected that the transmembrane potential would gradually approach its resting value and that the time record of the potential would have a simple course.

On the other hand, if one of the four factors changes at a much smaller rate than the others do, the time course of the potential record will be more complex.   Thus it may show a fairly rapid approach to values larger than the normal potential, with a subsequent slow return to the normal resting value.   This would account for the positive afterpotential. If the rapid changes leave the transmembrane potential at less than normal value, the record will show a slow negative afterpotential.   One would expect, *a priori*, that added chemical agents would have different effects on the rates of changes of the four factors.   This would account for the observed fact that different changes in the experimental conditions affect the different components of a complex action potential record in different ways.

The complexity of the action potential is brought out in the extensive and critical studies by Lorente de Nó (1947), who has presented, in essence, the following interpretation.   The membrane potential is regarded not as a diffusion potential but as being maintained at static double layers, with at least two and possibly three such double layers of charges. The electrostatic (Coulombic) attraction between the charged particles of a double layer is assumed balanced by non-Coulombic (chemical) forces which tend to separate the particles of opposite sign.   The complex nature of the action potential is assumed to be due to the fact that the normal values of the potentials in the separate double layers are recovered at different rates. Because of the importance of these views, it is of interest to examine the extent to which the interpretations expressed in the preceding discussion are consistent therewith.

Purely for convenience of reference, the two interpretations will be referred to as the static and the dynamic models, respectively. In both models the measured instantaneous transmembrane potential is assumed to consist of more than one component. In the static model, diffusion is given no important rôle. In the dynamic model, diffusion contributes to the potential, even in the resting state, for the reason that movement of ions is demonstrated by isotopic experiments, and wherever there is movement of ions with unequal mobilities there must be a diffusion component, E_M.

In the dynamic model there are two double layers of ions at the two surfaces of the membrane and a double layer separated by the membrane proper. The first two double layers are maintained by what may be called chemical forces, i.e., the differences in the solubilities of anions and cations in the membrane. The third layer is maintained by the diffusion of ions of unequal mobilities. In the static model the location of the double layers is not specified.

In the static model a slow afterpotential change is interpreted in terms of a slow change in some one of the assumed double layers. In the dynamic model the slow afterpotential is interpreted in terms of a slow reaction, which may effect changes in more than one of the three component potentials. Thus, if the outside surface of the membrane is subject to a slow change, both E_o and E_M suffer slow changes. However, since E is the algebraic sum of the three components, the experimental record of the transmembrane potential shows a single slow afterpotential. Both models assign to sodium an important rôle in nerve function. The static model does not attempt to intrepret in detail the nature of this rôle or the reason for the active transfer of sodium from the interior of the cell. The dynamic model interprets the sodium pump in terms of coupled diffusion outward. This process accounts for the exclusion of sodium and, at the same time, for the relatively high values of the resting transmembrane potential.

Note added in proof: The following recent publications deal with some of the topics discussed in this chapter: Butler (1952), Katz (1952), and Wyke (1951).

Physical Chemistry
of the Contractile Process
in Muscle[1, 2]

It was a Scholastic, William of Occam, who nearly a thousand years ago laid down the primary working principle for the development of scientific laws, or generalizations, as they might more properly be called: *Entia non sunt multiplicanda praeter necessitatem.* In Sir William Hamilton's amplification, "Neither more, nor more onerous, causes are to be assumed than are necessary to account for the phenomena." The great Newton, perhaps in an effort to reconcile his science with his religion, converted this to "Nature is simple." We biologists know with certainty that such is not the case, but we also know that it is necessary to proceed as if it were if we are ever to get any comprehension of nature.

C. Leonard Huskins, in *American Scientist*, October, 1951

A PHYSICOCHEMICAL MODEL OF THE CONTRACTILE MECHANISM

The problem of the contractility of muscle has attracted and held the attention of many investigators (Fenn, 1945). A great deal of progress in this field has been made. Recent progress in the chemical aspects of the problem is summarized in Mommaerts' monograph (1950). There are many aspects to this problem, and, although gratifying advances have been made with some, others are at a temporary standstill.

At the present time there is no satisfactory interpretation of the relation between the tension developed by a muscle and the length at which it is stimulated. Nor is there a satisfactory explanation of the manner in which the speed of shortening of a stimulated muscle is controlled by the prevailing conditions (Fenn, 1945). It is hoped that the theory presented

[1] The author of this chapter (M. J. P.) wishes to express his gratitude to the National Foundation for Infantile Paralysis for the aid which made possible the work on the problems discussed in this chapter.

[2] The writer is indebted to the *American Journal of Physiology* for permission to use most of the material of this chapter in the form in which it was originally published (Polissar, 1952a,b,c,d).

here (Polissar, 1952a,b,c,d) will lend support to Fenn's opinion that "The necessary methods of study seem to be ready for use, and much of the necessary information is at hand to complete the theory."

The idea that the tension developed by the muscle is due to shortening of filaments within the muscle fibers is well accepted by most investigators in this field.   We can bring to bear upon this old problem the points of view and the methods of approach of polymer chemistry and polymer physics, as well as the relatively rich store of empirical information already accumulated by these new sciences.

On examination of the progress made in the study of polymers (Schmidt and Marlies, 1948; Alfrey, 1948) one is impressed by the fact that the gains were made on the basis of relatively simple ideas, such as the independent chemical action of individual parts of a long polymer molecule and the law of mass action; also on rather simple mechanical pictures of the steric effects of side chains and the effects of the size of the side chain and of its polarity on such properties as tensile strength and elasticity.

It is the object of this chapter to show that the length-tension relation in stimulated muscle, the speed-load relation in an isotonic contraction, and other mechanochemical and thermal properties of muscle may be explained in terms of the simple assumptions which proved so fruitful in other branches of chemistry.   Specifically, it will be shown that an examination of the kinetics of the shortening of individual fibrils will not only produce the desired relations, but will also suffice to explain many of the facts of muscle behavior known to physiologists.

Experimental procedures and observations

The "reaction system" of the physiologist may consist of the whole muscle in an anesthetized animal, with one tendon cut and attached to the proper recording device; or it may be an excised muscle kept in a Ringer solution; or it may be a single muscle fiber.

An entire muscle consists of a tough connective tissue covering, which encloses more connective tissue, the intercellular fluid, and the contractile fibers.   The diameters of the *fibers* vary from 0.001 to 0.01 cm.   The outer cover of the individual fiber is called the *sarcolemma*.   Within the sarcolemma there is the intracellular fluid, called the *sarcoplasm* and the *myofibrils*, which constitute the working element of a contracting fiber.

The myofibrils run parallel to the fiber axis.   They consist of parallel filaments, which in measurements with an electron microscope are found to vary in diameter from 50 to 180 Å, with an average width of 100 Å. We shall be chiefly concerned with the behavior of these filaments in a stimulated muscle.

In voluntary muscles there are transverse striations along the fiber, at repeating distances of 10,000 to 20,000 Å, depending upon the source of the muscle. The repeating unit of the fiber between two similar striations is called a *sarcomere*. The myosin filaments extracted from a fiber may be of various lengths, but, in general, the maximum length is that of a sarcomere (Schmitt, Bear, Hall, and Jakus, 1947).

Application of a single electrical shock to a muscle produces a *twitch*. A succession of electrical shocks, frequent enough to cause the fusion of twitches, produces a *tetanus*, or *tetanic contraction*; the muscle is tetanized; a contraction may be isometric or isotonic. In an isometric contraction the length of the muscle is fixed. In an *isotonic contraction* the muscle is allowed to change its length while carrying a constant load. The term "contraction" as used by the physiologists is not synonymous with "shortening." Thus there is no overall shortening in an isometric contraction. The muscle merely develops a tension. Again, in an isotonic contraction in which the load is greater than the tension developed by the muscle, the muscle will lengthen.

The mechanical behavior of muscle is summarized best by a length-tension diagram for isometric contractions and by a speed-load diagram for isotonic contractions. The *passive stretch curve ABCDE* (Fig. 13.1) may be obtained by stretching the unstimulated muscle to various lengths and observing the tension at each length. The length of the muscle at which a passive tension just begins to appear on further stretch is called the *rest-length*. On a relative scale this length is assigned the magnitude 1.0.

The *active tension curve FGHI* may be obtained as follows: The muscle is tetanized at rest-length (step *A–I*), and the tension is observed. The muscle is allowed to relax, the relaxed muscle is given a little slack, after which it is stimulated again (steps *I–A–H*). By repeating these steps one obtains curve *FGHI*.

Curve *IJKL* (Fig. 13.2) is obtained by the succession of steps: stimulate, relax, stretch, stimulate, relax, etc.

Another method of obtaining a curve of the type *FGHI* is to tetanize the muscle at a certain length (Fig. 13.2, steps *A–G*) and then to change its length very slowly while it is in the tetanized state. On allowing the muscle to shorten, one gets curve *GF*. On stretching the muscle, one gets curve *GHI*. If the stretching is continued beyond the rest-length, curve *IJ'K'* is obtained. It is highly significant that in this process, in which the muscle is stretched in the stimulated state, the tension observed at each length (curve *IJ'K'*) is greater than the tension observed when the muscle is stretched in the unstimulated state and is stimulated afterward.

The speed-load relation in an isotonic contraction (Fig. 13.4) may be obtained as follows: The muscle is tetanized at rest-length; after full tension is developed, the muscle is released, while still in the tetanized state, and is allowed to shorten and lift a load. After a brief period of acceleration, the load reaches a maximum speed, the value of which depends upon the load. If the load is equal to W_r, the tension developed

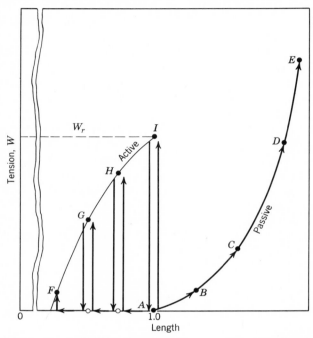

Fig. 13.1. Curve $ABCDE$: Length-tension curve for unstimulated muscle. Curve $FGHI$: Length-tension curve for tetanized muscle. The points of this curve are obtained by allowing the proper amount of slack before stimulating the muscle. W_r is the tension developed by the muscle when tetanized at rest-length. Abscissas: Relative length of the muscle, with rest-length taken as 1.0. (Schematic.)

at rest-length, the speed is zero. If the load is zero, the speed has its maximum value v_0. The relation between v/v_0 and W/W_r as obtained by Hill (1938) for frog's sartorius at 0°C is shown in diagram A of Fig. 13.4.

In an isotonic contraction a constant load is imposed on the muscle. The tension within the muscle remains constant and equal to the load. The muscle responds with a speed which for each load is variable and a function of the instantaneous length. If, by suitable mechanical arrangement, a constant speed of shortening or of lengthening is imposed on the muscle, the muscle responds with a tension whose instantaneous values depend both upon the instantaneous length and upon the imposed speed (Levin and Wyman, 1927). For very low speeds, the length-tension relation (Fig. 13.5) is the same as the isometric relation $FGHIJ'K'$ of Fig. 13.2 (Mommaerts, 1950, p. 41). For higher speeds there is a

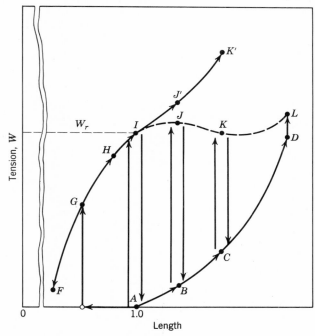

Fig. 13.2. Complete length-tension diagram. Curve $IJ'K'$ is obtained by stimulating the muscle at rest-length and stretching the muscle after the muscle is tetanized. Individual points of the curve $IJKL$ are obtained by stretching the muscle to the desired length *before* it is stimulated; the muscle is allowed to relax before it is stretched to the next length. (Schematic.)

deviation from the isometric curve, the deviation increasing with the magnitude of the imposed speed.

A muscle tetanized isometrically produces heat at constant rate, which is greater than the metabolic heat rate of resting muscle. This constant heat rate is called the *heat of maintenance*.

These are the observations which any molecular model of the contractile mechanism should be able to interpret. Other observations will be described as the need arises, and will be interpreted in terms of the physicochemical model proposed in this chapter.

The change of state of the fiber after stimulation

When a muscle is stimulated, the tension does not begin to rise at once. There is a latent period whose properties have been investigated by Sandow and other workers (for references, see Sandow, 1949).

It appears that the interior of the fiber in resting muscle is in a semifluid, solated state; on stimulation, the constituents are "welded" together to form the myofibrils whose subsequent shortening produces the outward manifestations of muscular contraction (Meyer and Picken, 1937; Morales, 1948; Astbury, 1950).

The latent period is probably associated with this sol-gel transformation. This period is relatively short as compared with the time of a twitch. The experimental evidence seems to indicate that the establishment of the active state follows shortly after stimulation (Hill, 1949). In the present chapter we will not be concerned with this preliminary period. Our "zero time" will be the time at which the sol-gel transformation is accomplished and the shortening of the filaments begins.

A physicochemical model of the contractile mechanism

We will accept the current idea that the shortening of active muscle is due to the shortening of the filaments and we will add the following assumptions. The filaments consist of smaller units, strung in series. Each unit within this series is capable of reacting with its chemical environment when the muscle is stimulated. These units alternate in an active muscle between a long state L and a short state S. We will call them *contractile units* in states L and S, respectively. The chemical behavior of each unit will be assumed to be independent of the states of other units in the filament.

We now have the following picture of what takes place when a muscle is stimulated isotonically: The stimulation of the muscle produces filaments consisting, at zero time, of contractile units in the L state. The chemical environment in active muscle is such as to make the following reactions possible: Reaction I, $L = S$; reaction II, $S = L$. These reactions proceed by different paths, and the combination of the two reactions will be given by the equation $L \rightleftarrows S$, to distinguish this cyclical process from the usual reversible reaction, such as $H_2O \rightleftarrows H^+ + OH^-$.

At first, reaction I predominates and the muscle shortens. Gradually, as the concentration of L decreases and that of S increases, a steady state is approached in which the two rates are equal; a tetanus is achieved.

If a load is attached to the shortened muscle, the tension created within the muscle speeds up reaction II and slows down reaction I. There follows a net reaction $S \to L$, which proceeds until a new steady state is reached, with a larger fraction of the units in state L; the muscle lengthens.

We visualize the ultimate length achieved by the muscle in a given isotonic contraction as the outward manifestation of the distribution of the contractile units between the L and the S states. This distribution is controlled by the tension within the muscle created by the imposed load. The heat of maintenance, observed in a tetanus, is due to the exothermic reactions in the sarcoplasm coupled with reactions I and II of the steady state cycle.

The statement that the speed of shortening of the muscle in an isotonic contraction is the net result of the complex of chemical reactions taking place in it would be fruitless without further elaboration. However, with the aid of our model, we can now declare that the speed of shortening is the outward manifestation of the rate of the net reaction $L \to S$.

In the proposed physicochemical model the constituent parts of the filaments do not undergo a permanent shortening lasting as long as the muscle is tetanized. Instead, they alternate between two states. This dynamic picture is an essential feature of the model; from it follow simple explanations of a fairly large number of the mechanical and thermal aspects of the physiological behavior of stimulated muscle. An examination of the literature shows that an assumption of a dynamic state on the molecular level has been made by others (Varga, 1946; Szent-Györgyi, 1947; Buchthal and Kaiser, 1948), but only recently has this idea been elaborated into quantitative treatments of the physiological behavior of tetanized muscle (Polissar, 1949, 1952a,b,c,d; Gergely and Laki, 1950; Buchthal and Kaiser, 1951[1]).

Although there is no direct experimental evidence of the existence of the dynamic state in tetanized muscle, the assumption is reasonable from a chemical point of view. Perhaps the number and the scope of the phenomena which may be explained with the use of this model will stimulate enough interest to produce more stringent experimental tests of the theory set forth in the following pages.

The length-tension diagram for an ideal muscle

Assume an idealized muscle containing a number of parallel filaments, each consisting of contractile units strung in series. If the muscle is stimulated isotonically, with no load to carry, then, at any instant, the length of the muscle is determined by the distribution of the contractile

---

[1] The study by Buchthal and Kaiser includes reference to a similar approach adopted by Burte and Halsey (1947) with regard to nylon, rubber, and wool.

units between the L and the S states.   This distribution is controlled by the two reactions and their respective rates, R_L and R_S, given below:

I: $L \to S$ $R_L = k_L(L)$ (13.1)

II: $S \to L$ $R_S = k_S(S)$ (13.2)

where (L) and (S) are the numbers of units in the L and S state, respectively.   In a short tetanus, in which the chemical environment is approximately constant, k_L and k_S are also approximately constant.

When complete tetanus is achieved, the shortening is at a maximum, the steady state is reached, the two rates are equal.   Combining equations (13.1) and (13.2), we obtain

$$k_L(L) = k_S(S)   (S)/(L) = k_L/k_S = K \tag{13.3}$$

Assume that the tetanized, fully shortened muscle is subjected to a pull W or is caused to carry a load W.   Because of the tension within the muscle, the Arrhenius energy of activation of reaction I will increase by a quantity $c_L W$ proportional to the tension.   The speed of reaction I will decrease by the factor $e^{-C_L W}$, where $C_L = c_L/RT$.   For the same reason the energy of activation of reaction II will decrease by a quantity $c_S W$, and the speed of this reaction will increase by the factor $e^{C_S W}(C_S = c_S/RT)$. The new rates, in the presence of a tension W, will be given by the following two equations:

$$R_L = k_L(L)e^{-C_L W}   R_S = k_S(S)e^{C_S W} \tag{13.4}$$

The two rates are not equal any more at the first instant, and the distribution is shifted in favor of formation of more L units, until a new distribution is reached in which the two rates are equal again. The new distribution is given by the equations

$$R_L = R_S   (S)/(L) = Ke^{-CW}   (C = C_L + C_S)   K = k_L/k_S \tag{13.5}$$

Equation (13.5) gives us the distribution of the units between the L and the S states in the presence of a tension W.   It includes equation (13.3) for the particular case when $W = 0$.

We now have the equation needed for the calculation of the length-tension relation in the idealized muscle.   We may illustrate the method by reproducing the calculation of one of the points of the curve ABC in Fig. 13.3.

Let the total number of contractile units in the muscle be 100, in terms of some arbitrary unit of quantity.   Let the aggregate length of all the contractile units strung along a filament extending through the entire muscle be $100a$, at zero time, in terms of some arbitrary unit of length a. Let the aggregate length of the links between the units and of the tendons be 25*a* on the same scale. (There is some arbitrariness in this choice of value. However, the relative magnitude is a reasonable one, and, besides, the calculated curve is rather insensitive to the assumed value.)

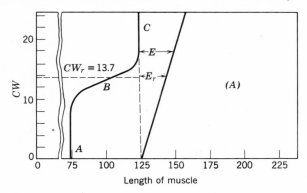

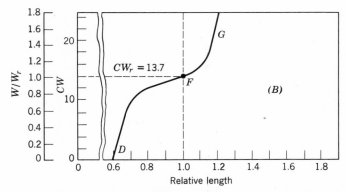

Fig. 13.3. Curve *ABC*: The theoretical length-tension relation in a model possessing no passive elasticity. Curve *DFG*: The theoretical length-tension relation in a model possessing passive elasticity. E_r is the passive elastic stretch at rest-length, at the corresponding tension W_r. The straight line in the upper diagram gives the stretch E at any other tension, assuming Hooke's law. Curve *DFG* is obtained from curve *ABC* by shifting each point of the latter through a horizontal distance equal to the corresponding value of E.

Abscissas: Length of muscle in arbitrary units (rest-length = 125) and in relative units. Ordinates: Tension in arbitrary units (CW_r = 13.7) and in relative units (W_r = 1.0).

We will calculate the length of the muscle for that particular load for which the value of CW of equation (13.5) is 11.0. The value of the exponential factor is 1.67×10^{-5}. The value of K will be taken as 3.8×10^5. The reason for this choice will be given in a later part of this chapter (p. 718).

The right side of equation (13.5) is equal to 6.34. Since the total number of units is 100, the number of S units and of L units must be 86.4 and 13.6 (in other words, 86.4 per cent of the units are converted into the S state when $CW = 11$).

To calculate the new length of the muscle we must know the relative lengths of the contractile unit in the two states. Hill's data (1938) indicate that the length of a fully contracted muscle is $0.6 \times$ rest-length. Allowing for the presence of unchanging links between the units and of the tendons, the assumption that the length of S is one-half the length of L will give results which are consistent with the net amount of shortening. It follows that the length of the muscle (when $CW = 11$) is $25a + 13.6a + 0.5 \times 86.4a = 81.8a$. Since the value of the rest-length was $125a$, the relative length of the muscle is 0.654.

Curve ABC of Fig. 13.3 shows the length of the muscle as a function of CW for values of the latter ranging from 0 to 24. This curve is, therefore, a length-tension curve with an arbitrary scale for W. Comparing this curve with curve $FGHIJ'K'$ of Fig. 13.2, we find that the former is a distorted version of the latter. The behavior of the ideal muscle differs from that of a real one in the following respects. The tetanized ideal muscle cannot be stretched beyond the rest-length; the curve for the ideal muscle has two practically vertical regions.

A physicochemical model possessing inactive tissue elasticity

An examination of the idealized model will disclose the reason for the discrepancies between its behavior and that of real muscle. The idealized model can change its length only through the chemical reaction $L \rightarrow S$ or its reverse. No allowance was made for the inactive elasticity possessed by body tissues. Gasser and Hill (1924) not only showed that the contractile mechanism possesses inactive elasticity but they also measured the extent of the elastic stretch.

These investigators used the following procedure: A muscle tetanized isometrically at rest-length was suddenly released and was allowed to shorten a small but predetermined distance. The sudden drop in tension was found to depend upon the amount of shortening allowed. If the amount of shortening allowed was beyond a certain value, the tension dropped to zero. In all experiments the tension would begin to rise soon after the initial drop. Assuming that during the brief time interval the contractile mechanism was too slow to change its length, they concluded that the change in length and the initial drop in tension were both due to the decrease in the inactive elastic stretch. Thus the amount of shortening needed to remove the tension completely must be equal to the original elastic stretch.

Using this method, Gasser and Hill estimated that the elastic stretch in an isometric tetanic contraction at rest-length amounted to 10 to 15 per cent of the length of the muscle.   We will assume an intermediate value of 12 per cent.[1]

We will modify the ideal model of the muscle by endowing it with inactive elasticity, in addition to its chemical contractility.   Since, on our scale, the rest-length of the muscle is $125a$, and since the experimental evidence indicates that in an isometric tetanus at rest-length the elastic stretch amounts to 12 per cent of the rest-length, the magnitude of stretch at the particular value W_r of the tension must be $15a$.   (The subscript r will be used consistently for the particular value exhibited by each quantity in an isometric contraction at rest-length.)

For the sake of concreteness, and as a first approximation, we will assume that the elastic stretch of muscle obeys Hooke's law.   In a later part of this chapter it will be shown that the value of CW_r is 13.7.   It follows that the elastic stretch at any value of W is given by the equation

$$E = E_r W/W_r \qquad (E_r = 15a \qquad CW_r = 13.7) \qquad (13.6)$$

In the elastic model the ratio of (S) to (L) is still given by equation (13.5).   However, the length of the elastic model at a particular value of W equals the calculated length of the ideal model at the same value of W, increased by the stretch E.   The length-tension curve of the elastic model may be obtained from curve ABC of the inelastic model by adding to each abscissa the value of E taken from the right side of the diagram.

Curve DFG of Fig. 13.3 shows the result of this calculation.   It will be seen that this curve reproduces well the characteristics of curve FIK' of Fig. 13.2.   The interpretation of the branch $IJKL$, obtained by stretching the muscle before stimulation, will be taken up later (p. 726).

Method of estimating the extent of the reaction $L = S$

When a muscle is tetanized isotonically with zero load, it contracts to approximately 60 per cent of its rest-length (Hill, 1938).   Since with zero load the tension within the muscle is zero, there is no inert elastic stretch and the entire shortening must be due to the reaction $L \to S$.   Later calculations will show that under these conditions the conversion of L

---

[1] Note added in proof: A more recent measurement of this constant [A. V. Hill, Proc. Roy. Soc. London, B 137, 273 (1950)] indicates that the value of the elastic stretch published by Gasser and Hill is too high by a factor of 4.   The new value of the elastic stretch calls for a different set of constants for the frog sartorius.   Unfortunately, Hill's paper came to the author's attention too late to permit the necessary changes. The sequence of steps needed for the evaluation of these constants is summarized on p. 718.

into S is practically 100 per cent complete. We therefore have the following relations:

0.4 muscle-length $= 100\%$ conversion from L to S

$\%$ conversion $= 100\%/0.4 \times$ (shortening, in muscle-lengths)   (13.7)

$\%$ conversion $= 250\% \times$ (shortening, in muscle-lengths)

The following example serves as an illustration of the use of equation (13.7). Suppose that it was found that in an isotonic contraction with zero load the muscle shortened at the rate of 0.00134 muscle-lengths per millisecond. Using equation (13.7), we find that the rate of conversion of L to S was $250\% \times 0.00134$, or 0.334 per cent per millisecond.

The extent of the conversion $L \rightarrow S$ in an isometric contraction at rest-length

When a muscle is tetanized isometrically at rest-length, the contractile mechanism begins to shorten, because of the reaction $L \rightarrow S$. Since the net length remains constant, there is an increasing elastic stretch E, and the tension begins to grow. Eventually the elastic stretch reaches a maximum value E_r, at which stage the rates of the two opposite reactions become equal and a steady state is achieved.

We have mentioned previously Gasser and Hill's observation (1924) that the elastic stretch under these conditions is approximately equal to 0.12 muscle-lengths. Using equation (13.7), we calculate that the extent of reaction in this state is

$$250\% \times 0.12 = 30\%$$

Thus we learn that, when the steady state is finally reached by a frog's sartorius, 30 per cent of the contractile units are in the S state, while 70 per cent are in the L state. We now proceed to develop the equations which will enable us to calculate the rate of turnover in this steady state cycle.

The speed-load relation in an isotonic contraction

To the best of the writer's knowledge, there is no theory known at present which would explain on a molecular basis the relation between the speed of shortening of a tetanized muscle and the load it is forced to carry. The chemical model described in this chapter offers a simple quantitative explanation of the speed of shortening.

Since in an isotonic contraction the tension within the muscle remains constant, the elastic stretch also remains constant. It follows that the shortening is an outward manifestation of the difference between the rate of reaction $L \rightarrow S$ and that of $S \rightarrow L$. The rates of the two reactions are given by equations (13.4). Calling the speed of shortening v when the load is W, we have the following equation:

$$v = \text{constant} \times [k_L(L)e^{-C_L W} - k_S(S)e^{C_S W}] \tag{13.8}$$

Examination of this equation shows that it will give the type of curve shown in diagram A of Fig. 13.4. The numerical values of the constants may be obtained by applying this equation to the data published by Hill (1938) for frog's sartorius at 0°C.

In Hill's experiments the muscle was first tetanized isometrically and was then released to carry a predetermined load W. The inertia of the system demands that the initial speed of the load must be zero and that this speed must approach the speed of shortening of the contractile mechanism only after a period of acceleration. In the meantime, the speed of the shortening of the contractile mechanism keeps changing because of the changes in (L), in (S), and in the tension prevailing within the muscle; clearly the tension within the muscle cannot be constant and equal the load during the accelerative period. A rigorous analysis of the speed of the load as a function of time is rather complicated.

Fortunately, the accelerative period must be very brief, as will be illustrated by the following calculation. Let us assume that the magnitude of the imposed load is one-third the magnitude of the isometric tension existing at the instant of release. In that case the initial instantaneous acceleration must be $2g$, or 1960 cm per sec per sec. With this load the experimental speed achieved was of the order of 1.5 cm per sec. If the acceleration remained constant, the accelerative period would last 1.5/1960 or 0.00077 sec. This time interval is very small compared with the total duration of the shortening, which was of the order of 0.2 sec or more. We must conclude that the accelerative period was very short, even though the average acceleration was several times smaller than the initial acceleration.

This conclusion simplifies the analysis of the speed of shortening; it enables us to assume that the maximum observed speed of the load equals the initial speed of shortening of the contractile mechanism; it also enables us to assume that the values of (S) and (L) at the instant of maximum observed speed are the same as the values $(S)_r$ and $(L)_r$, respectively, which prevailed in the steady state cycle at the instant of release.

Equation 13.8 is rather awkward to apply. Furthermore, the constant will vary from one muscle to another. It is convenient, in order to eliminate the constant, to derive the equation for the ratio v/v_0, as a function of W/W_r, where v_0 is the speed of shortening when the load is zero, and W_r, as before, is the tension developed in an isometric tetanic contraction at rest-length.

We will have frequent occasions to use the quantities $e^{C_L W_r}$, $e^{C_S W_r}$, and $e^{C W_r}$ ($C = C_L + C_S$). They may be conveniently replaced by the symbols A, B, and AB, respectively. Furthermore, it will be shown later on (p. 737) that $B = A^{(L)_r/(S)_r} = A^{70/30} = A^{7/3}$. It follows that $AB = A^{10/3}$. For the ratio W/W_r we will use the single letter Z.

Let us consider the rates of the two opposing reactions at the steady state, after tetanus is established. The two rates are equal; $R_L = R_S = R_r$, where R_r is the constant rate in the steady state cycle. After the release of the muscle, with the load W attached, and after the very brief accelerative period, the tension within the muscle drops to $W = Z W_r$. Using equations (13.4), we can see that the rate of the shortening reaction will increase by the factor A^{1-Z}. The rate of the lengthening reaction will decrease by the factor $1/B^{1-Z}$. The rate of the net reaction will be given by the difference between the two rates:

$$R_{net} = R_r(A^{1-Z} - 1/B^{1-Z}) \tag{13.9}$$

When W is zero, Z is zero, and the net rate is at its greatest, given by the following equation:

$$R_{net} \text{ (When } W = 0) = R_r(A - 1/B) \tag{13.10}$$

Since the speeds of shortening are proportional to the net rates of the reaction, we obtain the value of v/v_0 by dividing equation (13.9) by equation (13.10):

$$\frac{v}{v_0} = \frac{A^{1-Z} - 1/B^{1-Z}}{A - 1/B} = \frac{A^{-Z} - 1/AB^{1-Z}}{1 - 1/AB} \tag{13.11a}$$

$$\frac{v}{v_0} = \frac{A^{-Z} - 1/A^{10/3 - 7Z/3}}{1 - 1/A^{10/3}} \tag{13.11b}$$

A simple check will show that $v/v_0 = 1$ when $Z = 0$, and $v/v_0 = 0$ when $Z = 1$.

At first glance, equation (13.11b) may give the impression that it will be cumbersome to test it against experimental data. However, it turns out that, since A has a large value, then, for all values of Z smaller than 0.8, the second terms in the numerator and in the denominator are negligibly small, and equation (13.11b) may be replaced by the following equations:

$$v/v_0 = A^{-Z} \tag{13.12a}$$

$$\log_{10}(v/v_0) = -Z \log_{10} A \tag{13.12b}$$

To test equation (13.12b), and at the same time to obtain the value of A, we proceed as follows: The experimental values of $\log_{10}(v/v_0)$ are plotted against the corresponding values of $W/W_r (= Z)$. If equation (13.12b) fits the data, the points should fall on a straight line, except near the end, where the value of Z approaches 1.0. The slope of the line will be equal to $- \log_{10} A$. From the value of $\log_{10} A$ the value of A can be calculated.

This treatment was applied to Hill's data (1938) on the small sartorii of English frogs, at $0°C$.

Hill summarized the speed-load relation by the following equations:

$$(W + 14.35)(v + 1.03) = 87.6 \qquad (13.13)$$

where W is in grams, and speeds are in centimeters per second.

Substituting $v = 0$, we find $W_r = 70.7$ grams; substituting $W = 0$, we find $v_0 = 5.08$ cm per sec.

Intermediate values of v and W, obtained from Hill's equation, were subjected to the graphical treatment described above. On a plot of $\log_{10} (v/v_0)$ vs. Z the points fell on a straight line up to $Z = 0.8$. The slope of the line was $- 1.785$. From this slope the value of A was calculated: $A =$ antilog $1.785 = 61$.

Curve (A) of Fig. 13.4 shows the result of substitution of the value: $A = 61$ in the more exact equation (13.11). The solid circles represent Hill's equation. As will be seen, the agreement is quite satisfactory.

This agreement between theory and experiment should be taken with some caution. We are faced with a situation, common in graphical analysis, where a limited region of an experimental curve can be fitted by two entirely different equations. A few trials will show that arbitrary curves of this shape may be fitted both by Hill's equation (13.13) and by the chemical model equation (13.11). A more rigorous test of each of the two equations near the values $W/W_r = 1.0$ and 0.0 is impractical, since the data are not accurate enough for such a test. A rigorous test of the two equations is available (p. 715) when the load is greater than W_r and the muscle lengthens.

Since Hill's equation (13.13) is the only theoretical speed-load equation available at present (Fenn, 1945), it would be gratifying to find that equations (13.13) and (13.11) are based on assumptions which are similar in essence but differ in detail. However, this is not the case. Equation (13.13) can be written in a different form (Hill, 1938):

$$(W + a)v = b(W_r - W) \qquad (13.13a)$$

where a and b are constants for a given muscle (at a constant temperature). This equation, referred to by Hill as the characteristic equation connecting the load and the velocity, might have been classified as a purely empirical equation if it were not for the fact that the quantity a, obtained by fitting the experimental curve, equals approximately the heat of shortening per centimeter, obtained from an entirely different type of experiment. If this equality is not a mere coincidence, then it follows, as Hill pointed out, that the muscle is so organized that in separate experiments with different loads the total power of the muscle (i.e., rate of mechanical work + rate

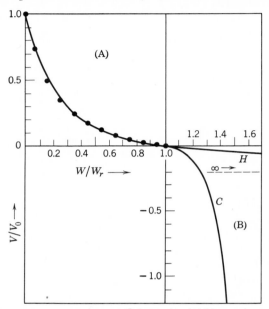

Fig. 13.4.   The solid curve shows the speed-load relation predicted by the use of the physicochemical model.   The circles represent the experimental values, summarized by Hill's equation.   Positive values of v/v_0 represent shortening with loads smaller than W_r; negative values represent lengthening with loads larger than W_r.   Curve H is the negative branch of Hill's curve. The dashed line is the asymptote to Hill's curve.   Branch C of the curve based on the physicochemical model is in qualitative agreement with Hill's observations on the "yielding" of the muscle under large loads.

of evolution of heat) is proportional to the difference between the maximum isometric tension and the load.

Hill's explanation of his equation is an elaboration of the statement that the total chemical activity is proportional to $(W_r - W)$ and does not constitute an interpretation on the molecular level.   On the other hand, equation (13.11) is based on the kinetics of the conversion of the contractile units from the L state to the S state.   Let us now turn to experimental observations which offer a crucial test between the two equations.

The rates of lengthening of a tetanized muscle with loads greater than W_r

Hill's equation is equivalent to the equilateral hyperbola: $W \cdot v =$ constant, translated parallel to the axes. It follows from this equation that loads larger than W_r will give negative values of v (i.e., the muscle must lengthen) and that v must approach some definite negative value as the load approaches infinity. Hill (1938, p. 162) called attention to this feature of the equation and pointed out that, in accordance therewith, it would take an infinite force to cause the muscle to lengthen at a rate which is only a relatively small fraction of the maximum rate of shortening.

On the other hand, equation (13.8), which differs from equation (13.11) by a change in scales, predicts that with large loads the rate of lengthening will be almost an exponential function of the load. Thus there is a crucial difference between the negative branches of the Hill equation and of the chemical model equation, as shown in curves H and C of Fig. 13.4.

It would be difficult to visualize a chemical contractile mechanism which would show a small constant lengthening with an infinite force, especially in view of the presence of some inert elasticity in the muscle. However, apart from this theoretical objection, the experimental data do not agree with the equation.

For example, when a heavy load is applied to a tetanized muscle the muscle lengthens rapidly at first, but the speed of lengthening eventually diminishes. Hill (1938, p. 162) regarded the initial rapid lengthening as a "give," or a "slip," analogous to the increase in length in a wire stretched beyond its elastic limit by a relatively great force; the initial lengthening of the muscle was viewed as "irreversible," and it was assumed that the rapid lengthening was accompanied by a sort of "collapse" of the contractile mechanism. However, we must take into account the fact that, as soon as the force is removed, the contractile machinery is set up again at once.

The chemical model provides a basis for understanding these observations. Under the influence of a large tension the rate of the net reaction $S \to L$ becomes fast at first. As the new steady state is approached, the rate of this net reaction decreases. There is no radical change in the contractile machinery, and, when the load is removed, the system reverts to the original steady state.

Interpretation of the Levin-Wyman experiment (1927)

The length-tension relations in a tetanized muscle upon which a constant rate of change of length is imposed is shown schematically in Fig. 13.5. The suggestion that at high speeds the muscle works against a viscous resistance which increases with speed has been shown to be inadequate to account for the effect of speed on the tension of the muscle (Fenn, 1945, 1930a,b).   On the other hand, the chemical model of muscle offers a plausible explanation of the observed results.

When the muscle is allowed to shorten at a small constant rate, the change in length is due partly to a decrease in the elastic stretch and partly

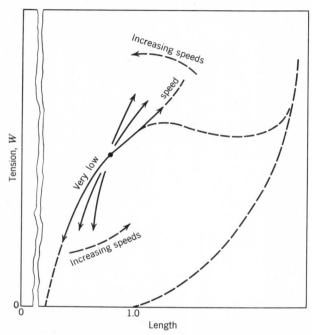

Fig. 13.5.   The length-tension relation of a tetanized muscle when a constant speed of shortening or lengthening is imposed upon it.   At very low speeds the chemical cycle reaches, at each length, the appropriate steady state.   When the muscle changes length at high speed, the chemical reaction is too slow to keep pace, and the change in length is due chiefly to the change in the passive elastic stretch.   The digression from the isometric curve increases with increasing speed.   (Schematic.)

to the reaction $L \to S$.   The tension at any particular length is given by curve DFG of Fig. 13.3.   If the rate of shortening is extremely high, most of the change is due to the decrease in the elastic stretch, since the chemical reaction is too slow by comparison.   As a result, the tension at any particular length is much smaller than that predicted by curve DFG.

The opposite effect takes place when the muscle is caused to lengthen. When the rate of lengthening is small, part of the change is due to an increase in the elastic stretch, part is due to the reaction $S \to L$.   When the muscle is stretched at a high rate, the contribution of the chemical reaction is small, almost the entire change in length is due to an increase in the elastic stretch, and the tension at any particular length is greater than that predicted by curve *DFG*.

Evaluation of the specific rate constant k_L

The speed-load equation (13.8) contains a proportionality constant whose value depends upon the units used in expressing the speed of shortening and the values of (L) and (S). We can eliminate the proportionality constant by the use of consistent units. Thus the speed of shortening can be expressed in muscle-lengths per second, and then changed by means of equation (13.7) into per cent conversion per second. With due attention to the meanings of the symbols A, B, Z, we can rewrite equation (13.8) as follows:

$$V = k_L(L)/A^Z - k_S(S)B^Z \qquad (13.14)$$

This equation is valid for all values of the variables. In particular, in an isometric tetanus at rest-length we have

$$v = k_L(L)_r/A - k_S(S)_r B \qquad \text{(since } Z = 1.0) \qquad (13.15a)$$

In the isometric tetanus the value of v is zero, and the two terms on the right side of equation (13.15a) must equal each other and must equal some constant rate of turnover R_r:

$$k_L(L)_r/A = R_r \qquad (13.15b)$$

$$k_S(S)_r B = R_r \qquad (13.15c)$$

In passing, we observe that, since A and B are both large numbers, the quantity $k_S(S)_r$ must be insignificantly small as compared with $k_L(L)_r$. We will later find this observation useful.

If the muscle is released, with zero load, the value of Z drops to zero (after a very brief accelerative period), and the speed of shortening is given by the following special case of equation (13.14):

$$v_0 = k_L(L)_r - k_S(S)_r \qquad \text{(since } Z = 0) \qquad (13.15d)$$

The second term on the right side of this equation is insignificantly small compared with the first term (see above); therefore equation (13.15d) may be replaced by the following equation, with a high degree of accuracy:

$$v_0 = k_L(L)_r \qquad (13.15e)$$

By means of this equation we can calculate the value of k_L. From Hill's data for a frog's sartorius at 0°C (1938), the value of v_0 was 5.08 cm per sec; since the length of the muscle was 3.8 cm, this speed amounts to

1.34 muscle-lengths per second. Equation (13.7) tells that this is equivalent to 334 per cent conversion per second (in other words, in the early stages of the experiment the instantaneous rate was such that 0.334 per cent of the total number of units was converted into the S state every millisecond).

Substituting this value of v_0 in equation (13.15e), as well as the value $(L)_r = 70$ per cent, we find that $k_L = 4.77$ sec^{-1}.

The rate of turnover in an isometric tetanus at rest-length

The rate of turnover at the steady state achieved in an isometric tetanus at rest-length is given both by equation (13.15b) and by equation (13.15c). We have all the data needed for the use of the former. Substituting the values $k_L = 4.77$ sec^{-1}, $(L)_r = 70$ per cent, $A = 61$, we get $R_r = 5.47$ per cent per sec, or $R_r = 0.0547$ sec^{-1}.

This calculation tells that every second 5.47 per cent of the total number of contractile units change from the L state to the S state, and an equal number change from the S state to the L state. The reciprocal of 0.0547 sec^{-1}, or 18.2 sec, is the average duration of a cycle at 0°C. Each contractile unit spends, on the average, 70 per cent of the period, or 12.7 sec, in the L state, and 30 per cent of the period, or 5.5 sec, in the S state.

Evaluation of the specific rate constant k_S

The value of k_S may be obtained either from equation (13.3) or from equation (13.15c). Using the latter, and substituting the known values $R_r = 5.47$ per cent per sec, $(S)_r = 30$ per cent, $B = A^{7/3} = 61^{7/3} = 14,600$, we obtain $k_S = 1.245 \times 10^{-5}$ sec^{-1}.

The value of the steady state constant K

The importance of this constant, defined in equation (13.3), lies in the fact that it gives the distribution of the contractile units between the two states when the muscle achieves full isotonic contraction in the absence of a load. Its value is given by the ratio k_L/k_S, and equals 3.8×10^5. The high value of $(S)/(L)$ in full contraction justifies the assumption made in the derivation of equation (13.7), namely, that in a full contraction with zero load, the conversion into the S state is practically 100 per cent complete.

Calculation of the values of the constants for muscles other than frog sartorius

Even if we assume that the contractile unit is the same in a variety of muscles, it does not follow that the characteristic constants needed in the various equations are the same. Some of the constants will be different because of a difference in the chemical environment of the myofibrils. The inert tissue elasticity may be different. Finally, a change in the temperature will introduce still other differences.

For the sake of clarity and continuity, the numerical values of some of the constants were used before the method of obtaining these values was indicated. In the way of a review, and also for the purpose of facilitating the application of the theory to other muscles, it will perhaps be useful to summarize the procedures used for the evaluation of the constants. The procedures will be listed in the order in which they were actually used.

The extent of the maximum shortening in an isotonic contraction with zero load, in muscle-lengths, will give the change in length corresponding to 100 per cent conversion from L to S. After the other constants are obtained, the assumption that the conversion is practically 100 per cent complete must be tested.

After the maximum shortening is obtained, the constant factor of equation (13.7) may be evaluated. This equation gives the proportionality factor from change in length to per cent conversion.

The value of the elastic stretch, E_r, in an isometric contraction at rest-length will give, with the use of equation (13.7), the per cent conversion from L to S in the steady state of the tetanus at rest-length.

A plot of the experimental values of $\log_{10} (v/v_0)$ against the corresponding values of Z ($Z = W/W_r$) will give the value of A ($A = e^{C_L W_r}$). The slope of the linear portion of the curve equals $-\log_{10} A$. This will be seen most directly on an examination of equation (13.11a); for small values of Z the ratio v/v_0 is proportional to A^{-Z}.

The most direct method of obtaining the value of B ($B = e^{C_s W_r}$) is to plot the experimental values of $\log_{10} (-v/v_0)$ against the corresponding values of Z. Equation (13.11a) may be rewritten as follows:

$$- v/v_0 = - \text{Constant} \times (A/A^Z - B^Z/B) \qquad (13.11c)$$

For values of Z much larger than 1.0 the expression within the parentheses becomes proportional to B^Z. It follows that the slope of the linear part for $Z > 1.0$ will give the value of $\log B$. Unfortunately, quantitative data on the rate of lengthening with loads greater than W_r are not available at present. For this reason the following indirect method was used:

As shown later (p. 735), the contractile unit theory demands that the heat of maintenance in an isometric tetanus be a function of the length at which the muscle is tetanized, and that it have a maximum value at some particular length. It will also be shown that, if the number of units in the steady state at this length are $(L)_m$ and $(S)_m$, respectively, the following equation must be satisfied:

$$B = A^{(L)_m/(S)_m} \qquad (13.16)$$

Since the heat of maintenance of frog's sartorius possesses a maximum at or very near the rest-length, the following value was used in this chapter: $B = A^{70/30}$.

With the values of A and B known, equation (13.11b) may be checked against the experimental results.

The values of the specific rate constant k_L, of the rate of turnover R_r, and of the specific rate constant k_S may be obtained with the use of equations (13.15e), (13.15b), and (13.15c), in the indicated order.

The value of the steady state constant K equals the ratio k_L/k_S. If this constant is large compared with unity, the assumption underlying the derivation of equation (13.7) is justified. On the other hand, should it turn out to be not much larger than 1.0, a method of successive approximations is called for.

With the value of K known, the values of the ratio $(S)/(L)$, for various values of CW may be calculated with the use of equation (13.5). Reasonable assumptions as to the length of the S unit, as compared with the L unit, together with an estimate of the aggregate length of connective inert links and tendons, will give the length-tension diagram similar to curve ABC of Fig. 13.3.

The value of e^{CW_r} equals the product AB, as will be seen from the definitions of A and B and the definition of C, given in equation (13.5). The natural logarithm of AB will give the value of CW_r, which fixes the level in diagram A of Fig. 13.3 at which the elastic stretch is E_r. By Hooke's law, the value of E for any other value of W may be calculated (or it may be obtained graphically from the upper diagram of Fig. 13.3). These values of E, added to the respective lengths of the non-elastic muscle, obtained from the upper diagram, will give the length-tension diagram appearing in the lower part of Fig. 13.3.

Up to this point the major features of the physicochemical model have been presented, and the model has been used to develop quantitative expressions for the length-tension relation and the speed-load relation in tetanized muscle. In the sections which follow the same model will be used as a basis for the interpretation of other mechanical features and some of the major features of the thermal properties of tetanized muscle, as well as to estimate the molecular weight of the contractile unit.

OTHER MECHANOCHEMICAL PROPERTIES OF MUSCLE

The time-tension relation in an isometric contraction at rest-length

When a muscle is stimulated electrically, an abrupt change of state takes place after a short latent period (Hill, 1949). For the purpose of the present calculation we will assume that the chemical environment

about the myofibrils is established and remains constant after the short
latent period.   The net reaction, $L \to S$, shortens the contractile units and
causes an elastic stretch, accompanied by a rise in tension.   Assuming,
as a first approximation, that the elastic force follows Hooke's law, the
instantaneous tension at any particular time is proportional to the extent
of the reaction.   It follows that $dW/dt = \text{constant} \times d(S)/dt$.   The rate

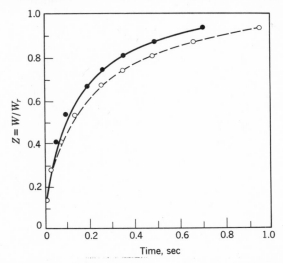

Fig. 13.6.   The time-tension relation for an isometric tetanic contraction
at 0°C.   The open circles represent the values calculated by numerical integration of the theoretical differential equation.   The solid curve shows Hill's
experimental values.   The solid circles were obtained in the same way as the
open circles, except that the rate constants obtained from the isotonic experiments were multiplied by the factor 1/0.743.

of the net reaction, $d(S)/dt$, is given by the difference between the rates
of the two opposing reactions:

$$d(S)/dt = R_L - R_S = k_L(L)e^{-C_L W} - k_S(S)e^{C_s W} \qquad (13.17)$$

In this equation (L), (S), W are all functions of time.   At any instant
$W/W_r = Z = (S)/(S)_r$.   The initial conditions are: $t = 0$; $(S) = 0$;
$W = 0$.

For frog's sartorius, at 0°C, the following values were calculated in the
preceding pages:

$$(S)_r = 30 \qquad k_L = 4.77 \text{ sec}^{-1} \qquad k_S = 1.25 \cdot 10^{-5} \text{ sec}^{-1}$$

$$e^{C_L W_r} = A = 61 \qquad e^{C_s W} = B = 14{,}600 \qquad (13.18)$$

Substitution of these values in (13.17) yields equation (13.19):

$$d(S)/dt = 4.77 \, (L)/61^Z - 1.25 \cdot 10^{-5}(S) \, 14{,}600^Z$$

$$\text{(frog's sartorius, at } 0°C) \quad (13.19)$$

Integration of equation (13.19) will give (S) as a function of time. The corresponding ratios $(S)/30$ will give Z as a function of time. A numerical integration may be carried out as follows:

The total increment in (S) (from 0 to 30) may be divided into a number of parts, with each part small enough to allow the calculation of average values of (L), (S), W for the duration of the increment. These average values, substituted in equation (13.19), will give the average rate, $d(S)/dt$, for the duration of the increment. The magnitude of the increment, divided by the average rate, will give the duration of the increment. Finally, the summation of the time increments up to a particular value of (S) will give t as a function of (S).

As an illustration of the method, we may calculate the time it takes the value of (S) to rise from 26 to 28.

Average values of (S) and (L): 27 and 73, respectively.

Average value of W: $(27/30)W_r$; $Z = 0.9$

Average value of $d(S)/dt$:

$$\frac{4.77 \times 73}{61^{0.9}} - 1.25 \times 10^{-5} \times 27 \times 14{,}600^{0.9}$$

$$= 6.67 \text{ units per sec} \quad (13.20)$$

Duration of this particular interval:

$$\frac{28 - 26}{6.67} = 0.300 \text{ sec}$$

By similar calculations and additions of intervals, it was found that $(S) = 26$ at $t = 0.665$ sec; it follows that $(S) = 28$ at $t = 0.665 + 0.300 = 0.965$ sec.

The Z values for $(S) = 26$ and 28 are 26/30 and 28/30, or 0.867 and 0.933, respectively.

The dashed curve of Fig. 13.6 shows the Z,t relation as calculated by this method. The last two points are the terminal values of the interval selected for the illustrative computation. The solid curve gives the experimental values obtained by Hill (1938; Fig. 15), for frog's sartorius at 0°C.

It is evident that the calculated and the experimental curves do not coincide. However, it is well known that in working with muscle it is very difficult to get quantitatively reproducible results. Thus, in Hill's measurements of W (1938, Table III, p. 174) some of the values obtained differ by as much as a factor of 2.

The solid circles of Fig. 13.6 were obtained by multiplying the t values of the theoretical curve by the factor 0.743.   This is equivalent to multiplying the rate constants of equation (13.3) by the factor $1/0.743$.   Considering that these constants were obtained from an entirely different type of experiment (isotonic), the agreement between the calculated and experimental curves is as good as could be expected.   The main significance of this calculation, however, is that it is found possible to give a quantitative interpretation of the rate of development of tension on the basis of a simple physicochemical model.

Chemical changes accompanying a single twitch

In a tetanic contraction the chemical environment within the muscle fiber is kept constant by a succession of electric shocks, in a manner as yet not understood.   On the other hand, isometric stimulation with a single electric shock produces a sequence of chemical changes whose outward manifestations consist of a rise in tension to a maximum, followed by a drop in tension during the relaxation period.   There are several lines of evidence (p. 730) which seem to indicate that in resting muscle the interior of each muscle fiber is in the solated state and that stimulation converts the interior into the gelated state.   Hill's experiments (1949) seem to indicate that the active state is established after a very short latent period.

Since the muscle reverts to the resting state after a single twitch, profound chemical changes must take place during the period of relaxation.   Since the tension does not drop abruptly, but changes gradually, we can visualize the following possibilities: (1) Individual molecular filaments change into the solated state, while a progressively smaller tension is maintained by the filaments remaining in the gelated state.   (2) A gradual change takes place in the chemical environment around the molecular filaments, a change which favors the reaction $S \to L$; eventually this must be followed by the solation of the filaments.   (3) A combination of (1) and (2) takes place.

No attempt will be made here to interpret the changes taking place during the relaxation phase of a twitch.   On the other hand, the physicochemical model of the contractile process may be used to interpret a number of observations made during the rising phase of a single twitch.

Extent of the reaction $L \to S$ in a twitch at 0°C

Hill found (1949, p. 405) that in a single twitch the maximum tension developed equals approximately 50 per cent of the tension developed in a tetanus.   Assuming Hooke's law, as a first approximation, we must conclude that the extent of the reaction $L \to S$ in a twitch is half as large as the extent of reaction established in the steady state of a tetanus.   It was estimated earlier that, in the latter, approximately 30 per cent of the units change into the S state.   It follows that in a twitch, at 0°C, the extent of the reaction is approximately 15 per cent.

The reversibility of the steady state $L = S$, and the effect of a quick stretch on the development of tension in a twitch

Hill (1949) studied the effect of an imposed stretch on the time course of the tension developed in a twitch.   His observations can be easily interpreted in terms of the two opposing reactions and the effect of tension on the rates of the two reactions.   In turn, these observations lend support to the proposed physicochemical model of the contractile process.

Hill experimented with the sartorii of the frog and the toad and studied the effect of the same stretch at varying time intervals following stimulation.   He also studied the effect of stretching the muscle by varying amounts, keeping constant the time at which the stretch was initiated. Let us examine the effect of stretching a toad's sartorius the same amount at various times after the stimulating shock.   Hill's observations (1949, Fig. 4) are redrawn in Fig. 13.7.

In this figure there are shown the results obtained in a series of seven experiments.   In each case the time of stimulation is indicated by a short vertical line.   The numbers in parentheses accompanying each curve give the time (in milliseconds), after the shock, at which the stretch was initiated. Thus, in experiment (a) the muscle was stretched 70 msec before the shock. In this experiment the stretch produced a *passive* tension which remained constant during the latent period of approximately 40 msec.   After the latent period the rate of development of tension must depend upon the rate of the net reaction $L \to S$.   This rate, equal to the difference between the rates of the two opposing reactions, is given by equation (13.17) for a constant chemical environment.   However, in a twitch the chemical environment does not remain constant; physiological relaxation sets in after a while, and for this reason the maximum tension developed in a twitch is smaller than the tension developed in a tetanus.

In experiment (d) the stretch was initiated 23 msec after the shock. At the termination of the imposed stretch (this event may be recognized, according to Hill, at the maxima of the respective curves), the tension within the muscle was subject to two opposing influences.   The reaction $L \to S$ tended to increase the tension.   On the other hand, the relaxation of the passive elastic component (a phenomenon following a quick stretch and common to passive elasticity of tissues) tended to decrease the tension. At first, the effect of the passive relaxation predominated, and the tension dropped. However, since the rate of passive relaxation decreased approximately exponentially, whereas the rate of the chemical reaction was approximately constant, the tension passed through a minimum, beyond which the effect of the chemical reaction was greater, and the tension began to rise.

In experiment (c), in which the stretch was initiated and terminated earlier than in (d), the net rate of the reaction $L \to S$ at the termination of the stretch was greater than at the end of the stretch in experiment (d),

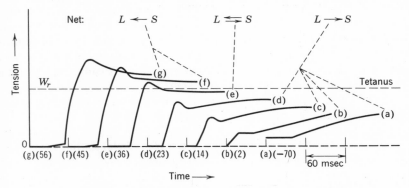

Fig. 13.7. Hill's observations on the effect of the time of stretch on the course of the time-tension curve. For the sake of clarity the curves have been shifted horizontally. Zero time for each experiment is the time of electrical stimulation. The number accompanying each curve gives the time, in milliseconds, at which the stretch was started. The slope of each curve near its end may be taken as an indication of the direction of the net reaction after the stretch. In experiments (a), (b), (c), (d) the reaction was $L \to S$. In experiments (f), (g) the reaction was $S \to L$. In experiment (e) the conditions were just right for a steady state.

since the number of L units was larger, and the prevailing tension was smaller. For this reason the minimum in curve (c) was less pronounced. Finally, in experiment (b) the net rate of the chemical reaction was just large enough to maintain the tension constant for a while. Eventually, however, the effect of the chemical reaction predominated, and the tension began to rise.

Turning our attention to equation (13.17), we can see that, if the stretch is imposed at a later time, when the concentration of S has reached a high value, and the value of W is already high, even before its increase by the stretch, then a further increase in W, caused by the stretch, may reverse the direction of the reaction. Experiment (g) offers a clear example of such a case. In this experiment the stretch was started 56 msec after the shock. For a while the net reaction was in the direction $L \to S$.

At some time during the stretch the values of (S), (L), and W were just right for the establishment of a steady state.   However, since the stretch was continued, the increasing tension reversed the direction of the net reaction in favor of $S \to L$.   The lengthening of the contractile mechanism during the end phase of the stretch accounts for the fact that the slope of the curve toward the end of the stretch was smaller than that in the other experiments.   A short period after the stretch was terminated the effect of the relaxation of the passive elasticity became insignificant.   However, since the remaining tension was still high, the reaction $S \to L$ continued, at a constantly decreasing rate, and the tension continued to drop.

Experiment (f) may be interpreted in a similar fashion.   In experiment (e) we have the interesting case where, at the end of the elastic relaxation, the values of (S), (L), and W were just right for a steady state, and the tension remained approximately constant.

The other curves given in Hill's paper can all be interpreted in a similar fashion, with the use of equation (13.17).

The length-tension relation in a muscle stretched before stimulation

It was shown earlier that the length-tension curve Aaa (Fig. 13.8), obtained by stretching a tetanized muscle very slowly, may be interpreted in terms of the changing steady state of the cycle $L \rightleftarrows S$ and the passive elasticity of the contractile filaments.   If the muscle is stretched before stimulation, the tension points may fall on a curve such as AAA, possessing a maximum and a minimum.   The maximum and minimum, however, are not the essential features of the curve.   Other muscles may give curve $A'a'a'$ when stretched after stimulation, and curve $A'A'A'$ when stretched before stimulation.   The essential difference between the two types of curve is that stretching the muscle before stimulation results in a tension which is smaller than that obtained when the muscle is first stimulated and subsequently stretched to the same length.

When an unstimulated muscle is stretched, the length-tension relation is given by a curve such as the passive stretch curve PPP.   Up to this point we have found no need to raise the question as to the seat of the elasticity responsible for the passive stretch tension.   However, in order to interpret an active tension curve such as AAA, we must raise and answer this question.

Let us consider two extreme cases.   In the first case the passive tension is due entirely to the sarcolemma and connective tissue.   In this case these structures operate in parallel with the contractile filaments when the muscle is stimulated, and the tension developed by the filaments is shown by the developed tension curve DDD, which is the difference between the observed tension AAA and the passive tension PPP.

In the second case the passive tension is due entirely to the contractile filaments. If this is so, the tension developed by the filaments on stimulation is the total observed tension AAA. It may be stated from the outset that this second assumption is less probable than the first. It would be

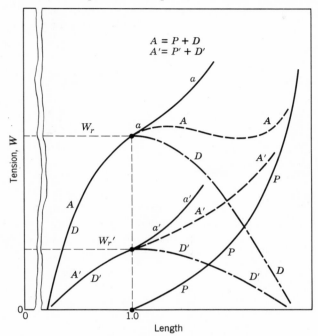

Fig. 13.8. The relation between the tension shown by a stretched passive muscle (PPP), the tension developed by the contractile mechanism (DDD), and the observed action tension (AAA). $A = P + D$. If the developed tension is relatively high, the active tension curve possesses a maximum and a minimum. If the developed tension is low (e.g., $D'D'D'$), the active tension curve $A'A'A'$ is monotonic. Stretching the muscle beyond the rest-length *after* stimulation produces higher tensions (curves aa and $a'a'$). The drop in the developed tension when the muscle is stretched *before* stimulation is probably caused by a conversion of part of the contractile units into an inactive state U. (Schematic.)

unlikely to find a contractile mechanism which shows a maximum, then a minimum, followed by a final rise in tension.

The seat of the passive tension and the nature of the developed tension

Ramsey and Street (1940) investigated this problem by comparing the passive tension of a single muscle fiber with that of the same fiber after the contractile mechanism has been crushed by gentle squeezing. They

concluded that the interior of the fiber does not contribute to the passive
·tension and that the whole passive tension is produced by the sarcolemma.

In their experiments with the human pectoralis, Ralston et al. (1947)
found that this muscle, which in the stimulated state may develop a
tension of over 40 lb, may be easily stretched in its passive state as much
as 30 per cent of its rest-length with the application of a force of less than
5 lb.   If the molecular filaments in the fibers of the passive muscle are
intact, it is difficult to see how these filaments can yield so easily to a
small force.   On the other hand, if the interior of the fiber is in the solated
state, the weak passive tension developed by this muscle is easily explained.
Sandow (1949), in his review of recent work on muscle, takes the position
that Ramsey's interpretation requires further experimental verification.
In this discussion we will tentatively accept Ramsey's view on the subject.
With this view accepted as a working assumption, we must accept the
conclusion that the contractile mechanism develops progressively smaller
tensions as the muscle is stretched to larger lengths before stimulation
(curve DD, Fig. 13.8).

As far back as 1895, Blix observed the drop in the developed tension
in a muscle stretched before stimulation.   Blix suggested that the change
in tension was due to a reduced contractility.   Buchthal (1942) has shown
that this is not due to a reduced irritability of the muscle and has also
ascribed the change to a reduced contractility.   Buchthal gave an explanation of the variation in the shape of the total tension curve (e.g., curves
AAA and $A'A'A'$ of Fig. 13.8).   If the total tension equals the sum of the
passive tension PPP and the developed tension, a weak developed tension
$D'D'D'$ will give the monotonic curve $A'A'A'$; on the other hand, a
strong developed tension DDD will give the S shaped curve AAA.

Ramsey's explanation of the decrease in contractility

Ramsey (1947) offered an explanation of the reduced contractility in
terms of Astbury's findings relative to the structure of the keratin-myosin-
epidermis-fibrinogen (k-m-e-f) family of substances.   According to
Astbury and Dickinson (1940) and Astbury (1947), members of this
family can exist in three states of folding: the superfolded state, the
half-folded state (α), and the unfolded state (β).   Stretching the normal
fiber converts it reversibly from the normal α-state to the β-state.

Ramsey accepts tentatively Astbury's conclusions relative to the
reversible conversion from the α-state to the β-state when the muscle is
stretched before stimulation.   His interpretation of the reduced contractility is based on the assumption that, in stimulated muscle, myosin
in the β-state develops no tension or develops much less tension than
myosin in the α-state.

Ramsey's views on the subject may be represented graphically as in Fig. 13.9. In resting muscle the filaments are in the α-state (point *A*). Stimulation converts part of the links into the superfolded state (point *B*); this creates a tension whose magnitude is given by the line *AB*. If the resting muscle (at *A*) is stretched, some of the links are converted reversibly into the unfolded β-state, and the muscle lengthens (point *E*). Stimulation brings about the conversion of some of the remaining α links into the superfolded state, and the tension *EF* is produced. Since the number of links in the α-state has been reduced previous to stimulation, the developed tension *EF* is smaller than *AB*.

This explanation, unless elaborated, cannot meet certain objections. Let us consider the stimulated muscle represented by point *B*. At this point some of the links are in the α-state, and some are in the superfolded state. It is not clear how it is possible for the filaments to maintain the tension *AB*, since a transition from the α- to the β-state in some of the links should relieve the tension.

If we assume that the tension *AB* is insufficient to cause the lengthening of any of the links from the α-state to the β-state, we are hard put to explain the transition of some of the links into the β-state in the process *AE*, where the tension is much smaller. Equally puzzling is the experimental evidence of Ramsey and Street (1940) that in a single fiber the tension at *E* is due to the sarcolemma, and that the interior of the fiber does not contribute to the tension.

This inconsistency is only apparent and can be removed if we take into consideration the difference between the interiors of the fibers of resting and of stimulated muscle. The indications are (Meyer and Picken, 1937; Frey-Wyssling, 1948; Morales, 1948; Astbury, 1950) that in the resting muscle the interior of the fiber is in a semifluid, solated state. On stimulation, a gelated state is achieved, in which state filaments capable of shortening and of maintaining a high tension are present. The solated state of the interior of the resting muscle accounts for the ease with which the resting muscle may be stretched. The gelated state of the stimulated muscle accounts for constancy of the tension in a tetanus.

An interpretation of the complete length-tension diagram of muscle

We can now combine Astbury's (1947) observations on the structure of myosin, the present dynamic interpretation of the contractile mechanism, and Ramsey's interpretation of the weakening of the mechanism with stretch (1947), to give a complete interpretation of the length-tension diagram first published by Blix (1895). Astbury's x-ray investigations deal with the fine structure of the contractile filament, without reference to the size of the elementary unit of contractility. The physicochemical model of contractility presented here assumes the existence of contractile units, without reference to the fine structure of the unit.   We can combine tentatively the two views by stating that in the short state (S) the contractile unit has the superfolded structure; in the long state (L) the unit possesses the intermediate α-structure.   Finally, in line with Astbury's observations, we assume that in stretched muscle the units possess a third,

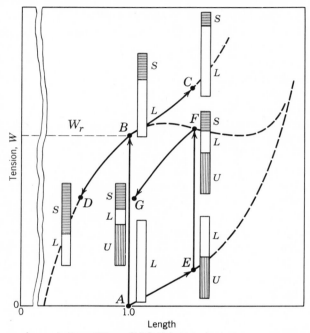

Fig. 13.9.   The relation between the length of the muscle, the previous treatment, and the observed tension.   The circles represent various states of the muscle, and the arrows indicate the path by which each state was reached. Each circle is accompanied by a bar diagram showing schematically the distribution of the contractile units between the U, L, and S states.   The interconversion between states U and L is relatively slow in stimulated muscle.   For further explanations see text.

unfolded structure corresponding to the β-state.   We will call this third state of the contractile unit the unfolded state and use the symbol U for this state.

Figure 13.9 shows, by means of block diagrams, the distribution of the contractile units among the three states, depending upon the previous history of the muscle.   Very little can be said at present about the nature of the solated state in resting muscle fibers.   When the muscle is stimulated, the interior of the fiber becomes gelated, and molecular filaments consisting of L units in series are formed (point A).   The reactions of the cycle $L \rightleftarrows S$ set in.   In an isometric contraction the net reaction $L \rightarrow S$ creates a tension, which rises (process AB) until the steady state is reached (point B).   At this point the tension is W_r.   If one end of the muscle is released, but is forced to carry a load W_r, there is no change in the statistical distribution of the units.   If the load is decreased very slowly, the decrease in tension favors the reaction $L \rightarrow S$, and the muscle shortens (process BD).   On the other hand, if, after tetanus is established at B, the load is increased slowly, the number of S units decreases and the muscle lengthens (process BC).

If the muscle is stretched before stimulation, from its rest-length 1.0, the solated interior of the fibers does not contribute to the tension.   The passive tension is due to the sarcolemma and connective tissue.   Little can be said at present about the changes taking place in the interior of the fiber on stretching before stimulation.   However, it may be safely assumed that, when the muscle is stimulated at the greater length, the gelation of the interior results in the formation of molecular filaments consisting partly of L units and partly of U units (point E).

As soon as the molecular filaments are formed, or shortly thereafter, the reactions of the cycle $L \rightleftarrows S$ set in.   If the length of the muscle is fixed, the tension grows (process EF) until the steady state is reached (point F).   The total tension is the sum of the passive tension at E and the developed tension EF, operating in parallel.

A comparison of the block diagrams accompanying points B and F (Fig. 13.9) shows that the greater length at F is accounted for chiefly by the presence of the longer U units.   If, at B, it were possible for some of the units to be converted into the longer state U, the tension would fall. The fact that the tension remains fairly constant in the isometric contraction at B indicates that the reaction $L \rightarrow U$ is either impossible in the gelated state or is entirely too slow to have any appreciable influence on the tension during the relatively short period of a tetanus.

The dependence of the behaviour of stimulated muscle on its previous history may be summarized by means of the following reaction scheme:

$$S \rightleftarrows L \qquad\qquad\qquad L \rightleftarrows U$$

In stimulated (gelated)   In unstimulated (solated)
muscle only   muscle only

Stretching the unstimulated muscle shifts the distribution in favor of U. Once the stretched muscle is stimulated, the distribution between L and U is "frozen," and only the remaining L units can participate in the cycle shown on the left.   The ease with which a muscle can be stretched before stimulation is accounted for by the solated state of the interior of the fibers.   The constancy of tension in an isometric tetanus at rest-length is accounted for by the fact that the change from L to U is impossible or is too slow in the stimulated muscle, in which the interior of the fiber is in a gelated state.

It remains to show why the developed tension EF (Fig. 13.9) is smaller than the developed tension AB.   For the sake of concreteness, we will consider the case when the stretch before stimulation is such that only 50 per cent of the total number of units are left in the active state L.   The decrease in the number of active units, taken by itself, does not account for the decrease in the developed tension.   Two muscles of equal cross sections, but of different lengths, develop the same tension, despite the fact that the number of contractile units differs from one muscle to the other.

The explanation will be found in the relation between the developed tension, the number of contractile units, and the inert elastic compliance of the molecular filaments in the muscle fibers.   When the length of the muscle is halved, the number of contractile units is halved, but the elastic compliance is also halved.   It follows that in the shorter muscle the same relative extent of the net reaction $L \to S$ will cause an elastic stretch which is half as large as in the longer muscle.   Since the compliance is half as large as in the longer muscle, the developed tension will be the same as in the large one, and the steady state conditions will have been satisfied (see equation 13.5).

The situation is different if the number of active contractile units is decreased, while the compliance of the molecular fiber is not appreciably changed.   This can be seen clearly by considering the extreme case when all but a very small fraction of the units are converted into the inactive state U.   In these circumstances, even if all the remaining L units were to be converted into the S state, the resulting elastic stretch would be very small, and, with a practically unchanged compliance, the developed tension must be small.

Returning to the analysis of process EF (Fig. 13.9), we conclude that, when the steady state is reached, at F, the per cent conversion from L to S must be greater than the per cent conversion at B, but the absolute number converted must be smaller; the bar diagrams accompanying points B and F show this feature schematically.

If, after the state of the muscle described by point F is reached, the muscle is allowed to shorten slowly to the rest-length (process FG), while still in the tetanized state, the steady state distribution is shifted in favor of the reaction $L \to S$.   Since the reaction $U \to L$ is either impossible or is too slow, the number of active units participating in the cycle is smaller at G than at B, and the developed tension AG is smaller than the developed tension AB.

THE THERMAL BEHAVIOR OF STIMULATED MUSCLE

Nature of the heat of maintenance, H

A rubber band maintaining a load does not require any expenditure of energy, since no physical work is performed. On the other hand, a tetanized muscle holding a load requires a continuous expenditure of energy, even though it does not perform any physical work. This energy leak, called the heat of maintenance, H, is usually given in calories per gram of muscle per second. The need for maintenance of energy is a common characteristic of cells performing their functions in a living organism. In the case of muscle it is possible to interpret the nature of the heat of maintenance in terms of the physicochemical model consisting of contractile units.

In the course of the last several years a large number of papers have been published on the reactions of myosin with other substances, particularly with adenosine triphosphate (ATP). (For references, see Mommaerts, 1950.) Unfortunately, despite the progress made in this field, there is no definite information at present regarding the nature of the coupling between the energy-yielding reaction and the tension-producing reaction: ATP is supposed to be more closely related to the fundamental process than any of the other potentially active substances (Mommaerts, 1950).

Despite the uncertainty about the nature of the coupling of the cycle $L \rightleftharpoons S$ with reactions in the sarcoplasm, we can assert that the two reactions of this cycle must be associated with net heat effects Q_{IL} and Q_{IIS}, respectively, as shown in Fig. 13.10. It is highly probable that both heat effects are positive, as may be seen from the following argument. Let us assume that the reaction $S \rightarrow L$ is endergonic. In that case, it must be coupled with an exergonic driving reaction, with all its associated sequel reactions. It is rather unlikely that the energies of the two reactions are so nicely balanced that there is no net heat effect. It is much more likely that the energies of the driving and the driven reactions are unequal and that there is spillage of thermal energy, Q_{IIS}.

If the reaction $S \rightarrow L$ is endergonic, it follows that the reaction $L \rightarrow S$ is exergonic. The latter reaction may be an isolated one, or it may drive another reaction; in either case we would expect that the heat effect Q_{IL} would be positive.

We can now formulate a quantitative expression for the rate of spillage of heat in a stimulated muscle. Multiplying the rate of each of the two reactions by the associated heat effect and adding the results, we get

$$\text{Rate of heat evolution} = R_L Q_{IL} + R_S Q_{IIS} \qquad (13.21a)$$

When the muscle is fully tetanized at a given length, the two rates are equal to some constant value R (which is a function of the length at which the muscle is tetanized). The total rate of evolution equals, by definition, the heat of maintenance, H. Thus we have the following equation for H:

$$H = R(Q_{IL} + Q_{IIS}) \qquad (13.21b)$$

Conversion of chemical energy into mechanical energy

Figure 13.10, which pictures the coupling of the cycle with reactions in the sarcoplasm, also illustrates the mechanism whereby chemical energy

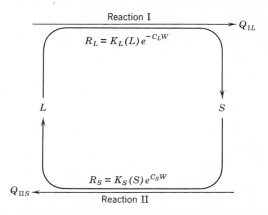

Fig. 13.10.   The cycle $L \rightleftarrows S$ and the coupled reactions I and II.   At the steady state the two rates, R_L and R_S, are equal.   The steady evolution of heat is due to the associated heats of reaction Q_{IL} and Q_{IIS}.   An increase in tension will decrease R_L and will increase R_S.   A decrease in tension will have the opposite effect.

is converted into mechanical energy, when needed.   In a tetanized muscle the free energy of the unspecified driving reaction is wasted as heat of maintenance.   However, before the tetanized state is established, part of the free energy is converted, by way of the net reaction $L = S$, into potential energy stored in the elastic component of the muscle.

In an isotonic contraction part of the free energy of the driving reaction is converted into mechanical work by way of the net reaction $L = S$.   After the muscle has shortened to the final length dictated by the imposed load, the entire free energy of the driving reaction is wasted in the form of heat of maintenance.

The instantaneous rate at which mechanical energy is developed is proportional to the product of the instantaneous net rate of the reaction $L = S$ and the instantaneous value of the tension W, i.e., to the product

$(R_L - R_S)W$. On the other hand, the instantaneous rate at which chemical energy is lost by the system is proportional to the sum $R_L F_{IL} + R_S F_{IIS}$, where F_{IL} and F_{IIS} are the free energy losses per mole in the two branches of the reaction cycle shown in Fig. 13.10.

The dependence of the heat of maintenance on the relative length of the muscle

It has been found experimentally that the heat of maintenance depends upon the length at which the muscle is tetanized. The magnitude of H passes through a maximum at or near the rest-length (Fenn, 1945; Ramsey, 1947). The following considerations show that the physicochemical model of the contractile mechanism calls for a maximum in the heat-length curve.

It was shown that the heat of maintenance is proportional to the rate of turnover, R, in the steady state. Because of the equality of the two rates at the steady state, R is given by one of the two equations (13.4). Choosing the first, we have

$$R = k_L(L)e^{-C_L W} \tag{13.22}$$

If the length at which the muscle is tetanized is changed, the value of R will change, because of the change in (L) and in W. W is not an independent variable, since it must satisfy equation (13.5). Furthermore, we have the relations: $(S) + (L) = \text{constant} = n$; $C_L + C_S = C$. From the physics of the model we can see that the steady state value of (L) increases continuously as the length at which the muscle is tetanized is increased. We can therefore seek possible maxima or minima in the heat of maintenance-length of muscle curve by investigating the behavior of the derivative $dR/d(L)$ considered as a function of (L).

It can be shown without additional assumptions, by using the ordinary rules of explicit and implicit differentiation, that the value of the derivative is given by the expression

$$\frac{dR}{d(L)} = \frac{k_L e^{-C_L W}[nC_S - (L)C]}{n - (L)} \tag{13.23}$$

Inspection of the numerator of the right side of (13.23) shows that there is only one value of (L) for which the right side of the equation equals zero, namely, the value of (L) which will satisfy the equation

$$(L)/n = C_S/C \tag{13.24}$$

The curve must have one, and one only, critical point. Further analysis of equation (13.22) shows that this critical point must be a maximum.

Thus the theory based on the physicochemical model predicts that the slope of the H-length curve should decrease progressively to zero and should eventually become negative.   The first part of this prediction is in agreement with observations (Fenn, 1945; Ramsey, 1947).   The slope of the curve is positive for lengths smaller than the rest-length and approaches zero at the rest-length or just before the rest-length is reached.   The experimental curve shows a negative slope beyond the rest-length.   However, this observation has no bearing on the validity of the theoretical prediction.   The theoretical calculation was based on the assumption that the total number of active units remains constant in the entire series of experiments.   This assumption is valid only if the tetanized state at lengths greater than the rest-length is reached by tetanizing the muscle at rest-length and only then slowly stretching the tetanized muscle to the desired length.   On the other hand, the experimental curve for relative lengths beyond the value 1.0 was obtained by stretching the muscle before stimulation and tetanizing it subsequently.   It was shown earlier that under these experimental conditions a part of the contractile units is converted into an inactive state U.   It follows that under these conditions the heat of maintenance must decrease because of the decrease in the number of active units.

Thus further experiments are needed to verify the prediction that, when stimulated muscle is stretched beyond its rest-length, the heat of maintenance decreases progressively.   When this is done, the investigator will have to take into consideration the effect discovered by Feng (1932), namely that when a resting muscle is stretched, the resting metabolism increases, sometimes as much as three-fold.   However, it may be assumed that, at least up to the rest-length the theoretical prediction agrees with experiment.

The numerical value of $e^{C_s W_r}$ for frog's sartorius at 0°C

The numerical value of $e^{C_L W_r}$ for frog's sartorius was found to be approximately 61, from an analysis of the relation between the rate of shortening of the muscle in an isotonic experiment and the load it is forced to carry.   The value of $e^{C_s W_r}$ may be obtained in a similar fashion from the rate of lengthening when the applied loads are larger than the load which the muscle is capable of carrying.   Unfortunately, this information is not available.   The data of Katz (1939b) cannot be used, since the speeds of lengthening with high loads were disregarded on the assumption that the muscle "yielded" with such loads.   Similarly, his data for loads only a little larger than W_r do not include the initial velocity, which was also ascribed to "yielding."   These are probably the reasons for the discrepancy between his results and those of Hill's equation.

Although it was shown earlier that Hill's equation cannot hold for very high loads, this equation, which gives an excellent fit for rates of shortening, should give a fairly good fit in the region close to the value of W_r.

In the absence of the data needed for the more direct method, we can calculate the value of $e^{C_S W}$ by an indirect method, making use of equation (13.24). Keeping in mind the relations $(L) + (S) = n$, and $C_L + C_S = C$, we can rewrite this equation as follows:

$$(L)/(S) = C_S/C_L \qquad (13.25)$$

Let us recall the physical meaning of this equation. It states that the heat of maintenance will have its maximum value at that particular length of the muscle at which the value of the ratio $(L)/(S)$ in the steady state equals the ratio C_S/C_L. Thus, if we knew the value of the right side of the equation, we could calculate the distribution of the contractile units between the two states at that length at which the heat of maintenance is at its maximum. Conversely, if we know the distribution of the contractile units at that length at which the heat of maintenance is at a maximum, we can use equation (13.25) to calculate the value of the ratio C_S/C_L.

Experimental observations show that the maximum occurs at or near the rest-length. It was estimated earlier that, in a tetanus at the rest-length, 70 per cent of the units are in the state L and 30 per cent are in the state S. It follows from equation (13.25) that C_S/C_L equals 7/3. Since the value of $e^{C_L W}$ is 61, it follows that $e^{C_S W} = 61^{7/3} \doteq 14,600$. This is the value which was used in the earlier part of the chapter.

The temperature coefficient of the speed of shortening in an isotonic contraction

According to the chemical model of the contractile process, the initial rate of shortening is proportional to the initial rate of the chemical reaction $L \rightarrow S$. It should be expected that the temperature coefficient of the rate of shortening will have the high value characteristic of chemical reactions, somewhere between 2 and 3 per 10°C.

This prediction is in agreement with the observations of Hill (1938), who found a temperature coefficient of 2.05. We can also compare our prediction with the data on single muscle fibers obtained by Buchthal and Kaiser (1949). Their three pairs of values for 0°C and 24°C, respectively, yield the coefficients 1.94, 2.04, and 2.13, average value 2.04 per 10°C.

Since the maximum rate of shortening is obtained when the load is zero, the rate of the reaction $L \rightarrow S$, with zero load, is given by the equation $R_L = k_L(L)$. Accepting the value 2.05 for the temperature coefficient of this reaction between 0° and 10°C, we can calculate the energy of activation, E, of this reaction from the modified Arrhenius equation,

$$\text{Temperature coefficient} = e^{\dfrac{E(T_2 - T_1)}{RT_1T_2}}$$

Substituting the values of R, T_1, T_2, we get $E = 11,000$ cal per mole.

The temperature coefficient of the rate of development of tension in an isometric tetanic contraction

The same reaction, $L \to S$, which causes the shortening of the muscle in an isotonic experiment causes an elastic stretch and the development of tension in an isometric experiment. We would expect, therefore, that the rate of development of tension would show the same temperature coefficient as the speed of shortening, namely 2.05 per 10°C. Hill (1938, Fig. 15) gives the tension-time curves for frog's sartorius at 0° and 16°C. From these curves it can be shown that for a temperature change of 16°C the relative rate of development of tension is greater by a factor of 2.4. This factor corresponds to a temperature coefficient of 1.73 per 10°C. The discrepancy between this value and the predicted value 2.05, amounting to a factor of 1.17, is undoubtedly due to the fact that in each of the two curves Hill gave the relative values of the instantaneous tensions in terms of the maximum tensions developed at the respective temperatures. Thus the assumption that the temperature coefficient of the developed tension is of the order of 1.17 will remove the discrepancy between the predicted and the observed temperature coefficients.

The temperature coefficient of the heat of maintenance, H

The value of H is given by equation (13.22). The value of R in this equation equals $k_L(L)e^{-C_LW_r}$ (equation 13.4 applied to the steady state). The specific rate constant k_L is expected to have a high temperature coefficient, of the order of 2.0. On the other hand, very little can be said, with the available information, about the nature of the temperature coefficient of (L) and of the exponential factor. Furthermore the quantities Q_{IL} and Q_{IIS} need not remain constant as the temperature is raised. Thus the reaction $L \to S$ may be coupled directly with some reaction, which we may call I_a: reaction I_a may be followed by reaction I_b, I_c, $\cdots$, in the indicated order. At a given temperature, Q_{IL} is the summation of the thermal effects produced by these consecutive reactions. Because of the lag between the successive reactions, reaction I_a may reach closer to the steady state rate while reaction I_c is still picking up speed. An increase in temperature will increase the speed of the approach of the successive reactions to their steady rate values, and will thus confer a temperature coefficient greater than 1.0 to the value of Q_{IL}. The same may be said about Q_{IIS}.

The experimentally observed values of the temperature coefficient of H are high. From Hill's values of H at 0° and 13°C (1938, Figs. 9 and 10), the calculated value of the temperature coefficient is 4.0 per 10°C. Hill (1926) gives a graphical summary of the heat production in a tetanus at four different temperatures. The temperature coefficient of H, calculated from these values, is 2.58 per 10°C.

The temperature coefficient of the isometric tension, W_r

The value of W_r is given by equation (13.5). Taking the natural logarithms of the two sides of the equation, we have

$$\ln [(S)/(L)] = \ln k_L - \ln k_S - CW_r \qquad (13.26)$$

Inspection of equation (13.26) shows that the temperature coefficients of the first three terms on the right side cannot be much different from 1.0, since they are logarithmic quantities. The quantity C contains the factor $1/T$, whose temperature coefficient is $273/283 = 0.965$ per 10°C, also a number close to 1.0. It follows that the developed tension W_r must also have a temperature coefficient which is not much different from 1.0.

It would be difficult to estimate the experimental value of this temperature coefficient from Hill's data (1938, Table III). Despite this investigator's careful efforts, the discrepancy between the data obtained for the same temperature is so high that no conclusion can be reached about the actual value of the coefficient. However, the data leave no doubt that the coefficient is small, not greater than 1.2 over the range of temperatures studied, in agreement with the theoretical prediction. The temperature coefficient of the tetanic tension in a single muscle fiber is about 1.12 (Ramsey, 1947).

The present theory, of course, is restricted to the condition that the effective amount of contractile substance is constant. There are data (D. E. Brown, unpublished), however, which may be interpreted as indicating that, over a wider range of temperatures and also under different hydrostatic pressures between 1 and 500 atm, the effective amount of contractile substance varies, or that additional reactions become involved in such manner that the tension is very significantly affected. The temperature-tension relations discussed by Weber (1952) are understandable on the same basis.

The economy of muscle and its temperature coefficient

To maintain a steady tension, a muscle requires the expenditure of energy in the form of the steady heat of maintenance. For the purpose of comparing the efficiencies of two different muscles, the economy of the muscle has been defined as the ratio

$$\frac{\text{(Tension, in grams)(Length of muscle)}}{\text{Heat of maintenance, in gram-cm per sec}} = \text{Economy} = \frac{W_r l}{H}$$

In this formula H is defined as the total heat produced by the muscle per second (Bozler, 1930).

Since the theory predicts that W_r must have a temperature coefficient not much different from 1.0, while H must have a large temperature coefficient, it follows that the economy of a given muscle must decrease greatly with an increase in temperature. This prediction is in agreement with observed results. A tetanus at 20°C is between two and three times as costly as a tetanus at 10°C (Fenn, 1945, p. 498; Hill, 1926, p. 43).

A chemical interpretation of the "catch mechanism" and of the high economy of some muscles

In some muscles the economy is so great that it has been argued that such muscles possess a "catch mechanism" which enables them to maintain tension without any expenditure of energy. Actually, there is probably a small expenditure which cannot be detected in the presence of the resting energy production (Fenn, 1945, p. 498). In the bivalve mollusc *Pecten*, there is a large striated adductor muscle whose function is to close the shell rapidly. It then relaxes, and a smaller smooth muscle, whose function is to hold the two valves together, takes over. The force needed to separate the valves is much larger than that needed to prevent them from closing. The valves may be closed for hours against a steady force and with the absorption of only relatively small amounts of oxygen (Starling, 1941: Bainbridge and Menzies, 1929). In general, slow action seems to be accompanied by a high economy.

Keeping in mind the physicochemical model of the contractile process, we can only speculate at this time about the reason for the high economy of these muscles. The tension developed by the muscle is given by equation (13.5). Two muscles with different enzymatic environments may have entirely different values of the rate constants k_L and k_S. If the ratio of the two rate constants is the same in the two muscles, both will develop the same tension per square centimeter. However, the muscle whose rate constants are smaller will show a greater economy.

On the other hand, if the values of k_L are the same in both muscles, and that of k_S is much smaller in one of them, the latter will develop a greater tension and at the same time will possess a greater economy.

If this interpretation of the "catch mechanism" and of the high economy of some muscles is correct, a low economy in tension is an obligatory condition for the ability of the muscle to perform fast work.

A proposal for a new measure of the effectiveness of muscle

The ratio (tension) (length of muscle)/(rate of heat loss), proposed by Bozler (1930), and called the economy of the muscle, has the dimension of time. Its value must depend upon the unit of time used. The value is different for different muscles; even for the same muscle, the value changes with the temperature. This dimensional ratio can be nothing more than some sort of an empirical index. Applied to a single muscle, it is sensitive to the experimental conditions; applied to different types of muscle, it emphasizes their differences. If there is any unity in the underlying mechanism of different types of muscle, this ratio will not reveal this unity.

The heat of maintenance, which is the rate of heat loss in an isometric tetanus, has the dimensions of power. It is to be expected that a more significant ratio will be obtained if this power is related to some other property of muscle which also has the dimensions of power. In seeking a suitable muscle function to be related to the heat of maintenance, we turn to an analogy which should help clarify the reason for the suggested choice.

Let us consider the hypothetical case of a single-cylinder steam locomotive standing still, but under full steam. The rate of heat loss of the locomotive is the analog of the heat of maintenance of muscle. The "heat of maintenance" of the locomotive does not represent wanton waste. It is the preparedness price paid for keeping the engine in readiness to deliver maximum power. The ratio (maximum thrust)(piston stroke)/(heat of maintenance) would have no special physical significance, even though it constitutes the analog of the economy of muscle. On the other hand, the ratio (heat of maintenance)/(maximum power) has a physical meaning and may be termed the preparedness-delivery-quotient.

By analogy, we may define the PDQ of the muscle (preparedness)/(delivery quotient) as the ratio (heat of maintenance)/(maximum power). Both the economy and the PDQ of the frog's sartorius can be calculated from the data published by Hill (1938, Fig. 9). Here the muscle was 3.45 cm long; its heat of maintenance was 11.5 g-cm per sec; it developed a maximum isometric tension of 44.7 grams. Substituting these values in the formula $W_r l/H$, we find that the economy of the muscle was 13.4 sec.

The speed of shortening with zero load at 0°C, v_0, may be estimated from the fact that the muscle shortens at the rate of 1.34 muscle-lengths per second (see p. 718). This gives the value $v_0 = 4.64$ cm per sec. At this speed there is no power delivered, since the load is zero. An analysis of the speed-load relation for this muscle shows that maximum power is delivered when the load is approximately equal to $0.3W_r$. With this load the speed of shortening is $0.3v_0$. Substituting these values in the formula for the PDQ of the muscle, we find

$$PDQ = \frac{H}{0.3W_r 0.3v_0} = 0.62 \qquad (13.27)$$

Thus the heat rate of keeping the muscle in a state of preparedness is 62 per cent of the maximum rate at which this organ can deliver work.

Thermal phenomena in a twitch

The rate of development of tension and the speed of shortening in an isotonic twitch both have a high temperature coefficient. Unlike the maximum tension in a tetanus, the maximum tension developed in a twitch decreases markedly with increasing temperature. Likewise, the total amount of heat developed per twitch decreases with increasing temperatures. On the other hand, the ratio (heat per twitch)/(maximum developed tension) is fairly independent of the temperature (Fenn, 1945).

The high temperature coefficients of the rate of development of tension and of the rate of shortening are easily explained, since they both reflect the high temperature coefficient of the reaction $L \rightarrow S$.

The commonly accepted explanation of the decrease in the tension developed in a twitch with increasing temperature is that the process responsible for relaxation has a higher temperature coefficient than does the process responsible for the development of tension. This, however, does not explain the constancy of the ratio (heat per twitch)/(developed tension). It is to be expected from the theory of the physicochemical model that the heat evolved per twitch will be proportional to the extent of the reaction $L \rightarrow S$ achieved by the time relaxation begins to decrease the tension. Since the maximum developed tension is also approximately proportional to the extent of the reaction, the constancy of the ratio (heat per twitch)/(developed tension) follows as a necessary consequence.

The nature of the heat of shortening

If a muscle is tetanized isometrically at rest-length and is subsequently allowed to shorten through a small predetermined distance, there is a sudden burst of energy which levels off to the steady heat of maintenance at the new length. If in this type of experiment the permitted excursion is increased, the excess energy liberated is proportional to the excursion (Hill, 1938; Fenn, 1945).

Hill called the excess heat evolution on shortening the "heat of shortening." If shortening is an exothermic process, one would expect a negative effect on lengthening the muscle. Hill's comment was that the negative effect "occurs so slowly, however, and is so small, that it proved impossible to measure it, or even to be quite sure of its existence." This would seem to be an understatement. The heat of shortening in tetanized muscle is so conspicuous that it is hard to see how the opposite effect on lengthening can be missed, if present. As a matter of fact, Hill observed that, if the load causing the muscle to lengthen is large, there is a rapid and large burst of energy which he ascribed to a "giving" of the contractile machinery. Since no damage is done to the muscle, and the active state is set up again as soon as the force is reduced (Hill, 1938), it is more likely that this burst of energy on lengthening is a normal characteristic of the contractile machinery.

With the use of the physicochemical model and equations (13.4), we can offer the following interpretation of Hill's observations: When the muscle is tetanized at rest-length, the tension within the muscle is W_r. The two reactions within the cycle proceed at steady and equal rates. The associated heats of reaction, Q_{IL} and Q_{IIS}, account for the steady heat of maintenance. When the muscle is released, the tension drops to zero. The rate of reaction II becomes insignificantly small, but the exponential increase in the rate of reaction I, with its associated heat, more than compensates for the decrease in the heat production by reaction II, and there is a burst of energy.

Since the allowed excursions were relatively small, the speed of shortening remained approximately constant, and the total heat of shortening was proportional to the excursion.

When the muscle is lengthened by the application of a large load, the converse takes place. The increase in the rate of reaction II more than compensates for the decrease in the rate of reaction I, and again there is a burst of energy.

Substitution of the expressions for R_L and R_S in equation (13.21) shows that the rate of evolution of heat, H, should have the following characteristics: For all values of W, H should be positive. When W is much lower or much higher than W_r, H is very large. For some one value of W near W_r, H passes through a minimum. However, the value of H at the minimum does not differ much from its value at the steady state (i.e., the heat of maintenance). Thus equation (13.21) accounts for the observations made by Hill.

The Fenn effect

The observation made by Fenn in 1923–24 constitutes an important milestone on the road toward the understanding of the contractile process

in muscle.   Before that time it was assumed that a muscle, upon stimulation, turns into a tensed spring.   The discrepancies between the behavior
of a muscle and that of a spring were ascribed to the damping effect of
the viscosity of the muscle.   A tensed spring possesses a fixed amount of
potential energy.   If the spring is allowed to shorten, its potential energy
is converted partly into mechanical work, partly into heat.   It was to be
expected that the more work the spring is caused to perform, the smaller
is the fraction of the potential energy converted into heat.

Fenn, investigating heat evolution in twitches, found that a muscle
lifting or lowering a load, far from developing less heat, actually develops
more heat than it does in a free twitch contraction.   He called attention
to the significance of this observation, namely, that the stimulated muscle
cannot be considered like a tensed spring, but like a machine capable of
converting chemical energy into work, as the need arises.   This point of
view is well established at present.

Granted that the muscle mobilizes additional chemical energy when the
need arises, there still remains the question of the mechanism used for
the purpose.   We shall not attempt to carry out a quantitative analysis
of Fenn's original observations.   There can be little doubt that the
chemical environment changes continuously in a twitch.   The kinetics of
a twitch, more complicated than that of a tetanic contraction, cannot be
handled by the methods described in the preceding pages.   Fortunately,
there is available a set of observations on the Fenn effect in tetanized
muscle (Hill, 1938; Fenn, 1945).

A frog's sartorius was tetanized at $0°C$.   In a series of four experiments
the muscle was released at 1.2 sec after stimulation, carrying the loads
3.0, 5.7, 13.9, and 24.9 grams, respectively; it was allowed to shorten a
small predetermined distance.   In each case there was an increase in the
rate of evolution of heat, while the load was in transit.   In each case the
rate eventually dropped to the steady value characteristic of the shortened
length.   As is to be expected, this instant occurred progressively later
with larger loads.   With the largest load, the steady rate was achieved at
approximately 2.3 sec after stimulation.   The observation was made that
the total heat evolved in all four experiments at 2.3 sec after stimulation
was approximately the same, despite the fact that the work done on the
heaviest load was eight times as large as that done on the smallest load.
Answers are needed to the following questions: What is the mechanism
which provides for the near-equality in the total excess energy evolved on
shortening?   What is the additional source of energy accounting for the
mechanical work done by the muscle?

The first question may be answered by making use of equations
(13.21a,b) and (13.22).   When the muscle is tetanized at rest-length, the

steady rate of turnover is R_r, and the heat of maintenance is given by the equation $H = R_r(Q_{IL} + Q_{IIS})$. The speed of shortening with a given load is proportional to $R_L - R_S$; therefore the total time of shortening is proportional to the reciprocal of this expression. The total excess heat developed during the shortening is proportional to the product of the increase in the rate of heat evolution and the time of shortening, and is given by the expression

$$\text{Excess heat} = \frac{R_L Q_{IL} + R_S Q_{IIS} - R_r Q_{IL} - R_r Q_{IIS}}{R_L - R_S} \times \text{constant} \tag{13.28a}$$

When the load is very small, R_L is much larger than R_r, and R_S is negligibly small compared with R_r. As a first approximation we can write

$$\text{Excess heat} = \frac{R_L Q_{IL}}{R_L} \times \text{constant} = Q_{IL} \times \text{constant} \tag{13.28b}$$

Thus it follows from the theory of the physicochemical model that the total excess heat evolved by a shortening muscle should be approximately constant, as observed by Hill. In order to carry out a more rigorous calculation, we need the relative values of Q_{IL} and of Q_{IIS}. Since this information is not available, we can carry out an illustrative calculation on the assumption that these two quantities are equal. This will give an approximate estimate of the relation between the total excess heat and the load.

Substitution of the value $Q_{IIS} = Q_{IL}$ in equation (13.28a) yields

$$\text{Excess heat} = \frac{R_L - R_S - 2R_r}{R_L - R_S} \times \text{constant} \times Q_{IL} \tag{13.29}$$

The variable part of the right-hand side of equation (13.29) may be calculated with the use of equation (13.4), which gives the effect of the load on the values of R_L and R_S. Table 13.1 was calculated with the use of the previously obtained values $e^{c_L W_r} = 61$ and $e^{c_S W_r} = 14,600$.

Inspection of the third column shows that the value of the excess heat evolved is rather insensitive to the load carried during shortening, for loads up to 30 per cent of the maximum developed tension. Even with a 50 per cent load, the excess heat evolved is only 23 per cent smaller than the heat evolved with zero load. Considering, on the one hand, the simplifications used in obtaining the values in the table, and, on the other hand, the degree of reproducibility to be expected from a series of experiments with muscle, the conclusion may be reached that the physicochemical model of muscle offers an adequate explanation of the approximate independence between the excess heat evolved and the load carried.

There still remains the question of the source of energy for the mechanical work of lifting the load. We turn our attention to the potential energy stored in the inert elastic component of the muscle just after stimulation. This energy must be smaller in the short position. When the load is very small, the difference between the two potential energies is converted into the kinetic energy of the load. This kinetic energy is wasted into heat when the load is suddenly stopped at the end of the excursion, but the heat is not registered by the thermopile, which is in direct contact with the muscle. When the load is increased progressively, a progressively larger fraction of the difference between the two potential energies is converted into the mechanical work of lifting the load.

Table 13.1.   Effect of the Load on the Excess Heat Evolved in Shortening

W/W_r	Value of Variable Factor	Relative Value of Variable Factor
0	0.97	1.00
0.05	0.96	0.99
0.10	0.95	0.98
0.20	0.93	0.96
0.30	0.89	0.92
0.40	0.83	0.85
0.50	0.75	0.77

The assumption that the mechanical work of lifting the load is provided by the potential energy stored in the elastic component may be tested as follows: Each load was lifted 0.52 cm. The work in lifting the load was 1.56, 2.96, 6.25, and 13 g-cm, respectively. The length of the muscle was 2.95 cm. The stretch of the elastic component at isometric contraction was 12 per cent of the length of the muscle (p. 709), or 0.35 cm.

Hill gives the value 45 grams for the tension in the longer position in his Fig. 7, and 43 grams in the text. We will take the lower figure, to make the test more stringent. Judging from the data in Hill's Fig. 7 and from the text, the tension in the shorter position was almost equal to the largest load lifted, or 24.9 grams. The potential energy in a Hooke spring equals the product of the tension and one-half the stretch. The potential energies for two different stretches are proportional to the squares of the tensions.

With these data we calculate that the potential energy in the long state was 7.5 g-cm, and in the shorter state it was 2.5 g-cm. The loss in potential energy was 5.0 g-cm.

This energy is ample to account for the lifting of the first two loads. It equals, within 20 per cent, the energy of lifting the third load. It is too small, by a factor of 2.6, to account for the energy of lifting the largest load.

Whether the discrepancy is due to the simplicity of the assumptions used or whether it is fatal to the explanation of the Fenn effect given here remains to be judged in the light of specially designed experiments. It is possible that muscle uses some additional mechanism to mobilize energy, when needed. There cannot be much doubt, however, that in the final explanation the speeding up of the two reactions while the load is in transit and the potential energy of the elastic component will have to be taken into consideration.

ESTIMATES OF THE SIZE OF THE CONTRACTILE UNIT

Estimate of the size of the contractile unit from the kinetics of the reactions $L \to S$ and $S \to L$

The distribution of the contractile units between the long and the short states in a tetanized muscle is affected by the tension prevailing within the muscle, since tension increases the difference between the potential energies of the two states. The difference between the potential energies of the two states equals the product of the tension exerted by each molecular filament and the difference between the lengths of the contractile unit in the two states. It follows that the mathematical expression showing the distribution of the contractile units between the two states as a function of the tension will contain the difference between the two lengths as one of the parameters, thus making it possible to form an estimate of the size of the contractile unit.

In a tetanized muscle contracted maximally in the absence of a load, a steady state is established. The two reactions of the steady state cycle and their respective rates are given by equations (13.1, 13.2).

Since the two rates are equal in the steady state, the distribution of the contractile units is given by equation (13.3).

In the first reaction the unit must pass through an active state L^*. We need not concern ourselves with the energy of activation in this process, but we must observe that in the presence of a tension the energy of activation is increased by an amount E_{L^*}, which is jointly proportional to the tension and the difference in lengths of the states L and L^*. The new rate of this reaction, in the presence of a tension, is given by equation (13.30):

$$R_L = k_L(L)e^{-E_{L^*}/RT} \qquad (13.30)$$

where R is the gas constant, and T is the absolute temperature at which the experiment is performed.

Similarly, in the second reaction the contractile unit must pass through an active state S^*. In the presence of a tension, the energy of activation of this process is decreased by an amount E_{S^*}, and the new rate of this reaction is given by equation (13.31):

$$R = k(S)e^{E_{S^*}/RT} \tag{13.31}$$

After the new steady state is established, the two rates are equal. Making use of this fact and combining equations (13.30, 13.31), we obtain the equation for the distribution of the contractile units between the two states in the presence of a tension:

$$\frac{(S)}{(L)} = Ke^{\dfrac{-(E_{L^*} + E_{S^*})}{RT}} \qquad \left(K = \frac{k_L}{k_S}\right) \tag{13.32}$$

The quantities E_{L^*} and E_{S^*} are proportional to the tension W. In an isothermal process T remains constant. By lumping together the several constants, we obtain a simplified form of equation (13.32):

$$\frac{E_{L^*} + E_{S^*}}{RT} = CW \qquad \frac{(S)}{(L)} = Ke^{CW} \tag{13.33}$$

This is the distribution equation used in the earlier parts of this chapter.

Let E_{LS} be the work done per mole of contractile units against the tension W when the units change from state L to state S. If the activated states L^* and S^* were precisely the same, or at least possessed the same lengths, it would follow that

$$E_{L^*} + E_{S^*} = E_{LS} \tag{13.34}$$

However, since the two reactions form two different branches of the cycle $L \rightleftarrows S$, equation (13.34) can be accepted only as a first approximation. With this qualification, we combine equations (13.33) and (13.34) and obtain equation (13.35):

$$E_{LS}/RT = CW \tag{13.35}$$

We may now proceed to evaluate the quantity E_{LS} in terms of the size of the contractile unit. Let A be the combined area of cross section of all the contractile molecular filaments in a given muscle. Let the area of a single filament be a. The number of filaments will be A/a. If the total tension is W, the tension per filament is Wa/A. If the length of the contractile unit in state L is h, and, if the unit shortens by the relative amount f when changing from state L to state S, the change in length equals fh. The work done by a single unit is given by the product of the tension per filament and the change in length, or $(Wa/A)(fh)$. Multiplying this quantity by Avogadro's number N we obtain the equation

$$E_{LS} = \frac{NWafh}{A} = \frac{Wf(Nah)}{A} \qquad (13.36)$$

Since a is the cross-sectional area of the molecular filament, it is also the area of the cross section of a single contractile unit. It follows that Nah is the effective molal volume of the contractile unit. We will call this quantity $\bar{V}$. Substituting this value in equation (13.36) and combining equations (13.36) and (13.35), we find the relation between the molecular volume and the quantity CW:

$$\bar{V} = \frac{RT(CW)}{f(W/A)} \qquad (13.37)$$

Inspection of equation (13.37) shows that a knowledge of the experimental values of both CW and of W/A for some particular experiment will enable us to calculate the value of $\bar{V}$.

We may use the data on frog's sartorius (Hill, 1938). The muscle used by Hill was 2.95 cm long and weighed 0.089 gram. It developed an isometric tension $W_r = 45$ grams. Taking the density of muscle as practically 1, we estimate that the area of the cross section of the muscle was 0.0304 sq cm. Muscle is known to contain approximately 10 per cent of myosin by weight. Since the density of protein is approximately 1.3, the combined cross-sectional area of the myosin in this muscle is estimated as 0.00234 sq cm. The value of W depends upon the length at which the muscle is tetanized. We will use the symbol W_r to indicate the fact that Hill measured the value of W at the rest-length of the muscle. Substituting the values of W_r and A for this particular muscle, we calculate the value of the ratio W_r/A. Thus, $W_r/A = 19,200$ g per sq cm $= 1.89 \times 10^7$ dynes per sq cm.

It was estimated earlier that the experimental value of CW_r for frog's sartorius at 0°C is 13.7. It was also estimated that the length of the unit in the S state is approximately half of its length in the L state; hence $f = 0.5$. Substituting these values of (W_r/A), f, CW_r, in equation (13.37), as well as the values $T = 273°K$, $R = 8.3 \times 10^7$ ergs per mole per degree Kelvin, we find the value $\bar{V} = 32,900$ cc. Since the density of the protein is 1.3, the molecular weight of the contractile unit is 43,000.

Estimate of the molecular weight of the contractile unit from the heat evolved per twitch

There is strong circumstantial evidence that the activity of myosin in stimulated muscle is in some way associated with the hydrolysis of adenosine triphosphate (ATP) (Mommaerts, 1950). It is not unlikely that the reaction of a single contractile unit is coupled with the hydrolysis of a single molecule of ATP. Since the heat of hydrolysis of ATP is known, it should be possible to calculate the molecular weight of the contractile unit from the heat evolved in a single twitch, as follows.

Let the total number of moles of contractile units in the whole muscle be n. In a twitch, only a fraction of the total number of units changes into the S state by the time relaxation begins to set in. Let the value of this fraction be p. It follows that the number of contractile units undergoing reaction in a single twitch is pn. By the time the muscle relaxes, the net chemical effect is the hydrolysis of pn moles of ATP. If the molecular weight of the contractile unit is M, the total weight of myosin in the muscle is nM. Since the myosin constitutes only 10 per cent of the weight of the muscle, the total weight of the muscle is $10nM$. We now have the following equation:

Number of moles of ATP hydrolyzed

$$\text{per gram of muscle per twitch} = \frac{pn}{10nM} = \frac{p}{10M} \qquad (13.38)$$

According to Hill (1950), a single twitch at 0°C sets free 0.003 cal per gram of muscle. This, according to Hill, corresponds to the liberation of 2.5×10^{-7} mole of phosphate per gram of muscle per twitch. The value of p was estimated earlier: $p = 0.15$. Substituting these values in equation (13.38), we find $M = 60,000$.

Considering the uncertainties in the values of the constants used in the two methods of estimating the molecular weight, this value is in fair agreement with the value 43,000 obtained by the first method.

Szent-Györgyi's estimate of the molecular weight of the "autone"

In a recent paper Szent-Györgyi (1949), states that his studies of the reactions of myosin with ATP and of the contraction of myosin in the presence of ATP suggest that this contractile matter consists of functional units, which he calls "autones." In this paper Szent-Györgyi uses consistently the value 35,000 for the molecular weight of the autone. However, he mentions that this value merely gives an indication of the order of magnitude of the molecular weight, and that the value may be as high as 70,000. It will be seen that the two values, 43,000 and 60,000, fall well within the range of values estimated by Szent-Györgyi.

Relation of the estimated molecular weight to Riseman and Kirkwood's theory of the elastic modulus of muscle

In a recent paper Riseman and Kirkwood (1948) have offered a theory of the elastic modulus of muscle. Their theory gives a value of the elastic modulus which is in fair agreement with the experimental value. The theory may also offer a clue to the relation between the activity of muscle and the hydrolysis of ATP.

The theory is based on the following assumptions: The myosin filament in the long state is electrically charged, whereas in the short state it is neutral.   The charges in the long state are due to phosphorylation of the —OH groups of the hydroxyamino acid residues of the myosin.   Each —H_2PO_4 group attached to the myosin is ionized to —HPO_4^-.   Excitation of the muscle consists of removal of these charges, resulting in an increase in the elastic modulus.   The original balance between the electrical force and the configurational force is destroyed, and the muscle shortens.

It appears from these authors' calculations that the phosphate charges are spaced 100 Å apart along the filaments, and that each charge is associated with a fraction of the filament whose molecular weight is 10,000.   The discrepancy between this value and the value of 47,000 calculated earlier in this paper cannot be due entirely to the fact that Riseman and Kirkwood used round figures for the values of the parameters entering their formula.   A bigger source of discrepancy is the value of the effective dielectric constant, $D_e = 100$, used by these authors.

The interaction between two charged particles immersed in an aqueous solution of amino acids or of protein, at a distance of several thousand angstroms, is influenced by the presence of the water molecules and of the highly polar amino acid molecules or protein molecules, whose orientation is responsive to the electric field.   In these circumstances the use of a dielectric constant whose value is higher than that of the dielectric constant of water is justified.   The situation is different, however, when the charges are embedded in the same protein molecule and are only a few angstroms apart.   The major contribution to the total electrical energy is due to the interaction of adjacent charges.   The lines of force run partly through the protein molecule, partly through the aqueous medium.   It is to be expected that the effective value of the dielectric constant will be much smaller than that of water.

This objection to the high value of the effective dielectric constant has already been voiced by Edsall (1950), who called attention to the difference between the macroscopic dielectric constant and the dielectric constant effective in the interaction between charges embedded in the same protein molecule.   In this connection Edsall mentions another paper (Kirkwood and Westheimer, 1938), in which a much smaller value of the effective dielectric constant was used in a situation similar to that under consideration.

According to the equation developed by Riseman and Kirkwood, the calculated value of the distance between the phosphate ions and the molecular weight per phosphate ion both vary inversely with the square root of the assumed value of D_e. A knowledge of the proper value of D_e would enable us to calculate the molecular weight associated with each phosphate ion. In the absence of the desired information, we may calculate the value of D_e which will give a molecular weight of 43,000. D_e should have a value which is smaller than the previously assumed value of 100 by a factor of $1/4.3^2$. This gives the value $D_e = 5.4$, which is much closer to values assumed for the interaction between charges attached to the same small molecule than the value $D_e = 100$. We may conclude that the molecular weight of 43,000 is not only in agreement with the theory of Riseman and Kirkwood as to order of magnitude, but also strengthens their theory by pointing to a more reasonable value of the effective dielectric constant.

Experimental evidence for the existence of macromolecular sub-units of the myosin molecule

The electron micrographs of Schmitt, Bear, Hall, and Jakus (1947) show that myosin filaments from muscle manifest discontinuities along their length, giving a nodose appearance. The axial distance between the beads or knots is approximately 400 Å. The beady appearance was also observed by Szent-Györgyi and his collaborators (Morgan et al., 1950).

Small-angle x-ray studies indicate the presence of a repeating fiber axis unit of 350 to 420 Å (Schmitt, Bear, Hall, and Jakus, 1947).

Since myosin and keratin show many similarities, Mercer's (Mercer and Rees, 1946; Farrant, Rees, and Mercer, 1947; Mercer, 1949) electron microscope observations on wool may be of some significance to the present problem. These studies have led to the conclusion that the long spacings, shown by x-rays, arise from a linear arrangement of corpuscular units along the fibers (1946, 1947). Mercer (1949) reported that the fibrils of wool are resolved into protofibrils of definite size. Both fibrils and matrix are corpuscular.

If the myosin of muscle is built from marcomolecular sub-units, it is to be expected that a suitable chemical procedure will disclose the existence of such sub-units. With this in view, it is interesting to note that Bailey (1948), and Astbury, Reed, and Spark (1948) have suggested that tropomyosin is the "monomer" of myosin. Astbury's observations that tropomyosin, like myosin, can exist in the α, β, and the supercontracted state lend support to this view.

A tentative estimate of the dimensions of the contractile unit

With a molal volume of 32,900 cc, the effective volume of a single unit would be 54,700 Å^3. If we assume that the particle is cylindrical and that its length is 400 Å, corresponding to the length of the beads observed in the electron micrographs, the estimated diameter of this particle is 13.2 Å.   Bailey et al. (1948) found that the molecular weight of tropomyosin is 90,000.   The approximate dimensions of the molecule of tropomyosin were estimated by Weber (1950).   With a molecular weight of 90,000, the molecules of tropomyosin would have the dimensions 990 Å × 11.8 Å.   If we assume that the contractile unit is the "monomer," while tropomyosin is an end-to-end "dimer," the calculated values for the contractile unit, 400 Å × 13.2 Å, molecular weight 43,000, are in good agreement with Weber's values.

We can only speculate at present on the relation of the contractile unit to the beads observed in electron micrographs.   The filaments observed by Schmitt, Bear, Hall, and Jakus (1947) varied in width from 50 to 200 Å. The variability in width is an indication that the beads do not represent an elementary contractile unit.   They are probably parallel aggregates of smaller units.   A 50 Å bead may contain over 20 units.   If the visible gradual shortening of muscle is due to a progressive increase in the number of units changed into the short state, it may very well be that a packet consisting of a large number of parallel units will give the appearance of a gradual change in the length of the bead.   It is hoped that F. O. Schmitt's tentative observations on this point (1950) will be expanded for the purpose of clarifying the question of the nature of the elementary unit of contractility.

Note added in proof: The following recent publications deal with some of the topics discussed in this chapter: Abbott and Wilkie (1953), Casella (1951), T. L. Hill (1952, 1953), Hill and Morales (1952), Mauro and Sten-Knudsen (1952), Morales and Botts (1952, 1953), Needham (1952), Tonomura, Watanabe, and Yagi (1953), Watanabe, Tonomura, and Shiokawa (1953), Tonomura and Watanabe (1953).

Potential Barriers
in Diffusion

... the mountain tarn barriered in by its stupendous crags. ...

John Ruskin, *Letters to the Clergy*

The elementary process in diffusion is the jumping of a molecule over a potential barrier arising from the hindrance to the jump offered by the surrounding medium. To scale this barrier the molecule in question must

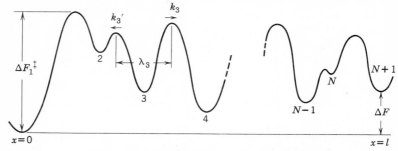

Fig. 14.1. Free energy profile of a sequence of barriers.

possess a certain minimum energy in the proper degrees of freedom, which will, in general, considerably exceed the average energy. The frequency with which this occurs has previously been shown (Glasstone, et al., 1941; Zwolinski et al., 1949; Eyring, Lumry, and Woodbury, 1949) to be

$$k_i = \kappa(kT/h)e^{-\Delta F_i{}^\ddagger/kT} \tag{14.1}$$

where $\Delta F^\ddagger$ is the free energy change necessary for the molecule to pass from its current equilibrium position to the top of the barrier, and the transmission coefficient κ is usually equal to unity. If the concentration of diffusing material is c_i molecules per cubic centimeter on the left of the barrier and c_{i+1} on the right, the net rate of permeation from left to right through 1 sq cm is given by

$$Q_i = c_i\lambda_i k_i - c_{i+1}\lambda_{i+1}k_{i+1}' \tag{14.2}$$

where λ_1 and λ_2 are lengths of the regions (i.e., the lattice distances) on either side from which molecules may jump across the barrier. An unprimed k indicates passage of a substance to the right; a primed k indicates passage to the left.

Let us now consider the steady state rate of permeation Q of a substance across an arbitrary sequence of N barriers (Fig. 14.1). Q_i in equation (14.2) must then be the same for each barrier:

$$Q_i = Q \quad \text{(all } i\text{)} \tag{14.3}$$

If c_1 and c_{N+1} are known, Q can be calculated in terms of the k's and λ's by consecutive substitutions:

$$c_2 = \frac{1}{v_2'}(c_1 v_1 - Q)$$

$$c_3 = \frac{1}{v_3'}(c_2 v_2 - Q) = \frac{v_1 v_2}{v_2' v_3'} c_1 - \frac{Q}{v_3'}\left(1 + \frac{v_2}{v_2'}\right)$$

$$c_{N+1} = \frac{v_1 v_2 \cdots v_N}{v_2' v_3' \cdots v_{N+1}'} c_1 - \frac{Q}{v_{N+1}'}\left(1 + \frac{v_N}{v_N'} + \cdots + \frac{v_N \cdots v_2}{v_N' \cdots v_2'}\right)$$

or $\quad Q = \dfrac{\left(v_1 c_1 - \dfrac{v_2' v_3' \cdots v_N'}{v_2 v_3 \cdots v_N} v_{N+1}' c_{N+1}\right)}{\left(1 + \dfrac{v_2'}{v_2} + \cdots + \dfrac{v_2' \cdots v_N'}{v_2 \cdots v_N}\right)}$ $\tag{14.4}$

where v has been written for λk. Use of equation (14.1) transforms (14.4) into

$$Q = \frac{\frac{kT}{h} e^{-\Delta F_1^\ddagger/kT}(\lambda_1 c_1 - \lambda_{N+1} c_{N+1} e^{\Delta F/kT})}{(1 + e^{\delta F_2^\ddagger/kT} + e^{\delta F_3^\ddagger/kT} + \cdots + e^{\delta F_N^\ddagger/kT})} \tag{14.5}$$

where $\delta F_i^\ddagger$ is the difference in free energy between the top of the ith and the top of the first barrier, and ΔF is the free energy change per molecule in going from the first to the last equilibrium position. If all the barriers are identical, $\delta F_i^\ddagger = 0$, for all i, and (14.5) becomes

$$Q = \frac{kT}{h} \lambda^2 e^{-\Delta F_1^\ddagger/kT}\left(\frac{c_1 - c_{N+1}}{l}\right) \tag{14.5a}$$

where $l = N\lambda$ is the thickness of the membrane. If the barrier sequence is such that $\lambda_1 = \lambda_{N+1}$ and $\Delta F = 0$, as is the case with a membrane separating two ideal solutions in the same solvent, then

$$Q = P(c_1 - c_{N+1}) \tag{14.5b}$$

where $\quad P = \dfrac{kT}{h} \lambda_1 e^{-\Delta F_1^\ddagger/kT} \Big/ \sum_{i=1}^{N} e^{\delta F_i^\ddagger/kT}$

is the permeability constant. It should be noted that the summation in the expression for P has the form of a partition function, and that in general, therefore, P may have a wide range of dependence on the temperature; it is only in the special case of equation (14.5a) that a plot of $\ln (P/T)$ versus $1/T$ will be linear.

If the λ and $\delta F^{\ddagger}$ can be expressed to a good approximation as continuous functions of the coordinate x in the direction of diffusion, the expression for P in equation (14.5b) becomes

$$P = \frac{kT}{h} \lambda_1 e^{-\Delta F_1^{\ddagger}/kT} \bigg/ \int_0^l \frac{1}{\lambda(x)} e^{\delta F_{(x)}^{\ddagger}/kT} \, dx \tag{14.6}$$

A constant force f exerted on each molecule will modify the free energy profile by the addition of a term $-fx$. The effect on P is therefore given by replacing $\delta F^{\ddagger}$ in equation (14.6) by $\delta F^{\ddagger} - fx$:

$$P = \frac{kT}{h} \lambda_1 e^{-\Delta F_1^{\ddagger}/kT} \left[\int_0^l \frac{1}{\lambda(x)} e^{\frac{1}{kT}\{\delta F_{(x)}^{\ddagger} - fx\}} \, dx \right]^{-1} \tag{14.7}$$

Furthermore (14.5b) must be rewritten

$$Q = P[c_{(0)} - c(l)e^{-fl/kT}] \tag{14.8}$$

since ΔF in equation (14.5) is now no longer zero.

A knowledge of P as a function of f and T gives

$$\int_0^l \frac{1}{\lambda_1 \lambda(x)} e^{\frac{\Delta F_1^{\ddagger} + \delta F_{(x)}^{\ddagger}}{kT}} e^{-\frac{fx}{kT}} \, dx = \frac{kT}{h} \cdot \frac{1}{P(f, T)} \tag{14.9}$$

This integral can, in principle at least, be inverted,[1] if it is assumed that neither T nor f has any effect on λ or $\delta F^{\ddagger}$ (which is, in general, only approximately true), to give

$$k(x, T) \equiv \frac{1}{\lambda_1 \lambda(x)} e^{\frac{\Delta F_1^{\ddagger} + \delta F_{(x)}^{\ddagger}}{kT}} \tag{14.10}$$

---

[1] Any integral of the type

$$P(f) = \int_a^b A(x)B(x, f) \, dx$$

can be inverted to give $A(x)$ if $B(x, f)$ is known. If no better means are available, the following approximate procedure will serve: Replace the integral by the corresponding summation

$$P(f_k) = \sum_{i=1}^N A(x_i)B(x_i, f_k) \, \Delta x \qquad (N \, \Delta x = b - a)$$

If $P(f_k)$ is known for N values of f_k, we have N simultaneous linear algebraic equations with the $B(x_i, f_k)$ as coefficients, which can be solved for the unknowns $A(x_i)$, thus giving $A(x)$ approximately at the N points x_i. By making Δx sufficiently small, this method can be made arbitrarily accurate.

If $\ln k$ is plotted against $1/kT$ for various values of x, the slopes will give $\Delta F_1^{\ddagger} + \delta F_{(x)}$ and the intercepts $\lambda_1 \lambda(x)$. The curves enveloping the peaks of the barriers can therefore be determined from permeability measurements at various temperatures and under the influence of various gravitational force fields, such as can be obtained in a centrifuge; to determine the curve enveloping the bottoms of the valleys requires some knowledge of conditions inside the membrane, such as the equilibrium concentration of diffusing material as a function of x.

The problem of finding P in terms of free energy profile and the initial and final concentration becomes enormously more complicated if the diffusing molecules interact with each other. In that event the profile is modified in a manner depending upon the concentration distribution within the membrane. As a special case of interacting particles, let us consider the steady state diffusion of electrolytes. In general, the barrier profile is different for the different ions constituting the solutions on either side, so these ions will not move at quite the same rate. This difference in diffusion rates leads to a very slight separation of charge which is, however, capable of producing an appreciable gradient of electric potential. We may expect the net concentration of charge to be almost negligible compared to the total concentration of the various ionic species, because even a small accumulation of free charge would produce an enormous electric field opposing any further charge separation; we may therefore employ the electroneutrality equation, which states that

$$\sum_j \epsilon^{(j)} c_i^{(j)} = 0 \qquad \text{(for all } i\text{)} \tag{14.11}$$

where $\epsilon^{(j)}$ is the charge (including sign) on the jth ionic species, present at concentration $c_i^{(j)}$. Because of the potential gradient present, equation (14.3) becomes, by an argument analogous to that used in deriving equations (14.7) and (14.8),

$$Q^{(j)} = c_i^{(j)} v_i^{(j)} e^{-\epsilon^{(j)} \mathscr{F} \Delta V_i / 2RT} - c_{i+1}^{(j)} v_{i+1}'^{(j)} e^{\epsilon^{(j)} \mathscr{F} \Delta V_i / 2RT} \tag{14.12}$$

ΔV_i being the potential difference across the ith barrier, and it having been assumed that each peak is midway between the two adjacent valleys. In addition to $c_1^{(j)}$ and $c_{N+1}^{(j)}$, we must know either the net current I flowing across the membrane or the total potential difference ΔV across it:

$$I = \sum_j \epsilon^{(j)} Q^{(j)} \tag{14.13}$$

$$\Delta V = \sum_i \Delta V_i \tag{14.14}$$

The $N - 1$ equations (14.11), together with the NJ ($J =$ number of components) equations (14.12) and equation (14.13) or equation (14.14), furnish a total of $N(J + 1)$ equations; for unknowns we have $(N - 1)J$ concentrations, J rates of permeation, and N potential differences across individual barriers, or a total of $N(J + 1)$ quantities to be determined. The relations enumerated above are therefore just sufficient to give us the distributions of voltages and concentrations within the membrane, as well as the relation among ΔV, I, T, the c_1's, and the c_{N+1}'s. It is, of course, possible to write equation (14.5) for this case also, but there is little to be gained by such a procedure, since the denominator of the right-hand side will contain the unknown ΔV_i's.

Clearly the solution of equations (14.11) to (14.14) is, in general, a very difficult matter. Making no attempt in that direction here, we proceed at once to the special situation where one barrier is very much higher than the others (Fig. 14.2). The rate-controlling process in this case is the permeation across the high barrier, and the concentrations to the right and left of this barrier may be assumed to have attained their equilibrium distributions. This follows from equation (14.12), where, for any of the lower barriers, $Q^{(j)}$ will be very much less than either of the terms on the right, so that, to a very good approximation,

$$\frac{c_{i+1}^{(j)}}{c_i^{(j)}} = \frac{\nu_i^{(j)}}{\nu_i'^{(j)}} e^{-\epsilon^{(j)} \mathscr{F} \Delta V_i / RT} \tag{14.15}$$

for all i as long as both position i and $i + 1$ are on the same side of the high barrier. Equations (14.15) can readily be combined to give

$$\frac{c_1^{(j)}}{c_I^{(j)}} = \frac{\lambda_I^{(j)}}{\lambda_1^{(j)}} e^{-\Delta F_1^{(j)}/RT} e^{-\epsilon^{(j)} \mathscr{F} \Delta V_1 / RT}$$

$$\frac{c_2^{(j)}}{c_{II}^{(j)}} = \frac{\lambda_{II}^{(j)}}{\lambda_1^{(j)}} e^{-\Delta F_2^{(j)}/RT} e^{\epsilon^{(j)} \mathscr{F} \Delta V_2 / RT} \tag{14.16}$$

with notation as shown in Fig. 14.2. Substitution of (14.16) into (14.11) yields, if we assume that we are dealing only with uni-univalent electrolytes ($\epsilon^{(j)} = \pm 1$),

$$\Delta V_1 = \frac{RT}{2\mathscr{F}} \ln \left[\frac{\sum\limits_{+} c_I^{(j)}(\lambda_I^{(j)}/\lambda_1^{(j)}) e^{-\Delta F_1^{(j)}/RT}}{\sum\limits_{-} c_I^{(j)}(\lambda_I^{(j)}/\lambda_1^{(j)}) e^{-\Delta F_1^{(j)}/RT}} \right]$$

$$\Delta V_2 = \frac{RT}{2\mathscr{F}} \ln \left[\frac{\sum\limits_{-} c_{II}^{(j)}(\lambda_{II}^{(j)}/\lambda_2^{(j)}) e^{-\Delta F_2^{(j)}/RT}}{\sum\limits_{+} c_{II}^{(j)}(\lambda_{II}^{(j)}/\lambda_2^{(j)}) e^{-\Delta F_2^{(j)}/RT}} \right] \tag{14.17}$$

where $\sum\limits_{+}$ extends over all the positive ions and $\sum\limits_{-}$ over all the negative ones. ΔV_1 and ΔV_2 thus depend only upon c_I and c_{II}, respectively, as do c_1 and c_2. So far as passage over the high barrier is concerned, we have

$$Q^{(j)} = c_1^{(j)}\lambda_1^{(j)}e^{\frac{-\Delta F_b^{(j)\ddagger}+\Delta F_1^{(j)}-\frac{1}{2}\epsilon^{(j)}\mathscr{F}\Delta V_b}{RT}}$$
$$- c_2^{(j)}\lambda_2^{(j)}e^{\frac{-\Delta F_b^{(j)\ddagger}+\Delta F_2^{(j)}+\frac{1}{2}\epsilon^{(j)}\mathscr{F}\Delta V_b}{RT}} \qquad (14.18)$$

Substitution of (14.18) into (14.13) yields

$$I = \alpha e^{-\mathscr{F}\Delta V_b/2RT} - \beta e^{\mathscr{F}\Delta V_b/2RT} \qquad (14.19)$$

where

$$\alpha = \sum_{+} c_1^{(j)}\lambda_1^{(j)}e^{(\Delta F_1^{(j)}-\Delta F_b^{(j)\ddagger})/RT} + \sum_{-} c_2^{(j)}\lambda_2^{(j)}e^{(\Delta F_2^{(j)}-\Delta F_b^{(j)\ddagger})/RT}$$

$$\beta = \sum_{+} c_2^{(j)}\lambda_2^{(j)}e^{(\Delta F_2^{(j)}-\Delta F_b^{(j)\ddagger})/RT} + \sum_{-} c_1^{(j)}\lambda_1^{(j)}e^{(\Delta F_1^{(j)}-\Delta F_b^{(j)\ddagger})/RT}$$

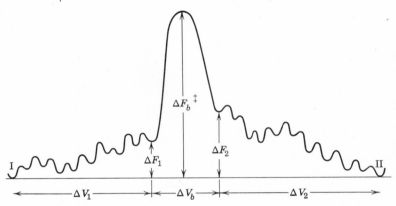

Fig. 14.2. Free energy profile of a sequence of barriers with one of the barriers much higher than the others.

Equation (14.19) can be rewritten

$$I = - 2(\alpha\beta)^{1/2} \sinh\left[(\mathscr{F}/2RT)(\Delta V - \Delta V_r)\right] \qquad (14.20)$$

where ΔV_r, the membrane potential at zero current, is given by

$$\Delta V_r = \Delta V_1 + \Delta V_2 + (RT/\mathscr{F})\ln(\alpha/\beta) \qquad (14.21)$$

ΔV_1 and ΔV_2, as well as the quantities $c_1^{(j)}$ and $c_2^{(j)}$ occurring in the expressions for α and β, can be calculated from equations (14.16) and (14.17). Equation (14.20) shows that, as ΔV becomes either positively or negatively infinite, the conductivity $[I/(\Delta V - \Delta V_r)]$ of the membrane also becomes infinite; this is not observed, possibly because sufficiently high potentials are never attained in practice. Furthermore, rectification is observed in biological membranes, whereas the conductivity from equation (14.20) is symmetric about ΔV_r. To fit the biological data, therefore, we must apply our theory to a more complex model than the one discussed above, such as that represented by equations (11.138a) and (11.138b).

The equations for the penetration of ions through membranes given in Chapter 11 (e.g., equation 11.37) are somewhat different from equation (14.12) given here. Under the restricted conditions that the barrier, in the absence of an electric field, is symmetric, that the concentrations on either side differ only infinitesimally, and that the potential change across the barrier is small, then in equation (14.12) $v_i^{(j)} = v_{i+1}'^{(j)} = v$, and the exponentials can be represented by their linear approximations. Then we may also express the $c^{(j)}$'s and the potential V as continuous functions of x, and replace equation (14.12) by

$$Q^{(j)} = - k^{(j)}\lambda^{(j)^2} \left\{ \frac{\partial c^{(j)}}{\partial x} + c^{(j)} \frac{\mathscr{F}\epsilon^{(j)}}{RT} \frac{\partial V}{\partial x} \right\} \qquad (14.22)$$

Calling $k^{(j)}\lambda^{(j)^2} = D^{(j)}$ the diffusion coefficient for the jth ionic species, equation (14.22) is equivalent to the differential equation (11.29) used in Chapter 11.

If the membrane has not yet attained a steady state, equations (14.12) or (14.22) are still valid, except that a subscript i must be appended to the $Q^{(j)}$'s, since the rates of permeation will now vary from barrier to barrier. The rates of accumulation of material are given by

$$\frac{\partial c_i^{(j)}}{\partial t} = \frac{Q_i^{(j)} - Q_{i+1}^{(j)}}{\lambda} \qquad (14.23)$$

or, if $c^{(j)}$ and $Q^{(j)}$ are continuous functions of x,

$$\frac{\partial c^{(j)}}{\partial t} = - \frac{\partial Q^{(j)}}{\partial x} \qquad (14.24)$$

Substitution of (14.22) into (14.24) yields

$$\frac{\partial c^{(j)}}{\partial t} = \frac{\partial}{\partial x} \left\{ D^{(j)} \left(\frac{\partial c^{(j)}}{\partial x} + c^{(j)} \frac{\mathscr{F}\epsilon^{(j)}}{RT} \frac{\partial V}{\partial x} \right) \right\} \qquad (14.25)$$

which is a slight generalization of Fick's law and becomes identical with it in the absence of a potential gradient.

Up to now we have tacitly assumed that when a molecule jumps over a barrier it will find a vacant site on the other side. The blocking of equilibrium positions is another form of interaction between diffusing molecules. The rate at which molecules cross a barrier in a given direction is then no longer just proportional to their concentration in the vicinity of the point of departure, but also to the concentration σ_i of vacant sites near the point of arrival:

$$Q = \lambda k c_i \sigma_{i+1} - \lambda k c_{i+1} \sigma_i \qquad (14.26)$$

where a symmetric barrier has been assumed and where k is now the rate constant for a second order reaction between a jumping molecule and a vacant site. We now suppose that there is a constant total concentration of diffusion sites σ^0, of which a part, $\sigma_i{}^{(d)}$, has been incapacitated by undergoing some transformation, while another part, $\sigma_i{}^{(P)}$, is reversibly poisoned by a narcotic or other drug. We then have the two equilibria:

$$\text{Vacant site} \overset{K_1}{\rightleftharpoons} \text{incapacitated site} \qquad (14.27)$$
$$\text{(Conc. } \sigma_i) \qquad \text{(Conc. } \sigma_i{}^{(d)})$$

$$\text{Vacant site} + r \text{ drug molecules} \overset{K_2}{\rightleftharpoons} \text{poisoned site} \qquad (14.28)$$
$$\text{Conc. } \sigma_i \qquad \text{Conc. } (P) \qquad \text{Conc. } \sigma_i{}^{(P)}$$

with the equilibrium constants K_1 and K_2, respectively. We may write as usual a conservation equation for the total number of sites:

$$\sigma^{(0)} = \sigma_i{}^{(d)} + \sigma_i{}^{(P)} + \sigma_i + c_i$$

$$= K_1 \sigma_i + K_2 \sigma_i (P)^r + \sigma_i + c_i \qquad (14.29)$$

whence
$$\sigma_i = \frac{\sigma^{(0)} - c_i}{1 + K_1 + K_2(P)^r} \qquad (14.30)$$

This result may be generalized to include any number of poisons or inhibitors. The membrane permeability P then takes the form

$$P = \frac{\lambda^2 k \sigma^{(0)}}{1 + K_1 + K_2(P)^r} \qquad (14.31)$$

If, more generally, the lattice points of concentration (σ), $(\sigma^{(d)})$, and $(\sigma^{(P)})$ have associated with themselves the jump frequencies k, $k^{(d)}$, and $k^{(P)}$, respectively, the corresponding permeability becomes

$$P = \frac{\lambda^2 \sigma^{(0)}(k + k^{(d)}K_1 + k^{(P)}K_2(P)^r)}{1 + K_1 + K_2(P)^r} \qquad (14.32)$$

Equation (14.31) exhibits the same effects of inactivation and poisoning on permeability which have previously been found affecting enzymes. Special experiments are thus required to tell whether a narcotic affects a nerve by modifying membrane permeability or by acting on an important enzyme. The modification of any intensive property such as temperature, pressure, potential gradient across the membrane, or a change of concentration of components, may modify the free energy change in any or all of the rate and equilibrium constants in equation (14.32).

If the process of adsorption of a substance on membranes is a cooperative one, (i.e., if adsorption facilitates the adsorption of still more), then a small variation in concentration may make the difference between almost no effect on the membrane and a complete transformation. In other words, under the right circumstances the membrane modification may take on the character of a phase change, as may be the case with nerve membranes. In this extreme case of a phase transition one associates a free energy change ΔF with the membrane transition impermeable $\rightarrow$ permeable. If ΔF is positive the membrane stays impermeable, becoming permeable when ΔF is negative. The degree of cooperation between sites fixes the sharpness of the membrane transition. In any case all changes in intensive properties will have a corresponding effect on ΔF and so bring about, or interfere with, the transition.

Sources of Illustrations

The following list gives the sources of previously published illustrations, reproduced by permission of living original authors and by permission of copyright owners. The sources of originally non-copyright illustrations and of data for figures which have been replotted in a different manner from the original are also listed. Figures that have been drawn from general knowledge or general principles are not listed.

All line drawings have been redrafted, and the relative dimensions of some have been altered from the originals in order to fit space requirements in this book.

Figure	*Source*
1.3	Eyring, Gershinowitz, and Sun, 1935. Jour. Chem. Phys., 3, p. 790, Fig. 3.
1.4A, B	Goodeve, 1934. Trans. Farad. Soc., 30. Line and stipple drawings made from photographs reproduced as Plates I and II, respectively, opposite p. 60.
1.6	Eyring and Magee, 1942. Jour. Cell. Comp. Physiol., 20, p. 174, Fig. 1.
1.7	Magee, Ri, and Eyring, 1941. Jour. Chem. Phys., 9, p. 422, Fig. 3.
1.10	Spikes, Lumry, Eyring, and Wayrynen, 1950. Proc. Nat. Acad. Sci., 36, p. 456, Fig. 1.
1.11	Spikes, 1950–51, Progress Report to Atomic Energy Commission, Contract No. AT(11–1)–82, Project No. 4, University of Utah, Fig. 9.
1.12	Benson, Kawachi, Hayes, and Calvin, 1952. Jour. Amer. Chem. Soc., 74, p. 4482 (Diagram in the text).
1.13	Spikes, 1950–51, Progress Report (cf. Fig. 1.11), Fig. 8.
1.14	Same, Fig. 12.
1.15	Spikes, 1950, to be published.
6.1	Altar and Eyring, 1936. Jour. Chem. Phys., 4, p. 661, Fig. 1.
6.2	Same, p. 661, Fig. 2.
6.3	Same, p. 664, Fig. 3.
6.4	Same, p. 665, Fig. 4.
6.5	Same, p. 666, Fig. 5.
6.6	Same, p. 668, Fig. 6.
6.7	Same, p. 668, Fig. 7.
7.1	Anderson, 1936. Jour. Cell. Comp. Physiol., 8, p. 268, Fig. 1.
7.3	Spruit, 1949. Enzymologia, 13, p. 196, Fig. 7.
7.4	Chase, 1943. Jour. Biol. Chem., 150, p. 442, Fig. 5.
7.5	van der Burg, 1943. Dissertation, p. 50, Fig. 18.
7.6	Spruit-van der Burg, 1950. Biochim. Biophys. Acta (Elsevier Publishing Co., New York–Amsterdam), 5, p. 177, Fig. 2.
7.8	Gaydon, 1950. Dissociation Energies and Spectra of Diatomic Molecules, Dover Publications, New York, p. 39, Fig. 5.
7.9	van der Burg, 1943. Dissertation, p. 60, Fig. 21b.
7.11A	Eyring, Walter, and Kimball, 1944. Quantum Chemistry, John Wiley & Sons, p. 327, Fig. 16.10.

Figure	Source
7.11B	Eyring, Walter, and Kimball, 1944. Quantum Chemistry, John Wiley & Sons, p. 327, Fig. 16.11.
7.12	Chase, 1945. Jour. Cell. Comp. Physiol., 25, p. 58, Fig. 3.
7.13	Same, p. 60, Fig. 4.
7.14	Chase, 1948. Jour. Cell. Comp. Physiol., 31, p. 179, Fig. 2.
7.16	van der Burg, 1943. Dissertation, p. 61, Fig. 22.
7.20A	Chase, 1949. Arch. Biochem., 23, p. 388, Fig. 1.
7.20B	Chase, 1950. Jour. Gen. Physiol., 33, p. 537, Fig. 1B.
7.21	Chase, 1949. Arch. Biochem., 23, p. 390, Fig. 2.
7.23	Johnson, van Schouwenburg, and van der Burg, 1939. Enzymologia, 7, p. 205, Fig. 9, and p. 206, Fig. 10.
8.1	Brown, Johnson, and Marsland, 1942. Jour. Cell. Comp. Physiol., 20, p. 156, Fig. 2.
8.2	D'Arcy Thompson, 1942. On Growth and Form, Cambridge University Press, p. 218, Fig. 62.
8.3	Monod, 1942. Recherches sur la croissance des cultures Bactériennes, Hermann et Cie, Paris, p. 109, Fig. 24.
8.4	Gray, 1928. British Jour. Exp. Biol., 6, p. 129, Fig. 2.
8.5	Ephrussi and Herold, 1945. Genetics, 30, p. 66, Fig. 2.
8.6	Terao and Tanaka, 1930. Jour. Imp. Fisheries Inst. Japan, 25, p. 67, Table I.
8.7	Buchanan and Fulmer, 1930 (from Blackman, 1905). Physiology and Biochemistry of Bacteria, Williams & Wilkins Co., Baltimore, Vol. 2, p. 76, Fig. 13.
8.8	Arrhenius, 1915 (data of Kjeldahl, 1881). Quantitative Laws in Biological Chemistry, G. Bell & Sons, Ltd., London, p. 57, Fig. 12d.
8.9	Hoagland and Perkins, 1934–35. Jour. Gen. Physiol., 18, p. 407, Fig. 5.
8.10	Crozier, 1924–25. Jour. Gen. Physiol., 7, p. 133, Fig. 6.
8.11	Same, p. 131, Fig. 5.
8.12	Same, p. 126, Fig. 2.
8.13	Morrison, 1924–25. Jour. Gen. Physiol., 7, p. 749, Fig. 3.
8.14	Buchanan and Fulmer, 1930. Physiology and Biochemistry of Bacteria. Williams & Wilkins Co., Baltimore, Vol. 2, p. 46, Fig. 5.
8.15	Crozier, 1924–25. Jour. Gen. Physiol., 7, p. 206, Fig. 12.
8.16	Same, p. 197, Fig. 5.
8.17	Sizer, 1942. Food Research, 7, p. 203, Fig. 1.
8.18	Same, p. 207, Fig. 3.
8.19	Morales, 1947. Jour. Cell. Comp. Physiol., 30, p. 304, Fig. 1.
8.20	Sizer, 1941. Jour. Bact., 41, 515, Fig. 2.
8.21	Sizer, 1939. Jour. Gen. Physiol., 22, 732, Fig. 5.
8.22	Hadidian and Hoagland, 1940. Jour. Gen. Physiol., 23, p. 96, Fig. 5.
8.23	Hoagland, 1936. Amer. Jour. Physiol., 116, p. 606, Fig. 6.
8.24	Johnson, Eyring, and Williams, 1942. Jour. Cell. Comp. Physiol., 20, p. 257. Data of Fig. 2B, with calculated curve in place of original one drawn by inspection.
8.25	Same, data of Fig. 2C.
8.26	Koffler, Johnson, and Wilson, 1947. Jour. Amer. Chem. Soc., 69, p. 1115. Control curves replotted from data of Figs. 1 and 2.
8.27	Johnson and Lewin, 1946. Jour. Cell. Comp. Physiol., 28, p. 59, Fig. 9.

Figure	Source
8.28	Johnson and Lewin, 1946. Jour. Cell. Comp. Physiol., **28**, p. 60, Fig. 10.
8.29	Same, p. 61, Fig. 11; the points and curve for rate of growth in quinine omitted.
8.30	Hedén and Wyckoff, 1949. Jour. Bact., **58**, p. 155, Fig. 3; p. 156, Fig. 6; p. 157, Fig. 7; and p. 159, Fig. 11. Prints from the original EMG plates arranged together for Fig. 8.30.
8.31	Johnson, Eyring, et al., 1945. Jour. Gen. Physiol., **28**, p. 502, Fig. 21.
8.32	Same, p. 503, Fig. 22.
8.33	Same, p. 504, Fig. 23.
8.34	Chase, 1950. Jour. Gen. Physiol., **33**, p. 539, Fig. 3A.
8.35	Wright and Schomaker, 1948. Jour. Amer. Chem. Soc., 70, p. 358, Fig. 8.
8.36	Chase, 1950. Jour. Gen. Physiol., **33**, p. 541, Fig. 4.
8.37	Same, p. 543, Fig. 5.
8.38	Kunitz, 1948. Jour. Gen. Physiol., **32**, p. 248, Fig. 2.
8.39	Same, p. 248, Fig. 3a.
8.40	Same, p. 253, Fig. 5b.
8.41	Same, p. 258, Fig. 6.
8.42	Field, Fuhrman, and Martin, 1944. Jour. Neurophysiol., **7**, p. 122, data of Fig. 4 replotted on a logarithmic scale of the ordinate.
8.43A	Redrawn from Astbury, 1941. Jour. Soc. Chem. Indus., **60**, p. 494, Fig. 3.
8.43B	Same, p. 491 (diagram).
8.43C	Same, p. 491 (diagram).
8.43D, E	Pauling, Corey, and Branson, 1951. Proc. Nat. Acad. Sci., **37**, p. 207, Figs. 2 and 3.
8.44	Bull, 1945. Jour. Amer. Chem. Soc., **67**, p. 5, Fig. 2.
8.45	Bodine and Allen, 1938. Jour. Cell. Comp. Physiol., **12**, p. 75, Fig. 3.
8.46	Same, p. 79, Fig. 8.
8.47	Boyer, Lum, Ballou, Luck, and Rice., 1946. Jour. Biol. Chem., **162**, p. 183, Fig. 1.
8.48	Boyer, Ballou, and Luck, 1946. Jour. Biol. Chem., **162**, p. 201, Fig. 2.
8.49	Casey and Laidler, 1951. Jour. Amer. Chem. Soc., **73**, p. 1456, Fig. 4.
8.50	Steinhardt, 1937. Det. Kgl. Danske Videnskabernes Selskab-Math-Fys. Meddeleser, **14**, p. 17, Fig. 1.
8.51	Same, p. 21, Fig. 2.
8.52	Lauffer, 1943. Jour. Amer. Chem. Soc., **65**, p. 1798, Fig. 4.
8.53	Same, p. 1800, Fig. 5.
8.54	Jacobsen and Christensen, 1948. Nature, **161**, p. 30, Fig. 1.
8.55	Same, p. 30, Fig. 2.
8.56	Foster, Johnson, and Miller, 1949. Jour. Gen. Physiol., **33**, p. 9, Fig. 6.
9.1	Lauffer and Dow, 1941. Jour. Biol. Chem., **140**, p. 514, Fig. 1.
9.2	Matthews, Dow, and Anderson, 1940. Jour. Biol. Chem., **135**, p. 701, Fig. 3.
9.3	Same, p. 702, Fig. 4.
9.4	Curl and Jansen, 1950. Jour. Biol. Chem., **184**, p. 148, Fig. 1.
9.5	Same, p. 49, Fig. 3.
9.6	Curl and Jansen, 1950. Jour. Biol. Chem., **185**, p. 715, Fig. 1.
9.7	Same, p. 716, Fig. 2.
9.8	Brown, Johnson, and Marsland, 1942. Jour. Cell. Comp. Physiol., **20**, p. 161, Fig. 5.

Figure	*Source*
9.9	Brown, D. E. S. Previously unpublished; by courtesy of Professor Brown.
9.10	Johnson, Eyring, et al., 1945. Jour. Gen. Physiol., **28**, 487, Fig. 14.
9.11	Edwards and Brown, 1934. Jour. Cell. Comp. Physiol., **5**, 14, Fig. 6.
9.12	Landau and Marsland, 1952. Jour. Cell. Comp. Physiol., **40**, 374, Fig. 2.
9.13	Same, p. 376, Fig. 3A.
9.14	Same, p. 372, Fig. 1.
9.15	Pease and Kitching, 1939. Jour. Cell. Comp. Physiol., **14**, p. 138, Fig. 2.
9.17	Same, p. 137, Fig. 1.
9.19	Benthaus, 1941–42. Biochem. Zeitschr., **311**, p. 113, Fig. 3.
9.20	Johnson and Campbell, 1946. Jour. Biol. Chem., **163**, p. 694, Fig. 4.
9.21	Johnson, Baylor, and Fraser, 1948. Arch. Biochem., **19**, p. 241, Figs. 2 and 3.
9.22	Same, p. 242, Fig. 4.
9.23	Eyring, Johnson, and Gensler, 1946. Jour. Phys. Chem., **50**, p. 458, Fig. 4.
9.24	Same, p. 459, Fig. 5.
9.25	Foster, Johnson, and Miller, 1949. Jour. Gen. Physiol., **33**, p. 6, Fig. 3.
9.26	Linderstrøm-Lang, 1950. Cold Spr. Harb. Symp., **14**, p. 119, Fig. 1.
9.27	Chantrenne, Linderstrøm-Lang, and Vandendriessche, 1947. Nature, p. 877, Fig. 2.
9.28	Same, Fig. 3.
9.29	Curl and Jansen, 1950. Jour. Biol. Chem., **185**, p. 719, Fig. 3.
9.30	Heilbrunn, 1924. Amer. Jour. Physiol., **68**, p. 647, Fig. 1.
9.31	Marsland, 1942. The Structure of Protoplasm, Iowa State College Press, Ames, p. 132, Fig. 2.
9.32	Pease, 1940. Jour. Cell. Comp. Physiol., **16**, p. 371, Plate I.
9.33	Marsland and Brown, 1936. Jour. Cell. Comp. Physiol., **8**, p. 171, Fig. 4.
9.34	Marsland, 1942. The Structure of Protoplasm, Iowa State College Press, Ames, p. 142, Fig. 6.
9.35	Marsland, 1938. Jour. Cell. Comp. Physiol., **12**, p. 59, Fig. 1.
9.36	Marsland, 1950. Jour. Cell. Comp. Physiol., **36**, p. 215, Fig. 4.
9.37	Same, p. 220, Fig. 6.
9.38	Johnson and Lewin, 1946. Jour. Cell. Comp. Physiol., **28**, p. 188, Fig. 12.
9.39	ZoBell and Oppenheimer, 1950. Jour. Bact., **60**, p. 776, Fig. 3.
9.40	Fleming, Voureka, Kramer, and Hughes, 1950. Jour. Gen. Microbiol., **4**, p. 268, Figs. 1 and 2.
9.41	Foster and Johnson, 1951. Jour. Gen. Physiol., **34**, p. 544, Fig. 12.
10.1	Johnson, 1948. Sci. Mon., **47**, p. 232, Fig. 9.
10.2	Johnson and Chase, 1942. Jour. Cell. Comp. Physiol., **20**, p. 153, Fig. 1.
10.3	Johnson and Moore, 1941. Proc. Soc. Exp. Biol. Med., **48**, p. 324, Fig. 1.
10.4	Johnson, Brown, and Marsland, 1942. Science, **95**, p. 201, Fig. 1.
10.5	Johnson, Eyring, et al., 1945. Jour. Gen. Physiol., **28**, p. 492, Fig. 17.
10.6	Same, p. 493, Fig. 19.
10.7	Same, p. 494, Fig. 20.
10.8	Quastel and Wooldridge, 1928. Biochem. Jour., **22**, p. 696, Fig. 1.
10.9	Same, p. 696, Fig. 2.
10.11	Johnson, Eyring, et al., 1945. Jour. Gen. Physiol., **28**, p. 484, Fig. 11.
10.12	Same, p. 483, Fig. 10.
10.13	Chase, 1948. Jour. Cell. Comp. Physiol., **31**, 183, Fig. 5.
10.14	Steinhardt, Fugitt, and Harris, 1941. Jour. Res. Nat. Bur. Stand., **26**, p. 299, Fig. 1.

Figure	*Source*
10.15	Steinhardt and Zaiser, 1950. Jour. Biol. Chem., **183**, p. 794, Fig. 3.
10.16	Johnson, Eyring, et al., 1945. Jour. Gen. Physiol., **28**, p. 485, Fig. 12.
10.17	Same, p. 486, Fig. 13.
10.18	Same, p. 489, Fig. 15.
10.19	Lee, Epstein, and Foley, 1943. Proc. Soc. Exp. Biol. Med., **53**, p. 246, Fig. 1.
10.20	Johnson and Lewin, 1947. Antonie van Leewenhoek, **12**, p. 182, Fig. 1D.
10.21	Johnson, Brown, and Marsland, 1942. Jour. Cell. Comp. Physiol., **20**, p. 271, Fig. 1.
10.22	Johnson, Eyring, et al., 1945. Jour. Gen. Physiol., **28**, p. 511, Fig. 31.
10.23	Same, p. 517, Fig. 35.
10.24	Same; new figure plotted from data of Fig. 31, p. 511.
10.25	Same, p. 518, Fig. 36.
10.26	Same; new figure plotted from data of Fig. 35, p. 517.
10.27	Same; new figure plotted from data of Fig. 31, p. 511, plus data of Fisher and Stearn, 1942, Jour. Cell. Comp. Physiol., **19**, p. 113, Fig. 1.
10.28	Clowes and Krahl, 1936. Jour. Gen. Physiol., **20**, p. 161, Fig. 8; Krahl and Clowes, 1936, *ibid.*, p. 175, Fig. 2.
10.29	Koffler, Johnson, and Wilson, 1947. Jour. Amer. Chem. Soc., **69**, p. 1115, Fig. 1.
10.30	Same, Fig. 2.
10.31	Johnson, Eyring, et al., 1945. Jour. Gen. Physiol., **28**, p. 519, Fig. 37.
10.32	Same, p. 521, Fig. 38.
10.33	Same, p. 522, Fig. 39.
10.34	Same, p. 523, Fig. 40.
10.35	Same, p. 524, Fig. 41.
10.36	Johnson, Flagler, Simpson, and McGeer, 1951. Jour. Cell. Comp. Physiol., **37**, p. 4, Fig. 1.
10.37	Same, p. 7, Fig. 3.
10.38	Same, p. 8, Fig. 4.
10.39	Same, p. 9, Fig. 5.
10.40	Johnson, Eyring, et al., 1945. Jour. Gen. Physiol., **28**, p. 505, Fig. 24.
10.41	Same, p. 506, Fig. 25.
10.42	Same, p. 507, Fig. 26.
10.43	Fraser, Johnson, and Baker, 1949. Arch. Biochem., **24**, p. 317, Fig. 2.
10.44	Johnson and Campbell, 1946. Jour. Biol. Chem., **163**, p. 695, Fig. 7.
10.45	Johnson, Eyring, et al., 1945. Jour. Gen. Physiol., **28**, p. 509, Fig. 28.
10.46	Data of Jowett, 1938. Jour. Physiol., **92**, p. 326, Fig. 2, replotted on logarithmic scale of the ordinate.
10.48	Johnson and Gray, 1949. Jour. Bact., **58**; portions of three figures: p. 678, Fig. 2; p. 684, Fig. 36; and p. 684, Fig. 39.
10.49	Chick, 1930. In; A System of Bacteriology in Relation to Medicine, Medical Research Council, London, **1**, p. 181, Fig. 1.
10.51	Same, data plotted from Table IV, p. 200.
10.52	Same, data plotted from Table II, p. 196.
10.53	Johnson and ZoBell, 1949. Jour. Bact., **57**, p. 361, Fig. 1.
10.54	Johnson, Eyring, and Kearns, 1943. Arch. Biochem., **3**, p. 18, Fig. 7.
10.55	Same, p. 17, Fig. 6.
10.56	Same, p. 15, Fig. 4.

Bibliography
and Author Index

(The number of the page, or of the pages, on which each bibliographic reference is cited in this book, is given in italics at the end of the reference. The bibliography includes a few references that are not specifically cited in the text. These references are to successive publications, bearing on the same subject, by authors of papers that are specifically cited in the text.)

Abbott, B. C., and D. R. Wilkie, 1953. The relation between velocity of shortening and the tension-length curve of skeletal muscle. J. Physiol., **120**: 214–223. *(753)*

Abraham, E. P. (See Chain, Florey, Abraham, and Heatley, 1949.)

Abramowitz, A. A., 1939. Color changes in animals. Tabulae Biologicae, **17**: 267–337. *(350)*

Adair, G. S. (See Roche, Roche, Adair, and Adair, 1932.)

Adair, G. S., and M. E. Adair, 1934a. The determination of the membrane potentials of protein solutions and the valence of protein ions. Biochem. Jour., **28**: 199–221. *(254)*

Adair, G. S., and M. E. Adair, 1934b. The determination of the isoelectric and isoionic points of hemoglobin from measurements of membrane potentials. Biochem. Jour., **28**: 1230–1258.

Adair, G. S., and M. E. Robinson, 1930. The analysis of the osmotic pressures of the serum proteins, and the molecular weights of albumins and globulins. Biochem. Jour., **24**: 1864–1889. *(253)*

Adair, M. E. (See Adair and Adair, 1934a, 1934b; Roche, Roche, Adair, and Adair, 1932.)

Adam, N. K., 1926. The structure of thin films. VII. Critical evaporation phenomena at low compressions. Proc. Roy. Soc. Lond., A **110**: 423–441. *(262)*

Adams, D. H., and R. H. S. Thompson, 1948. The selective inhibition of cholinesterases. Biochem. Jour., **42**: 170–175. *(489, 490, 493)*

Adrian, E. D., and K. Yamagiwa, 1935. The origin of the Berger rhythm. Brain, **58**: 323–351. *(214)*

Aeschlimann, J. A., and A. Stempel, 1946. Some Analogs of Prostigmin. Hoffmann-La Roche, Basle, Switzerland. Jubilee volume dedicated to Emil Barrell, pp. 306–313. *(490, 491)*

Akiyama, H. (See Tamamushi and Akiyama, 1938; 1939.)

Albrecht, H. O., 1928. Ueber die Chemiluminescenz des Aminophthalsäurehydrazids. Zeitschr. physik. Chem., **136**: 321–330. *(137, 164)*

Alder, M. G., and H. Eyring, 1952. Radiation-induced decomposition of certain organic molecules in solution. Nucleonics, **10**: 54–57. *(33)*

Alfrey, T., Jr., 1948. Mechanical Behavior of High Polymers. Interscience Publishers, New York. (*700*)

Allard, H. A. (See Giddings, Allard, and Hite, 1929.)

Allen, A. C. (See Bond, Swift, Allen, and Fishler, 1950.)

Allen, A. O., 1947. Effective radiation on materials. U.S. Atomic Energy Commission. Declassified Document No. MDDC 962, pp. 1–17, N.D. 520, 1947. (*32, 33*)

Allen, D. E. (See Collier and Allen, 1942.)

Allen, F. M. (See Crossman, Ruggiero, Hurley, and Allen, 1942.)

Allen, F. M., 1938. Resistance of peripheral tissues to asphyxia at various temperatures. Surg. Gynecol. Obstet., **67**: 746–751.   (*502*)

Allen, F. M., 1939. Surgical considerations of temperature in ligated limbs. Amer. Jour. Surg., **45**: 459–464.   (*502*)

Allen, F. M., 1941. Reduced temperatures in surgery. I. Surgery of limbs. Amer. Jour. Surg., **52**: 225–237.   (*502*)

Allen, F. M., 1942. Reduced temperatures in surgery. III. Experiments on pelvic and abdominal refrigeration with especial reference to traumatic and military surgery. Amer. Jour. Surg., **55**: 451–466.   (*502*)

Allen, F. M., 1943. Refrigeration anesthesia for limb operations. Anesthesiol., **4**: 12–16.   (*502*)

Allen, F. W., and J. J. Eiler, 1941. The action of crystalline ribonuclease on ribonucleic acid. Jour. Biol. Chem., **137**: 757–763.   (*341*)

Allen, T. H. (See Bodine and Allen, 1938; Bodine, Allen, and Boell, 1937.)

Altar, W., and H. Eyring, 1936. Absolute rates of four-atom reactions. Jour. Chem. Phys., **4**: 661–673.   (*103*)

Amberson, W. R., 1922. Kinetics of the bioluminescent reaction in *Cypridina*. Jour. Gen. Physiol., **4**: 517–534, 535–558.   (*174*)

Anderson, A. K. (See Matthews, Dow, and Anderson, 1940.)

Anderson, R. C. (See Chen, Anderson, Henderson, and Mills, 1943; Chen, Anderson, Steldt, and Mills, 1943.)

Anderson, R. S., 1933. The chemistry of bioluminescence. 1. Quantitative determination of luciferin. Jour. Cell. Comp. Physiol., **3**: 45–59.   (*127, 158*)

Anderson, R. S., 1935. Studies in bioluminescence. II. The partial purification of *Cypridina* luciferin. Jour. Gen. Physiol., **19**: 301–305.   (*127*)

Anderson, R. S., 1936. Chemical studies on bioluminescence. III. The reversible reaction of *Cypridina* luciferin with oxidizing agents and its relation to the luminescent reaction. Jour. Cell. Comp. Physiol., **8**: 261–276.   (*128, 129, 152, 172, 181*)

Anderson, R. S., 1937. Chemical studies of bioluminescence. IV. Salt effects on the total light emitted by a chemiluminescent reaction. Jour. Amer. Chem. Soc., **59**: 2115–2117.   (*153, 155, 157, 171*)

Anderson, T. F. (See Harkins and Anderson, 1938.)

Anson, M. L. (See Mirsky and Anson, 1929.)

Anson, M. L., 1944. Denaturation of proteins. In: C. L. A. Schmidt (Ed.), The Chemistry of the Amino Acids and Proteins, pp. 1115–1124. Charles C Thomas, Springfield, Ill.   (*252*)

Anson, M. L., 1945. Protein denaturation and the properties of protein groups. Adv. Protein Chem., **2**: 361–386.   (*217, 252*)

Anson, M. L., and A. E. Mirsky, 1931a. Protein coagulation and its reversal. Jour. Gen. Physiol., **14**: 725–732.   (*217*)

Anson, M. L., and A. E. Mirsky, 1931b. The reversibility of protein coagulation. Jour. Phys. Chem., **35**: 185–193.   (*217*)

Anson, M. L., and A. E. Mirsky, 1933–1934. The equilibrium between active native trypsin and inactive denatured trypsin. Jour. Gen. Physiol., **17**: 393–398.   (*216*)

Antopol, W. (See Glick and Antopol, 1939.)

Armstrong, C. W. J., and K. C. Fisher, 1940. A comparison of the effects of the respiratory inhibitors azide and cyanide on the frequency of the embryonic fish heart. Jour. Cell. Comp. Physiol., **16**: 103–112.   (*384, 417*)

Arnow, L. E., 1936. Effects produced by the irradiation of proteins and amino acids. Physiol. Rev., **16**: 671–685.   (*252*)

Arrhenius, S. (See Watson, Arrhenius, and Williams, 1936.)

Arrhenius, S., 1889. Über die Reaktionsgeschwindigkeit bei der Inversion von Rohrzucker durch Säuren. Zeitschr. physik. Chem., **4**: 226–248.   (*2*)

Arrhenius, S., 1907. Immunochemistry. The Macmillan Co., New York. (*197, 198, 199, 271, 272*)

Arrhenius, S., 1908. Immunochemie. Ergeb. Physiol., **7**: 480–551.   (*197*)

Arrhenius, S., 1915. Quantitative Laws in Biological Chemistry, G. Bell and Sons, Ltd., London.   (*1, 4, 197, 198, 199*)

Ashworth, J. N. (See Scatchard, Strong, Hughes, Ashworth, and Sparrow, 1945.)

Astbury, W. T., 1933. Some problems in the X-ray analysis of the structure of animal hairs and other protein fibres. Trans. Farad. Soc., **29**: 193–211.

Astbury, W. T., 1941. Jubilee Memorial Lecture. Proteins. Jour. Soc. Chem. Ind., **60**: 491–497.   (*257*)

Astbury, W. T., 1943. X-rays and the stoichiometry of proteins. Adv. Enzymol., **3**: 63–108.

Astbury, W. T., 1946. Progress of X-ray analysis of organic and fibre structures. Nature, **157**: 121–124.   (*30*)

Astbury, W. T., 1947. Croonian Lecture: On the structure of biological fibres and the problem of muscle. Proc. Roy. Soc. Lond., B **134**: 303–328. (*728, 730*)

Astbury, W. T., 1950. In: A discussion on muscular contraction and relaxation: their physical and chemical basis, pp. 58–63. Proc. Roy. Soc. Lond., B **137**: 40–87.   (*30, 704, 730*)

Astbury, W. T., and F. O. Bell, 1941. Nature of the intramolecular fold in alpha-keratin and alpha-myosin. Nature, **147**: 696–699.   (*256, 257*)

Astbury, W. T., C. E. Dalgliesh, S. E. Darmon, and G. B. B. M. Sutherland, 1948. Studies on the structure of synthetic polypeptides. Nature, **162**: 596–600. (*260*)

Astbury, W. T., and S. Dickinson, 1940. X-ray studies of the molecular structure of myosin. Proc. Roy. Soc. Lond., B **129**: 307–332.   (*257, 728*)

Astbury, W. T., S. Dickinson, and K. Bailey, 1935. The X-ray interpretation of denaturation and the structure of the seed globulins. Biochem. Jour., **29**: 2351–2360.   (*257*)

Astbury, W. T., and R. Lomax, 1935. An X-ray study of the hydration and denaturation of proteins. Jour. Chem. Soc., 846–851.   (*253, 254, 257*)

Astbury, W. T., R. Reed, and L. C. Spark, 1948. An X-ray and electron microscope study of tropomyosin. Biochem. Jour., **43**: 282–287.   (*752*)

Astbury, W. T., and W. A. Sisson, 1935. X-ray studies of the structure of hair, wool and related fibers. III. The configuration of the keratin molecule and its orientation in the biological cell. Proc. Roy. Soc. Lond., A 150: 533–551. (256)

Astbury, W. T., and H. J. Woods, 1934. X-ray studies of the structure of hair, wool and related fibres. II. The molecular structure and elastic properties of hair keratin. Trans. Roy. Soc. Lond., A 232: 333–394.

Bailey, K. (See Astbury, Dickinson, and Bailey, 1935.)

Bailey, K., 1948. Tropomyosin: A new asymmetric protein component of the muscle fibril. Biochem. Jour., 43: 271–279. (752)

Bailey, K., H. Gutfreund, and A. G. Ogston, 1948. Molecular weight of tropomyosin from rabbit muscle. Biochem. Jour., 43: 279–281. (753)

Bainbridge, F. A., and J. A. Menzies, 1929. Essentials of Physiology, Ed. by H. Hartridge. Longmans, Green and Co. (740)

Baker, R. S. (See Fraser, Johnson, and Baker, 1949.)

Baldwin, D. M. (See Krueger and Baldwin, 1934.)

Baldwin, E., 1948. Dynamic Aspects of Biochemistry. The Macmillan Co., New York. (137)

Ball, E. G., 1944. Energy relationships of the oxidative enzymes. Ann. N. Y. Acad. Sci., 45: 363–375. (375)

Ball, E. G., and P. A. Ramsdell, 1944. The flavin-adenine dinucleotide content of firefly lanterns. Jour. Amer. Chem. Soc., 66: 1419–1420. (135)

Ballentine, R. (See Chakravorty and Ballentine, 1941; McElroy and Ballentine, 1944.)

Ballou, G. A. (See Boyer, Ballou, and Luck, 1946, 1947; Boyer, Lum, Ballou, Luck, and Rice, 1946.)

Ballou, G. A., P. D. Boyer, and J. M. Luck, 1945. The electrophoretic mobility of human serum albumin as affected by lower fatty acid salts. Jour. Biol. Chem., 159: 111–116. (271)

Ballou, G. A., P. D. Boyer, J. M. Luck, and F. G. Lum, 1944. The heat coagulation of human serum albumin. Jour. Biol. Chem., 153: 589–605. (271)

Bancroft, W. D., and G. H. Richter, 1931. The chemistry of anesthesia. Jour. Phys. Chem., 35: 215–268. (450)

Barbour, H. G., 1936. Pharmacological action of inhalation anesthetics. Amer. Jour. Surgery, 34: 435–445. (484)

Barbu, E. (See Vignais, Barbu, Basset, and Macheboeuf, 1951.)

Bardach, M. (See Basset, Wollman, Macheboeuf, and Bardach, 1933, 1935; Wollman, Macheboeuf, Bardach, and Basset, 1936.)

Barker, H. A., 1936. The oxidative metabolism of the colorless alga, Prototheca Zopfii. Jour. Cell. Comp. Physiol., 8: 231–250. (397)

Barlund, H. (See Collander and Barlund, 1933.)

Barlund, H., 1938. Einfluss des Äthyläthers auf die Permeabilität der Chara-Zellen. Protoplasma, 30: 70–78. (500)

Barron, E. S. G., 1946. Effects of X-rays on tissue metabolism. Atomic Energy Commission. Declassified Document No. AECD-2316, pp. 1–22 (Declassified, Sept., 1948). (32)

Barron, E. S. G., 1951. Thiol groups of biological importance. Adv. Enzymol., 11: 201–266. (211)

Barron, E. S. G., and S. Dickman, 1949. Studies on the mechanism of action of ionizing radiations. II. Inhibition of sulfhydryl enzymes by alpha, beta and gamma rays. Jour. Gen. Physiol., **32**: 595–605.

Barron, E. S. G., S. Dickman, J. A. Muntz, and T. P. Singer, 1949. Studies on the mechanism of action of ionizing radiations. I. Inhibition of enzymes by X-rays. Jour. Gen. Physiol., **32**: 537–552. (*32*)

Barron, E. S. G., and T. P. Singer, 1943. Enzyme systems containing active sulfhydryl groups. The rôle of glutathione. Science, **97**: 356–358. (*252*)

Basset, J. (See Lepine, Basset, and Macheboeuf, 1936; Macheboeuf and Basset, 1934; Macheboeuf, Basset, and Levy, 1933; Vignais, Barbu, Basset, and Macheboeuf, 1951; Wollman, Macheboeuf, Bardach, and Basset, 1936.)

Basset, J., A. Gratia, M. Macheboeuf, and P. Manil, 1938. Action of high pressure on plant viruses. Proc. Soc. Exp. Biol. Med., **38**: 248–251. (*293*)

Basset, J., M. Lisbonne, and M. A. Macheboeuf, 1933. Action des ultra-pressions sur le suc pancréatique. Compt. rend. acad. sci., **196**: 1540–1542. (*292*)

Basset, J., and M. A. Macheboeuf, 1932. Étude sur les effets biologiques des ultrapressions: résistance des bactéries, des diastases et des toxines aux pressions très élevées. Compt. rend. acad. sci., **195**: 1431–1433. (*294*)

Basset, J., and M. A. Macheboeuf, 1933. Études sur les effets biologiques des ultrapressions. Études sur l'immunité: influence des pressions très élevées sur certains antigènes et anticorps. Compt. rend. acad. sci., **196**: 67–69. (*294*)

Basset, J., M. Macheboeuf, and J. J. Perez, 1935. Études sur les effets biologiques des ultra-pressions. Modification de la specificité antigénique des sérums sous l'influence des pressions très élevées. Compt. rend. acad. sci., **200**: 496–498. (*294*)

Basset, J., M. Macheboeuf, and G. Sandor, 1933. Études sur les effets biologiques des ultrapressions. Action des pressions très élevées sur les protéides. Compt. rend. acad. sci., **197**: 796–798. (*292*)

Basset, J., S. Nicolau, M. A. Macheboeuf, 1935. L'action de l'ultrapression sur l'activité pathologique de quelques virus. Compt. rend. acad. sci., **200**: 1882–1884. (*293*)

Basset, J., E. Wollman, M. A. Macheboeuf, and M. Bardach, 1933. Études sur les effets biologiques des ultra-pressions: action des pressions très élevées sur les bactériophages et sur un virus invisible (virus vaccinal). Compt. rend. acad. sci., **196**: 1138–1139. (*293, 294*)

Basset, J., E. Wollman, M. A. Macheboeuf, and M. Bardach, 1935. Études sur les effets biologiques des ultra-pressions: action des pressions élevées sur les tumeurs. Compt. rend. acad. sci., **200**: 1247–1248. (*294, 295*)

Basset, J., E. Wollman, Mme. E. Wollman, and M. A. Macheboeuf, 1935. Études sur les effets biologiques des ultra-pressions; action des pressions très élevées sur les bactériophages des spores et sur les autolysines. Compt. rend. acad. sci., **200**: 1072–1074. (*293, 294*)

Batelli, F., and L. Stearn, 1913a. Einfluss der Anaesthetica auf die Oxydone. Biochem. Zeitschr., **52**: 226–252. (*452*)

Batelli, F., and L. Stearn, 1913b. Einfluss der Aldehyde auf die Oxydone. Biochem. Zeitschr., **52**: 253–270.

Bateman, J. B. (See Chambers, Bateman, and Calkins, 1940.)

Bateman, J. B., 1945. Some properties of films and membranes. In: Hoeber (Ed.), Physical Chemistry of Cells and Tissues, pp. 187–216, Blakiston Co., Philadelphia. (260)

Bateman, J. B., and L. A. Chambers, 1939. "Surface Elasticity" of protein films. I. Egg albumin. Jour. Chem. Phys., 7: 244–250. (263)

Bateman, J. B., and L. A. Chambers, 1941. "Surface elasticity" of protein films. II. Properties of partially and of completely spread films. Jour. Phys. Chem., 45: 209–222. (263)

Bates, R. W. (See Gerlough and Bates, 1932.)

Baum, F., 1899. Zur Theorie der Alkoholnarkose. II. Ein physikalisch-chemische Beitrag zur Theorie der Narkotika. Arch. exp. Path. Pharm., 42: 119–137. (508)

Baumberger, J. P., 1917. Hibernation: a periodical phenomenon. Ann. Entomol. Soc. Amer., 10: 179–186. (269)

Bawden, F. C., and N. W. Pirie, 1940. The inactivation of some plant viruses by urea. Biochem. Jour., 34: 1258–1275. (282, 284)

Baylor, M. B. (See Johnson, Baylor and Fraser, 1948.)

Beamer, P. R., and F. W. Tanner, 1939. Heat resistance studies on selected yeasts. Zentr. Bakt. Parasitenk. Infek., II, 100: 202–211. (455)

Bear, R. S. (See Schmitt, Bear, Hall, and Jakus, 1947.)

Beauvallet, M., 1937. Inversions des effets d'une substance contracturante par une autre substance contracturante. Compt. rend. soc. biol., 124: 727–729. (351)

Becquerel, P., 1910. Recherches expérimentelles sur la vie latente des spores des Mucorinées et des Ascomycètes. Compt. rend. acad. sci., 150: 1437–1439. (187)

Becquerel, P., 1925. La suspension de la vie des graines dans le vide a la température de l'hélium liquid. Compt. rend. acad. sci., 181: 805–807. (187)

Becquerel, P., 1929. La vie latente des grains de pollen dans le vide à 271°C au-dessous de zéro. Compt. rend. acad. sci., 188: 1308–1310. (187)

Becquerel, P., 1932. La vie latente des spores des Mousses aux basses températures. Compt. rend. acad. sci., 194: 1378–1380. (187)

Becquerel, P., 1936. La vie latente de quelques Algues et animaux inférieurs aux basses températures et la conservation de la vie dans l'univers. Compt. rend. acad. sci., 202: 978–981. (188)

Beijerinck, M. W., 1916. Die Leuchtbakterien der Nordsee im August und September. Folio Microbiol., 4: 1–26. (218)

Beijerinck, M. W., and H. C. Jacobsen, 1908. Influence des températures absolues de 82 et 20 degrés centigrades sur la vitalité des microbes. Verzamelde Geschriften van M. W. Beijerinck, 4: 324–332. Delft, 1921. (187)

Bělehrádek, J., 1930. Temperature coefficients in biology. Biol. Rev. Proc. Camb. Phil. Soc., 5: 30–58. (197, 214)

Bělehrádek, J., 1935. Temperature and Living Matter. Gebrüder Borntraeger, Berlin. (214, 345, 381)

Bell, F. O. (See Astbury and Bell, 1941.)

Bell, P. H., and R. O. Roblin, 1942. Studies in chemotherapy. VII. A theory of the relation of structure to activity of sulfanilamide-type compounds. Jour. Amer. Chem. Soc., 64: 2905–2917. (401)

Benaglia, A. E. (See Levy and Benaglia, 1950.)

Bengen, F., 1940. German patent application o.z. 12438 (March 18, 1940); Technical Oil Mission, Reel 6, frames 263–270 in German; Reel 143, pp. 135–139 in English. (*483*)

Bengen, F., and W. Schlenk, 1949. Über neuartige Additionsverbindungen des Harnstoffs. Experientia, **5**: 200. (*483*)

Bennett, L. R. (See Dowdy, Bennett, and Chastain, 1950.)

Benson, A. A., S. Kawachi, P. Hayes, and M. Calvin, 1952. The path of carbon in photosynthesis. XVI. Kinetic relationships of the intermediates in steady state photosynthesis. Jour. Amer. Chem. Soc., **74**: 4477–4482. (*37, 38*)

Benthaus, J., 1937. Über den Einfluss hoher Drucke auf Gewebekulturen. Pflüg. Arch. ges. Physiol., **239**: 107–119. (*295*)

Benthaus, J., 1941–1942. Ueber den Einfluss hoher komprimierender Drucke auf die Wirkung von Verdauungsfermenten. Biochem. Zeitschr., **311**: 108–118. (*313, 315, 325*)

Berger, H., 1929. Über das Elektrenkephalogramm des Menschen. Arch. Psychiat. Nervenkr., **87**: 527–570. (*214*)

Berger, J. (See Lehr and Berger, 1949.)

Bernal, J. D., and R. H. Fowler, 1933. A theory of water and ionic solution, with particular reference to hydrogen and hydroxyl ions. Jour. Chem. Phys., **1**: 515–548. (*304*)

Bernard, Claude, 1875. Leçons sur les anaesthesiques et sur l'asphixie. Librairie J.-B. Balliere et Fils, Paris. (*452, 484, 486*)

Bernfeld, P. (See Meyer and Bernfeld, 1945a, b.)

Bernstein, J., 1902. Untersuchungen zur Thermodynamik der bioelektrischen Ströme. Pflüg. Arch. ges. Physiol., **92**: 521–562. (*621, 625*)

Berry, J. A., and C. A. Magoon, 1934. Growth of micro-organisms at and below 0°. Phytopath., **24**: 780–796. (*188*)

Bessey, C. A., and E. A. Bessey, 1898. Further notes on thermometer crickets. Amer. Nat., **32**: 263–264. (*201*)

Bessey, E. A. (See Bessey and Bessey, 1898.)

Bibra, E., and E. Harless, 1847. Die Wirkung des Schwefeläthers in chemischer und physiologischer Beziehung. Erlangen (cf. Winterstein, 1926). (*508*)

Bigger, J. W., 1944. Treatment of staphylococcal infections with penicillin. Lancet, **247**: 497–500. (*404*)

Bilinsky, B. M. (See Schmitt, Skow, and Bilinsky, 1936.)

Binz, C., 1877. Zur Wirkungsweise schlafmachender Stoffe. Arch. exp. Path. Pharm., **6**: 310–317. (*452*)

Binz, C., 1880. Aphorismen und Versuche über schlafmachende Stoffe. Arch. exp. Path. Pharm., **13**: 157–168.

Birstein, G. (See Paul, Birstein, and Reuss, 1910.)

Blackman, F. F., 1905. Optima and limiting factors. Ann. Bot., **19**: 281–295. (*194, 195, 196*)

Blackman, F. F., and G. Matthaei, 1905. Experimental researches in vegetable assimilation and respiration. IV. A quantitative study of carbon-dioxide assimilation and leaf temperature in natural illumination. Proc. Roy. Soc. Lond., B **76**: 402–460. (*195*)

Blair, E. A. (See Erlanger and Blair, 1931.)

Blair, H. A., 1932. On the intensity-time relations for stimulation by electric currents. Jour. Gen. Physiol., **15**: 709–729. (*623*)

Blanchard, M. H.   (See Cohn, McMeekin, Edsall, and Blanchard, 1934.)

Blinks, L. R., and M. L. J. Darsie, 1936–1937.   Effects of oxygen tension and temperature change on the bioelectric potential of Halicystis.   Proc. Soc. Exp. Biol. Med., **35**: 522–524.   (*502*)

Blix, M., 1895.   Die Länge und die Spannung des Muskels.   Skand. Arch. Physiol., **5**: 150–206.   (*728, 730*)

Block, E.   (See Rona and Block, 1921.)

Blodgett, K. B., 1934.   Monomolecular films of fatty acids on glass.   Jour. Amer. Chem. Soc., **56**: 495.   (*265*)

Blodgett, K. B., and I. Langmuir, 1937.   Built-up films of barium stearate and their optical properties.   Phys. Rev., **51**: 964–982.   (*265*)

Blout, E. R.   (See Uzman and Blout, 1950.)

Blumenthal, G.   (See Mazia and Blumenthal, 1948.)

Bodansky, O.   (See Mazur and Bodansky, 1946.)

Bodine, J. H., 1945a.   Action of $HgCl_2$ upon variously activated tyrosinase.   Arch. Biochem., **6**: 479.   (*267*)

Bodine, J. H., 1945b.   Tyrosinase and phenols.   Action of diversely activated tyrosinase on monohydric and *o*-dihydric phenols.   Proc. Soc. Exp. Biol. Med., **58**: 205–209.   (*267*)

Bodine, J. H., and T. H. Allen, 1938.   Enzymes in ontogenesis (Orthoptera).   V. Further studies on the activation of the enzyme, tyrosinase.   Jour. Cell. Comp. Physiol., **12**: 71–84.   (*267, 268, 269*)

Bodine, J. H., T. H. Allen, and E. J. Boell, 1937.   Enzymes in ontogenesis (Orthoptera).   III. Activation of naturally occurring enzymes (tyrosinase).   Proc. Soc. Exp. Biol. Med., **37**: 450–453.   (*267*)

Bodine, J. H., and L. R. Fitzgerald, 1949.   Effect of urea, thiourea, phenylthiourea and thiouracil on the oxygen consumption of blocked and active embryonic cells.   Biol. Bull., **96**: 1–8.   (*268*)

Bodine, J. H., J. Hall, and L. D. Carlson, 1940.   Enzymes in ontogenesis (Orthoptera).   X. The effects of temperature on the activity of the naturally occurring and other activators of protyrosinase.   Jour. Cell. Comp. Physiol., **16**: 71–83.   (*267*)

Bodine, J. H., and D. L. Hill, 1945.   The action of synthetic detergents on protyrosinase.   Arch. Biochem., **7**: 21–32.   (*267*)

Bodine, J. H., and T. N. Tahmisian, 1943.   The effect of heavy metals on the activation and injury of the enzyme tyrosinase.   Arch. Biochem., **2**: 403–411.   (*267*)

Bodine, J. H., T. N. Tahmisian, and D. L. Hill, 1944.   Effect of heat on protyrosinase.   Heat activation and injury of protyrosinase and tyrosinase.   Arch. Biochem., **4**: 402–412.   (*267*)

Boell, E. J.   (See Bodine, Allen, and Boell, 1937.)

Boell, E. J., and D. Nachmansohn, 1940.   Localization of choline esterase in nerve fibers.   Science, **92**: 513–514.   (*497*)

de Boer, R. B.   (See Cohen and de Boer, 1913.)

Böttger, I.   (See Fischer, Böttger, and Lehmann-Echternacht, 1942.)

Bohr, N., 1913.   On the constitution of atoms and molecules.   Phil. Mag. (6) **26**: 1–25, 476–502, 857–875.   (*63*)

Bond, V. P., M. N. Swift, A. C. Allen, and M. C. Fishler, 1950.   Sensitivity of abdomen of rat to x-radiation.   Amer. Jour. Physiol., **161**: 323–330.   (*32*)

Bonner, J. T., W. W. Clarke, Jr., C. L. Neely, Jr., and M. K. Slifkin, 1950. The orientation to light and the extremely sensitive orientation to temperature gradients in the slime mold Dictyostelium discoideum. Jour. Cell. Comp. Physiol., **36**: 149–158.   (*188*)

Bonner, W. D., W. L. Gore, and D. M. Yost, 1935. The thermal reaction between gaseous iodine monochloride and hydrogen. Jour. Amer. Chem. Soc., **57**: 2723–2724.   (*114, 121*)

Booij, H. L., and H. P. Wolvekamp, 1944. Catenary processes, master reactions and limiting factors. Bibliotheca Biotheoretica, Series D, **1**: 145–224. (*207*)

Booth, N., 1930. The denaturation of proteins. VII. Denaturation in the presence of alcohol. Biochem. Jour., **24**: 1699–1705.   (*275*)

Borrowman, S. R., 1950. Kinetics of the formic dehydrogenase system. Dissertation. University of Utah.   (*315, 332*)

Botts, J., F. H. Johnson, and M. F. Morales, 1951. The behavior of free-weighted actomyosin threads under pressure. Jour. Cell. Comp. Physiol., **37**: 247–254. (*512*)

Bowers, J. Z.   (See Warren and Bowers, 1950.)

Bowman, K. M.   (See Himwich, Bowman, Fazekas, and Goldfarb, 1940.)

Boyarsky, L. L., A. D. Rosenblad, S. Postel, and R. W. Gerard, 1949. Action of methyl fluoroacetate on respiration and potential of nerve. Amer. Jour. Physiol., **157**: 291–298.   (*508*)

Boyarsky, L. L., J. M. Tobias, and R. W. Gerard, 1947. Nerve conduction after inactivation of choline esterase. Proc. Soc. Exp. Biol. Med., **64**: 106–108. (*496, 498*)

Boyer, P. D.   (See Ballou, Boyer, and Luck, 1945; Ballou, Boyer, Luck, and Lum, 1944.)

Boyer, P. D., G. A. Ballou, and J. M. Luck, 1946. The combination of fatty acids and related compounds with serum albumin. V. Stabilization against urea and guanidine denaturation. Jour. Biol. Chem., **162**: 199–208.   (*271*)

Boyer, P. D., G. A. Ballou, and J. M. Luck, 1947. The combination of fatty acids and related compounds with serum albumin. Jour. Biol. Chem., **167**: 407–424.   (*270, 271*)

Boyer, P. D., F. G. Lum, G. A. Ballou, J. M. Luck, and R. G. Rice, 1946. The combination of fatty acids and related compounds with serum albumin. I. Stabilization against heat denaturation. Jour. Biol. Chem., **162**: 181–198. (*270, 271*)

Boyle, Robert, 1667. Concerning the relation between light and air (in shining wood and fish). Phil. Trans. Roy. Soc. Lond., **2**: Number 31, 581–600. (*124*)

Bozler, E., 1930. The heat production of smooth muscle. Jour. Physiol., **69**: 442–462.   (*740, 741*)

Branson, H. R.   (See Pauling, Corey, and Branson, 1951.)

Brazier, M. A. B., 1951. The Electrical Activity of the Nervous System. The Macmillan Co., New York.   (*604, 684*)

Bresler, S. E., 1947. The principle of enzymic synthesis under pressure. Compt. rend. acad. sci. U.R.S.S., **55**: 141–143.   (*292, 336*)

Bridgman, P. W., 1912. Water, in the liquid and five solid forms, under pressure. Proc. Amer. Acad. Arts Sci., **47**: 441–558.   (*304*)

Bridgman, P. W., 1914. The coagulation of albumen by pressure. Jour. Biol. Chem., **19**: 511–512. (*292*)

Bridgman, P. W., 1931. The Physics of High Pressure. G. Bell and Sons, Ltd., London. (*290*)

Bridgman, P. W., 1946. Recent work in the field of high pressures. Revs. Mod. Phys., **18**: 1–93. (*290*)

Bridgman, P. W., and J. B. Conant, 1929. Irreversible transformations of organic compounds under high pressures. Proc. Nat. Acad. Sci., **15**: 680–683. (*292*)

Briggs, G. E., and J. B. S. Haldane, 1925. A note on the kinetics of enzyme action. Biochem. Jour., **19**: 338–339. (*176*)

Brigham, E. H. (See Chase and Brigham, 1951; Kauzmann, Chase, and Brigham, 1949.)

Brink, F., and J. M. Posternak, 1948. Thermodynamic analysis of the relative effectiveness of narcotics. Jour. Cell. Comp. Physiol., **32**: 211–234. (*429, 432*)

Bronk, J. R., E. N. Harvey, and F. H. Johnson, 1952. The effects of hydrostatic pressure on luminescent extracts of the ostracod crustacean, *Cypridina*. Jour. Cell. Comp. Physiol., **40**: 347–365. (*314*)

Brooks, G., 1940. Observations sur la phosphorescence des trois derniers anneaux du ver luisant. Compt. rend. acad. sci., **210**: 228–230. (*135*)

Brooks, S. C., 1918. A theory of the mechanism of disinfection, hemolysis, and similar processes. Jour. Gen. Physiol., **1**: 61–80. (*455*)

Brooks, V. B., R. E. Ransmeier, and R. W. Gerard, 1949. Action of anticholinesterases, drugs and intermediates on respiration and electrical activity of the isolated frog brain. Amer. Jour. Physiol., **157**: 299–316. (*498, 508*)

Brown, D. E. (See Edwards and Brown, 1934; Johnson, Brown, and Marsland, 1942a, 1942b; Marsland and Brown, 1936, 1942; Shanes and Brown, 1942.)

Brown, D. E., 1934a. The pressure coefficient of "viscosity" in the eggs of *Arbacia punctulata*. Jour. Cell. Comp. Physiol., **5**: 335–346. (*290, 350, 352*)

Brown, D. E., 1934b. The pressure-tension-temperature relation in cardiac muscle. Amer. Jour. Physiol., **109**: 16. (*290, 307, 308, 311*)

Brown, D. E., 1934–1935. Cellular reactions to high hydrostatic pressure. Annual Report of Tortugas Laboratory, Carnegie Institution of Washington, pp. 76, 77, issued Dec. 13, 1935. (*290, 307, 308, 311*)

Brown, D. E., 1936. The sequence of events in the isometric twitch at high pressure. Cold Spr. Harb. Symp., **4**: 242–251. (*309*)

Brown, D. E., F. H. Johnson, and D. A. Marsland, 1942. The pressure-temperature relations of bacterial luminescence. Jour. Cell. Comp. Physiol., **20**: 151–168. (*25, 190, 215, 219, 309, 310, 312, 319, 326*)

Brown, D. E., and D. A. Marsland, 1936. The viscosity of *Amoeba* at high hydrostatic pressure. Jour. Cell. Comp. Physiol., **8**: 159–165. (*352*)

Buchanan, R. E. (See Fulmer and Buchanan, 1923.)

Buchanan, R. E., and E. I. Fulmer, 1930. Physiology and Biochemistry of Bacteria, Vol. II. Effects of Environment upon Microörganisms. Williams & Wilkins Co., Baltimore, Md. (*194, 195, 204*)

Buchner, E., 1897. Alkoholische Gärung ohne Hefezellen. Ber. deutsch. chem. Gesellsch., **30**: 117–124. (*289*)

Buchner, H., 1897. Die Bedeutung der activen löslichen Zellproducte für den Chemismus der Zelle. Münch. med. Wschr., **44**: 299–302. (*289*)

Buchthal, F., 1942. The mechanical properties of the single striated muscle fibre at rest and during contraction and their structural interpretation. Det. Kgl. Danske Videnskabernes Selskab-Biologiske Meddelelser, **17**: 1–140. (*728*)

Buchthal, F., and E. Kaiser, 1948. Communication to the VI Physiological Congress, Oslo, August, 1948. (*705*)

Buchthal, F., and E. Kaiser, 1949. Optimum mechanical conditions for the work of skeletal muscle. Acta psychiat. Neurolog., **24**: 333–352. (*737*)

Buchthal, F., and E. Kaiser, 1951. The rheology of the cross striated muscle fibre. Det. Kgl. Danske Videnskabernes Selskab-Biologiske Meddelelser, **21**: 1–318. (*705*)

Bull, H. B. (See Neurath and Bull, 1938.)

Bull, H. B., 1938a. Protein denaturation. Cold Spr. Harb. Symp., **6**: 140–149. (*263*)

Bull, H. B., 1938b. Monolayers of denatured egg albumin. Jour. Biol. Chem., **125**: 585–598. (*261, 263, 264*)

Bull, H. B., 1940. Viscosity of solutions of denatured and of native egg albumin. Jour. Biol. Chem., **133**: 39–49. (*253*)

Bull, H. B., 1945a. Monolayers of egg albumin on concentrated salt solutions. Jour. Amer. Chem. Soc., **67**: 4–8. (*262, 263, 264*)

Bull, H. B., 1945b. Monolayers of β-lactoglobulin on concentrated salt solutions. Jour. Amer. Chem. Soc., **67**: 8–10. (*264*)

Bull, H. B., 1946. Monolayers of β-lactoglobulin. II. Film molecular weight. Jour. Amer. Chem. Soc., **68**: 745–747. (*263, 264*)

Bull, H. B., 1947. Spread monolayers of protein. Adv. Protein Chem., **3**: 95–121. (*252, 260, 262*)

Bullock, T. H., H. Grundfest, D. Nachmansohn, and M. Rothenberg, 1947. Effect of di-isopropyl fluorophosphate (DFP) on action potential and cholinesterase of nerve II. Jour. Neurophysiol., **10**: 63–78. (*498*)

Bullock, T. H., H. Grundfest, D. Nachmansohn, M. A. Rothenberg, and K. Sterling, 1946. Effect of di-isopropyl fluorophosphate (DFP) on action potential and choline esterase of nerve. Jour. Neurophysiol., **9**: 253–260. (*489, 496*)

Bullock, T. H., D. Nachmansohn, and M. A. Rothenberg, 1946. Effects of inhibitors of choline esterase on the nerve action potential. Jour. Neurophysiol., **9**: 9–22. (*489, 498*)

van der Burg, A. (See Johnson, van Schouwenburg, and van der Burg, 1939; Kluyver, van der Kerk, and van der Burg, 1942; van Schouwenburg and van der Burg, 1940.)

van der Burg, A., 1943. Spektrale onderzoekingen over chemo- en bioluminescentie. Thesis. Utrecht. (*125, 135, 137, 140, 141, 146, 147, 161, 162*)

Burk, D. (See Lineweaver and Burk, 1934; Winzler, Burk, and du Vigneaud, 1944.)

Burk, N. F., 1932. Osmotic pressure, molecular weight, and stability of serum albumin. Jour. Biol. Chem., **98**:353–377. (*253*)

Burk, N. F., 1937a. Osmotic pressure, molecular weight, and stability of amandin and excelsin and certain other proteins. Jour. Biol. Chem., **120**: 63–83. (*254*)

Burk, N. F., 1937b. Osmotic pressure, molecular weight, and stability of serum globulin. Jour. Biol. Chem., **121**: 373–402. *(253)*

Burk, N. F., 1938. Osmotic pressure, molecular weight and stability of gliadin. Jour. Biol. Chem., **124**: 49–70. *(253)*

Burk, N. F., 1940. Osmotic pressure, molecular weight and dissociation of *Limulus* hemocyanin. Jour. Biol. Chem., **133**: 511–520. *(254)*

Burt, R. L., 1945. Narcosis and cell division in *Colpoda steinii*. Biol. Bull., **88**: 12–29. *(450)*

Burte, H., and G. Halsey, 1947. A new theory of nonlinear viscous elasticity. Textile Research Jour., **17**: 465–476. *(705)*

Burton, A. C., 1939. The properties of the steady state compared to those of equilibrium as shown in characteristic biological behavior. Jour. Cell. Comp. Physiol., **14**: 327–349. *(207)*

Burton, K., 1951. The stabilization of *d*-amino acid oxidase by flavin-adenine dinucleotide, substrates and competitive inhibitors. Biochem. Jour., **48**: 458–467. *(500)*

Butler, J. A. V., 1937. The energy and entropy of hydration of organic molecules. Trans. Farad. Soc., **33**: 229–238. *(431, 462)*

Butler, J. A. V. (Ed.), 1952. Electrical Phenomena at Interfaces. The Macmillan Co., New York. *(603, 698)*

Calkins, H. E. (See Chambers, Bateman, and Calkins, 1940.)

Callery, G., and P. Portier, 1910. Influence des pressions élevées sur les phénomenès osmotiques. Compt. rend. soc. biol., **69**: 245–247. *(290)*

Calvin, M. (See Benson, Kawachi, Hayes, and Calvin, 1952.)

Cameron, D. E. (See Hoagland, Rubin, and Cameron, 1937.)

Campbell, D. H. (See Johnson and Campbell, 1945; 1946.)

Campbell, D. H., and F. H. Johnson, 1946. Pressure and specific precipitation. Jour. Amer. Chem. Soc., **68**: 725. *(266)*

Campbell, H. A., and K. P. Link, 1941. Studies on the hemorrhagic sweet clover disease. IV. The isolation and crystallization of the hemorrhagic agent. Jour. Biol. Chem., **138**: 21–33. *(465)*

Campbell, H. A., W. K. Smith, W. L. Roberts, and K. P. Link, 1941. Studies on the hemorrhagic sweet clover disease. II. The bioassay of hemorrhagic concentrates by following the prothrombin level in the plasma of rabbit blood. Jour. Biol. Chem., **138**: 1–20. *(465)*

Cann, J. R., and J. G. Kirkwood, 1950. The fractionation of proteins by electrophoresis-convection. Cold Spr. Harb. Symp., **14**: 9–23. *(255)*

Carlson, L. D. (See Bodine, Hall, and Carlson, 1940.)

Carnot, S., 1824. Réflexions sur la puissance motrice du feu et sur les machines propres a développer cette puissance. Bachelier, Paris. *(42, 44)*

Carpenter, F. H. (See Loring and Carpenter, 1943.)

Carver, C. M. (See Johnson, Carver, and Harryman, 1942.)

Casella, C., 1951. Tensile force in total striated muscle, isolated fibre and sarcolemma. Acta Physiol. Scand., **21**: 380–401. *(753)*

Casey, E. J., and K. J. Laidler, 1950. The mechanism of the heat inactivation of pepsin. Science, **111**: 100–111. *(273)*

Casey, E. J., and K. J. Laidler, 1951. The kinetics and mechanism of the heat inactivation of pepsin. Jour. Amer. Chem. Soc., **73**: 1455–1457. (*273, 276, 277*)

Castiglione, A., 1947. A History of Medicine. Translated by E. B. Krumbhaar, Alfred A. Knopf, New York. (*501*)

Cattell, McK. (See Edwards and Cattell, 1930.)

Cattell, McK., and D. J. Edwards, 1930. The influence of hydrostatic pressure on the contraction of cardiac muscle in relation to temperature. Amer. Jour. Physiol., **93**: 97–104. (*290, 307*)

Cattell, McK., and D. J. Edwards, 1932. Conditions modifying the influence of hydrostatic pressure on striated muscle, with special reference to the role of viscosity changes. Jour. Cell. Comp. Physiol., **1**: 11–36. (*290, 307, 308*)

Certes, A., 1884a. Note relative à l'action des hautes pressions sur la vitalité des microörganisms d'eau douce et d'eau de mer. Compt. rend. soc. biol., **36**: 220–222. (*288*)

Certes, A., 1884b. Sur la culture, à l'abri des germes atmosphériques, des eaux et des sediments rapportés par les expeditions du "Travailleur" et du "Talisman"; 1882–1883. Compt. rend. acad. sci., **98**: 690–693. (*288*)

Certes, A., 1884c. De l'action des hautes pressions sur les phénomènes de la putrefaction et sur la vitalité des microörganismes d'eau douce et d'eau mer. Compt. rend. acad. sci., **99**: 385–388. (*288*)

Certes, A., and D. Cochin, 1884. Action des hautes pressions sur la vitalité de la levure et sur les phénomènes de la fermentation. Compt. rend. soc. biol., **36**: 639–640. (*288, 289*)

Chaffee, E. (See Hobby, Meyer, and Chaffee, 1942.)

Chain, E. (See Gardner and Chain, 1942.)

Chain, E., H. W. Florey, E. P. Abraham, and N. G. Heatley, 1949. The action of penicillin on micro-organisms. In: Antibiotics, by H. W. Florey, E. Chain, N. G. Heatley, M. A. Jennings, A. G. Sanders, and M. E. Florey. Vol. I, Chapter 35, pp. 1137–1188. Oxford University Press. (*366*)

Chakravorty, P. N., and R. Ballentine, 1941. On the luminescent oxidation of luciferin. Jour. Amer. Chem. Soc., **63**: 2030–2031. (*127, 130, 131, 133*)

Chamberlain, M. M. (See Loeb and Chamberlain, 1915.)

Chamberland, Ch. (See Pasteur, Jaubert, and Chamberland, 1878.)

Chambers, L. A. (See Bateman and Chambers, 1939, 1941.)

Chambers, L. A., J. B. Bateman, and H. E. Calkins, 1940. Further studies of the orientation of reactive sites in thin films of streptococcal antigens. Jour. Immunol., **40**: 483–496. (*266*)

Chance, B., E. N. Harvey, F. Johnson, and G. Millikan, 1940. The kinetics of bioluminescent flashes. A study in consecutive reactions. Jour. Cell. Comp. Physiol., **15**: 195–215. (*157, 172, 177*)

Chang, H-C, W-M Hsiek, and Y-M Lu, 1939. Light-pituitary reflex and the adrenergic-cholinergic sympathetic nerve in a teleost. Proc. Soc. Exp. Biol. Med., **40**: 455–456. (*351*)

Chang, J. J. (See Strehler, Harvey, Chang, and Cormier, 1954.)

Chantrenne, H., K. Linderstrøm-Lang, and L. Vandendriessche, 1947. Volume change accompanying the splitting of ribonucleic acid by ribonuclease. Nature, **159**: 877. (*341, 342, 362*)

Chaplin, H. (See Johnson, Eyring, Steblay, Chaplin, Huber, and Gherardi, 1945.)

Chase, A. M. (See Giese and Chase, 1940; Johnson and Chase, 1942; Kauzmann, Chase, and Brigham, 1949; McElroy and Chase, 1952.)

Chase, A. M., 1940. Changes in the absorption spectrum of *Cypridina* luciferin solutions during oxidation. Jour. Cell. Comp. Physiol., **15**: 159–172. (*159*)

Chase, A. M., 1942. The reaction of *Cypridina* luciferin with azide. Jour. Cell. Comp. Physiol., **19**: 173–181.   (*372, 384, 417*)

Chase, A. M., 1943. The absorption spectrum of luciferin and oxidized luciferin. Jour. Biol. Chem., **150**: 433–445.   (*136, 137, 138*)

Chase, A. M., 1945. The visible absorption band of reduced luciferin. Jour. Biol. Chem., **159**: 1–4.   (*136, 137*)

Chase, A. M., 1946. Reversible heat inactivation of *Cypridina* luciferase. Jour. Cell. Comp. Physiol., **27**: 121–124.   (*218*)

Chase, A. M., 1948a. The chemistry of *Cypridina* luciferin. Ann. N. Y. Acad. Sci., **49**: 353–375.   (*128*)

Chase, A. M., 1948b. Effects of hydrogen ion concentration and of buffer systems on the luminescence of the *Cypridina* luciferin-luciferase reaction. Jour. Cell. Comp. Physiol., **31**: 175–192.   (*158, 392, 393, 398*)

Chase, A. M., 1949a. Studies on cell enzyme systems. I. The effect of ferri-cyanide on the reaction of *Cypridina* luciferin and luciferase and the combining weight of luciferin. Jour. Cell. Comp. Physiol., **33**: 113–122. (*128*)

Chase, A. M., 1949b. Studies on cell enzyme systems. II. Evidence for enzyme-substrate complex formation in the reaction of *Cypridina* luciferin and luciferase. Arch. Biochem., **23**: 385–393.   (*173, 174, 176*)

Chase, A. M., 1950. Studies on cell enzyme systems. IV. The kinetics of heat inactivation of *Cypridina* luciferase. Jour. Gen. Physiol., **33**: 535–546. (*137, 238, 240, 243, 244, 245, 250*)

Chase, A. M., and E. H. Brigham, 1951. The ultraviolet and visible absorption spectra of *Cypridina* luciferin solutions. Jour. Biol. Chem., **190**: 529–536. (*137*)

Chase, A. M., and J. H. Gregg, 1949. Analysis of *Cypridina* luciferin for nitro-gen. Jour. Cell. Comp. Physiol., **33**: 67–71.   (*127, 133*)

Chase, A. M., and E. N. Harvey, 1942. A note on the kinetics of *Cypridina* luminescence. Jour. Cell. Comp. Physiol., **19**: 242–243.   (*174*)

Chase, A. M., and P. B. Lorenz, 1945. Kinetics of the luminescent and non-luminescent reactions of *Cypridina* luciferin at different temperatures. Jour. Cell. Comp. Physiol., **25**: 53–63.   (*153, 154, 155, 156, 158, 177, 219, 243*)

Chase, A. M., E. H. Reppert, and R. M. Ruch, 1944. Reversible heat inactivation of invertase. Jour. Cell. Comp. Physiol., **23**: 27–30.   (*330*)

Chase, A. M., J. Schryver, and K. Stern, 1948. Exploratory electrophoretic ex-periments on luciferase preparations. Jour. Cell. Comp. Physiol., **31**: 25–33. (*126*)

Chastain, S. M. (See Dowdy, Bennett, and Chastain, 1950.)

Chaucer, G., 1385. The Legend of Good Women. "The legend of Hypermnestra," p. 2670.   (*486*)

Chen, K. K., R. C. Anderson, F. G. Henderson, and C. A. Mills, 1943. Potency of cymarin and coumingine hydrochloride as influenced by environmental temperature. Proc. Soc. Exp. Biol. Med., **53**: 200–202.   (*465*)

Chen, K. K., R. C. Anderson, F. A. Steldt, and C. A. Mills, 1943. Environmental temperature and drug action in mice. Jour. Pharmacol. Exp. Therap.,
79: 127–132.   (*465*)

Chen, K. K., C. L. Rose, and G. H. A. Clowes, 1934. Comparative values of
several antidotes in cyanide poisoning. Amer. Jour. Med. Sci., **188**: 767–781.
(*485*)

Cheng, T. H. (See Fan, Cheng, and Richards, 1948.)

Chevrotier, J. (See Lumière and Chevrotier, 1914.)

Chick, H., 1908. An investigation of the laws of disinfection. Jour. Hyg., **8**:
92–158.   (*438, 454, 460, 461*)

Chick, H., 1910. The process of disinfection by chemical agencies and hot water.
Jour. Hyg., **10**: 237–286.   (*454, 460*)

Chick, H., 1912. The bactericidal properties of blood serum. I. The reaction-
velocity of the germicidal action of normal rabbit-serum on *B. coli commune*
and the influence of temperature thereon. Jour. Hyg., **12**: 414–435.   (*454*)

Chick, H., 1930. In: A System of Bacteriology in Relation to Medicine. Vol. I,
Chapter V, pp. 178–207. Medical Research Council, London.   (*454, 460,
461*)

Chick, H., and C. J. Martin, 1910. On the "heat coagulation" of proteins. Jour.
Physiol., **40**: 404–430.   (*195, 271*)

Chick, H., and C. J. Martin, 1911. On the "heat coagulation" of proteins. Part
II. The action of hot water upon egg-albumen and the influence of acid and
salts upon reaction velocity. Jour. Physiol., **43**: 1–27.   (*195, 271, 274*)

Chick, H., and C. J. Martin, 1912a. On the "heat coagulation" of proteins.
Part III. The influence of alkali upon reaction velocity. Jour. Physiol.,
45: 61–69.   (*271*)

Chick, H., and C. J. Martin, 1912b. On the "heat coagulation" of proteins. Part
IV. The conditions controlling the agglutination of proteins already acted
upon by hot water. Jour. Physiol., **45**: 261–295.   (*271*)

Chin, Y-C, 1939. Does acetylcholine play a part in the mechanism of melanophores expansion? Proc. Soc. Exp. Biol. Med., **40**: 454–455.   (*351*)

Chouaïech, M. (See Roche and Chouaïech, 1940.)

Chow, B. F. (See Rothen, Chow, Greep, and Van Dyke, 1941.)

Christensen, L. K. (See Jacobsen and Christensen, 1948.)

Christensen, L. Korsgaard, 1949. Trypsin splitting and denaturation of β-lactoglobulin. Nature, **163**: 1003.   (*335, 340*)

Christian, W. (See Warburg and Christian, 1936.)

Christopherson, A. R. (See Hecht, Woodbury, Woodbury, and Christopherson,
1950; Woodbury, Hecht, and Christopherson, 1951.)

Clark, A. J., 1926a. The reaction between acetyl choline and muscle cells. Jour.
Physiol., **61**: 530–546.   (*499*)

Clark, A. J., 1926b. The antagonism of acetyl choline by atropine. Jour. Physiol.,
61: 547–556.   (*499*)

Clark, A. J., 1937. General Pharmacology. In: Heffter's Handbuch der experi-
mentellen Pharmakologie. Vol. 4. Springer, Berlin.   (*382, 485, 487*)

Clark, D. G. (See Curtis and Clark, 1950.)

Clark, W. G. (See Tenenberg, Tsuchiya, Clark, and Strakosch, 1942; Tsuchiya,
Tenenberg, Clark, and Strakosch, 1942.)

Clarke, W. W., Jr. (See Bonner, Clarke, Neely, and Slifkin, 1950.)

Clausius, R., 1850. Ueber die bewegende Kraft der Wärme und die Gesetze, Welche sich daraus für die wärmelehre selbst ableiten lassen. Ann. Phys. Chem. (Pogg.), **79**: 368–397. (*43*)

Clemence, G. M., 1952. Time and its measurement. Amer. Sci., **40**: 260–269. (*9*)

Clendenning, K. A., and P. R. Gorham, 1950. Storage of isolated chloroplasts without loss of photochemical activity. Canadian Jour. Res., (C) **28**:513–524. (*39*)

Clifton, C. E., 1937a. Prevention of assimilation in respiring cells. Nature, **140**: 318. (*398*)

Clifton, C. E., 1937b. On the possibility of preventing assimilation in respiring cells. Enzymologia, **4**: 246–253. (*398*)

Clifton, C. E., 1946. Microbial assimilations. Adv. Enzymol., **6**: 269–308. (*396*)

Clowes, G. H. A. (See Chen, Rose, and Clowes, 1934; Krahl and Clowes, 1938; Krahl, Keltch, and Clowes, 1940.)

Clowes, G. H. A., 1951. The inhibition of cell division by substituted phenols with special reference to the metabolism of dividing cells. Ann. N. Y. Acad. Sci., **51**: 1409–1431. (*396, 397, 416, 417*)

Coates, C. W. (See Nachmansohn, Cox, Coates, and Machado, 1943.)

Cobb, D. M. (See Fenn and Cobb, 1936.)

Coblentz, W. W., and C. W. Hughes, 1926. Spectral energy distribution of the light emitted by plants and animals. Sci. Papers U. S. Bur. Stand., **21**: 521–534. (*138*)

Cochin, D. (See Certes and Cochin, 1894.)

Cohen, B., 1922. Disinfection studies. The effects of temperature and hydrogen ion concentration upon the viability of *Bact. coli* and *Bact. typhosum* in water. Jour. Bact., **7**: 183–230. (*455*)

Cohen, E., and R. B. de Boer, 1913. Piezochemische Studien. X. Der Einfluss des Druckes auf die Reaktionsgeschwindigkeit in kondensierten Systemen. I. Zeitschr. physik. Chem., **84**: 41–82. (*306*)

Cohen, E., and H. F. G. Kaiser, 1914–1915. Piezochemische Studien. XIII. Der Einfluss des Drucks auf die Reaktionsgeschwindigkeit in kondensierten Systemen. II. Zeitschr. physik. Chem., **89**: 338–364. (*306*)

Cohen, E., and A. M. Valeton, 1916–1918. Piezochemische Studien. XIV. Der Einfluss des Druckes auf die Reaktionsgeschwindigkeit in kondensierten Systemen. III. Zeitschr. physik. Chem., **92**: 433–470. (*306*)

Cohn, E. J. (See McMeekin, Cohn, and Weare, 1935.)

Cohn, E. J., and J. T. Edsall, 1943. Proteins, Amino Acids and Peptides. Reinhold Publishing Co., N. Y. (*263, 590, 691*)

Cohn, E. J., T. L. McMeekin, J. T. Edsall, and M. H. Blanchard, 1934. Studies in the physical chemistry of amino acids, peptides and related substances. I. The apparent molal volume and the electrostriction of the solvent. Jour. Amer. Chem. Soc., **56**: 784–794. (*336*)

Cole, K. S. (See Curtis and Cole, 1940; 1942; 1950.)

Cole, K. S., 1941. Rectification and inductance in the squid giant axon. Jour. Gen. Physiol., **25**: 29–51. (*582, 583, 689*)

Cole, K. S., 1949. Dynamic electrical characteristics of the squid axon membrane. Arch. Sci. physiol., **3**: 253–258. (*635*)

Cole, K. S., and H. J. Curtis, 1939. Electric impedance of the squid giant axon during activity. Jour. Gen. Physiol., **22**: 649–670. (*622, 625, 688*)

Cole, K. S., and H. J. Curtis, 1941. Membrane potential of the squid giant axon during current flow. Jour. Gen. Physiol., **24**: 551–563. (*626, 689*)

Collander, R., and H. Barlund, 1933. Permeabilitätsstudien an *Chara ceratophylla*. Acta Bot. Fennica., **11**: 1–114. (*500*)

Collier, H. B., and D. E. Allen, 1942. Enzyme inhibition by derivatives of phenothiazine. II. Inhibition of cholinesterase. Canadian Jour. Res., (B) **20**: 189–193. (*490*)

Combette, R. (See Roche and Combette, 1937.)

Commoner, B., 1939. The effect of cyanide on the respiration of bakers' yeast in various concentrations of dextrose. Jour. Cell. Comp. Physiol., **13**: 121–138. (*417*)

Conant, J. B. (See Bridgman and Conant, 1929.)

Conant, J. B., 1936. The Chemistry of Organic Compounds. The Macmillan Co., New York. (*24*)

Conway, E. J., 1951. The biological performance of osmotic work. A redox pump. Science, **113**: 270–273. (*672*)

Cook, R. P., and M. Stephenson, 1928. Bacterial oxidations by molecular oxygen. I. The aerobic oxidation of glucose and its fermentation products in its relation to the viability of the organism. Biochem. Jour., **22**: 1368–1386. (*397*)

Coolidge, A. S. (See James and Coolidge, 1933.)

Cooper, E. A. (See Morgan and Cooper, 1912.)

Cooper, E. A., and J. Mason, 1927. Studies of selective bactericidal action. Jour. Hyg., **26**: 118–126. (*453*)

Cooper, G. R. (See Neurath, Cooper, and Erickson, 1942a; 1942b.)

Coraboeuf, E., and S. Weidmann, 1949a. Potentiel de repos et potentiels d'action du muscle cardiaque, mesurés à l'aide d'électrodes internes. Compt. rend. soc. biol., **143**: 1329–1331. (*496*)

Coraboeuf, E., and S. Weidmann, 1949b. Potentiels d'action du muscle cardiaque obtenus à l'aide de microélectrodes intracellulaires. Presence d'une inversion de potentiel. Compt. rend. soc. biol., **143**: 1360–1361. (*496*)

Corey, R. B. (See Pauling and Corey, 1950; 1951a-g; 1952; Pauling, Corey, and Branson, 1951.)

Corey, R. B., 1948. X-ray studies of amino acids and peptides. Adv. Prot. Chem., **4**: 385–406. (*256*)

Cormier, M. J. (See Strehler and Cormier, 1953; Strehler, Harvey, Chang, and Cormier, 1954.)

Cormier, M. J., and B. L. Strehler, 1953. The identification of KCF: requirement of long-chain aldehydes for bacterial extract luminescence. Jour. Amer. Chem. Soc., **75**: 4864–4865. (*186*)

Cornman, I., 1950a. Inhibition of sea-urchin egg cleavage by a series of substituted carbamates. Jour. Nat. Can. Inst., **10**: 1123–1138. (*434*)

Cornman, I., 1950b. Temperature alteration of carbamate narcosis of dividing Arbacia eggs. Biol. Bull., **99**: 338. (*432*)

Cornman, I., and M. E. Cornman, 1951. The action of podophyllin and its fractions on marine eggs. Ann. N. Y. Acad. Sci., **51**: 1443–1487. (*360*)

Cornman, M. E. (See Cornman and Cornman, 1951.)

Coster, J. H. (See McMeekin, Polis, Della Monica, and Coster, 1948.)

Coulombre, J. (See McElroy, Hastings, Sonnenfeld and Coulombre, 1953.)

Cowan, S. L., 1934. The action of potassium and other ions on the injury potential and action current in *Maia* nerve. Proc. Roy. Soc. Lond., B **115**: 216–260. (*501*)

Cox, R. T. (See Nachmansohn, Cox, Coates, and Machado, 1943.)

Crane, M. M., 1921. The effect of hydrogen ion concentration on the toxicity of alkaloids for *Paramoecium*. Jour. Pharmacol. Exp. Therap., **18**: 319–339. (*403*)

Crescitelli, F., 1948. The dual action of carbamates on the resting potential of frog nerve. Jour. Cell. Comp. Physiol., **32**: 187–210. (*438*)

Crescitelli, F., G. B. Koelle, and A. Gilman, 1946. Transmission of impulses in peripheral nerves treated with di-isopropyl fluorphosphate (DFP). Jour. Neurophysiol., **9**: 241–252. (*496, 498*)

Crossman, L. W., W. F. Ruggiero, V. Hurley, and F. M. Allen, 1942. Reduced temperatures in surgery; amputations for peripheral vascular disease. Arch. Surg., **44**: 139–156. (*502*)

Crozier, W. J., 1924–1925a. On the critical thermal increment for the locomotion of a Diplopod. Jour. Gen. Physiol., **7**: 123–136. (*200*)

Crozier, W. J., 1924–1925b. On biological oxidations as a function of temperature. Jour. Gen. Physiol., **7**: 189–216. (*200, 201, 205, 208*)

Crozier, W. J., 1926. The distribution of temperature characteristics for biological processes; critical increments for heart rates. Jour. Gen. Physiol., **9**: 531–546. (*200, 209*)

Crozier, W. J., and H. Federighi, 1924–1925a. Critical thermal increment for the movement of *Oscillatoria*. Jour. Gen. Physiol., **7**: 137–149. (*200, 202*)

Crozier, W. J., and H. Federighi, 1924–1925b. Temperature characteristic for heart rhythm of the silk worm. Jour. Gen. Physiol., **7**: 565–570. (*200*)

Crozier, W. J., and G. F. Pilz, 1924. The locomotion of *Limax*. I. Temperature coefficient of pedal activity. Jour. Gen. Physiol., **6**: 711–721. (*200*)

Crozier, W. J., and T. B. Stier, 1924–1925a. Critical thermal increments for rhythmic respiratory movements in insects. Jour. Gen. Physiol., **7**: 429–447. (*200*)

Crozier, W. J., and T. B. Stier, 1924–1925b. The temperature characteristic for pharyngeal breathing rhythm of the frog. Jour. Gen. Physiol., **7**: 571–579. (*200*)

Crozier, W. J., and T. B. Stier, 1924–1925c. Critical increment for opercular breathing rhythm of the gold fish. Jour. Gen. Physiol., **7**: 699–704. (*200*)

Crozier, W. J., and T. B. Stier, 1924–1925d. Temperature characteristic for heart beat frequency in *Limax*. Jour. Gen. Physiol., **7**: 705–708. (*200*)

Cubin, H. K., 1929. The denaturation of proteins. Part V. Denaturation by acid. Biochem. Jour., **23**: 25–30. (*274*)

Curl, A. L., and E. F. Jansen, 1950a. Effect of high pressures on trypsin and chymotrypsin. Jour. Biol. Chem., **184**: 45–54. (*293, 299, 301, 302*)

Curl, A. L., and E. F. Jansen, 1950b. The effect of high pressures on pepsin and chymotrypsinogen. Jour. Biol. Chem., **185**: 713–724. (*293, 297, 299, 300, 302, 343*)

Curme, H. G. (See Klotz and Curme, 1948.)

Curran, H. R. (See Evans and Curran, 1943.)

Curran, H. R., and F. R. Evans, 1945. Heat activation inducing germination in the spores of thermotolerant and thermophilic aerobic bacteria. Jour. Bact., 49: 335–346. (268)

Curtis, H. J. (See Cole and Curtis, 1939; 1941.)

Curtis, H. J., 1951. The biological effects of radiations. Ann. Rev. Physiol., 13: 41–56. (32)

Curtis, H. J., and K. S. Cole, 1940. Membrane action potentials from the squid giant axon. Jour. Cell. Comp. Physiol., 15: 147–157. (496)

Curtis, H. J., and K. S. Cole, 1942. Membrane resting and action potentials from the squid giant axon. Jour. Cell. Comp. Physiol., 19: 135–144. (623, 684)

Curtis, H. J., and K. S. Cole, 1950. Nervous system: excitation and propagation of nerve. In: Medical Physics. Vol. II, Glaser, O. (Ed.). Year Book Publishers, Chicago. (582, 583, 604, 617, 619, 625, 626, 678, 689)

Curtis, O. F., and D. G. Clark, 1950. An Introduction to Plant Physiology. McGraw-Hill Book Co., New York. (269)

Cutkomp, L. K. (See Richards and Cutkomp, 1946.)

Cutting, W. C. (See Tainter and Cutting, 1933.)

Dalgliesh, C. E. (See Astbury, Dalgliesh, Darmon, and Sutherland, 1948.)

Danielli, J. F. (See Davson and Danielli, 1943.)

Danielli, J. F., 1941. On the permeability change of stimulated nerve. Jour. Physiol., 100: 117–124. (691)

Danielli, J. F., 1950. Cell Physiology and Pharmacology. Elsevier Publishing Co., New York. (509, 511)

Danielli, J. F., 1952. Structural factors in cell permeability and in secretion. Soc. Exp. Biol. Symp., 6: 1–15. (603)

Darmon, S. E. (See Astbury, Dalgliesh, Darmon, and Sutherland, 1948.)

Darmon, S. E., and G. B. B. M. Sutherland, 1949. Evidence from infra-red spectroscopy on the structure of proteins. Nature, 164: 440–441. (260)

Darsie, M. L. J. (See Blinks and Darsie, 1936–1937.)

Davis, B. D., 1943. The binding of sulfonamide drugs by plasma proteins. A factor in determining the distribution of drugs in the body. Jour. Clin. Invest., 22: 753–762. (401)

Davis, B. D., and W. B. Wood, 1942. Studies on antibacterial action of sulfonamide drugs. III. Correlation of drug activity with binding to plasma proteins. Proc. Soc. Exp. Biol. Med., 51: 283–285. (401)

Davis, E. F. (See Mason and Davis, 1942.)

Davis, H., 1926. The conduction of the nerve impulse. Physiol. Rev., 6: 547–595. (502)

Davisson, C., and L. H. Germer, 1927. Diffraction of electrons by a crystal of nickel. Phys. Rev., 30: 705–740. (68)

Davson, H., 1940a. Ionic permeability. The comparative effects of environmental changes on the permeability of the cat erythrocyte membrane to sodium and potassium. Jour. Cell. Comp. Physiol., 15: 317–330. (518)

Davson, H., 1940b. The influence of the lyotropic series of anions on cation permeability. Biochem. Jour., 34: 917–925. (519)

Davson, H., and J. F. Danielli, 1943. The Permeability of Natural Membranes. The Macmillan Co., New York. (517, 518)

Dean, R. B., 1941. Theories of electrolyte equilibrium in muscle. Biol. Symp., J. Cattell (Ed.), **3**: 331–348. (*670*)

de Broglie, L., 1925. Recherches sur la théorie des quanta. Ann. physique, (10) **3**: 22–128. (*68*)

De Jong, D. A., 1922. Micro-organismes et basses températures. Arch. Néerl. physiol., **7**: 588–591. (*187*)

Delbrück, M., 1941. A theory of autocatalytic synthesis of polypeptides and its application to the problem of chromosome reproduction. Cold Spr. Harb. Symp., **4**: 122–126. (*31*)

Delbrück, M., 1946. Bacterial viruses or bacteriophages. Biol. Rev. Proc. Camb. Phil. Soc., **21**: 30–40. (*366*)

Delbrück, M., and S. E. Luria, 1942. Interference between bacterial viruses. I. Interference between two bacterial viruses acting upon the same host, and the mechanism of virus growth. Arch. Biochem., **1**: 111–141. (*367*)

Della Monica, E. S. (See McMeekin, Polis, Della Monica, and Coster, 1948.)

Derbyshire, A. J. (See Simpson and Derbyshire, 1934.)

Deuticke, H. J., and U. Ebbecke, 1937. Über die chemischen Vorgänge bei der Kompressions-verkürzung des Muskels. Hoppe-Seyler's Zeitschr. physiol. Chem., **247**: 70–103. (*308*)

Deuticke, H. J., and F. Harren, 1938. Über den Ablauf fermentativer Reaktionen unter hohem Druck. Hoppe-Seyler's Zeitschr. physiol. Chem., **256**: 169–183. (*313*)

Deutsch, H. F., 1951. A highly active horse erythrocyte catalase. Acta Chem. Scand., **5**: 815–819. (*255*)

Devaux, H., 1903a. Sur une réaction nouvelle et générale des tissus vivants. Essai de détermination directe des dimensions de la micelle albuminoïde. Proc.-ver. séances soc. sci. phys. nat. Bordeaux, 1903–1904, pp. 3–7. (*260*)

Devaux, H., 1903b. Recherches sur les lames très minces, liquides ou solides; existence d'un minimum d'epaisseur. Proc.-ver. séances soc. sci. phys. nat. Bordeaux, 1903–1904, pp. 9–14. (*260*)

Devaux, H., 1904a. Membranes de coagulation par simple contact de l'albumine avec l'eau; application au protoplasma. Proc.-ver. séances soc. sci. phys. nat. Bordeaux, 1903–1904, pp. 34–38. (*260*)

Devaux, H., 1904b. Comparaison de l'épaisseur critique de lames très minces avec le diamètre théorique de la molecule. Proc.-ver. séances soc. sci. phys. nat. Bordeaux, 1903–1904, pp. 76–80. (*260*)

Dewar, J., 1910. Light reactions at low temperatures. Proc. Roy. Inst. Gr. Brit., **19**: 921–928. (*187*)

Dickinson, S. (See Astbury and Dickinson, 1940; Astbury, Dickinson, and Bailey, 1935.)

Dickman, S. (See Barron and Dickman, 1949; Barron, Dickman, Muntz, and Singer, 1949.)

Diebold, W., and L. Juhling, 1938. Fibrinogen, Thrombin und Harnstoff. Biochem. Zeitschr., **296**: 389–409. (*282*)

Diehl, H. S. (See Larson, Hartzell, and Diehl, 1918.)

Dinerstein, R. A. (See Zimmerschied, Dinerstein, Weitkamp, and Marchner, 1949.)

Dittler, R., 1925. Die "Reizzeit" von Induktionsschlägen verschiedener Stärke. Zeitschr. Biol., **83**: 29–44. (*616*)

Dodge, B. O.   (See Shear and Dodge, 1927.)

Dorn, F. J. P.   (See Gorter, van Ormondt, and Dorn, 1932.)

Doudoroff, M., 1938.   Lactoflavin and bacterial luminescence.   Enzymologia, 5: 239–243.   (135)

Dow, R. B.   (See Grant, Dow, and Franks, 1941; Lauffer and Dow, 1941; Matthews, Dow, and Anderson, 1940.)

Dow, R. B., and J. E. Matthews, 1939.   The disintegration of erythrocytes and denaturation of hemoglobin by high pressure.   Phil. Mag., 27: 637–639. (295)

Dow, R. B., J. E. Matthews, Jr., and W. T. S. Thorp, 1940.   The effect of high pressure treatment on the physiological activity of insulin.   Amer. Jour. Physiol., 131: 382–387.   (292)

Dowdy, A. H., L. R. Bennett, and S. M. Chastain, 1950.   Study of the effects of varying oxygen tensions on the response of mammalian tissues to Roentgen irradiation.   Atomic Energy Commission Declassified Document No. UCLA-55, pp. 1–15.   (32)

Drabkin, D. L., 1939.   Action of urea upon hemoglobin.   Spectrophotometric study of progress of a protein denaturation.   Proc. Soc. Exp. Biol. Med., 41: 225–227.   (282)

Drew, H. D. K., 1939.   Chemiluminescence in the oxidation of certain organic substances.   Trans. Farad. Soc., 35: 207–216.   (137, 142, 143, 160, 162, 164, 167)

Drew, H. D. K., and F. H. Pearman, 1937.   Chemiluminescent organic compounds. Part IV, Amino- and Hydrazino-cyclophthalhydrazides and their relative luminescent power.   Jour. Chem. Soc., 26: 586–592.   (140)

DuBois, A. S.   (See Valko and DuBois, 1944.)

Dubois, R., 1885.   Fonction photogénique des pyrophores.   Compt. rend. soc. biol., 37: 559–562.   (125)

Dubois, R., 1887.   Note sur la fonction photogénique chez les Pholades.   Compt. rend. soc. biol., 39: 564–566.   (125)

Dubois, R., and P. Regnard, 1889.   Note sur l'action des hautes pressions sur la fonction photogénique du Lampyre.   Compt. rend. soc. biol., 36: 675–676. (288)

Du Bois-Reymond, E., 1843.   Vorläufiger Abriss einer Untersuchung über den sogenannten Froschstrom und über die electromotorischen Fische.   Ann. Phys. Chem., 58: 1–30.   (496)

DuFait, R. P.   (See Massart and DuFait, 1940.)

Duggan, E. L., and J. M. Luck, 1948.   The combination of organic amides with serum albumin.   IV. Stabilization against urea denaturation.   Jour. Biol. Chem., 172: 205–220.   (271)

Dutcher, J. D.   (See Winterstein and Dutcher, 1943.)

Eagle, H., H. J. Magnuson, and R. Fleischman, 1947.   The effect of hyperpyrexia on the therapeutic efficacy of penicillin in experimental syphilis.   Amer. Jour. Syph., Gonor. Ven. Dis., 31: 239–245.   (468)

Eagle, H., and A. D. Musselman, 1944.   The spirochaeticidal action of penicillin in vitro and its temperature coefficient.   Jour. Exp. Med., 80: 493–505. (404)

Ebbecke, U.   (See Deuticke and Ebbecke, 1937.)

Ebbecke, U., 1914. Wirkung allseitiger Kompression auf den Froschmuskel. Pflüg. Arch. ges. Physiol., **157**: 79–116. (*290, 309, 504*)

Ebbecke, U., 1935a. Über die Wirkung hoher Drucke auf herzschlag und Elektrokardiogramm. Pflüg. Arch. ges. Physiol., **236**: 416–426. (*308, 309*)

Ebbecke, U., 1935b. Über die Wirkungen hoher Drucke auf marine Lebewesen. Pflüg. Arch. ges. Physiol., **236**: 648–657. (*288, 309, 512*)

Ebbecke, U., 1935c. Das Verhalten von Paramecien unter der Einwirkung hohen Druckes. Pflüg. Arch. ges. Physiol., **236**: 658–661. (*309, 347*)

Ebbecke, U., 1935d. Kompressions verkürzung und idiomuskuläre Kontraktion und die Beziehung zwischen elektrischer und mechanischer Reizung. Pflüg. Arch. ges. Physiol., **236**: 662–668. (*308, 309*)

Ebbecke, U., 1935e. Muskelzuckung und Tetanus unter den Einfluss der Kompression durch hoher Drucke. Pflüg. Arch. ges. Physiol., **236**: 669–677. (*308, 309*)

Ebbecke, U., 1935f. Kompression und Kontraktion des Muskels unter der Einwirkung hoher Drucke. Proc. Internat. Physiol. Congr. Leningrad & Moscow, **15**: 224. (*308, 309*)

Ebbecke, U., 1936a. Einwirkung hoher Drucke auf glattmusklige Organe (Froschmagenpreparat). Pflüg. Arch. ges. Physiol., **237**: 771–784. (*309*)

Ebbecke, U., 1936b. Über das Verhalten des Zentralnervensystems (Rückenmarkfrosch) unter der Einwirkung hoher Drucke. Pflüg. Arch. ges. Physiol., **237**: 785–789. (*308, 309*)

Ebbecke, U., 1936c. Über plasmatische Kontraktionen von roten Blutkörperchen, Paramäcien, und Algenzellen unter der Einwirkung hoher Drucke. Pflüg. Arch. ges. Physiol., **238**: 452–466. (*309, 347*)

Ebbecke, U., 1936d. Über das Verhalten der Querstreifung und des Muskelspektrums bei der Kompressionsverkürzung. Pflüg. Arch. ges. Physiol., **238**: 749–752. (*295, 309, 355*)

Ebbecke, U., 1936e. Über Kompression und Narkose. Pflüg. Arch. ges. Physiol., **238**: 441–451. (*309, 503*)

Ebbecke, U., 1937. Über Sporocytenbildung und submikroskopische Feinstruktur der roten Blutkörperchen. Pflüg. Arch. ges. Physiol., **239**: 533–543. (*295, 347*)

Ebbecke, U., and O. Hasenbring, 1935. Über die Kompressions Verkürzung des Muskels bei Einwirkung hoher Drucke. Pflüg. Arch. ges. Physiol., **236**: 405–415. (*309*)

Ebbecke, U., and O. Hasenbring, 1936. Über die Spannungsleistung bei der Kompressionverkürzung. Pflüg. Arch. ges. Physiol., **238**: 753–757. (*309*)

Ebbecke, U., and R. Haubrich, 1939. Weiteres Untersuchungen über die Kompressionsbeeinflussung der Blutgerinnung. Pflüg. Arch. ges. Physiol., **243**: 34–38. (*308*)

Ebbecke, U., and H. Schaefer, 1935. Über den Einfluss hoher Drucke auf den Aktionsstrom von Muskeln und Nerven. Pflüg. Arch. ges. Physiol., **236**: 678–692. (*309*)

Edelmann, A., 1950a. Radiant energy. Ann. Rev. Physiol., **12**: 27–46. (*32*)

Edelmann, A., 1950b. Adrenal cortex and survival of rats after x-irradiation. Fed. Proc., **9**: 36. (*32*)

Edes, R. T., 1899. Relation of the chirping of the tree cricket (*Oecanthus nivens*) to temperature. Amer. Nat., **33**: 935–938. (*201*)

Edie, E. S., 1914.   On the resistance of trypsin solutions to heat.   Biochem. Jour.,
    8: 84–89.   (*215*)

Edsall, J. T.   (See Cohn and Edsall, 1943; Cohn, McMeekin, Edsall, and Blanch-
    ard, 1934.)

Edsall, J. T., 1950.   From comments at the discussion on muscular contraction.
    (See Hill et al., 1950.)   (*751*)

Edwards, D. J.   (See Cattell and Edwards, 1930; 1932.)

Edwards, D. J., and D. E. Brown, 1934.   The action of pressure on the form of
    the electromyogram of auricle muscle.   Jour. Cell. Comp. Physiol., **5**: 1–19.
    (*308, 317*)

Edwards, D. J., and McK. Cattell, 1930.   The action of compression on the con-
    traction of heart muscle.   Amer. Jour. Physiol., **93**: 90–96.   (*290, 307*)

Ehrenfest, E., and E. Ronzoni, 1933.   Effect of dinitrophenol on oxidation of
    tissues.   Proc. Soc. Exp. Biol. Med., **31**: 318–319.   (*396*)

Eijkman, C., 1892.   Lichtgevende Bacterien.   Geneeskund. Tijdschr. Nederland.
    Indië, **32**: 435–441.   (*218*)

Eijkman, C., 1908.   Die Ueberlebungskurve bei Abtötung von Bakterien durch
    Hitze.   Biochem. Zeitschr., **11**: 12–20.   (*455*)

Eijkman, C., 1909.   Investigations on the subject of disinfection.   K. Acad.
    Wetens. Amsterdam, Vol. 11, pt. 2, 668–674.   (*455*)

Eijkman, C., 1912.   Untersuchungen über die Reaktionsgeschwindigkeit der
    Mikroörganismen.   Folia Microbiol., **1**: 359–376.   (*455, 458*)

Eiler, J. J.   (See Allen and Eiler, 1941.)

Einstein, A., 1905.   Ist die Trägheit eines Körpers von seinem Energieinhalt
    abhängig?   Ann. Physik, **18**: 639–641.   (*43*)

Einstein, A., 1906.   Zur Theorie der Lichterzeugung und Lichtabsorption.   Ann.
    Physik, **20**: 199–206.   (*62*)

Eisenberg, M. A., and G. W. Schwert, 1951.   The reversible heat denaturation
    of chymotrypsinogen.   Jour. Gen. Physiol., **34**: 583–606.   (*31, 217*)

Ellis, S., F. L. Plachte, and O. H. Straus, 1943.   Studies on physostigmine and
    related substances.   II. The destruction of physostigmine in buffered solutions
    and in serum.   Jour. Pharmacol. Exp. Therap., **79**: 295–308.   (*489*)

Embree, N. D.   (See Harned and Embree, 1934.)

Englehardt, H., 1922.   Untersuchungen über das Mechanismus den Sublimatwirk-
    ung auf Bakterien.   Disinfektion, **7**: 63–65, 81–83.   (*438*)

Ephrussi, B., and J. L. Herold, 1945.   Studies of pigments of *Drosophila*.   II.
    Effect of temperature on the red and brown pigments in the mutant blood
    (*w*^{b1}).   Genetics, **30**: 62–70.   (*192*)

Epstein, J. A.   (See Lee, Epstein, and Foley, 1943; Lee, Foley, and Epstein, 1944.)

Erickson, J. O.   (See Neurath, Cooper, and Erickson, 1942a, 1942b; Neurath,
    Greenstein, Putnam, and Erickson, 1944.)

Erickson, J. O., and H. Neurath, 1943.   Antigenic properties of native and re-
    generated horse serum albumin.   Jour. Exp. Med., **78**: 1–8.   (*217*)

Erlanger, J., and E. A. Blair, 1931.   The irritability changes in nerve in response
    to subthreshold constant currents, and related phenomena.   Amer. Jour.
    Physiol., **99**: 129–155.   (*619*)

Erlanger, J., and H. S. Gasser, 1937.   Electrical Signs of Nervous Activity.
    Oxford University Press, London.   (*604*)

Euler, H. von, and I. Lauren, 1919. Über die Temperaturempfindlichkeit der Saccharase (Invertase). Zeitschr. physiol. Chem., **108**: 64–114. (*272*)

Evans, F. R. (See Curran and Evans, 1945.)

Evans, F. R., and H. R. Curran, 1943. The accelerating effect of sublethal heat on spore germination in mesophilic aerobic bacteria. Jour. Bact., **46**: 513–523. (*268*)

Evans, M. G. (See Polanyi and Evans, 1935.)

Eymers, J. G., and K. L. van Schouwenburg, 1936. On the luminescence of bacteria. I. A quantitative study of the spectrum of the light emitted by *Photobacterium phosphoreum* and by some chemiluminescent reactions. Enzymologia, **1**: 107–119.

Eymers, J. G., and K. L. van Schouwenburg, 1937a. On the luminescence of bacteria. II. Determination of the oxygen consumed in the light emitting process of *Photobacterium phosphoreum*. Enzymologia, **1**: 328–340.

Eymers, J. G., and K. L. van Schouwenburg, 1937b. On the luminescence of bacteria. III. Further quantitative data regarding spectra connected with bioluminescence. Enzymologia, **3**: 235–241. (*125, 135, 138*)

Eyring, H. (See Alder and Eyring, 1952; Altar and Eyring, 1936; Glasstone, Laidler, and Eyring, 1941; Johnson and Eyring, 1944; Johnson, Eyring, and Kearns, 1943; Johnson, Eyring, Steblay, Chaplin, Huber, and Gherardi, 1945; Johnson, Eyring, and Williams, 1942; Magee, Ri, and Eyring, 1941; Spikes, Lumry, Eyring, and Wayrynen, 1950; Stearn and Eyring, 1940, 1941; Wheeler, Topley, and Eyring, 1936; Wynne-Jones and Eyring, 1935; Zwolinski, Eyring, and Reese, 1949.)

Eyring, H., 1930. Verwendung optischer Daten zur Berechnung der Aktivierungs-wärme. Naturwiss., **18**: 914. (*14*)

Eyring, H., 1935a. The activated complex in chemical reactions. Jour. Chem. Phys., **3**: 107–115. (*12, 22, 121*)

Eyring, H., 1935b. The activated complex and the absolute rate of chemical reactions. Chem. Rev., **17**: 65–77. (*22*)

Eyring, H., 1936. Viscosity, plasticity, and diffusion as examples of absolute reaction rates. Jour. Chem. Phys., **4**: 283–291. (*533*)

Eyring, H., 1938. The theory of absolute reaction rates. Trans. Farad. Soc., **34**: 41–48. (*22*)

Eyring, H., H. Gershinowitz, and C. E. Sun, 1935. The absolute rate of homogeneous reactions. Jour. Chem. Phys., **3**: 786–796. (*14, 15*)

Eyring, H., F. H. Johnson, and R. L. Gensler, 1946. Pressure and reactivity of proteins, with particular reference to invertase. Jour. Phys. Chem., **50**: 453–464. (*31, 315, 330, 331, 362*)

Eyring, H., and G. E. Kimball, 1933. The quantum mechanics of seven and eight electrons with spin degeneracy. Jour. Chem. Phys., **1**: 239–246. (*87*)

Eyring, H., R. Lumry, and J. W. Woodbury, 1949. Some applications of modern rate theory to physiological systems. Record Chem. Prog., **10**: 100–114. (*671, 684, 691, 754*)

Eyring, H., and J. L. Magee, 1942. Application of the theory of absolute reaction rates to bacterial luminescence. Jour. Cell. Comp. Physiol., **20**: 169–177. (*25, 127, 215, 219, 309, 312*)

Eyring, H., and M. Polanyi, 1930. Zur Berechnung der Aktivierungswärme. Naturwiss., **18**: 914–915. (*14*)

Eyring, H., and M. Polanyi, 1931. Ueber einfache Gasreaktionen. Zeitschr. physik. Chem., B **12**: 279–311.   (*14, 16, 104*)

Eyring, H., and A. E. Stearn, 1939. The application of the theory of absolute reaction rates to proteins. Chem. Rev., **24**: 253–270.   (*215, 252, 272, 274, 277, 278, 280*)

Eyring, H., J. Walter, and G. E. Kimball, 1944. Quantum Chemistry. John Wiley & Sons, New York.   (*70, 146, 150*)

Fager, E. W. (See Gaffron and Fager, 1951.)

Fairfield, J., 1948. Effects of cold on infant rats: body temperatures, oxygen consumption, electrocardiograms. Amer. Jour. Physiol., **155**: 355–365. (*188*)

Falk, I. S., 1923. The rôle of certain ions in bacterial physiology. A review. Abs. Bact., **7**: 87–103, 133–147.   (*455*)

Falk, I. S., and C.-E. A. Winslow, 1926. A contribution to the dynamics of toxicity and the theory of disinfection. Jour. Bact., **11**: 1–26.   (*455*)

Famulener, L. W., and T. Madsen, 1908. Die Abschwächung der Antigene durch Erwärmung (Vibriolysin, Tetanolysin, Ziegenserum-Häemolysin). Biochem. Zeitschr., **11**: 186–209.   (*272*)

Fan, H. Y., T. H. Cheng, and A. G. Richards, 1948. The temperature coefficient of DDT action in insects. Physiol. Zool., **21**: 48-59.   (*466*)

Fankuchen, I., 1945. X-ray diffraction and protein structure. Adv. Prot. Chem., **2**: 387–405.   (*252*)

Farrant, J. L., A. L. G. Rees, and E. H. Mercer, 1947. Structure of fibrous keratin. Nature, **159**: 535–536.   (*752*)

Fawcett, E. W. (See Gibson, Fawcett, and Perrin, 1935.)

Fawcett, E. W., and R. O. Gibson, 1934a. The influence of pressure on a number of organic reactions in the liquid phase. Jour. Chem. Soc., 386–395. (*306*)

Fawcett, E. W., and R. O. Gibson, 1934b. The influence of pressure on the rate of formation of cetylpyridinium halides. Jour. Chem. Soc., 396–400. (*306*)

Fazekas, J. F. (See Himwich, Bowman, Fazekas, and Goldfarb, 1940.)

Federighi, H. (See Crozier and Federighi, 1924–1925a; 1924–1925b.)

Feld, E. A. (See Nachmansohn and Feld, 1947; Nachmansohn, Rothenberg, and Feld, 1947.)

Feld, E. A., H. Grundfest, D. Nachmansohn, and M. Rothenberg, 1948. Effect of di-isopropyl fluorophosphate (DFP) on action potential and cholinesterase of nerve. IV. Jour. Neurophysiol., **11**: 125–132.   (*498*)

Feng, T. P., 1932. The effect of length on the resting metabolism of muscle. Jour. Physiol., **74**: 441–454.   (*736*)

Fenn, W. O., 1923–1924a. A quantitative comparison between the energy liberated and the work performed by the isolated sartorius muscle of the frog. Jour. Physiol., **58**: 175–203.   (*743*)

Fenn, W. O., 1923–1924b. The relation between the work performed and the energy liberated in muscular contraction. Jour. Physiol., **58**: 373–395. (*743*)

Fenn, W. O., 1930a. Frictional and kinetic factors in the work of sprint running. Amer. Jour. Physiol., **92**: 583–611.   (*716*)

Fenn, W. O., 1930b. Work against gravity and work due to velocity changes in running. Amer. Jour. Physiol., 93: 433–462. *(716)*

Fenn, W. O., 1945. Contractility. In: Physical Chemistry of Cells and Tissues, R. Höber (Ed.). Pp. 445–522. Blakiston Co., Philadelphia. *(699, 713, 716, 735, 736, 740, 742, 744)*

Fenn, W. O., and D. M. Cobb, 1936. Electrolyte changes in muscle during activity. Amer. Jour. Physiol., 115: 345–356. *(669)*

Ferguson, J., 1939. The use of chemical potentials as indices of toxicity. Proc. Roy. Soc. Lond., B 127: 387–404. *(431, 432)*

Field, J. (See Fuhrman and Field, 1943, 1948; Hollinger, Fuhrman, Lewis, and Field, 1949; Peiss and Field, 1948, 1950; Pierce and Field, 1949.)

Field, J., F. A. Fuhrman, and A. W. Martin, 1944. Effect of temperature on the oxygen consumption of brain tissue. Jour. Neurophysiol., 7: 117–126. *(250, 251)*

Field, J., and V. E. Hall, 1944. Physiological effects of heat and cold. Ann. Rev. Physiol., 6: 69–94. *(502)*

Field, J., A. W. Martin, and S. M. Field, 1933. Action of 1,2,4-dinitrophenol on yeast respiration and fermentation. Proc. Soc. Exp. Biol. Med., 31: 56–57. *(396)*

Field, S. M. (See Field, Martin, and Field, 1933.)

Fildes, P., 1940. Mechanism of antibacterial action of mercury. Brit. Jour. Exp. Path., 21: 67–73. *(438)*

Fischer, E., 1902. Ueber einige Derivate des Glykocolls, Alanins und Leucins. Ber. deut. chem. Gesellsch., 35: 1095–1106. *(256)*

Fischer, F. G., I. Böttger, and H. Lehmann-Echternacht, 1942. Über die Thymopolynucleotidase aus Pankreas. Nucleinsauren. V. Zeitschr. physiol. Chem., 271: 246–264. *(341)*

Fischgold, H. (See Rona and Fischgold, 1933.)

Fisher, K. C. (See Armstrong and Fisher, 1940; Ormsbee and Fisher, 1943.)

Fisher, K. C., and R. J. Henry, 1943. The effect of urethane and chloral hydrate on oxygen consumption and cell division in the egg of the sea-urchin, *Arbacia punctulata*. Jour. Gen. Physiol., 27: 469–481. *(417)*

Fisher, K. C., and R. Öhnell, 1940. The steady state frequency of the embryonic fish heart at different concentrations of cyanide. Jour. Cell. Comp. Physiol., 16: 1–13. *(384, 407, 417, 418, 448)*

Fisher, K. C., and J. R. Stearn, 1942. The separation of an "activity" metabolism from the total respiration of yeast by the effects of ethyl carbamate. Jour. Cell. Comp. Physiol., 19: 109–122. *(384, 414, 415, 417)*

Fishler, M. C. (See Bond, Swift, Allen, and Fishler, 1950.)

Fitzgerald, L. R. (See Bodine and Fitzgerald, 1949.)

Flagler, E. A. (See Johnson and Flagler, 1951; Johnson, Flagler, Simpson, and McGeer, 1951.)

Fleischman, R. (See Eagle, Magnuson, and Fleischman, 1947.)

Fleming, A., A. Voureka, I. R. H. Kramer, and W. H. Hughes, 1950. The morphology and motility of *Proteus vulgaris* and other organisms cultured in the presence of penicillin. Jour. Gen. Microbiol., 4: 257–269. *(366)*

Fleming, R. H. (See Sverdrup, Johnson, and Fleming, 1942.)

Flett, L. H., R. C. Haring, A. F. Guiteras, and R. Shapiro, 1945. The revival of organisms presumably killed by phenol. Jour. Bact., **50**: 591–595. (*439*)

Florey, H. W. (See Chain, Florey, Abraham, and Heatley, 1949.)

Foley, E. J. (See Lee, Epstein, and Foley, 1943; Lee and Foley, 1945; Lee, Foley, and Epstein, 1944.)

Fontaine, M., 1927a. De l'influence des fortes pressions sur l'imbibition des tissus. Compt. rend. acad. sci., **184**: 1198–1200. (*290*)

Fontaine, M., 1927b. Du mode d'action des fortes pressions sur les tissus. Compt. rend. acad. sci., **184**: 1345–1347. (*290*)

Fontaine, M., 1927c. Influence des fortes pressions sur le volume globulaire. Compt. rend. soc. biol., **97**: 1656–1657. (*290*)

Fontaine, M., 1928a. De l'influence des fortes pressions sur les tissus musculaires immergés dans des solutions hypertoniques. Compt. rend. soc. biol., **98**: 28. (*290*)

Fontaine, M., 1928b. Sur les analogies existant entre les effets d'une tétanisation et ceux d'une compression. Compt. rend. acad. sci., **186**: 99–101. (*290*)

Fontaine, M., 1928c. Sur les réactions aux fortes pressions, du gastrocnémien de grenouille immergé dans une solution hypotonique. Compt. rend. acad. sci., **186**: 323–325. (*290*)

Fontaine, M., 1928d. Les fortes pressions et la consommation d'oxygène de quelques animaux marins. Influence de la taille de l'animal. Compt. rend. soc. biol., **99**: 1789–1790. (*290, 326*)

Fontaine, M., 1929a. De l'action des fortes pressions sur la respiration des algues. Compt. rend. acad. sci., **189**: 647–649. (*290*)

Fontaine, M., 1929b. De l'augmentation de la consommation d'oxygène des animaux marins sous l'influence des fortes pressions. Ses variations en fonction de l'intensité de la compression. Compt. rend. acad. sci., **188**: 460–461. (*290, 326*)

Fontaine, M., 1929c. De l'augmentation de la consommation d'oxygène des animaux marins sous l'influence des fortes pressions. Ses variations en fonction de la durée de la compression. Compt. rend. acad. sci., **188**: 662–663. (*290*)

Fontaine, M., 1929d. De l'influence de la durée et de l'intensité de la compression sur l'imbibition de gastrocnémien de grenouille. Compt. rend. soc. biol., **101**: 32–33. (*290*)

Fontaine, M., 1929e. De l'action des fortes pressions sur les cellules végétales. Compt. rend. soc. biol., **101**: 452–454. (*290*)

Fontaine, M., 1929f. De l'influence comparée de la pression sur la respiration et la photosynthèse des algues. Compt. rend. soc. biol., **102**: 912–914. (*290, 326*)

Fontaine, M., 1930. Recherches expérimentales sur les réactions des êtres vivants aux fortes pressions. Ann. inst. océanogr., **8**(N.S.): 1–99. (*290*)

Formánek, Em., 1900. Über die Einwirkung von chloroform und Chloralhydrat auf den Blutfarbstoff. Zeitschr. physiol. Chem., **29**: 416–422. (*452*)

Forst, A. W., 1928. Zur Entgiftung der Blausäure. Arch. exp. Path. Pharm., **128**: 1–66. (*485*)

Forst, A. W., 1932. Zum Antagonismus Kohlenhydrate-Blausaure. Arch. exp. Path. Pharm., **167**: 108–111. (*485*)

Foster, R. A. C., and F. H. Johnson, 1951. Influence of urethane and of hydro-static pressure on the growth of bacteriophages T2, T5, T6 and T7. Jour. Gen. Physiol., **34**: 529–550. (*284, 366, 367*)

Foster, R. A. C., F. H. Johnson, and V. K. Miller, 1949. The influence of hydro-static pressure and urethane on the thermal inactivation of bacteriophage. Jour. Gen. Physiol., **33**: 1–16. (*284, 285, 333, 334*)

Fourt, L. (See Harkins, Fourt, and Fourt, 1940.)

Fourt, L., and F. O. Schmitt, 1936. Unimolecular films of nerve proteins. Jour. Phys. Chem., **40**: 989–996. (*264*)

Fourt, P. C. (See Harkins, Fourt, and Fourt, 1940.)

Fowler, R. H. (See Bernal and Fowler, 1933.)

Fowler, R. H., 1936. Statistical Mechanics. The Theory of the Properties of Matter in Equilibrium. The Macmillan Co., New York. (*88, 96*)

Fowler, R. H., and E. A. Guggenheim, 1939. Statistical Thermodynamics. The Macmillan Co., New York. (*5*)

Franck, J., 1951. A critical survey of the physical background of photosynthesis. Ann. Rev. Plant Physiol., **2**: 53–86. (*34*)

Franck, J., and W. E. Loomis, (Eds.), 1949. Photosynthesis in Plants. Iowa State College Press, Ames, Iowa. (*34*)

Franks, W. R. (See Grant, Dow, and Franks, 1941.)

Fraser, D. (See Johnson, Baylor, and Fraser, 1948.)

Fraser, D., and F. H. Johnson, 1951. The pressure-temperature relationship in the rate of casein digestion by trypsin. Jour. Biol. Chem., **190**: 417–421. (*315, 332*)

Fraser, D., F. H. Johnson, and R. S. Baker, 1949. The acceleration of the thermal denaturation of tobacco mosaic virus by urethan at normal and increased pressure. Arch. Biochem., **24**: 314–320. (*285, 441, 442*)

Frensdorff, H. K. (See Simpson, Watson, Levedahl, Schellman, Frensdorff, and Kauzmann, 1951.)

Freundlich, H., 1937. Some recent work on gels. Jour. Phys. Chem., **41**: 901–910. (*344*)

Frey-Wyssling, A., 1948. Submicroscopic Morphology of Protoplasm and Its Derivatives. Elsevier Publishing Co. (*730*)

Frobisher, M., 1928. Relations of surface tension to bacterial phenomena. Jour. Inf. Dis., **38**: 66–91. (*366*)

Fröhlich, F. W., 1904. Zur Kenntnis der Narkose des Nerven. Zeitschr. allgem. Physiol., **3**: 75–88. (*504*)

Frumkin, A., 1925. Einige Bemerkungen zur Theorie der Adsorption und Ver-teilung. Zeitschr. physik. Chem., **116**: 501–503. (*432*)

Fühner, H., 1904. Ueber die Einwirkung verschiedener Alkohole auf die Ent-wicklung der Seeigel. Arch. exp. Path. Pharm., **51**: 1–10. (*432*)

Fühner, H., 1921a. Die narkotische Wirkung des Benzins und seiner Bestandteile (Pentan, Hexan, Heptan, Octan). Biochem. Zeitschr., **115**: 235–268. (*432*)

Fühner, H., 1921b. Die Wirkungsstärke der Narcotics. I. Versuche am isolierten Froschherzen. Biochem. Zeitschr., **120**: 143–163. (*432*)

Fühner, H., and E. Neubauer, 1907. Hämolyse durch Substanzen homologer Reihen. Arch. exp. Path. Pharm., **56**: 333–345. (*432*)

Fugitt, C. H. (See Steinhardt, Fugitt, and Harris, 1940, 1941, 1942.)

Fuhrman, F. A. (See Field, Fuhrman, and Martin, 1944; Hollinger, Fuhrman, Lewis, and Field, 1949.)

Fuhrman, F. A., 1946. The effect of body temperature on drug action. Physiol. Rev., **26**: 247–274. (*466*)

Fuhrman, F. A., and J. Field, 1943. Action of diphenyloxazolidinedione on brain respiration at varied temperature levels. Jour. Pharmacol. Exp. Therap., **77**: 229–237. (*486*)

Fuhrman, F. A., and J. Field, 1948. Inhibition of brain respiration by ethyl alcohol at varied temperature levels. Proc. Soc. Exp. Biol. Med., **69**: 331–332. (*446, 486*)

Fuhrman, G., and E. W. Weymouth, 1946. The effect of dinitrophenol on the oxygen consumption of albino mice at graded levels of environmental temperature. Amer. Jour. Physiol., **147**: 527–530. (*466*)

Fulmer, E. I. (See Buchanan and Fulmer, 1930.)

Fulmer, E. I., and R. E. Buchanan, 1923. Study on toxicity. Jour. Gen. Physiol., **6**: 77–89. (*455*)

Gaffron, H., and E. W. Fager, 1951. The kinetics and chemistry of photosynthesis. Ann. Rev. Plant Physiol., **2**: 87–114. (*34*)

Gardner, A. D., 1940. Morphological effects of penicillin on bacteria. Nature, **146**: 837–838. (*366*)

Gardner, A. D., and E. Chain, 1942. Proactinomycin: A "bacteriostatic" produced by a species of *Proactinomyces*. Brit. Jour. Exp. Path., **23**: 123–127. (*366*)

Gasser, H. S. (See Erlanger and Gasser, 1937.)

Gasser, H. S., 1931. Nerve activity as modified by temperature changes. Amer. Jour. Physiol., **97**: 254–269. (*502, 503*)

Gasser, H. S., and A. V. Hill, 1924. The dynamics of muscular contraction. Proc. Roy. Soc. Lond., B **96**: 398–437. (*708, 710*)

Gaydon, A. G., 1950. Dissociation Energies and Spectra of Diatomic Molecules. Dover Publications, New York. (*144*)

Gegenbauer, V., 1921. Studien über die Desinfektionswirkung des Sublimates. Arch. Hyg., **90**: 23–81. (*438*)

Gehenio, P. M. (See Luyet and Gehenio, 1940.)

Gellhorn, E., 1929. Das Permeabilitätsproblem. Julius Springer, Berlin. (*500*)

Gemmill, C. L., and L. Hellerman, 1937. The reversible inhibition of muscle glycolysis. Amer. Jour. Physiol., **120**: 522–531. (*438*)

Gensler, R. L. (See Eyring, Johnson, and Gensler, 1946; Johnson, Kauzmann, and Gensler, 1948.)

Gerard, R. W. (See Boyarsky, Rosenblad, Postel, and Gerard, 1949; Boyarsky, Tobias, and Gerard, 1947; Brooks, Ransmeier, and Gerard, 1949; Graham and Gerard, 1946; Ling and Gerard, 1948, 1949.)

Gerard, R. W., 1930. The response of nerve to oxygen lack. Amer. Jour. Physiol., **92**: 498–541. (*507*)

Gergely, J., and K. Laki, 1950. A thermodynamic discussion of the length-tension diagram of muscle. Enzymologia, **14**: 272–276. (*705*)

Gerlach, W., and O. Stern, 1922a. Der experimentelle Nachweiss der Richtungsquantelung im Magnetfeld. Zeitschr. Physik, **9**: 349–352. (*81*)

Gerlach, W., and O. Stern, 1922b. Das magnetische Moment des Silberatoms. Zeitschr. Physik, **9**: 353–355. (*81*)

Gerlough, T. D., and R. W. Bates, 1932. The purification and some properties of insulin. Jour. Pharmacol. Exp. Therap., **45**: 19–51. (*272, 274, 275*)

Gerlough, T. D., and W. White, 1934. Some factors influencing the rate of thermal destruction of the tetanus antitoxin of antitetanic horse plasma at 60° and 66°C. Jour. Immunol., **27**: 367–377. (*239*)

Germer, L. H. (See Davisson and Germer, 1927.)

Gershinowitz, H. (See Eyring, Gershinowitz, and Sun, 1935.)

Gherardi, G. (See Johnson, Eyring, Steblay, Chaplin, Huber, and Gherardi, 1945.)

Gibbs, E. L. (See Gibbs, Gibbs, and Lennox, 1937.)

Gibbs, F. A., E. L. Gibbs, and W. G. Lennox, 1937. The various cerebral dysrhythmias of epilepsy, and measures for their control. Trans. Amer. Neurol. Assoc., **63**: 129–134. (*505*)

Gibbs, J. W., 1874–1878. On the equilibrium of heterogeneous substances. Trans. Conn. Acad., **3**: 108–248, 343–524. (*42, 50*)

Gibson, R. O. (See Fawcett and Gibson, 1934; Williams, Perrin, and Gibson, 1936.)

Gibson, R. O., E. W. Fawcett, and M. W. Perrin, 1935. The effect of pressure on reactions in solution. I. Sodium ethoxide and ethyl iodide to 3000 kg/cm^2. II. Pyridine and ethyl iodide to 8500 kg/cm^2. Proc. Roy. Soc. Lond., A **150**: 223–240. (*306*)

Giddings, N. J., H. A. Allard, and B. H. Hite, 1929. Inactivation of the tobacco-mosaic virus by high pressure. Phytopath., **19**: 749–750. (*293*)

Giese, A. C., and A. M. Chase, 1940. The effects of cyanide on *Cypridina* luciferin. Jour. Cell. Comp. Physiol., **16**: 237–246. (*126, 128, 130, 372*)

Gilbert, C. A. (See Lee and Gilbert, 1918.)

Gillham, E. M. (See Potter and Gillham, 1946.)

Gilman, A. (See Crescitelli, Koelle, and Gilman, 1946; Goodman and Gilman, 1941; Koelle and Gilman, 1949.)

Glasstone, S., K. J. Laidler, and H. Eyring, 1941. The Theory of Rate Processes. McGraw-Hill Book Co., New York. (*5, 22, 100, 122, 359, 533, 754*)

Gleu, K., and W. Petsch, 1935. Die Chemiluminescenz der Dimethyl-diacridyliumsalze. Zeitschr. angew. Chem., **48**: 57–59. (*136, 160*)

Glick, D., and W. Antopol, 1939. The inhibition of choline esterase by thiamine (Vitamin B$_1$). Jour. Pharm. Exp. Therap., **65**: 389–394. (*490*)

Goddard, D. R., 1935. The reversible heat activation inducing germination and increased respiration in the ascospores of *Neurospora tetrasperma*. Jour. Gen. Physiol., **19**: 45–60. (*269*)

Goldacre, R. J., and I. J. Lorch, 1950. Folding and unfolding of protein molecules in relation to cytoplasmic streaming, amoeboid movement and osmotic work. Nature, **166**: 497–500. (*30*)

Goldfarb, W. (See Himwich, Bowman, Fazekas, and Goldfarb, 1940.)

Goldman, D. E., 1943. Potential, impedance, and rectification in membranes. Jour. Gen. Physiol., **27**: 37–60. (*562*)

Goldman, M. C. (See Jacobson, Robson, Marks, and Goldman, 1949.)

Goldstein, A., 1944. The mechanism of enzyme-inhibitor-substrate reactions illustrated by the cholinesterase-physostigmine-acetylcholine system. Jour. Gen. Physiol., **27**: 529–580. (*407*)

Goodeve, C. F., 1934. Three dimensional models of the potential energy of triatomic systems. Trans. Farad. Soc., **30**: 60–69. (*16*)

Goodman, L., and A. Gilman, 1941. The Pharmacological Basis of Therapeutics. The Macmillan Co., New York. (*432, 464*)

Gordy, W., 1948. Microwave spectroscopy. Rev. Mod. Phys., **20**: 668–717. (*9*)

Gore, W. L. (See Bonner, Gore, and Yost, 1936.)

Gorham, P. R. (See Clendenning and Gorham, 1950.)

Gorter, E., 1935. The spreading of pepsin and of trypsin. Jour. Gen. Physiol., **18**: 421–426. (*261*)

Gorter, E., 1936. Discussion on surface phenomena—films. Proc. Roy. Soc. Lond., A **155**: 707–708. (*265*)

Gorter, E., 1941. Properties of protein monolayers. Ann. Rev. Biochem., **10**: 619–636. (*260*)

Gorter, E., and F. Grendel, 1926. On the spreading of proteins. Trans. Farad. Soc., **22**: 477–483.

Gorter, E., and F. Grendel, 1928. Die Eiweissbreitung als Methode zur Bestimmung von Serumalbumin und Serumglobulin. Biochem. Zeitsche., **201**: 391–411. (*261*)

Gorter, E., L. Maaskant, and G. J. van Lookeren Campagne, 1936. On the spreading of fibrinogen. Proc. Akad. Wetens. Amsterdam, **39**: 1187–1191. (*261*)

Gorter, E., and J. van Ormondt, 1933. The spreading of insulin and of zein. Proc. Akad. Wetens. Amsterdam, **36**: 922–926. (*261*)

Gorter, E., and J. van Ormondt, 1935. The spreading of myosin. Biochem. Jour., **29**: 48–52. (*261*)

Gorter, E., J. van Ormondt, and F. J. P. Dorn, 1932. The spreading of ovalbumin. Proc. Akad. Wetens. Amsterdam, **35**: 838–843. (*261*)

Gorter, E., and G. Th. Philippi, 1934. The influence of time on the spreading of proteins. Proc. Akad. Wetens. Amsterdam, **37**: 788–793. (*261*)

Goth, A. (See Sulkin, Goth, and Zarafonetis, 1946; Sulkin, Zarafonetis, and Goth, 1945.)

Gotschlich, E., 1893. Ueber den Einfluss der Wärme auf Länge und Dehnbarkeit des elastischen Gewebes und des quergestreiften Muskels. Pflüg. Arch. ges. Physiol., **54**: 109–164. (*215, 217*)

Gottlieb-Billroth, H. (See Meyer and Gottlieb-Billroth, 1920.)

Gottschalk, A. (See Lipschitz and Gottschalk, 1921.)

Goudsmit, S. (See Uhlenbeck and Goudsmit, 1925, 1931.)

Gould, B. S., 1939. The nature of animal and plant tyrosinase. The oxidation of mono and dihydric phenols as a function of temperature. Enzymologia, **7**: 292–296. (*170*)

Gould, B. S., and I. W. Sizer, 1938. The mechanism of bacterial dehydrogenase activity in vivo. I. Anaerobic dehydrogenase activity of *Escherichia coli* as a function of temperature. Jour. Biol. Chem., **124**: 269–279. (*208*)

Graham, J., and R. W. Gerard, 1946. Membrane potentials and excitation of impaled single muscle fibers. Jour. Cell. Comp. Physiol., **28**: 99–117. (*496*)

Graham-Smith, G. S., 1920. The behavior of bacteria in fluid cultures as indicated by daily estimates of the numbers of living organisms. Jour. Hyg., **19**: 133–204. (*191*)

Gralén, N., 1939. The splitting of hemoglobin by acids. Biochem. Jour., **33**: 1907–1912. (*254*)

Gramenitzki, M. J., 1910. Der Einfluss verschiedener Temperaturen auf die Fermente und die Regeneration fermentativer Eigenschaften. Hoppe-Seyler's Zeitschr. physiol. Chem., **69**: 286–300. (*215*)

Gramenizky, M. J., 1913. Der Zusammenhang zwischen dem aktiven und inaktiven Zustand des Ferments und der Oberflächenspannung desselben. Biochem. Zeitschr., **52**: 142–154. (*215*)

Gramenizky, M. J., 1913. Über den Einfluss von Säuren und Alkalien auf das im Stadium der Regeneration befindliche diastatische Ferment. Biochem. Zeitschr., **56**: 78–81. (*215*)

Grant, E. A., R. B. Dow, and W. R. Franks, 1941. Denaturation of egg albumin by pressure. Science, **94**: 616. (*292*)

Grassheim, K. (See Rona and Grassheim, 1923.)

Grassmann, W., 1932. Proteolytische Enzyme des Tier- und Pflanzenreiches. Ergeb. Enzymforsch., **1**: 128–167. (*185*)

Grassmann, W., and F. Schneider, 1936. Proteasen. Ergeb. Enzymforsch., **5**: 79–116. (*185*)

Gratia, A. (See Basset, Gratia, Macheboeuf, and Manil, 1938.)

Gray, D. H. (See Johnson and Gray, 1949.)

Gray, J., 1923. The mechanism of ciliary movement. III. The effect of temperature. Proc. Roy. Soc. Lond., B **95**: 6–15. (*202, 250*)

Gray, J., 1928. The growth of fish. III. The effect of temperature on the development of the eggs of *Salmo fario*. Brit. Jour. Exp. Biol., **6**: 125–130. (*191*)

Gray, J., 1929. The kinetics of growth. Brit. Jour. Exp. Biol., **6**: 248–274. (*191*)

Green, R. E. (See Wescoe, Green, McNamara, and Krop, 1948.)

Greenstein, J. P. (See Neurath, Greenstein, Putnam, and Erickson, 1944.)

Greenstein, J. P., and J. Wyman, 1936. Further studies on dielectric constant and electrostriction of amino acids and peptides. Jour. Amer. Chem. Soc., **58**: 463–465. (*336*)

Greep, R. O. (See Rothen, Chow, Greep, and Van Dyke, 1941.)

Gregerson, J. P., 1916. Untersuchungen über die desinfizierende Kraft der desinfizierenden Stoffe im Verhältnis zu ihrer Konzentration. Zentr. Bakt. Parasitenk. Infek., Abt. I, Orig., **77**: 168–185. (*455, 461*)

Gregg, J. H. (See Chase and Gregg, 1949.)

Grendell, F. (See Gorter and Grendell, 1926, 1928.)

Grob, D., 1950. The anticholinesterase activity in vitro of the insecticide parathion (*p*-nitrophenyl diethyl thionophosphate). Johns Hopkins Hosp. Bull., **87**: 95–105. (*489*)

Grob, D., A. M. Harvey, O. R. Langworthy, and J. L. Lilienthal, 1947. The administration of di-isopropyl fluorophosphate (DFP) to man. III. Effect on the central nervous system with special reference to electrical activity of the brain. Johns Hopkins Hosp. Bull., **81**: 257–265.

Grob, D., J. L. Lilienthal, and A. M. Harvey, 1947. The administration of di-isopropyl fluorophosphate (DFP) to man. II. Effect on intestinal motility and use in treatment of abdominal distension. Johns Hopkins Hosp. Bull., **81**: 245–256.

Grob, D., J. L. Lilienthal, A. M. Harvey, and B. F. Jones, 1947. The administration of di-isopropyl fluorophosphate (DFP) to man. I. Effect on plasma and erythrocyte cholinesterase; general systemic effects; use in study of hepatic function and erythropoiesis; and some properties of plasma cholinesterase. Johns Hopkins Hosp. Bull., **81**: 217–244. (*498*)

Grossberg, A. L. (See Pauling, Pressman, and Grossberg, 1944.)

Grundfest, H. (See Bullock, Grundfest, Nachmansohn, and Rothenberg, 1947; Bullock, Grundfest, Nachmansohn, Rothenberg, and Sterling, 1946; Feld, Grundfest, Nachmansohn, and Rothenberg, 1948.)

Grundfest, H., 1936. Effects of hydrostatic pressure upon the excitability, the recovery, and the potential sequence of frog nerve. Cold Spr. Harb. Symp., **4**: 179–187. (*308*)

Grundfest, H., 1940. Bioelectric potentials. Ann. Rev. Physiol., **2**: 213–242. (*678*)

Grundfest, H., D. Nachmansohn, and M. Rothenberg, 1947. Effect of di-isopropyl fluorophosphate (DFP) on action potential and cholinesterase of nerve. III. Jour. Neurophysiol., **10**: 155–164. (*498*)

Guastalla, J., 1939. Films trés dilués de quelques protéines; essai de détermination des masses moleculaires. Compt. rend. acad. sci., **208**: 1078–1080. (*263*)

Guggenheim, E. A. (See Fowler and Guggenheim, 1939.)

Guiteras, A. F. (See Flett, Haring, Guiteras, and Shapiro, 1945.)

Gutfreund, H. (See Bailey, Gutfreund, and Ogston, 1948.)

Haas, E., 1944. The effect of atabrine and quinine on isolated respiratory enzymes. Jour. Biol. Chem., **155**: 321–331. (*374*)

Haas, E., C. J. Harrer, and T. R. Hogness, 1942. Cytochrome reductase. II. Improved methods of isolation; inhibition and inactivation; reaction with oxygen. Jour. Biol. Chem., **143**: 341–349. (*396*)

Hadidian, Z., and H. Hoagland, 1940. Chemical pacemakers. Part I. Catalytic brain iron. Part II. Activation energy of chemical pacemakers. Jour. Gen. Physiol., **23**: 81–99. (*211, 212*)

Hadidian, Z., and H. Hoagland, 1941. Chemical pacemakers. III. Activation energies of some rate-limiting components of respiratory systems. Jour. Gen. Physiol., **24**: 339–352. (*211*)

Haldane, J. B. S. (See Briggs and Haldane, 1925.)

Haldane, J. B. S., 1930. Enzymes. Longmans, Green & Co., New York. (*174, 176*)

Hall, C. E. (See Schmitt, Bear, Hall, and Jakus, 1947.)

Hall, J. (See Bodine, Hall, and Carlson, 1940.)

Hall, V. E. (See Field and Hall, 1944.)

Halsey, G. (See Burte and Halsey, 1947.)

Haneda, Y. (See Harvey and Haneda, 1952.)

Hansen, E. C., 1894. Recherches sur les bactéries acétifiantes. Résumé compt. rend. trav. lab. Carlsberg, **3**: 182–216. (*192*)

Hardy, J. D., 1950. Physiological responses to heat and cold. Ann. Rev. Physiol., **12**: 119–144. (*188*)

Haring, R. C. (See Flett, Haring, Guiteras, and Shapiro, 1945.)

Harkins, W. D., and T. F. Anderson, 1938. Protein monolayers; films of oxidized cytochrome C. Jour. Biol. Chem., **125**: 369–376. (*264*)

Harkins, W. D., L. Fourt, and P. C. Fourt, 1940. Immunochemistry of catalase. II. Activity in multilayers. Jour. Biol. Chem., **132:** 111–118. *(266)*

Harless, E. (See Bibra and Harless, 1847.)

Harned, H. S., and N. D. Embree, 1934. The ionization constant of formic acid from 0 to 60°. Jour. Amer. Chem. Soc., **56:** 1042–1044, 2797. *(27, 225)*

Harren, F. (See Deuticke and Harren, 1938.)

Harrer, C. J. (See Haas, Harrer, and Hogness, 1942; Stotz, Harrer, Schultze, and King, 1937–1938.)

Harris, M. (See Sookne and Harris, 1937; Steinhardt, Fugitt, and Harris, 1940, 1941, 1942.)

Harris, M. M., and R. S. Harris, 1944. Effect *in vitro* of curare alkaloids and crude curare preparations on "true" and pseudo-cholinesterase activity. Proc. Soc. Exp. Biol. Med., **56:** 223–225. *(492)*

Harris, R. S. (See Harris and Harris, 1944.)

Harryman, W. K. (See Johnson, Carver, and Harryman, 1942.)

Hartmann, F. W. (See McClure, Hartmann, Schnedorf, and Schelling, 1939.)

Hartree, E. F. (See Keilin and Hartree, 1938.)

Hartzell, T. B. (See Larson, Hartzell, and Diehl, 1918.)

Harvey, A. M. (See Grob, Harvey, Langworthy, and Lilienthal, 1947; Grob, Lilienthal, and Harvey, 1947; Grob, Lilienthal, Harvey, and Jones, 1947.)

Harvey, E. N. (See Bronk, Harvey, and Johnson, 1952; Chance, Harvey, Johnson, and Millikan, 1940; Chase and Harvey, 1942; Johnson and Harvey, 1938; Johnson, Rexford, and Harvey, 1949; McElroy and Harvey, 1951; Strehler, Harvey, Chang, and Cormier, 1954.)

Harvey, E. N., 1913. The temperature limits of phosphorescence of luminous bacteria. Biochem. Bull., **2:** 456–457. *(187, 218)*

Harvey, E. N., 1917a. The chemistry of light production in living organisms. Pub. Carnegie Inst. Wash. No. 251, pp. 171–234. *(128, 179)*

Harvey, E. N., 1917b. Studies on bioluminescence. IV. The chemistry of light production in a Japanese ostracod crustacean, *Cypridina hilgendorfii*, Müller. Amer. Jour. Physiol., **42:** 318–341. *(169, 218)*

Harvey, E. N., 1917c. Studies on bioluminescence. VIII. The mechanism of the production of light during oxidation of pyrogallol. Jour. Biol. Chem., **31:** 311–336. *(160)*

Harvey, E. N., 1920. The Nature of Animal Light. J. B. Lippincott, Philadelphia. *(124, 218)*

Harvey, E. N., 1923. The minimum concentration of luciferin to give a visible luminescence. Science, **57:** 501–503. *(136)*

Harvey, E. N., 1924. Recent advances in bioluminescence. Physiol. Rev., **4:** 639–671. *(124)*

Harvey, E. N., 1926. Oxygen and luminescence, with a description of methods for removing oxygen from cells and fluids. Biol. Bull., **51:** 89–97. *(124)*

Harvey, E. N., 1927. Bioluminescence. Bull. Nat. Res. Council No. 59, pp. 50–62. *(124)*

Harvey, E. N., 1932. The evolution of bioluminescence and its relation to cell respiration. Proc. Amer. Phil. Soc., **71:** 135–141. *(183)*

Harvey, E. N., 1935. Luciferase, the enzyme concerned in luminescence of living organisms. Ergeb. Enzymforsch., **4:** 365–379. *(124)*

Harvey, E. N., 1940. Living Light. Princeton University Press. (*124, 125, 136, 159*)

Harvey, E. N., 1941. Review of bioluminescence. Ann. Rev. Biochem., **10**: 531–552. (*124*)

Harvey, E. N., 1942. Hydrostatic pressure and temperature in relation to stimulation and cyclosis in *Nitella flexilis*. Jour. Gen. Physiol., **25**: 855–863. (*355*)

Harvey, E. N., 1944. The nature of the red and green luminescence of the South American "Railroad worm," *Phryxothrix*. Jour. Cell. Comp. Physiol., **23**: 31–38. (*139*)

Harvey, E. N., 1951. Enzymes in luminescence. In: The Enzymes, Sumner and Myrbåck (Eds.). Chapter 61, pp. 581–608. Academic Press, New York. (*124*)

Harvey, E. N., 1952. Bioluminescence. Academic Press, New York. (*124, 125*)

Harvey, E. N., and Y. Haneda, 1952. Adenosine triphosphate and bioluminescence of various organisms. Arch. Biochem. Biophys., **35**: 470–471. (*135*)

Harvey, E. N., and I. M. Korr, 1938. Luminescence in absence of oxygen in the Ctenophore, *Mnemiopsis leidyi*. Jour. Cell. Comp. Physiol., **12**: 319–323. (*124*)

Harvey, E. N., and T. F. Morrison, 1923. The minimum concentration of oxygen for luminescence by luminous bacteria. Jour. Gen. Physiol., **6**: 13–19. (*124*)

Harvey, E. N., and P. A. Snell, 1931. The analysis of bioluminescences of short duration, recorded with photo-electric cell and string galvanometer. Jour. Gen. Physiol., **14**: 529–545. (*174*)

Hasenbring, O. (See Ebbecke and Hasenbring, 1935, 1936.)

Hastings, J. W. (See McElroy, Hastings, Sonnenfeld, and Coulombre, 1953.)

Hastings, J. W., 1952. Oxygen concentration and bioluminescence intensity. Jour. Cell. Comp. Physiol., **39**: 1–30. (*124*)

Haubrich, R. (See Ebbecke and Haubrich, 1939.)

Haubrich, R., 1937. Über die Druckresistenz der Erythrocyten. Pflüg. Arch. ges. Physiol., **239**: 304–313. (*295*)

Haubrich, R., 1939. Über die Retraktion bei der Blutgerinnung unter Druck. Pflüg. Arch. ges. Physiol., **243**: 39–42. (*308*)

Haurowitz, F., 1950. Chemistry and Biology of Proteins. Academic Press, New York. (*31*)

Hawkins, J. E. (See Maddock, Hawkins, and Holmes, 1939.)

Hawkins, R. D., and B. Mendel, 1949. Studies on cholinesterase. 6. The selective inhibition of true cholinesterase in vivo. Biochem. Jour., **44**: 260–264. (*490, 491, 493*)

Hayes, P. (See Benson, Kawachi, Hayes, and Calvin, 1952.)

Heatley, N. G. (See Chain, Florey, Abraham, and Heatley, 1949.)

Hecht, H. H. (See Woodbury, Hecht, and Christopherson, 1951; Woodbury, Woodbury, and Hecht, 1950.)

Hecht, H. H., L. A. Woodbury, J. W. Woodbury, and A. R. Christopherson, 1950. Observations on the origin of the electrocardiogram: Potential variations of single heart muscle fibers *in situ*. Jour. Clin. Invest., **29**: 820–821. (*496*)

Hedén, C-G., and R. W. G. Wyckoff, 1949. The electron microscopy of heated bacteria. Jour. Bact., **58**: 153–160.   (*232, 233*)

Heilbrunn, L. V., 1924a. The colloid chemistry of protoplasm. III. The viscosity of protoplasm at various temperatures. Amer. Jour. Physiol., **68**: 645–648. (*345*)

Heilbrunn, L. V., 1924b. The colloid chemistry of protoplasm. IV. The heat coagulation of protoplasm. Amer. Jour. Physiol., **69**: 190–199.   (*345, 453*)

Heilbrunn, L. V., 1925. The action of ether on protoplasm. Biol. Bull., **49**: 461–475.   (*500*)

Heilbrunn, L. V., 1943. An Outline of General Physiology. W. R. Saunders Co., Philadelphia.   (*487*)

Heitler, W., and F. London, 1927. Wechselwirkung neutraler Atome und homöopolare Bindung nach der Quantenmechanik. Zeitschr. Physik., **44**: 455–472.   (*14, 86*)

Hellerman, L. (See Gemmill and Hellerman, 1937.)

Hellerman, L., 1937. Reversible inactivations of hydrolytic enzymes. Physiol. Rev., **17**: 454–484.   (*438*)

Hellerman, L., 1939. Reversible processes in the control of activity of certain enzymes; with a preliminary note on the oxidation of urease by porphyrindine. Cold Spr. Harb. Symp., **7**: 165–173.   (*438*)

Helmholtz, H., 1850. Messungen über den zeitlichen Verlauf der Zuckung animalischer Muskeln und die Fortpflanzungsgeschwindigkeit der Reizung in den Nerven. Arch. Anat. Physiol. wissensch. Med., pp. 276–364.   (*503*)

Helmholtz, H., 1882. Die Thermodynamik chemischer Vorgänge. Sitzungsber. Akad. Wiss. Berlin, **1**: 22–39.   (*49*)

Hemmi, H. (See Meyer and Hemmi, 1935.)

Henderson, F. G. (See Chen, Anderson, Henderson, and Mills, 1943.)

Henderson, P., 1907. Zur Thermodynamik der Flüssigkeiten. Zeitschr. physik. Chem., **59**: 118–127.   (*559*)

Henderson, P., 1908. Zur Thermodynamik der Flüssigkeiten. Zeitschr. physik. Chem., **63**: 325–345.   (*559*)

Henderson, V. E., 1930. The present status of the theories of narcosis. Physiol. Rev., **10**: 171–220.   (*284, 487, 508, 509*)

Henrici, A. T., 1928a. Morphologic variations of bacteria in the lag phase. Jour. Inf. Dis., **38**: 54–65.   (*365*)

Henrici, A. T., 1928b. Morphologic Variation and the Rate of Growth of Bacteria. Baillière, Tindall and Cox, London.   (*365*)

Henry, R. J. (See Fisher and Henry, 1943.)

Henry, R. J., 1944. The Mode of Action of Sulfonamides. Josiah Macy, Jr., Foundation, Review Series, vol. 2, No. 1, New York.   (*378*)

Heppel, L. A., 1939. The electrolytes of muscle and liver in potassium-depleted rats. Amer. Jour. Physiol., **127**: 385–392.   (*669*)

Heppel, L. A., 1940. The diffusion of radioactive sodium into the muscles of potassium-deprived rats. Amer. Jour. Physiol., **128**: 449–454.   (*669*)

Hermann, L., 1866. Über die Wirkungsweise einer Gruppe von Giften. Arch. Anat. Physiol. wiss. Med., pp. 27–40.   (*509*)

Herold, J. L. (See Ephrussi and Herold, 1945.)

Herriott, R. M. (See Northrop, Kunitz, and Herriott, 1948.)

Herzfeld, K. F., 1919a. Zur Theorie der Reaktionsgeschwindigkeit in Gasen. Zeitschr. Elektrochem., **25**: 301–304. (*22*)

Herzfeld, K. F., 1919b. Zur Theorie der Reaktionsgeschwindigkeiten in Gasen. Ann. Physik, Ser. 4, **59**: 635–667. (*22*)

Heymann, E., 1935. Studies on sol-gel transformation. I. Inverse sol-gel transformation of methyl cellulose in water. Trans. Farad. Soc., **31**: 846–864. (*344, 347*)

Heymann, E., 1936a. Studies on sol-gel transformation. II. Dilatometric investigations on iron hydroxide, gelatin, methyl cellulose, silicic acid and viscose. Trans. Farad. Soc., **32**: 462–473. (*344, 347*)

Heymann, E., 1936b. Dilatometric investigations on the heat denaturation of proteins. Biochem. Jour., **30**: 127–131. (*335, 342*)

Hill, A. V. (See Gasser and Hill, 1924.)

Hill, A. V., 1926. Muscular Activity. Williams & Wilkins Co., Baltimore. (*739, 740*)

Hill, A. V., 1935. Excitation and accommodation in nerve. Proc. Roy. Soc. Lond., B **119**: 305–355. (*623*)

Hill, A. V., 1938. The heat of shortening and the dynamic constants of muscle. Proc. Roy. Soc. Lond., B **126**: 136–195. (*702, 708, 709, 711, 713, 715, 717, 722, 737, 738, 739, 741, 742, 743, 744, 749*)

Hill, A. V., 1949. The abrupt transition from rest to activity in muscle. Proc. Roy. Soc. Lond., B **136**: 399–420. (*704, 720, 723, 724*)

Hill, A. V., and others, 1950. A discussion on muscular contraction and relaxation: their physical and chemical basis. Proc. Roy. Soc. Lond., B **137**: 40–87. (*709, 750*)

Hill, D. L. (See Bodine and Hill, 1945; Bodine, Tahmisian, and Hill, 1944.)

Hill, R., 1937. Oxygen evolved by isolated chloroplasts. Nature, **139**: 881–882. (*35*)

Hill, T. L., 1952. Some models for the transfer of chemical free energy into contractile work in muscle. Record Chem. Progr., **13**: 101–108. (*753*)

Hill, T. L., 1953. Energetics and molecular mechanisms in muscle action. Part II. Statistical thermodynamical treatment of contractile systems. Discussions Farad. Soc., 1953, No. 13, 132–145. (*753*)

Hill, T. L., and M. F. Morales, 1952. Thermodynamics of free energy transfer in certain models of muscle action. Arch. Biochem. and Biophysics, **37**: 425–441. (*753*)

Himwich, H. E., K. M. Bowman, J. F. Fazekas, and W. Goldfarb, 1940. Temperature and brain metabolism. Amer. Jour. Med. Sci., **200**: 347–353. (*250*)

Hinshelwood, C. N., 1933. The Kinetics of Chemical Change in Gaseous Systems. Oxford University Press. (*5*)

Hinshelwood, C. N., 1940. The Kinetics of Chemical Change. Oxford University Press. (*5*)

Hinshelwood, C. N., 1946. The Chemical Kinetics of the Bacterial Cell. Clarendon Press, Oxford. (*455*)

Hite, B. H. (See Giddings, Allard, and Hite, 1929.)

Hoagland, H. (See Hadidian and Hoagland, 1940; 1941.)

Hoagland, H., 1936a. Some pacemaker aspects of rhythmic activity in the nervous system. Cold Spr. Harb. Symp., **4**: 267–284. (*201*)

Hoagland, H., 1936b. Temperature characteristics of the "Berger rhythm" in man. Science, **83**: 84–85. (*214*)

Hoagland, H., 1936c. Pacemakers of human brain waves in normals and in general paretics. Amer. Jour. Physiol., **116**: 604–615. (*201, 213, 214*)

Hoagland, H., and C. T. Perkins, 1934–1935. Some temperature characteristics in man. Jour. Gen. Physiol., **18**: 399–408. (*200*)

Hoagland, H., M. A. Rubin, and D. E. Cameron, 1937. The electroencephalogram of schizophrenics during insulin hypoglycemia and recovery. Amer. Jour. Physiol., **120**: 559–570. (*505*)

Hobbiger, F., 1951. Inhibition of cholinesterases by irreversible inhibitors *in vitro* and *in vivo*. Brit. Jour. Pharm. Chem., **6**: 21–30. (*499*)

Hobby, G. L., K. Meyer, and E. Chaffee, 1942. Observations on the mechanism of action of penicillin. Proc. Soc. Exp. Biol. Med., **50**: 281–285. (*404*)

Hock, R. (See Scholander, Hock, Walters, and Irving, 1950.)

Hodgkin, A. L. (See Nastuk and Hodgkin, 1950.)

Hodgkin, A. L., 1937. Evidence for electrical transmission in nerve. Jour. Physiol., **90**: 183–232. (*664, 665, 666*)

Hodgkin, A. L., 1951. The ionic basis of electrical activity in nerve and muscle. Biol. Rev. Proc. Camb. Phil. Soc., **26**: 339–409. (*496, 604, 610, 668, 669, 670, 680, 684, 685, 687*)

Hodgkin, A. L., and A. F. Huxley, 1939. Action potentials recorded from inside a nerve fiber. Nature, **144**: 710–711. (*496, 623, 684*)

Hodgkin, A. L., and A. F. Huxley, 1945. Resting and action potentials in single nerve fibers. Jour. Physiol., **104**: 176–195. (*496, 623, 684, 685*)

Hodgkin, A. L., and A. F. Huxley, 1952a. Currents carried by potassium and sodium ions through the membrane of the giant axon of *Loligo*. Jour. Physiol., **116**: 449–472. (*641, 695, 696*)

Hodgkin, A. L., and A. F. Huxley, 1952b. The components of membrane conductance in the giant axon of *Loligo*. Jour. Physiol., **116**: 473–496. (*641, 695*)

Hodgkin, A. L., and A. F. Huxley, 1952c. The dual effect of the membrane potential on sodium conductance in the giant axon of *Loligo*. Jour. Physiol., **116**: 497–506. (*641, 695*)

Hodgkin, A. L., and A. F. Huxley, 1952d. A quantitative description of membrane current and its application to conduction and excitation in nerve. Jour. Physiol., **117**: 500–544. (*641, 696*)

Hodgkin, A. L., A. F. Huxley, and B. Katz, 1949. Ionic currents underlying activity in the giant axon of the squid. Arch. Sci. Physiol., **3**: 129–150. (*687, 689, 690*)

Hodgkin, A. L., A. F. Huxley, and B. Katz, 1952. Measurement of current-voltage relations in the membrane of the giant axon of *Loligo*. Jour. Physiol., **116**: 424–448. (*636, 637, 639, 641, 695*)

Hodgkin, A. L., and B. Katz, 1949a. The effect of sodium ions on the electrical activity of the giant axon of the squid. Jour. Physiol., **108**: 37–77. (*562, 564, 622, 623, 626, 674, 685*)

Hodgkin, A. L., and B. Katz, 1949b. The effect of temperature on the electrical activity of the giant axon of the squid. Jour. Physiol., **109**: 240–249. (*502–503*)

Höber, R., 1907. Beiträge zur physikalischen chemie der Erregung und der Narkose. Pflüg. Arch. ges. Physiol., **120**: 492–516. (*500*)

Höber, R., 1926. Physikalische Chemie der Zelle und der Gewebe. Englemann, Leipzig. (*500*)

Höber, R., 1945. In: Physical Chemistry of Cells and Tissues, R. Höber (Ed.). The Blakiston Co., Philadelphia. Chapter on the influence of narcotics on cell activity, and section on passive penetration and active transfer in animal and plant tissues. (*429, 500, 509, 604, 670*)

Höber, R., 1946. The membrane theory. Ann. N. Y. Acad. Sci., **47**: 381–394. (*684*)

Hoefler, K., and F. Weber, 1926. Die wirkung der Äthernarkose auf die Harnstoffpermeabilität von Pflanzenzellen. Jahr. wiss. Bot., **65**: 643–738. (*500*)

van't Hoff, J. H., 1884. Études de Dynamique Chimique. Frederik Muller and Co., Amsterdam. (*3*)

Hofmeister, F., 1902. Über Bau und Gruppierung der Eiweisskörper. Ergeb. Physiol., **1**: 759–802. (*256*)

Hogness, T. R. (See Haas, Harrer, and Hogness, 1942.)

Holder, H. G., and E. M. MacKay, 1942. Wound therapy. With special reference to application of carbamide-sulfonamide mixtures to contaminated and infected wounds. Military Surgeon, **90**: 509–518. (*482*)

Holder, H. G., and E. M. MacKay, 1943. Carbamide-sulfonamide mixtures in wound therapy. Surgery, **13**: 677–682. (*482*)

Holdheide, W., 1931. Über Plasmoptyse bei *Hydrodictyon utriculatum*. Planta, **15**: 244–298. (*500*)

Hollinger, H., F. A. Fuhrman, J. J. Lewis, and J. Field, 1949. The effect of sodium azide on respiration of rat skeletal muscle and brain cortex *in vitro*, with special reference to temperature. Jour. Cell. Comp. Physiol., **33**: 223–246. (*466*)

Holman, R. T. (See Schlenk and Holman, 1950.)

Holmes, E. (See Maddock, Hawkins, and Holmes, 1939.)

Holtham, S. B., and F. Schütz, 1949. The effect of cyanate on the stability of proteins. Biochimica Biophysica Acta, **3**: 65–81. (*271*)

Holyoke, E. D., and F. H. Johnson, 1951. The influence of hydrostatic pressure and *p*H on the rate of lysis of *Micrococcus lysodeikticus* by lysozyme. Arch. Biochem. Biophys., **31**: 41–48. (*315*)

Hooker, D., 1914. Amoeboid movement in the corial melanophores of frogs. Anat. Record, **8**: 103. (*353*)

Hopkins, F. G., 1930. Denaturation of proteins by urea and related substances. Nature, **126**: 328–330, 383–384. (*274, 282, 284*)

Hotchkiss, R. D. (See Linderstrøm-Lang, Hotchkiss, and Johansen, 1938.)

Hotchkiss, R. D., 1944. Gramicidin, tyrocidine and tyrothricin. Adv. Enzymol., **4**: 153–199. (*396*)

Houck, C. R., 1942. The effects of bichloride of mercury upon the luminescence and respiration of the luminous bacterium, *Achromobacter fischeri*. Jour. Cell. Comp. Physiol., **20**: 277–293. (*375, 384*)

Hsiek, W-M. (See Chang, Hsiek, and Lu, 1939.)

Huang, T-C, and H. Wu, 1930. Studies on denaturation of proteins. X. Osmotic pressure of denatured egg albumin and methemoglobin in concentrated urea solutions. Chinese Jour. Physiol., **4**: 221–229. (*253, 254*)

Huber, C. (See Johnson, Eyring, Steblay, Chaplin, Huber, and Gherardi, 1945.)

Huebner, C. J. (See Stahman, Huebner, and Link, 1941.)

Huggins, M. L., 1943. The structure of fibrous proteins. Chem. Rev., **32**: 195–218. (*258*)

Hughes, C. W. (See Coblentz and Hughes, 1926.)

Hughes, W. H. (See Fleming, Voureka, Kramer, and Hughes, 1950.)

Hughes, W. L. (See Scatchard, Strong, Hughes, Ashworth, and Sparrow, 1945.)

Hurley, V. (See Crossman, Ruggiero, Hurley, and Allen, 1942.)

Huskins, C. L., 1951. Science, Cytology, and Society. American Scientist, **39**: 688–699. (*699*)

Huxley, A. F. (See Hodgkin and Huxley, 1939, 1945, 1952a–d; Hodgkin, Huxley, and Katz, 1949, 1952.)

Huxley, A. F., and R. Stämpfli, 1951. Effect of potassium and sodium on resting and action potentials of single myelinated nerve fibres. Jour. Physiol., **112**: 496–508. (*685*)

Ikeda, K., 1897. Allegemiene Beziehungen zwischen Concentration und Giftwirkung der Quecksilberchloridlösungen. Zeitschr. Hyg. Infek., **25**: 95–101. (*454, 460*)

Ilefeld, F. W., 1943. Carbamide sulfonamide mixtures. Use in treatment of compound fractures and traumatic wounds. Surg., Gynecol. Obstet., **76**: 427–437. (*482*)

Inman, V. T. (See Ralston, Inman, Strait, and Shaffrath, 1947.)

Irving, L. (See Scholander, Hock, Walters, and Irving, 1950.)

Isaacs, M. L., 1932. A theory of disinfection. Science, **75**: 46–48. (*455*)

Ito, M. (See Miyake and Ito, 1923; 1924.)

Jacobs, M. H., 1935. Diffusion processes. Ergebn. Physiol., **12**: 1–160. (*516*)

Jacobs, M. H., and A. K. Parpart, 1932. Osmotic properties of the erythrocyte. IV. Is the permeability of the erythrocyte to water decreased by narcotics? Biol. Bull., **62**: 313–327. (*500*)

Jacobs, M. H., and A. K. Parpart, 1937. The influence of certain alcohols on the permeability of erythrocytes. Biol. Bull., **73**: 380–381. (*500*)

Jacobsen, C. F. (See Linderstrøm-Lang and Jacobsen, 1941.)

Jacobsen, C. F., 1942. The contraction accompanying the splitting of peptide bonds in synthetic substrates for trypsin and chymotrypsin. Compt. rend. trav. lab. Carlsberg, sér. chim., **24**: 281–286. (*335, 336*)

Jacobsen, C. F., 1947. The activation of chymotrypsinogen. Compt. rend. trav. lab. Carlsberg, sér. chim., **25**: 325–437. (*335, 344*)

Jacobsen, C. F., 1949. A comparison of different β-lactoglobulin samples. Compt. rend. trav. lab. Carlsberg, sér. chim., (18) **26**: 455–475. (*255*)

Jacobsen, C. F., and L. K. Christensen, 1948. Influence of temperature on the urea denaturation of β-lactoglobulin. Nature, **161**: 30–31. (*282, 283*)

Jacobsen, C. F., and K. Linderstrøm-Lang, 1949. Salt linkages in proteins. Nature, **164**: 411. (*280, 336*)

Jacobsen, H. C. (See Beijerinck and Jacobsen, 1908.)

Jacobson, L. O., M. E. Robson, E. K. Marks, and M. C. Goldman, 1949. The effect of X-radiation on antibody formation. Jour. lab. clin. med., **34**: 1612–1613. (*32*)

Jaffee, O. (See Marsland and Jaffee, 1949.)

Jakus, M. A. (See Schmitt, Bear, Hall, and Jakus, 1947.)

James, H. M., and A. S. Coolidge, 1933. The ground state of the hydrogen molecule. Jour. Chem. Phys., 1: 825–835. (86)

Jansen, E. F. (See Curl and Jansen, 1950a; 1950b.)

Jaubert, J. (See Pasteur, Jaubert, and Chamberland, 1878.)

Johansen, A., and J. E. Thygesen, 1948. Direct dilatometry of peptidase activity of normal human serum and hemolysate. Compt. rend. trav. lab. Carlsberg, 26: 369–402. (335)

Johansen, G. (See Linderstrøm-Lang, Hotchkiss, and Johansen, 1938.)

John, H. M. (See Nachmansohn and John, 1944, 1945; Nachmansohn, John, and Wallach, 1943.)

Johnson, F. (See Scholander, Hock, Walters, Johnson, and Irving, 1950.)

Johnson, F. H. (See Botts, Johnson, and Morales, 1951; Bronk, Harvey, and Johnson, 1952; Brown, Johnson, and Marsland, 1942; Campbell and Johnson, 1946; Chance, Harvey, Johnson, and Millikan, 1940; Eyring, Johnson, and Gensler, 1946; Foster and Johnson, 1951; Foster, Johnson, and Miller, 1949; Fraser and Johnson, 1951; Fraser, Johnson, and Baker, 1949; Holyoke and Johnson, 1951; Koffler, Johnson, and Wilson, 1947; Schlegel and Johnson, 1949; Strehler and Johnson, 1954; ZoBell and Johnson, 1949.)

Johnson, F. H., 1934. Action of 2,4-dinitrophenol on the respiration and oxidations of *Aerobacter cloacae*. Jour. Tenn. Acad. Sci., 9: 288–291. (396)

Johnson, F. H., 1936. The aerobic oxidation of carbohydrates by luminous bacteria, and the inhibition of oxidation by certain sugars. Jour. Cell. Comp. Physiol., 8: 439–463.

Johnson, F. H., 1938. Hexose oxidation by luminous bacteria. III. The escape of respiration and luminescence from inhibition by alpha methylglucoside, with a note on urethanes. Jour. Cell. Comp. Physiol., 12: 281–294. (180)

Johnson, F. H., 1939. Total luminescence of bacterial suspensions in relation to the reactions concerned in luminescence. Enzymologia, 7: 72-81. (180)

Johnson, F. H., 1942. Mechanism of p-aminobenzoic acid action and the parallel effects of ethyl carbamate (urethane). Science, 95: 104–105. (485)

Johnson, F. H., 1947. Bacterial luminescence. Adv. Enzymol., 7: 215–264. (182)

Johnson, F. H., 1948. Bioluminescence: A reaction rate tool. Sci. Mon., 67: 225–235. (766)

Johnson, F. H., M. B. Baylor, and D. Fraser, 1948. The thermal denaturation of tobacco mosaic virus in relation to hydrostatic pressure. Arch. Biochem., 19: 237–245. (328, 329)

Johnson, F. H., D. E. Brown, and D. A. Marsland, 1942a. A basic mechanism in the biological effects of temperature, pressure and narcotics. Science, 95: 200–203. (215, 218, 309, 380, 422)

Johnson, F. H., D. E. Brown, and D. A. Marsland, 1942b. Pressure reversal of the action of certain narcotics. Jour. Cell. Comp. Physiol., 20: 269–276. (309, 408, 422)

Johnson, F. H., and D. H. Campbell, 1945. The retardation of protein denaturation by hydrostatic pressure. Jour. Cell. Comp. Physiol., 26: 43–46. (327, 329)

Johnson, F. H., and D. H. Campbell, 1946. Pressure and protein denaturation. Jour. Biol. Chem., 163: 689–698. (327, 444)

Johnson, F. H., C. M. Carver, and W. K. Harryman, 1942. Luminous bacterial auxanograms in relation to heavy metals and narcotics, self-photographed in color. Jour. Bact., 44: 703–714. (485)

Johnson, F. H., and A. M. Chase, 1942. Sulfonamide and urethane inhibition of Cypridina luminescence in vitro. Jour. Cell. Comp. Physiol., 19: 151–161. (181, 377, 378, 471, 473)

Johnson, F. H., and H. Eyring, 1944. The nature of the luciferin-luciferase system. Jour. Amer. Chem. Soc., 66: 848. (132, 136)

Johnson, F. H., H. Eyring, and W. Kearns, 1943. A quantitative theory of synergism and antagonism among diverse inhibitors, with special reference to sulfanilamide and urethane. Arch. Biochem., 3: 1–31. (429, 430, 469, 472, 473, 474, 475, 477, 478, 479)

Johnson, F. H., H. Eyring, R. Steblay, H. Chaplin, C. Huber, and G. Gherardi, 1945. The nature and control of reactions in bioluminescence. With special reference to the mechanism of reversible and irreversible inhibitions by hydrogen and hydroxyl ions, temperature, pressure, alcohol, urethane, and sulfanilamide in bacteria. Jour. Gen. Physiol., 28: 463–537. (181, 316, 326, 333, 378, 385, 386, 387, 391, 392, 399, 400, 409, 410, 419, 423, 424, 426, 427, 428, 439, 441, 445)

Johnson, F. H., H. Eyring, and R. W. Williams, 1942. The nature of enzyme inhibitions in bacterial luminescence: sulfanilamide, urethane, temperature and pressure. Jour. Cell. Comp. Physiol., 20: 247–268. (181, 215, 219, 226, 227, 309, 373, 383, 419)

Johnson, F. H., and E. A. Flagler, 1951a. Hydrostatic pressure reversal of narcosis in tadpoles. Science, 112: 91–92. (512, 513)

Johnson, F. H., and E. A. Flagler, 1951b. Activity of narcotized amphibian larvae under hydrostatic pressure. Jour. Cell. Comp. Physiol., 37: 15–25. (512, 513)

Johnson, F. H., E. A. Flagler, R. Simpson, and K. McGeer, 1951. The inhibition of bacterial luminescence by a homologous series of carbamates. Jour. Cell. Comp. Physiol., 37: 1–14. (334, 429, 430, 431, 432, 434, 435, 436)

Johnson, F. H., and D. H. Gray, 1949. Nuclei and large bodies of luminous bacteria in relation to salt concentration, osmotic pressure, temperature and urethane. Jour. Bact., 58: 675–688. (361, 365, 450, 451)

Johnson, F. H., and E. N. Harvey, 1938. Bacterial luminescence, respiration and viability in relation to osmotic pressure and specific salts of sea water. Jour. Cell. Comp. Physiol., 11: 213–232. (182)

Johnson, F. H., W. J. Kauzmann, and R. L. Gensler, 1948. The urethan inhibition of invertase activity in relation to hydrostatic pressure. Arch. Biochem., 19: 229–236. (330, 434)

Johnson, F. H., and I. Lewin, 1946a. The action of quinine on dehydrogenases of E. coli. Jour. Cell. Comp. Physiol., 28: 1–22. (208, 444)

Johnson, F. H., and I. Lewin, 1946b. The disinfection of E. coli in relation to temperature, hydrostatic pressure and quinine. Jour. Cell. Comp. Physiol., 28: 23–45. (333, 455, 458, 462)

Johnson, F. H., and I. Lewin, 1946c. The growth rate of *E. coli* in relation to temperature, quinine and coenzyme. Jour. Cell. Comp. Physiol., **28**: 47–75. (*230, 231, 403*)

Johnson, F. H., and I. Lewin, 1946d. The influence of pressure, temperature and quinine on the rates of growth and disinfection of *E. coli* in the logarithmic growth phase. Jour. Cell. Comp. Physiol., **28**: 77–97. (*326, 333, 363, 364, 366, 462*)

Johnson, F. H., and I. Lewin, 1947. The rates of growth and disinfection of *Escherichia coli* in relation to *p*H, quinine and temperature. Ann. Leeuw., **12**: 177–185. (*404*)

Johnson, F. H., and K. Moore, 1941. Sulfonamide inhibition of bacterial luminescence. Proc. Soc. Exp. Biol. Med., **48**: 323–325. (*379*)

Johnson, F. H., D. Rexford, and E. N. Harvey, 1949. The hypothetical structure of luciferin. Jour. Cell. Comp. Physiol., **33**: 133–136. (*133*)

Johnson, F. H., and F. McK. Schlegel, 1948. Hemoglobin oxygenation in relation to hydrostatic pressure. Jour. Cell. Comp. Physiol., **31**: 421–425. (*254*)

Johnson, F. H., K. L. van Schouwenburg, and A. van der Burg, 1939. The flash of luminescence following anaerobiosis of luminous bacteria. Enzymol., **7**: 195–224. (*130, 183, 184, 185*)

Johnson, F. H., and G. G. Wright, 1946. Influence of hydrostatic pressure on the denaturation of *Staphylococcus* antitoxin at 65°C. Proc. Nat. Acad. Sci., **32**: 21–25. (*267*)

Johnson, F. H., and C. E. ZoBell, 1949a. The retardation of thermal disinfection of *Bacillus subtilis* spores by hydrostatic pressure. Jour. Bact., **57**: 353–358. (*333, 463*)

Johnson, F. H., and C. E. ZoBell, 1949b. The acceleration of spore disinfection by urethan and its retardation by hydrostatic pressure. Jour. Bact., **57**: 359–362. (*463*)

Johnson, M. W. (See Sverdrup, Johnson, and Fleming, 1942.)

Jones, B. F. (See Grob, Lilienthal, Harvey, and Jones, 1947.)

Jonxis, J. H. P., 1939. On the spreading of different haemoglobins, muscle haemoglobins and cytochrome C. Biochem. Jour., **33**: 1743–1751. (*264*)

Josephson, E. S. (See Sizer and Josephson, 1942.)

Joule, J. P., 1849. On the mechanical equivalent of heat. Proc. Roy. Soc. Lond., **5**: 839. (*43*)

Jowett, M., 1938. The action of narcotics on brain respiration. Jour. Physiol., **92**: 322–335. (*446, 447, 448, 449, 505, 506*)

Jowett, M., and J. H. Quastel, 1937. The effects of ether on brain oxidations. Biochem. Jour., **31**: 1101–1112. (*446, 505*)

Juhling, L. (See Diebold and Juhling, 1938.)

Kaiser, E. (See Buchthal and Kaiser, 1948, 1949, 1951.)

Kaiser, H. F. G. (See Cohen and Kaiser, 1914–1915.)

Kamm, O., 1921. The relation between structure and physiological action of the alcohols. Jour. Amer. Pharm. Assoc., **10**: 87–89. (*462*)

Kanda, S., 1924. Physico-chemical studies on bioluminescence V. The physical and chemical nature of the luciferine of *Cypridina hilgendorfii*. Amer. Jour. Physiol., **68**: 435–444. (*127*)

Kanda, S., 1929. Physico-chemical studies on bioluminescence VII. The solubility of *Cypridina* luciferin in organic solvents. Sci. Papers Inst. Phys. Chem. Res. Tokyo, **10**: 91–98.   (*127*)

Kanitz, A., 1915. Temperatur und Lebensvorgänge. Gebrüder Borntraeger, Berlin.   (*195*)

Karush, F., 1950a. Heterogeneity of the binding sites of bovine serum albumin. Jour. Amer. Chem. Soc., **72**: 2705–2713.   (*255, 415*)

Karush, F., 1950b. The competitive interaction of organic anions with bovine serum albumin. Jour. Amer. Chem. Soc., **72**: 2714–2718.   (*415*)

Karush, F., and M. Sonnenberg, 1949. Interaction of homologous alkyl sulfates with bovine serum albumin. Jour. Amer. Chem. Soc., **71**: 1369–1376. (*415*)

Kasha, M. (See Lewis and Kasha, 1944.)

Katz, B. (See Hodgkin, Huxley, and Katz, 1949, 1952; Hodgkin and Katz, 1949a, 1949b.)

Katz, B., 1937. Experimental evidence for a non-conducted response of nerve to subthreshold stimulation. Proc. Roy. Soc. Lond., B **124**: 244–276. (*614, 615*)

Katz, B., 1939a. Electric Excitation of Nerve. Oxford University Press.   (*604, 610, 612, 624, 655, 661*)

Katz, B., 1939b. The relation between force and speed in muscular contraction. Jour. Physiol., **96**: 45–64.   (*736*)

Katz, B., 1952. The properties of the nerve membrane and its relation to the conduction of impulses. Soc. Exp. Biol. Symp., **6**: 16–38.   (*698*)

Kauzmann, W. J. (See Johnson, Kauzmann, and Gensler, 1948; Simpson, Watson, Levedahl, Schellman, Frensdorff, and Kauzmann, 1951.)

Kauzmann, W., A. M. Chase, and E. H. Brigham, 1949. Studies on cell enzyme systems. III. Effects of temperature on the constants in the Michaelis-Menton relation for the luciferin-luciferase system. Arch. Biochem., **24**: 281–288. (*126, 176, 177, 314*)

Kavanau, J. L., 1950. Enzyme kinetics and the rate of biological processes. Jour. Gen. Physiol., **34**: 193–209.   (*206*)

Kawachi, S. (See Benson, Kawachi, Hayes, and Calvin, 1952.)

Kearns, W. (See Johnson, Eyring, and Kearns, 1943.)

Keilin, D., 1930. Cytochrome and intracellular oxidase. Proc. Roy. Soc. Lond., B **106**: 418–444.   (*374*)

Keilin, D., and E. F. Hartree, 1938. Cytochrome oxidase. Proc. Roy. Soc. Lond., B **125**: 171–186.   (*374*)

Keltch, A. K. (See Krahl, Keltch, and Clowes, 1940.)

Kelvin, William Thomson, 1853. On the dynamical theory of heat, with numerical results deduced from Mr. Joule's equivalent of a thermal unit, and M. Regnault's observations on steam. Trans. Roy. Soc. Edinburgh, **20**: 261–288. (*43*)

van der Kerk, G. J. M. (See Kluyver, van der Kerk, and van der Burg, 1942.)

van der Kerk, G. J. M., 1942. Onderzoekingen over de bioluminescentie der lichtbacteriën. Thesis. Utrecht.   (*133, 178*)

Keynes, R. D., 1949. The movements of radioactive ions in resting and stimulated nerve. Arch. Sci. Physiol., **3**: 165–176.   (*549, 626, 644, 676*)

Kilpatrick, M. (See Shinohara and Kilpatrick, 1934.)

Kimball, G. E. (See Eyring and Kimball, 1933; Eyring, Walter, and Kimball, 1944.)

Kimler, A. (See Shoup and Kimler, 1934.)

King, C. G. (See Stotz, Harrer, Schultze, and King, 1937–1938.)

Kipnis, D. M. (See McElroy and Kipnis, 1947.)

Kirkwood, J. G. (See Cann and Kirkwood, 1950; Riseman and Kirkwood, 1948.)

Kirkwood, J. G., and F. H. Westheimer, 1938. The electrostatic influence of substituents on the dissociation constants of organic acids. Parts I and II. Jour. Chem. Phys., 6: 506–517. (751)

Kistiakowsky, G. B., and R. Lumry, 1949. Anomalous temperature effects in the hydrolysis of urea by urease. Jour. Amer. Chem. Soc., 71: 2006–2013. (211)

Kitching, J. A. (See Pease and Kitching, 1939.)

Kitching, J. A., and D. C. Pease, 1939. The liquefaction of the tentacles of suctorian protozoa at high hydrostatic pressures. Jour. Cell. Comp. Physiol., 14: 410–412. (347)

Kjeldahl, J., 1881. Nogle Iagttagelser over Invertin. Medd. Carlsberg Lab. I. Bind. Tredie Hefte, pp. 331–338. (197, 198)

Klotz, I. M., 1944. The mode of action of sulfonamides. Jour. Amer. Chem. Soc., 66: 459–464. (401)

Klotz, I. M., 1950. The nature of some ion-protein complexes. Cold Spr. Harb. Symp., 14: 97–112. (415)

Klotz, I. M., and H. G. Curme, 1948. The thermodynamics of metallo-protein combinations. Copper with bovine serum albumin. Jour. Amer. Chem. Soc., 70: 939–943. (415)

Kluyver, A. J., 1931. The Chemical Activities of Micro-organisms. University Press, London. (24)

Kluyver, A. J., G. J. M. van der Kerk, and A. van der Burg, 1942a. The effect of radiation on light emission by luminous bacteria I. Proc. Nederl. Akad. Wetensch., 45: 886–894. (131, 133)

Kluyver, A. J., G. J. M. van der Kerk, and A. van der Burg, 1942b. The effect of radiation on light emission by luminous bacteria II. Proc. Nederl. Akad. Wetensch., 45: 962–967. (131, 133)

Knaysi, G., 1930. Do bacteria die logarithmically? Jour. Inf. Dis., 47: 322–327. (455)

Koch, Robert, 1881. Ueber Disinfection. Mitt. Kaiserlichen Gesundheitsamte, 1: 234–282. (460)

Kochmann, M., 1923. Einfluss der Narkotica der Fettreihe auf den Quellungszustand der Zellkolloide. Biochem. Zeitschr., 136: 49–65. (432)

Koelle, G. B. (See Crescitelli, Koelle, and Gilman, 1946.)

Koelle, G. B., 1946. Protection of cholinesterase against irreversible inactivation by di-isopropyl fluorophosphate in vitro. Jour. Pharm. Exp. Therap., 88: 232–237. (500)

Koelle, G. B., and A. Gilman, 1949. Anticholinesterase drugs. Pharm. Revs., 1: 166–216. (488)

Koffler, H., F. H. Johnson, and P. W. Wilson, 1947. Combined influence of temperature and urethane on the respiration of Rhizobium. Jour. Amer. Chem. Soc., 69: 1113–1117. (208, 228, 229, 419, 420, 421)

Kohn, H. I., 1943. Antagonists (excluding *p*-aminobenzoic acid), dynamists and synergists of the sulfonamides. Ann. N. Y. Acad. Sci., **44**: 503–524. (*377*)

Kopac, M. J. (Chairman), 1951. The Mechanisms of Cell Division. Ann. N. Y. Acad. Sci., **51**: 1279–1546. (*353*)

Kornmüller, A. E., 1935. Die bioelektrischen Erscheinungen architektonischer Felder der Grosshirnrinde. Biol. Rev. Proc. Camb. Phil. Soc., **10**: 383–426. (*214*)

Korr, I. M. (See Harvey and Korr, 1938.)

Korr, I. M., 1935. The relation between cell integrity and bacterial luminescence. Biol. Bull., **68**: 347–354. (*178*)

Korr, I. M., 1936. The luciferin-oxyluciferin system. Jour. Amer. Chem. Soc., **58**: 1060. (*129*)

Korsgaard Christensen. (See Christensen, L. Korsgaard.)

Krahl, M. E., and G. H. A. Clowes, 1938. Physiological effects of nitro- and halo-substituted phenols in relation to extracellular and intracellular hydrogen ion concentration. II. Experiments with *Arbacia* eggs. Jour. Cell. Comp. Physiol., **11**: 21–39. (*397*)

Krahl, M. E., A. K. Keltch, and G. H. A. Clowes, 1940. Inhibition of flavoprotein oxidative catalysis by substituted phenols. Jour. Biol. Chem., **136**: 563–564. (*396*)

Kraines, S. H., 1937. The correlation of oxygen-deprivation with intelligence, constitution and blood pressure. Amer. Jour. Psychiatry, **93**: 1435–1446. (*504*)

Kramer, I. R. H. (See Fleming, Voureka, Kramer, and Hughes, 1950.)

Krause, P., 1902. Ueber durch Pressung gewonnenen Zellsaft des *Bacillus pyocyaneus* nebst einer kurzen mitteilung über die Einwirkung des Druckes auf Bakterien. Centralbl. Bakt., Abt. I (orig.), **31**: 673–678. (*290*)

Kreezer, E. H. (See Kreezer and Kreezer, 1947.)

Kreezer, G. L., and E. H. Kreezer, 1947. The form of the light-response of luminous bacteria to a sudden increase in temperature and its analysis as a transient. Jour. Cell. Comp. Physiol., **30**: 173–202. (*326*)

Krönig, B., and Th. Paul, 1897. Die chemische Grundlage der Lehre von der Giftwirkung und Disinfektion. Zeitschr. Hyg., **25**: 1–112. (*454, 460*)

Krop, S. (See Wescoe, Green, McNamara, and Krop, 1948.)

Krueger, A. P., and D. M. Baldwin, 1934. The reversible inactivation of bacteriophage by bichloride of mercury. Jour. Gen. Physiol., **17**: 499–505. (*438*)

Kuhn, L. R., 1949. Effect of elevated body temperatures on cryptococcosis in mice. Proc. Soc. Exp. Biol. Med., **71**: 341–343. (*467*)

Kuhn, R., and H. Rudy, 1936. Lactoflavin als Co-Ferment; Wirkstoff und Träger. Ber. deut. chem. Gesellsch., **69**: 2557–2567. (*136*)

Kunitz, M. (See Northrop, Kunitz, and Herriott, 1948.)

Kunitz, M., 1940. Crystalline ribonuclease. Jour. Gen. Physiol., **24**: 15–32. (*341*)

Kunitz, M., 1945. Crystallization of a trypsin inhibitor from soybean. Science, **101**: 668–669. (*246*)

Kunitz, M., 1946. Crystalline soybean trypsin inhibitor. Jour. Gen. Physiol., **29**: 149–154. (*246*)

Kunitz, M., 1947a. Crystalline soybean trypsin inhibitor. II. General properties. Jour. Gen. Physiol., **30**: 291–310. (*127, 246*)

Kunitz, M., 1947b. Isolation of a crystalline protein compound of trypsin and of soybean trypsin-inhibitor. Jour. Gen. Physiol., **30**: 311–320. (*246*)

Kunitz, M., 1948. The kinetics and thermodynamics of reversible denaturation of crystalline soybean trypsin inhibitor. Jour. Gen. Physiol., **32**: 241–263. (*127, 246, 247, 248, 249, 250*)

Kunitz, M., and J. H. Northrop, 1933–1934. Inactivation of crystalline trypsin. Jour. Gen. Physiol., **17**: 591–615. (*216*)

Kunkel, L. O., 1936. Heat treatments for the cure of yellows and other virus diseases of peach. Phytopath., **26**: 809–830. (*468*)

Laidler, K. J. (See Casey and Laidler, 1950, 1951; Glasstone, Laidler, and Eyring, 1941.)

Laidler, K. J., 1950. Chemical Kinetics. McGraw-Hill Book Co., New York. (*5*)

Laidler, K. J., 1951. The influence of pressure on the rates of biological reactions. Arch. Biochem., **30**: 226–236. (*313, 314, 315*)

Laki, K. (See Gergely and Laki, 1950.)

Lamanna, C., 1942. Growth stimulation by sulfanilamide in low concentration. Science, **95**: 304–305. (*485*)

Lamb, C. A. (See Shaw, Steele, and Lamb, 1937.)

La Mer, V. K., 1937. Energy of activation of protein denaturations. Science, **86**: 614. (*278*)

La Mer, V. K., and M. L. Miller, 1935. Temperature dependence of the energy of activation in the dealdolization of diacetone alcohol. Jour. Amer. Chem. Soc., **57**: 2674–2680. (*5*)

Landau, J., and D. A. Marsland, 1952. Temperature-pressure studies on the cardiac rate in tissue culture explants from the heart of the tadpole (*Rana pipiens*). Jour. Cell. Comp. Physiol., **40**: 367–381. (*318, 319, 320*)

Landauer, M. (See Lüers and Landauer, 1922.)

Landsteiner, K. (See Rothen and Landsteiner, 1942.)

Langmuir, I. (See Blodgett and Langmuir, 1937.)

Langmuir, I., 1917. The constitution and fundamental properties of solids and liquids. II. Liquids. Jour. Amer. Chem. Soc., **39**: 1848–1906. (*432*)

Langmuir, I., 1938. Protein monolayers. Cold Spr. Harb. Symp., **6**: 171–189. (*260, 261*)

Langmuir, I., and V. J. Schaefer, 1938. Activities of urease and pepsin monolayers. Jour. Amer. Chem. Soc., **60**: 1351–1360. (*265*)

Langmuir, I., and V. J. Schaefer, 1939. Properties and structure of protein monolayers. Chem. Rev., **24**: 181–202. (*265*)

Langworthy, O. R. (See Grob, Harvey, Langworthy, and Lilienthal, 1947.)

Larrabee, M. G. (See Posternak and Larrabee, 1948.)

Larson, W. P., T. B. Hartzell, and H. S. Diehl, 1918. The effect of high pressures on bacteria. Jour. Inf. Dis., **22**: 271–279. (*294, 295*)

Lauffer, M. A. (See Stanley and Lauffer, 1939.)

Lauffer, M. A., 1943. The denaturation of tobacco mosaic virus by urea. II. Kinetic aspects. Jour. Amer. Chem. Soc., **65**: 1793–1802. (*277, 281, 282*)

Lauffer, M. A., 1945. Thermal destruction of influenza A virus hemagglutinin. I. The kinetic process. Arch. Biochem., **8**: 265–274. (*277*)

Lauffer, M. A., 1949. Physical chemistry of viruses. Record Chem. Prog., Fall issue, 205–211. (*297*)

Lauffer, M. A., and R. B. Dow, 1941. The denaturation of tobacco mosaic virus at high pressures. Jour. Biol. Chem., **140**: 509–518. (*293, 296*)

Lauffer, M. A., and W. C. Price, 1940. Thermal denaturation of tobacco mosaic virus. Jour. Biol. Chem., **133**: 1–15. (*277, 297, 328, 329*)

Lauren, I. (See von Euler and Lauren, 1919.)

Lawrence, C. A., 1940. Effect of temperature on bacteriostatic action of sulfanilamide on members of the Enterococcus group. Proc. Soc. Exp. Biol. Med., **43**: 52–55. (*401*)

Lea, D. E., 1946. Actions of Radiations on Living Cells. Cambridge University Press, England (1947, The Macmillan Co., New York). (*32, 455*)

Lee, R. E., and C. A. Gilbert, 1918. On the application of the mass law to the process of disinfection—being a contribution to the "mechanistic theory" as opposed to the "vitalistic theory." Jour. Phys. Chem., **22**: 348–372. (*455*)

Lee, S. W., J. A. Epstein, and E. J. Foley, 1943a. Synergism of urea and sulfathiazol on *E. coli*. Effect of inoculum size. Proc. Soc. Exp. Biol. Med., **54**: 107–108. (*482*)

Lee, S. W., J. A. Epstein, and E. J. Foley, 1943b. Temperature and the bacteriostatic action of sulfathiazol and other drugs. II. *Streptococcus pyogenes*. Proc. Soc. Exp. Biol. Med., **53**: 245–247. (*402*)

Lee, S. W., and E. J. Foley, 1945. Effect of temperature on the action of penicillin *in vitro*. Proc. Soc. Exp. Biol. Med., **60**: 133–136. (*404*)

Lee, S. W., E. J. Foley, and J. Epstein, 1944. Mode of action of penicillin. I. Bacterial growth and penicillin activity—*Staphylococcus aureus* FDA. Jour. Bact., **48**: 393–399. (*404*)

Lehmann-Echternacht, H. (See Fischer, Böttger, and Lehmann-Echternacht, 1942.)

Lehr, H., and J. Berger, 1949. The isolation of a crystalline actinomycin-like antibiotic. Arch. Biochem., **23**: 503–504. (*137*)

Leïpunskiï, O. I., 1940. Coagulation of gelatin under pressure. (In Russian.) Jour. Phys. Chem., U.S.S.R., **14**: 1517–1519. (*292*)

Lennox, W. G. (See Gibbs, Gibbs, and Lennox, 1937.)

Lepeschkin, W. W., 1923. Ueber das Wesen der Koagulation der Eiweisstoffe durch Alcohol und andere organische Substanzen. Kolloid Zeitschr., **32**: 100–103. (*453*)

Lepeschkin, W. W., 1924. Kolloidchemie des Protoplasmas. Springer, Berlin. (*453*)

Lepine, P., J. Basset, and M. Macheboeuf, 1936. Action des ultrapressions sur le virus de la peste aviaire. Pouvoir antigène du virus ultrapressé. Compt. rend. soc. biol., **121**: 202–203. (*293*)

Levedahl, B. (See Simpson, Watson, Levedahl, Schellman, Frensdorff, and Kauzmann, 1951.)

Levene, P. A. (See Schmidt and Levene, 1938.)

Levin, A., and J. Wyman, 1927. The viscous elastic properties of muscle. Proc. Roy. Soc. Lond., B **101**: 218–243. (*703, 715*)

Levy, G. (See Macheboeuf, Basset, and Levy, 1933.)

Levy, M., and A. E. Benaglia, 1950. The influence of temperature and pH upon the rate of denaturation of ricin. Jour. Biol. Chem., **186**: 829–847.   (*278*)

Lewin, I. (See Johnson and Lewin, 1946a–d, 1947.)

Lewis, G. N., 1916. The atom and the molecule. Jour. Amer. Chem. Soc., **38**: 762–785.   (*81*)

Lewis, G. N., 1923. Valence and the Structure of Atoms and Molecules. Chemical Catalog Co., New York.   (*81*)

Lewis, G. N., and M. Kasha, 1944. Phosphorescence and the triplet state. Jour. Amer. Chem. Soc., **66**: 2100–2116.   (*147*)

Lewis, G. N., and M. Randall, 1923. Thermodynamics and the Free Energy of Chemical Substances. McGraw-Hill Book Co., New York.   (*49, 225*)

Lewis, J. J. (See Hollinger, Fuhrman, Lewis, and Field, 1949.)

Lewis, P. S., 1926a. The kinetics of protein denaturation. Part I. The effect of variation in the hydrogen ion concentration on the velocity of the heat denaturation of oxyhaemoglobin. Biochem. Jour., **20**: 965–977.   (*272, 274, 275*)

Lewis, P. S., 1926b. The kinetics of protein denaturation. Part II. The effect of variation in the hydrogen ion concentration on the velocity of the heat denaturation of egg-albumin; the critical increment of the process. Biochem. Jour., **20**: 978–983.   (*272, 275*)

Lewis, P. S., 1926c. The kinetics of protein denaturation. Part III. The influence of neutral salts on the velocity of the heat denaturation of oxyhaemoglobin. Biochem. Jour., **20**: 984–992.

Lewis, W. C. McC., 1918. Studies in catalysis. Part IX. The calculation in absolute measures of velocity constants and equilibrium constants in gaseous systems. Jour. Chem. Soc., **113**: 471–492.   (*5*)

Li, C. H., 1946. Electrophoretic inhomogeneity of crystalline β-lactoglobulin. Jour. Amer. Chem. Soc., **69**: 2746–2747.   (*255*)

Li, N. (See Sherman and Li, 1936.)

Libet, B., 1948. Adenosinetriphosphatase in nerve. Fed. Proc., **7**: 72.   (*693*)

Lilienthal, J. L. (See Grob, Harvey, Langworthy, and Lilienthal, 1947; Grob, Lilienthal, and Harvey, 1947; Grob, Lilienthal, Harvey, and Jones, 1947.)

Lillie, R. S., 1909. On the connection between changes of permeability and stimulation and on the significance of changes in permeability to carbon dioxide. Amer. Jour. Physiol., **24**: 14–44.   (*500*)

Lillie, R. S., 1912. Antagonism between salts and anesthetics. I. On the conditions of the anti-stimulating action of anesthetics with observations of their protective or antitoxic action. Amer. Jour. Physiol., **29**: 372–397.   (*500*)

Lillie, R. S., 1913. Antagonism between salts and anesthetics. III. Further observations showing parallel decrease in stimulating, of permeability-increasing, and toxic actions of salt solutions in the presence of anesthetics. Amer. Jour. Physiol., **31**: 255–287.   (*500*)

Lillie, R. S., 1916. The theory of anesthesia. Biol. Bull., **30**: 311–366.   (*500*)

Lillie, R. S., 1932. Protoplasmic and Nervous Action. University of Chicago Press, Chicago, 2nd ed.   (*500*)

Linderholm, H., 1952. Active transport of ions through frog skin with special reference to the action of certain diuretics. Acta Physiol. Scand., **27**: 1–144.   (*603*)

Linderstrøm-Lang, K. (See Chantrenne, Linderstrøm-Lang, and Vandendriessche, 1947; Jacobsen and Linderstrøm-Lang, 1949.)

Linderstrøm-Lang, K., 1950. Structure and enzymatic breakdown of proteins. Cold Spr. Harb. Symp., 14: 117–126. (256, 336, 339, 340)

Linderstrøm-Lang, K., R. D. Hotchkiss, and G. Johansen, 1938. Peptide bonds in globular proteins. Nature, 142: 996. (284)

Linderstrøm-Lang, K., and C. F. Jacobsen, 1941. The contraction accompanying enzymatic breakdown of proteins. Compt. rend. trav. lab. Carlsberg, sér. chim., 24: 1–46. (302, 335, 336, 337, 339, 340)

Lindquist, A. W., A. H. Madden, and H. O. Schroeder, 1946. Effect of temperature on knockdown and kill of mosquitoes and bedbugs exposed to DDT. Jour. Kansas Entomol. Soc., 19: 13–15. (466)

Lindquist, A. W., H. G. Wilson, H. O. Schroeder, and A. H. Madden, 1945. Effect of temperature on knockdown and kill of houseflies exposed to DDT. Jour. Econ. Entomol., 38: 261–264. (466)

Lineweaver, H., and D. Burk, 1934. The determination of enzyme dissociation constants. Jour. Amer. Chem. Soc., 56: 658–666. (175, 407)

Ling, G., and R. W. Gerard, 1949a. The normal membrane potential of frog Sartorius fibers. Jour. Cell. Comp. Physiol., 34: 383–395. (496, 502)

Ling, G., and R. W. Gerard, 1949b. The influence of stretch on the membrane potential of the striated muscle fiber. Jour. Cell. Comp. Physiol., 34: 397–405. (496)

Ling, G., and R. W. Gerard, 1949c. The membrane potential and metabolism of muscle fibers. Jour. Cell. Comp. Physiol., 34: 413–438. (496, 502, 508)

Ling, G., and J. W. Woodbury, 1949. Effect of temperature on the membrane potential of frog muscle fibers. Jour. Cell. Comp. Physiol., 34: 407–412. (496, 502)

Link, K. P. (See Campbell and Link, 1941; Campbell, Smith, Roberts, and Link, 1941; Stahman, Huebner, and Link, 1941.)

Lipman, C. B., 1936. Normal viability of seeds and bacterial spores after exposure to temperatures near absolute zero. Plant Physiol., 11: 201–205. (187)

Lipmann, F. (See Loomis and Lipmann, 1948.)

Lipmann, F., 1941. Metabolic generation and utilization of phosphate bond energy. Adv. Enzymol., 1: 99–162. (507)

Lipschitz, W., and A. Gottschalk, 1921. Die Reduktion der aromatischen Nitrogruppe als Indikator von Teilvorgängen der atmung und der Gärung. Eine Method zur vergleichend-quantitativen Bestimmung biologischen oxydo-Reduktionen. Pflüg. Arch. ges. Physiol., 191: 1–32. (484)

Lisbonne, M. (See Basset, Lisbonne, and Macheboeuf, 1933.)

Lloyd, D. J., and T. Moran, 1934. Pressure and the water relations of proteins. I. Isoelectric gelatin gels. Proc. Roy. Soc. Lond., A 147: 382–395. (292)

Lloyd, D. P. C., 1950. Chapters on Electrical Properties of Nerve and Muscle and Functional Properties of Neurons. In: Textbook of Physiology, J. F. Fulton (Ed.). W. B. Saunders Co., Philadelphia. (604, 619)

Loeb, J., and M. M. Chamberlain, 1915. An attempt at a physico-chemical explanation of certain groups of fluctuating variation. Jour. Exp. Zool., 19: 559–568. (205)

Loeb, J., and J. H. Northrop, 1917. On the influence of food and temperature upon the duration of life. Jour. Biol. Chem., **32**: 103–121.   (*193, 455*)

Loeb, J., and H. Wasteneys, 1911. Sind die Oxydationsvorgänge unabhängige Variable in dem Lebenserscheinungen? Biochem. Zeitschr., **36**: 345–356. (*205*)

Loeb, J., and H. Wasteneys, 1913. Is narcosis due to asphyxiation? Jour. Biol. Chem., **14**: 517–523.   (*504*)

Lomax, R. (See Astbury and Lomax, 1935.)

London, F. (See Heitler and London, 1927.)

London, F., 1928. Über den Mechanismus der homöopolaren Bindung. In: Probleme der moderne Physik (Sommerfeld Festschrift). Pp. 104–113. S. Hirzel, Leipzig.   (*14*)

London, F., 1929. Quantenmechanische deutung des Vorgangs der Aktivierung. Zeitschr. Elektrochem., **35**: 552–555.   (*14, 104*)

van Lookeren Campagne, G. I. (See Gorter, Maaskant, and van Lookeren Campagne, 1936.)

Loomis, W. E. [See Franck and Loomis (Eds.), 1949.]

Loomis, W. F., and F. Lipmann, 1948. Reversible inhibition of the coupling between phosphorylation and oxidation. Jour. Biol. Chem., **173**: 807–808. (*396*)

Lorch, I. J. (See Goldacre and Lorch, 1950.)

Lorente de Nó, R., 1947. A Study of Nerve Physiology. Studies from the Rockefeller Institute for Medical Research, New York, Vols. 131 and 132. (*503, 507, 604, 682, 697*)

Lorenz, P. B. (See Chase and Lorenz, 1945.)

Loring, H. S. (See Stanley and Loring, 1938.)

Loring, H. S., and F. H. Carpenter, 1943. The isolation of mononucleotides after hydrolysis of ribonucleic acid by crystalline ribonuclease. Jour. Biol. Chem., **150**: 381–388.   (*341*)

Lu, Y-M. (See Chang, Hsiek, and Lu, 1939.)

Luck, J. M. (See Ballou, Boyer, and Luck, 1945; Ballou, Boyer, Luck, and Lum, 1944; Boyer, Ballou, and Luck, 1946, 1947; Boyer, Lum, Ballou, Luck, and Rice, 1946; Duggan and Luck, 1948.)

Lucké, B., 1931. The effect of certain narcotics (urethanes) on permeability of living cells to water. Biol. Bull., **60**: 72–79.   (*500*)

Lüers, H., and M. Landauer, 1922. Über die Kinetik der Hitzegerinnung von Proteinen. Zeitschr. angew. Chem., **35**: 469–471.   (*272*)

Lüers, H., and W. Wasmund, 1922. Über die Wirkungsweise der Amylase. Fermentforsch., **5**: 169–235.   (*272*)

Lum, F. G. (See Ballou, Boyer, Luck, and Lum, 1944; Boyer, Lum, Ballou, Luck, and Rice, 1946.)

Lumière, A., and J. Chevrotier, 1914. Sur la résistance du gonocoque aux basses températures. Compt. rend. acad. sci., **158**: 139–140.   (*188*)

Lumry, R. (See Eyring, Lumry, and Woodbury, 1949; Kistiakowsky and Lumry, 1949; Spikes, Lumry, Eyring, and Wayrynen, 1950.)

Lundgren, H. P., 1939. Protein stability as revealed by ultracentrifugal analysis. Nature, **143**: 896.   (*244, 253*)

Lundgren, H. P., 1941. The catalytic effect of active crystalline papain on the denaturation of thyroglobulin. Jour. Biol. Chem., **138**: 293–303.   (*340*)

Lundgren, H. P., 1945.   Synthetic protein fibers from protein detergent complexes. Textile Research Jour., **15**: 335–353.   (*258*)

Lundgren, H. P., and J. W. Williams, 1939.   Ultracentrifugal analysis and stability in protein systems. Jour. Phys. Chem., **43**: 989–1002.   .(*244, 253*)

Luria, S. E.   (See Delbrück and Luria, 1942.)

Luyet, B., 1937a.   Sur le mécanisme de la mort cellulaire par les hautes pressions; l'intensité et la durée des pressions léthales pour la levure. Compt. rend. acad. sci., **204**: 1214–1215.   (*295*)

Luyet, B., 1937b.   Sur le mécanisme de la mort cellulaire par les hautes pressions; modifications cytologiques accompagnant la mort chez la levure. Compt. rend. acad. sci., **204**: 1506–1508.   (*295*)

Luyet, B. J., 1952.   Survival of cells, tissues and organisms after ultra-rapid freezing. In: Freezing and Drying, R. J. C. Harris (Ed.). Pp. 77–98. Published by the Institute of Biology, Tavistock House South, London. Haffner, New York.   (*188*)

Luyet, B. J., and P. M. Gehenio, 1940.   Life and Death at Low Temperatures. Biodynamica. Normandy, Missouri.   (*188*)

Maaskant, L.   (See Gorter, Maaskant, and van Lookeren Campagne, 1936.)

McCalla, T. M., 1940.   Cation adsorption by bacteria. Jour. Bact., **40**: 23–32.   (*438*)

McClure, R. D., F. W. Hartmann, J. G. Schnedorf, and V. Schelling, 1939. Anoxia.   A source of possible complications in surgical anesthesia. Ann. Surg., **110**: 835–850.   (*504*)

McDonald, A.   (See Weinstein and McDonald, 1945.)

McElroy, W. D., 1943.   The application of the theory of absolute reaction rates to the action of narcotics. Jour. Cell. Comp. Physiol., **21**: 95–116.   (*419*)

McElroy, W. D., 1947.   The energy source for bioluminescence in an isolated system. Proc. Nat. Acad. Sci., **33**: 342–345.   (*135*)

McElroy, W. D., 1951.   Properties of the reaction utilizing adenosine triphosphate for bioluminescence. Jour. Biol. Chem., **191**: 547–557.   (*135*)

McElroy, W. D., and R. Ballentine, 1944.   The mechanism of bioluminescence. Proc. Nat. Acad. Sci., **30**: 377–382.   (*132, 133, 134*)

McElroy, W. D., and A. M. Chase, 1952.   Purification of *Cypridina* luciferase. Jour. Cell. Comp. Physiol., **38**: 401–408.   (*126*)

McElroy, W. D., J. W. Hastings, V. Sonnenfeld, and J. Coulombre, 1953.   The requirement of riboflavin phosphate for bacterial luminescence. Science, **118**: 385–386.   (*186*)

McElroy, W. D., and E. N. Harvey, 1951.   Differences among species in the response of firefly extracts to adenosine triphosphate. Jour. Cell. Comp. Physiol., **37**: 83–90.   (*135*)

McElroy, W. D., and D. M. Kipnis, 1947.   The mechanism of inhibition of bioluminescence by naphthoquinones. Jour. Cell. Comp. Physiol., **30**: 359–380. (*134, 181, 182*)

McElroy, W. D., and B. L. Strehler, 1949.   Factors influencing the response of the bioluminescent reaction to adenosine triphosphate. Arch. Biochem., **22**: 420–433.   (*135*)

Macfadyen, A., 1900.   On the influence of the temperature of liquid air on bacteria. Proc. Roy. Soc. Lond., B **66**: 180–182.   (*187*)

Macfadyen, A., and S. Rowland, 1900a. Further note on the influence of liquid air on bacteria. Proc. Roy. Soc. Lond., B **66**: 339–340.   (*187*)

Macfadyen, A., and S. Rowland, 1900b. Influence of the temperature of liquid air on bacteria. Proc. Roy. Soc. Lond., B **66**: 488–489.   (*187*)

McGeer, K. (See Johnson, Flagler, Simpson, and McGeer, 1951.)

McGillivray, I. H., 1930. The inactivation of pancreatic lipase by heat. Biochem. Jour., **24**: 891–904.   (*272*)

Machado, A. L. (See Nachmansohn, Cox, Coates, and Machado, 1943; Nachmansohn and Machado, 1943.)

Macheboeuf, M. A. (See Basset, Gratia, Macheboeuf, and Manil, 1938; Basset, Lisbonne, and Macheboeuf, 1933; Basset and Macheboeuf, 1932, 1933; Basset, Macheboeuf, and Perez, 1935; Basset, Macheboeuf, and Sandor, 1933; Basset, Nicolau, and Macheboeuf, 1935; Basset, Wollman, Macheboeuf, and Bardach, 1933, 1935; Basset, Wollman, Wollman, and Macheboeuf, 1935; Vignais, Barbu, Basset, and Macheboeuf, 1951; Wollman, Macheboeuf, Bardach, and Basset, 1936.)

Macheboeuf, M. A., and J. Basset, 1934. Die Wirkung sehr hoher Drucke auf Enzyme. Ergeb. Enzymforsch., **3**: 303–308.   (*292*)

Macheboeuf, M., J. Basset, and G. Levy, 1933. Influence des pressions très élevées sur les diastases. Ann. physiol. physicochim. biol., **9**: 713–722. (*292*)

Macht, D. I., 1921. A toxicological study of some alcohols, with especial reference to isomers. Jour. Pharmacol. Exp. Therap., **16**: 1–10.   (*462*)

McIlwain, H., 1941. A nutritional investigation of the antibacterial action of acriflavine. Biochem. Jour., **35**: 1311–1319.   (*439*)

McIlwain, H., 1942. The biochemical specificity of sulfanilamide and of other antibacterial agents. Science, **95**: 509–511.   (*481*)

MacInnes, D. A., 1939. The Principles of Electrochemistry. Reinhold Publishing Co., New York.   (*558, 559*)

MacKay, E. M. (See Holder and MacKay, 1942; 1943.)

Mackworth, J. F., and E. C. Webb, 1948. The inhibition of serum cholinesterases by alkyl fluorophosphonates. Biochem. Jour., **42**: 91–98.   (*489, 490, 493, 496*)

McLaren, A. D. (See Werbin and McLaren, 1951a; 1951b.)

McMeekin, T. L. (See Cohn, McMeekin, Edsall, and Blanchard, 1934.)

McMeekin, T. L., E. J. Cohn, and J. H. Weare, 1935. Studies in the physical chemistry of amino acids, peptides and related substances. III. The solubility of derivatives of the amino acids in alcohol-water mixtures. Jour. Amer. Chem. Soc., **57**: 626–633.   (*336*)

McMeekin, T. L., B. D. Polis, E. S. Della Monica, and J. H. Coster, 1948. Heterogeneity of β-lactoglobulin. Jour. Amer. Chem. Soc., **70**: 881–882. (*255*)

McNamara, B. P. (See Wescoe, Green, McNamara, and Krop, 1948.)

Madden, A. H. (See Lindquist, Madden, and Schroeder, 1946; Lindquist, Wilson, Schroeder, and Madden, 1945.)

Maddock, S., J. E. Hawkins, and E. Holmes, 1939. The inadequacy of substances of the "glucose cycle" for maintenance of normal cortical potentials during hypoglycemia produced by hepatectomy with abdominal evisceration. Amer. Jour. Physiol., **125**: 551–565.   (*505*)

Madsen, T. (See Famulener and Madsen, 1908.)

Madsen, Th., and M. Nyman, 1907. Zur theorie der disinfektion. I. Zeitschr. Hyg. Infek., **57**: 388–404.   *(454)*

Magee, J. L. (See Eyring and Magee, 1942.)

Magee, J., T. Ri, and H. Eyring, 1941. Theory of acid strength. Temperature effect. Jour. Chem. Physics, **9**: 419–427.   *(27, 224, 225)*

Magnuson, H. J. (See Eagle, Magnuson, and Fleischman, 1947.)

Magoon, C. A. (See Berry and Magoon, 1934.)

Manil, P. (See Basset, Gratia, Macheboeuf, and Manil, 1938.)

Mann, P. J. G., M. Tennenbaum, and J. H. Quastel, 1938. On the mechanism of acetylcholine formation in brain *in vitro*. Biochem. Jour., **32**: 243–261.   *(502, 507)*

Marchner, R. F. (See Zimmerschied, Dinerstein, Weitkamp, and Marchner, 1949.)

Marinesco, G., 1912. Forschungen über den kolloiden Bau der Nervenzellen und ihre erfahrungsgemässen Veranderungen. Kolloid Zeitschr., **11**: 209–225.   *(450)*

Mark, H. (See Meyer and Mark, 1951.)

Mark, H., and A. V. Tobolsky, 1950. Physical Chemistry of High Polymeric Systems. Interscience Publishers, New York.   *(169)*

Marks, E. K. (See Jacobson, Robson, Marks, and Goldman, 1949.)

Marlies, C. A. (See Schmidt and Marlies, 1948.)

Marmont, G., 1949. Studies on the axon membrane. Jour. Cell. Comp. Physiol., **34**: 351–382.   *(635)*

Marsland, D. A. (See Brown, Johnson, and Marsland, 1942; Brown and Marsland, 1936, 1942; Johnson, Brown, and Marsland, 1942a, 1942b; Landau and Marsland, 1952; Pease and Marsland, 1939; Rugh and Marsland, 1943.)

Marsland, D. A., 1938. The effects of high hydrostatic pressure upon cell division in *Arbacia* eggs. Jour. Cell. Comp. Physiol., **12**: 57–70.   *(326, 354, 356, 357, 364)*

Marsland, D. A., 1939. The mechanism of cell division. Hydrostatic pressure effects upon dividing egg cells. Jour. Cell. Comp. Physiol., **13**: 15–22.   *(354)*

Marsland, D. A., 1942. Protoplasmic streaming in relation to gel structure in the cytoplasm. In: The Structure of Protoplasm. A monograph of the Society of Plant Physiologists, William Seifriz (Ed.). Pp. 127–161. The Iowa State College Press, Ames.   *(347, 348, 351, 352)*

Marsland, D. A., 1944. Mechanism of pigment displacement in unicellular chromatophores. Biol. Bull., **87**: 252–261.   *(347, 351, 352)*

Marsland, D. A., 1948. Protoplasmic contractility. Pressure experiments on the motility of living cells. Sci. Mon., **67**: 193–200.   *(347)*

Marsland, D. A., 1950. The mechanisms of cell division; temperature-pressure experiments on the cleaving eggs of *Arbacia punctulata*. Jour. Cell. Comp. Physiol., **36**: 205–227.   *(354, 357, 358)*

Marsland, D. A., 1951. The action of hydrostatic pressure on cell division. Ann. N. Y. Acad. Sci., **51**: 1327–1335.   *(354)*

Marsland, D. A., and D. E. Brown, 1936. Amoeboid movement at high hydrostatic pressure. Jour. Cell. Comp. Physiol., **8**: 167–178.   *(347, 350)*

Marsland, D. A., and D. E. Brown, 1942. The effects of pressure on sol-gel equilibria, with special reference to myosin and other protoplasmic gels. Jour. Cell. Comp. Physiol., **20**: 295–305.   *(313, 347)*

Marsland, D. A., and O. Jaffee, 1949. Effects of pressure on the cleaving eggs of the frog (*Rana pipiens*). Jour. Cell. Comp. Physiol., **34**: 439–450. (*354, 355, 357*)

Martin, A. W. (See Field, Fuhrman, and Martin, 1944; Field, Martin, and Field, 1933.)

Martin, C. J. (See Chick and Martin, 1910, 1911, 1912.)

Martin, G., 1951. Biological Antagonism. Blakiston Co., Philadelphia. (*377, 378*)

Mason, H. S., 1952a. *Cypridina* luciferin. Arch. Biochem. Biophys., **35**: 472. (*127, 131, 133*)

Mason, H. S., 1952b. The beta-luciferin of *Cypridina*. Jour. Amer. Chem. Soc., **74**: 4727. (*137*)

Mason, H. S., and E. F. Davis, 1952. *Cypridina* luciferin. Partition chromatography. Jour. Biol. Chem., **197**: 41–45. (*127, 136*)

Mason, J. (See Cooper and Mason, 1927.)

Massart, L., and R. P. DuFait, 1940. Hemmung der Acetylcholin-Esterase durch Farbstoffe und durch Eserine. Enzymologia, **9**: 364–368. (*490*)

Matthaei, G. (See Blackman and Matthaei, 1905.)

Matthaei, G. L. C., 1905. Experimental researches on vegetable assimilation and respiration. III. On the effect of temperature on carbon dioxide assimilation. Phil. Trans. Roy. Soc. Lond., B **197**: 47–105. (*194, 195*)

Matthews, H. D., 1942. On the stridulations of insects. Science, **95**: 324–325. (*201*)

Matthews, J. E. (See Dow and Matthews, 1939.)

Matthews, J. E., Jr. (See Dow, Matthews, and Thorp, 1940.)

Matthews, J. E., Jr., R. B. Dow, and A. K. Anderson, 1940. The effects of high pressure on the activity of pepsin and rennin. Jour. Biol. Chem., **135**: 697–705. (*252, 293, 297, 298, 299*)

Mauro, A., and O. Sten-Knudsen, 1952. The rôle of the sarcolemma in muscle physiology. Acta Medica Scand., **142**: Supplement 266, 715–724. (*753*)

Mayeda, S., 1928. Die Wirkungsstärke der Alkaloide und ihr Hydrolysengrad in gepufferten Lösungen als Funktion der Wasserstoffionenkonzentration des Mediums. Biochem. Zeitschr., **197**: 410–417. (*403*)

Mazia, D., and G. Blumenthal, 1948. Inactivation of enzyme-substrate films by small doses of X-rays. Proc. Nat. Acad. Sci., **34**: 328–336. (*34*)

Mazur, A., and O. Bodansky, 1946. The mechanism of *in vitro* and *in vivo* inhibition of cholinesterase activity by di-isopropyl fluorophosphate. Jour. Biol. Chem., **163**: 261–276. (*489, 493, 496*)

de Meester, W. A. T. (See Moesveld and de Meester, 1928.)

Mellanby, J., and V. J. Woolley, 1913. The ferments of the pancreas. Part III. The properties of trypsin, trypsinogen and enterokinase. Jour. Physiol., **47**: 339–360. (*215*)

Mendel, B. (See Hawkins and Mendel, 1949.)

Mendel, B., D. B. Mundell, and H. Rudney, 1943. Studies on cholinesterase. 3. Specific tests for true cholinesterase and pseudocholinesterase. Biochem. Jour., **37**: 473–476. (*493*)

Mendel, B., and H. Rudney, 1943. Studies on cholinesterase. 1. Cholinesterase and pseudocholinesterase. Biochem. Jour., **37**: 59–63. (*488*)

Menton, M. L. (See Michaelis and Menton, 1913.)

Menzies, J. A.   (See Bainbridge and Menzies, 1929.)

Mercer, E. H.   (See Farrant, Rees, and Mercer, 1947.)

Mercer, E. H., 1949.   Electron microscopic study of wool.   In: Experimental Cell Research.   Proc. of the 6th Int. Congr. of Exp. Cytology, Stockholm, 1947.   T. Caspersson and L. Monné (Eds.).   Pp. 60–62.   Academic Press, New York.   *(752)*

Mercer, E. H., and A. L. G. Rees, 1946.   Structure and elasticity of the cortex of keratin fibers—an electron microscopic study.   Austral. Jour. Exp. Biol. Med. Sci., **24**: 175–183.   *(752)*

Meyer, H. H., 1899.   Zur Theorie der Alkoholnarkose.   Erste Mittheilung.   Welche Eigenschaft der Anästhetika bedingt ihre narkotische Wirkung?   Arch. exp. Path. Pharm., **42**: 109–118.   *(464, 508)*

Meyer, H. H., 1901.   Zur Theorie der Alkoholnarkose.   III. Mitt.   Der Einfluss Wechselnder Temperatur auf Wirkungsstärke und Teilungskoefficient der Narkotica.   Arch. exp. Path. Pharm., **46**: 338–346.   *(509)*

Meyer, K.   (See Hobby, Meyer, and Chaffee, 1942.)

Meyer, K. H., 1929.   Über Feinbau, Festigkeit und Kontraktilität tierischer Gewebe.   Biochem. Zeitschr., **214**: 253–281.   *(30)*

Meyer, K. H., 1937.   Contributions to the theory of narcosis.   Trans. Farad. Soc., **33**: 1062–1068.   *(509, 510, 511)*

Meyer, K. H., 1951.   Mechanische Eigenschaften und molecularer Feinbau biologischer Systeme.   Zeitschr. Elektrochem., **55**: 453–459.   *(30)*

Meyer, K. H., and P. Bernfeld, 1945a.   La perméabilité des membranes.   VII. L'influence de la solubilité des ions dans la membrane.   Helv. Chim. Acta, **28**: 962–980.

Meyer, K. H., and P. Bernfeld, 1945b.   La perméabilité des membranes.   VIII. Prescriptions pour la preparation de membranes sélectives et non sélectives.   Helv. Chim. Acta, **28**: 972–980.   *(565, 578)*

Meyer, K. H., and H. Gottlieb-Billroth, 1920.   Theorie der Narkose durch Inhalationsanästhetika.   Hoppe-Seyler's Zeitschr. physiol. Chem., **112**: 55–79.   *(509)*

Meyer, K. H., and H. Hemmi, 1935.   Beiträge zur Theorie der Narkose.   III. Biochem. Zeitschr., **277**: 39–76.   *(432)*

Meyer, K. H., and H. Hopff, 1923.   Theorie der Narkose durch Inhalationsanästhetika.   Hoppe-Seyler's Zeitschr. physiol. Chem., **126**: 281–298.   *(509)*

Meyer, K. H., and H. Mark, 1951.   Biological significance of folding and unfolding of protein molecules.   Nature, **167**: 736.   *(30)*

Meyer, K. H., and L. E. R. Picken, 1937.   The thermoelastic properties of muscle and their molecular interpretation.   Proc. Roy. Soc. Lond., B **124**: 29–56.   *(704, 730)*

Meyer, K. H., and J. F. Sievers, 1936a.   La perméabilité des membranes.   I. Théorie de la perméabilité ionique.   Helv. Chim. Acta, **19**: 649–664.   *(565)*

Meyer, K. H., and J. F. Sievers, 1936b.   La perméabilité des membranes.   II. Essais avec des membranes sélectives artificielles.   Helv. Chim. Acta, **19**: 665–677.   *(578)*

Meyer, K. P., 1942.   Nachweis und Messung geringer Konzentrationen an freiem Sauerstoff vermittels Leuchtbakterien.   Helv. Phys. Acta, **15**: 2–22.   *(124)*

Meyerhof, O., 1918.   Notiz über Eiweissfällungen durch Narkotika.   Biochem. Zeitschr., **86**: 325–328.   *(284, 452)*

Michaelis, L., and M. L. Menton, 1913.   Der Kinetik der Invertinwirkung.   Bio-chem. Zeitschr., **49**: 333–369.   (*174*)

Michaelis, M., and J. H. Quastel, 1941.   The site of action of narcotics in respira-tory processes.   Biochem. Jour., **35**: 518–533.   (*506, 507*)

Michaelis, L., and P. Rona, 1910.   Beiträge zur allgemeinen Eiweisschemie.   III. Mitteilung.   Die Denaturierung des Serumsalbumins.   Biochem. Zeitschr., **29**: 494–500.   (*216*)

Mikhel'son, M. J., 1943.   Effect of narcotics on cholinesterase activity.   Experi-ment *in vitro* after Sheiner's method.   (In Russian.)   Farmakol. i Toksikol., **6**: 49–51.   No. 5.   (*490*)

Mikhel'son, M. Ya., 1946.   Influence of narcotics on cholinesterase activity.   IV. Comparison of narcotic strengths of narcotics with their hindering activity on cholinesterase activity.   (In Russian.)   Fiziol. Zhur. U.S.S.R., **32**: 745–756.   (*492*)

Miller, G. L., 1944.   Influence of *p*H and of certain other conditions on the stability of the infectivity and red cell agglutinating activity of influenza virus.   Jour. Exp. Med., **80**: 507–520.   (*277*)

Miller, L., 1939.   Digestion of crystalline lactoglobulin by crystalline trypsin and chymotrypsin.   Compt. rend. trav. lab. Carlsberg, sér. chim., **23**: 45–53.   (*340*)

Miller, M. L.   (See La Mer and Miller, 1935.)

Miller, V. K.   (See Foster, Johnson, and Miller, 1949.)

Millikan, G.   (See Chance, Harvey, Johnson, and Millikan, 1940.)

Mills, C. A.   (See Chen, Anderson, Henderson, and Mills, 1943; Chen, Anderson, Steldt, and Mills, 1943.)

Mirsky, A. E.   (See Anson and Mirsky, 1931, 1933–1934; Ris and Mirsky, 1949.)

Mirsky, A. E., 1936.   The visual cycle and protein denaturation.   Proc. Nat. Acad. Sci., **22**: 147–149.   (*254*)

Mirsky, A. E., 1938.   Protein denaturation.   Cold Spr. Harb. Symp., **6**: 150–163.   (*252*)

Mirsky, A. E., and M. L. Anson, 1929.   Protein coagulation and its reversal.   The reversal of the coagulation of hemoglobin.   Jour. Gen. Physiol., **13**: 133–143.   (*217*)

Mirsky, A. E., and L. Pauling, 1936.   On the structure of native, denatured and coagulated proteins.   Proc. Nat. Acad. Sci., **22**: 439–447.   (*252, 258, 277*)

Mitchell, J. S., 1935.   Some aspects of the equation of state of monolayers.   Trans. Farad. Soc., **31**: 980–986.   (*262*)

Miyake, K., and M. Ito, 1923.   The lethal temperature of Koji-diastase in aqueous solution and the recovery of its action after heating.   Jour. Biochem. Japan, **2**: 255–270.   (*215*)

Miyake, K., and M. Ito, 1924.   Lethal temperature of pure Koji-diastase in aqueous solutions and recovery of its action after heating.   Jour. Biochem. Japan, **3**: 177–194.   (*215*)

Mock, H. E., and H. E. Mock, Jr., 1943.   Refrigeration anesthesia in amputations.   Jour. Amer. Med. Assoc., **123**: 13–17.   (*502*)

Mock, H. E., Jr.   (See Mock and Mock, 1943.)

Moelwyn-Hughes, E. A., 1932.   The kinetics of certain bimolecular reactions in solution.   Chem. Rev., **10**: 241–264.   (*5*)

Moelwyn-Hughes, E. A., 1933; 1947. The Kinetics of Reactions in Solution. Oxford University Press. (5)

Moesveld, A. L. Th., 1922–1923. Piezochemische Studien. XVII. Der Einfluss des Druckes auf die Reaktionsgeschwindigkeit in homogenen flüssigen Systemen. Zeitschr. physik. Chem., 103: 486–504. (306)

Moesveld, A. L. Th., 1923. Piezochemische Studien. XXIII. Der Einfluss des Druckes auf die Reaktionsgeschwindigkeit in homogenen flüssigen Systemen. V. In Flüssigkeitsgemischen. Zeitschr. physik. Chem., 105: 455–471. (306)

Moesveld, A. L. Th., and W. A. T. de Meester, 1928. Piezochemische Studien. XXIX. Der Einfluss des Druckes auf die Reaktionsgeschwindigkeit. Die Rolle des Mediums in homogen flüssigen Systemen. Zeitschr. physik. Chem., 138: 169–225. (306)

Mommaerts, W. F. H. M., 1950. Muscular Contraction—A Topic in Molecular Physiology. Interscience Publishers, New York. (699, 703, 733, 750)

Monnier, A. M., 1934. L'Excitation Electrique des Tissues. Hermann et Cie., Paris. (623)

Monod, J., 1942. Recherches sur la Croissance des Cultures Bactériennes. Librairie Scientifique, Hermann et Cie., Paris. (191)

Moore, B., and H. E. Roaf, 1904. On certain physical and chemical properties of solutions of chloroform in water, saline, serum and haemoglobin. A contribution to the chemistry of anaesthesia. Proc. Roy. Soc. Lond., 73: 382–412. (452)

Moore, B., and H. E. Roaf, 1905. On certain physical and chemical properties of solutions of chloroform and other anaesthetics. A contribution to the chemistry of anaesthesia. Proc. Roy. Soc. Lond., B 77: 86–102.

Moore, K. (See Johnson and Moore, 1941.)

Morales, M. F. (See Botts, Johnson, and Morales, 1951.)

Morales, M. F., 1947. A note on limiting reactions and temperature coefficients. Jour. Cell. Comp. Physiol., 30: 303–314. (207, 209)

Morales, M. F., 1948. Some qualitative considerations on the mechanism of striated muscle contraction. Biochimica Biophysica Acta, 2: 618–623. (704, 730)

Morales, M. F., and J. Botts, 1952. A model for the elementary process in muscle action. Arch. Biochem. and Biophysics, 37: 283–300. (753)

Morales, M. F., and J. Botts, 1953. Energetics and molecular mechanisms in muscle action. Part I. Outline of a theory of muscle action and some of its experimental basis. Discussion Farad. Soc., 1953, No. 13, pp. 125–132. (753)

Moran, T. (See Lloyd and Moran, 1934.)

Morgan, C., G. Rozsa, A. Szent-Györgyi, and R. W. G. Wyckoff, 1950. Macromolecular arrangement within muscle. Science, 111: 201–202. (752)

Morgan, G. T., and E. A. Cooper, 1912. The influence of the chemical constitution of certain organic hydroxyl and aminic derivatives on their germicidal power. Eighth Int. Cong. Appl. Chem., 19: 243–257. (462)

Morrison, T. F. (See Harvey and Morrison, 1923.)

Morrison, T. F., 1924–1925. Studies on luminous bacteria. II. The influence of temperature on the intensity of the light of luminous bacteria. Jour. Gen. Physiol., 7: 741–753. (203, 218)

Morse, P. M., 1929. Diatomic molecules according to the wave mechanics. II. Vibrational levels. Phys. Rev., **34**: 57–64. (*11*)

Mudge, C. S., and F. R. Smith, 1935. Relation of action of chlorine to bacterial death. Amer. Jour. Pub. Health, **25**: 442–447. (*439*)

Müller, A. (See Süpfle and Müller, 1920.)

Muller, H. J., 1922. Variation due to change in the individual gene. Amer. Nat., **56**: 32–50. (*31*)

Muller, H. J., 1937. Physics in the attack on the fundamental problems of genetics. Sci. Mon., **44**: 210–214. (*31*)

Mulliken, R. S., 1925. The isotope effect in band spectra, II: The spectrum of boron monoxide. Phys. Rev., **75**: 259–294. (*144, 145, 146*)

Mulliken, R. S., and C. A. Rieke, 1941. Molecular electronic spectra, dispersion and polarization. The theoretical interpretation and computation of oscillator strengths and intensities. Repts. Progr. Phys., **8**: 231–273. (*152*)

Mundell, D. B. (See Mendel, Mundell, and Rudney, 1943.)

Muntz, J. A. (See Barron, Dickman, Muntz, and Singer, 1949.)

von Muralt, A., 1946. Die Signalübermittlung im Nerven. Verlag Birkhäuser, Basel. (*406*)

Murray, T. J. (See Winchester and Murray, 1936.)

Musselman, A. D. (See Eagle and Musselman, 1944.)

Nachmansohn, D. (See Boell and Nachmansohn, 1940; Bullock, Grundfest, Nachmansohn, and Rothenberg, 1947; Bullock, Grundfest, Nachmansohn, Rothenberg, and Sterling, 1946; Bullock, Nachmansohn, and Rothenberg, 1946; Feld, Grundfest, Nachmansohn, and Rothenberg, 1948; Grundfest, Nachmansohn, and Rothenberg, 1947; Weber and Nachmansohn, 1929.)

Nachmansohn, D., 1945. The role of acetyl choline in the mechanism of nerve activity. In: R. S. Harris and K. V. Thimann, Vitamins and Hormones, **3**: 337–377. (*497*)

Nachmansohn, D., 1946. Chemical mechanism of nerve activity. Ann. N. Y. Acad. Sci., **47**: 395–428. (*497*)

Nachmansohn, D., R. T. Cox, C. W. Coates, and A. L. Machado, 1943. Action potential and enzyme activity in the electric organ of *Electrophorus electricus*. II. Phosphocreatine as energy source of the action potential. Jour. Neurophysiol., **6**: 383–395. (*502*)

Nachmansohn, D., and E. A. Feld, 1947. Studies on cholinesterase. IV. On the mechanism of diisopropyl fluorophosphate action *in vivo*. Jour. Biol. Chem., **171**: 715–724. (*498*)

Nachmansohn, D., and H. M. John, 1944. Inhibition of choline acetylase by α-keto acids. Proc. Soc. Exp. Biol. Med., **57**: 361–362. (*507*)

Nachmansohn, D., and H. M. John, 1945. Studies on choline acetylase. 1. Effect of amino acids on the dialyzed enzyme. Inhibition by α-keto acids. Jour. Biol. Chem., **158**: 157–171. (*507*)

Nachmansohn, D., H. M. John, and H. Waelsch, 1943. Effect of glutamic acid on the formation of acetylcholine. Jour. Biol. Chem., **150**: 485–486. (*507*)

Nachmansohn, D., and A. L. Machado, 1943. The formation of acetylcholine. A new enzyme: "choline acetylase." Jour. Neurophysiol., **6**: 397–403. (*507*)

Nachmansohn, D., M. A. Rothenberg, and E. A. Feld, 1947. The *in vitro* reversibility of cholinesterase inhibition by DFP. Arch. Biochem., **14**: 197–211. (*494, 495*)

Nachmansohn, D., and H. Schneemann, 1945. On the effect of drugs on cholinesterase. Jour. Biol. Chem., **159**: 239–240. (*491, 492*)

Nagai, H., 1905. Erstickung und Narkose des Flimmerepithels. Zeitschr. allgem. Physiol., **5**: 34–42. (*504*)

Nastuk, W. L., and A. L. Hodgkin, 1950. The electrical activity of single muscle fibers. Jour. Cell. Comp. Physiol., **35**: 39–73. (*496, 502, 684, 685*)

Needham, D. M., 1952. Adenosine triphosphate and the structural proteins in relation to muscle contraction. Adv. Enzymol., **13**: 151–197. (*753*)

Neely, C. L., Jr. (See Bonner, Clarke, Neely, and Slifkin, 1950.)

Nernst, W., 1906. Über die Berechnung chemisch Gleichgewichte aus thermischer Messungen. Nachr. kgl. Ges. Wiss. Göttingen Math.-physik. Klasse, **1**: 1–40. (*49*)

Neter, E., 1941. Combined bacteriostatic activity of sulfanilamide and azochloramide upon Group A hemolytic Streptococcus and Enterococcus. Proc. Soc. Exp. Biol. Med., **47**: 303–305. (*481*)

Neter, E., 1942. An *in vitro* study on the synergistic action of sulfamido compounds and azochloramid upon various pathogenic organisms. Jour. Pharm. Exp. Therap., **74**: 52–60. (*481*)

Neubauer, E. (See Fühner and Neubauer, 1907.)

Neurath, H. (See Erickson and Neurath, 1943.)

Neurath, H., 1936. The influence of denaturation on the spreading of proteins on a water surface. Jour. Phys. Chem., **40**: 361–368. (*261, 264*)

Neurath, H., 1940. Intramolecular folding of polypeptide chains in relation to protein structure. Jour. Phys. Chem., **44**: 296–305. (*256*)

Neurath, H., and H. B. Bull, 1938. The surface activity of proteins. Chem. Rev., **23**: 391–435. (*260, 263*)

Neurath, H., G. R. Cooper, and J. O. Erickson, 1942a. The denaturation of proteins and its appparent reversal. I. Horse serum albumin. Jour. Biol. Chem., **142**: 249–263. (*217, 253*)

Neurath, H., G. R. Cooper, and J. O. Erickson, 1942b. The denaturation of proteins and its apparent reversal. II. Horse serum pseudoglobulin. Jour. Biol. Chem., **142**: 265–276. (*217, 254*)

Neurath, H., J. P. Greenstein, F. W. Putnam, and J. O. Erickson, 1944. The chemistry of protein denaturation. Chem. Rev., **34**: 157–265. (*217, 252, 253, 254, 277*)

Nickerson, W. J., 1951. Metabolic aspects of bacterial growth in the absence of cell division. Proc. Fifth Intern. Congr. Microbiol., Rio de Janeiro (August, 1950). In press. (*366*)

Nicloux, M., 1904. Étude de l'action lipolytique du cytoplasma de la graine de ricin. Compt. rend. soc. biol., **56**: 839–843. (*272*)

Nicolai, H. W. (See Rona and Nicolai, 1927.)

Nicolau, S. (See Basset, Nicolau, and Macheboeuf, 1935.)

van Niel, C. B., 1949a. The "Delft School" and the rise of general microbiology. Bact. Rev., **13**: 161–174. (*24*)

van Niel, C. B., 1949b. The comparative biochemistry of photosynthesis. In: Photosynthesis in Plants, Franck, J., and W. E. Loomis (Eds.). Pp. 437–495. Iowa State College Press, Ames. (*24*)

Nigrelli, R. F. (See Shanes and Nigrelli, 1941.)

Nims, L. F., 1949. Radiation. Ann. Rev. Physiol., **11**: 527–544.   (*32*)

Northey, E. H., 1948. The Sulfonamides and Related Compounds. Reinhold Publishing Corp., New York.   (*378*)

Northrop, J. H. (See Kunitz and Northrop, 1933–1934; Loeb and Northrop, 1917.)

Northrop, J. H., 1932. Crystalline trypsin. IV. Reversibility of the inactivation and denaturation of trypsin by heat. Jour. Gen. Physiol., **16**: 323–337. (*216*)

Northrop, J. H., 1939. Crystalline Enzymes. Columbia University Press, New York.   (*217*)

Northrop, J. H., M. Kunitz, and R. M. Herriott, 1948. Crystalline Enzymes. Columbia University Press, New York.   (*217, 344*)

Nyman, M. (See Madsen and Nyman, 1907.)

Ochoa, S. (See Vishniac and Ochoa, 1951.)

Ochoa, S., and W. Vishniac, 1952. Carboxylation reactions and photosynthesis. Science, **115**: 297–301.   (*38*)

Ogston, A. G. (See Bailey, Gutfreund, and Ogston, 1948.)

Öhnell, R. (See Fisher and Öhnell, 1940.)

Oppenheimer, C. H. (See ZoBell and Oppenheimer, 1950.)

van Ormondt, J. (See Gorter and van Ormondt, 1933, 1935; Gorter, van Ormondt, and Dorn, 1932.)

Ormsbee, R. A., and K. C. Fisher, 1943. The effect of urethane on the consumption of oxygen and the rate of cell division in the ciliate *Tetrahymena geleii*. Jour. Gen. Physiol., **27**: 461–468.   (*417*)

Örström, Å., 1932. Zur Analyse der Atmungsteigerung bei der Befruchtung des Seeigeleis auf der Grundlage von Versuchen über Oxydation und Reduktion von Dimethylparaphenylendiamin in der Eizelle. Protoplasma, **15**: 566–589. (*417*)

Ostwald, W., 1890. Electrische Eigenschaften halbdurchlässiger Scheidewände. Zeitschr. physik. Chem., **6**: 71–82.   (*515*)

Overton, E., 1901. Studien über Narkose, zugleich ein Beitrag zur allgemeinen Pharmakologie. Fischer, Jena.   (*429, 430, 508*)

Pace, J., 1930. The inactivation of trypsin by heat. Biochem. Jour., **24**: 606–614. (*272*)

Pace, J., 1931. The heat-inactivation of the proteinase of the pancreas. Biochem. Jour., **25**: 1485–1490.

Parker, G. H., 1939. General anesthesia by cooling. Proc. Soc. Exp. Biol. Med., **42**: 186–187.   (*189*)

Parker, G. H., 1940a. Neurohumors as chromatophore activators. Proc. Amer. Acad. Arts Sci., **73**: 165–195.   (*350, 351*)

Parker, G. H., 1940b. The chromatophore system in the catfish *Ameiurus*. Biol. Bull., **79**: 237–251.   (*350, 351*)

Parker, G. H., 1940c. On the neurohumors of the color changes in catfishes and on fats and oils as protective agents for such changes. Proc. Amer. Phil. Soc., **83**: 379–403.   (*350, 351*)

Parker, G. H., 194\-1941. Melanophore bands and areas due to nerve cutting, in relation to the protracted activity of nerves. Jour. Gen. Physiol., **24**: 483–504. (*351*)

Parker, G. H., 1941. The method of activation of melanophores and the limitations of melanophore responses in the catfish *Ameiurus*. Proc. Amer. Phil. Soc., **85**: 18–24. (*351*)

Parker, G. H., 1941–1942. The activity of peripherally stored neurohumors in catfishes. Jour. Gen. Physiol., **25**: 177–184. (*351*)

Parker, J. M. (See White and Parker, 1938.)

Parpart, A. K. (See Jacobs and Parpart, 1932, 1937.)

Pasteur, L., J. Jaubert, and Ch. Chamberland, 1878. La théorie des germs et ses applications à la médicine et à la chirugie. Bull. Acad. Med., 2nd ser., **7**: 432–453. (*467*)

Patt, H. M., M. N. Swift, and E. B. Tyree, 1948. Influence of temperature on radiosensitivity in the frog (*Rana pipiens*). Fed. Proc., **7**: 90–91. (*32, 34*)

Paul, T., G. Birstein, and A. Reuss, 1910. Beiträge zur kinetik des asterbens der Bakterien in Sauerstoff verschiedener Konzentration und bei verschiedener Temperaturen. Biochem. Zeitschr., **25**: 367–400. (*455*)

Paul, T., and F. Prall, 1907. Die Wertbestimmung von Desinfektionsmitteln mit Staphylokokken, die bei der Temperatur der flüssigen Luft aufbewahrt wurden. Arb. Reichsgesundh. Amt., **26**: 73–129. (*187*)

Paul, Th. (See Krönig and Paul, 1897.)

Pauli, W., 1925. Über den Zusammenhang des Abschlusses der Elektronengruppen im Atom mit der Komplexstructur der Spektren. Zeitschr. Physik, **31**: 765–783. (*84*)

Pauling, L. (See Mirsky and Pauling, 1936.)

Pauling, L., 1933. The calculation of matrix elements for Lewis electronic structures of molecules. Jour. Chem. Phys., **1**: 280–283. (*87*)

Pauling, L., 1940a. The Nature of the Chemical Bond. Cornell University Press, Ithaca, N. Y. (*10, 81, 165*)

Pauling, L., 1940b. A theory of the structure and process of formation of antibodies. Jour. Amer. Chem. Soc., **62**: 2643–2657. (*30, 255*)

Pauling, L., and R. B. Corey, 1950. Two hydrogen-bonded spiral configurations of the polypeptide chain. Jour. Amer. Chem. Soc., **72**: 5349. (*31, 258*)

Pauling, L., and R. B. Corey, 1951a. Atomic coordinates and structure factors for two helical configurations of polypeptide chains. Proc. Nat. Acad. Sci., **37**: 235–240. (*31, 258*)

Pauling, L., and R. B. Corey, 1951b. The structure of synthetic polypeptides. Proc. Nat. Acad. Sci., **37**: 241–250. (*31, 258*)

Pauling, L., and R. B. Corey, 1951c. The pleated sheet, a new layer configuration of polypeptide chains. Proc. Nat. Acad. Sci., **37**: 251–256. (*31, 258*)

Pauling, L., and R. B. Corey, 1951d. The structure of feather rachis keratin. Proc. Nat. Acad. Sci., **37**: 256–261. (*31, 258*)

Pauling, L., and R. B. Corey, 1951e. The structure of hair, muscle, and related proteins. Proc. Nat. Acad. Sci., **37**: 261–271. (*31, 258*)

Pauling, L., and R. B. Corey, 1951f. The structure of fibrous proteins of the collagen-gelatin group. Proc. Nat. Acad. Sci., **37**: 272–281. (*31, 258*)

Pauling, L., and R. B. Corey, 1951g. The polypeptide-chain configuration in hemoglobin and other globular proteins. Proc. Nat. Acad. Sci., 37: 282–285. (*31, 258*)

Pauling, L., and R. B. Corey, 1952. Configurations of polypeptide chains with equivalent cis amide groups. Proc. Nat. Acad. Sci., 38: 86–93. (*258*)

Pauling, L., R. B. Corey, and H. R. Branson, 1951. The structure of proteins: Two hydrogen-bonded helical configurations of the polypeptide chain. Proc. Nat. Acad. Sci., 37: 205–211. (*30, 31, 258, 259*)

Pauling, L., D. Pressman, and A. L. Grossberg, 1944. The serological properties of simple substances. VII. A quantitative theory of the inhibition by haptens of the precipitation of heterogeneous antisera with antigens, and comparison with experimental results for polyhaptenic simple substances and for azo-proteins. Jour. Amer. Chem. Soc., 66: 784–792. (*239*)

Pearman, F. H. (See Drew and Pearman, 1937.)

Pease, D. C. (See Kitching and Pease, 1939.)

Pease, D. C., 1940a. Hydrostatic pressure effects upon protoplasmic streaming in plasmodium. Jour. Cell. Comp. Physiol., 16: 361–375. (*347, 349*)

Pease, D. C., 1940b. The effects of hydrostatic pressure upon the polar lobe and cleavage pattern in the chaetopterus egg. Biol. Bull., 78: 103–110. (*349, 354*)

Pease, D. C., 1941. Hydrostatic pressure effects upon the spindle figure and chromosome movement. I. Experiments on the first mitotic division of urechis eggs. Jour. Morphol., 69: 405–441. (*348, 362*)

Pease, D. C., 1942. The inhibition of fertilization and membrane elevation by high hydrostatic pressures. Jour. Cell. Comp. Physiol., 19: 1–3. (*360*)

Pease, D. C., 1946. Hydrostatic pressure effects upon the spindle figure and chromosome movement. II. Experiments on the meiotic divisions of *Tradescantia* pollen mother cells. Biol. Bull., 91: 145–169. (*347, 348, 361*)

Pease, D. C., and J. A. Kitching, 1939. The influence of hydrostatic pressure upon ciliary frequency. Jour. Cell. Comp. Physiol., 14: 135–142. (*318, 321, 323, 324*)

Pease, D. C., and D. A. Marsland, 1939. The cleavage of *Ascaris* eggs under exceptionally high pressure. Jour. Cell. Comp. Physiol., 14: 407–408. (*354, 355*)

Pease, D. C., and D. Regnery, 1941. *Drosophila* salivary chromosomes subjected to high hydrostatic pressure. Jour. Cell. Comp. Physiol., 17: 397–398. (*361*)

Peiss, C. N., and J. Field, 1948. A comparison of the influence of 2,4-dinitrophenol on the oxygen consumption of rat brain slices and homogenates. Jour. Biol. Chem., 175: 49–56. (*396*)

Peiss, C. N., and J. Field, 1950. The respiratory metabolism of excised tissues of warm- and cold-adapted fishes. Biol. Bull., 98: 213–224. (*189*)

Pelzer, H., and E. Wigner, 1932. Über die Geschwindigkeitskonstante von Austauschreaktionen. Zeitschr. physik. Chem., B 15: 445–471. (*12*)

Perez, J. J. (See Basset, Macheboeuf, and Perez, 1935.)

Perkins, C. T. (See Hoagland and Perkins, 1934–1935.)

Perrin, M. W. (See Gibson, Fawcett, and Perrin, 1935; Williams, Perrin, and Gibson, 1936.)

Peters, R. A., 1920. Variations in the resistance of protozoan organisms to toxic agents. Jour. Physiol., 54: 260–266. (*455*)

Petsch, W. (See Gleu and Petsch, 1935.)

Philippi, G. Th. (See Gorter and Philippi, 1934.)

Philippi, G. Th., 1934. On the spreading of ovalbumin. Rec. trav. chim., **53**: 81–90. *(261)*

Philippi, G. Th., 1936. On the Nature of Proteins. Thesis. Leiden. *(261)*

Picken, L. E. R. (See Meyer and Picken, 1937.)

Pierce, F. T., and J. Field, 1949. The effect of 2,4-dinitrophenol on hexokinase and glycogenolysis. Jour. Biol. Chem., **180**: 895–900. *(396)*

Pilz, G. F. (See Crozier and Pilz, 1924.)

Pirie, N. W. (See Bawden and Pirie, 1940.)

Planck, M., 1890. Ueber die Potentialdifferenz zwischen zwei verdünnten Lösungen binärer Electrolyte. Ann. Physik, **40**: 561–576. *(558)*

Planck, M., 1901. Über das Gesetz der Energieverteilung im Normalspectrum. Ann. Physik, (4) **4**: 553–563. *(62)*

Polanyi, M. (See Eyring and Polanyi, 1930; 1931.)

Polanyi, M., and M. G. Evans, 1935. Some applications of the transition state method to the calculation of reaction velocities, especially in solution. Trans. Farad. Soc., **31**: 875–894. *(12)*

Polis, B. D. (See McMeekin, Polis, Della Monica, and Coster, 1948.)

Polissar, M. J., 1938. A kinetic approach to the theory of conductance of infinitely dilute solutions, based on the "cage" model of liquids. Jour. Chem. Phys., **6**: 833–844. *(533)*

Polissar, M. J., 1949. The physical chemistry of the contractile process in muscle fiber. Abstracts of Papers, 115th Meeting, Amer. Chem. Soc., San Francisco, p. 8F. *(704, 705)*

Polissar, M. J., 1952a. Physical chemistry of contractile process in muscle. A physicochemical model of contractile mechanism. Amer. Jour. Physiol., **168**: 766–781. *(699, 700, 704, 705)*

Polissar, M. J., 1952b. Physical chemistry of contractile process in muscle. II. Analysis of other mechano-chemical properties of muscle. Amer. Jour. Physiol., **168**: 782–792. *(699, 700, 704, 705)*

Polissar, M. J., 1952c. Physical chemistry of contractile process in muscle. III. Interpretation of thermal behavior of stimulated muscle. Amer. Jour. Physiol., **168**: 793–804. *(699, 700, 704, 705)*

Polissar, M. J., 1952d. Physical chemistry of contractile process in muscle. IV. Estimates of size of contractile unit. Amer. Jour. Physiol., **168**: 805–811. *(699, 700, 704, 705)*

Polissar, M. J., 1952e. Concentration and potential pattern within membrane and its relation to penetration of ions and to time constants of electrotonus and accommodation. Fed. Proc., **11**: 124. *(604)*

Popoff, M., 1908. Experimentelle Zellstudien. Arch. Zellforsch., **1**: 245–379. *(192)*

Portier, P. (See Callery and Portier, 1910.)

Postel, S. (See Boyarsky, Rosenblad, Postel, and Gerard, 1949.)

Posternak, J. M. (See Brink and Posternak, 1948.)

Posternak, J. M., and M. G. Larrabee, 1948. Action of narcotics on synapses compared to action on axons in sympathetic ganglia. Fed. Proc., **7**: (1) p. 96. *(432)*

Potter, C., and E. M. Gillham, 1946. Effects of atmospheric environment, before and after treatment, on the toxicity to insects of contact poisons. Ann. Appl. Biol., **33**: 142–159.   (*466*)

Prall, F.   (See Paul and Prall, 1907.)

Pressman, D.   (See Pauling, Pressman, and Grossberg, 1944.)

Price, W. C.   (See Lauffer and Price, 1940.)

Price, W. C., 1940.   Thermal inactivation rates of four plant viruses. Arch. ges. Virusforsch., **1**: 373–386.   (*277*)

Przibram, H., 1923.   Temperatur und Temperatoren in Tierreiche. F. Deuticke, Leipsig u. Wien.   (*195*)

Puder, S., 1927.   Insulin und Dextrose als Gegengifte des Cyans. Med. Klin., **23**: 704–705.   (*485*)

Purr, A., 1935a.   Studies on the reversible inactivation of papain and cathepsin. Biochem. Jour., **29**: 5–12.   (*371*)

Purr, A., 1935b.   The activation phenomena of papain and cathepsin. Biochem. Jour., **29**: 13–20.   (*371*)

Putnam, F. W.   (See Neurath, Greenstein, Putnam, and Erickson, 1944.)

Pütter, A., 1914.   Temperaturkoeffizienten. Zeitschr. allgem. Physiol., **16**: 574–627.   (*196*)

Quastel, J. H.   (See Jowett and Quastel, 1937; Mann, Tennenbaum, and Quastel, 1938; Michaelis and Quastel, 1941.)

Quastel, J. H., 1939.   Respiration in the central nervous system. Physiol. Rev., **19**: 135–183.   (*487, 504, 505*)

Quastel, J. H., 1943.   Effects of narcotics and benzedrine on metabolic processes in the central nervous system. Trans. Farad. Soc., **39**: 348–359.   (*450, 504, 506*)

Quastel, J. H., M. Tennenbaum, and A. H. M. Wheatley, 1936.   Choline ester formation in, and choline esterase activities of, tissues *in vitro*. Biochem. Jour., **30**: 1668–1681.   (*507*)

Quastel, J. H., and M. D. Whetham, 1924.   The equilibria existing between succinic, fumaric, and malic acids in the presence of resting bacteria. Biochem. Jour., **18**: 519–534.   (*208*)

Quastel, J. H., and W. R. Wooldridge, 1927.   The effects of chemical and physical changes in the environment on resting bacteria. Biochem. Jour., **21**: 148–168.   (*438*)

Quastel, J. H., and W. R. Wooldridge, 1928.   Some properties of the dehydrogenating enzymes of bacteria. Biochem. Jour., **22**: 689–702.   (*387, 388*)

Rabinowitz, I., 1945.   Photosynthesis and Related Processes. Vol. 1. Interscience Publishers, New York.   (*34*)

Rabinowitz, I., 1951.   Photosynthesis and Related Processes. Vol. 2, Part 1. Interscience Publishers, New York.   (*34*)

Rahm, P. G., 1923.   Biologische und physiologische Beiträge zur Kenntnis der Moosfauna. Zeitschr. allgem. Physiol., **20**: 1–34.   (*188*)

Rahn, O., 1934.   Chemistry of death. Cold Spr. Harb. Symp., **2**: 70–77.   (*455*)

Rahn, O., 1943.   The problem of the logarithmic order of death in bacteria. Biodynamica, **4**: 81–130.   (*455*)

Rahn, O., 1945a.   Physical methods of sterilization of micro-organisms.   Bact. Rev., 9: 1–47.   (455)

Rahn, O., 1945b.   Injury and Death of Bacteria by Chemical Agents.   Biodynamica.   Normandy, Missouri.   (455)

Ralston, H. J., V. T. Inman, L. A. Strait, and M. D. Shaffrath, 1947.   Mechanics of human isolated voluntary muscle.   Amer. Jour. Physiol., 151: 612–620. (728)

Ramsdell, P. A.   (See Ball and Ramsdell, 1944.)

Ramsey, R. W., 1947.   Muscle: Physics.   In: Medical Physics, Glaser, O. (Ed.). Year Book Publishers, Chicago.   (728, 730, 735, 736, 739)

Ramsey, R. W., and S. F. Street, 1940.   The isometric length-tension diagram of isolated skeletal muscle fibers of the frog.   Jour. Cell. Comp. Physiol., 15: 11–34.   (727, 730)

Randall, M.   (See Lewis and Randall, 1923.)

Ranke, H., 1867.   Studien zur Wirkung des Chloroforms, Äthers und Amylens. Centralbl. med. Wissensch., 5: 209–213.   (452)

Ranke, H., 1877.   Zur Wirkungsweise der Anaesthetica.   Centralbl. med. Wissensch., 15: 609–614.   (452)

Ransmeier, R. E.   (See Brooks, Ransmeier, and Gerard, 1949.)

Raper, H. S., 1932.   Tyrosinase.   Ergeb. Enzymforsch., 1: 270–279.   (143, 170)

Rashevsky, N., 1933.   Outline of a physico-mathematical theory of excitation and inhibition.   Protoplasma, 20: 42–56.   (623)

Rashevsky, N., 1948.   Mathematical Biophysics.   University of Chicago Press, Chicago (rev. ed.).   (662)

Rashevsky, N., 1950.   Nervous system: mathematical theory of its functions.   In: Medical Physics, Otto Glasser (Ed.).   Vol. II.   Year Book Publishers, Chicago. (623)

Reed, G. B., 1937.   Independent variation of several characteristics in S. marcescens.   Jour. Bact., 34: 255–266.   (365)

Reed, R.   (See Astbury, Reed, and Spark, 1948.)

Rees, A. L. G.   (See Farrant, Rees, and Mercer, 1947; Mercer and Rees, 1946.)

Reese, C. E.   (See Zwolinski, Eyring, and Reese, 1949.)

Regnard, P.   (See Dubois and Regnard, 1889.)

Regnard, P., 1884a.   Note sur les conditions de la vie dans les profondeurs de la mer.   Compt. rend. soc. biol., 36: 164–168.   (286, 288, 308)

Regnard, P., 1884b.   Note relative a l'action des hautes pressions sur quelques phénomènes vitaux (mouvement des cils vibratiles, fermentation).   Compt. rend. soc. biol., 36: 187–188.   (286, 288)

Regnard, P., 1884c.   Sur la cause de la rigidité des muscles soumis aux très hautes pressions.   Compt. rend. soc. biol., 36: 310–311.   (286, 288)

Regnard, P., 1884d.   Effet des hautes pressions sur les animaux marins.   Compt. rend. soc. biol., 36: 394–395.   (286, 288)

Regnard, P., 1885a.   Influence des hautes pressions sur l'éclosion des oeufs de poisson.   Compt. rend. soc. biol., 37: 48.   (288)

Regnard, P., 1885b.   Sur un appareil, permettant de suivre par la vue les phénomènes qui se passent sous l'influence des hautes pressions.   Compt. rend. soc. biol., 37: 210–211.   (288)

Regnard, P., 1885c. Phénomènes objectifs que l'on peut observer sur le animaux soumis aux hautes pressions. Compt. rend. soc. biol., **37**: 510–515.   (*288, 308*)

Regnard, P., 1886. Actions des hautes pressions sur les tissus animaux. Compt. rend. acad. sci., **102**: 173–176.   (*288*)

Regnard, P., 1887a. Les phénomènes de la vie sous les hautes pressions—la contraction musculaire. Compt. rend. soc. biol., **39**: 265–269.   (*288*)

Regnard, P., 1887b. Influence des hautes pressions sur la rapidité du courant nerveux. Compt. rend. soc. biol., **39**: 406–408.   (*288*)

Regnard, P., 1891. Recherches expérimentales sur les conditions physiques de la vie dans les eaux. Librairie de l'Academie de Médecine, Paris.   (*286, 288*)

Regnard, P., and W. Vignal, 1884. Des lésions que produisent sur les tissus animaux les hautes pressions. Compt. rend. soc. biol., **36**: 403–404.   (*288*)

Regnery, D. (See Pease and Regnery, 1941.)

Reichel, H., 1909. Zur Theorie der Desinfektion. Die Desinfektionswirkung des Phenols (I, II, and III). Biochem. Zeitschr., **22**: 149–176 (I), 177–199 (II), 201–231 (III).   (*455*)

Reichenbach, H., 1911. Die Absterbeordnung der Bakterien und ihre Bedeutung für Theorie und Praxis der Desinfektion. Zeitschr. Hyg. Infekt., **69**: 171–222. (*455*)

Reid, A. (See Thompson and Reid, 1927.)

Reiner, J. M. (See Spiegelman and Reiner, 1942; Young and Reiner, 1937.)

Reiner, J. M., 1937. Diffusion and biological membrane permeability. I. Growth, **1**: 313–327.   (*516*)

Reiner, J. M., 1941. Diffusion and biological membrane permeability. II. Phil. Sci., **8**: 105–114.   (*516*)

Reiner, J. M., and S. Spiegelman, 1947. The mechanism of inhibition of carbohydrate assimilation by dinitrophenol and azide. Jour. Cell. Comp. Physiol., **30**: 347–357.   (*398*)

Reinicke, D. (See Rona and Reinicke, 1921.)

Reppert, E. H. (See Chase, Reppert, and Ruch, 1944.)

Reuss, A. (See Paul, Birstein, and Reuss, 1910.)

Rexford, D. (See Johnson, Rexford, and Harvey, 1949.)

Ri, T. (See Magee, Ri, and Eyring, 1941.)

Rice, R. G. (See Boyer, Lum, Ballou, Luck, and Rice, 1946.)

Richards, A. G. (See Fan, Cheng, and Richards, 1948.)

Richards, A. G., and L. K. Cutkomp, 1946. Correlation between the possession of a chitinous cuticle and sensitivity to DDT. Biol. Bull., **90**: 97–108.   (*466*)

Richards, R. K., 1943. Influence of fever upon the action of 3,3′-methylene-bis-(4-hydroxy-coumarin) (dicumarol). Science, **97**: 313.   (*466*)

Richet, Ch., 1893. Note sur le rapport entre la toxicité et les propriétés physiques des corps. Compt. rend. soc. biol., **45**: 775–776.   (*429*)

Richter, G. H. (See Bancroft and Richter, 1931.)

Rideal, E. K. (See Schulman and Rideal, 1937.)

Rideal, E. K., 1939. Film reactions as a new approach to biology. Science, **90**: 217–225.   (*265*)

Rieke, C. A. (See Mulliken and Rieke, 1941.)

Ris, H., and A. E. Mirsky, 1949. The state of the chromosomes in the interphase nucleus. Jour. Gen. Physiol., **32**: 489–509. (*361*)

Riseman, J., and J. G. Kirkwood, 1948. Remarks on the physico-chemical mechanism of muscular contraction and relaxation. Jour. Amer. Chem. Soc., **70**: 2820–2821. (*750*)

Roaf, H. E. (See Moore and Roaf, 1904; 1905.)

Roberts, W. L. (See Campbell, Smith, Roberts, and Link, 1941.)

Robinow, C., 1945. Nuclear apparatus and cell structure of rod-shaped bacteria. (*Addendum* to: Dubos, R. J., The Bacterial Cell. Harvard University Press, Cambridge, Mass.) (*233, 450, 451*)

Robinson, M. E. (See Adair and Robinson, 1930.)

Roblin, R. O. (See Bell and Roblin, 1942.)

Robson, M. E. (See Jacobson, Robson, Marks, and Goldman, 1949.)

Roche, A. (See Roche, Roche, Adair, and Adair, 1932.)

Roche, J., and M. Chouaïech, 1940. Sur la reversibilité de la dénaturation de la sérumalbumine. Compt. rend. soc. biol., **133**: 474–478. (*217*)

Roche, J., and R. Combette, 1937. Recherches sur les globines. IV. Combinaison des globines à la protohematine et poids moleculaire des hémoglobines artificielles. Bull. soc. chim. biol., **19**: 627–641. (*217*)

Roche, J., A. Roche, G. S. Adair, and M. E. Adair, 1932. The osmotic pressure of globin. Biochem. Jour., **26**: 1811–1828. (*254*)

Roger, H., 1895. Action des hautes pressions sur quelques bactéries. Arch. physiol. norm. pathol., 5th ser., **7**: 12–17. (*294, 295*)

Rohdewald, M. (See Willstätter and Rohdewald, 1934.)

Rona, P. (See Michaelis and Rona, 1910.)

Rona, P., and E. Block, 1921. Beiträge zum studium der Giftwirkung. Ueber die Wirkung des Chinins auf Invertase. Biochem. Zeitschr., **118**: 185–212. (*403*)

Rona, P., and H. Fischgold, 1933a. Dilatometrische Untersuchungen bei der Spaltung von Eiweisskörpern und deren Bausteinen. I. Mitteilung: Spaltung von Dipeptiden. Biochem. Zeitschr., **261**: 66–75. (*335*)

Rona, P., and H. Fischgold, 1933b. Dilatometrische Untersuchungen bei der Spaltung von Eiweisskörpern und ihren Bausteinen. II. Mitteilung: Spaltung von Ovalbumin und Casein. Biochem. Zeitschr., **261**: 366–373. (*335*)

Rona, P., and K. Grassheim, 1923. Studien zur Zellatmung. II. Mitteilung. Die Wirkung von Chinin auf die Atmung lebender Hefezellen. Biochem. Zeitschr., **140**: 493–516. (*403*)

Rona, P., and H. W. Nicolai, 1927. Untersuchungen über die Giftwirkung der Chininkörper auf das Gasvermögen lebender Hefe. Biochem. Zeitschr., **189**: 331–347. (*403*)

Rona, P., and D. Reinicke, 1921. Beiträge zum Studium der Giftwirkung. Ueber die Wirkung des Chinins auf Serumlipase. Biochem. Zeitschr., **118**: 213–231. (*403*)

Rona, P., and M. Takata, 1922. Ueber die Wirkung des chinins und der Chininderivate auf Magenlipase. Biochem. Zeitschr., **134**: 118–130. (*403*)

Ronzoni, E. (See Ehrenfest and Ronzoni, 1933.)

Root, C. W., 1932. The relation between respiration and light intensity of luminous bacteria, with special reference to temperature. I. Temperature and light intensity. Jour. Cell. Comp. Physiol., **1**: 195–208. (*203, 218*)

Rose, C. L.   (See Chen, Rose, and Clowes, 1934.)

Rosenberg, S., 1926.   Sind Insulin und Blausäure Gegengifte?   Med. Klin., **22**: 1650.   (*485*)

Rosenberg, T., 1948.   On accumulation and active transport in biological systems. I. Thermodynamic considerations.   Acta Chem. Scand., **2**: 14–33.   (*516*)

Rosenblad, A. D.   (See Boyarsky, Rosenblad, Postel, and Gerard, 1949.)

Ross, R. W. N. L., 1946.   Inhibition of various clostridia by penicillin in human serum.   Jour. Path. Bact., **58**: 441–447.   (*366*)

Rothen, A., 1942.   The present status of molecular weights of proteins.   Ann. N. Y. Acad. Sci., **43**: 229–241.   (*253*)

Rothen, A., 1947.   Films of protein in biological processes.   Adv. Prot. Chem., **3**: 123–137.   (*252, 260, 265*)

Rothen, A., B. F. Chow, R. O. Greep, and H. B. Van Dyke, 1941.   Specific properties of films of protein.   Cold Spr. Harb. Symp., **9**: 272–277.   (*266*)

Rothen, A., and K. Landsteiner, 1942.   Serological reactions of protein films and denatured proteins.   Jour. Exp. Med., **76**: 437–450.   (*266*)

Rothenberg, M. A.   (See Bullock, Grundfest, Nachmansohn, and Rothenberg, 1947; Bullock, Grundfest, Nachmansohn, Rothenberg, and Sterling, 1946; Bullock, Nachmansohn, and Rothenberg, 1946; Feld, Grundfest, Nachmansohn, and Rothenberg, 1948; Grundfest, Nachmansohn, and Rothenberg, 1947; Nachmansohn, Rothenberg, and Feld, 1947.)

Rottier, P. B., 1942.   Fluorometrische en spectrophotometrische bepaling van lactoflavine in micro-organismen.   Dissertation. Delft.   (*135*)

Roubaud, E., 1919.   Études sur le sommeil d'hiver pré-imaginal des muscides. Les cycles d'asthénie et l'athermobiose réactivante spécifique.   Bull. Biol. Fr. Belg., **56**: 455–544.   (*269*)

Rowland, S.   (See Macfadyen and Rowland, 1900a, 1900b.)

Rozsa, G.   (See Morgan, Rozsa, Szent-Györgyi, and Wyckoff, 1950.)

Rubin, M. A.   (See Hoagland, Rubin, and Cameron, 1937.)

Ruch, R. M.   (See Chase, Reppert, and Ruch, 1944.)

Rudney, H.   (See Mendel, Mundell, and Rudney, 1943; Mendel and Rudney, 1943.)

Rudy, H.   (See Kuhn and Rudy, 1936.)

Ruggiero, W. F.   (See Crossman, Ruggiero, Hurley, and Allen, 1942.)

Rugh, R., and D. A. Marsland, 1943.   The effect of hydrostatic pressure upon the early development of the frog's egg (*Rana pipiens*).   Proc. Amer. Phil. Soc., **86**: 459–466.   (*354, 357, 361*)

Sabine, J. C.   (See Wright and Sabine, 1943.)

Sachs, J., 1864.   Ueber die obere Temperatur-Gränze der Vegetation.   Flora, (N.R.) **22**, No. 5, pp. 65–75.   (*215, 217*)

Sailer, R. I., 1950.   A thermophobic insect.   Science, **112**: 743.   (*188*)

Salkowski, E., 1888.   Über die antiseptische Wirkung des Chloroformwassers. Deut. med. Wochenschr., **14**: 309–311.   (*452*)

Salkowski, E., 1900.   Über die eiweissfällende Wirkung des Chloroforms.   Hoppe-Seyler's Zeitschr. physiol. Chem., **31**: 329–337.   (*452*)

Sandor, G.   (See Basset, Macheboeuf, and Sandor, 1933.)

Sandow, A., 1949.   Muscle.   Ann. Rev. Physiol., **11**: 297–334.   (*704, 728*)

Sastri, B. M.   (See Sreenivasaya, Sastri, and Sreevangachar, 1934.)

Saubert, G. G. P., 1937. The influence of alcohols on the protoplasmic membrane and colloid models. Rec. trav. bot. néerl., **34**: 709–797.   (*500*)

Scatchard, G., 1952. Molecular interactions in protein solutions. Amer. Sci., **40**: 61–83.   (*415*)

Scatchard, G., L. E. Strong, W. L. Hughes, J. N. Ashworth, and A. H. Sparrow, 1945. Chemical, clinical and immunological studies on the products of human plasma fractionation. XXVI. The properties of solutions of human serum albumin of low salt content. Jour. Clin. Invest., **24**: 671–679. (*271*)

Schaefer, H. (See Ebbecke and Schaefer, 1935.)

Schaefer, H., 1944. Elektrophysiologie, I Band: Allgemeine Elektrophysiologie. J. W. Edwards, Publisher Inc., Ann Arbor.   (*604, 610, 612, 655, 691*)

Schaefer, V. J. (See Langmuir and Schaefer, 1938, 1939.)

Schaffer, J. M. (See Tilley and Schaffer, 1926.)

Schaller, K., 1942. Über die Cholinesterase des menschlichen Blutes. Zeitschr. klin. Med., **141**: 565–589.   (*500*)

Schelling, V. (See McClure, Hartmann, Schnedorf, and Schelling, 1939.)

Schellman, J. (See Simpson, Watson, Levedahl, Schellman, Frensdorff, and Kauzmann, 1951.)

Schlegel, F. McK. (See Johnson and Schlegel, 1948.)

Schlegel, F. McK., and F. H. Johnson, 1949. The influence of temperature and hydrostatic pressure on the denaturation of methemoglobin by urethanes and salicylate. Jour. Biol. Chem., **178**: 251–257.   (*334*)

Schlenk, H., and R. T. Holman, 1950. The urea complexes of unsaturated fatty acids. Science, **112**: 19–20.   (*483*)

Schlenk, W. (See Bengen and Schlenk, 1949.)

Schlenk, W., 1949. Die Harnstoff-Addition der aliphatischen Verbindungen. Liebigs Ann. Chem., **565**: 204–240.   (*483*)

Schmelkes, F. C., and O. Wyss, 1942. Inactivation of sulfonamide inhibitor by azochloramid. Proc. Soc. Exp. Biol. Med., **49**: 263–267.   (*481*)

Schmidt, A. X., and C. A. Marlies, 1948. Principles of High-Polymer Theory and Practice. McGraw-Hill Book Co., New York.   (*700*)

Schmidt, C. L. A. (Ed.), 1943. The Chemistry of the Amino Acids and Proteins. C. C. Thomas, Springfield, Ill.   (*256*)

Schmidt, G., and P. A. Levene, 1938. Ribonucleodepolymerase (The Jones-Dubos enzyme). Jour. Biol. Chem., **126**: 423–434.   (*341*)

Schmidt, H., 1936. Plasmolyse und Permeabilität. Jahr. wiss. Bot., **83**: 470–512. (*500*)

Schmitt, F. O. (See Fourt and Schmitt, 1936.)

Schmitt, F. O., 1950. Morphology in muscle and nerve physiology. Biochimica Biophysica Acta, **4**: 68–77. Reprinted in: Metabolism and Function, D. Nachmansohn (Ed.). Elsevier Publishing Co., Amsterdam.   (*753*)

Schmitt, F. O., R. S. Bear, C. E. Hall, and M. A. Jakus, 1947. Electron microscope and x-ray diffraction studies of muscle structure. Ann. N. Y. Acad. Sci., **47**: 799–812.   (*701, 752, 753*)

Schmitt, F. O., and O. H. A. Schmitt, 1931. The nature of the nerve impulse. II. The effect of cyanides upon medulated nerves. Amer. Jour. Physiol., **97**: 302–314.   (*507*)

Schmitt, F. O., R. K. Skow, and B. M. Bilinsky, 1936. Cyanide inhibition of frog tissues. Proc. Soc. Exp. Biol. Med., **34**: 397–399.   (*417*)

Schmitt, O. H., 1951.   In: Nerve Impulse, Transactions of the Second Conference, March 1–2, New York, p. 86.   D. Nachmansohn (Ed.), Josiah Macy, Jr., Foundation, Publisher.   (*670*)

Schmitt, O. H. A.   (See Schmitt and Schmitt, 1931.)

Schnedorf, J. G.   (See McClure, Hartmann, Schnedorf, and Schelling, 1939.)

Schneemann, H.   (See Nachmansohn and Schneemann, 1945.)

Schneider, F.   (See Grassmann and Schneider, 1944.)

Schoepfle, G. M., 1940.   Kinetics of luminescent flashes in the bacterium, *Achromobacter fischeri* at different temperatures.   Jour. Cell. Comp. Physiol., **16**: 341–360.   (*183, 326*)

Schoepfle, G. M., 1941.   Kinetics of bacterial luminescent flashes: effects of veronal, dinitrophenol and osmotic pressure.   Jour. Cell. Comp. Physiol., **17**: 109–116.   (*183*)

Scholander, P. F., R. Hock, V. Walters, and L. Irving, 1950.   Adaptation to cold in arctic and tropical mammals and birds in relation to body temperature, insulation, and basal metabolic rate.   Biol. Bull., **99**: 259–271.   (*189*)

Scholander, P. F., R. Hock, V. Walters, F. Johnson, and L. Irving, 1950.   Heat regulation in some arctic and tropical mammals and birds.   Biol. Bull., **99**: 237–258.   (*189*)

Schomaker, V.   (See Wright and Schomaker, 1948a, 1948b.)

van Schouwenburg, K. L.   (See Eymers and van Schouwenburg, 1936, 1937a, 1937b; Johnson, van Schouwenburg, and van der Burg, 1939.)

van Schouwenburg, K. L., 1938.   On Respiration and Light Emission in Luminous Bacteria.   Dissertation.   Delft.   (*128, 179, 180, 371*)

van Schouwenburg, K. L., and A. van der Burg, 1940.   On the influence of carbon monoxide on respiration and light emission of luminous bacteria.   Enzymologia, **9**: 34–42.   (*183*)

Schroeder, H. O.   (See Lindquist, Madden, and Schroeder, 1946; Lindquist, Wilson, Schroeder, and Madden, 1945.)

Schroedinger, E., 1926.   Quantisierung als Eigenwertproblem.   Ann. Physik, **79**: 361–376, 489–527; **80**: 437–490; **81**: 109–139.   (*69*)

Schroedinger, E., 1946.   "What Is Life?"   Cambridge University Press.   (*23*)

Schryver, J.   (See Chase, Schryver, and Stern, 1948.)

Schuiling, A. L.   (See Spruit and Schuiling, 1945.)

Schulman, J. H., 1941.   The orientation at the oil/water interface of esters and their digestion by pancreatin.   Trans. Farad. Soc., **37**: 134–139.   (*265*)

Schulman, J. H., and E. K. Rideal, 1937a.   Molecular interaction in monolayers. I. Complexes between large molecules.   Proc. Roy. Soc. Lond., B **122**: 29–45.   (*261*)

Schulman, J. H., and E. K. Rideal, 1937b.   Molecular interaction in monolayers. II. The action of haemolytic and agglutinating agents or lipo-protein monolayers.   Proc. Roy. Soc. Lond., B **122**: 46–57.   (*261*)

Schultze, M. O.   (See Stotz, Harrer, Schultze, and King, 1937–1938.)

Schütz, F.   (See Holtham and Schütz, 1949.)

Schwert, G. W.   (See Eisenberg and Schwert, 1951.)

Seastone, C. V., 1938.   The measurement of surface films formed by hemocyanin, tobacco mosaic virus, vaccinia, and *Bacterium gallinarum*.   Jour. Gen. Physiol., **21**: 621–629.   (*261*)

Sexton, W. A., 1950.   Chemical Constitution and Biological Activity.   D. Van Nostrand Co., New York.   (*377*)

Shaffrath, M. D. (See Ralston, Inman, Strait, and Shaffrath, 1947.)

Shanes, A. M., 1944. The effect of high potassium concentrations on the aerobic and anaerobic fractions of the resting potential of frog nerve. Jour. Cell. Comp. Physiol., **23**: 193–196. *(501)*

Shanes, A. M., and D. E. Brown, 1942. The effect of metabolic inhibitors on the resting potential of frog nerve. Jour. Cell. Comp. Physiol., **20**: 1–13. *(507)*

Shanes, A. M., and R. F. Nigrelli, 1941. The chromatophores of *Fundulus heteroclitus* in polarized light. Zoologica, **26**: 237–245. *(353)*

Shapiro, H., 1934. The light intensity of luminous bacteria as a function of oxygen pressure. Jour. Cell. Comp. Physiol., **4**: 313–328. *(124)*

Shapiro, R. (See Flett, Haring, Guiteras, and Shapiro, 1945.)

Shapley, H., 1920. Thermokinetics of *Liometopum apiculatum* Mayr. Proc. Nat. Acad. Sci., **6**: 204–211. *(202)*

Shaw, J. L., B. F. Steele, and C. A. Lamb, 1937. Effect of anesthesia on the blood oxygen. I. A study of the effect of ether anesthesia on the oxygen in the arterial and in the venous blood. Arch. Surg., **35**: 1–10. *(504)*

Shear, C. L., and B. O. Dodge, 1927. Life histories and heterothallism of the red bread mold fungi of the *Monilia sitophila* group. Jour. Agric. Res., **34**: 1019–1042. *(269)*

Sherman, A., and N. Li, 1936. Theoretical considerations concerning the mechanism of the thermal reaction between gaseous iodine monochloride and hydrogen. Jour. Amer. Chem. Soc., **58**: 690–691. *(114)*

Shinohara, K., and M. Kilpatrick, 1934. The stability of cysteine in acid solution. Jour. Biol. Chem., **105**: 241–251. *(272)*

Shoup, C. S. (See Strehler and Shoup, 1953.)

Shoup, C. S., 1929. The respiration of luminous bacteria and the effect of oxygen tension upon oxygen consumption. Jour. Gen. Physiol., **13**: 27–45. *(124)*

Shoup, C. S., and A. Kimler, 1934. The sensitivity of the respiration of luminous bacteria for 2,4-dinitrophenol. Jour. Cell. Comp. Physiol., **5**: 269–276. *(396)*

Shull, A. F., 1907. The stridulation of the snowy tree-cricket (*Oecanthus niveus*). Canadian Entomol., **39**: 213–225. *(201)*

Sievers, J. F. (See Meyer and Sievers, 1936a; 1936b.)

Simpson, H. N., and A. J. Derbyshire, 1934. Electrical activity of the motor cortex during cerebral anemia. Amer. Jour. Physiol., **109**: 99. *(504)*

Simpson, R. B. (See Johnson, Flagler, Simpson, and McGeer, 1951.)

Simpson, R. B., M. T. Watson, B. Levedahl, J. Schellman, H. K. Frensdorff, and W. Kauzmann, 1951. The kinetics of protein denaturation. Unpublished account, privately circulated, November, 1951. Published, while this book was in press, as a series of papers, Jour. Amer. Chem. Soc., **75**: 5139–5172 (1953). *(31)*

Singer, T. P. (See Barron, Dickman, Muntz, and Singer, 1949; Barron and Singer, 1943.)

Sisson, W. A. (See Astbury and Sisson, 1935.)

Sizer, I. W. (See Gould and Sizer, 1938.)

Sizer, I. W., 1939. Temperature activation of the urease-urea system using crude and crystalline urease. Jour. Gen. Physiol., **22**: 719–741. *(209, 211)*

Sizer, I. W., 1941. Temperature activation of the urease-urea system using urease of *Proteus vulgaris*. Jour. Bact., **41**: 511–527.   *(209, 210)*

Sizer, I. W., 1942a. The activity of yeast invertase as a function of oxidation-reduction potential. Jour. Gen. Physiol., **25**: 399–409.   *(211)*

Sizer, I. W., 1942b. The action of certain oxidants and reductants upon the activity of bovine phosphatase. Jour. Biol. 'Chem., **145**: 405–414.   *(211)*

Sizer, I. W., 1943. Effects of temperature on enzyme kinetics. Adv. Enzymol., **3**: 35–62.   *(170, 208, 209)*

Sizer, I. W., and E. S. Josephson, 1942. Kinetics as a function of temperature of lipase, trypsin, and invertase activity from −70 to 50°C (−94 to 122°F). Food Research, **7**: 201–209.   *(206, 207)*

Sizer, I. W., and A. A. Tytell, 1941. The activity of crystalline urease as a function of oxidation-reduction potential. Jour. Biol. Chem., **138**: 631–642. *(211)*

Sklar, A. L., 1939. The near ultraviolet absorption of substituted benzenes. Jour. Chem. Phys., **7**: 984–993.   *(152)*

Skow, R. K. (See Schmitt, Skow, and Bilinsky, 1936.)

Slator, A., 1911. The rate of alcoholic fermentation. Jour. Inst. Brewing, **17**: 147–169.   *(204)*

Slator, J. C., 1931. Molecular energy levels and valence bonds. Phys. Rev., ser. 2, **38**: 1109–1144.   *(85, 87)*

Slifkin, M. K. (See Bonner, Clarke, Neely, and Slifkin, 1950.)

Smith, F. R. (See Mudge and Smith, 1935.)

Smith, H. W., 1936. The retention and physiological role of urea in the Elasmobranchii. Biol. Rev. Proc. Camb. Phil. Soc., **11**: 49–82.   *(282)*

Smith, J. H., 1921. The killing of *Botrytis* spores by phenol. Ann. Appl. Biol., **8**: 27–50.   *(455)*

Smith, J. H., 1923. The killing of *Botrytis cinerea* by heat, with a note on the determination of temperature coefficients. Ann. Appl. Biol., **10**: 335–347. *(455)*

Smith, W. K. (See Campbell, Smith, Roberts, and Link, 1941.)

Snell, P. A. (See Harvey and Snell, 1931.)

Sobotka, H., 1944. Monomolecular layers: their application in physiology and medicine. In: Glaser, O., Medical Physics. P. 763. Year Book Publishers, Chicago.   *(265)*

Sollner, K., 1950. Recent advances in the electrochemistry of membranes of high ionic selectivity. Jour. Electrochem. Soc., **97**: 139C–151C.   *(516)*

Sonnenberg, M. (See Karush and Sonnenberg, 1949.)

Sonnenfeld, V. (See McElroy, Hastings, Sonnenfeld and Coulombre, 1953.)

Sookne, A. M., and M. Harris, 1937. Stress-strain characteristics of wool as related to its chemical constitution. Jour. Res. Nat. Bur. Stand., **19**: 535–549 (RP 1043).   *(272)*

Spaeth, R. A., 1916. Evidence proving the melanophore to be a disguised type of smooth muscle cell. Jour. Exp. Zool., **20**: 193–215.   *(351, 353)*

Spark, L. C. (See Astbury, Reed, and Spark, 1948.)

Sparrow, A. H. (See Scatchard, Strong, Hughes, Ashworth, and Sparrow, 1945.)

Spiegelman, S. (See Reiner and Spiegelman, 1947.)

Spiegelman, S., and J. M. Reiner, 1942. A kinetic analysis of potassium accumulation and sodium exclusion. Growth, **6**: 367–389.   *(680)*

Spiegel-Adolf, M., 1926. Hitzveränderungen des albumins. Biochem. Zeitschr., **170**: 126–172. (*217*)

Spikes, J. D., 1950–1951. Progress Report, Atomic Energy Commission, Contract No. AT(11–1)—82, Project No. 4, University of Utah. (*39, 40*)

Spikes, J. D., 1952. Stoichiometry of the photolysis of water by illuminated chloroplast fragments. Arch. Biochem. Biophys., **35**: 101–109. (*37*)

Spikes, J. D., R. Lumry, H. Eyring, and R. Wayrynen, 1950. Potential changes in chloroplast suspensions and in whole cytoplasm preparations of plant cells on illumination. Proc. Nat. Acad. Sci., **36**: 455–460. (*35, 36*)

Spruit, C. J. P., 1946. Naphthoquinonen en Bioluminescentie. Thesis. Utrecht. (*133, 181, 182, 183*)

Spruit, C. J. P., 1947. Carbonyl-substituted naphthoquinones. Part I. Methyl ketones unsubstituted in the side chain. Rec. trav. chim., **66**: 655–672. (*133*)

Spruit, C. J. P., 1948. Carbonyl-substituted naphthoquinones. Part II. Ketones of the type $C_{10}H_7O_2COCH_2R$. Rec. trav. chim., **67**: 285–297. (*133*)

Spruit, C. J. P., 1949. The chemical nature of the luciferins. Enzymologia, **13**: 191–200. (*131, 133, 134*)

Spruit, C. J. P., and A. L. Schuiling, 1945. On the influence of naphthoquinones on the respiration and light emission of *Photobacterium phosphoreum*. Rec. trav. chim., **64**: 219–228. (*134, 181, 182, 183, 375*)

Spruit-van der Burg, A., 1950. Emission spectra of luminous bacteria. Biochimica Biophysica Acta, **5**: 175–178. (*135, 141*)

Sreenivasaya, M. (See Sreevangachar and Sreenivasaya, 1935.)

Sreenivasaya, M., B. M. Sastri, and H. B. Sreerangachar, 1934. Dilatometric studies in the proteoclastic degradation of proteins. I. Tryptic hydrolysis. Biochem. Jour., **28**: 351–355. (*335*)

Sreenivasaya, M., and H. B. Sreerangachar, 1934. Dilatometric studies in the proteoclastic degradation of proteins. II. Peptic hydrolysis. Biochem. Jour., **28**: 1219–1221. (*335*)

Sreerangachar, H. B. (See Sreenivasaya, Sastri, and Sreerangachar, 1934; Sreenivasaya and Sreerangachar, 1934.)

Sreerangachar, H. B., and M. Sreenivasaya, 1935. Dilatometric determination of the relative digestibility of proteins. Biochem. Jour., **29**: 291–294. (*335*)

Stahman, M. A., C. J. Huebner, and K. P. Link, 1941. Studies on the hemorrhagic sweet clover disease. V. Identification and synthesis of the hemorrhagic agent. Jour. Biol. Chem., **138**: 513–527. (*465*)

Stämpfli, R. (See Huxley and Stämpfli, 1951.)

Stanley, W. M., and M. A. Lauffer, 1939. Disintegration of tobacco mosaic virus in urea solutions. Science, **89**: 345–347. (*254*)

Stanley, W. M., and H. S. Loring, 1938. Properties of virus proteins. Cold Spr. Harb. Symp., **6**: 341–360. (*297*)

Stannard, J. N., 1939. Separation of the resting and activity oxygen consumptions of frog muscle by means of sodium azide. Amer. Jour. Physiol., **126**: 196–213. (*417*)

Starling, E. H., 1941. Starling's Principles of Human Physiology, edited and revised by C. L. Evans. Lea and Febiger, Philadelphia. (*740*)

Stearn, A. E. (See Eyring and Stearn, 1939.)

Stearn, A. E., 1949. Kinetics of biological reactions with special reference to enzyme processes. Adv. Enzymol., **9**: 25–74. (*207*)

Stearn, A. E., and H. Eyring, 1940. Absolute rates of solid reactions: diffusion. Jour. Phys. Chem., **44**: 955–980. (*533*)

Stearn, A. E., and H. Eyring, 1941. Pressure and rate processes. Chem. Rev., **29**: 509–523. (*287, 305, 306*)

Stearn, J. R. (See Fisher and Stearn, 1942.)

Stearn, L. (See Batelli and Stearn, 1913.)

Steblay, R. (See Johnson, Eyring, Steblay, Chaplin, Huber, and Gherardi, 1945.)

Steele, B. F. (See Shaw, Steele, and Lamb, 1937.)

Steinbach, H. B., 1940. Sodium and potassium in frog muscle. Jour. Biol. Chem., **133**: 695–701. (*669*)

Steinhardt, J., 1937. The stability of crystalline pepsin. Det. Kgl. Danske Videnskabernes Selskab-Math.-Fys. Meddelelser, **14**: (11) pp. 1–53. (*272, 277, 278, 279*)

Steinhardt, J., 1938. Solubility behavior of crystalline pepsin and other proteins. Proc. 32nd Ann. Meeting Amer. Biol. Chem., March 30, 1938. Jour. Biol. Chem., **123**: CXV–CXVI. (*272*)

Steinhardt, J., 1941. Participation of anions in the combination of proteins with acids. Ann. N. Y. Acad. Sci., **41**: 287–320. (*393, 394*)

Steinhardt, J., 1942. Calculation of protein-anion affinity constants from acid titration data. Jour. Res. Nat. Bur. Stand., **28**: 191–199. (*393*)

Steinhardt, J., C. H. Fugitt, and M. Harris, 1940. Combination of wool protein with acid and base: the effect of temperature on the titration curve. Jour. Res. Nat. Bur. Stand., **25**: 519–544. (*393*)

Steinhardt, J., C. H. Fugitt, and M. Harris, 1941. Relative affinities of the anions of strong acids for wool protein. Jour. Res. Nat. Bur. Stand., **26**: 293–320. (*393, 394*)

Steinhardt, J., C. H. Fugitt, and M. Harris, 1942. Further investigations of the affinities of anions of strong acids for wool protein. Jour. Res. Nat. Bur. Stand., **28**: 201–216.

Steinhardt, J., and E. M. Zaiser, 1950. Combination of wool protein with cations and hydroxyl ions. Jour. Biol. Chem., **183**: 789–802. (*393, 395*)

Steldt, F. A. (See Chen, Anderson, Steldt, and Mills, 1943.)

Stempel, A. (See Aeschlimann and Stempel, 1946.)

Stephenson, M. (See Cook and Stephenson, 1928.)

Sterling, K. (See Bullock, Grundfest, Nachmansohn, Rothenberg, and Sterling, 1946.)

Stern, K. (See Chase, Schryver, and Stern, 1948.)

Stern, O., 1896. Ueber den Einfluss des Druckes auf die Inversionskonstante einiger Säuren. Ann. Phys. Chem., **59**: 652–663. (*306*)

Stevens, K. P., 1927. Studies on the amount of light emitted by mixtures of *Cypridina* luciferin and luciferase. Jour. Gen. Physiol., **10**: 859–873. (*174*)

Stier, T. B. (See Crozier and Stier, 1924–1925a–d.)

Stotz, E., C. J. Harrer, M. O. Schultze, and C. G. King, 1937–1938. The oxidation of ascorbic acid in the presence of guinea pig liver. Jour. Biol. Chem., **122**: 407–418. (*374*)

Strait, L. A. (See Ralston, Inman, Strait, and Shaffrath, 1947.)

Strakosch, E. A. (See Tenenberg, Tsuchiya, Clark, and Strakosch, 1942; Tsuchiya, Tenenberg, Clark, and Strakosch, 1942.)

Street, S. F. (See Ramsey and Street, 1940.)

Strehler, B. L. (See Cormier and Strehler, 1953; McElroy and Strehler, 1949.)

Strehler, B. L., 1953. Luminescence in cell-free extracts of luminous bacteria and its activation by DPN. Jour. Amer. Chem. Soc., 75: 1264. (185)

Strehler, B. L., and M. J. Cormier, 1953. Factors affecting the luminescence of cell-free extracts of the luminous bacterium, Achromobacter fischeri. Arch. Biochem. Biophys., 47: 16–33. (186)

Strehler, B. L., E. N. Harvey, J. J. Chang, and M. J. Cormier, 1954. The luminescent oxidation of reduced riboflavin or reduced riboflavin phosphate in the bacterial luciferin-luciferase reaction. Proc. Nat. Acad. Sci., 40: 10–12. (186)

Strehler, B. L., and F. H. Johnson, 1954. The temperature-pressure-inhibitor relationships of bacterial luminescence in vitro. (To be published.) (186)

Strehler, B. L., and C. S. Shoup, 1953. The chemiluminescence of riboflavin. Arch. Biochem. Biophys., 47: 8–15. (186)

Strong, L. E. (See Scatchard, Strong, Hughes, Ashworth, and Sparrow, 1945.)

Strutt, R. J., 1912. The molecular statistics of some chemical actions. Proc. Roy. Soc. Lond., A 87: 302–309. (5)

Sugiura, Y., 1927. Über die Eigenschaften des Wasserstoffmoleküls im Grundstande. Zeitschr. Physik, 45: 484–492. (14, 86)

Sulkin, S. E., A. Goth, and C. Zarafonetis, 1946. Influence of anesthesia on experimental western equine encephalomyelitis. Science, 104: 53–54. (468)

Sulkin, S. E., C. Zarafonetis, and A. Goth, 1945. Combined anesthesia and hyperimmune serum therapy in the treatment of experimental western equine encephalomyelitis. Proc. Soc. Exp. Biol. Med., 60: 163–165. (468)

Sun, C. E. (See Eyring, Gershinowitz, and Sun, 1935.)

Süpfle, K., and A. Müller, 1920. Ueber die Rolle der Adsorption bei der Einwirkung von Sublimat auf Bakterien. Arch. Hyg., 89: 351–354. (438)

Sutherland, G. B. B. M. (See Astbury, Dalgliesh, Darmon, and Sutherland, 1948; Darmon and Sutherland, 1949.)

Sverdrup, H. U., M. W. Johnson, and R. H. Fleming, 1942. The Oceans. Their Physics, Chemistry and General Biology. Prentice-Hall, Inc., New York. (303)

Sveshnikov, B. J. (See Zelinsky and Sveshnikov, 1942.)

Swift, M. N. (See Bond, Swift, Allen, and Fishler, 1950; Patt, Swift, and Tyree, 1948.)

Szent-Györgyi, A. (See Morgan, Rozsa, Szent-Györgyi, and Wyckoff, 1950.)

Szent-Györgyi, A., 1947, 1951. Chemistry of Muscular Contraction. Academic Press, New York. (30, 353, 705)

Szent-Györgyi, A., 1949. Free-energy relations and contraction of actomyosin. Biol. Bull., 96: 140–161. (750)

Szolnoki, J., 1926. Sind Insulin und Blausäure Gegengifte? Deut. med. Wochenschr., 52: 1427. (485)

Tahmisian, T. N. (See Bodine and Tahmisian, 1943; Bodine, Tahmisian, and Hill, 1944.)

Tainter, M. L., and W. C. Cutting, 1933. Febrile, respiratory, and some other actions of dinitrophenol. Jour. Pharm. Exp. Therap., **48**: 410–429. (*396*)

Takata, M. (See Rona and Takata, 1922.)

Tamamushi, B., 1943. Die Quantenausbeute der Chemiluminescenten Reaktionen in Lösung. Sci. Papers Inst. Phys. Chem. Res. Tokyo, **41**: 166–176. (*160*)

Tamamushi, B., and H. Akiyama, 1938. Zum Mechanismus der Chemilumi-nescenz des 3-Aminophthalsäurehydrazids. Zeitschr. physik. Chem., B **38**: 400–406. (*137, 164*)

Tamamushi, B., and H. Akiyama, 1939. Notes on the chemiluminescence of dimethyldiacridilium-nitrate. Trans. Farad. Soc., **35**: 491–494. (*160*)

Tammann, G., 1895. Zur. wirkung ungeformter Fermente. Zeitschr. physik. Chem., **18**: 426–442. (*195, 272*)

Tammann, G., 1900. Ueber die Grenzen des festen Zustandes. IV. Ann. Physik, **2**: 1–31. (*304*)

Tanaka, T. (See Terao and Tanaka, 1930.)

Tanner, F. W. (See Beamer and Tanner, 1939.)

Tarchanoff, J., 1901. Lumière des bacilles phosphorescents de la mer Baltique. Compt. rend. acad. sci., **133**: 246–249. (*218*)

Tarr, H. L. A., 1933. Some observations on the respiratory catalysts present in the spores and vegetative cells of certain aerobic bacilli. Biochem. Jour., **27**: 136–145. (*226*)

Taylor, G. W., 1934. The effect of narcotics on respiration and luminescence in bacteria, with special reference to the relation between the two processes. Jour. Cell. Comp. Physiol., **4**: 329–355. (*179, 430, 485*)

Taylor, G. W., 1936. The effect of ethyl urethane on bacterial respiration and luminescence. Jour. Cell. Comp. Physiol., **7**: 409–415. (*179*)

Taylor, H. S., 1941. Large molecules through atomic spectacles. Proc. Amer. Phil. Soc., **85**: 1–12. (*258*)

Tenenberg, D. J. (See Tsuchiya, Tenenberg, Clark, and Strakosch, 1942.)

Tenenberg, D. J., H. M. Tsuchiya, W. G. Clark, and E. A. Strakosch, 1942. *In vitro* effect of sulfonamides plus urea on *Escherichia coli* in presence of para-aminobenzoic acid. Proc. Soc. Exp. Biol. Med., **51**: 247–249. (*481*)

Tennenbaum, M. (See Mann, Tennenbaum, and Quastel, 1938; Quastel, Ten-nenbaum, and Wheatley, 1936.)

Teorell, T., 1935. Diffusion effect on ionic distribution. I. Theoretical considera-tions. Proc. Nat. Acad. Sci., **21**: 152–161. (*565, 681*)

Teorell, T., 1937. Studies on diffusion effect upon ionic distribution. II. Experi-ments on ionic accumulation. Jour. Gen. Physiol., **21**: 107–122. (*681*)

Teorell, T., 1949a. Permeability. Ann. Rev. Physiol., **11**: 545–564. (*519, 540*)

Teorell, T., 1949b. Membrane electrophoresis in relation to bio-electrical polariza-tion effects. Arch. Sci. Physiol., **3**: 205–219. (*539*)

Teorell, T., 1951. Zur quantitativen Behandlung der Membranpermeabilität. Zeitschr. Elektrochem., **55**: 460–469. (*539, 565*)

Teorell, T., 1953. Transport processed and electrical phenomena in ionic mem-branes. Progress in Biophysics and Biophysical Chem., **3**: 305–369. (*603*)

Terao, A., and T. Tanaka, 1930. Duration of life of the water-flea, *Moina macro-copa* Strauss, in relation to temperature. Jour. Imp. Fisheries Inst. Japan, **25**: 67. (*193*)

Thompson, D'Arcy, 1942. On Growth and Form. Cambridge University Press. *(190, 192)*

Thompson, G. P., 1928. Experiments on the diffraction of cathode rays. Proc. Roy. Soc. Lond., A 117: 600–609. *(68)*

Thompson, G. P., and A. Reid, 1927. Diffraction of cathode rays by a thin film. Nature, 119: 890. *(68)*

Thompson, R. H. S. (See Adams and Thompson, 1948.)

Thörner, W., 1920. Untersuchungen über Wärmeerregung und Wärmelähmung und den Erscheinungskomplex der "Gewöhnung" bei der letzteren. Zeitschr. allgem. Physiol., 18: 226–276. *(503)*

Thörner, W., 1929. Beobachtungen über peripheren Kreislauf und Melanophoren unter den Einfluss von Degeneration und Kationwirkung in Durchspülungsversuchen am Frosch. Pflüg. Arch. ges. Physiol., 222: 52–70. *(351)*

Thornton, F. E., 1935. The action of sodium, potassium, calcium and magnesium ions on the plasma gel of *Amoeba proteus* at different temperatures. Physiol. Zool., 8: 246–254. *(345)*

Thorp, W. T. S. (See Dow, Matthews, and Thorp, 1940.)

Thygesen, J. E. (See Johansen and Thygesen, 1948.)

Tilley, F. W., 1942. An experimental study of the influence of temperature on the bactericidal activities of alcohols and phenols. Jour. Bact., 43: 521–525. *(460)*

Tilley, F. W., and J. M. Schaffer, 1926. Relation between the chemical constitution and germicidal activity of the monohydric alcohols and phenols. Jour. Bact., 12: 303–309. *(432, 462)*

Tishler, M. (See Waksman and Tishler, 1942.)

Tobias, J. M. (See Boyarsky, Tobias, and Gerard, 1947.)

Tobolsky, A. V. (See Mark and Tobolsky, 1950.)

Tollhausen, P., 1889. Untersuchungen über *Bacterium phosphorescens* Fischer. Thesis. Wurzburg. *(218)*

Toman, J. E. P., J. W. Woodbury, and L. A. Woodbury, 1947. Mechanism of nerve conduction block produced by anticholinesterases. Jour. Neurophysiol., 10: 429–441. *(496, 497)*

Tonomura, Y., and S. Watanabe, 1953. Supplementary remarks to the "Interaction between actomyosin and adenosine triphosphate." Jour. Biochem., 40: 403–406. *(753)*

Tonomura, Y., S. Watanabe, and K. Yagi, 1953. Mechanism of muscular contraction. I. Interaction between actomyosin and adenosine triphosphate. Jour. Biochem., 40: 27–54. *(753)*

Topley, B. (See Wheeler, Topley, and Eyring, 1936.)

Topley, W. W. C., and G. S. Wilson, 1936. Principles of Bacteriology and Immunity. William Wood and Co., Baltimore. *(188)*

Townes, C. H., 1952. Microwave spectroscopy. Amer. Sci., 40: 270–290. *(9)*

Traube, J., 1891. Über die Capillaritätskonstanten organischer Stoffe in Wässerigen Lösungen. Liebigs Ann. Chem., 265: 27–55. *(429)*

Traube, J., 1904. Theorie der Osmose und Narkose. Pflüg. Arch. ges. Physiol., 105: 541–558. *(429)*

Traube, J., 1910. Die Theorie des Haftdrucks (Oberfläschendrucks) und ihre Bedeutung für die Physiologie. Pflüg. Arch. ges. Physiol., 132: 511–538. *(429)*

Traube, J., 1913. Theorie der Narkose. Pflüg. Arch. ges. Physiol., **153**: 276–308. (*429*)

Trautz, M., 1905. Studien über chemlumineszenz. Zeitschr. physik. Chem., **53**: 1–111. (*143*)

Trautz, M., 1916. Das Gesetz der Reaktionsgeschwindigkeit und der Gleichgewichte in Gasen. Bestätigung der Additivität von C_v-3/2R. Neue Bestimmung der Integrationskonstanten und der Moleküldurchmesser. Zeitschr. anorg. allgem. Chem., **96**: 1–28. (*5*)

Troland, L. T., 1917. Biological enigmas and the theory of enzyme action. Amer. Nat., **51**: 321–350. (*31*)

Tsuchiya, H. M. (See Tenenberg, Tsuchiya, Clark, and Strakosch, 1942.)

Tsuchiya, H. M., D. J. Tenenberg, W. G. Clark, and E. A. Strakosch, 1942. Antagonism of anti-sulfonamide effect of methionine, and enhancement of bacteriostatic action of sulfonamide by urea. Proc. Soc. Exp. Biol. Med., **50**: 262–266. (*481*)

Tyree, E. B. (See Patt, Swift, and Tyree, 1948.)

Tytell, A. A. (See Sizer and Tytell, 1941.)

Uhlenbeck, G. E., and S. Goudsmit, 1925. Ersetzung der Hypothese vom unmechanischen Zwang durch eine Forderung bezüglich des inneren Verhaltens jedes einzelnen Elektrons. Naturwiss., **13**: 953–954. (*81*)

Uhlenbeck, G. E., and S. Goudsmit, 1926. Spinning electrons and the structure of spectra. Nature, **117**: 264–265. (*81*)

Ussing, H. H., 1949a. The distinction by means of tracers between active transfer and diffusion. Acta Physiol. Scand., **19**: 43–56. (*539, 682*)

Ussing, H. H., 1949b. Transport of ions across cellular membranes. Physiol. Rev., **29**: 117–155. (*604, 670, 677, 680*)

Ussing, H. H., 1951. Unterscheidung zwischen aktivem Transport und Diffusion mit Hilfe von radioaktiven Isotopen. Zeitschr. Elektrochem., **55**: 470–475. (*539*)

Ussing, H. H., 1952. Some aspects of the application of tracers in permeability studies. Adv. Enzym., **13**: 21–65. (*603*)

Ussing, H. H., 1953. Transport through biological membranes. Ann. Rev. Physiol., **15**: 1–20. (*603*)

Uzman, L. L., and E. R. Blout, 1950. Infra-red spectra of films of native and denatured pepsin. Nature, **166**: 862–863. (*260*)

Valeton, A. M. (See Cohen and Valeton, 1916–1918.)

Valko, E. I., and A. S. DuBois, 1944. The antibacterial action of surface active cations. Jour. Bact., **47**: 15–25. (*439*)

Vandendriessche, L. (See Chantrenne, Linderstrøm-Lang, and Vandendriessche, 1947.)

Vandendriessche, L., 1951. An enzymatic study on the structure of yeast ribose nucleic acid. Compt. rend. lab. Carlsberg, sér. chim., **27**: 341–391. (*341, 362*)

Van Dyke, H. B. (See Rothen, Chow, Greep, and Van Dyke, 1941.)

Varga, L., 1946. The relation of temperature and muscular contraction. Hungarica, Acta Physiologica, **1**: 1–8. (*705*)

Vernon, H. M., 1912. The action of homologous alcohols and aldehydes on the tortoise heart. Jour. Physiol., **43**: 325–342. (*432*)

Vernon, H. M., 1913. The changes in the reactions of growing organisms to narcotics. Jour. Physiol., **47**: 15–29. (*432*)

Verworn, M., 1909. Über Narkose. Deut. med. Wochenschr., **35**: 1593–1595. (*504*)

Vignais, P., E. Barbu, J. Basset, and M. Macheboeuf, 1951. Modifications de l'état des acides ribonucléiques sous hautes pressions en présence ou en absence de nucléodépolymérase. Compt. rend. acad. sci., **232**: 2364–2366. (*292*)

Vignal, W. (See Regnard and Vignal, 1884.)

du Vigneaud, V. (See Winzler, Burk, and du Vigneaud, 1944.)

Violle, H., 1926. De la neutralization "in vivo" de l'acide cyanhydrique par le glucose. Bull. acad. méd. Paris, **95**: 644–647. (*485*)

Vishniac, W. (See Ochoa and Vishniac, 1952.)

Vishniac, W., and S. Ochoa, 1951. Photochemical reduction of pyridine nucleotides by spinach grana and coupled carbon dioxide fixation. Nature, **167**: 768. (*38*)

Voureka, A. (See Fleming, Voureka, Kramer, and Hughes, 1950.)

Wagner, K. E., 1890. Contribution à l'étude de l'immunité. Le charbon des poules. Ann. Inst. Pasteur., **4**: 570–602. (*467*)

Waksman, S. A., and M. Tishler, 1942. The chemical nature of actinomycin, an antimicrobial substance produced by *Actinomyces antibioticus*. Jour. Biol. Chem., **142**: 519–538. (*137*)

Wald, G., 1935. Carotenoids and the visual cycle. Jour. Gen. Physiol., **19**: 351–371. (*254*)

Wallach, H. (See Nachmansohn, John, and Wallach, 1943.)

Walter, J. (See Eyring, Walter, and Kimball, 1944.)

Walters, V. (See Scholander, Hock, Walters, and Irving, 1950.)

Warburg, O., 1910. Über die oxydationen in lebenden Zellen nach Versuchen am Seeigelei. Hoppe-Seyler's Zeitschr. physiol. Chem., **66**: 305–340. (*504*)

Warburg, O., 1911. Über Hemmung der Blausäurewirkung in lebenden Zellen. Hoppe-Seyler's Zeitschr. physiol. Chem., **76**: 331–346. (*484*)

Warburg, O., 1921. Physikalische Chemie der Zellatmung. Biochem. Zeitschr., **119**: 134–166. (*429, 430, 432*)

Warburg, O., and W. Christian, 1936. Pyridin, der wasserstoffübertragende Bestandteil von Gärungsfermenten. Helv. Chim. Acta, **19**: E79-E88. (*136*)

Warburg, O., and R. Wiesel, 1912. Ueber die Wirkung von Substanzen homologer Reihen auf Lebensvorgänge. Pflüg. Arch. ges. Physiol., **144**: 465–488. (*452, 504*)

Waring, H., 1942. The co-ordination of vertebrate melanophore responses. Biol. Rev. Proc. Camb. Phil. Soc., **17**: 120–150. (*350*)

Warren, G. H., 1945. The antigenic structure and specificity of luminous bacteria. Jour. Bact., **49**: 547–561. (*182*)

Warren, S., and J. Z. Bowers, 1950. The acute radiation syndrome in man. Ann. Intern. Med., **32**: 207–216. (*32*)

Wasmund, W. (See Lüers and Wasmund, 1922.)

Wasteneys, H. (See Loeb and Wasteneys, 1911; 1913.)

Watanabe, S., Y. Tonomura, and H. Shiokawa, 1953. Mechanism of muscular contraction. II. Kinetic studies on muscle ATP-ase. Jour. Biochem., **40**: 387–402. (*753*)

Watkins, J. H., and C.-E. A. Winslow, 1932. Factors determining the rate of mortality of bacteria exposed to alkalinity and heat. Jour. Bact., **24**: 243–265. (*455*)

Watson, C. C. (See Williams and Watson, 1937.)

Watson, C. C., S. Arrhenius, and J. W. Williams, 1936. Physical chemistry of zein. Nature, **137**: 322–323. (*253*)

Watson, H. E., 1908. A note on the variation of the rate of disinfection with change in concentration of the disinfectant. Jour. Hyg., **8**: 536–542. (*455, 461*)

Watson, M. T. (See Simpson, Watson, Levedahl, Schellman, Frensdorff, and Kauzmann, 1951.)

Wayrynen, R. (See Spikes, Lumry, Eyring, and Wayrynen, 1950.)

Weare, J. H. (See McMeekin, Cohn, and Weare, 1935.)

Webb, E. C. (See Mackworth and Webb, 1948.)

Webb, E. C., 1948. The action of alkyl fluorophosphonates on esterases and other enzymes. Biochem. Jour., **42**: 96–98. (*494*)

Webb, M., 1948. The influence of magnesium on cell division. 1. The growth of *Clostridium welchii* in complex media deficient in magnesium. Jour. Gen. Microbiol., **2**: 275–287. (*366*)

Webb, M., 1949a. The influence of magnesium on cell division. 2. The effect of magnesium on the growth and cell division of various bacterial species in complex media. Jour. Gen. Microbiol., **3**: 410–417. (*366*)

Webb, M., 1949b. The influence of magnesium on cell division. 3. The effect of magnesium on the growth of bacteria in simple chemically defined media. Jour. Gen. Microbiol., **3**: 418–424. (*366*)

Webb, M., 1949c. The chemistry of bacterial cell division. Jour. Soc. Chem. Ind. Lond., **68** (Part 2): 319–321. (*366*)

Webb, M., 1951a. The influence of magnesium on cell division. 4. The specificity of magnesium. Jour. Gen. Microbiol., **5**: 480–484. (*366*)

Webb, M., 1951b. The influence of magnesium on cell division. 5. The effect of magnesium on the growth of bacteria in chemically-defined media of varying complexity. Jour. Gen. Microbiol., **5**: 485–495. (*366*)

Weber, F. (See Hoefler and Weber, 1926.)

Weber, F., 1931. Plasmolyse-Resistenz und -Permeabilität bei Narkose. Protoplasma, **14**: 179–191. (*500*)

Weber, G., 1950. Fluorescence of riboflavin and flavin-adenine dinucleotide. Biochem. Jour., **47**: 114–121. (*136*)

Weber, H. H., 1930. Die Bjerrumsche Zwitterionentheorie und die Hydratation der Eiweisskörper. Biochem. Zeitschr., **218**: 1–35. (*336, 337*)

Weber, H. H., 1950. Muscle contraction and muscle proteins. Proc. Roy. Soc. Lond., B **137**: 50–58. (*753*)

Weber, H. H., 1952. Is the contracting muscle in a new elastic equilibrium? Proc. Roy. Soc. Lond., B **139**: 512–521. (*739*)

Weber, H. H., and D. Nachmansohn, 1929. Die Unabhängigkeit der Eiweisshydratation von der Eiweissionisation. Biochem. Zeitschr., **204**: 215–252. (*336*)

Wegler, R., 1937. Chemiluminescenz cyclischer Hydrazide. Jour. prakt. Chem., **148**: 135–160. *(143)*

Weidmann, S. (See Coraboeuf and Weidmann, 1949a; 1949b.)

Weinstein, L., and A. McDonald, 1945. The effect of urea, urethane, and other carbamates on bacterial growth. Science, **101**: 44–45. *(481)*

Weitkamp, A. W. (See Zimmerschied, Dinerstein, Weitkamp, and Marchner, 1949.)

Welch, A. D., 1945. Interference with biological processes through the use of analogs of essential metabolites. Physiol. Rev., **25**: 687–715. *(376)*

Werbin, H., and A. D. McLaren, 1951a. The effect of high pressure on the rates of proteolytic hydrolysis. I. Chymotrypsin. Arch. Biochem. Biophys., **31**: 285–293. *(315)*

Werbin, H., and A. D. McLaren, 1951b. The effect of high pressure on the rate of proteolytic hydrolysis. II. Trypsin. Arch. Biochem. Biophys., **32**: 325–337. *(315, 332)*

Werkman, C. H. (See Wood and Werkman, 1935; 1936.)

Werkman, C. H., and H. G. Wood, 1942. Heterotrophic assimilation of carbon dioxide. Adv. Enzymol., **2**: 135–182. *(38)*

Wescoe, W. C., R. E. Green, B. P. McNamara, and S. Krop, 1948. The influence of atropine and scopolamine on the central effects of DFP. Jour. Pharm. Exp. Therap., **92**: 63–72. *(499)*

Westheimer, F. H. (See Kirkwood and Westheimer, 1938.)

Weymouth, E. W. (See Fuhrman and Weymouth, 1946.)

Wheeler, A., B. Topley, and H. Eyring, 1936. The absolute rates of reaction of hydrogen with the halogens. Jour. Chem. Phys., **4**: 178–187. *(115)*

Whetham, M. D. (See Quastel and Whetham, 1924.)

White, H. J., and J. M. Parker, 1938. The bactericidal effect of sulfanilamide upon beta hemolytic streptococci *in vitro*. Jour. Bact., **36**: 481–498. *(401)*

White, W. (See Gerlough and White, 1934.)

Wiesel, R. (See Warburg and Wiesel, 1912.)

Wigglesworth, V. B., 1933. The physiology of the cuticle and of ecdysis in *Rhodnius prolixus* (Treatomidae, Hemiptera); with special reference to the function of the oenocytes and of the dermal glands. Quart. Jour. Micr. Sci., **76**: 269–318. *(269)*

Wigglesworth, V. B., 1934. The physiology of ecdysis in *Rhodnius prolixus* (Hemiptera). II. Factors controlling moulting and "metamorphosis." Quart. Jour. Micr. Sci., **77**: 191–222. *(269)*

Wigglesworth, V. B., 1936. The function of the corpus allatum in the growth and reproduction of *Rhodnius prolixus* (Hemiptera). Quart. Jour. Micr. Sci., **79**: 91–121. *(269)*

Wigglesworth, V. B., 1947. The Principles of Insect Physiology (3rd ed.). Methuen & Co., London.

Wigner, E. (See Pelzer and Wigner, 1932.)

Williams, E. G., M. W. Perrin, and R. O. Gibson, 1936. The effect of pressure up to 12,000 kg/cm^2 on reactions in solution. Proc. Roy. Soc. Lond., A **154**: 684–703. *(306)*

Williams, J. W. (See Lundgren and Williams, 1939; Watson, Arrhenius, and Williams, 1936.)

Williams, J. W., and C. C. Watson, 1937. Dissociation of ovalbumin in urea solvent. Nature, **139**: 506–507. (*253*)

Williams, R. W. (See Johnson, Eyring, and Williams, 1942.)

Willstätter, R., and M. Rohdewald, 1934. Über den Zustand des Glykogens in der Leber, in Muskel und in Leukocyten. Hoppe-Seyler's Zeitschr. physiol. Chem., **225**: 103–124. (*382*)

Wilson, G. S. (Topley and Wilson, 1936.)

Wilson, H. G. (See Lindquist, Wilson, Schroeder, and Madden, 1945.)

Wilson, P. W. (See Koffler, Johnson, and Wilson, 1947.)

Winchester, G., and T. J. Murray, 1936. Effect of liquid air temperature on bacteria. Proc. Soc. Exp. Biol. Med., **35**: 165–166. (*187*)

Winslow, C.-E. A. (See Watkins and Winslow, 1932.)

Winterstein, H., 1900. Über die Wirkung der Kohlensäure auf das Centralnervensystem. Arch. Anat. Physiol. Suppl., 177–192. (*504*)

Winterstein, H., 1902. Zur Kenntnis der Narkose. Zeitschr. allgem. Physiol., **1**: 19–33. (*504*)

Winterstein, H., 1913. Beiträge zur Kenntnis der Narkose. I. Mitteilung. Kritische übersicht über die Beziehungen zwischen Narkose und Sauerstoffatmung. Biochem. Zeitschr., **51**: 143–170. (*504*)

Winterstein, H., 1926. Die Narkose. Julius Springer, Berlin. (*284, 452, 487, 500*)

Winterstein, O., and J. D. Dutcher, 1943. Curare alkaloids from *Chondodendron tomentosum*. Science, **97**: 467–470. (*492*)

Winzler, R. J., D. Burk, and V. du Vigneaud, 1944. Biotin in fermentation, respiration, growth and nitrogen assimilation by yeast. Arch. Biochem., **5**: 25–47. (*396*)

Wolff, H. G., 1936. The cerebral circulation. Physiol. Rev., **16**: 545–596. (*504*)

Wollman, E., M. Macheboeuf, M. Bardach, and J. Basset, 1936. Action des ultra-pressions sur deux tumeurs de lapin; le carcinome de Brown-Pearce et le papillome de Shope. Compt. rend. soc. biol., **123**: 588–592. (*294, 295*)

Wollman, E. (See Basset, Wollman, Macheboeuf, and Bardach, 1933, 1935; Basset, Wollman, Wollman, and Macheboeuf, 1935.)

Wollman, Mme. E. (See Basset, Wollman, Wollman, and Macheboeuf, 1935.)

Wolvenkamp, H. P. (See Booij and Wolvenkamp, 1944.)

Wood, H. G. (See Werkman and Wood, 1942.)

Wood, H. G., and C. H. Werkman, 1935. The utilization of CO_2 by the propionic acid bacteria in the dissimilation of glycerol. Jour. Bact., **30**: 332. (*38*)

Wood, H. G., and C. H. Werkman, 1936. The utilisation of CO_2 in the dissimilation of glycerol by the propionic acid bacteria. Biochem. Jour., **30**: 48–53. (*38*)

Wood, W. B. (See Davis and Wood, 1942.)

Woodbury, J. W. (See Eyring, Lumry, and Woodbury, 1949; Hecht, Woodbury, Woodbury, and Christopherson, 1950; Ling and Woodbury, 1949; Toman, Woodbury, and Woodbury, 1947; Woodbury, Woodbury, and Hecht, 1950.)

Woodbury, J. W., and L. A. Woodbury, 1950. Membrane resting and action potentials from excitable tissues. Fed. Proc., **9**: 139–140. (*496*)

Woodbury, L. A. (See Hecht, Woodbury, Woodbury, and Christopherson, 1950; Toman, Woodbury, Woodbury, 1947; Woodbury and Woodbury, 1950.)

Woodbury, L. A., H. H. Hecht, and A. R. Christopherson, 1951. Membrane resting and action potentials of single cardiac muscle fibers of frog ventricle. Amer. Jour. Physiol., **164**: 307–318.   *(496)*

Woodbury, L. A., J. W. Woodbury, and H. H. Hecht, 1950. Membrane resting and action potentials of single cardiac muscle fibers. Circulation, **1**: 264–266. *(496, 684)*

Woods, D. D., 1940. The relation of *p*-aminobenzoic acid to the mechanism of action of sulfanilamide. Brit. Jour. Exp. Path., **21**: 74–90.   *(377)*

Woods, H. J. (See Astbury and Woods, 1934.)

Wooldridge, W. R. (See Quastel and Wooldridge, 1927; 1928.)

Wooley, D. W., 1947. Recent advances in the study of biological competition between structurally related compounds. Physiol. Rev., **27**: 308–333. *(377)*

Wooley, D. W., 1951. A Study of Antimetabolites. John Wiley & Sons, New York. *(377, 378)*

Wooley, V. J. (See Mellanby and Wooley, 1913.)

Wright, C. E., and J. C. Sabine, 1943. The inactivation of choline esterase by morphine, dilaudid, codeine, and desomorphine. Jour. Pharm. Exp. Therapeutics, **78**: 375–383.   *(492, 493)*

Wright, E. B., 1947. The effects of asphyxiation and narcosis on peripheral nerve polarization and conduction. Amer. Jour. Physiol., **148**: 174–184.   *(507)*

Wright, G. G. (See Johnson and Wright, 1946.)

Wright, G. G., 1944. Studies on the denaturation of antibody. I. The action of urea on diphtheria antitoxin. Jour. Exp. Med., **79**: 455–461.   *(238, 239)*

Wright, G. G., 1945. Studies on the denaturation of antibody. II. The effect of protein concentration on the rate of denaturation of diphtheria antitoxin by urea. Jour. Exp. Med., **81**: 647–653.   *(238)*

Wright, G. G., and V. Schomaker, 1948a. Studies on the denaturation of antibody. III. Kinetic aspects of the inactivation of diphtheria antitoxin by urea. Jour. Amer. Chem. Soc., **70**: 356–364.   *(238, 239, 240, 242)*

Wright, G. G., and V. Schomaker, 1948b. Studies on the denaturation of antibody. IV. The influence of pH and certain other factors on the rate of inactivation of staphylococcus antitoxin in urea solutions. Jour. Biol. Chem., **175**: 169–177.   *(238, 334)*

Wrinch, D. M., 1937a. On the pattern of proteins. Proc. Roy. Soc. Lond., A **160**: 59–86.   *(256)*

Wrinch, D. M., 1937b. On the structure of insulin. Trans. Farad. Soc., **33**: 1368–1380.   *(256)*

Wrinch, D. M., 1937c. On the structure of pepsin. Phil. Mag., ser. 7, **24** (Suppl.): 940–953.   *(256)*

Wu, H. (See Huang and Wu, 1930.)

Wu, H., 1927. Studies on denaturation of proteins. II. Coagulation by alcohol. Chinese Jour. Physiol., **1**: 81–88.   *(254)*

Wu, H., and E-F. Yang, 1932. Molecular weights of natural and denatured hemoglobins and globin. Chinese Jour. Physiol., **6**: 51–58.   *(253)*

Wyckoff, R. W. G. (See Hedén and Wyckoff, 1949; Morgan, Rozsa, Szent-Györgyi, and Wyckoff, 1950.)

Wyke, B. G., 1951. Biophysical aspects of nerve function. Progr. Biophysics, **2**: 117–192.   *(698)*

Wyman, J.   (See Greenstein and Wyman, 1936; Levin and Wyman, 1927.)

Wynne-Jones, W. F. K., and H. Eyring, 1935.   The absolute rate of reactions in condensed phases.   Jour. Chem. Phys., **3**: 492–502.   (*12, 22*)

Wyss, O.   (See Schmelkes and Wyss, 1942.)

Yakushiji, E., 1940.   Zur Kenntnis der Polyphenolasen.   Proc. Imp. Acad. Tokyo, **16**: 39–41.   (*143*)

Yamagiwa, K.   (See Adrian and Yamagiwa, 1935.)

Yang, E-F.   (See Wu and Yang, 1932.)

Yost, D. M.   (See Bonner, Gore, and Yost, 1935.)

Young, G., and J. M. Reiner, 1937.   Mechanical forces and torque on an ellipsoid in diffusion fields in connection with the problem of orientation of colloidal micellae in biological systems.   Growth, **1**: 251–261.   (*588*)

Zaiser, E. M.   (See Steinhardt and Zaiser, 1950.)

Zarafonetis, C.   (See Sulkin, Goth, and Zarafonetis, 1946; Sulkin, Zarafonetis, and Goth, 1945.)

Zelinsky, V. V., and B. J. Sveshnikov, 1942.   Absorption spectra of phthalcyclo-hydrazides at different pH.   Compt. rend. acad. sci. U.R.S.S., **34**: 252–255. (*161*)

Zeller, E. A., 1942a.   Über die Hemmung der Cholin-esterase durch p-Amino-benzolsulfonsäure-amide und Diamine.   Helv. Chim. Acta, **25**: 216–229. (*492*)

Zeller, E. A., 1942b.   Hemmung der Cholin-esterase durch Pyrazolone, zugleich ein Beitrag zur Differenzierung der Cholin-esterasen verschiedener Herkunft. Helv. Chim. Acta, **25**: 1099–1110.   (*492*)

Zilva, S. S., 1914.   The rate of inactivation by heat of peroxidase in milk. I. Biochem. Jour., **8**: 656–669.   (*272*)

Zimmerschied, W. J., R. A. Dinerstein, A. W. Weitkamp, and R. F. Marchner, 1949.   Complexes of urea with linear aliphatic compounds.   Jour. Amer. Chem. Soc., **71**: 2947.   (*483*)

Zirpolo, G., 1933.   Ricerche criobiologiche sui batteri luminosi dei Cefalopodi. Arch. Zool. Ital., **18**: 359–405.   (*187*)

ZoBell, C. E.   (See Johnson and ZoBell, 1949.)

ZoBell, C. E., 1952.   Bacterial life at the bottom of the Philippine trench.   Science, **115**: 507–508.   (*364*)

ZoBell, C. E., and F. H. Johnson, 1949.   The influence of hydrostatic pressure on the growth and viability of terrestrial and marine bacteria.   Jour. Bact., **57**: 179–189.   (*189, 289, 354, 355, 356, 363*)

ZoBell, C. E., and C. H. Oppenheimer, 1950.   Some effects of hydrostatic pressure on the multiplication and morphology of marine bacteria.   Jour. Bact., **60**: 771–781.   (*364, 365*)

Zwolinski, B. J., H. Eyring, and C. E. Reese, 1949.   Diffusion and membrane permeability.   Jour. Phys. Coll. Chem., **53**: 1426–1452.   (*533, 754*)

Subject Index